GRANT'S *Method of Anatomy*

GRANT'S *Method*

J. C. Boileau Grant, *M.C.,* M.B., Ch.B.,
Hon. D. Sc. (Man.), F.R.C.S. (Edin.)

Professor Emeritus of Anatomy in the University of Toronto and Curator of the Anatomy Museum; Visiting Professor of Anatomy in the University of California, Los Angeles; formerly Professor of Anatomy in the University of Manitoba

J. V. Basmajian, M.D.

Professor and Head of the Department of Anatomy, Queen's University, Kingston, Ontario, Canada

Baltimore / *1965*

of Anatomy

BY REGIONS

DESCRIPTIVE AND DEDUCTIVE

SEVENTH EDITION

THE WILLIAMS & WILKINS COMPANY

428 E. Preston Street
Baltimore, Md. 21202 U.S.A.

Made in the United States of America

First Edition, October, 1937
Reprinted August, 1938
Second Edition, March, 1940
Reprinted February, 1941
Reprinted November, 1943
Reprinted February, 1944
Third Edition October, 1944
Reprinted September, 1945
Reprinted April, 1946
Reprinted November, 1946
Reprinted November, 1947
Fourth Edition, August, 1948
Reprinted September, 1949
Reprinted February, 1951
Fifth Edition, July, 1952
Reprinted November, 1953
Sixth Edition, December, 1958
Reprinted April, 1962
Reprinted November, 1963
Reprinted August, 1964
Seventh Edition, 1965

Library of Congress Catalog Card Number 65-21119

The figures on the front cover are from the great anatomical work of Andreas Vesalius, *De Humani Corporis Fabrica,* published in Basle in 1543. Vesalius does some few of the illustrations himself; however, the great portion of them (including those on the cover) are generally attributed to the great Venetian artist, Titian, and his pupils. The scenic view at the feet of the figures when arranged in sequence presents a panoramic view of the countryside near Padua, where Vesalius was a professor of surgery. Some slight modifications have been made in the figures to adapt them to their purely decorative use in this edition of *Grant's Method of Anatomy.*

Composed and printed at the
Waverly Press, Inc.
Mt. Royal & Guilford Aves.
Baltimore, Md. 21202 U.S.A.

PREFACE TO THE SEVENTH E

This edition of the *Method* appears in a new format adapted to modern needs. To make the student's task easier, the 27 chapters of the previous edition have been broken into 50 chapters and these have been provided with lists of contents, and more headings and subheadings.

Thirty-eight new illustrations have been added; others have been improved or enlarged, a few reduced in size, and 42 have been relettered to conform with the New International Nomenclature (N.A.P.), which is used throughout the text.

Although these improvements take up much space, the total number of pages has been reduced from 833 to 736. This has been accomplished by deletions of obsolete or redundant material from the text, by more concise expression, by putting into small type material that the student should not need to read twice, and by eliminating text where an illustration conveys the information effectively. Many parts of the text have been rearranged, and new and important material has been added.

The purpose of the book remains the same as that stated in the preface to the first edition, which is repeated on the next page. It is meant to be simple and explanatory with a view to aiding and encouraging the student to understand and to correlate rather than to try to memorize. It is so to relieve his memory that facts, once known but now forgotten, can be recalled.

I express my thanks to those who have taken the time and trouble to make suggestions for improvements, particularly to Professor A. von Hochstetter for his penetrating observations, to Professor G. F. Lewis for his enduring interest, and to Dr. S. Sahay who has devoted many hours to careful proofreading.

The new illustrations are mainly the work of Miss Nancy Joy, but also of Miss Jill Leland, Mrs. Dorothy Chubb, Miss Annette Porter, and Dr. C. H. Bridgman, to each of whom I am deeply grateful.

And, finally, Professor John V. Basmajian has joined me as co-editor. Once a distinguished undergraduate student of mine, he later became an assistant and a colleague. I am fortunate to have been able to enlist his aid.

J. C. B. Grant

University of Toronto
May, 1965

PREFACE TO THE FIRST EDITION

The study of human anatomy may be attempted in either of two ways. One consists in collecting facts and memorizing them. This demands a memory which is wax to receive impressions and marble to retain them. Even so endowed a student will not master the infinite complexities of the subject. The other way consists in correlating facts, that is, studying them in their mutual relationships. This leads inevitably to the apprehending of the underlying principles involved, and the *raison d'être* of such relationships. The student will thus learn to reason anatomically and will find the acquisition of new and related facts an easier task. It is the purpose of this book to lead the student to approach the subject from this viewpoint, and it involves certain departures from tradition.

The human body is here considered by regions. In most regions some feature predominates. It may be a muscle, a vessel, a nerve, a bony landmark, or other palpable structure, or it may be a viscus. The regions are for the most part built up around the dominant or central feature.

The markings, lines and ridges, depressions and excrescences, on a bone tell a story as do the scars and irregularities on the earth's surface. Because they are in the main to be interpreted by reference to the soft parts that surround and find attachment to them, the bones are not described together under the heading "osteology" as though they were things apart. The shafts of the bones are considered with the surrounding soft parts; the ends with the joints into which they enter. The bones of the foot are primarily considered as a single mechanism —so are those of the hand and of the skull. The correct orientation of certain bones is given in cases where without this information the actions of certain muscles (e.g., Gluteus Medius, Teres Major) could not be understood.

It is not the mere presence of a ligament or its name that is of interest, but the functions it serves. These depend commonly on the direction of the fibers of the ligament; occasionally on their precise attachments. Many fibrous bands bearing individual names are really members of a community. A challenge thrown at one must be taken up by all. They act in unison, and therefore they are considered together as a unit.

In the consideration of viscera the subject is elucidated by reference to comparative anatomy and to embryology. These are cognate sciences which throw light about the existing structure of man. The positions of the viscera are referred to selected vertebral levels, the vertebral column being an ever present and ever ready measuring rod.

Surface Anatomy is largely dispensed with as an independent subject. Its study is undertaken as a review of Gross Anatomy, distances being measured, wherever feasible, in terms of structures. For example, instead of stating that the posterior tibial artery lies half an inch from the tibial malleolus—which would be a new fact to memorize—it is spoken of as being the breadth of two tendons from the malleolus, the tendons being the tibialis posterior and flexor digitorum muscles—a fact already learned by dissection. Again, by regarding the left renal vein as the vein of the three left paired abdominal glands (adrenal, renal, and sex) its length is easily calculated as being the length of the right renal vein, plus the width of the vanished left inferior vena cava, plus the breadth of the aorta, say $1\frac{1}{2} + 1 + 1 = 3\frac{1}{2}$ inches. And, again, the memory is not strained to recollect that the adrenal gland lies at the level of the 12th thoracic vertebra when the fact can profitably and readily be deduced from a series of related circumstances.

Illustrations to be of value must be simple, accurate, and convey a definite idea. It is for these reasons that they consist entirely of line drawings. Their simplicity encourages the student to reproduce them; and though diagrammatic in nature they are based on measurements and observations of a great deal of carefully dissected material. Their accuracy therefore, in those details they are intended to illuminate, has been the object of very considerable work. Many of the original dissections are to be found in the anatomy museum of the University of Toronto. In many instances the names of the structures in the illustrations have with care been grouped to form tables which are complete in themselves, as in figures 160 and 666. It is hoped that this tabular arrangement will add to the usefulness of the illustrations.

With few exceptions The Birmingham Revision (B. R.) of the B. N. A. terminology is employed in this book. Such synonymous and alternative terms as differ considerably from the B. R. terms, and such as are likely to die hard, are recorded within brackets in the text immediately after the B. R. terms.

The book is meant to be a working instrument designed to make Anatomy rational, interesting, and of direct application to the problems of medicine and surgery. The bare, dry, and unrelated facts of Anatomy tend rapidly to disappear into forgetfulness. That is largely because its guiding principles are not grasped so as to capture the imagination. Once they are grasped it will be found that details and relationships will remain within certain and easy recall.

I am indebted to many of my friends and colleagues for the help they have given me in this plan and I take this opportunity of expressing to them my very grateful thanks. I mention in particular: Dr. Brock Brown, who has so willingly and ably assisted with most of the illustrations and therein has displayed his artistic skill; Mr. J. G. Watt, who has so successfully executed the illustrations on the thorax; Mr. E. M. Davidson, whose experienced pencil laid the foundation of many of the figures; Dr. J. C. Watt and Dr. H. A. Cates, who have read many sections of the manuscript and have offered valuable criticisms; Dr. C. G. Smith and Mr. H. C. Elliott, who have read the entire proofs with great care; Dr. R. K. George, who has prepared the index; Dr. B. L. Guyatt, who has made many dissections and has helped to verify the innumerable points on which the figures are based; and Mr. H. E. LeMasurier, who has rendered many diverse and valuable services.

J. C. BOILEAU GRANT

University of Toronto
September, 1937

INTRODUCTION

There are few words with a longer history than the word *Anatomy*. If we write anatome, we use the name that Aristotle gave to the Science of Anatomy 2300 years ago. He made the first approach to accurate knowledge of the subject, although it was derived from dissections of the lower animals only. The word means cutting up—the method by which the study of the structure of living things is made possible.

The boundaries of the subject have widened. Through the use of the microscope and with the aid of stains the field of Anatomy has come to include microscopical anatomy or *histology* and the study of development before birth or *embryology*. The study of the anatomy of other animals, *comparative anatomy*, has been pursued exhaustively partly in an endeavor to explain the changes in form, *morphology*, of different animals including man. *Physical Anthropology*, or the branch of the study of mankind that deals chiefly with the external features and the measurements of different races and groups of people, and with the study of prehistoric remains commands interest of the anatomist. The hereditary, nutritional, chemical, and other factors controlling and modifying the growth of the embryo, of the child, and of animals are within his legitimate field; so also is the growth of tissues in test-tubes, *tissue culture*. Feeding and other experiments on animals play leading parts in many investigations.

Individuals differ in outward form and features; for example, how varied are fingerprints and the arrangement of the veins visible through the skin; individuals differ also in their internal makeup. Textbooks, for the most part, describe average conditions where weights and measures are concerned, and the commonest conditions where arrangements and patterns are concerned. Owing to the variety of these the commonest may have less than a 50 per cent incidence; therefore, it may not be truly representative. As data on variations accumulate, the subject of *Statistical Anatomy* emerges. Some variations are so rare as to be abnormalities or *anomalies*. Among the different races of mankind there are percentage differences in the form and arrangement of structures, just as there are among the different races of the apes and other animals. But relatively little is known as yet of *Racial Anatomy*, which is a branch of physical anthropology.

The human body is generally dissected by regions, *Regional Anatomy*, and described by systems, *Systematic Anatomy*. The regions of the body comprise (1) the head and neck, (2) the trunk, and (3) the limbs. These can be divided and subdivided indefinitely. The trunk is divisible into thorax, abdomen, and pelvis. The systems of the body comprise the skeleton (the study of which is osteology), the joints (arthrology), the muscles (myology), the nervous system (neurology, which includes the brain, spinal cord, organs of special sense, the nerves, and the autonomic nervous system), the cardio-vascular system which includes the heart, blood vessels, and lymph vessels. The viscera of the body (exclusive of the heart and parts of the nervous system) comprise four tubular systems—

the digestive, respiratory, urinary, and genital—and the ductless or endocrine glands. All these are wrapped up in the skin and subcutaneous tissue.

Anatomy considered with special reference to its medical and surgical bearing is called *Applied Anatomy.* Anatomy can be studied profitably, although to a limited extent, by means of cross-sections, *Cross-Section Anatomy.* In the living subject a great deal can be learned by inspection and palpation of surface parts. This and the relating of deeper parts to the skin surface, *Surface Anatomy,* are a necessary part of a medical education. And, the X-ray reveals much that cannot be investigated by other means.

Regarding nomenclature, it may be said briefly that over 30,000 anatomical terms were in use in the various textbooks of Anatomy and in the journals when, in the year 1895, the German Anatomical Society, meeting in Basle, approved a list of about 5000 terms to designate the various macroscopic structures of the human body. As a result of the work of the distinguished anatomists who undertook to compile the list, which was very largely selected from the multiplicity of terms then in use, it became possible all at once to sweep away 25,000 redundant terms. This selected list of anatomical terms is known as the Basle Nomina Anatomica, or as the B.N.A. In time it found wide acceptance. Six terse rules, set down by the Commission for its own guidance, are worth recording here. They are as follows: (1) Each part shall have only one name. (2) Each term shall be in Latin. (3) Each term shall be as short and simple as possible. (4) The terms shall be merely memory signs. (They need lay no claim to description or to speculative interpretation.) (5) Related terms shall, as far as possible, be similar, e.g., femoral nerve, femoral artery, and femoral vein. (6) Adjectives, in general, shall be arranged as opposites, e.g., major and minor, superior and inferior.

In the year 1933, The Anatomical Society of Great Britain and Ireland, meeting in Birmingham, adopted a revision of the B.N.A., known as the B.R.; in 1935, the German Anatomical Society, meeting in Jena, likewise adopted a revision, known as the J.N.A. or I.N.A. Despite their many excellent points, these found only local and restricted acceptance. In 1955, the Sixth International Congress of Anatomists, meeting in Paris, gave approval to a somewhat conservative revision of the B.N.A. which was submitted to it, and which contained many B.R. and I.N.A. terms. It is hoped and believed that this Nomina Anatomica Parisiensia, or N.A.P. for short, will come to be used exclusively and universally and that it will become the truly international vocabulary and a boon to all concerned.

DESCRIPTIVE TERMS

In describing the relationship of one structure to another it is obviously highly necessary—if we would have our description understood—that we employ certain accepted terms. Only by so doing can we avoid ambiguity and misunderstanding.

For descriptive purposes the human body is regarded as standing erect, the eyes looking forward to the horizon, the arms by the sides, and the palms of the hands and the toes directed forward; this is the **Anatomical Position.** The cadaver may be placed on the table lying on its back, on its side, or on its face, but for descriptive purposes it is assumed to be standing erect in the anatomical position. The palms of the hands can be made to face any direction: resting on the table they face downward (inferiorly); turn them round and they face upwards (superiorly); as they hang by the sides they may face each other (medially), away from each other (laterally), backwards (posteriorly), or forward (anteriorly). One of these positions, namely, the forward facing one, is by convention selected as the anatomical one—despite the fact that it is not the most comfortable. That is to say, the palm of the hand is understood to be the anterior surface of the hand and it is not permissible to refer to it variously as the posterior, inferior, superior, medial, or lateral surface according to passing fancy or because it happens temporarily to face one of these directions. From these remarks it should be evident that to misapply terms of relationship is to court confusion (*fig. 1*).

The body is divided into two halves, a right and a left, by the *median* or *midsagittal plane.* The anterior and posterior borders of this plane reach the skin surface at the front and back of the body at the *median line* or *midline.*

Terms of Relationship. Three pairs of relative terms suffice to express the relationship of any given structure to another (*fig. 2*). They are:

1. {Anterior or in front = nearer the front surface of the body.
   Posterior or behind = nearer the back surface of the body.
2. {Superior or above = nearer the crown of the head.
   Inferior or below = nearer the soles of the feet.
3. {Medial = nearer the median plane of the body.
   Lateral = farther from the median plane of the body.

The foregoing terms are applicable to all regions and all parts of the body—always provided that the body is, or is assumed to be, in the anatomical position.

Terms of Comparison. When it is desired to compare the relationship of some structure in man with the same structure in, for example, a dog, it is necessary to use a different set of terms, terms related not to space but to parts of the body, such as the head, tail, belly, and back. For example, in man standing erect the heart lies above the diaphragm; in the dog standing on all fours it lies in front of the diaphragm; but in both instances its position relative to other parts of the body is the same; so, *speaking comparatively*, one would say that both in man and

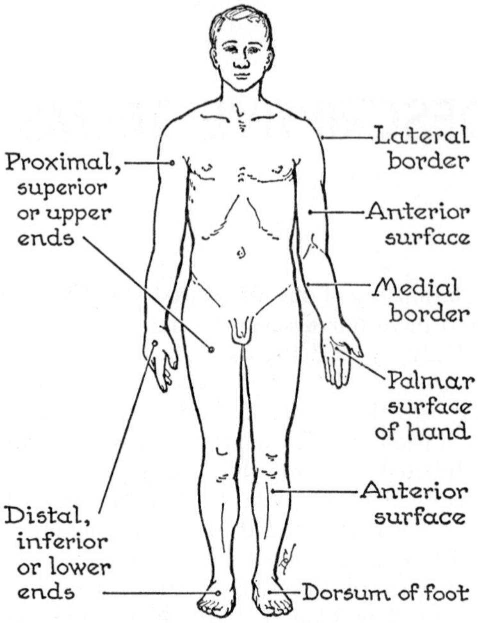

FIG. 1. The subject in the Anatomical Position—except for the right forearm, which is pronated.

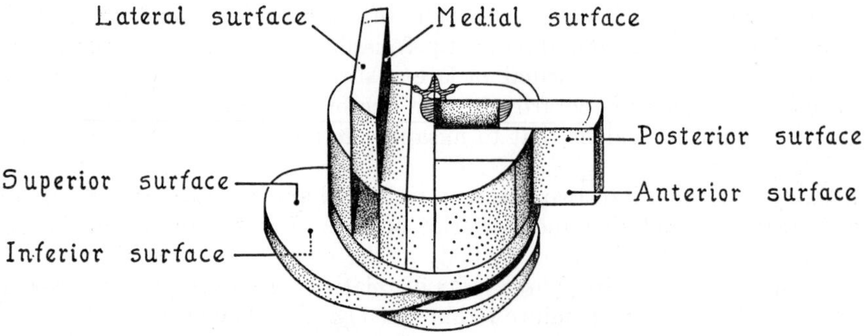

FIG. 2. Three pairs of surfaces involving six essential descriptive terms. They are related to the three fundamental planes in the body.

in the dog the heart is on the head, cranial, or cephalic side of the diaphragm (*fig. 3*).

Hence, the terms *ventral* and *dorsal*, *cranial* and *caudal*, as well as *medial* and *lateral* are applicable to the trunk or torso (thorax, abdomen, and pelvis) irrespective of the position assumed by the body. Moreover, it is desirable to employ these terms in embryology and comparative embryology, and it is quite correct to employ them in human anatomy—for no misunderstanding can arise from their use as synonyms for anterior, posterior, superior, and inferior.

In the limbs, terms are coupled with reference to (1) the proximity to the trunk, *proximal* = nearer the trunk and is synonymous with superior; *distal* = farther from the trunk and is synonymous with inferior; (2) the morphological borders, *preaxial* = the lateral or radial border (i.e., thumb side) of the upper limb and the medial or tibial border (i.e., big toe side) of the lower limb; *post-*

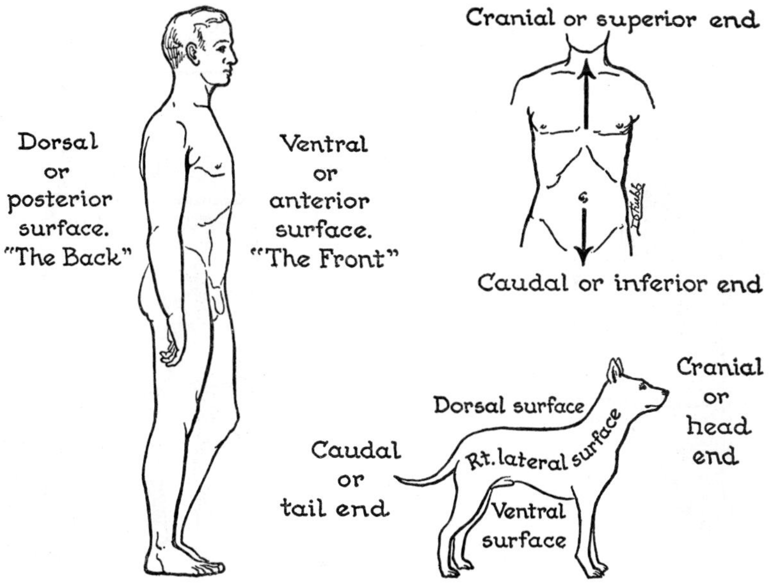

FIG. 3 Three pairs of terms necessary to comparative anatomy and of more general application than those given in figure 2.

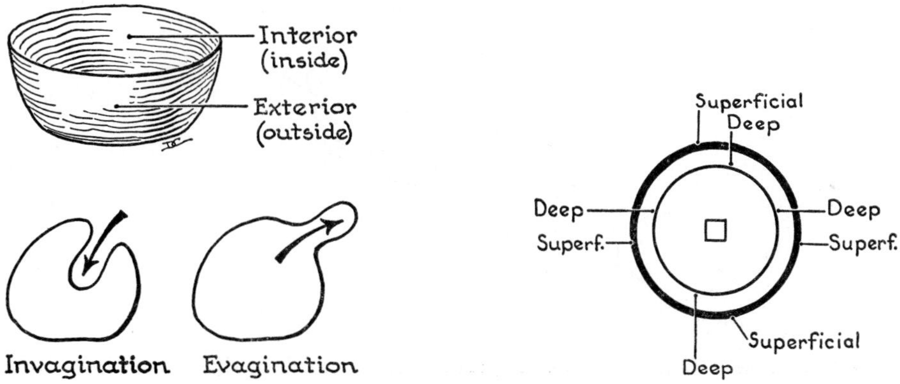

FIGS. 4, 5, AND 6. Three pairs of contrasting terms

axial = the medial or ulnar border of the upper limb and the lateral or fibular border of the lower limb; and (3) the functional surfaces, *flexor* and *extensor*, the flexor surface being anterior in the upper limb and posterior in the lower limb.

The anterior surface of the hand is generally called the *palmar* (or volar) surface, and the inferior surface of the foot the *plantar* surface. The opposite surfaces are called the *dorsum* of the hand and foot.

Other Terms. *Inside, interior,* or *internal* and *outside, exterior,* or *external,* are reserved (1) for bony cavities, such as the pelvic, thoracic, cranial, and orbital, and (2) for hollow organs, such as the heart, mouth, bladder, and intestine (*fig. 4*).

An *invagination* and an *evagination* (L. vagina = a sheath or scabbard) are inward and outward bulgings of the wall of a cavity (*fig. 5*).

Superficial and *deep* denote nearness to and remoteness from the skin surface

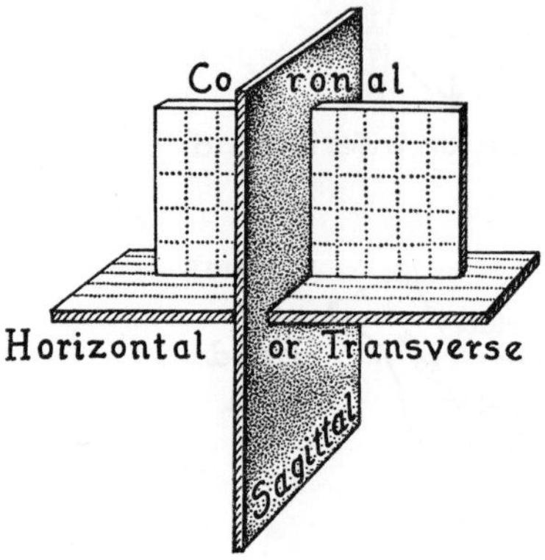

FIG. 7. The three fundamental planes

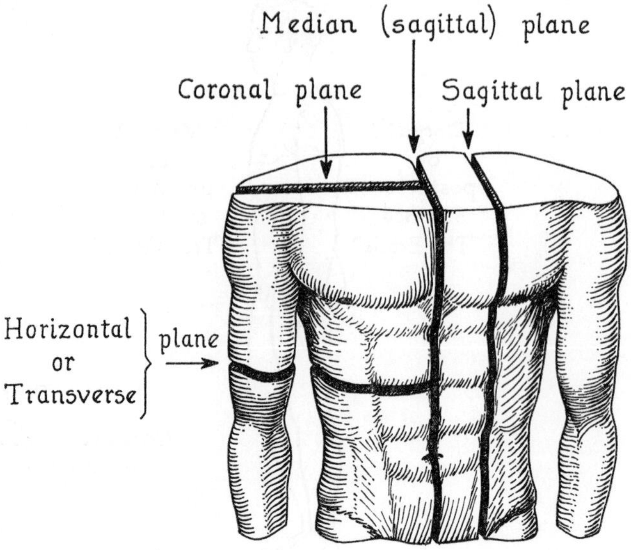

FIG. 8. Fundamental planes in the body

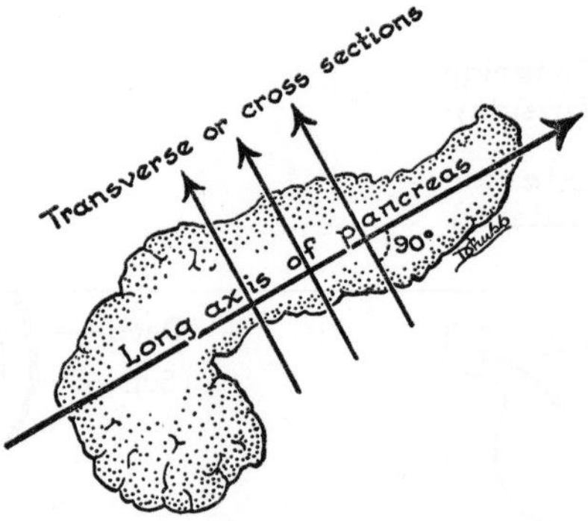

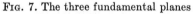

FIG. 9. A cross section of an organ or part is a section made at right angles to its long axis.

irrespective of whether at the front, side, or back. These two terms may be applied to organs, such as the liver and lung (*fig. 6*).

On, over, and *under* are terms to beware of. They should be used in a general sense and without specific regard to the anatomical position. Just as a fly may be *on* the ceiling, wall, or floor, so a tubercle may be *on* any part of a bone, and a sulcus may be *on* any surface of the brain. A vessel may pass *under* or *over* an arch or bridge; and a nerve may lie *under* the deep fascia. Used in these senses the terms are explicit. Carefully avoid using them loosely in place of "superior to" and "inferior to," for such misuse is the cause of much misunderstanding.

In relation to (related to) is not an informative term unless it is specified what the relationship is, e.g., close, intimate, remote, occasional.

Ipsilateral refers to the same side of the body, e.g., the right arm and the right leg. *Contralateral* refers to opposite sides of the body, e.g., the right temporal and the left pterygoid muscles.

Planes. (1) A *sagittal plane* is any vertical antero-posterior plane parallel to and including the median plane. It is also parallel to the sagittal suture of the skull. (2) A *coronal* or *frontal plane* is any vertical side-to-side plane at right angles to the sagittal plane. It is approximately parallel to the coronal suture of the skull. (3) A *transverse plane* is any plane at right angles to 1 and 2, i.e., at right angles to the long axis of the body or limb. In the case of an organ or other structure a *transverse* or *cross section* is a section at right angles to the long axis of that organ or structure. (4) An *oblique plane* may lie at any other angle. (See *figs. 7–9.*)

Attachments of Muscles. Muscles are attached at both ends. The proximal attachment of a limb muscle is its *origin;* the distal end is its *insertion.*

Note. It would be logical to regard the fixed end as the origin and the moving end as the insertion, if they were constant; but they are not constant; they are reversible. Thus, when pulling on an oar, the Latissimus Dorsi draws the humerus backward, toward the body; but when climbing a tree, it draws the body towards the humerus. Similar examples are numerous in the lower limb due to the fact that in walking the right foot is stationary on the ground while the left foot is advancing; and this condition is reversed when the next step is taken. Hence, the origins and insertions of the muscles of the lower limb are alternately fixed and moving.

Vessels. Arteries are likened to trees with *branches;* veins are likened to rivers with *tributaries.* Before Harvey discovered that blood moved "in a circle" both arteries and veins were spoken of as having branches, and there is no objection today to referring to the branch of a vein.

Movements at Joints. To *flex* is to bend or to make an angle.

To extend is to stretch out or to straighten. Movements of flexion and extension take place at the elbow joint.

To abduct is to draw away laterally from the median plane of the body.

To adduct is the opposite movement in the same plane (L. ab = from; ad = to; duco = I lead). Movements of abduction and adduction, as well as of flexion and extension, take place at the wrist joint.

The middle finger is regarded as lying in the *axial line of the hand;* and the 2nd toe as lying in the *axial line of the foot.* Abduction and adduction of the fingers and toes are movements from and toward these axial lines. The movements of the thumb are named differently; see page 146.

To circumduct (L. circum = around) is to perform the movements of flexion, abduction, extension, and adduction in sequence, thereby describing a cone, as can be done at the shoulder, hip, wrist, and metacarpo-phalangeal joints.

To rotate is to turn or revolve on a long axis, as the arm at the shoulder joint, the femur at the hip joint, the radius on the ulna, and certain vertebrae on each other.

To pronate was originally to bend or flex the body forward as in obeisance in prayer, that is to face downward or prone. Applied to the forearm, *to pronate* means to turn it so that the palm of the hand faces downwards on a table or, when you are seated, rests on your knee, which is the equivalent of facing backward when it hangs by the side. Pronation is, therefore, a movement of medial rotation.

To supinate is to rotate the forearm laterally so that the dorsum of the hand rests on the table or faces backward when the limb hangs by the side. Supine = lying on the back.

To protract (L. pro = forward; traho = I pull) is to move forward.

To retract is to move backwards. Protraction and retraction are terms applied to the movements of the lower jaw and shoulder girdle.

For every reason the student should, from the first, use, use only, and use correctly the accepted terms.

CONTENTS

Section V
LOWER LIMB

Section VI
THORAX

Section VII
HEAD AND NECK

SECTION I

General Considerations

CHAPTER 1

LOCOMOTOR SYSTEMS

BONE

Physical Properties; Functions; Structure; Classification.

Markings on Dried Bones: Terms; A Living Bone; The Parts of a Young Bone; Epiphyses; Nutrient Artery and Canal; Ossification; Bone Marrow; Vessels and Nerves; Historical.

CARTILAGE

Hyaline Cartilage; Fibrocartilage; Elastic Cartilage.

VERTEBRAL COLUMN

PARTS OF A TYPICAL VERTEBRA AND THEIR FUNCTIONS—*Body; Vertebral Arch; Processes; Ossification.*

ARTICULATED VERTEBRAL COLUMN—*Intervertebral Discs; Bodies of the Vertebrae; Curvatures; Varying Stature; Line of Gravity; Transverse Processes; Pedicles; Laminae; Vertebral Foramina and Vertebral Canal; Articular Processes; Spinous Processes.*

ARTICULATIONS OR JOINTS

SKULL TYPE—*Suture and Synchondrosis; Synostosis.*

VERTEBRAL TYPE—*Symphysis; Symphysis between Two Vertebral Bodies; Syndesmosis; Vertebral Syndesmoses.*

LIMB TYPE—*Synovial Joint: articular capsule, joint cavity, synovial membrane and folds, synovia, fat-pads, articular discs, ligaments, articular cartilage, lubrication, labra, nerves, and vessels.*

Classification of Synovial Joints.

MUSCLES

Types of Muscles.

Skeletal Muscles: Fibers; Parts; Insertions; Synovial Bursa; Synovial Sheath.

Internal Structure; Contraction; Investigation; Electromyography; Muscle Action.

Blood Supply; Nerves; Nomenclature; Variations; Accessory Muscles.

BONE

In this chapter our main concern is with bone as a tissue and its general characteristics; but the vertebrae are described in detail because an understanding of them is fundamental to several regions. The student should not proceed with a study of regional anatomy until this chapter and the succeeding ones are read and understood.

A bone of a living man is itself a living thing. It has blood vessels, lymph vessels, and nerves. It grows. It is subject to disease.

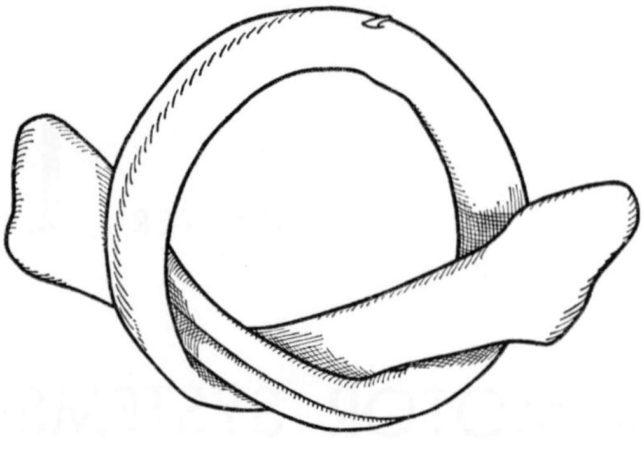

FIG. 10. A decalcified fibula can be tied in a knot

When fractured it heals itself; and if the fracture is so improperly set that the parts have lost their previous alignment, its internal structure undergoes remodeling in order that it may continue to withstand strains and stresses as it did before. Unnecessary bone is resorbed. For example, following the extraction of a tooth, the walls of the socket, thus rendered empty, disappear; also, the bones of a paralyzed limb atrophy (become thinner and weaker) from disuse. Conversely, when bones have increased weight to support, they hypertrophy (become thicker and stronger).

Bones have an *organic framework* of fibrous tissue and cells, among which *inorganic salts* —notably, phosphate of calcium—are deposited in a characteristic fashion. The fibrous tissue gives the bones resilience and toughness; the salts give them hardness and rigidity and make them opaque to X-rays. One-third is organic; two-thirds are inorganic.

Physical Properties. By submerging a bone in a mineral acid the salts are removed, but the organic material remains and still displays in detail the shape of the untreated bone. Such a specimen is flexible. For example, a decalcified fibula can be tied in a knot (*fig. 10*); when the knot is untied, the fibula springs back into shape.

The organic material of a bone, long buried near the surface of the earth, is removed by bacterial action (i.e., decomposition), and only the salts remain. The same result can be achieved more speedily by burning with fire. A bone so treated, being more brittle than porcelain, will crumble and fracture unless handled with care.

Bones that have lain buried in a limestone cave become petrified (i.e., calcium carbonate replaces the organic material); so, they endure; so do those that are mineralized through lying in soils containing, e.g., iron, lead, or zinc.

Moisture being necessary to bacterial action, bones that have remained thoroughly dry (mummified) retain their organic framework and therefore much of their toughness. The anthropologist about to exhume fragile bones first toughens them them by "petrifying" artificially, i.e., by impregnating them with shellac dissolved in in spirit or with cellulose dissolved in acetone.

Functions of Bones. In addition to being (1) the rigid supporting framework of the body, bones serve as (2) levers for muscles; (3) they afford protection to certain viscera (e.g., brain and spinal cord, heart and lungs, liver and bladder); (4) they contain marrow, which is the factory for blood cells; and (5) they are the storehouses of calcium and phosphorus.

Structure of a dried bone seen on section is shown in figure 11. MACROSCOPICALLY, there are two forms of bony tissue (1) *spongy* or cancellous and (2) *compact* or dense.

All bones have a complete outer casing of compact bone; the interior is filled with spongy bone except where replaced by a medullary cavity or an air sinus (see below). In a long bone, such as the humerus, the compact bone is thickest near the middle of the shaft and it becomes progessively thinner as the bone expands toward its articular ends, these being covered with a mere shell of compact bone. Conversely, spongy bone fills the expanded ends and extends for a variable distance along the shaft but leaves a tubular space, the *medullary cavity*. The *lamellae* or plates of the spongework are arranged in lines of pressure and of tension, and in an X-ray photograph the pressure lines are seen to pass across joints from bone to bone (*fig. 496* of the hip joint).

Classification. The bones of the body may be classified variously.

DEVELOPMENTALLY: according to whether

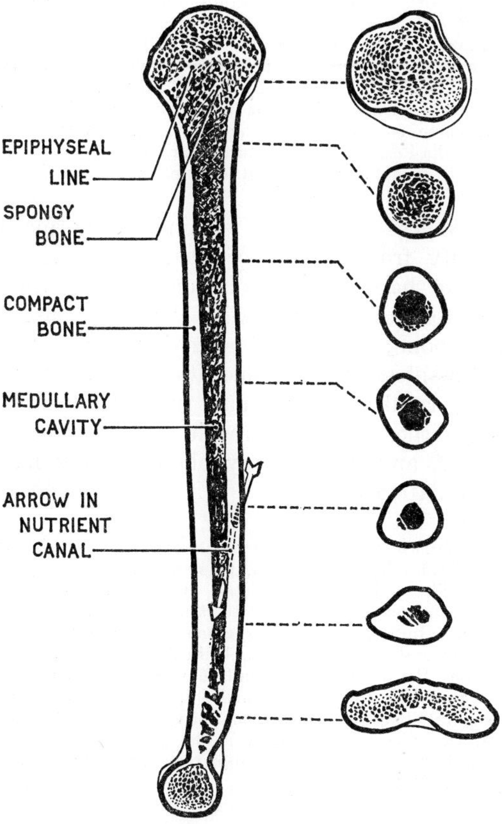

FIG. 11. The structure of a dried bone as shown by longitudinal and transverse sections of a humerus.

they developed (1) in cartilage or (2) in membrane.

REGIONALLY:

Axial Bones	Skull	cranium, face	22
		auditory ossicles	6
		hyoid	1
	Vertebrae		26
	Ribs		24
	Sternum		1
Appendicular Bones	Upper limb: Girdle (shoulder), Free bones		64
	Lower limb: Girdle (pelvic), Free bones		62
			206

This number is not exact. It varies with age and with the individual, being larger in youth while the various parts of compound bones (e.g., frontal, sacrum) are still discrete and when accessory or supernumerary bones are present, and being smaller when two bones have fused (e.g., fusion of lunate and triquetrum, or of two vertebrae) and when a bone is suppressed or congenitally absent (e.g., absent phalanx or vertebra).

ACCORDING TO SHAPE:

1. Long } peculiar to the limbs.
2. Short }
3. Flat } peculiar to the axial skeleton and the
4. Irregular } girdles.
5. Sesamoid—in certain tendons.

1. Long Bones are tubular. They are confined to the limbs, where they serve as levers for muscles.

A long bone has a body or shaft and two ends. The *ends*, being articular, are smooth, covered with cartilage, either convex or concave, and enlarged.

The *shaft* is hollow (medullary cavity) as a straw is hollow, thus obtaining most strength with least expenditure of material and with least weight. It, typically, has three borders which separate three surfaces, so on cross-section it is triangular rather than circular (*fig. 12*).

Long bones develop (are preformed) in cartilage. The shaft of every long bone begins to ossify (primary center) about the 2nd to 3rd month of intra-uterine life. One or both ends begin to ossify (secondary centers) soon after birth.

Exceptions. Every long bone does not conform to all the foregoing specifications. For example, the *clavicle* and the *ribs* have no medullary cavity, but they fulfil the func-

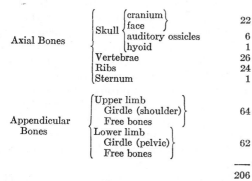

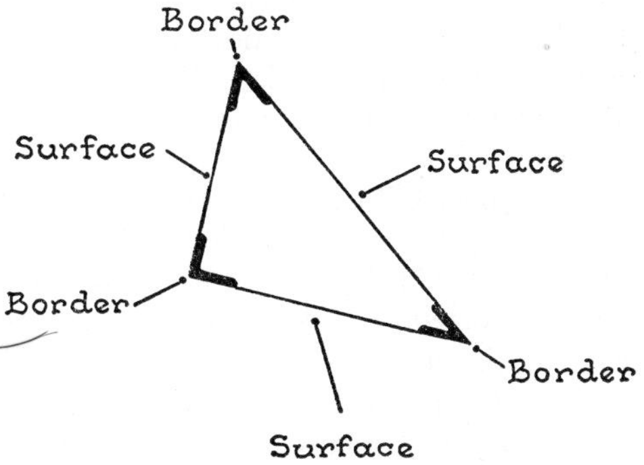

FIG. 12. The three borders are unbendable, like angle-iron.

tions of long bones. The *vertebrae* are classified as irregular bones, but their bodies possess most of the features of a long bone.

2. Short Bones are cubical or modified cubes. They are confined to the carpus and tarsus. They have six surfaces of which four (or less) are articular, leaving two (or more) free for the attachment of ligaments and for the entry of blood vessels. They develop in cartilage, and they begin to ossify soon after birth.

»» Of the short bones, 3 (calcaneus, talus, and cuboid) start ossifying before birth; so do the epiphyses of 3 long bones (knee end of femur and of tibia and commonly the shoulder end of humerus).

3. Flat Bones resemble sandwiches. They consist of two layers or plates of compact bone with spongy bone and marrow spread between them. Many of the skull bones, the sternum, scapulae, and parts of other bones, are of the flat type. Most flat bones help to form the walls of rounded cavities and therefore are curved. At birth a flat bone consists of a single plate. In the flat bones of the skull the spongy bone, here called *diploe,* and its contained marrow appears some years later and splits the plate into two.

4. Irregular Bones have any irregular or mixed shape. All skull bones, not of the flat type, are irregular (e.g., sphenoid, maxilla); so are the vertebrae and the hip bones. They are composed of spongy bone and marrow within a compact covering.

Pneumatic Bones. Evaginations of the mucous lining of the nasal cavities and of the middle ear and mastoid antrum invade the diploe of certain flat and irregular bones of the skull thereby producing *air cells* or *air sinuses.* This pneumatic method of construction may be economical in bony material, but it invites "colds in the head" and other infections of the nose to extend to these sinuses.

5. Sesamoid Bones are nodules of bone that develop in certain tendons where they rub on convex bony surfaces ("Sesamoid" of Arabic origin = like a seed). The free surface of the nodule is covered with articular cartilage; the rest is buried in the tendon; it possesses no periosteum.

The largest, the *patella* or *knee-cap,* occurs in the Quadriceps Femoris tendon.

»» Perhaps the most important, the two at the head of the first metatarsal, occur in the tendons of Flexor Hallucis Brevis. Two occur at the head of the first metacarpal, in the tendons of Adductor Pollicis and Flexor Pollicis Brevis. The foregoing are constant.

Others commonly occur in the lateral head of Gastrocnemius, Peroneus Longus (at side of cuboid), Tibialis Posterior (behind navicular tuberosity), and at heads of metacarpals 2 and 5 (in palmar plates).

Accessory Bones. Certain bones normally ossify from several centers, and it sometimes happens that one or more of these centers fails to unite with the main mass of the bone; again, an abnormal or extra center of ossification may make its appearance and the resulting bone may remain discrete. In either case, the result is an accessory bone, and in an X-ray photograph it may simulate a fracture.

»» *Examples:* (1) The frontal bone may persist in right and left halves, i.e., persisting metopic suture. (2) The upper (interparietal) part of the occipital squama may remain discrete, and is typical of West Coast Indians. (3) The zygomatic bone may be in upper and lower parts notably in Asiatics. (4) Sutural bones, the size of a finger nail, may occur in the sutures of the skull. (5) The acromial epiphysis may remain a separate bone. (6) The 5th lumbar vertebra is commonly in two pieces (*fig. 321*). (7) The patella may be bipartite (*fig. 518*). (8) Supernumerary carpals and tarsals occur (p. 459).

Markings on a Dried Bone. The surface of a dried bone is smooth, in fact almost polished, over areas covered with cartilage and where tendons play in grooves (e.g., head of humerus; upper and under surfaces of sustentaculum tali). Near the ends of a long bone there are large vascular foramina for veins and arteries, and piercing the shaft obliquely is the nutrient canal, for the nutrient vessels, which may be 2 inches long.

Markings occur wherever fibrous tissue is attached—no matter whether it be a ligament, tendon, aponeurosis, fascia, or intermuscular septum. Fibrous tissue markings are, however, not present at birth nor in the young (e.g., they are not seen on a soup bone). They appear about puberty and they become progressively better marked with advancing age.

Terms. Markings take the form of (1) elevations, (2) facets, and (3) depressions.

Elevations, in order of prominence: a linear elevation is a *line, ridge,* or *crest;* a rounded elevation is a *tubercle, tuberosity, malleolus,* or *trochanter;* a sharp elevation is a *spine* or *styloid process.*

Small, smooth, flat areas are called *facets* (*cf.* the facet of a diamond).

A *depression* is a *pit* or *fovea,* if small; a *fossa,* if large; a *groove* or *sulcus,* if it has length. A *notch* or *incisura,* when bridged by a ligament or by bone, is a *foramen* (i.e., a perforation or hole), and a foramen that has length is a *canal* or *meatus.* A canal has an *orifice* [*os* or *ostium*] at each end.

The portion of a notch, foramen, or orifice of a canal over which an emerging vessel or nerve rolls is rounded, but elsewhere it is sharp. Therefore, even on a dried bone the direction taken by the emerging occupant is evident (*cf.* lesser sciatic notch, anterior sacral foramina, infra-orbital canal).

Areas covered with articular cartilage are called *articular facets,* if approximately flat. Certain rounded articular areas are called *heads;* others are called *condyles* (= knuckles). A *trochlea* is a pulley.

The fleshy fibers of a muscle make no mark on a bone.

A Living Bone or a Dissecting Room Specimen before Maceration. The articular parts are covered with *hyaline* (articular) *cartilage.* This is not equally thick at all points; so, its contour is not identical with that of the underlying bone. Hence, macerated bones do not articulate perfectly.

Periosteum envelops all parts not covered with cartilage and not giving attachment to ligaments and tendons. It consists of two layers: (1) an outer, fibrous membrane and (2) an inner, vascular one lined with bone-forming cells, the *osteoblasts.* The periosteum is easily scraped off with the handle of the scalpel, leaving, however, many osteoblasts adhering to the bone. *Fibrocartilage* lines the grooves where tendons exert pressure. Some elevations seen in the macerated bone are but shadows of what they were before maceration, because in life they had fibrocartilaginous extensions, now shed (e.g., dorsal radial tubercle).

The Parts of a Young Bone (*fig. 13*). At birth both ends of a long bone are cartilaginous, *cartilaginous epiphyses.* The part of the bone between the cartilaginous ends is the *diaphysis* (Gk. dia = in between, across).

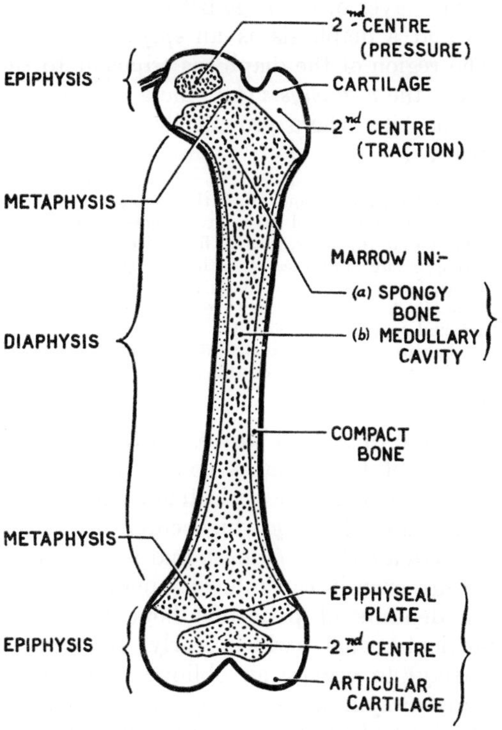

FIG. 13. The parts of a young bone as shown by a longitudinal section of a femur.

It comprises a casing of compact bone which encloses a medullary cavity at its middle and spongy bone at each end, and all is filled with red marrow. The diaphysis is clothed in *periosteum* (Gk. peri = around; osteon = bone). When the developing bone was in the cartilaginous state, the periosteum was known as *perichondrium* (Gk. chondros = cartilage).

Epiphyses (Gk. epi = upon, physis = growth). (1) During the 1st and 2nd years one (or both) of the cartilaginous ends begins to ossify subjacent to the site of articulation, constituting a *pressure epiphysis* (e.g., head of humerus, condyles of femur). (2) Later, generally about puberty, independent ossific centers appear in the cartilage at the sites of attachment of certain tendons, constituting *traction epiphyses* (e.g., tubercles of humerus, trochanters of femur). (3) A third type of epiphysis is the *atavistic epiphysis.* Atavistic epiphyses phylogenetically were independent bones now grafted on to other bones (e.g., coracoid process of scapula).

The layer of cartilage between an epiphysis and a diaphysis is an *epiphyseal plate.* The region of the diaphysis adjacent to the plate, the *metaphysis* (Gk. meta = beyond), is the site where growth in length takes place.

»» All long bones—including the metacarpals, metatarsals, phalanges, and ribs—have a pressure epiphysis at one end or the other, whereas five paired bones *always* have pressure epiphyses at both ends (viz., humerus, radius, femur, tibia, and fibula), and a few bones *occasionally* have them at both ends (viz., clavicle, 1st and 2nd metacarpals, and 1st metatarsal). The ulna also has an epiphysis at each end, but the proximal one is a traction epiphysis for the tendon of the Triceps (*fig. 197*).

Nutrient Artery and Canal. The blood supply of living bones comes from many small vessels in the periosteum and from a large *nutrient artery* which enters the shaft through a *nutrient foramen* and is a constant feature even in early development. Increasing deposits of periosteal bone allow the nutrient canal (which early ran transversely) to occupy an oblique position directed away from the epiphyseal end (*fig. 11*). Check any bone (clavicle, phalanx, rib) and observe that it is so. In cases where there is an epiphysis at both ends, the canal is directed away from the more actively growing end.

It is roughly estimated that the shoulder end of the humerus and the wrist ends of the ulna and radius grow 3 to 4 times as much as their elbow ends; the knee end of the femur between 2 and 4 times as much as the hip end; and the knee end of the tibia slightly more than the ankle end (*fig. 197*) (Digby and Phemister). Hence, in these bones the nutrient canals are directed—to the elbow I go, from the knee I flee (Hughes).

Where there are two epiphyseal ends, the end that has the more work to do is the first to start work (ossifying) and the last to stop (to fuse with the diaphysis). When fusion (synostosis) takes place, growth in length ceases.

Ossification. Except for certain bones of the skull and the clavicle, all the bones of the body pass through a cartilaginous stage. About the 8th intra-uterine week ossification of the long bones begins. There are two types of ossification: (1) intracartilaginous or enchondral and (2) periosteal or intramembranous.

In the shaft of a long bone both types take place concurrently, as described in text books of Histology (see Ham and Leeson).

After birth, at the center of one or both cartilaginous ends, the process of enchondral ossification begins, as shown in figure 13, and a bony epiphysis takes form. Ossification progresses in the epiphysis until only two sheets of cartilage remain: (1) the *articular cartilage* which covers the end of the bone and persists throughout life, and (2) a residual plate, the *epiphyseal plate,* placed between the diaphysis and the bony epiphysis forming a synchondrosis. Ultimately, when the bone has attained its adult length, the plate also ossifies—the site commonly being marked by an *epiphyseal line* (*fig. 11*). In technical terms, a synchondrosis has been converted into a synostosis.

Short bones (i.e., carpal and tarsal) ossify enchondrally like epiphyses.

The bones of the skull, except those of the base, do not pass through a cartilaginous stage but ossify directly from membrane.

»» Those preformed in cartilage are (1) occipital, save the interparietal part, (2) sphenoid, save the greater wings and the pterygoid laminae, (3) ethmoid, (4) inferior conchae, and (5) petromastoids and styloid processes of the temporal bones.

Sexual Difference. Ossification starts earlier in females than in males and it is completed earlier—even by as much as 2 to 3 years.

Bone Marrow. Blood cells, made by bone marrow, have but a short life, the red cells living about 120 days, and the birth rate necessarily keeps pace with the death rate.

At birth, spongy bone, which at this age is limited in quantity, and the medullary cavities of the long bones are filled with red (blood-forming) marrow. By the 7th year, the amount of spongy bone has increased and the red marrow has extended into it, but at the same time has receded from the medullary cavities only to be replaced there by yellow (fatty) marrow. About the 18th year, red marrow is almost entirely replaced by yellow in the limb bones; thereafter, it is confined to the axial skeleton—skull, vertebrae, ribs, sternum, hip bones, and upper ends of femur and humerus (A. Piney and M. M. Wintrobe).

In certain conditions (e.g., pernicious anemia) where the death rate of the red cells is high, the yellow marrow reverts to red in an endeavor to support the birth rate.

Vessels and Nerves. ARTERIES supply long bones thus: (1) *periosteal twigs* enter the shaft at many points, run in the Haversian canals, and supply the outer part of the compact bone of the shaft (*fig. 13.1*); (2) twigs from *articular arteries*, which anastomose around the joint usually between the bone and the reflexion of the synovial membrane, supply the epiphyses, the metaphyseal region, and the capsule; (3) the *nutrient artery* (medullary a.), on entering the medullary cavity, divides into a proximal and a distal branch, each of which supplies the inner part of the compact bone, the marrow, and the metaphyseal region. It is the main artery of the shaft (Trueta and Cavadias.) The blood flow through the cortex runs in a centrifugal and not in a centripetal direction (Brookes *et al.*).

The anastomoses between the branches of the nutrient and periosteal arteries seem to be feeble. Though many of the metaphyseal branches of the nutrient artery are end arteries, some of them anastomose with the metaphyseal branches of the articular arteries. Indeed, when the shaft of a long bone is fractured, one or other branch of the nutrient artery is necessarily torn across. It then falls to the anastomoses effected with the articular arteries to replenish the torn nutrient artery with blood.

VEINS. There are periosteal veins and nutrient veins, but the chief veins, enriched with young blood cells, are said to escape by the large foramina near the ends of the bone.

LYMPH VESSELS exist in the periosteum and in the perivascular lymph spaces in Haversian canals.

NERVES. Sensory nerves are plentiful in the periosteum, and nerves (? to blood vessels) accompany the nutrient artery.

Historical Data. One day in 1736, John Belchier, surgeon on the staff of Guy's Hospital, London, was dining with a friend. A joint of pork was served, and it was commented that the bones were red. The host,

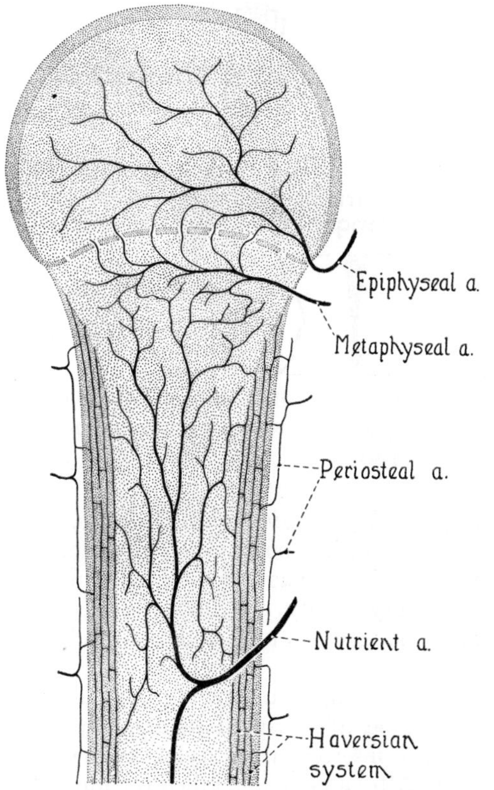

FIG. 13.1. Blood supply to a long bone (schematic).

who was a calico-printer, explained that he utilized bran soaked in madder from his dye vats to feed his pigs, and to this fact he attributed the color. Belchier communicated this information to the Royal Society, and it was printed in its transactions.

Duhamel, a French squire, read Belchier's paper and, being curious, fed madder to some of his fowls and pigs; and with the same red result. He then conducted a number of experiments on pigs and found that if the animals were killed while the feeding of madder was in progress, the bones appeared red, and that if the feeding of madder had ceased for a period, the bones appeared white. On laying open the bones, he found that though they were white outside they were red inside. By alternately feeding food with madder and without, he produced bones with alternating red and white rings or layers, so he concluded that *bones increase in girth like trees and that the periosteum is*

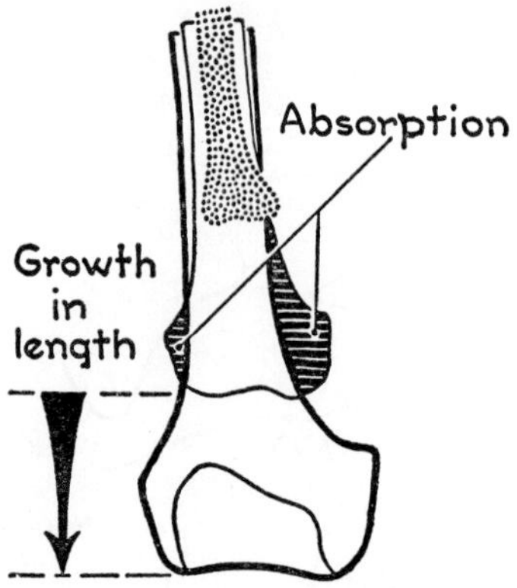

FIG. 14. Remodelling of bone. As a long bone grows, sites once occupied by the expanded ends become parts of the more slender shaft.

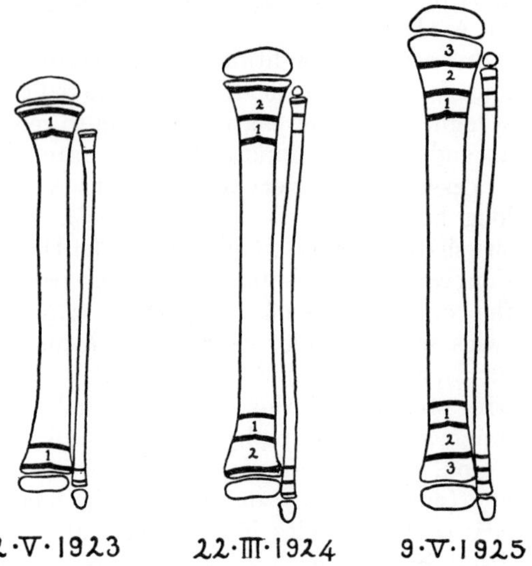

FIG. 15. Outlines of three radiograms of the leg bones of a young girl taken over a period of 2 years. Observe that the three lines of arrested growth, denoting three successive illnesses, remain equidistant. (After H. A. Harris.)

responsible for laying down the rings. He encircled growing bones with rings of silver wire and in time he found the wire inside the medullary cavity, because the cavity too had enlarged—but he did not understand how.

In the shaft of a growing bone Duhamel bored holes at measured distances apart, and in them inserted silver stylets to keep them open. After a period he killed the animal and found that, although the length of the bone had increased, the holes remained the same distance apart, so he concluded that *growth in length takes place at the ends of the long bones.*

John Hunter sought further explanation. Knowing that the lower jaw has no epiphyses and that the milk teeth of a child fill the body of the jaw right back to the ramus, he wondered how space was found for the three additional teeth, the three permanent molars. He surmised that the *growth of bone entails two processes—one of deposition* (addition), *the other of absorption* (subtraction). Only thus could he account for the growth of the jaw, the formation and progressive enlargement of medullary cavities, and for changes in the neck of the femur. About 1764, John Hunter—employing on pigs madder-feeding experiments and using controls—put his theory to the test and proved it to be correct (*fig. 14*). (Consult "Menders of the Maimed" by Sir Arthur Keith.)

»» There is general agreement that the bones of the base of the skull, being mainly cartilaginous bones, grow as such, the chief epiphyseal plate being between the basi-occipital and the body of the sphenoid.

The bones of the vault of the skull are membranous bones. Regarding their growth there are two conflicting views: (1) In one view, the essential mode of growth is by deposition of bone on the exterior and resorption from the interior, modeling taking place as for long bones (J. C. Brash). (2) The other view is that growth is mainly sutural in all parts of the skull, with depositions and resorptions taking place in various areas both inside and out (J. P. Weinmann and H. Sicher, and L. W. Mednick and S. L. Washburn).

In support of the latter view, if the coronal suture closes prematurely and the metopic and sagittal remain open, the skull becomes unduly broad and high and short (R. K. Rau); whereas, if the metopic and sagittal sutures close prematurely, the result is a long narrow skull (B. H. Dawson and D. A. N. Hoyte).

The growing skeleton is sensitive to relatively slight and transient illnesses and to periods of malnutrition. When a child is ill or starved, his epiphyseal plates, ceasing to proliferate, become heavily calcified; and when growth is resumed, this line of arrested growth appears as a veritable scar. (The annual rings in deciduous trees and on the scales of fish likewise bear evidence of growth retarded or arrested and its resumption.) Figure 15 makes clear that "since the transverse striations remain parallel and equidistant, . . . all growth in length takes place by the apposition of new bone to the ends of the diaphysis at the growth cartilages" (H. A. Harris).

When a particulate radio-opaque substance, such as thorotrast, is injected into the bloodstream, it is taken up by the reticulo-endothelial cells, and apparently it is retained by them indefinitely. Hence, the spleen and liver cast a positive shadow on an X-ray plate, and so does the bone marrow. Employing this technique experimentally in young animals, Mortensen and Guest have shown that, while the expanded ends of a long bone grow farther apart and the medullary cavity enlarges correspondingly, the shadow cast by the part of the marrow infiltrated remains constant in length and the actively growing ends gradually recede from it. This substantiates the work referred to above.

CARTILAGE

Hyaline Cartilage; Fibrocartilage; Elastic Cartilage.

Cartilage or gristle is a connective tissue in which a solid ground substance replaces tissue fluids. It has no blood vessels, lymph vessels, or nerves; so, it is insensitive. There are three types of cartilage: (1) hyaline, (2) fibro- and (3) elastic.

Hyaline Cartilage (Gk. (h)ualos = a transparent stone) is white and resilient. It is potentially bone; in fact, all the bones, except certain skull bones and the clavicle, were preformed in hyaline cartilage.

»» Hyaline cartilage persists in the adult only at the articular ends of bones as articular cartilage, at the sternal ends of the ribs as costal cartilage, and as the cartilages of the nose, larynx, trachea, and bronchi. The thyroid, cricoid, and 1st costal cartilages commonly begin to calcify about the 40th year.

Fibrocartilage has the same structure as fibrous tissue (aponeurosis, ligament, *fig. 53*) save that, the ground substance being solid, the cells are not squeezed into stellate form by the bundles of fibrous tissue, but are round (*fig. 53*). Fibrocartilage bears the same resemblance to fibrous tissue as a starched collar bears to a soft collar. Wherever fibrous tissue is subjected to great pressure, it is replaced by fibrocartilage, which is tough, strong, and resilient.

»» It occurs in intervertebral discs, articular discs (e.g., semilunar cartilages of the knee), glenoid and acetabular labra, and the surface layers of tendons and ligaments that are pressed on by bone. It lines certain bony grooves in which tendons play, and it caps certain bony prominences.

Elastic Cartilage. Here cartilage cells are numerous and the solid ground work is pervaded by elastic fibers; so, it looks yellow. Being elastic, it springs back into shape after being bent.

It is found only in the auricle, external acoustic meatus, auditory tube, and the cartilages guarding the entrance to the larynx.

VERTEBRAL COLUMN

PARTS OF A TYPICAL VERTEBRA AND THEIR FUNCTIONS—*Body; Vertebral Arch; Processes; Ossification.*

ARTICULATED VERTEBRAL COLUMN—*Intervertebral Discs; Bodies of the Vertebrae; Curvatures; Varying Stature; Line of Gravity; Transverse Processes; Pedicles; Laminae; Vertebral Foramina and Vertebral Canal; Articular Processes; Spinous Processes.*

Parts of a Typical Vertebra and Their Functions

The vertebral column is made up of 33 vertebrae, arranged as follows: 7 cervical, 12 thoracic, 5 lumbar, 5 sacral, and 4 coccygeal. The sacral and the coccygeal vertebrae unite to form composite bones, called the os sacrum and coccyx. The 5 sacral vertebrae have completely fused to form a single mass by the 23rd year; a gap, however, often persists between the 1st and 2nd sacral bodies until the 32nd year (McKern and Stewart). The last three pieces of the coccyx fuse together in middle life and these in turn fuse with the first piece still later. There are, therefore, 24 presacral or true vertebrae, of which 12 bear ribs and 12 do not.

Not only have the bones of each region features characteristic of their particular region but every bone in each region has one or more distinguishing features of its own.

A vertebra is composed of the following parts (*fig. 16*):

1. A weight-bearing part—the *body*.
2. A part that protects the spinal cord—the *vertebral arch*.
3. Three levers on which muscles pull—the *spinous process* and the right and left *transverse processes*.
4. Four projections which restrict movements—two superior and two inferior *articular processes*.

The Body of a vertebra (*fig. 17*) resembles the long bones of the limbs in that it is weight-supporting, constricted about its "waist," and enlarged at its two ends, which are articular (although rather flat). Also, it has a primary center of ossification for the "diaphysis" which appears early, and

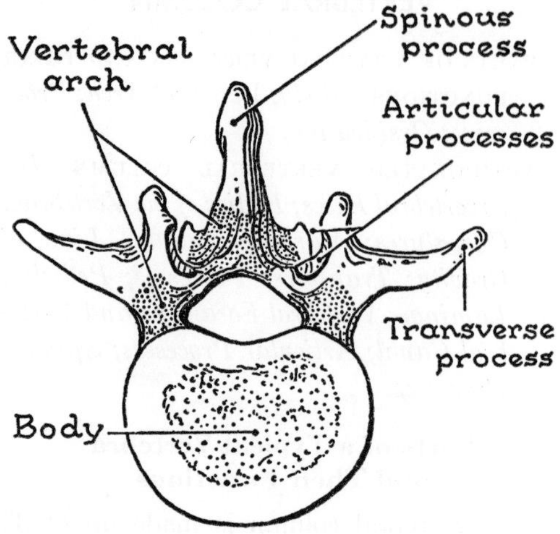

FIG. 16. The parts of a vertebra, from above

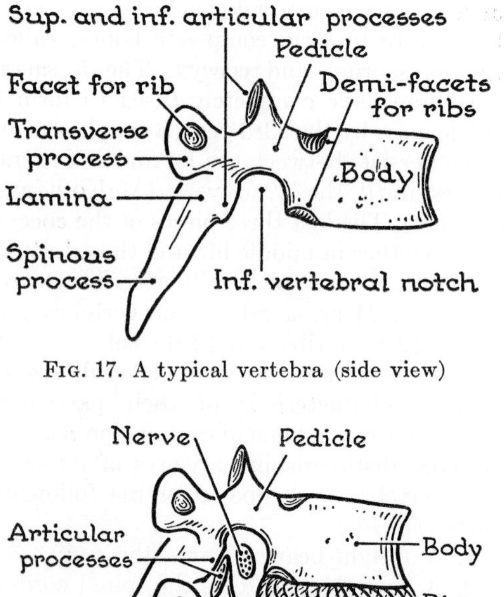

FIG. 17. A typical vertebra (side view)

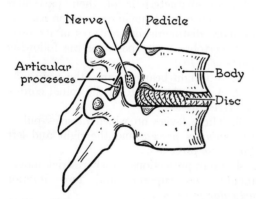

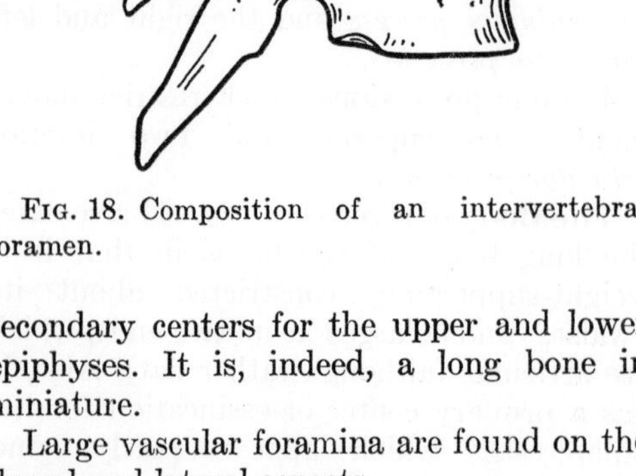

FIG. 18. Composition of an intervertebral foramen.

secondary centers for the upper and lower epiphyses. It is, indeed, a long bone in miniature.

Large vascular foramina are found on the dorsal and lateral aspects.

The Vertebral Arch protects the spinal medulla (spinal cord) from injury, as the roof of the cranium protects the brain. Immediately behind its attachment to its body, each half of the arch is crossed, both above and below, by a spinal nerve. Accordingly, this part of the arch, called the *pedicle* (root) is grooved above and below, but especially below, to allow ample space for the passage of a nerve. The grooves are the *superior* and *inferior vertebral notches.*

The posterior band-like portions of each arch, the *right* and *left laminae,* meet behind in the median plane. A vertebral arch and the posterior aspect of a body enclose a space, the *vertebral foramen,* in which the spinal medulla (spinal cord) and its membranes are lodged.

Transverse and Spinous Processes. The movement of one body on another is effected in part through the actions of muscles on the lever-like transverse and spinous processes, which project like the spokes of a capstan. The transverse processes project laterally on each side from the junction of a pedicle and a lamina; the spinous process or spine projects backward in the median plane from the site of union of a right and a left lamina.

Articular Processes arise near the junction of pedicle and lamina. The superior processes spring rather from pedicles and face in a backward direction (backward and upward in the cervical region; backward and laterally in the thoracic; backward and medially in the lumbar), whereas inferior articular processes spring from laminae and face in contrary directions. It is evident that in all regions the contact established between upper and lower articular processes prevents forward displacement of an upper vertebra on a lower.

The upper and lower surfaces of the bodies are the real articular surfaces of the vertebrae. The articular processes (except those of the atlas and axis) do not transmit weight. Their presence interferes with the unrestricted mobility the bodies might otherwise enjoy and decrees in what direction movements between two adjacent vertebrae shall be allowed. There are, however, circumstances in which they bear weight, e.g., on rising from the stooping position.

Collectively, the vertebral foramina constitute the *vertebral canal.*

Collectively, two adjacent vertebral notches constitute an *intervertebral foramen.* Entering into the composition of an intervertebral foramen are: above and below, pedicles; in front, an intervertebral disc and parts of the two bodies it unites; and behind, two articular processes and the capsule uniting them (*fig. 18*).

Ossification. At birth a vertebra is in three parts—a *centrum* and the right and left sides of a *neural arch,* united to each other by hyaline cartilage (*fig. 19*). The site of union of a centrum and a neural arch is a *neuro-central synchondrosis.*

On a thoracic vertebra, the facets for the heads of the ribs are situated on the neural arches just behind the neuro-central synchondroses; they are not on the sides of the centrum.

Synostosis of the two halves of the arch takes place posteriorly during the 1st year, and of the arch and centrum between the 3rd and 6th years.

Epiphyses. Pressure and traction epiphyses appear about puberty and fuse not later than the 24th year. In most mammals the pressure epiphyses take the form of plates, but in man they are rings, that overlie the upper and lower surfaces of the centrum and extend on to the neural arch (*fig. 27*).

»» The body of a vertebra is a composite of the upper and lower epiphyses and the mass of bone between them. It includes the centrum, parts of the neural arch, and the facets for the heads of the ribs. The terms "body" and "centrum" are not, therefore, strictly speaking interchangeable; neither are the terms "vertebral arch" and "neural arch".

Scale-like traction epiphyses appear on the tips of the spinous and transverse processes.

The advanced student requiring details should consult the following: Cervical vertebrae (p. 642), thoracic vertebrae (p. 464), lumbar vertebrae (p. 285), sacrum and coccyx (p. 315).

ARTICULATED VERTEBRAL COLUMN

The bodies of the vertebrae contribute three-fourths to the total length of the presacral portion of the articulated column; the intervertebral discs contribute one-fourth (*fig. 20*).

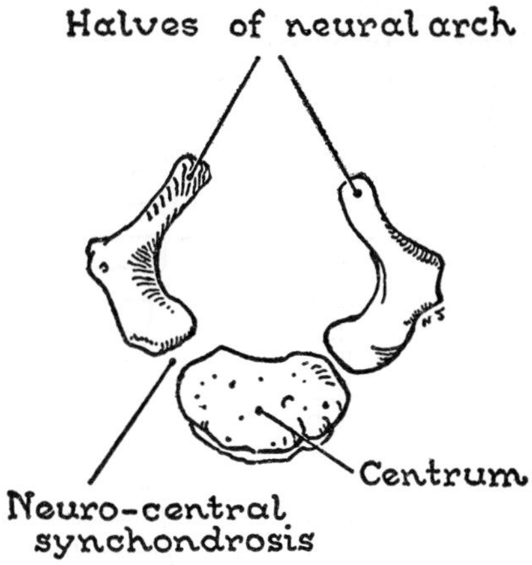

FIG. 19. A vertebra at birth

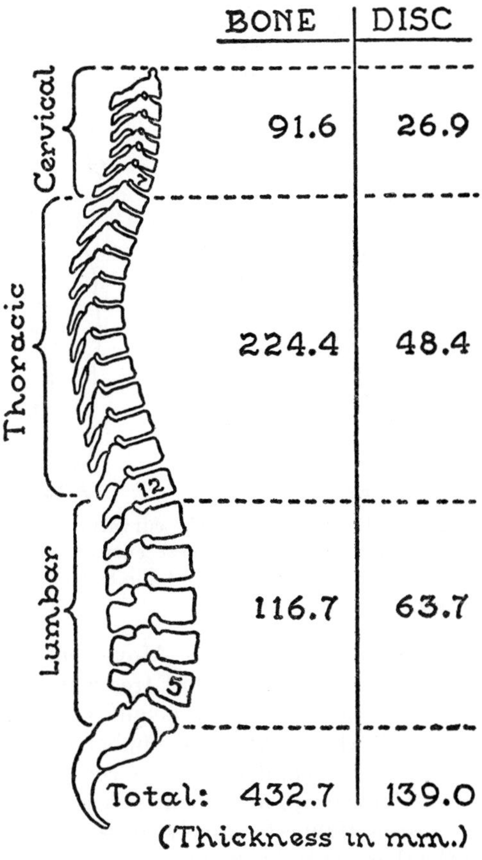

BONE
DISC
Cervical
91.6
26.9
Thoracic
224.4
48.4
12
Lumbar
116.7
63.7
5
Total: 432.7
139.0
(Thickness in mm.)

FIG. 20. Proportions of bone and disc in the presacral parts of the vertebral column (with the use of Todd's data).

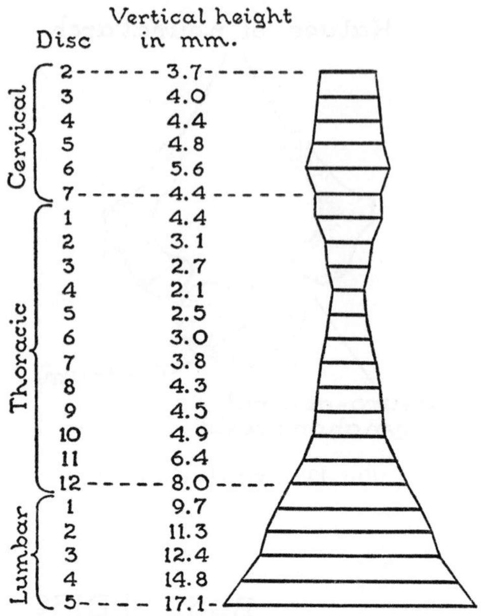

FIG. 21. Graph of the vertical heights of the intervertebral discs. (With the use of Todd's data.)

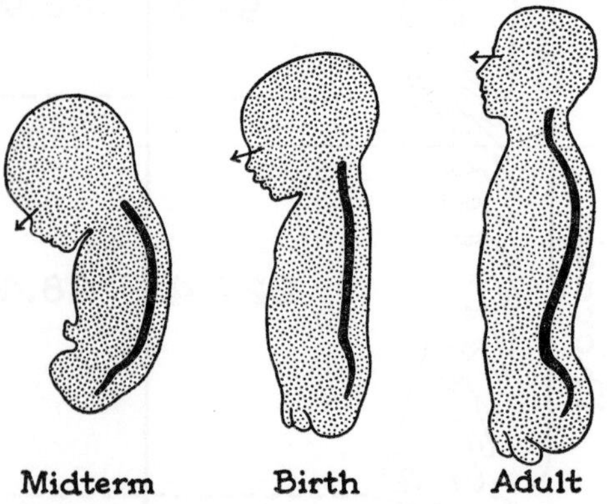

FIG. 22. Development of the curvatures of the spine; the thoracic and sacral curvatures are primary, and the cervical and lumbar are secondary.

Intervertebral Discs. Movement between two vertebrae is most free where the disc is thickest (vertical height greatest), namely, in the cervical and lumbar regions, where the vertebral column is convex forward. Conversely, movement is least where the disc is thinnest, namely, in the regions of the thoracic and pelvic cavities, where the column is concave forward. Indeed, the sacral discs are largely ossified in the adult to form part of the composite sacral bone. Thus, they are thickest in the lower lumbar region and thinnest in the midthoracic region (T. 2–6) (*fig. 21*).

Further, in the cervical and lumbar regions each disc is thicker ventrally than dorsally whereas in the thoracic region the converse is the case; hence, in each region the disc contributes to the curvature of the column.

Bodies of the Vertebrae. As might be expected, the size of the weight-bearing surface of a body depends upon the weight it supports. Accordingly, the upper and lower surfaces increase progressively from above downward to the first piece of the sacrum, and from there to the tip of the coccyx they diminish progressively. This is because the superimposed weight is transferred from the first three pieces of the sacrum to the ilium, thence to the femora when standing up and to the ischial tuberosities when sitting down (*fig. 356*).

The 1st and 2nd cervical vertebrae—the atlas and axis—are highly specialized and their bodies are modified. During development, the tissue that might have become the body of the atlas becomes attached to the upper surface of the axis, forming a tooth-like upward prolongation, the *dens* of the axis. The support of the skull is shifted to a pair of concave facets on the atlas.

In lieu of a body, the *atlas* has an anterior arch which lies in front of the dens and of the plane of the bodies generally; it holds the lateral masses of the atlas together.

The upper surface of the body of a *cervical* vertebra is oblong and, having upturned back and sides and, being rounded off in front, it resembles a seat. The lower surface is the counterpart of this. The upper and lower surfaces of the thoracic and lumbar bodies are flat, the *thoracic* being heart-shaped with long diameter anteroposterior and the *lumbar* being kidney-shaped with long diameter transverse.

Curvatures. In prenatal life the vertebral column is uniformly curved so as to be concave ventrally (*fig. 22*). In the thoracic and sacro-coccygeal regions these concavities persist and thereby add to the capacity of the thoracic and pelvic cavities.

The bodies of the thoracic and of most sacral vertebrae conform to the curvatures in being deeper behind than in front. The cervical and lumbar regions do not partake in cavities; so, by way of compensation, they are convex ventrally. The cervical curvature (convexity) appears when the infant learns to hold its head erect and to direct its visual axes forward, about the 3rd month. The lumbar curvature (convexity) appears when the child acquires the art of walking erect, about the 18th month. The thoracic and sacral curvatures, therefore, are *primary curvatures;* the cervical and lumbar are *secondary or compensatory.*

You might surmise that since the thoracic and sacral bodies are deeper behind than in front, the cervical and lumbar bodies would be deeper in front than behind. But, it is not so. These two unhampered regions are rich in intervertebral disc and therefore are supple. In the cervical region the bodies are of equal depth in front and behind; so, the cervical curvature is due solely to disc. In the lumbar region the 5th and 4th bodies are deeper in front, the 3rd and 2nd are variable, and the 1st is deeper behind.

Varying Stature. One may be shorter in the evening than in the morning because with fatigue (1) the curvatures of the spine may increase, (2) the turgor of the pulp of the intervertebral discs may be reduced; and (3) the height of the arches of the feet may be lessened. On the other hand, the stature increases when one lies down.

The **Line of Gravity** passes through the dens of the axis, just in front of the sacral promontory, behind the centers of the hip joints, and in front of the knee and ankle joints (*fig. 23*).

FIG. 23. The line of gravity

Transverse Processes arise between upper and lower articular processes at the junctions of pedicles with laminae, and project laterally. In the *thoracic* region they act not only as levers for muscles but also as fulcra for the ribs; so, they are strong and stout and, in conformity with the backward curving of the ribs, they have a backward and upward inclination. Their tips bear articular facets, the shape and direction of which vary for reasons concerned with the mechanism of respiration (p. 497 and *fig. 554*). The 11th and 12th ribs are floating; so, the transverse processes of the 11th and 12th vertebrae are reduced in size and carry no facets. The spread of the thoracic transverse processes diminishes from 1st to 12th.

Each *cervical* transverse process has a circular foramen, the *foramen transversarium.* The upper six foramina transmit the vertebral artery; the 7th transmits only veins. Each process, therefore, has two roots, a posterior and an anterior. All posterior roots end in tubercles for tendons; but of the anterior roots only the 3rd, 4th, 5th, and 6th have tubercles, the 6th being the largest. The processes and bodies collectively form an approximately flat anterior surface.

The *lumbar* transverse processes may be regarded as ossifications extending into the posterior aponeurosis of the Transversus

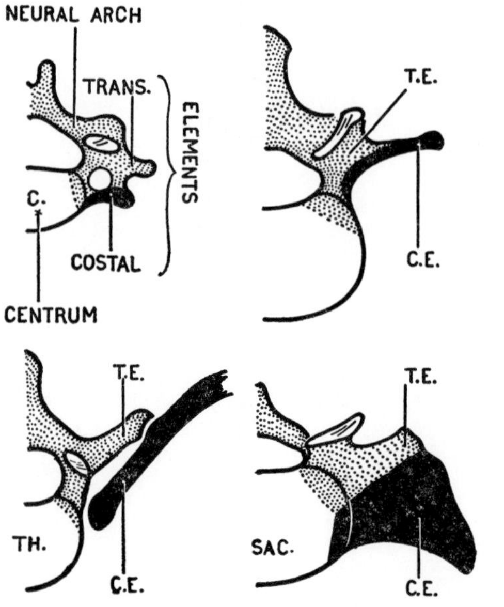

FIG. 23.1. Homologous parts of cervical, thoracic, lumbar, and sacral vertebrae. (*Clear* = centrum; *Stippled* = neural arch, transverse and spinous processes; *black* = costal element.)

Abdominis; so, they are thin and flat, except at their tips which take the pull of the muscle (*fig. 323*). From 1st to 5th their roots creep progressively farther forward toward the bodies. Conforming to the shape of the rounded abdominal cavity, they are directed slightly backward. They are not noted for their strength. Since the 4th lumbar vertebra lies at the level of the highest part of the iliac crest, it follows that the 5th lumbar vertebra must lie below the highest part of the crest (see page 320).

Morphology of the Transverse Processes. Except in the thoracic region, a transverse process comprises two elements—a *costal* or rib element and a true or *morphological* transverse process, as is made clear by figure 23.1.

Pedicles spring from the upper half of the sides of the bodies; vertebral notches mainly lie behind the lower half. *Intervertebral foramina* increase in size from above downward to the midlumbar region (*figs. 17 and 18*).

Laminae overlap markedly in the thoracic region and slightly in the cervical region. In the lumbar region there are *interlaminar gaps*, and also in the cervical region when the neck is bent. The largest gaps are between skull and atlas, atlas and axis, 4th and 5th lumbar vertebrae, and 5th lumbar vertebra and sacrum.

Vertebral Foramina and Vertebral Canal. In the thoracic region the vertebral canal is circular and of the diameter of a signet ring, circular because the spinal cord is here cylindrical; but in the regions from which the brachial and lumbo-sacral plexuses spring the canal is larger and triangular, or rather it is expanded transversely in adaptation to the more laterally expanded cord. Hence, when exposing the spinal cord, be careful to make the saw cuts converge on a canal no larger than a finger (*fig. 24*).

In the upper three cervical vertebrae, the vertebral canal is very roomy—so roomy that free movement between the head and the neck does not constrict the spinal cord [medulla].

Articular Processes. In all three regions —cervical, thoracic, lumbar—the articular processes prevent the vertebrae from slipping forwards, and they allow flexion and extension. In addition, the *cervical articular processes* allow one to look sideways and upward, because their upper facets mostly face obliquely upward, laterally, and back-

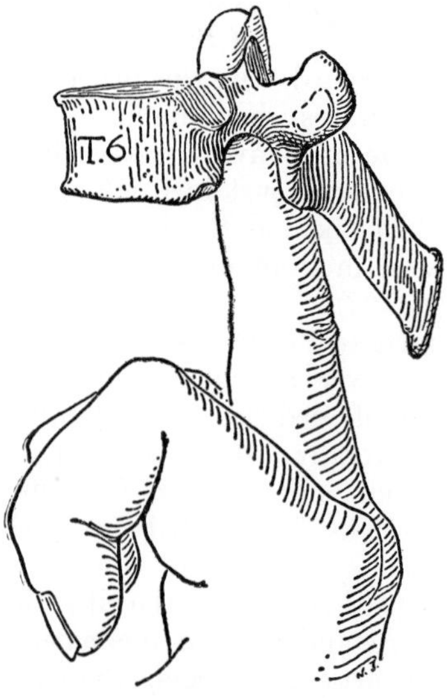

FIG. 24. A vertebral foramen is not larger than a finger-ring.

ward. The *thoracic* processes allow rotation, because they are set vertically on the arc of a circle (*fig. 545*). The *lumbar* processes prevent rotation, but allow side bending. They change direction progressively: the inferior processes of L. 1 facing laterally, and those of L. 5 forward.

Note on the laminae the arresting grooves made on full extension by the inferior articular processes of the vertebra next above.

Spinous Processes. The spinous processes become more massive as they are followed from higher to lower levels. The pull on each, as in rising from the stooping posture, is mainly a caudalward one; hence, each is directed caudalward. That of the 1st *cervial* is reduced to a tubercle. In modern man, cervical spines 2–6 are bifid. The 7th ends in a tubercle and is prominent, but not so prominent as the 1st thoracic. In the *thoracic* region the middle four spines—those behind the pericardium—are markedly overlapping (*figs. 543 and 548*). The 1st and 2nd, and the 11th and 12th are nearly horizontal. The *lumbar* spines are thick oblong plates with thickened ends. The 5th (and 4th) *sacral* spines and laminae are absent and the sacral canal is exposed. The sacral articular processes on each side fuse to form an irregular crest which ends below in a cornu (horn). This cornu articulates with the cornu of the coccyx.

ARTICULATIONS OR JOINTS

SKULL TYPE—*Suture and Synchondrosis; Synostosis.*

VERTEBRAL TYPE—*Symphysis; Symphysis between Two Vertebral Bodies; Syndesmosis; Vertebral Syndesmoses.*

LIMB TYPE—*Synovial Joint: articular capsule, joint cavity, synovial membrane and folds, synovia, fat-pads, articular discs, ligaments, articular cartilage, lubrication, labra, nerves, and vessels.*

Classification of Synovial Joints.

A joint is a junction between two or more bones. Joints may be classified as immovable, slightly movable, and freely movable; but perhaps it is more helpful to consider them as:

1. The *skull type:* Immovable or temporary joint.
2. The *vertebral type:* Slightly movable or secure joint.
3. The *limb type:* Freely movable, insecure, or synovial joint.

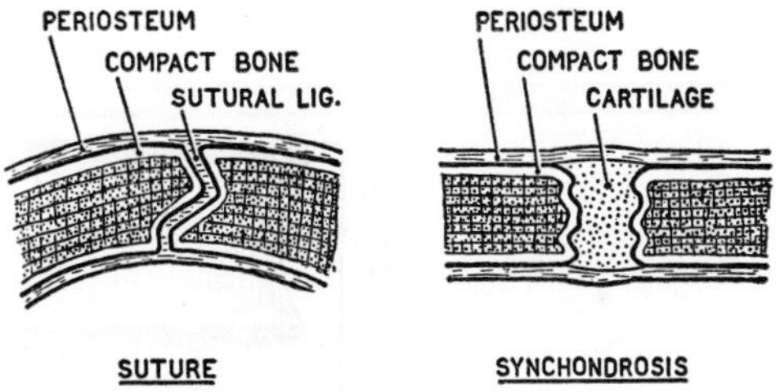

FIG. 25. A suture and a synchondrosis

Skull Type of Joint

The skull type is either a suture or a synchondrosis depending on whether the bones concerned ossify in membrane or in cartilage; it is immovable (*fig. 25*).

Suture. When the growing edges of two bones (or ossific centers) developing in membrane come together, a residual film of membrane may persist unossified between them for some years, till middle age, or indefinitely. Such a union is called a suture; and sutures are confined to the skull (*fig. 25*). The edges may interlock in jig-saw fashion, or like the teeth of a saw (*fig. 667*). They may be bevelled and overlapping or relatively flat and abutting. A ridge may fit into a groove, as it does between sphenoid and vomer.

Synchondrosis. Similarly when the growing edges of two bones (or ossific centers) developing in a single mass of cartilage come together, a residual plate of cartilage may persist unossified between them for a number of years. Such a union is a synchondrosis.

»»*Sites.* Synchondroses occur at the base of the skull between the basi-occipital and basi-sphenoid, sphenoid and ethmoid, petrous-temporal and basi-occipital, and petrous-temporal and jugular process. Their distribution however is widespread, for is it not by synchrondroses (epiphyseal plates) that epiphyses are united to bones? (*fig. 13.*)

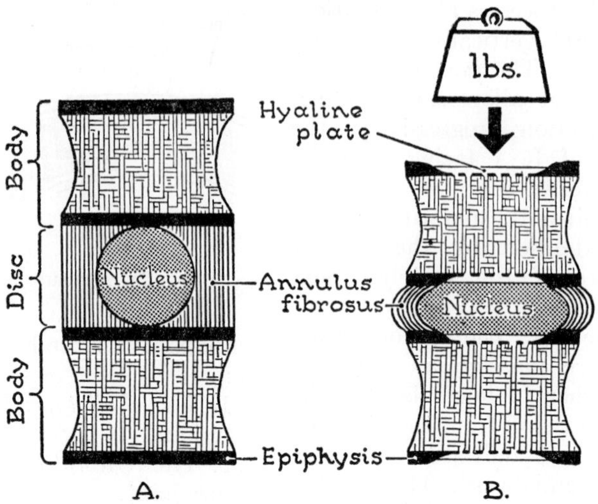

FIG. 26. Scheme of an intervertebral disc (*Annulus*, old terminology = *Anulus*, N. A. P.)

Synostosis is the obliteration of a suture or a synchondrosis by bone. It is associated with cessation of growth locally.

Vertebral Type of Joint

The vertebral type is either a symphysis or a syndesmosis. Intervertebral joints are built for strength and security; so, their opposed bony surfaces are firmly bound together. This minimizes the risk of dislocation, which here would be disastrous; it also greatly restricts mobility.

A **Symphysis** is a joint where two opposed bony surfaces are coated with hyaline cartilage, are united by fibrocartilage, and are further united in front and behind by ligamentous bands. There is no joint cavity, but a small cleft may be present.

»»*Sites.* Symphyses occur (1) between the bodies of vertebrae, (2) between the pubic bones, and (3) between the manubrium and body of the sternum. They are all situated in the median plane.

The Symphysis between Two Vertebral Bodies. The upper and lower surfaces of the body of a vertebra each consist of hyaline cartilage. In the periphery of the cartilage a ring-shaped bony epiphysis appears (*fig. 27*) and finally fuses with the rest of the body in early adult life. The cartilaginous plate persists and must be regarded as helping to enclose an intervertebral disc.

Intervertebral Discs (*fig. 26*). Adjacent

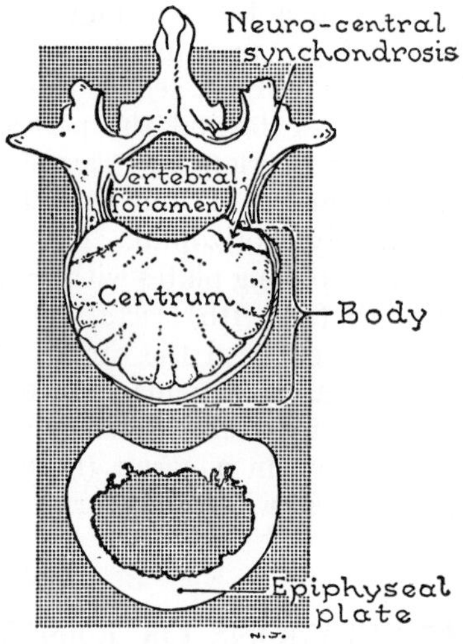

FIG. 27. A vertebra in childhood

bodies are united by a fibro-cartilaginous disc whose peripheral part is composed of about a dozen concentric layers of fibers, the *anulus fibrosus.* The fibers in alternate layers cross like the limbs of the letter X. The center of the disc is filled with a fibrogelatinous pulp, the *nucleus pulposus,* which acts as a cushion or shock absorber.

Longitudinal Ligaments of the Bodies, an anterior and a posterior, extend from sacrum to base of skull: the one is attached to the intervertebral discs and adjacent margins of the vertebral bodies anteriorly; the other is attached to them posteriorly, within the vertebral canal. The anterior ligament is a broad, strong band, except above, where it becomes a cord that gains attachment to the anterior tubercle of the atlas and extends above it to the pharyngeal tubercle of the basi-occipital. The posterior ligament is weak and narrow, but it widens where it is attached to the backs of the discs. Its upper end is the membrana tectoria (p. 647).

»» *Note.* (1) The hyaline plate is apt to crack and the nucleus pulposus to herniate through it into the cancellous body of the vertebra; and (2) the pulp may burst through the anulus fibrosus posteriorly, where it is thinnest, and protrude under cover of the posterior longitudinal ligament. These accidents happen commonly.

Vessels and Nerves. Small blood vessels from the marrow spaces pass through the hyaline plate to supply the disc until the 8th year, and some of these may persist until the 20th or 30th years. (Coventry et al.; and others.) Branches of the spinal nerves have been traced to the longitudinal ligaments and to the anulus (Roofe; and others).

A **Syndesmosis** is a union by ligamentous fibers, the bony points united being some distance apart.

»» *Sites.* Syndesmoses occur between the vertebral arches, and between the lever-like processes of the vertebrae, also between coracoid and clavicle (coracoclavicular lig.), and between the bones of the forearm and of the leg (interosseous membranes) including the inferior tibio-fibular joint.

Vertebral Syndesmoses. The laminae of adjacent vertebrae are united by yellow elastic fibers, called a *ligamentum flavum.* These broad bands unite the upper border and posterior surface of one lamina to the lower border and anterior surface of the lamina above. By virtue of their elasticity, the ligamenta flava serve as "muscle sparers," i.e., they assist in the recovery to the erect posture after bending forward and they are particularly strong in the lumbar region.

The adjacent borders of the spinous processes are united by weak *interspinous ligaments* and their tips are united by the strong *supraspinous ligament,* which in the neck become the *ligamentum nuchae* (p. 560). The transverse processes may be connected by weak *intertransverse ligaments.*

The articular processes of the vertebrae are united by articular capsules to form *Joints of the Limb Type.* These have synovial folds and fat-pads.

»» In the lumbar region lateral extensions of the plate-like ligamenta flava close the joint cavities anteriorly.

So, typical vertebrae are united to each other by three types of joints: symphyses, syndesmoses, and synovial joints.

Limb Type of Joint
(Synovial Joint or Articulation)

The limbs being primarily organs of locomotion have joints that permit free movement; so, the site which in a symphysis is occupied by fibrocartilage becomes a synovial joint cavity. This makes for insecurity.

At the limb type of joint the ends of two (or more) bones are capped with hyaline cartilage and are united by an *articular capsule* (*fig 28*). This consists of a short sleeve of fibrous tissue, called the *fibrous capsule,* which extends well beyond the articular (hyaline) cartilage, and it is lined with an inner sleeve of synovial membrane (the synovial capsule). The synovial membrane is reflected from the fibrous capsule on to the bone, and this it covers right up to the articular cartilage.

A Synovial or Joint Cavity develops as a

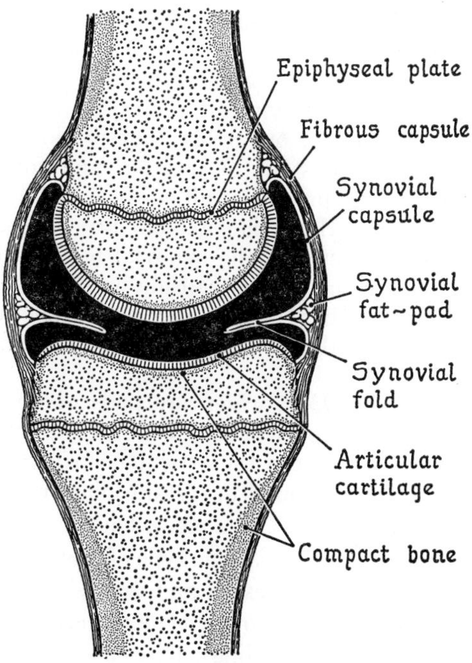

FIG. 28. A synovial joint, on section

cleft between the ends of the primitive bones, and it may be helpful to think of it as being originally lined throughout with synovial membrane, and to think of this synovial membrane as persisting except where it is worn away at areas of pressure and of friction. At these sites there is articular cartilage.

Synovial or joint cavities, then, are lined either with articular cartilage or with synovial membrane.

A Synovial Membrane is a thin sheet of areolar tissue (*fig. 53*) which is characterized by its richness in blood vessels and lymphatics, and the absence of a continuous lining of mesothelial cells (such as is possessed by peritoneum, the membrane lining the abdominal cavity).

The membrane can be dissected from the fibrous capsule and from the bone, but it is intimately adherent to the pressure surfaces of such fibrocartilages and tendons as enter into joints. The film of lubricating and nourishing fluid within the synovial cavity resembles white of egg; hence, it is called synovia or synovial fluid.

Synovia or Synovial Fluid is a dialysate of blood plasma plus a mucin, called *hyaluronic acid*, and to it the viscosity and lubricating properties of the synovia are due.

Transparent *folds of synovial membrane* containing fat at their attached borders project into all synovial joints, commonly for a centimeter or farther. These folds are practically constant in position and form, and they are present at all ages (*fig. 203*).

Fat-pads (Haversian glands) are pads of fat placed between the synovial membrane and either the fibrous capsule or the bone. Fat being very pliant, the pads can accommodate themselves to changing conditions.

Articular Discs, which are pads of fibrocartilage (or of condensed fibrous tissue) interposed between the articular surfaces of two bones, are found in certain joints where double movements take place. On the proximal surface of the disc one type of movement takes place (e.g., flexion and extension); on the distal surface another type of movement (e.g., rotation or gliding). Discs are nonvascular and non-nervous, except at their

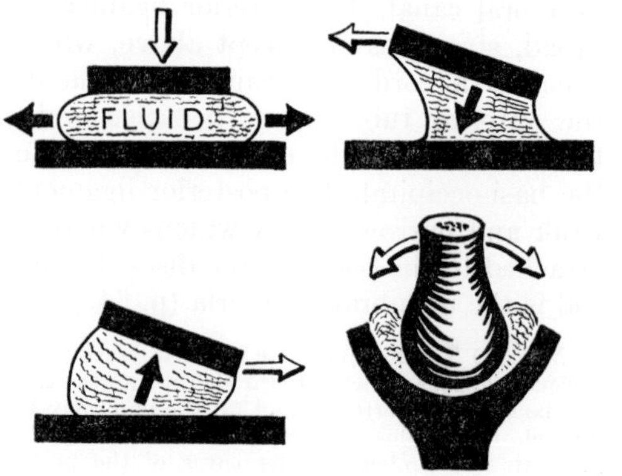

FIG. 29. Lubrication, with the use of a convergent film of viscous fluid.

peripheral attachments. They are nourished by synovial fluid.

»» *Sites*. Discs are found in the temporo-mandibular, sterno-clavicular, acromio-clavicular, radio-ulnar, and knee joints. (In the carnivora, however, only hinge movement is allowed at the temporo-mandibular joint, despite the presence of a disc.)

Ligaments. The fibrous capsule is thickened in parts to form cords and bands, called *ligaments*, which withstand temporary strains. Other ligaments are independent of the capsule.

Articular Cartilage, having neither blood vessels nor lymphatics (nor has it any nerves), must receive its nourishment by the diffusion of fluids. There is evidence that the synovial fluid nourishes the cartilage from its free surface and the epiphyseal vessels from its attached surface (Ekholm). It is known that detached pieces of articular cartilage can live, and even grow, in synovial fluid.

Lubrication (*fig. 29*). The articular components of a synovial joint are incongruous; that is, they do not fit each other reciprocally, as do structures made by machine. If apposing surfaces are parallel or congruous, there can be no self-lubrication. Self-lubrication seems to be dependent upon the presence of (1) a thin, convergent, or wedge-shaped space, (2) a viscous fluid, and (3) a certain speed of movement. Given these three factors, two bearing surfaces will be completely separated by a film of lubricant (MacConaill).

Articular discs, menisci, and synovial fat-pads and folds are important aids to the formation of thin wedge-shaped films. When at rest, there is no film between weight-bearing surfaces. Indeed, Charnley holds that such a film plays no important role. He emphasizes "boundary lubrication," which depends upon entrapped hyaluronic acid in the spongy articular cartilage. Davies has shown that in cattle and sheep the viscosity of the synovial fluid varies considerably from joint to joint.

Labra. Fibrous tissue, subjected to great pressure and friction, gives place to fibro-cartilage, e.g., articular discs. The shoulder and hip joint each has its socket deepened by a pliable ring of fibro-cartilage called its labrum (L., lip).

Epiphyseal Plates. In some joints the line of attachments of the fibrous capsule may be "beyond" the edges of the epiphyseal plate (e.g., hip joint, *fig. 496*).

Nerve Endings are found in the fibrous capsule and synovial membrane. Those in the fibrous capsule are of a type associated with position-sense or proprioception (Ruffini corpuscles) and with pain (free endings). Those in the synovial membrane and its prolongations are believed to be pain receptors and, being associated with blood vessels, they probably supply them (E. Gardner). Articular cartilage has no nerves, nor have discs except at their attached margins.

Blood and Lymph Vessels are a feature of synovial membrane, but they are absent from articular cartilage.

Main arteries keep to the flexor surfaces of joints. Here they are protected from injury, but, during flexion of the joint, they are bent and may thus be occluded; hence, a collateral circulation, such as is found at the elbow, wrist, knee, and ankle, serves as a useful by-pass.

Bursae. See page 24.

Classification of Synovial Joints

1. Plane. *Arthrodial or gliding joint:* The apposed bony surfaces are approximately flat, e.g., carpal joints and joints of the small tarsals.

2. Uniaxial. (*1*) *Hinge or ginglymus joint:* one surface is concave, the other convex, and movement takes place on a horizontal axis, e.g., the elbow and ankle. (*2*) *Pivot or trochoid joint:* a ring encircles a pivot set on a vertical axis, and rotation takes place as with a door on a hinge, viz., atlanto-axial and proximal radio-ulnar joints.

3. Biaxial. Circumduction is permitted; i.e., on performing the movements of flexion, abduction, extension, and adduction in sequence, a cone is described.

(*1*) *Condyloid joint:* one bony surface is a ball and the other a socket, but rotation is not a conspicuous feature, e.g., the metacarpo-phalangeal (knuckle) joints. (*2*) *Ellipsoid joint:* one surface is an oval and the other a socket, e.g., the radio-carpal (wrist) joint.

4. Multiaxial. Movements of circumduction and of axial rotation are permitted. (*1*) *Ball and socket joint:* a ball fits into a socket and provides a universal joint; the shoulder and hip joints. (*2*) *Saddle joint:* the surfaces are reciprocally saddle-shaped; the carpo-metacarpal joint of the thumb.

MUSCLES

Types of Muscles.
Skeletal Muscles: Fibers; Parts; Insertions; Synovial Bursa; Synovial Sheath.
Internal Structure; Contraction; Investigation; Electromyography; Muscle Action.
Blood Supply; Nerves; Nomenclature; Variations; Accessory Muscles.

It is from the fancied resemblance certain muscles bear to mice, the tendons presumably being their tails, that the diminutive term "muscle" is derived (L. mus = a mouse).

There are three types of muscular tissue. (1) *skeletal* or voluntary, such as occurs in the muscles of the limbs, body wall, and face, (2) *heart* or cardiac, which is confined to the heart, and (3) *smooth*, visceral, or involuntary, such as is found in the stomach, bladder, and blood vessels.

Skeletal muscles are under the control of the will; hence, they are alternatively called voluntary muscles. Histologically their fibers possess light and dark cross-striations. Heart muscle also is striated, but neither heart muscle nor smooth muscle is under voluntary control; they are both involuntary. The accompanying table indicates that the terms striated and involuntary are comprehensive.

Appearance	Restrictive Name	Control
Striated	{skeletal	or voluntary
	{heart	involuntary
Nonstriated or smooth		involuntary

To contract and to relax is the function of all three types of muscle. Skeletal or voluntary muscles mostly pass from one bone across a joint (or joints) to another bone, and by contracting they approximate their sites of attachment; hence, they act upon joints. Heart muscle and smooth muscle mostly form the walls of cavities and tubes, and by contracting they expel the contents.

The distinction between voluntary and smooth muscle on the basis of their ability to be controlled by the will is not always clear. Thus, the diaphragm is structurally a voluntary muscle like the Biceps, and though it can be controlled voluntarily, as on taking a deep breath or on holding the breath, ordinarily it works automatically. Again, the upper part of the esophagus is supplied with voluntary muscle and the lower part with smooth, yet voluntary control cannot be exercised over either part.

It would appear that the distribution of voluntary and smooth muscle is determined not so much by the type of control required as by the character of the contraction required, voluntary (skeletal) muscle having the property of rapid contraction; smooth muscle, of slow sustained contraction without fatigue.

Skeletal or Voluntary Muscle is the subject of the remainder of this section. The red or lean of a roast of beef is voluntary muscle. Voluntary muscles form about 43% of the total body weight. They are the engines or motors of the body. When they contract, by bringing two bony points closer together, they act on joints, producing movement.

Fibers. The "fibers" of a voluntary muscle are in reality elongated cells consisting of protoplasm or sarcoplasm, several nuclei, and a cell membrane, the *sarcolemma* (Gk. sarx = flesh; lemma = a husk or skin; *cf.* sarcophagus, sarcoma). The fibers range from about 1 mm. to 41 mm. in length. Around each individual fiber there is some loose areolar tissue (endomysium), around a collection of fibers there is more (perimysium), and around the entire muscle still more (the muscle sheath). This areolar tissue permits swelling, gliding and, indeed, independent action of the enclosed fiber or collection of fibers. In a length of muscle, such as the Sartorius, several fibers are arranged more or less end to end. Regarded macroscopically such a chain of fibers is commonly referred to as a fiber, which, in a functional sense, it is.

In some animals muscle fibers are *red* or *dark*, as in the leg of a chicken; others are *white* or *pale*, as in the breast. In man, red and white fibers are said to be mixed in different proportions in different muscles, but this needs confirmation (E. W. Walls).

Exceptions. Though skeletal muscles typically cross at least one joint and are attached at both ends to bone, the attachment is commonly in part via the medium of deep fascia, intermuscular septa, interosseous membranes, or ligaments, which being fibrous will not stretch. But certain voluntary muscles, particularly those of the face, are by one end attached to *skin*—through them we express our emotions; others, articular muscles, are by one end attached to the synovial capsules of joints—an *articular muscle*, by withdrawing the capsule saves it from being nipped; still others form rings or *sphincters* around the entrance to the orbital cavity, mouth, and anal canal—these close the eyelids, lips, and anus, respectively. The *constrictors* of the pharynx constitute what practically is a tubular muscle; the striated muscle of the esophagus actually is tubular. The Transversus Abdominis and the diaphragm are constrictors or compressors of the abdominal contents.

The Parts of a Muscle. The proximal attachment of a limb muscle is called the

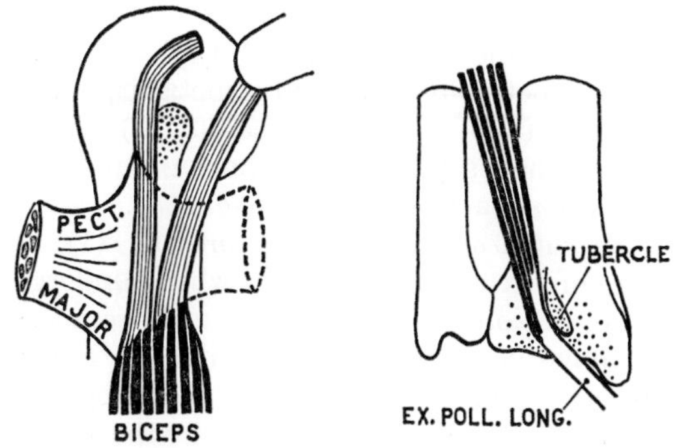

FIG. 30. Two examples demonstrating a principle: where a muscle is subjected to pressure or friction its fleshy fibers are replaced by tendon or aponeurosis.

origin, and the distal attachment the *insertion*, for reasons given on page xv. The fleshy part of a muscle is sometimes referred to as the *fleshy belly*. Some muscles are fleshy from end to end, but most are fibrous at one end or at both. The fibrous end has the same histological structure as ligament. When rounded it is called a *tendon*, when flattened and membranous, an *aponeurosis*, which suggests that it is nervous—but the ancients did not distinguish between nerves, ligaments, and tendinous structures.

The two chief component parts of a voluntary muscle, then, are (1) the fleshy and (2) the fibrous (tendon or aponeurosis). These have contrasting properties: *fleshy fibers* are highly specialized, contractile, vascular, expensive in upkeep, and resistant to infection, but they cannot survive pressure or friction; *tendons* are unspecialized, inelastic, nonvascular, and inexpensive in upkeep. They are designed to withstand pressure, but owing to their meager blood supply they readily die (slough) when exposed to infection. Where a muscle presses on bone, ligament, tendon, or other unyielding structure, the fleshy fibers always give place to tendon (*fig. 30*). Further, if the tendon is subjected to friction, a lubricating device—a synovial *bursa* or a *synovial sheath*—is always interposed.

It is a matter of common observation that the cross-sectional area of the tendon of a muscle is much less than that of the fleshy belly (*figs. 30.1* and *61.1*). Hence, a muscle that arises by fleshy fibers and is inserted by tendon has a much more extensive origin than insertion. Hence, the precise site of attachment of a tendon, where the force of a muscle pull is concentrated and focused, is of much greater practical importance than that of a wide spread fleshy attachment. At fleshy attachments forces are dissipated and make no mark on the bone, but at tendinous attachments forces are concentrated and do. Thus, tendinous attachments create ridges, tubercles, and facets, and if large they may produce traction epiphyses.

Tendons are immensely strong; it is estimated that a tendon whose cross-sectional area is 1 inch square is capable of supporting a weight of from 9,700 to 18,000 lbs. (Cronkite).

The fibers of a tendon are not strictly parallel, but plaited; they twine about each other in such a manner that fibers from any given point at the fleshy end of the tendon are represented at all points at the insertional end (*fig. 31 A*); hence, the pull of the whole muscle can be transmitted to any part of the insertion. The fan-shaped manner in which most tendons

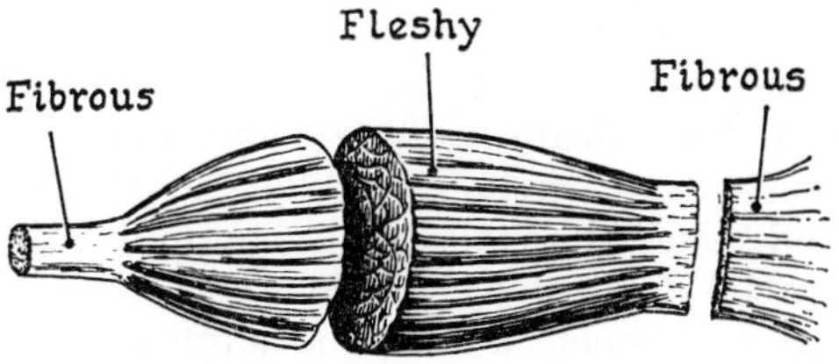

FIG. 30.1. Cross sections of tendons and fleshy belly compared.

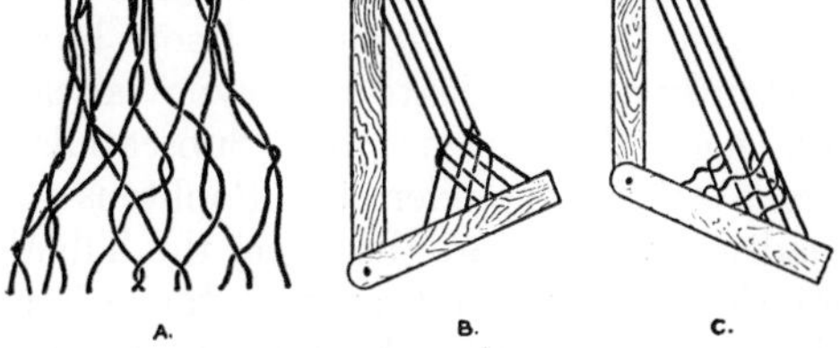

FIG. 31. *A*, the fibers of a tendon are plaited. *B* and *C*, in different positions of a joint different fibers take the strain. (After Mollier.)

are inserted into bone ensures that successive parts of the insertion shall take the full pull of the muscle as the angle of the joint changes (*fig. 31, B* and *C*).

The fibers of tendons, ligaments, and other fibrous structures commonly pass through a pad of fibrocartilage before plunging into their bony attachment. Like the rubber pad employed by the electrician at the junction of the free and the fixed point of a wire, the pads help to prevent fraying from frequent flexing.

Insertions. Muscles are usually inserted near the proximal end of a bone (or lever), close around a joint, close to an axis of movement (e.g., Biceps, Brachialis, and Triceps at the elbow). So, they help to retain in apposition the ends of the bones taking part in the joint, and thereby give it strength. By being thus inserted they produce, on contracting, rapid movement of the distal end.

Some muscles are inserted near the middle of the shaft of a bone (e.g., Deltoid, Coracobrachialis, Pronator Teres, Adductors of the thigh) and a few are inserted near the distal end (e.g., Brachio-radialis, part of Adductor Magnus).

A Synovial Bursa (L. bursa = a purse) is a closed sac differentiated out of areolar tissue. It is roughly the size and shape of a coin. Its delicate walls are separated from each other merely by a film of slippery fluid, like white of egg. As a lubricating device, diminishing friction and allowing free movement, a bursa is more effective than areolar tissue.

Bursae may be classified thus—subtendinous, articular, and subcutaneous.

Subtendinous bursae are found wherever tendons rub against resistant structures, such as bone, cartilage, ligament, or other tendons; hence, they are commonest in the limbs (*fig. 122*). Certain subtendinous bursae constantly communicate with synovial cavities, e.g., the Biceps and Subscapularis bursae at the shoulder, the Popliteus and Quadriceps bursae at the knee, the Tibialis Anterior bursa at the tarso-metatarsal joint; others do so inconstantly, e.g., the Psoas b. at the hip and the Gastrocnemius b. at the knee.

"Articular" bursae play the part of joint cavities between dens of the axis and transverse ligament of the atlas (*figs. 746 and 747*), between adjacent metacarpophalangeal (and metatarso-phalangeal) joints where they separate neighboring capsules, and the subacromial bursa (*fig. 183*).

Subcutaneous bursae are present (1) at the convex surface of joints which undergo acute flexion, because here the skin requires to move very freely, e.g., behind the elbow (olecranon b.), in front of the knee (prepatellar b.) and, sometimes, dorsal to the metacarpo-phalangeal and interphalangeal joints; (2) over bony and ligamentous points subjected to considerable pressure and friction. Most of these, being acquired or occupational, are inconstant, e.g., those lying superficial to: acromion, ischial tuberosity, lig. patellae, tuberosity of the tibia, malleoli, insertion of the tendo calcaneus, and head of the first metatarsal (medial side).

A Synovial Sheath is a tubular bursa that envelops a tendon. In fact, it is two tubes, one within the other. The inner or *visceral tube* adheres closely to the tendon and is separated from the outer or *parietal tube* by the synovial cavity. The visceral and parietal tubes are united longitudinally, along the surface least subjected to pressure, by a synovial fold, the *mesotendon*, which transmits vessels to the tendon (*fig. 32*). If the range of movement of the tendon is considerable, the mesotendon may disappear (e.g., Peronei Longus et Brevis) or be represented by threads, *vincula* (e.g., long digital flexors).

A synovial sheath is required only where a tendon is subjected to friction or pressure on two or more surfaces (front and back). This condition obtains only at the hand, foot, and shoulder. In all instances it so happens that the friction results from the presence of bone on one surface and of a

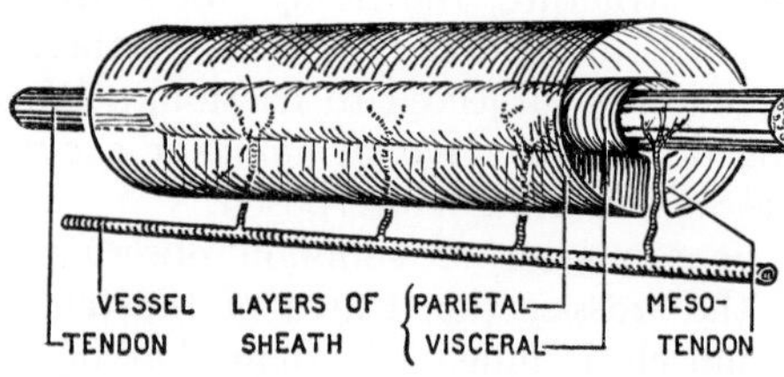

Fig. 32. Diagram of a synovial sheath

retinacular ligament on the other. In order to allow ample play such sheaths extend about ½″ above and below the sites of friction.

Architecture or Internal Structure. The fleshy fibers of a muscle may be disposed either (1) parallel to the long axis of the muscle, (2) obliquely, like the barbs of a feather, or (3) radially like a fan.

The functional differences between the parallel and the oblique type is this. The parallel type has long fibers (or chains of fibers) but relatively few of them, therefore it can lift a light weight through a long distance. The oblique type has short fibers, but they are very numerous; therefore, it can lift a heavy weight through a short distance.

1. Fibers Parallel to the Long Axis of the Muscle or approximately so (*fig. 33*). The fleshy fibers may be *parallel* from end to end, perhaps having a short tendon or aponeurosis at one end or at both ends. This includes many strap-like and flat muscles (e.g., Sternomastoid, Rhomboids, Rectus Abdominis, Gluteus Maximus, and Sartorius). Here may be included the *fusiform type*, which has a tendon at one end or at both ends (e.g., Biceps Brachii, Semitendinosus, and Fl. Carpi Radialis).

2. Fibers Oblique to the Long Axis of the Muscle (*fig. 34*). From their resemblance to feathers these muscles are called *pennate*, the fleshy fibers corresponding to the barbs of the feather and the tendon to the shaft, for they are all inserted by tendon. They are (1) *unipennate* when the fleshy fibers have a linear or narrow origin (e.g., Ext. Digitorum Longus, Peroneus Tertius), for in this case the appearance is that of one-half of a feather; (2) *bipennate* when the fleshy fibers arise from a long broad surface (e.g., Peroneus Longus, Fl. Hallucis Longus), for in this case the appearance is that of a whole feather; (3) *multipennate* when septa (partitions) extend into the origin and the insertion (e.g., Deltoid, Subscapularis, *fig. 84*), the appearance being that of many feathers; and finally, (4) muscles (e.g., Tibialis Anterior) whose fibers converge from the walls of a cylindrical space to a buried central tendon may be spoken of as "*circumpennate*".

»» Note that a bipennate muscle arises not only from two lines but also from the surface between those lines; hence, it is many times more powerful than a unipennate muscle. Multipennate and "circumpennate" muscles are correspondingly still more powerful.

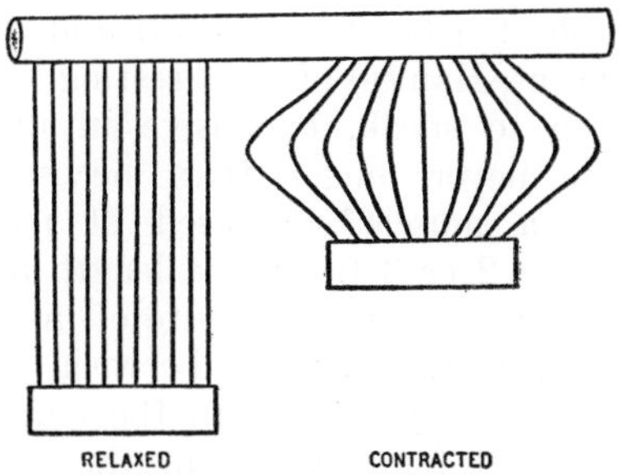

Fig. 33. On contracting, fleshy fibers shorten by one-third to one-half of their resting length and swell correspondingly.

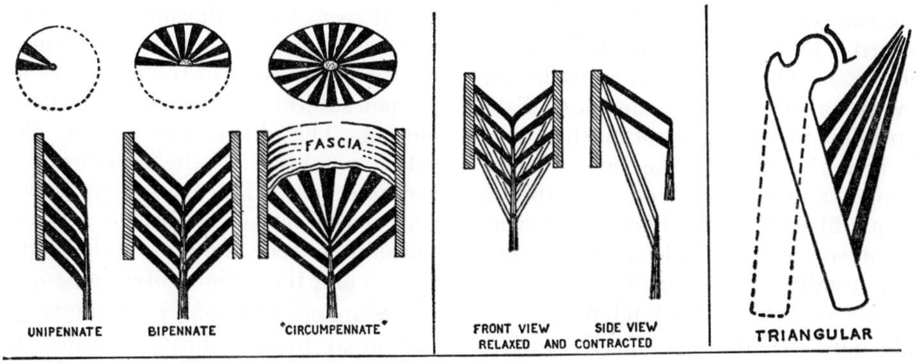

Fig. 34. Diagrams showing the architecture or internal structure of pennate and triangular muscles. Pennate muscles, obviously, are powerful muscles. (After Pfuhl.)

3. In a Radial, Triangular or Fan-shaped Muscle (*fig. 34*) the fleshy fibers converge from a wide origin or base to an apex. Obviously, the cross-sectional area of the apex is much smaller than that of the base; hence, the apex is necessarily fibrous. And, it creates a rough mark, line or ridge on the bone (Pectoralis Minor, Adductor Longus) or pulls out a process (Temporalis) or produces an epiphysis (Gluteus Medius).

The radial type is commonly segmented radially, and it can contract by segments.

Contraction. When muscle fibers contract or shorten, they necessarily increase in circumference (*fig. 33*)—they swell, as exemplified in gross form by the Biceps Brachii in changing from its relaxed to its contracted state. In pennate muscles the side or upward thrust imparted by each swelling fiber to its neighbor is no negligible factor in raising the tendon during the contraction of the muscle.

On contracting, the fleshy fibers of a muscle shorten between a third and a half (57 per cent, Haines) of their resting length. Being, so to speak, expensive in upkeep they are never longer than necessary—those of a muscle composed of parallel fibers being 2 or 3 times the length of the distance through which the site of insertion can move. If the distance between origin and insertion is greater than the length of fiber required for full action, the surplus length is fibrous, i.e., tendinous or aponeurotic (e.g., Sartorius, p. 369; Rectus Femoris, p. 371). A tendon can be any length.

As a corollary, knowing the range of movement of the bony point into which a muscle is inserted, the length of the fleshy fibers (or chains of fibers) of that muscle can usually be calculated, and the most distal point possible for its origin established (e.g., Biceps Femoris, p. 385). The various fleshy fibers (or chains of fibers) of a parallel or an oblique fibered muscle have equal work to do, and so are equal in length; therefore, one can usually reason out the aspect of the muscle on which the tendon appears, for this must be on the opposite surface from the origin (e.g., Fl. Digitorum Profundus, *fig. 122;* Fl. Pollicis Longus, *fig. 123*). The fleshy fibers of a triangular muscle whose base is inserted into a limb bone (e.g., Anconeus at the elbow, Pectineus and Adductor Longus at the hip) are longer on the distal side than on the proximal. They require to be so, because the most distal point of insertion makes the greatest excursion.

Investigation. In investigating the action of muscles five methods are available.

1. In the cadaver a muscle may be freed from surrounding structures and pulled upon, and the resultant position of the joints upon which it acts taken to indicate the actions of the muscle in life.

2. In the living subject a muscle may be stimulated to contract by the suitable application of the electrodes of an induction coil to the skin, one being placed over the motor point (p. 28) of the muscle. This was Duchenne's method of approach, and his work forms the basis of our knowledge of the actions of muscles (Kaplan).

3. A living person may be instructed to execute a specified movement while an observer, by inspection and palpation of the muscles of the region, determines which are in action. Precautions must be taken to avoid confusing antagonists and synergists with prime movers (p. 27).

4. Clinical information may be gained from the study of the effects (1) of nerve injuries—and these were plentiful during the war—and (2) of transplanting tendons surgically in cases of paralysis. These fall into the category of experiments performed accidentally and by design.

5. *Electromyography.* Inman, Saunders, and Abbott introduced a new method which would seem to be the ultimate, or at least the penultimate, method. It consists in planting electrodes in the muscle of a living human subject, and having him perform a motion. The differences in the electrical action potentials of the muscle are amplified and recorded mechanically. Now, it has been determined that there is a direct relationship between the tension developed in a muscle and the action potential; so, by this procedure one can analyze the activity of an individual muscle during motion, noting, for example, during what stage of a movement it comes into action and during what

stage it exhibits its greatest activity. Further, by using a number of amplifiers the simultaneous actions of a group of muscles can be studied (p. 182).

Methods 1 and 2 give information as to what an individual muscle acting alone would do. Since, however, instances of a muscle acting singly are few (e.g., closing the eye), these have less practical importance than methods 3 and 4. Method 5 is throwing much light on the subject and is revealing errors in our present teaching (Basmajian).

Muscle Action. The structural unit of a muscle is a muscle fiber. The functional unit, known as a *motor unit,* consists of a nerve cell, situated in the anterior horn of the spinal cord, and all the muscle fibers, usually 100 or more, controlled by the nerve fiber of that cell.

When an impulse is carried by the nerve fiber to its muscle fibers, they all contract almost simultaneously and for a total time that is quite brief (5 to 8 milliseconds). The result is a twitch of a tiny volume of the whole muscle.

Where great precision is required, as with the extrinsic muscles of the eyeball, one nerve fiber controls only about a dozen muscle fibers. Only a small proportion of motor units are in action at a given moment—at least they are in different phases of activity, because impulses are discharged by the central nervous system asynchronously.

Movements are produced by throwing an increasing number of motor units into action and at the same time relaxing, to various degrees, the antagonistic muscles (reflex relaxation).

Most bodily actions, even ordinary ones, call into play principal muscles and many assistants. The principal muscles, *prime movers* or agonists, by actively contracting (shortening) produce the desired movement. The muscles that are so situated that they would usually produce movements in the opposite direction are called *antagonists.*

Again, when a prime mover passes over more than one joint, certain muscles are called upon to steady the intervening joints; such muscles are *synergists* (Gk. syn = together; ergon = work). When antagonists contract normally during a movement, their role is synergistic. Still other muscles, *fixators,* are called upon to steady the more proximal parts of the limb or trunk. Obviously, the same muscle may act as prime mover, antagonist, synergist, or fixator under different circumstances.

Examples. (1) When you lay your hand and forearm on the table and abduct your thumb, not only is the Abductor Pollicis Longus (at the lateral border of the wrist) felt to become taut but also the Flexor and Extensor Carpi Ulnaris—the medial edge of the former is felt on deep pressure just proximal to the pisiform, of the latter just proximal to the base of metacarpal V. These two ulnar muscles act as synergists; they fix the wrist joint lest it too be abducted. (2) The long flexors of the fingers flex the interphalangeal and metacarpophalangeal joints and also the wrist joint. Now, on clenching the fist or on closing the hand, say on a broom handle, the tendons of the Extensores Carpi Radiales and Ulnaris can be felt to contract (see p. 163). They do so in order to prevent flexion of the wrist; they act as synergists.

Resistance may be a substitute for an antagonist. Example: If your elbow is rigidly flexed at a right angle, both your Biceps and Triceps can be felt to be contracted. If now you place your palm under the edge of a heavy table and make an effort to raise it, the Triceps is felt at once to relax, demonstrating that the resistance of the table replaces the action of the Triceps.

Gravity is a valuable aid to some movements, depending upon the position of the limb or of the body. Example: On raising the arm from the side, the multipennate portion of the Deltoid (*fig. 84*) is the prime mover; gravity (certainly if there is a weight in the hand) is a sufficient antagonist; the anterior and posterior long fibers of the Deltoid act as synergists; the Trapezius and Serratus Anterior fix the shoulder girdle (*fig. 176B*) and, so, become fixation muscles—in fact, without them the movements become completely disorganized.

Conversely, on lowering the arm, gravity becomes the prime mover and Deltoid, the antagonist. If resistance is encountered, as on pressing the hand downward on the table, the anterior and posterior folds of the axilla become taut because the Pectoral muscles and the Latissimus Dorsi come into play as prime movers, and the Deltoid relaxes. Similarly, in walking the raised limb tends of its own weight to fall to the ground.

Blood Supply. The chief vessels enter a muscle with the nerve constantly in some muscles (Biceps Brachii and Gastrocnemius), and with varying frequencies in others; others again have multiple entries (Fl. Digit. Profundus). Accessory vessels, unaccompanied by nerves are present in many muscles, forming good anastomoses in some (Pectoralis Major) and poor in others (Sartorius and Hamstrings) (J. C. Brash). The vessels in a muscle anastomose to form a rectangular network of large and small interconnecting branches. This assures every muscle cell of adequate nutrition. *Anastomosis* (Gk. stoma = a mouth) means the junction or intercommunication of hollow tubes—usually blood vessels—by means of open mouths. The term has been extended illogically to mean the junction of solid structures, such as nerve fibers.

The veins in the muscles, like those in the limbs in general, have valves; so, muscular exercise, by massaging these veins, aids in circulating the blood.

LYMPH VESSELS run with the blood vessels.

Nerve Supply. The nerve to a muscle, called a motor nerve, is a mixed nerve, being about three-fifths efferent (motor), two-fifths afferent (sensory) and containing sympathetic fibers. (1) The efferent fibers pass to *motor end-plates* (i.e., areas of granular, nucleated sarcoplasm under the sarcolemma in which a nerve fibril branches like an open hand). (2) The afferent fibers begin as: *free endings* on the muscle fibers, *encapsulated endings* in the connective tissue, *muscle-spindles* (a spindle being a fusiform swelling, 1 to 4 mm. long, containing poorly developed muscle fibers over which an afferent nerve fiber spreads or around which it forms a spiral) and, *tendon-spindles* at musculo-tendinous junctions. (They are similar to muscle-spindles, but collagen fibers replace muscle fibers (Bridgman).)

It is through the sensory nerves in muscles, tendons, and joints that one is kept informed of the position of the parts of one's body in space; so, even with the eyes shut or in the dark, one can walk without stumbling, feed oneself without spilling, and shave without a mirror; further, one knows whether a joint is extended or, if flexed, the degree. (3) The sympathetic fibers supply the vessels.

Most motor nerves are derived from more than one spinal segment, and the segments are always consecutive (e.g., the nerve to the Deltoid muscle arises from Cervical 5 and 6; that of Sartorius from Lumbar 2, 3, and 4). Muscles placed near the surface of the body may be made to contract on applying an electrode to the skin near, but not at, the point of entry of the nerve. The most effective point of electrical stimulation for each muscle (which overlies the greatest concentration of nerve endings on muscle fibers) is called the *motor point* of that muscle.

Nomenclature. The names given to muscles are descriptive of their *shape* (e.g., Triangularis, Trapezius, Rhomboidei, Teres (round), Quadratus Femoris); of their *general form* (e.g., Longus, Serratus (like a saw), Latissimus, Piriformis, Gracilis, Vasti); of the number of *heads* or *bellies* (e.g., Biceps, Triceps, Quadriceps, Digastric), of their *structure* (e.g., Semitendinosus, Semimembranosus); of their *location* (e.g., Temporalis, Supraspinatus, Intercostales, Iliacus, Tibialis Anterior); of their *attachments* (e.g., Stylo-hyoideus, Ilio-costalis, Brachio-radialis); of their *action* (e.g., Flexor and Extensor Carpi Ulnaris, Abductor and Adductor Hallucis, Levator Scapulae, Depressor Anguli Oris, Supinator, Pronator Teres, Rotatores, Tensor Palati); of their *direction* (e.g., Rectus Abdominis, Obliquus Oculi Superior, Transversus Linguae); of *contrasting features* (e.g., Pectoralis Major and Minor, Peroneus Longus and Brevis, Pterygoideus Medialis and Lateralis, Tibialis Anterior and Posterior, Gemellus Superior and Inferior, Obturator Internus and Externus; Gluteus Maximus, Medius, and Minimus; Vastus Medialis, Intermedius, and Lateralis).

Variations. Muscles are subject to variation, and books have been written about their variations (Le Double). The muscles that vary most are muscles that are either "coming" or "going", that is, muscles that are appearing in the species and muscles that are disappearing.

»» The *Palmaris Longus and Plantaris* are disappearing (the one is absent in 13.7 per cent of 771 limbs, the other in 6.6 per cent of 740 limbs) and when present the sites of origin and insertion and the size of the fleshy bellies vary greatly. The *Peroneus Tertius* is appearing (it is absent in 6.25 per cent of 400 limbs) and when present it is inserted anywhere along the dorsum of metatarsals 3, 4, or 5 or to the interosseous membrane between them. The *Peroneus Longus* has migrated across the sole of the foot to be attached to metatarsal 1. In 72.3 per cent of 213 limbs it is attached also to cuneiform 1, and in 48.3 per cent to metatarsal 2 also. The short muscles to the little finger and little toe are commonly in part suppressed (J.C.B.G.).

It is obvious that the wide spread fleshy origin of a muscle may spread either a little more or a little less without affecting the action of the muscle (e.g., the Pectoralis Minor, typically arising from ribs 3, 4, and 5, may extend upward to the 2nd rib or downward to the 6th; on the other hand, the lower portions of the Trapezius and Pectoralis Major are not uncommonly wanting). Equally obvious, the site of insertion of a tendon, where the pull of the muscle is concentrated, cannot vary without altering the action of the muscle.

Accessory Muscles mostly lend themselves to explanation on morphological grounds; they are not clinically important. The Sternalis and the Axillary Arch are of considerable interest (q.v.). Sometimes the Biceps Brachii has three origins and the Coraco-brachialis three insertions, as in some primates, and occasionally they have four.

CHAPTER 2

CARDIOVASCULAR AND NERVOUS SYSTEMS

CARDIOVASCULAR SYSTEM

(Heart, blood vessels, and lymphatics)

The blood vascular system comprises (1) the heart and (2) the blood vessels (arteries—capillaries—veins). These form a tubular system which, with few exceptions, is closed, lined throughout with a single layer of flat cells, *endothelium,* and filled with blood. It receives the lymph and chyle brought to it from the lymphatic system.

Blood. The volume of blood in the body is about 10 pints, and it equals about one-eleventh of the total body weight. It is composed of plasma and cells. The *plasma* or fluid portion of the blood = 91 per cent water and 9 per cent solids (e.g. proteins, salts, products of digestion, and waste products), also respiratory gases (O_2 and CO_2), internal secretions, enzymes, etc. The *cells* = red corpuscles (erythrocytes), white corpuscles (leukocytes), and blood platelets; these are in suspension.

Animals, like plants, absorb their food in fluid form. The fluid products of digestion are absorbed from the digestive tract into the bloodstream for distribution to the various tissues and organs of the body for their growth, maintenance, and diverse activities (e.g., contraction in muscles, secretion in glands). Oxygen from the air passes into the lungs and thence into the bloodstream, the plasma dissolving a small amount, the red cells combining with 60 times as much. This also is distributed to the tissues. The waste products of metabolism, formed in the tissues, enter the bloodstream and are brought by it to the excretory organs (kidneys, bowel, lungs, and skin). It is through the thin walls of the capillaries, which consist only of endothelium, that these various interchanges take place.

Definitions. The *Heart* is a hollow muscular pump. Its duty is to pump the blood to the capillaries. *Capillaries* are tubes whose walls consist of thin semipermeable membranes—permeable to water and crystalloids, but impermeable to the proteins of the blood plasma and to other substances of large molecular composition. Through them nutritive materials and O_2 pass from the blood to the tissues; and through them waste products and CO_2 return from the tissues to the blood.

Arteries are tubes that conduct blood from the heart to the capillaries. *Veins* are tubes that conduct it back from the capillaries to the heart.

Circulation of blood. The blood traverses two separate circuits (*fig. 35*), the *pulmonary* and the *systemic*, each with its own pump.

1. The right side of the heart pumps the blood through the vessels of the lungs—these constitute the pulmonary or lesser circuit.

2. The left side of the heart pumps the blood through the vessels of the body generally—these constitute the systemic or greater circuit.

To serve these two circuits, the heart has four chambers, two on the right side and two on the left. One of these on each side is a thin walled receiving chamber, the *atrium*, the other is a thick walled distributing or pumping chamber, the *ventricle*.

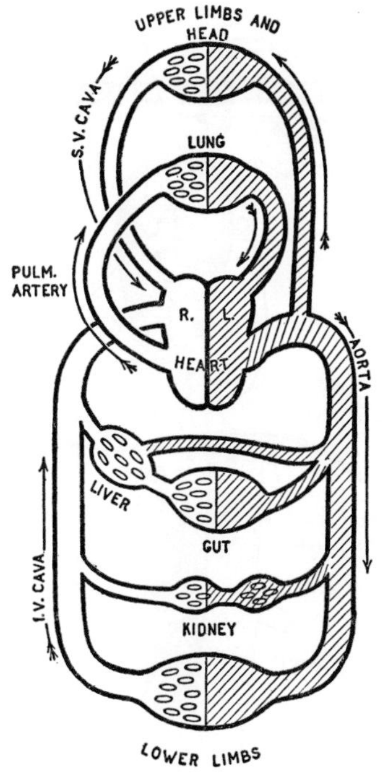

Venous Arterial

FIG. 35. Diagram of the circulatory system. Hatched vessels conduct oxygenated blood; clear vessels conduct blood laden with carbon dioxide. Note the pulmonary and systemic circuits and the double set of capillaries on the subsidiary digestive and renal circuits.

The Pulmonary Circuit: The blood entering the right atrium (via the s. v. cava, i. v. cava, and veins of the heart itself) passes to the right ventricle which pumps it through the pulmonary arteries to the capillaries of the lungs, thence through the pulmonary veins to the left atrium.

The Systemic Circuit: From the left atrium the blood passes to the left ventricle which pumps it through the aorta and its various arterial branches to the capillaries of all the rest of the body, thence through veins which become increasingly larger and fewer till finally the superior and inferior venae cavae and the cardiac veins return to the right atrium the same volume of blood as the left ventricle ejects into the aorta, and at the same rate (*fig. 36*).

Normally blood is red when the oxygen content is high and bluish when it is low. Oxygen is taken up by the capillaries in

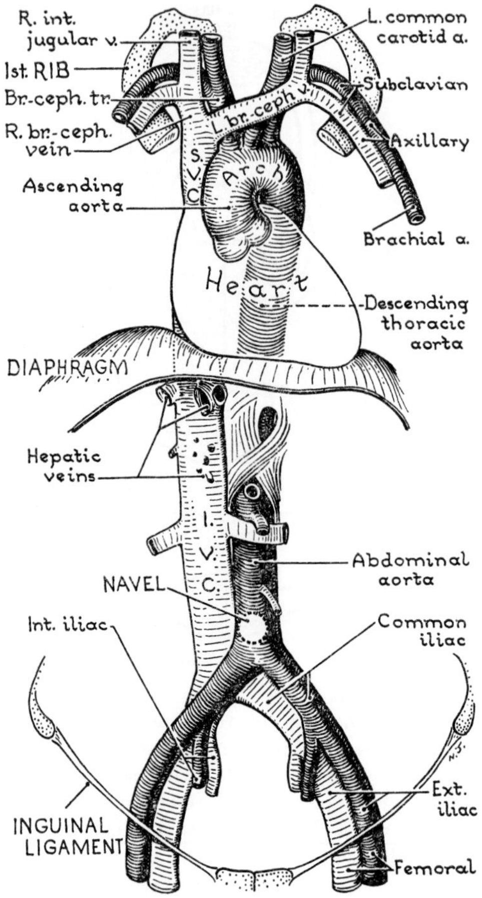

FIG. 36. The great arteries and veins of the systemic circuit.

the lung and carbon dioxide is given off. The reverse process occurs in the systemic capillaries. It follows, therefore, that blood is *red* in the pulmonary veins, left side of the heart, and systemic arteries; and *"blue"* in the systemic veins, right side of the heart, and pulmonary arteries. It is customary in illustrations to color the parts red and blue accordingly.

Though the capacity of each of the four heart chambers is practically the same (60–70 cc.), the resistance offered by the pulmonary vessels is obviously much less than that offered by the systemic ones; accordingly, the wall of the right ventricle is much thinner than that of the left.

Structure of Cardiac Wall. (L. Cor, and Gk. Kardia = Heart.) The main layer of the cardiac wall is the middle or muscular layer, the *myocardium*. Internally, the myocardium is lined throughout with *endocardium*. This is an areolar membrane, lined with flat endothelial cells continuous with those of the blood vessels. The endocardium is thickest in the atria, where the muscle is thinnest. Externally the myocardium is covered with *epicardium* (visceral pericardium), which is similar to endocardium. In the areolar layer of the epicardium run the main cardiac vessels often embedded in much fat. For heart valves, see Chapter 32.

Blood Vessels (arteries, capillaries, veins). The main systemic artery (the *aorta*) and the *pulmonary trunk*, each about 30 mm. in diameter, branch and rebranch like a tree, the branches becoming smaller as they become progressively more numerous. When reduced to a diameter of about 0.3 mm. and just visible to the naked eye they are called *arterioles*. These break up into a number of *capillaries* (L. capillus = a hair), each about ½–1 mm. long and large enough (7 μ or more) to allow the passage of the red blood cells in single file.

The capillaries form an anastomosing network or *rete*. The cross-sectional area of the entire systemic rete or capillary bed is about 800 times greater than that of the aorta. In this rete the smallest veins, called *venules*, have their source.

Veins accompany arteries and have the same tree-like pattern as arteries but, owing to the direction of the blood current within them, they are usually likened not to trees but to rivers, the branches being called *tributaries*.

Below the elbow and knee, and elsewhere, arteries are closely accompanied by paired veins, *venae comitantes*, one on each side. These veins are united to each other by short branches which form a network around their artery. The pulsations of the artery, by indenting the veins, perhaps aid slightly in forcing the venous blood onward toward the heart. Veins also run independently of arteries (e.g., superficial veins); veins are more numerous than arteries and their caliber is greater.

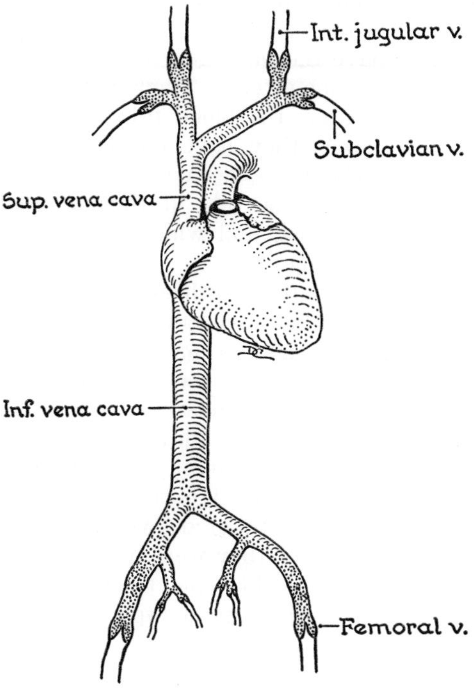

FIG. 37. The venous blood is imprisoned in the trunk by valves.

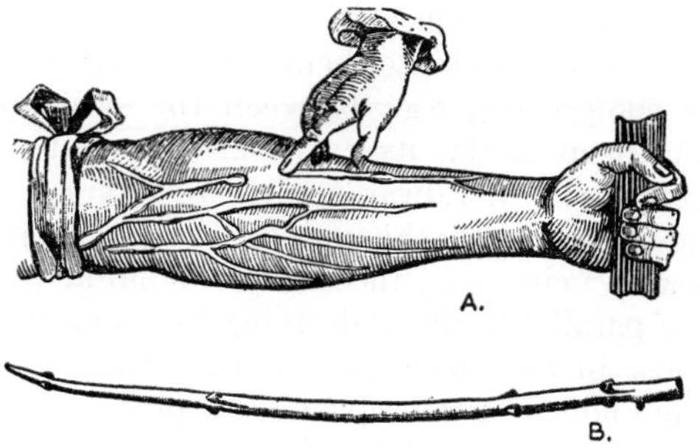

FIG. 38. *A*, demonstrating the sites of the valves in the veins of the forearm during life (after William Harvey—*The motion of the heart and blood in animals*, 1628). *B*, a vein turned inside out imperfectly showing the valves (after Fabricius, 1603).

Venous Valves. The inner tunic of most medium and small veins is thrown at intervals into delicate folds, called *valvules* or *cusps*. Each cusp forms with the wall of the vein a semilunar bulging pocket or *sinus*. These pockets are mostly arranged in pairs, facing each other, to form valves. Like the gates of a canal lock, they open in one direction, namely, toward the heart. Around the valve the wall of the vein is dilated, as at the aortic valve (*fig. 601*), to allow back eddies to close the cusps.

The nearest valves to the heart lie at the ends of the internal jugular, subclavian, and femoral veins (*fig. 37*). They imprison the venous blood within the trunk, and during periods of increased intra-abdominal pressure (e.g., during defecation) and during increased intra-thoracic pressure (e.g., during expiration), they prevent it from being forced back into the limbs, head, and neck.

There are no functioning valves in the *Portal System*, that is, in the veins that bring blood from the stomach and intestines (guts) to the liver; and only rarely do those (two or three) in the cardiac veins function. Valves are most numerous in the veins of the limbs, and they are commonly placed just distal to the mouth of a tributary.

To Demonstrate Valves in the superficial veins of the forearm: Circumduct your limb vigorously at the shoulder joint in order to cause the veins to fill; then, keeping the forearm below the level of the heart so that the veins shall not empty, with the tip of your index obstruct a prominent vein about the middle of the forearm and, by stroking proximally with your thumbnail, empty a long segment of the vein. Note that on removing the thumb the vein fills from above as far as the nearest valve, and that on removing the index the empty segment fills from below (*fig. 38*).

The superficial veins are elliptical on cross-section, the long axis of the ellipse being parallel to the overlying skin. This is notably the case at the sites of valves (*fig. 39*). The

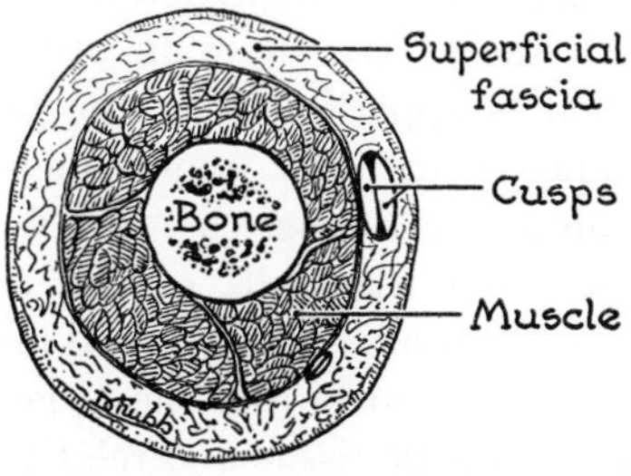

FIG. 39. Veins tend to be elliptical on cross section. The long axes of the cusps of their valves are so disposed that external pressure does not impair their function.

two cusps of each valve arise from the long curves of the ellipse; hence, when the valve is compressed, e.g., between the skin and the deep fascia, its cusps are brought together (E. A. Edwards). A similar arrangement exists at the valves of the deeper seated veins, e.g., those in the femoral vein are parallel to the underlying Psoas muscle; those in the subclavian vein are parallel to the underlying 1st rib—and so probably for venous valves in general.

Structure. *Arteries* typically have three coats or tunics. (1) The *tunica intima* or inner coat has a lining of endothelial cells, with a little subendothelial areolar tissue and, outside this, a tube of elastic tissue (the internal elastic membrane); (2) the *tunica media* or middle coat is composed of alternate layers of smooth muscle and elastic tissue in an areolar bedding; (3) the *tunica adventitia* or outer coat is a fibro-areolar tube of considerable strength containing some elastic fibers.

Both muscular tissue and elastic tissue are elastic, like rubber, and after being stretched they tend to return to normal length, i.e., they contract passively. Muscles can also contract actively; elastic tissue cannot. Hence, muscle needs a large blood supply; elastic tissue needs but little—it is a muscle sparer; its upkeep is inexpensive.

The blood ejected at each heart beat into the aorta causes it to expand. As the expanded aorta returns to normal, it continues to maintain sufficient pressure to drive the blood through the arteries and arterioles into the capillary bed. The amount escaping into the capillary bed in a given region, however, is regulated by the need of the tissue at the time. In other words, the blood is apportioned to the organs in accordance with their requirements. The mechanism controlling the distribution is the muscle in the walls of the arterioles which, so to speak, can be turned on and off like a tap. The aorta and the large arteries have much elastic tissue and relatively little muscle in their walls; whereas the arterioles are essentially muscular.

Capillaries have but one coat, namely, the endothelial lining common to all vessels and the heart.

Veins have the same general structure as their companion arteries. Their caliber, however, is greater; the blood pressure within them is lower; they have less muscle and much less elastic tissue. A vein may be described as an areolar tube in which a muscle coat is embedded, and which possesses an endothelial lining.

Some hours after death all the muscular tissue in the body contracts; hence, the corpse becomes rigid, in *rigor mortis*, and the blood is driven from the more muscular arteries into the less muscular veins. Even after the rigor passes off and the vessels relax, the arteries are empty and the veins are filled with blood. Arteries (Gk. and L. arteria = an air tube) derive their name from the fact that they were believed to be conductors of air like the trachea, which was known as the arteria aspera or rough air tube.

Vasa Vasorum. The heart wall is supplied by the coronary arteries and the cardiac veins. Arteries and veins with a diameter greater than 1 mm. are supplied by small vessels, *vasa vasorum.*

Distribution of Blood and Its Nervous Regulation. The volume of blood pumped into the aorta in a given time equals that returning to the right atrium, which in turn equals that pumped into the pulmonary artery and returning to the left atrium. If it were otherwise, there would be temporary or permanent local congestion, which, in fact occurs with heart failure. The blood pressure within the aorta is about 120 mm. of mercury, at the arterial end of the capillaries about 30 mm., at the venous end 12 mm., and in the great veins 5 mm. This determines the direction of the blood flow.

The rate of flow in the aorta, when the subject is resting, is about 0.5 meter per second, in the capillaries about 0.5 mm. per second, and in the veins it gradually increases until in the venae cavae it nearly equals the rate in the aorta.

The Heart is supplied by efferent vagal and sympathetic fibers. Stimulation of the vagus results in slowing of the heart; stimulation of the sympathetic in acceleration.

When the blood pressure in the arteries rises, afferent fibers of the vagus distributed to the aortic arch (aortic nerve) and of the glossopharyngeal nerve distributed to a swelling on the internal carotid artery, called the *carotid sinus* (sinus nerve), are stimulated; this reflexly brings about slowing of the heart and vasodilatation of the vessels with consequent fall in blood pressure.

The Blood Vessels, particularly the arterioles, are supplied by efferent nerve fibers of the sympathetic nervous system—which almost always cause vasoconstriction—and perhaps in some locations by parasympathetic fibers having an opposite effect. Various degrees of vasoconstriction allow the blood to be partly shut off from one part of the body and diverted to another, e.g., during digestion it is diverted to the abdominal viscera; during hot weather it is diverted to the skin so that heat may be lost.

Anastomoses and Variations. During development, networks of vessels sprout into actively growing parts (e.g., organs and limbs) and, as the parts enlarge, the networks advance farther into them. Certain channels through these networks are chosen to be permanent arteries and veins and their branches; the others disappear (*fig. 446*). There being a wide choice of channels in the network, it is not suprising that those selected for permanency should vary somewhat from individual to individual. By way of demonstrating this fact, pull up your sleeve and compare the pattern of the superficial veins on the front of your forearm with that of your neighbor; minor if not major differences will be seen; even between your right and left limbs the patterns differ.

Although the number of channels in the network retained to form main arteries is restricted, commonly to one or two, the peripheral parts persist as capillary channels and the communications between these and neighboring capillaries are called anastomoses (i.e., furnished with stomata or mouths). Anastomoses also occur between certain large vessels (e.g., the arterial circle at the base of the brain; the palmar arches, *fig. 148;* the intestinal arcades, *fig. 238*) and between many small vessels and precapillary vessels (e.g., around joints and in the heart). In cases of obstruction of the larger arteries, it is by the enlargement of these anastomoses that a collateral circulation is established and the vitality of distant (or neighboring) parts preserved.

An arterial channel, which under ordinary circumstances disappears, may persist as an *accessory* or *supernumerary* artery (e.g., renal, *fig. 311 B*); if the normal artery disappears the persisting artery will act as a substitute for it (e.g., brachial, *fig. 111;* profunda, *fig. 114*). Such *abnormal* arteries, acting as substitutes, account for the erratic courses sometimes taken by certain arteries and for the unusual relationships they may bear to neighboring nerves and other structures. The same remarks apply to veins.

It is easily understood that arteries are *sinuous* or *tortuous* when supplying parts that are highly mobile like the cheeks and lips, protrudable like the tongue, or expansile like the uterus and colon. It is not so obvious why other arteries (e.g., splenic artery) should be so.

In the aged the temporal artery may become visibly sinuous and the brachial and radial arteries can be felt to be so, owing to degenerative changes in their elastic walls.

Arterio-venous Anastomoses. In some regions arterioles communicate directly with venules, e.g., in the skin of the palm of the hand and of the terminal phalanges, in the nail bed, in the skin of the lips, nose, and eyelids and at the tip of the tongue. This is in addition to the regular communications by capillaries.

End-arteries are arteries that do not anastomose with neighboring arteries except through terminal capillaries. Obstruction of such an artery is likely to lead to local death, resulting in the case (1) of a cerebral artery, in paralysis, (2) of the central artery to the retina, in blindness, (3) of a branch of the renal or splenic artery, in death of a segment of the kidney or spleen, and (4) of several adjacent vasa recta of the gut, in gangrene of the gut.

Sinusoids. In parts of certain organs (e.g., liver, spleen, bone marrow, suprarenal glands) the place of capillaries is taken by irregularly wide, tubular spaces, called *sinusoids.* The lining cells differ somewhat from endothelial cells, many of them being phagocytic, that is to say, capable of engulfing particulate matter, and they are supported by reticular fibers—not by areolar tissue.

Cavernous Tissue. In the erectile tissue of the external genitals (penis in the male, clitoris in the female), there are innumerable venous spaces lined with endothelium and separated by fibrous septa containing smooth muscle. In the nasal cavities, especially over the middle and inferior conchae, arterioles open into wide and abundant venous spaces and from these venules arise. Therefore, the mucous membrane of the nasal passages also is erectile. When one has a "cold in the head", the venous spaces dilate and may obstruct the air way.

Vascularity. *Cellular tissues* are vascular, e.g., muscles being the cellular engines of the body require much fuel; glands (kidney, thyroid, suprarenal, and liver) are very vascular; so, obviously, are the lungs. *Connective tissues* are only slightly vascular; thus, areolar tissue and the fibrous tissues (e.g., deep fascia, tendons, ligaments) have a very meager blood supply; adipose tissue and bone have a fair supply, but hyaline cartilage, the cornea, and the epidermis are nonvascular.

Nervous tissue. The gray matter of the brain and spinal medulla, being cellular, is more vascular than the white matter and the peripheral nerves.

LYMPHATIC SYSTEM

Tissue fluid is the fluid that bathes the cells (and fibers) of the tissues of the body, and it resembles blood plasma in chemical composition. From this fluid the cells get their nutritive material; to it they give their waste products; and through it they respire. Between the tissue fluid and the plasma of the circulating blood a constant interchange of fluid and dissolved substances takes place through the semipermeable walls of the capillaries, and by this means the tissue fluid is refreshed.

Most of the constituents of the blood plasma that transude through the walls of the capillaries into the tissue spaces, for the nourishment of the tissues, after undergoing metabolic change, transude back again and return to the heart via the veins. Some, however, transudes into the *lymph capillaries* whence it is drained by *lymph vessels* through *lymph nodes* to the great veins at the root of the neck where it rejoins the blood stream.

The fluid in the lymphatics is clear and colorless and is called *lymph* (L. lympha = pure, clear water); lymphocytes are added to it as it passes through the lymph nodes, otherwise it is free from blood cells.

Lymph Capillaries occur only where there are blood capillaries, and like blood capillaries they form a closed network, but with a larger mesh. They are especially numerous in the skin and in mucous membranes. In two regions hollow finger-like cul-de-sacs project from the networks: (1) the papillae of the skin, and (2) the villi of the intestines.

The **Lymph Vessels** draining the networks are thin-walled, ½ to 1 mm. in diameter, and beaded due to numerous valves. They run in layers of areolar tissue. Though more plentiful than veins, they tend to accompany veins and to drain corresponding territories. With the exception of a few lymph vessels at the root of the neck, all lymph vessels are interrupted by lymph nodes.

Lymph Nodes (Glands) vary *in size* from a pin's head to an olive, and are somewhat flattened. *In color,* they are pink in life and brownish in the embalmed cadaver; but those draining the lungs are black from inhaled carbon, and after a meal those draining the intestines are white from emulsified fat. The nodes act as filters for lymph and factories for lymphocytes.

»» *Note.* Just as the renal blood passes through two sets of (arterial) capillaries (*fig. 48*), and the portal blood through two sets of (venous) capillaries, so lymph passes through two sets of (lymph) capillaries: (1) in the tissues, and (2) in the sinuses of the nodes or series of nodes.

The flow of lymph in an immobile limb is almost negligible, but during muscular activity it is very active. Lymph flows in the same direction as venous blood, that is, toward the heart, due probably to (1) rhythmical contraction of the vessels, (2) intermittent pressure (e.g., muscular action) on the valved vessels, (3) negative pressure or suction within the thorax, and (4) positive pressure within the abdomen during inspiration. Hence, when massaging a part, the stroking should be toward the heart.

We all know that when small blood vessels and capillaries are cut, the blood soon clots, bleeding is arrested, and the cut is sealed. A broken lymph capillary, however, may remain open for days, permitting the entry of debris, fluid, and poisons if they are present (Clark and Clark).

Main Channels. Three paired lymph trunks (1) the *jugular* accompanying the internal jugular vein in the neck, (2) the *subclavian* accompanying the subclavian vein in the upper limb, and (3) the *bronchomediastinal* from thoracic viscera, end either separately or together near the angle of confluence of the internal jugular and subclavian veins. A fourth channel, the *thoracic duct,* drains the chest wall and the territory below the diaphragm (the liver in part excepted); it is described on p. 531 and depicted in *fig. 640.*

Lymphatico-venous Communications. It has been conjectured that communications must exist between lymphatics and veins (Rusznyák *et al.*). Pressman and Simon seem to have proved this to be true; they injected air and then saline into lymph nodes (of the dog) and, in colored motion pictures, saw these appear simultaneously in efferent lymphatics of the nodes and in the adjacent veins.

Investigation. By forcing valves, main lymph trunks may be injected in retrograde direction, but not the smaller ones. These and the lymph nodes into which they drain can be rendered conspicuous from the network end. This is done by plunging a hypodermic needle at random into an areolar plane (e.g., subcutaneous, submucous, subserous, fascial) and injecting Prussian blue (or some other pigment that is insoluble in water and tissue fluids) dissolved in ether and turpentine. As the solvents evaporate the pigment is deposited within the lymphatics, which can be dissected. Naturally, the point of the needle will not in all instances enter a lymphatic, if such is present, at the first attempt.

If, while thus injecting, e.g., the subserous network of the stomach, you deliberately obstruct the efferent vessel in which the colored fluid is visible flowing toward a lymph node, it will be observed to find egress by one of several neighboring vessels. From this you will appreciate that the normal anatomical outflow may be greatly diverted in pathological (e.g., cancerous) conditions associated with obstruction.

Exceptions. Lymph capillaries are not present in epithelium (e.g., epidermis), cartilage, or other tissues devoid of blood vessels, neither are they present in the bone marrow and the main tissues of the spleen and liver. In the spleen and liver, the blood passing between the cells in irregular spaces (called sinusoids) appears to provide the sole drainage of the active tissues. However, the fibrous tissues of both organs have lymphatics. There are no lymphatics in the brain.

Lymph capillaries do not accompany the blood capillaries between the alveoli of the lungs, or in the glomeruli of the kidneys, since these capillaries are not nutritive in function; but in the lungs, lymph vessels do accompany the bronchial vessels.

Lymphoid Tissues are collections of enormous numbers of migratory and semimigratory scavenger cells called lymphocytes. Lymphocytes are usually classed with the white blood cells for they are discharged with lymph into the blood stream. Lymphoid tissue occurs in lymph nodes, the palatine, lingual and pharyngeal tonsils, the solitary and aggregated follicles of the intestine, the appendix, the thymus and the corpuscles of the spleen. It is best developed in youth, and diseases of this tissue are commonest in youth.

FETAL CIRCULATION

Red blood cells appear very early in the embryo, but until the 2nd month they are immature in type (nucleated). Nucleated red cells are found until a few days after birth, but they cannot be recovered from the maternal blood because the two circulations—fetal and maternal—are separate and closed. In the placenta, the two circulations come into close apposition with each

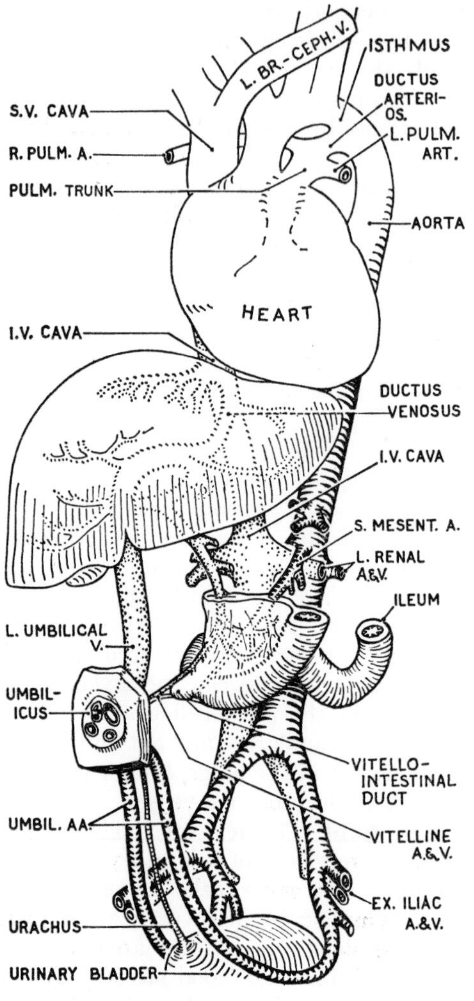

FIG. 40. The fetal circulation. (After Cullen.)

other being separated by semipermeable walls. Nutritive material and oxygen permeate from mother to fetus; waste products and carbon dioxide permeate from fetus to mother. The functions of the placenta, therefore, are concerned with nutrition, excretion, and respiration. In the fetus the pulmonary, portal, and renal circulations are of little account; the placental circulation is paramount.

Fetal blood, charged with nutritive material and oxygen, leaves the placenta in the *umbilical vein*. This vein traverses the umbilical cord outside the fetus and the free edge of a membrane, the falciform ligament of the liver inside, to end in the left portal vein. Some of the blood, thus brought to the left portal vein, then flows through the liver, leaves it by the hepatic veins, and enters the inferior vena cava; but most of the blood by-passes the liver, being short-circuited by the ductus venosus.

The *ductus venosus*, which occupies a sulcus behind the liver, connects the left portal vein to the inferior vena cava just below the diaphragm (*fig. 40*). Hence, the purest blood to reach the fetal heart travels through the terminal part of the i.v. cava to the right atrium.

In the fetus the blood from the i.v. cava is directed across the right atrium and through an opening in the interatrial septum, the *foramen ovale*, into the left atrium, thereby short-circuiting the pulmonary circuit. Thence it passes through the left ventricle into the ascending aorta and aortic arch, and by their branches it is distributed to the walls of the heart, the head and neck (including the brain), and the upper limbs, which therefore receive "pure" blood. It is blood that has been purified in the placenta and returned by the umbilical vein and ductus venosus to the i. v. cava and so to the right atrium (*fig. 40*).

The blood from the head and neck and upper limbs returns via the superior vena cava to the right atrium, whence it passes through the right ventricle into the pulmonary trunk. Some of this blood then follows the pulmonary circuit through the lungs to the left atrium, but most of it is short-circuited to the aorta by a vessel, the *ductus arteriosus*, that connects the left pulmonary artery to the aortic arch just beyond the origin of the left subclavian artery. Beyond this connection the united streams descend through the aorta and common iliac arteries —some to be distributed to the abdomen and lower limbs, some to the placenta. The umbilical or placental arteries, one on each side, pass by the sides of the bladder and up the anterior abdominal wall to the umbilicus, thence along the umbilical cord to the placenta where waste products and carbon dioxide are discharged.

From this account it would appear (1) that the kidney has no short circuit, (2) that the liver has one (ductus venosus), and (3) that the lungs have two (foramen ovale and ductus arteriosus), and, furthermore, that the heart, head, neck, and upper limbs receive the purest blood.

Changes at Birth. LUNGS. The child cries; the lungs begin to expand (Chapter 31) and assume their functions, whereupon the foramen ovale and the ductus arteriosus close—the former to be represented by the *fossa ovalis*, the latter by a fibrous cord, the *ligamentum arteriosum.*

PLACENTA. The cord is tied about 2 inches from the umbilicus, cut, and discarded with the placenta; so, the right and left umbilical arteries become thrombosed and fibrous, and are known as the obliterated umbilical arteries; and the umbilical vein, behaving likewise, becomes the *round ligament* of the liver.

LIVER. The ductus venosus also becomes a fibrous thread, the *ligamentum venosum;* so, all the blood in the portal vein must now pass through the liver.

X-ray Findings. Barclay, Barcroft, Barron, Franklin and Prichard, after injecting radio-opaque substances into veins of living fetal sheep and taking moving X-ray pictures, observed that (1) the whole of the superior caval blood passes through the right atrium, right ventricle, and pulmonary trunk, and thence (a) via the right and left pulmonary arteries to the lungs and (b) via the ductus arteriosus into the descending aorta; (2) the major part of the inferior caval blood passes through the foramen ovale into the left atrium, and the minor part passes with the superior caval blood into the right ventricle; (3) the ductus arteriosus, which may be regarded as a long muscular sphincter, closes functionally a few

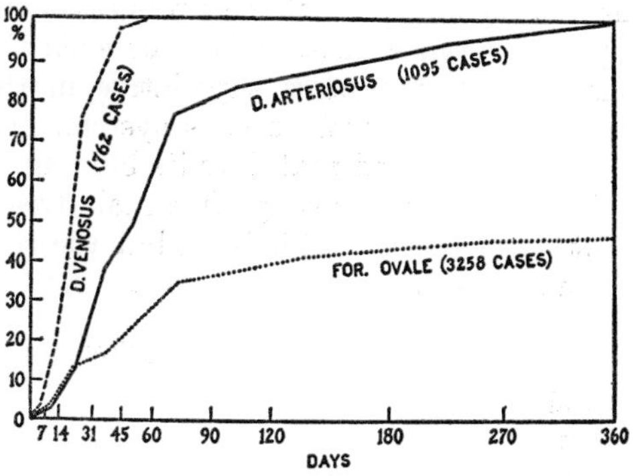

FIG. 41. Dates of permanent closure of the ductus venosus, ductus arteriosus and foramen ovale during the 1st year of life. (After Scammon and Norris.)

minutes after delivery; (4) subsequent injections, made at 5-minute intervals for nearly 2 hours after delivery, show that the ductus remains closed (although perhaps opening intermittently); and (5) the functional closure of the foramen ovale, which tends to precede that of the ductus, is apparently dependent on the onset of respiration.

»» Patten concludes that the changes that occur in the heart and great vessels are more gradual than is usually supposed. His evidence is based on measurements of the diameters of the foramen ovale, ductus arteriosus, and great vessels about the heart made in children at term and during the weeks following birth.

Physiological occlusion is not to be confused with anatomical obliteration.

From the accompanying chart (*fig. 41*) it is seen that the times of complete obliteration of the orifices are highly variable. The foramen ovale, though closed functionally, remains unobliterated (i.e., admits a probe) in about 25 per cent of adults.

NERVOUS SYSTEM

SUBDIVISIONS.

SPINAL MEDULLA OR CORD—*Membranes; Structure; Neuron.*

PERIPHERAL NERVES—*Macroscopic or Gross Structure; Microscopic Structure; Plexuses; Blood Supply.*

Autonomic Nervous System

SYMPATHETIC SYSTEM—*Structure; Cerebral Control; Supply of Individual Regions and Organs (upper limb, lower limb, head and neck, thorax, abdomen and pelvis).*

PARASYMPATHETIC SYSTEM—*Oculomotor Nerve; Facial Nerve; Glossopharyngeal Nerve; Vagus Nerve; Pelvic Splanchnic Nerves.*

Man is not the largest of the animals, nor are his vision, hearing, or sense of smell the most acute; he is not the strongest of the animals, the most fleet of foot, or even the longest-lived; but he is superlative in the quality of his central nervous system, and he possesses a hand that does its bidding.

The brain requires preferential treatment not given it in this book but the rest of the nervous system is described.

Subdivisions of the Nervous System

Central Nervous System	Brain Spinal medulla or cord	
Peripheral Nervous System	Peripheral nerves	Cranial nerves—12 pairs Spinal nerves—31 pairs
	Autonomic nervous system	Sympathetic Parasympathetic

The central nervous system controls the voluntary muscles of the body and is concerned with things both above and below the level of consciousness. The autonomic nervous system, also called the involuntary, or visceral nervous system, controls the parts over which we do not exercise voluntary control and of which, for the most part, we are unconscious (e.g., action of the heart, movements of the viscera, the state of the blood vessels, and the secretion of glands).

Spinal Medulla or Cord

The spinal cord lies within the vertebral canal. The vertebral canal (or a vertebral foramen), being too small to admit a finger (*fig. 24*), the cord obviously must be of smaller diameter than a finger, but in length (18″) it equals the femur.

The cord is surrounded by three **membranes:** (1) the *pia mater* which, like a delicate skin, clings tenderly to the cord, (2) the *arachnoid mater* (Gk. = like a cobweb) which is joined to the pia by threads and is flimsy, and (3) the *dura mater* which is tough and fibrous, but is easily split longitudinally, owing to the direction of its fibers. The arachnoid mater is separated from the pia by a space, the *subarachnoid space,* filled with cerebrospinal fluid. This fluid presses the arachnoid against the dura thereby obliterating a potential space, the *subdural space.*

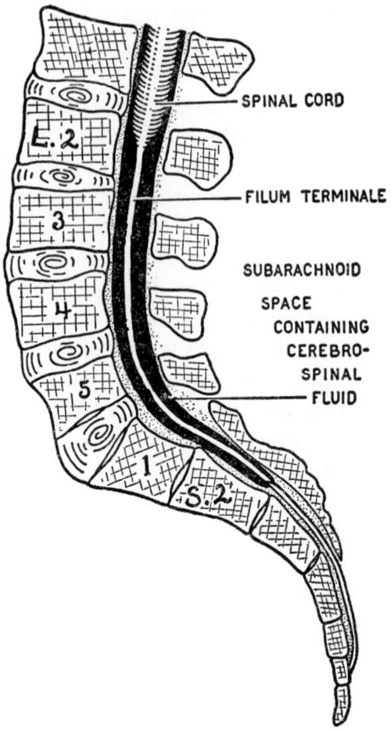

FIG. 42. The spinal cord ends at lumbar vertebra 1–2, the subarachnoid space at sacral vertebra 2.

In the fetus the spinal cord extends down to the coccyx, but as development proceeds, owing to the greater growth of the vertebral column, it is drawn upwards, so that at birth it extends only to vertebra L. 3, and in the adult to the upper part of L. 2 (*fig. 42*). Flexing the column draws the cord temporarily higher. A strong, glistening thread, the *filum terminale,* largely composed of pia mater, attaches the end of the cord to the back of the coccyx even in the adult.

A broad band of pia, the *ligamentum denticulatum,* projects like a long lateral fin from each side of the cord and lies between the ventral and dorsal nerve roots. From the free margin of this ligament strong tooth-like processes, one for each segment, pass through the arachnoid to become firmly attached to the dura. The highest tooth or dens of each ligament is at the level of the foramen magnum; the lowest tooth varies in level from T. 12 to L. 2 (I. B. Macdonald). Hence, the spinal cord within its water-bath is fixed cranially to the brain, caudally via filum terminale to the coccyx, and laterally via ligamenta denticulata to the dura.

The *spinal dura* is free within the vertebral canal. It is, however, adherent to the margin of the foramen magnum and is there continuous with the cranial dura. It is fixed caudally to the coccyx by the filum terminale which, as it passes beyond the closed end of the dural sac, acquires an adherent dural covering. It is fixed on each side by the ventral and dorsal spinal nerve roots (described below). These likewise acquire adherent dural coverings which add to their thickness and give them strength.

Meningeal Nerves. At each segmental level, rami pass through the intervertebral foramina to the dura. Their fibers can be traced to the spinal ganglia (sensory) and to the gray rami communicantes (Kimmel).

On *flexing the spinal column*, the spinous processes spread apart, the vertebral canal lengthens (up to 7 cm.), and the dural sac stretches. In the cadaver, full flexion of the column exerts traction on the dural sac so that nerves L. 1 and 2 are drawn from 2 to 5 mm. within the intervertebral foramina. L. 3 is withdrawn less, and L. 4 negligibly. On the other hand, "*straight-leg raising*" through 15° to 30° exerts traction on the sciatic nerve; through 60° to 80° it pulls L. 5, S. 1, and S. 2 downward through 2 to 5 mm., but again the effect on L. 4 is negligible (Inman and Saunders).

Similarly, traction on the outstretched hand pulls the roots of the brachial plexus caudally, in the intervertebral foramina, C. 6 and 7 moving the most (Smith).

In the adult, the subarachnoid space and the contained cerebrospinal fluid extend to the body of sacral vertebra 2. So, between L. 2 and S. 2, in place of cord there is filum terminale surrounded by the roots of the lower spinal nerves which have been drawn upwards with the cord. These loosely occupy the sac of cerebrospinal fluid, here somewhat dilated, in which they lie, and from their resemblance to a horse's tail they are called the *cauda equina*.

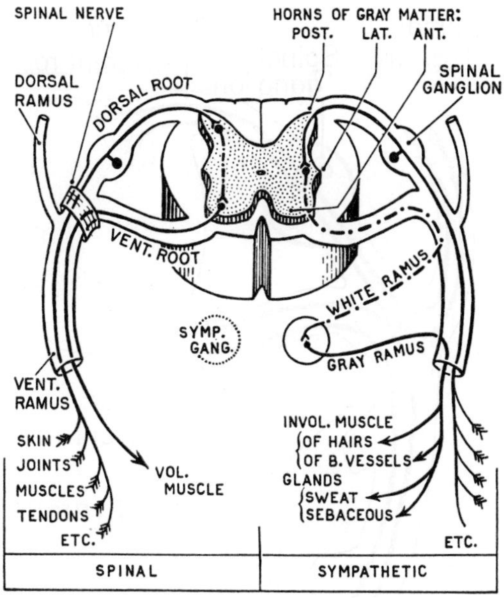

FIG. 43. The composition of a peripheral nerve

»» *Note.* A hollow needle entering the subarachnoid space to draw off CSF above L. 2 may puncture and so damage the spinal cord; entering lower down it would merely push the nerves of the cauda equina apart.

Structure. The spinal cord or spinal medulla, as seen on cross section, has an H-shaped field of gray matter enveloped in a zone of white matter (*fig. 43*). The anterior and posterior limbs of the H, called the *anterior* and *posterior horns* or *gray columns*, divide the white matter of each side into *anterior*, *lateral*, and *posterior white columns*. A groove in front, the *antero-median fissure*, and a septum behind, the *postero-median septum*, separate the right and left sides of white matter. A canal, the *central canal of the cord*, continuous with the ventricles of the brain, runs through the gray matter.

Two continuous rows of delicate *nerve rootlets or fila* (L. filum = a thread) are attached to each side of the cord along the lines of the apices of the anterior and posterior columns of gray matter. The fila of the anterior row converge laterally in groups of a dozen or so to form *ventral or anterior nerve roots*, and the fila of the posterior row do likewise to form *dorsal or posterior nerve roots*.

The respective ventral and dorsal roots pierce the dura about 2 mm. apart, one in

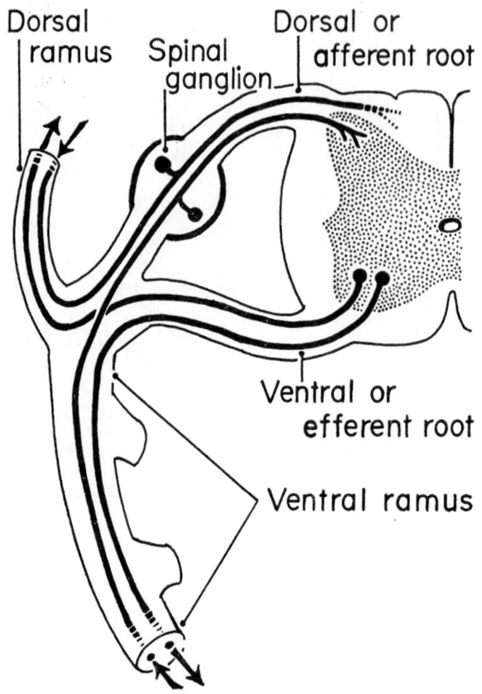

FIG. 43.1. The fibers in the two roots and two primary rami of a spinal nerve.

front of the other—or rather they carry it before them. They then continue laterally to the intervertebral foramina where each dorsal root is swollen because it contains the bodies of (sensory) nerve cells; the swelling is a *spinal ganglion* (posterior root ganglion). Just beyond this, the two roots unite and their fibers mingle to form a *nerve trunk*. This, after a few millimeters, divides into a large *ventral* and a small *dorsal ramus* (L. ramus = branch) (*fig. 43.1*).

The length of cord to which the fila of one pair of spinal nerves is attached is called a *spinal segment*. Since there are 31 pairs of spinal nerves, the cord is said to have 31 segments. But segmentation of the cord is incidental—not fundamental—and in cases where one side of a vertebra fails to develop the corresponding fila group themselves with fila of the neighboring roots.

Neuron. The structural unit of the nervous system is a nerve cell or neuron. A neuron has the following parts: (1) the cell body, (2) a process or *dendrite* (or processes) which transmits impulses to the cell body and (3) a process or *axon* which transmits impulses from the cell body. An entire neuron may be microscopic in size; on the other hand, a process may be several feet long (e.g., a fiber of the sciatic nerve).

Peripheral Nerves

Macroscopic or Gross Structure. The peripheral nerves met with in dissection (e.g., facial, median, sciatic) are made up of bundles of nerve fibers, both afferent and efferent (*fig. 43*). A loose sheath of areolar tissue (epineurium), continuous with the surrounding areolar tissue, encases the entire nerve and unites the individual bundles. Each bundle has a thicker sheath, the *perineurium*, which branches when the bundle branches and which accompanies every fiber to its destination. Between the fibers are some delicate areolar septa (endoneurium).

Microscopic Structure. A nerve fiber consists of a central thread, the *axis cylinder*, encased in a tube of white fatty material of varying thickness, the *myelin sheath*, around which there is a thin, but tough, nucleated membrane, the *neurilemma*. A nerve fiber may be likened to a pencil, the axis cylinder being the lead, the myelin sheath the wooden shaft, and the neurilemma the enamel coating. The axis cylinder is the essential part of the fiber. It is continuous throughout the length of the fiber and at the periphery it separates into many *fibrils*.

White versus Gray. It is the myelin sheath that gives whiteness to nerves and to nerve tracts in the spinal cord and brain; in its absence nerve tissue looks gray.

If a fiber is pinched, the axis cylinder and the myelinated sheath will rupture, but the neurilemma may remain intact.

Nerves transmit messages or impulses quite rapidly, but the speed is variable, being about 60 meters per second in motor nerves. Certain chemicals, *hormones*, secreted by glands enter the bloodstream and carry messages to distant parts, but this blood-borne transmission is relatively slow.

Functions. A dorsal nerve root transmits impulses to the cord; it is *afferent* or sensory. A ventral nerve root transmits impulses from the cord; it is *efferent* or motor. (L.

ad-ferens = bringing to; ex-ferens = bringing from, the CNS here being understood.)

The cell bodies of the afferent nerve fibers lie within the spinal ganglia. Those of the efferent nerve fibers lie in the anterior horn of the gray matter of the cord (*fig. 43.1*).

Afferent or sensory spinal nerve fibers bring impulses from the endings in the skin, muscles, joints, etc. to the spinal ganglia, and thence, via the fila of the dorsal roots to the cord. Within the cord the fibers branch: some branches ascend in the cord, others descend, still others at once turn into the gray matter of the posterior horn where they synapse (i.e., make contact) with the dendrites of short *connector* (*intercalated*) *cells* whose axons in turn synapse with the dendrites of large multipolar cells in the anterior horn. The axons of these motor cells emerge in the anterior root fila and end in motor end-plates of voluntary muscles.

These neurons—afferent, connector, and efferent—constitute a simple spinal *reflex arc.* The arc functions thus: if one's finger is touched, even during sleep, one moves it; if it is pricked or burnt, one withdraws the limb. In the one case a simple reflex arc is invoked; in the other, afferent impulses spread more widely, even to the opposite side of the body, perhaps arousing consciousness, due to the ascending and descending and crossing fibers by which impulses spread to other parts of the cord and to the brain.

Contrasts. The area of distribution of a severed artery can, if the anastomosis is ample, be taken over by other arteries. Not so with nerves; just as cutting a telephone wire isolates a house, so cutting a motor nerve isolates the muscle fibers supplied by it, and they wither away.

Nerve Plexuses. Ventral nerve rami and their branches communicate with adjacent rami and branches to form plexuses, thereby widening the influence of the individual segments of the spinal cord. Close to the vertebral column the ventral rami of nerves C. 1–4 form the cervical plexus, those of C. 5—Th. 1 the brachial plexus, L. 1–4 the lumbar plexus, L. 4–S. 4 the sacral plexus, and S. 4–Co. 1 the coccygeal plexus.

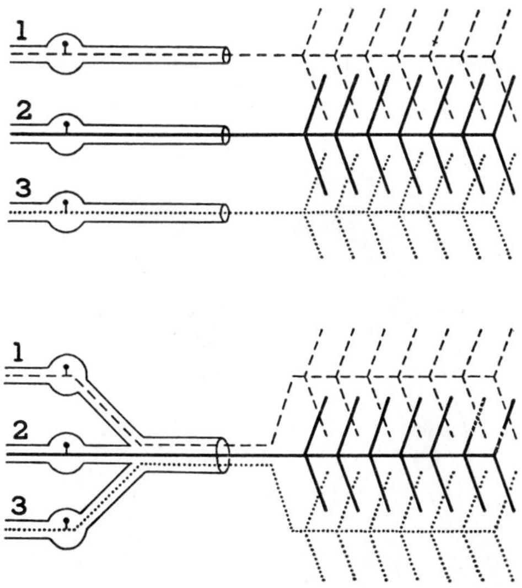

FIG. 43.2. The distribution of a series of spinal nerves overlap. (After Haymaker and Woodhall, modified.)

Nerves communicate more peripherally also, e.g., the musculocutaneous and median usually communicate in the arm; the median and ulnar communicate in the upper part of the forearm, superficially in the palm, and again deep in the palm under cover of the thenar muscles. Cutaneous nerves communicate freely with adjacent nerves and overlap them with the result that severing a cutaneous nerve diminishes sensation in its territory without as a rule abolishing it (*figs. 43.2 and 43.3*).

Peripheral nerves are themselves plexuses: their fibers do not run parallel courses but are plaited, not unlike the tendon fibers in figure 31*A*. The branch of a nerve is usually bound to the parent stem for between ½″ and 2½″ by areolar tissue, and the level at which it leaves the parent stem varies within this range. Proximal to this, the strands of the branch take part in the plait, and attempts to free the branch more proximally lead to its destruction (*fig. 43.4*).

»» *Note.* If the individual motor nerves, supplying a group of muscles developed from a common muscle mass, are traced proximally up the parent stem, they will be found to form a single bundle. This bundle can be traced but a short distance before its fibers separate and become plaited with the fibers of the parent stem (e.g., the nerves to the Gastrocnemius, Soleus, and Plantaris spring from a common bundle, but the nerve to the Popliteus does not spring from this bundle,

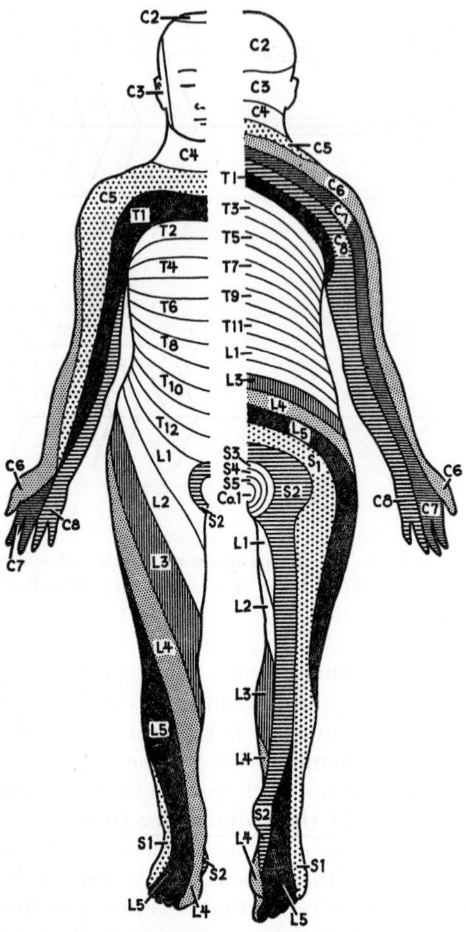

FIG. 43.3. Dermatomes: the strips of skin supplied by the various levels or segments of the spinal cord. (After Keegan, modified.)

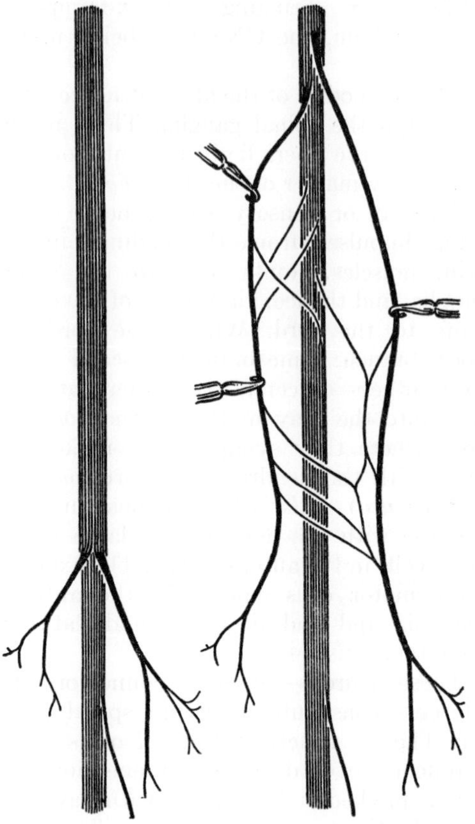

FIG. 43.4. Two branches of a nerve dissected proximally.

for the reason that the Popliteus is not related to these three muscles developmentally, although it chances to be closely related to them topographically).

Blood Supply. The peripheral nerves are supplied by a succession of anastomosing nutrient vessels, *arteriae nervorum* derived from the nearest arteries which are seldom more than ¼″ to ½″ away. In number, size, and origin they are inconstant. Thus, occasionally the median nerve may receive no artery between axilla and elbow, the circulation being maintained by a large intraneural descending vessel which enters it at the axilla; but, when the nutrient vessels are small, they are necessarily numerous. On reaching a nerve the artery usually divides into ascending and descending branches, which, by anastomosing with longitudinal chains near the surface of the nerve (epineural) and between the nerve bundles (interfascicular), form a series of arterial "ladders". From these, finer branches pass into the nerve bundles (intrafascicular) where they form a more or less oblong network that runs throughout the length of the nerve.

The veins, *venae nervorum*, have an intraneural pattern similar to that of the arteries. Some of the veins from the cutaneous nerves end in the cutaneous veins, but most of them pierce the deep fascia and end in muscle veins. The veins of the deep nerves end either in muscle veins or in the venous plexus around an artery (Sunderland).

AUTONOMIC NERVOUS SYSTEM

This system of nerves and ganglia distributes efferent impulses to (1) the heart, (2) smooth muscle, wherever situated, and (3) glands, and it collects afferent impulses from them. It has two parts,

(1) the sympathetic system and
(2) the parasympathetic system.

The sympathetic system (*fig. 44.2*) has central connections with the thoraco-lumbar part of the spinal medulla or cord from the 1st thoracic to the 2nd (or 3rd) lumbar segment (i.e., the first 8 and the last 8 of the 31 segments of the spinal cord are excluded). *The Parasympathetic System,* which has (1) a cranial part and (2) a sacral part, has central connections with the brain through cranial nerves III, VII, IX, and X, and with the spinal cord at sacral segments (2), 3, and 4.

Sympathetic System

In the *sympathetic system* there are neurons corresponding to the efferent, connector, and afferent neurons of the voluntary system (*figs. 44* and *44.1*). The equivalent of the efferent or anterior horn cells, called *excitor cells,* occur (1) in the *paravertebral ganglia* or ganglia of the sympathetic trunk, (2) in the *prevertebral ganglia* (or visceral ganglia, cardiac, celiac, intermesenteric, hypogastric, and subsidiary ganglia) which are but detached parts of paravertebral ganglia, and (3) in the medulla of the suprarenal gland.

The gray matter of the spinal cord from segments Th. 1—L. 2 possesses an intermedio-lateral column (horn), and it is in this intermedio-lateral column that the sympathetic *connector cells* are lodged (*fig. 44.1*). Their axons pass as fine, medullated *preganglionic fibers* (2.6 μ) via the ventral nerve roots and white rami communicantes (Th. 1—L. 2) to the paravertebral ganglia, and there form synapses with the excitor cells.

Some preganglionic fibers, however, ascend and descend in the sympathetic trunk to form synapses with excitor cells in ganglia at various levels; whereas other preganglionic fibers pass through the paravertebral ganglia

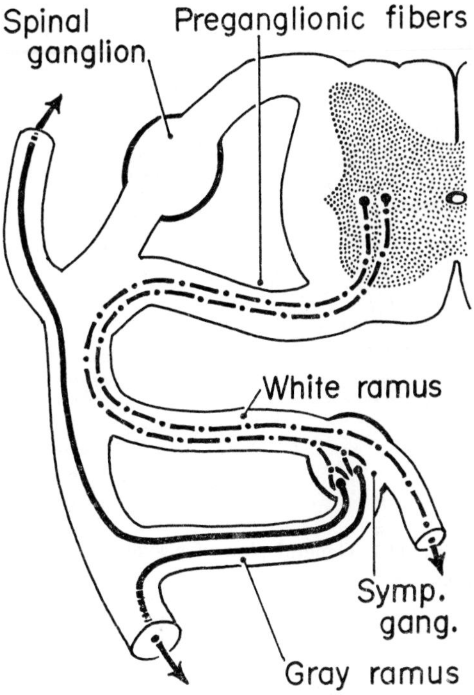

FIG. 44. The typical sympathetic contribution to a spinal nerve.

without synapsing, to form *splanchnic nerves* (*fig. 44.1*).

The *postganglionic fibers,* or axons of the excitor cells, are mostly nonmedullated and therefore gray. One or more bundles of these gray fibers called *gray rami communicantes* pass laterally from the ganglia of the sympathetic trunk to each and every spinal nerve and, with other postganglionic fibers relayed from the superior cervical ganglion to the face, which is the territory of the trigeminal nerve (*fig. 44.4*), they reach the blood vessels, sweat and sebaceous glands, and arrectores pilorum muscles of the entire cutaneous surface of the body and of somatic structures (limbs and body wall).

The thoracic and lumbar *Splanchnic Nerves* are, in a sense, elongated white rami communicantes containing preganglionic fibers that pass without interruption through paravertebral ganglia (Th. 5–L. 2) to synapse with excitor cells in prevertebral ganglia.

The greater (Th. 5–10), lesser (Th. 10, 11), and lowest (Th. 12) thoracic splanchnic

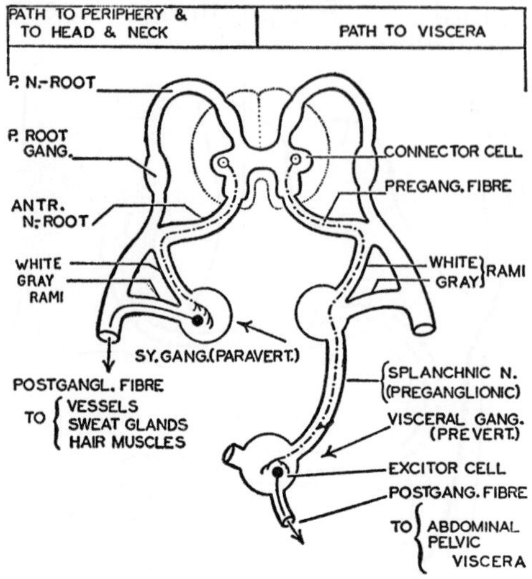

FIG. 44.1. General plan of a sympathetic ganglion.

nerves and the four lumbar splanchnic nerves end in the celiac and other prevertebral ganglia, whence they are relayed almost entirely as perivascular branches to the abdominal and pelvic viscera (*figs. 44.1* and *44.5*).

The *suprarenal gland* is peculiar in its nerve supply in that branches of the splanchnic nerves ramify among the cells of its medulla, which therefore represent excitor cells (p. 269). They are derived from cord segments Th. 10–L. 1, (2).

The cervical and upper thoracic sympathetic ganglia, although paravertebral in location, represent both para- and prevertebral ganglia of more caudal levels; that is to say, the postganglionic fibers of the excitor cells in these ganglia pass (1) on the one hand, as rami communicantes to the spinal nerves and, so, to somatic structures, and (2) on the other hand, as visceral fibers to such structures as the eye, salivary glands, heart, and lungs.

The *visceral afferent* (sensory) fibers of the sympathetic system travel with the visceral efferent fibers. They pass via the white rami communicantes to the spinal ganglia (dorsal root ganglia) where, like the afferent fibers of the voluntary system, they have their cell stations. They enter the spinal cord through the dorsal roots mainly of Th. 1–L. 2, and synapse with the connector cells in the intermedio-lateral column of gray matter. Many, however, first ascend or descend in the sympathetic trunk.

THE SYMPATHETIC TRUNK ITSELF is composed of ascending and descending fibers some of which are preganglionic efferent, postganglionic efferent, and also afferent fibers. The paravertebral ganglia (ganglia of the trunk) are formed by synapses between preganglionic efferent neurons and the cell bodies of postganglionic neurons. The influence of a single preganglionic neuron is diffused over a wide area due to the fact that each preganglionic fiber synapses with a number of postganglionic neurons.

CEREBRAL CONTROL over the autonomic system is exercised by centers in the hypothalamic region, which lies toward the lower and front part of the 3rd ventricle. From here descending tracts influence the connector cells.

THE SYMPATHETIC SUPPLY OF INDIVIDUAL REGIONS AND ORGANS will be considered by diagram and comment. Figures 44.2 to 44.5 indicate for the different regions and organs (1) the probable segmental locations of the connector cells in the intermedio-lateral column of gray matter; (2) the ganglia in which they synapse with effector cells; and (3) the ultimate distribution of the postganglionic fibers.

Upper Limb (*fig. 44.4*). Preganglionic fibers from cord segments Th. (2), 3–6, (7) ascend in the sympathetic trunk to the upper thoracic, inferior cervical, and middle cervical ganglia. Thence a dozen or so postganglionic, gray rami pass to the roots of the brachial plexus to be distributed to the limb. Most of these fibers travel in the lower trunk of the plexus (? where they may be subjected to pressure by the 1st rib) and in the median and ulnar nerves. A few "accessory gray rami" derived from the vertebral (sympathetic) plexus also pass to the upper five or six cervical nerves.

»» The gray ramus from ganglion Th. 2 to the ventral ramus of Th. 1 (Kuntz's nerve, *fig. 579*) must not be overlooked in operations intended to denervate the vessels of the upper limb.

Gray rami pass directly from the stellate ganglion to the subclavian artery, and ex-

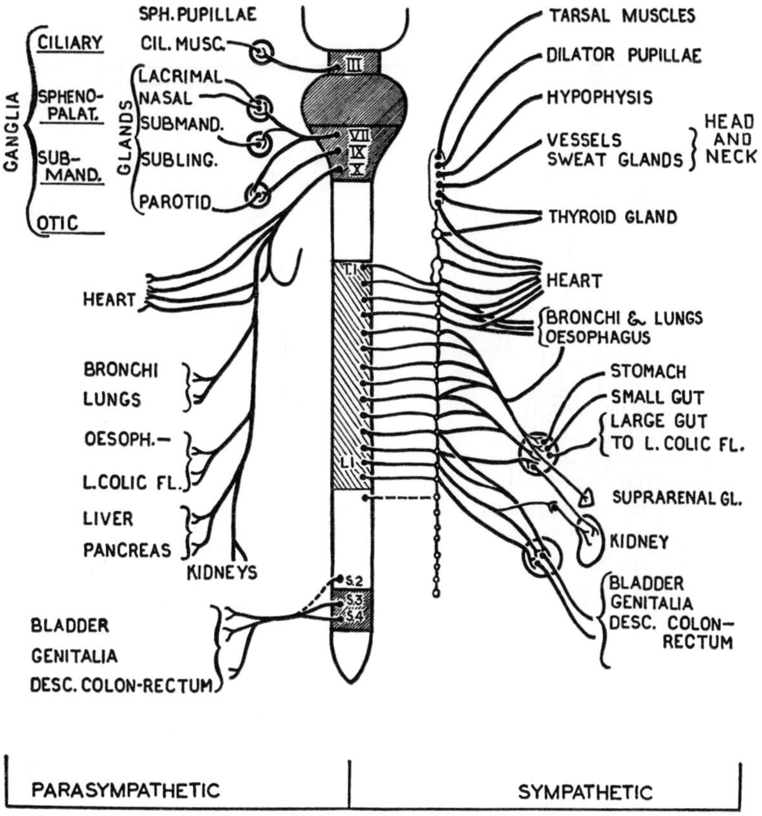

FIG. 44.2. General plan of the autonomic nervous system. (After Stopford.)

tend along it to the beginning of the axillary artery (*fig. 724*), but most of the axillary artery and the arteries distal to it are supplied at intervals with vaso-motor and vaso-sensory twigs from sympathetic fibers traveling with the nerves of the limb.

Lower Limb (*fig. 44.4*). Preganglionic fibers from cord segments Th. (10), 11, 12, L. 1 and 2 descend in the sympathetic trunk to ganglia L. 2–S. 3. Thence, as post-ganglionic fibers (gray rami) they pass to the nerves of the lumbar and sacral plexuses. The upper part of the femoral artery is supplied by an extension from the aortic plexuses along the common and external iliac arteries; but as in the upper limb so in the lower, most of the femoral artery and the arteries distal to it are supplied locally.

Head and Neck (*fig. 44.2*). Cord segments are mainly Th. 1 and 2, i.e., connector cells are situated in segments Th. 1 and 2, though some may extend lower. The excitor cells lie mainly in the superior cervical ganglion, and from it postganglionic fibers pass to the arrectores pilorum, sweat glands, and vessels of the skin; to the heart; and, via the int. carotid nerve, to the vessels of the nasal cavity (through the deep petrosal nerve), to the dura, to the cerebral vessels, and to the orbital cavity (tarsal muscles, Dilator Pupillae, and vaso-constrictors).

The orbital fibers arise mainly in cord segment Th. 1 (*fig. 766*), pass to the 1st thoracic ganglion, and ascend partly in the ansa subclavia (hence, traction on the subclavian artery may damage these fibers, causing Horner's syndrome) to the excitor cells in the superior cervical ganglion.

Thorax. Cord segments are mainly Th. 2, 3, and 4. For the *heart,* the cord segments are Th. 1–4, (5). From relay stations in the three cervical and upper 4, (5) thoracic ganglia, cardiac nerves pass to the cardiac plexus (*fig. 44.3*). Pain impulses travel in the afferent fibers (but apparently not by way of the superior cervical ganglion) and have

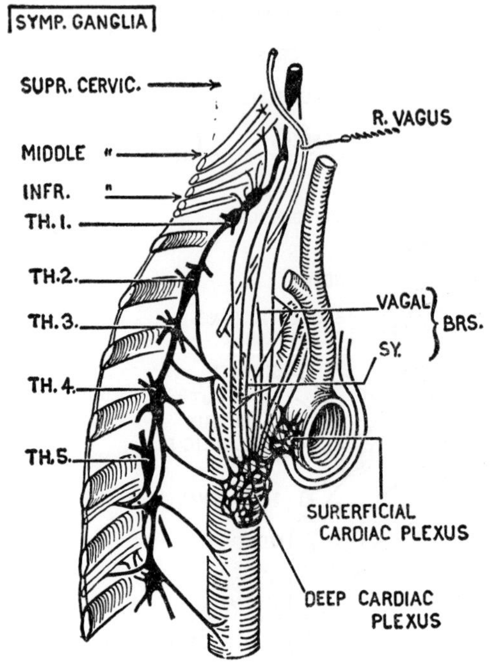

FIG. 44.3. Cardiac plexuses. (From White, after Kuntz and Morehouse.)

their cell stations in the upper 4, (5) thoracic spinal ganglia.

For the lungs, the cord segments are Th. 2–6, (7); for the esophagus, Th. 4, 5, and 6.

Abdomen and Pelvis. Cord segments are Th. 5–L. 2. For the stomach, liver, and pancreas they are Th. 6–9, (10), and for the gall bladder Th. 4–9, (10).

For the small intestine the cord segments are Th. (8), 9, 10, (11); for the cecum and appendix Th. 10, 11 and 12; for colon to left colic flexure Th. (11), 12, and L. 1; and for left colic flexure to rectum L. 1 and 2.

For kidney the cord segments are Th. (11), 12, L. 1, (2); for ureter L. 1 and 2; and for bladder (? Th. 11, 12), L. 1 and 2. (The foregoing data are largely from Mitchell.)

From the cord segments, connector fibers pass through the thoracic and lumbar parasympathetic ganglia, as the thoracic and lumbar splanchnic nerves, to be relayed in the celiac, renal, mesenteric, and superior and inferior hypogastric ganglia.

For other pelvic viscera see page 353 and figures 44.5 and 49.

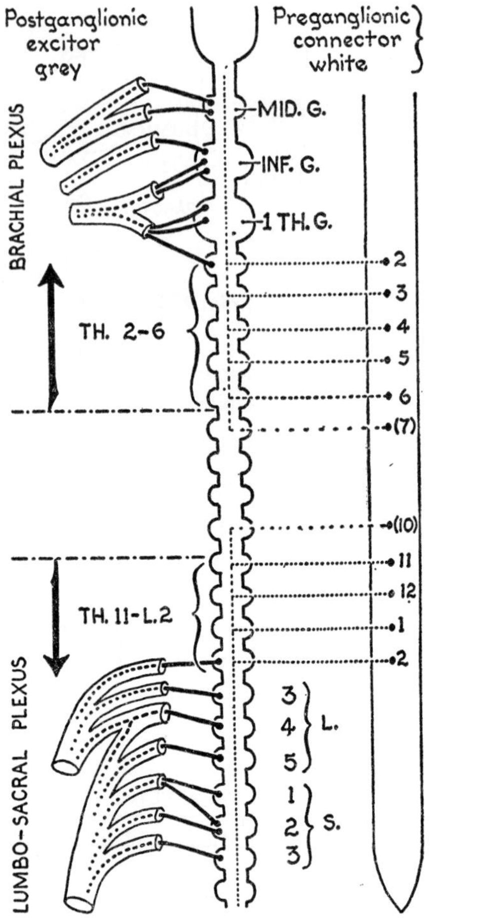

FIG. 44.4. The sympathetic supply to the upper and lower limbs.

Parasympathetic System

Parasympathetic nerve fibers (efferent) are contained in cranial nerves III, VII, IX, and X and in sacral nerves (2), 3, and 4.

Many branches of the trigeminal nerve (N. V) are accompanied in the terminal parts of their courses by efferent parasympathetic fibers from other nerves (e.g., the lingual nerve by the chorda tympani, see below).

»» *Afferent* parasympathetic nerve fibers are contained in cranial nerves IX and X and in sacral nerves (2), 3, and 4.

Oculomotor Nerve. This nerve (N. III) sends fibers to the ciliary ganglion,

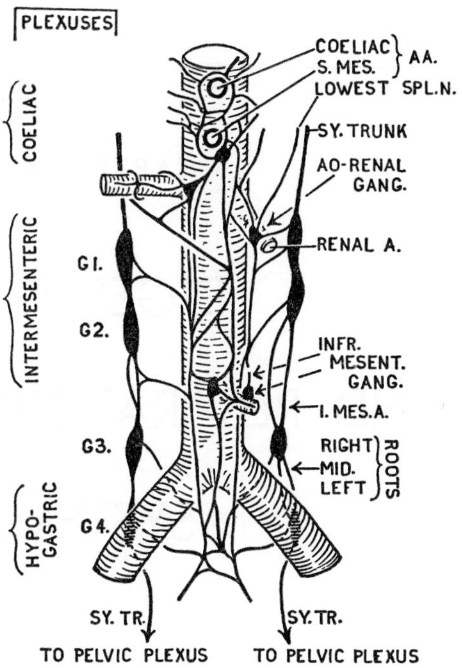

FIG. 44.5. The intermesenteric and superior hypogastric plexuses. (From a dissection by K. Baldwin.)

whence they are relayed by short ciilary nerves to the sphincter pupillae and the ciliary muscle, mediating contraction of the pupil and accommodation of the lens to near vision (*fig. 766*).

Facial Nerve. (N. VII; see *fig. 797* and p. 713). *The Efferent Fibers* of the nervus intermedius (pars intermedia of the facial nerve) carry secreto-motor and vaso-dilator impulses to the lacrimal, nasal, palatine, and salivary glands. They run thus: (1) via the *greater (superficial) petrosal nerve* to the pterygopalatine ganglion, whence as post-ganglionic fibers they accompany (a) the zygomatic nerve to the orbit, where, leaving it, they join the lacrimal nerve and so to the lacrimal gland (*fig. 786.1*), and (b) branches of nerve V^2 to the nasal and palatine glands (*fig. 796* and p. 688); and (2) via the *chorda tympani*, which, after passing through the tympanum, joins the lingual nerve which conducts it as far as the submandibular ganglion from which it is relayed to the submandibular and sublingual glands (*fig. 786* and p. 678), and (3) a *twig of the facial nerve* joins the lesser (superficial) petrosal nerve perhaps bringing accessory secretory fibers to the parotid gland.

»» The *Afferent Fibers* of the nervus intermedius are: (1) mainly taste fibers coming (a) from the anterior two-thirds of the tongue in the chorda tympani, and (b) from the soft palate in the lesser palatine nerves, through the pterygopalatine ganglion and on via the greater (superficial) petrosal nerve. These fibers have their cell station in the geniculate ganglion. (2) The fibers of deep sensibility in the face also have their cell station in the geniculate ganglion and travel in the nervus intermedius.

Glossopharyngeal Nerve. The tympanic branch of this nerve (N. IX, *fig. 761*) traverses the tympanum in the tympanic plexus, receives a twig from the facial nerve, and, as the lesser (superficial) petrosal nerve, runs to the otic ganglion, and thence by the auriculotemporal nerve to the parotid gland. If the twig from the facial nerve is secretory (secreto-motor), then the parotid gland has a double nerve supply—from IX and from VII.

The *Afferent Fibers* are (1) fibers of taste from the posterior one-third of the tongue, (2) fibers of general sensation from the posterior one-third of the tongue, the fauces, pharynx, and tympanum, and (3) pressor fibers in the sinus nerve. Their cell station is in the ganglia on the root of nerve IX.

Vagus Nerve. This nerve (N. X) supplies the digestive and respiratory passages and the heart, as described on page 657 and shown in figure 762. The relay stations of the efferent fibers of the vagus are in terminal ganglia, situated in (or near) the walls of the organ or part it supplies. The vagus causes hollow organs to contract and their sphincters to relax. It is secreto-motor. The cell stations of its afferent fibers are in the ganglia on the root of the vagus. Its afferent fibers do not carry impulses of pain from the heart or from abdominal organs.

Pelvic Splanchnic Nerves. These nerves (S. 2, 3, and 4) behave as vagal fibers, and are described on page 353. The vagus supplies the gastro-intestinal tract as far as the left colic flexure, via a branch of the posterior vagal trunk (*fig. 306*); the pelvic splanchnic nerves supply the gut distal to that point. Their afferent fibers are conductors of pain impulses.

CHAPTER **3**

DIGESTIVE AND RESPIRATORY SYSTEMS

DIGESTIVE SYSTEM

Parts; Mouth; Mastication; Oral Glands: Parotid, Submandibular, Sublingual; Pharynx and Esophagus; Stomach; Intestine; Liver; Pancreas; Spleen.

RESPIRATORY SYSTEM

Parts; Nasal Cavities; Pharynx; Auditory Tube; Larynx; Trachea; Bronchi; Lungs; Respiratory Act; Epithelial Surfaces.

DIGESTIVE SYSTEM

Animals, like plants, absorb their food in fluid form. In order that solid food shall become fluid, preparatory to being taken into the blood stream, it must undergo certain mechanical and chemical changes. The parts of the body set aside for this purpose are known as the digestive system. This is essentially (1) a long hollow tube, the digestive passage, through which food is propelled, and (2) certain accessory glands (*fig. 45*).

The *digestive passage* (alimentary canal) begins at the lips, traverses the neck, thorax, abdomen and pelvis, and ends at the anus.

Its successive **parts** are:

Mouth
Pharynx
Esophagus
Stomach
Small intestine
  duodenum, jejunum, and ileum.
Large intestine
  appendix, cecum, colon, rectum, anal canal and anus.

Its **accessory glands** are:

Glands of the mouth
  parotid,
  submandibular, and
  sublingual
Liver
Pancreas, with which is associated the Spleen.

Mouth. To survive, animals must eat. And, in search for food, they advance, mouth end foremost. Around the mouth the organs of special sense are developed: the eyes to locate food by *sight*, the nose by *smell*, and the lips and tongue by *touch.*

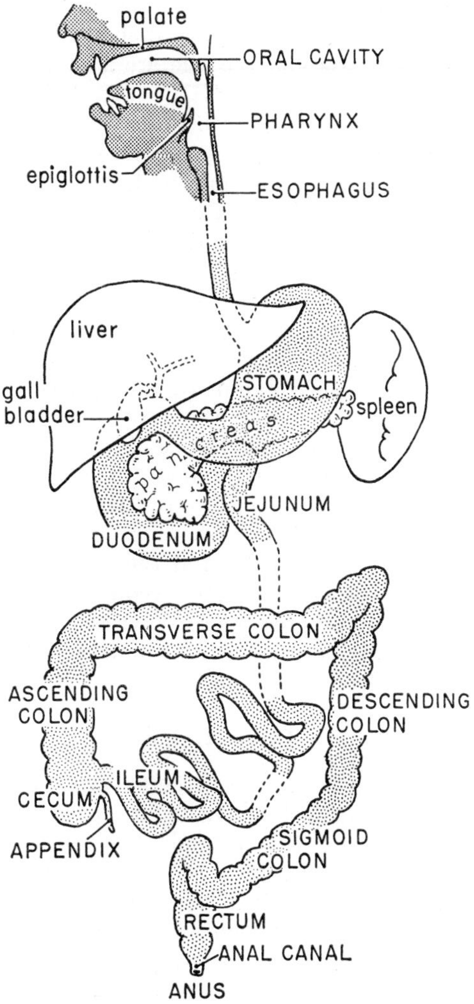

FIG. 45. Diagram of the digestive tract

When the food is in the mouth, the *taste buds* decide if it is good, in which case it is swallowed; if not, it is rejected. The ears advise if there is *sound* of danger, when safety may be sought in flight. Hence, the brain establishes itself at the mouth end of the body.

The mouth, or oral cavity, is bounded externally by the cheeks and lips. The cleft between the upper and lower lips is the *aperture* of the mouth. The *teeth* form two dental arches, one set in the upper jaw or maxillae and the other in the lower jaw or mandible. The horseshoe-shaped space external to the teeth and gums is the *vestibule* of the mouth. The space bounded externally by the teeth and gums is the *mouth proper*. From the floor of the mouth rises the *tongue;* the roof comprises the *hard* and *soft palates* and the median finger-like process, the *uvula*, in which the soft palate ends.

Mastication. The incisor teeth (L. incidere = to cut) bite off pieces of food, and the molar teeth (L. mola = a millstone) grind them. The food is commonly coarse; so, the mouth requires a protective lining. It is lined with stratified squamous epithelium, resembling epidermis, but the surface cells, although flattened, retain their nuclei and do not cornify. The epithelium is lubricated and kept moist by the secretions of small glands, the size of pin-heads, that line the palate, lips, and cheeks. These secretions augment those of the three large, paired, **Oral Glands** (Salivary Glands) (parotid, submandibular, and sublingual).

The **Parotid Gland** lies below the ear (*fig. 45.1*). Its long duct opens into the vestibule of the mouth beside the 2nd upper molar tooth.

The **Submandibular** (SUBMAXILLARY) **Gland** lies under shelter of the mandible; its duct opens on to a papilla beside its fellow, behind the lower incisor teeth. On opening your mouth and raising the tip of the tongue, watery secretion may be seen welling up from the orifices.

Each **Sublingual Gland** produces a

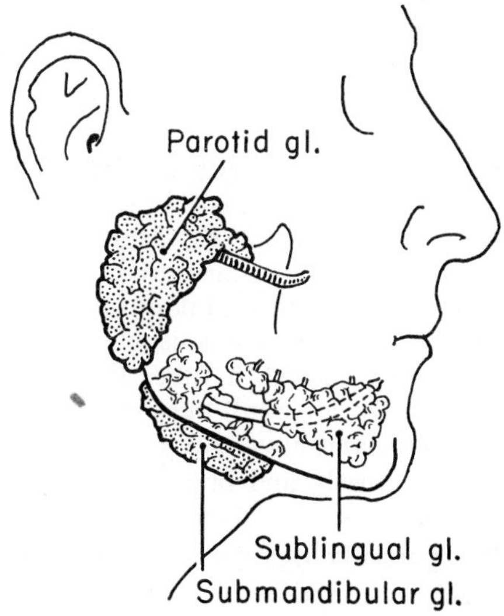

FIG. 45.1. The three oral (salivary) glands

ridge on the side of the floor of the mouth beneath the tongue. Its many fine ducts open on to the ridge (*figs. 45.1* and *785*).

The salivary glands have either a mucous secretion or a serous secretion or both; the serous secretion (ptyalin) digests free starch but cannot break down the cellulose enclosing the starch.

The saliva moistens the food which has been ground into small particles by the teeth. This the tongue rolls into a bolus or lubricated mass easily swallowed—dry food is swallowed with difficulty. Saliva keeps the lips and mouth pliable in speaking.

The **Pharynx and Esophagus** are merely passages and, like the mouth, are protected by stratified squamous epithelium. The muscular coat of the pharynx and upper half of the esophagus, though voluntary in structure, is not under voluntary control; in the lower half of the esophagus (and onward to the anus) it is involuntary or smooth.

The **Stomach** lies in the abdomen and, being a receptacle for food and requiring to expand, to contract and to move about, it possesses a serous (peritoneal) coat, such as the relatively inexpansible pharynx and esophagus do not require. It secretes a protective mucus. Some of the cells of its test-tube-like glands secrete hydrochloric acid which is necessary to the action of the pepsin secreted by the remaining cells. Pepsin initiates the digestion of proteins. The outlet of the stomach, the **Pylorus** (Gk. = a gatekeeper) is guarded by a strong sphincter of circular fibers, the *pyloric sphincter* (*figs. 233* and *280*).

The **Intestine** or gut is divisible into two parts: (1) the small intestine, about 20 feet long, and (2) the large intestine, about 6 feet long, as measured at autopsy (B. M. L. Underhill). But during life, the whole digestive passage is usually from 8 to 10 feet long. Indeed, a tube, 10 feet long, swallowed by an adult may project from both mouth and anus. After death the gut lengthens greatly and progressively (W. C. Alvarez).

The partially digested food leaving the stomach is mixed with hydrochloric acid and pepsin, is fluid, and is relatively free from bacteria. In the upper part of the small gut (3″ beyond the pylorus) the ferments of the pancreas and the bile are added to the intestinal ferments. Here digestion continues and absorption of water and digested products begins. These processes are most active in the duodenum and they diminish as the large gut is approached. The essential function of the large gut is to dehydrate the intestinal contents. The bacteria, present in enormous numbers, exemplify symbiosis, for they make an important contribution to the welfare of their host. In addition to the production of vitamin B, they convert bile salts into molecules that are resorbed and used for producing hemoglobin. They also in part break down cellulose, which is almost undigested in the small intestine.

As the distance from the entrance of the pancreatic juices and the bile increases the intestinal contents become less fluid and their progress more slow; hence, in the large gut more lubricating mucus is manufactured.

Liver (Hepar)

The liver is the largest organ in the body. Attached to its under surface is the *gall bladder;* this extends backward to a transverse fissure, the *porta hepatis*, through which the *hepatic ducts* conduct bile from the liver and through which the *portal vein* (conducting blood laden with products of digestion) and the *hepatic artery* (conducting oxygenated blood) enter the liver. After the blood has circulated through the liver, it leaves the posterior surface via the hepatic veins to enter the inferior vena cava.

The liver is a gland of compound tubular design. The cells of the tubules elaborate an *exocrine* (*external*) *secretion,* called bile, into the tiny lumina of the tubules. Each tubule, called a *bile capillary* or *canaliculus*, is really a continuous series of minute spaces between two contiguous rows of liver cells. At the periphery of the lobule (see below) it drains into a system of ducts, the *bile passages*, which communicate with the gall bladder and with the duodenum (*fig. 274*, p. 243).

The same liver cells also elaborate an *endocrine* (*internal*) *secretion*. This is possible, since the surfaces of the cells not forming

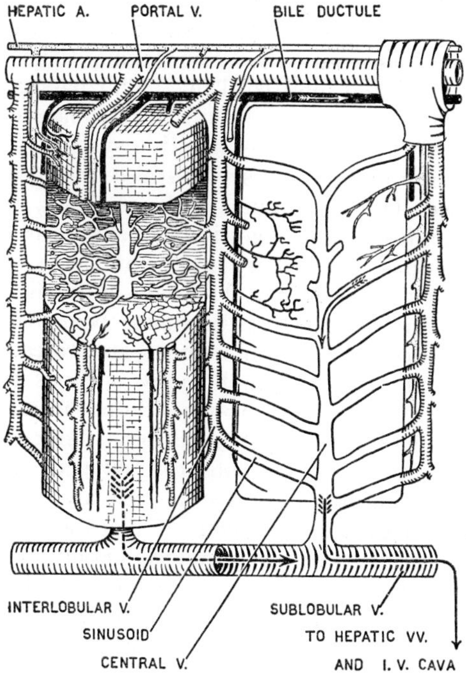

FIG. 46. Diagram of the blood flow through 2 lobules of the liver and of the course of bile, according to the traditional description.

canaliculi are in apposition with blood capillaries. These are not simple capillaries but *sinusoids* (p. 35). Helping to line the sinusoids are phagocytic cells, *Kupffer's cells.*

Blood flow through the Liver. Traditionally, the liver is composed of hexagonal lobules (*fig. 46*) where distributing (interlobular) branches of the portal vein, placed peripherally, send sinusoids converging on a receiving (central) radicle of the hepatic vein, placed centrally.

A different plan is now recognized (*fig. 46.1*); it is one in which a distributing (preterminal) portal vein, placed centrally, sends diverging sinusoids to three receiving hepatic veins, placed peripherally. To this Rappaport has given the name "Liver acinus." The design is that of a trefoil of three "simple acini."

A preterminal hepatic artery accompanies each preterminal portal vein and bile passage, and it empties into the sinuses.

Each simple acinus is divided into three zones which are related to the declining influence of the artery.

The *bile passages* conduct bile in the reverse direction (i.e., toward the porta). *Lymph vessels* run both with the portal vein and the hepatic veins.

Functions. As the blood moves leisurely though the sinusoids, the cells of the liver elaborate bile. They also regulate the amount of sugar (glucose) in the blood by removing the excess after a meal and temporarily storing it as glycogen. They also store vitamin A. They elaborate urea which the kidneys dispose of, also fibrinogen and heparin.

The Kupffer cells, like similar reticulo-endothelial cells in the spleen and bone marrow, help to dispose of effete red blood cells, and are concerned with resistance to disease and with immunity.

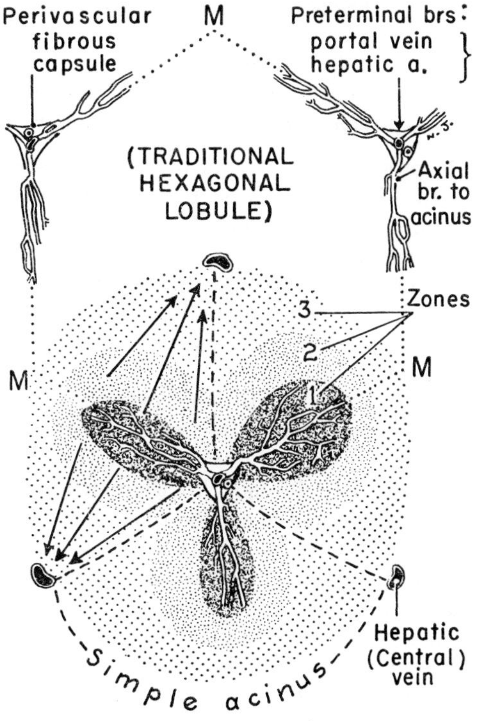

FIG. 46.1. According to the modern view, the acinus is the liver unit. It incorporates sectors of several (3) adjacent lobules, a preterminal branch of the portal vein and of the hepatic artery being central and several (3) initial hepatic veins being peripheral. *Zones 1* are supplied with better blood than *Zones 2*, and *2* than *3*. (Courtesy of Rappaport *et al.*)

Pancreas

The pancreas is known as the sweetbread in animals that are used by man for food. This long gland extends across the abdomen and lies behind the stomach. It has an external secretion which passes to the duodenum where it is changed into ferments that act upon proteins, carbohydrates, and fats. And, it has an internal secretion, called insulin, the reduction of which leads to diabetes.

Spleen (Lien)

The spleen is included here for convenience; but its association with the digestive system is incidental. It is a soft sponge filled with blood, about the size of a clenched fist, and colored like the liver (*fig. 282*).

Structure and Function. See page 230.

RESPIRATORY SYSTEM

Parts; Nasal Cavities; Pharynx; Auditory Tube; Larynx; Trachea; Bronchi; Lungs; Respiratory Act; Epithelial Surfaces.

Respiration is a chemical reaction essential to life; it involves the taking up of oxygen and giving off of carbon dioxide. In unicellular organisms this interchange of gases (O_2 and CO_2) takes place directly between the cell and the medium (which in all cases is water) in which the cell lives. But in a large multicellular organism (such as man) all cells, except the external ones, being removed from the surrounding medium (in this case air), require that the oxygen shall be brought to them from the exterior and that the carbon dioxide shall in turn be taken away. The transfer is made in two stages: the first stage is from the exterior via the air passages to the lungs, which act as a halfway house; the second stage is via the bloodstream to the watery medium (tissue fluids) that bathes the cells.

Two systems, then, the respiratory and the circulatory, are here allied in the common purpose of permitting the individual cells to breathe (exchange gases) like unicellular organisms. The lungs are sponges filled with air; their septa, being thin, moist, and membranous, allow transfusion of gases in solution. Being removed from the surface of the body, they are, in a measure, protected from mechanical injury and from desiccation; moreover, the air reaching them is warmed and moistened by the air passages.

The respiratory system is developmentally an offshoot from the digestive system. The urinary and genital systems also are closely allied. Of these four tubular systems, the respiratory and digestive have absorptive functions; the urinary and genital have not—they are excretory. The walls of the digestive and respiratory passages, being thus exposed to germs from without, are protected by a barrier of lymphocytes, such as the urinary and genital passages do not possess.

The digestive system absorbs food; the respiratory system absorbs oxygen, the absorption taking place in the alveoli of the lungs. The products of digestion and the oxygen (which combines loosely with the hemoglobin pigment in the red blood cells to form oxyhemoglobin) are conveyed by the blood to the tissues of the body where the products of digestion are oxidized and energy thereby released. The carbon dioxide, formed in the process, returns in the blood to the lungs and is there eliminated.

The respiratory system has two portions (*fig. 47*): (1) conducting and (2) respiratory.

The *Conducting Portion*, or air passages, comprises:

Nasal cavities
Pharynx
Larynx
Trachea
Bronchi and Bronchioles

The *Respiratory Portion* comprises:

Lungs (having respiratory bronchioles, alveolar ductules, alveolar sacs, and alveoli)

The **Nasal Cavities,** a right and a left are separated from each other by a thin median partition, the *nasal septum.* The entrance to each cavity, called the *nostril* or naris, opens into a *vestibule* which is lined with skin.

From the side wall of each cavity three downwardly curved shelves, the *conchae,* overhang three antero-posteriorly running passages, the *meatuses.* Opening into the inferior meatus is the *tear duct* (naso-lacrimal duct); opening into the other meatuses are

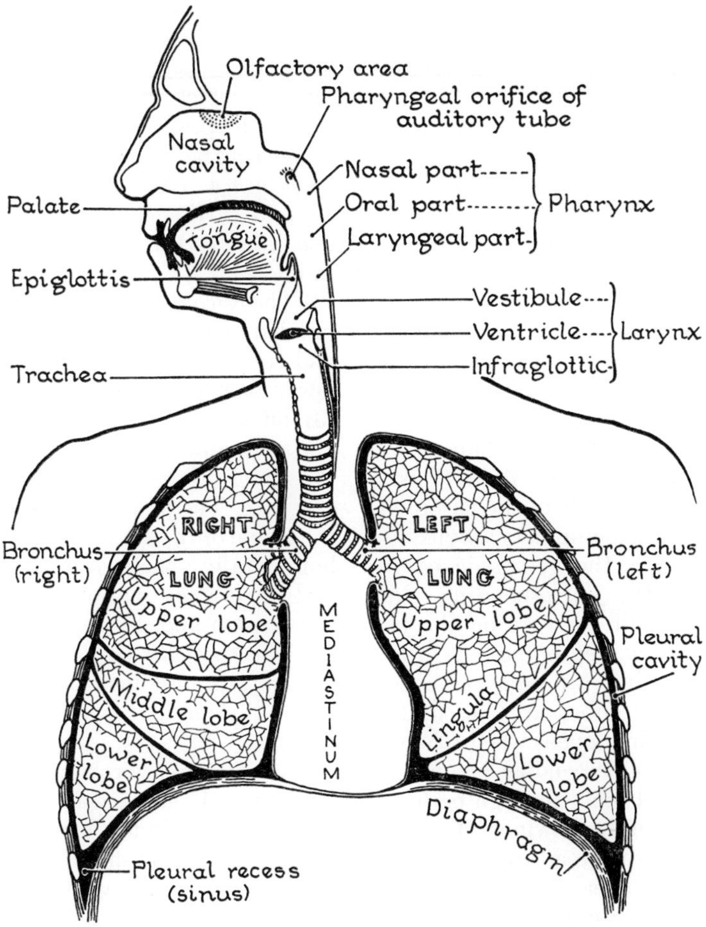

FIG. 47. Diagram of the respiratory system

the orifices of large *air sinuses* (air cells). These sinuses, inflated with air, invade the surrounding bones causing them to be large enough to carry the upper teeth and to form the framework of a large face in the adult, without adding great weight.

The mucous membrane lining the nasal cavities and air sinuses is almost inseparable from the periosteum; hence, the two collectively are called *muco-periosteum.* The muco-periosteum covering the inferior concha, and to a lesser extent that covering the middle concha, contains dilatable *venous sinuses* which warm and humidify the inhaled air. The muco-periosteum has a covering of stratified ciliated epithelium; in it are mucus-producing "goblet cells"; there are also mucous and serous glands, diffuse lymphoid tissue, and lymphoid follicles. The mucus catches inhaled dust and bacteria, and acts a sterilizing agent. The cilia waft the mucus, and the foreign matter entangled in it, backward to the pharynx.

The uppermost part (2 square cm. in each nasal cavity) of the medial and lateral walls is the *olfactory area.* Here the olfactory nerves, which stream through the thin perforated roof (*cribriform plate*) of the nasal cavity, end freely among the epithelial cells. This area is much more extensive in certain lower animals, such as the dog. The olfactory area is above the level reached by the air passing to and from the lungs, but eddies of air can be made to circulate here on sniffing, so that weaker stimuli may be appreciated.

The **Pharynx** is a fibro-muscular chamber, 5″ long. It is attached above to the base of the skull; it is continuous below with the esophagus. Communicating with it in front are the nasal, oral, and laryngeal cavities. Accordingly, it is divisible into three parts (upper, middle, and lower), called the nasal, oral, and laryngeal parts, respectively.

The nasal part or *nasopharynx* is the backward extension of the nasal cavities, and it cannot be shut off from these cavities, but it can be, and is, shut off from the oral part by the soft palate and uvula during the act of swallowing. Were it not so, food would be forced from the oral part into the nasal part and so to the nasal cavities—a person with a paralyzed soft palate (e.g., after diphtheria) may find that this may happen.

An air duct, the **Auditory Tube** (Eustachian) opens on to each side of the nasopharynx. Each tube, by bringing the pharynx into communication with the tympanic cavity (middle ear) of the corresponding side, serves to keep the air pressure on the two sides of the tympanic membrane (ear drum) equal under changing atmospheric conditions. Normally the tubes are closed, but the act of swallowing opens them; hence, persons ascending or descending heights, as in an aeroplane, find relief through performing the movement of swallowing. The tubes also allow infection to spread from the nasopharynx to the middle ear.

On each side of the entrance to the oral pharynx, and visible from the mouth, is a mass of lymphoid tissue, the size and shape of half a walnut, called "*the tonsil*" or the palatine tonsil. Its upper pole extends upward from the side of the tongue far into the soft palate; its lower pole cannot be seen unless the tongue is depressed.

The nasal part of the pharynx is, then, part of the respiratory passage; the oral part and the upper half of the laryngeal part are common to the respiratory and digestive passages.

The **Larynx** or voice box opens off the lowest part of the pharynx and is continuous below with the trachea. This box is kept rigid by a number of hyaline and elastic cartilages which are united by membranes. It is lined with mucous membrane internally and covered with voluntary muscles externally (*fig. 810*).

The chief cartilages of the larynx are: (1) The *thyroid cartilage*, which resembles an angular shield, has two perpendicular *laminae* which meet in front in the median plane, the prominent upper end of the angle of meeting being conspicuous as the *laryngeal prominence* (Adam's apple). Below, the thyroid cartilage grips the cricoid cartilage (*fig. 47.1*) as the knees of a horseman grip a saddle.
(2) The *cricoid cartilage* is a complete ring expanded posteriorly into a lamina or plate and so resembles a signet ring; it keeps the lower part of the larynx perpetually open. (3) The *arytenoid cartilages* are paired, small, and pyramidal; their bases articulate with the upper border of the lamina of the cricoid cartilage. The paired *vocal cords* extend from the inside of the angle of the thyroid cartilage horizontally backward to the arytenoid cartilages whose various movements control the tension and distance apart of the cords. (4) The *epiglottic cartilage* is shaped like an elm leaf, its stalk being attached to the angle of the thyroid cartilage just above the vocal cords.

The **Trachea** or windpipe is an elastic tube over 4″ long, with a caliber equal to the root of the index finger. It is kept patent by about 20 U-shaped rings of hyaline cartilage which are open posteriorly.

When you throw back your head you can readily feel the thyroid and cricoid cartilages rise, and perhaps feel the tracheal rings separate.

At the level of the sternal angle, 2″ below the jugular notch, the trachea bifurcates into a right and a left bronchus.

The **Bronchi** have the same structure as the trachea. After an oblique course of 2″, each enters the respective lung at the hilus and descends toward the base, giving off branches which in turn branch and rebranch like a tree (*figs. 585–589*). Within the lung the U-shaped rings give place to flakes of hyaline cartilage which surround the tube and hold it open. When the bronchi are reduced to the diameter of 1.0 mm., they are called *bronchioles*.

The terminal bronchioles divide into a number (2 to 11) of alveolar ductules which end in dilated air sacs, *alveolar sacs*. The

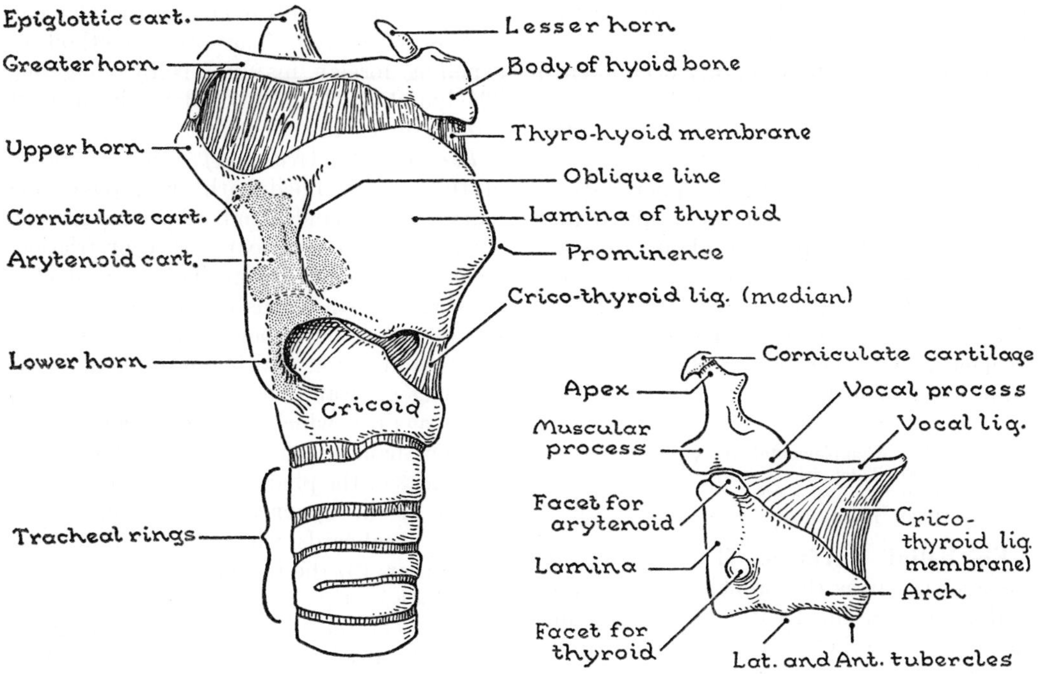

FIG. 47.1. Cartilages and ligaments of the larynx, side view

walls of these sacs being themselves sacculated, resemble a bunch of grapes, and hence they are called alveoli (L. alveolus = a bunch of grapes) (*fig. 590*). Adjacent *alveolar* sacs are practically contiguous—between them there is room only for a close-meshed network of capillaries through which the blood cells hurry in single file giving off CO_2 and taking up O_2 from the alveoli.

The **Lungs,** a right and a left, are spongeworks of elastic tissue which on section and in consistency resemble rubber sponges. In this highly elastic framework a bronchus and a pulmonary artery and a pulmonary vein ramify, the bronchus conducting air to and from the alveoli, the vessels conducting blood.

The lungs occupy the conical thorax, each lung forming half a cone. The right lung is divided by two complete fissures into three separate lobes; the left is divided by one fissure into two lobes.

Each lobe of each lung has a delicate and inseparable "skin", the *visceral pleura.* This is a perfectly smooth, moist, serous membrane, identical in structure and in origin with peritoneum, i.e., a fine areolar sheet with a surface of squamous (mesothelial) cells. Another layer of pleura lines the ribs, diaphragm, and mediastinum (containing the heart); this is *parietal pleura.* Between the visceral and parietal layers of pleura there is a potential space, the *pleural cavity,* best explained by figure 561. It allows the lung to expand and contract without friction.

The **Respiratory Act** has two phases—inspiration and expiration. On inspiration the diaphragm descends, thereby increasing the vertical diameter of the thorax; and the ribs rise from a sloping to a more horizontal position, thereby increasing both the antero-posterior and the side-to-side diameter, as you can determine by palpation. The atmospheric pressure is 14.7 lbs. to the square inch at sea level; therefore, on enlarging the thorax (inspiration) air rushes down the trachea and bronchi into the lungs so that they expand, thereby avoiding the formation of a vacuum in the pleural cavities. Expiration is largely a matter of elastic recoil; that is, the highly elastic tissue contracts, the stretched abdominal muscles act like an elastic belt on the abdominal contents forcing the diaphragm upward; and the cartilages of the ribs, which underwent twisting during inspiration, now untwist.

The respiratory act has aptly been likened to a fire bellows in action, the thoracic cage being the framework of the bellows, the trachea the nozzle.

As the table shows, during quiet respiration about 500 cc. of air are inspired and expired. On full inspiration about an extra 2500 cc. can be taken in; and on full expiration an extra 1000 cc. can be forced out. Even then there remain in the alveolar sacs, trachea, and bronchi about 1000 cc. which cannot be expelled.

	cc		
Total capacity	2500	Complemental air	Vital capacity
	500	Tidal air	
	1000	Supplemental air	
	1000	Residual air	

Epithelial Surfaces. The respiratory passages as far as the bronchioles of 1 mm. in diameter are lined with stratified columnar, ciliated epithelium containing scattered goblet cells. In the mucous membrane are mucous and serous glands, also lymphoid tissue both diffuse and aggregated.

In the protective mucus that lines the larynx, trachea, and bronchi inhaled dust and other foreign material is caught and entangled. The cilia cause the lining tube of mucus to move ever upward, like a moving carpet or escalator, to the entrance of the larynx where it spills over into the pharynx and is swallowed. The other method of expelling foreign material is by coughing. The lymphoid tissue also is defensive against foreign invasion.

Exceptional Areas (1) The vestibule of the nose is lined with skin, possessing hairs, sweat glands, and sebaceous glands; (2) areas subjected to pressure or friction, where cilia could not survive, are protected by stratified squamous epithelium, viz., (a) the parts of the upper surface of the soft palate and uvula which are applied to the pharyngeal wall during swallowing; (b) areas against which the food comes into contact, namely, the entire oral and laryngeal parts of the pharynx and also the dorsal aspect of the upper half of the epiglottis; (c) the vocal cords, which vibrate and strike each other; (3) the terminal and respiratory bronchioles, the epithelium of which is cubical; (4) the alveoli, whose continuous lining of epithelium cells is so extremely thin that its existence was doubted until it was shown by electron microscopy; (5) the olfactory (smell) epithelium.

The cilia in the nasal cavities sweep backward toward the pharynx; those in the trachea and bronchi upward toward the pharynx; those in the air sinuses spirally around the walls to the orifices.

CHAPTER 4

UROGENITAL SYSTEM AND THE SKIN

URINARY SYSTEM

The urinary system and the genital system are closely associated in their development and are commonly described together as the *urogenital system.* In the human male, but not in the female, the urethra serves as a common outlet for the products of both systems.

The urinary system comprises the following parts (*fig. 47.2*):

Kidneys, Ureters	bilateral and paired
Bladder, Urethra	median and unpaired

The *kidneys* excrete urine. This passes down two muscular tubes, one on each side, the *ureters,* into a muscular reservoir, the *urinary bladder,* where it is stored until such time as it may conveniently be discharged through the *urethra.*

Kidneys. Each of the two kidneys is of conventional kidney shape, is about 4½″ long, and weighs about 4½ oz. Its

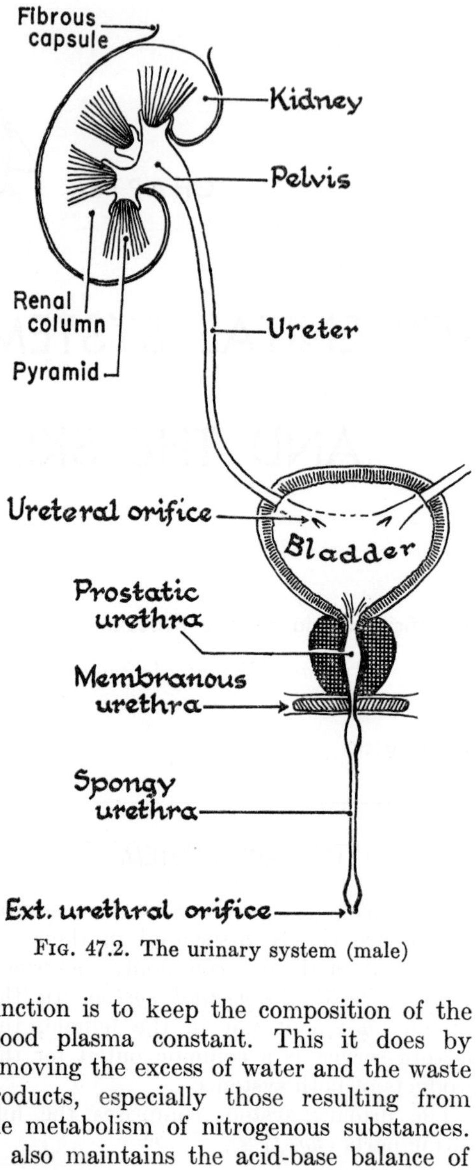

FIG. 47.2. The urinary system (male)

function is to keep the composition of the blood plasma constant. This it does by removing the excess of water and the waste products, especially those resulting from the metabolism of nitrogenous substances. It also maintains the acid-base balance of the blood by selective elimination of certain electrolytes.

Structure (*fig. 48*). Occupying the inner two-thirds of the cut surface of a kidney are dark, striated areas, the *pyramids*. The apices, *papillae*, of the pyramids project into the calyces of the pelvis. The outer one-third of the kidney, i.e., the part lying external to the bases of the pyramids, is *cortex*. Cortical tissue, under the name *renal column*, extends between the pyramids. These columns and the pyramids constitute the *medulla*.

»» A kidney contains about 1,000,000 microscopical units. Each unit or *nephron* has two parts, (1) a *glomerulus* and (2) a *uriniferous tubule*.

A glomerulus (L. glomus = a ball) is a spherical bunch of looped capillaries which invaginates the expanded blind end of a uriniferous tubule, called a *glomerular capsule* or *Bowman's capsule*. The surface area of all the glomeruli of each kidney is estimated to be 0.3813 sq. meter (M. H. Book). The two layers of glomerular capsule, outer and inner or invaginated, plus the glomerulus are known as a *renal* or *Malpighian corpuscle*. But the term is variously applied. Malpighi, who first saw the corpuscles through the microscope, likened them to apples hanging from a tree.

The capsule is succeeded by the proximal convoluted tubule, the descending and ascending limbs of Henle's loop, the distal convoluted tubule and finally the junctional tubule which discharges into a system of collecting tubules. About a dozen collecting tubules open on to the papilla of each pyramid (*fig. 309*) and discharge their contents into the pelvis of the kidney.

Each named part of the tubule has a distinctive epithelium and, accordingly, a different function. The glomeruli and the convoluted tubules occupy the labyrinth of the kidney; the limbs of Henle's loops and the collecting tubules occupy the pyramids.

The **Renal Arteries,** a right and a left, carry far more blood to the kidneys than is needed for their nourishment, and all the blood first passes through the glomeruli.

Each renal artery typically divides into five *segmental arteries* (commonly arising irregularly) which, after entering the renal sinus, send branches up along

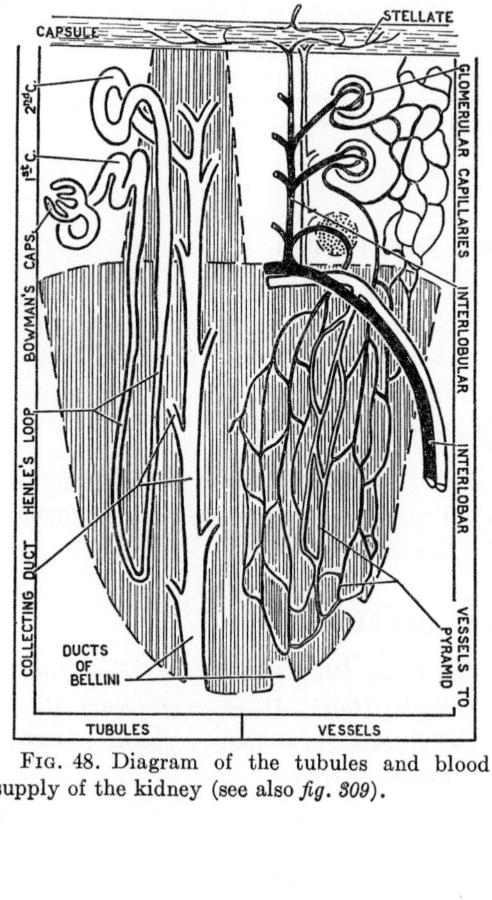

FIG. 48. Diagram of the tubules and blood supply of the kidney (see also *fig. 309*).

the sides of the pyramids and, because the pyramids are spoken of as lobes of the kidney, the arteries are called *interlobar arteries*. At the junction between medulla and cortex, the interlobar arteries divide into many *arcuate arteries* which curve between these two parts, forming arcs but not arches.

From the arcuate arteries, *interlobular arteries* pass radially toward the capsule, each giving off many short *intralobular arteries* to the cortex round about, and from them spring short arterioles, *vasa afferentia*, which pass to the glomeruli.

Each *vas afferens* enters a glomerulus and there forms capillary loops, as noted. These unite and leave the glomerulus as a *vas efferens*, which breaks up into capillaries which ramify throughout the renal substance. Thus, (1) the *vasa efferentia* from the outermost glomeruli (those nearest the capsule) provide a capillary network among the convoluted tubules; (2) the vasa from the innermost glomeruli send long meshed capillaries, arteriolae rectae, to the pyramids; and (3) the intermediate vasa do both. The "arcuate" arteries are end arteries—they do not anastomose with their fellows to form arches.

The **interlobular veins** begin under the capsule as stellate veins and may be seen on stripping it off. The tributaries of the renal veins anastomose freely.

Ureters, Urinary Bladder and Urethra. From the kidney the urine is propelled by peristaltic action along a 10-inch muscular tube, the *ureter*, into a hollow muscular reservoir, the *urinary bladder*. Through a cystoscope introduced into the bladder, jets of urine are seen to leave the ureteral orifices two or three times a minute.

The bladder has a capacity of ½ to 1 pint. From its lowest part a fibro-muscular tube, the *urethra*, leads to the exterior of the body. It is about 6″ to 8″ long in the male, 1¼″ in the female.

At the junction of the bladder and urethra (i.e., at the neck of the bladder) the bladder is guarded by a sphincter of involuntary muscle, the *sphincter vesicae*—whose existence is denied by some investigators (Woodburne)—and beyond this (i.e., between the fasciae of the urogenital diaphragm) it is guarded by a sphincter of voluntary muscle, the *sphincter urethrae*.

Nerve Supply. The student will be required later to learn individual nerve supplies. However, these are brought together here for convenience rather than for memorization.

KIDNEY. The strong clinical evidence is that the kidney receives sympathetic fibers that pass via the lowest splanchnic nerve and the visceral rami of ganglion L. 1 to the renal plexus and thence along the renal vessels to the kidney. The nerve fibers are vasoconstrictor, vasodilator, and afferent. Cutting dorsal nerve roots of T. 12, L. 1, and L. 2 relieves renal pain (White and Smithwick). A denervated kidney continues to excrete normal urine.

THE URETER. In its upper part the ureter receives *Sympathetic* nerve fibers from the renal and intermesenteric plexuses; in its middle part from the superior hypogastric plexus (and hypogastric nerve) in association with the spermatic plexus; and in its lower part from the inf. hypogastric plexus [pelvic plexus] which lies at the side of the bladder, vesicle and prostate (Mitchell). Its spinal or cord segments are L. 1 and 2. The peristalsis of the ureter is not disturbed by lumbar sympathectomy; in fact, by the withdrawal of inhibitory sympathetic influences the functions of a dilated (hydronephrotic) ureter and of a dilated colon (megacolon) are improved.

Parasympathetic. Vagal fibers via the celiac plexus may be supposed to supply the kidney and upper part of the ureter, and pelvic splanchnic nerve fibers for the lower part.

THE BLADDER AND URETHRA (*fig. 49*). *Parasympathetic.* The pelvic splanchnic nerves (S. 2, 3, 4) are the motor nerves to the bladder; when they are stimulated, the bladder empties, the blood vessels dilate, and the penis becomes erect. They are also the sensory nerves to the bladder.

Sympathetic, through its superior hypogastric plexus (lower thoracic, and lumbar 1, 2, 3), is motor to a continuous muscle sheet comprising the ureteric musculature, the trigonal muscle, and the muscle of the urethral crest. It also supplies the muscle of the epididymis, ductus (vas) deferens, seminal vesicle, and prostate. When the plexus is stimulated, the seminal fluid is ejaculated into the urethra but is hindered from entering the bladder perhaps by the muscle sheet which is drawn towards the internal urethral orifice. The sympathetic is also vaso-constrictor, and to some slight extent it is sensory to the trigonal region.

The pudendal nerve is motor to the sphincter urethrae and sensory to the glans penis and the urethra.

It would seem that the sympathetic

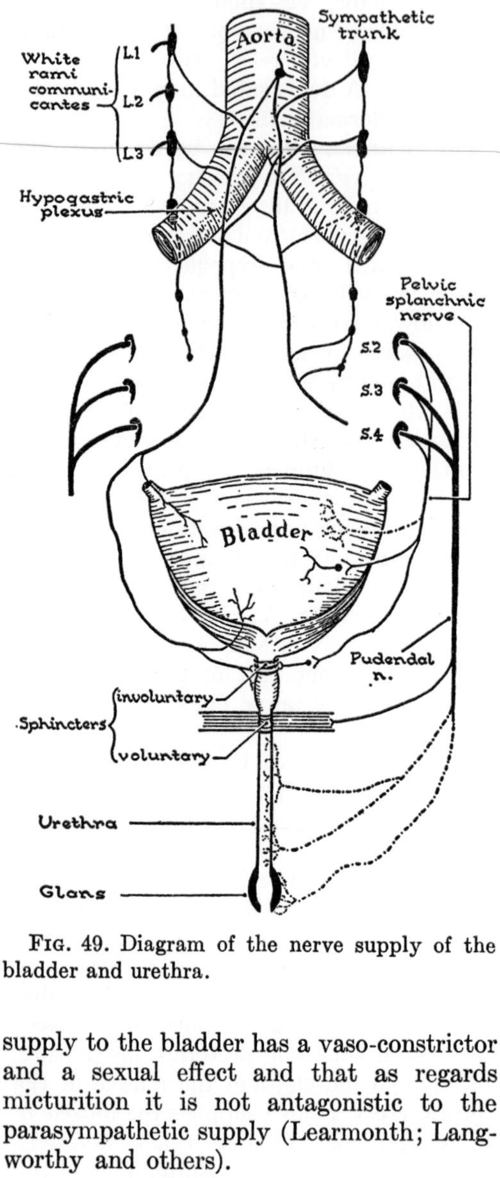

FIG. 49. Diagram of the nerve supply of the bladder and urethra.

supply to the bladder has a vaso-constrictor and a sexual effect and that as regards micturition it is not antagonistic to the parasympathetic supply (Learmonth; Langworthy and others).

GENITAL SYSTEM

The male and female organs of reproduction are fundamentally the same, and in early fetal life are very similar. In both sexes they pass through an indifferent stage during which there is a pair of parallel ducts—mesonephric (Wolffian) and paramesonephric (Mullerian)—on each side of the body. In the male, the mesonephric ducts are utilized as genital ducts and the paramesonephric ducts largely disappear or remain vestigial; in the female the converse is true (*figs. 49.1, 50,* and *51*).

Each sex has (1) a symmetrical pair of reproductory or sex glands, which produce germ cells—spermatozoa in the male and ova in the female; (2) two different pairs of passages through which these germ cells ultimately find their way to the exterior of the body; one being well developed in each sex and largely vestigial in the opposite sex; (3) accessory glands; and (4) external genitals.

Homologous Male and Female Parts

	Male	Female
Sexual Gland	Testis	Ovary
MALE PASSAGES Mesonephric tubules & duct	 Epididymis paradidymis Ductus Deferens	Appendix (W) (?) *Epoophoron* *Paroophoron* *Duct of Gartner (of epoophoron)*
	Urethra: prostatic penile	 Urethra Labia Minora, enclosing vestibule
FEMALE PASSAGES Paramesonephric duct	*Appendix (M)* (?) *Prostatic Utricle* (?)	Uterine tube Uterus Vagina
Accessory glands	Seminal vesicle Prostate Bulbo-urethral gland Urethral glands	— Para-urethral ducts Greater vestibular gland Lesser vestibular glands
External genitals	Penis bulb of penis Scrotum	Clitoris Bulbs of vestibule Labia Majora

MALE GENITAL SYSTEM

The male reproductive organs are:

Testis
Epididymis
Deferent Duct
Seminal Vesicle
Ejaculatory Duct
Prostate
Bulbo-urethral Gland

The external genital parts include:

Penis
Urethra
Scrotum

Rudimentary or vestigial structures:
Prostatic Utricle
Paradidymis
Aberrant ductules

The Testes or male sex glands, one on each side, lie in the scrotum (*figs. 49.1, 225, 226,* and *227*). Each testis is ovoid and 1½″ long. Like the eyeball, it has a thick, white, inelastic, fibrous outer coat, the *tunica albuginea.* Within this covering are numerous, delicate, threadlike, macroscopic *seminiferous tubules,* the linings of which produce enormous numbers of microscopic *spermatozoa.* These are provided with long whiplike tails which later provide propulsive power.

The testis is covered in front and at the sides with a bursal sac, the *tunica vaginalis testis,* which before birth was continuous with the peritoneal cavity.

The Ducts of the Testis. From 6 to 12 fine *efferent ductules,* lead out of the upper part of the testis into the *duct of the epididymis.* This duct, although about 20 feet long, is so folded as to form a compact body, the *epididymis* (Gk. epi = upon; didumos = a twin; i.e., the testes are twins), which caps the upper pole of the testis and is applied to its posterior border. The cells

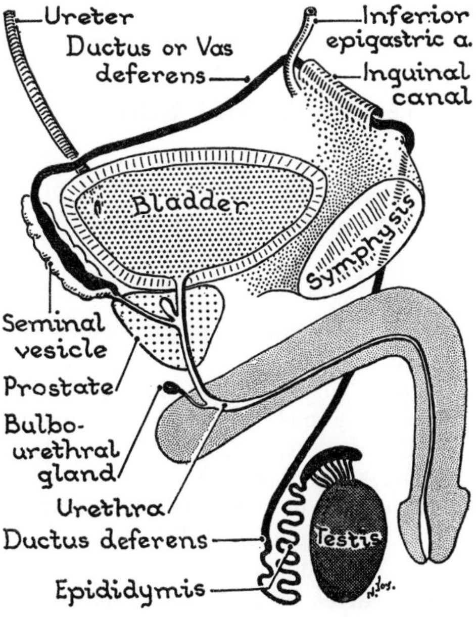

FIG. 49.1. The male genital system

lining the duct of the epididymis discharge a mucoid secretion.

The *ductus* or *vas deferens* connects the duct of the epididymis to the urethra. It is about 18″ long. It ascends through the upper part of the scrotum to the abdominal wall. This it pierces obliquely in a tunnel, the *inguinal canal.* Continuing, it runs under cover of the peritoneum to the base of the bladder, and then descends between the bladder and the rectum. Its terminal ¾″, the *ejaculatory duct,* pierces the prostate and opens into the urethra close to its fellow, about an inch beyond the bladder. From this point onward the male urethra is the common duct of the urinary and genital systems.

Accessory Glands. 1. The **Seminal Vesicles,** one on each side, are tubular outgrowths from the last part of the deferent ducts, which they resemble in structure (*figs. 367* and *368*). They secrete a yellowish sticky liquid.

2. The **Prostate** (Gk. pro = before, istanai = to stand), the size and shape of a large chestnut, surrounds the first 1¼″ of the urethra just beyond the bladder. It is partly glandular, partly muscular and partly fibro-areolar. It secretes into the urethra an opalescent liquid, free from mucus. It is pierced by the ejaculatory ducts.

3. The **Bulbo-urethral Glands** (of Cowper), the size of a pea, lie one on each side of the membranous urethra. Their ducts are 1″ long and open into the spongy urethra. They secrete a mucus-like substance.

4. The **Urethral Glands** (p. 327).

The Penis (L. penis = a tail) is the male organ of copulation (*see fig. 333*). It comprises three parallel fibrous tubes, two paired and one unpaired, which have innumerable cavernous spaces, filled with blood. It is enclosed in a single loosely fitting tube of skin and subcutaneous tissue. The paired tubes, the right and left *corpora cavernosa,* are fused side by side. In front they present a rounded end; behind they diverge into right and left *crura* (L. crus = a leg) which are firmly attached to the pubic arch. The c. cavernosa are the "supporting skeleton" of the penis.

The unpaired tube, the *corpus spongiosum,*

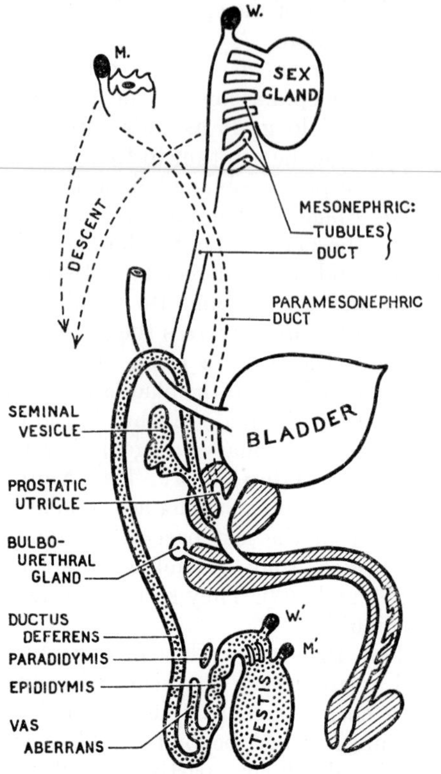

Fig. 50
Diagram of the male genital system
(side view)

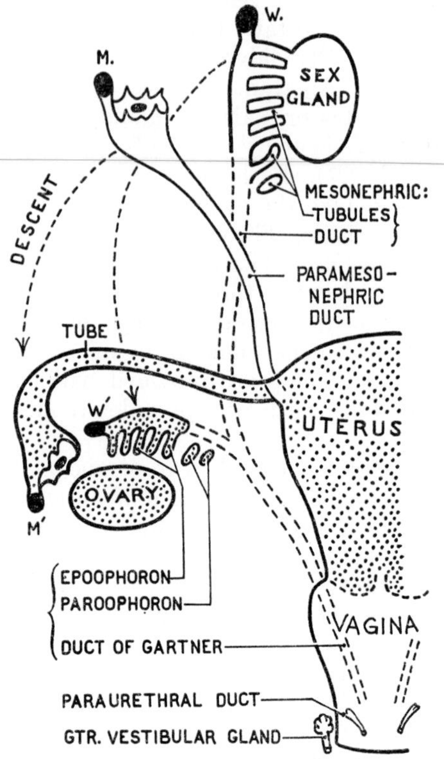

Fig. 51
Diagram of the female genital system
(front view)

In the upper halves of both figures the parts are shown in their early or indifferent state. Most of the paramesonephric (Mullerian) structures disappear in the male, and of the mesonephric (Wolffian) in the female. (M = Mullerian appendage; W = Wolffian appendage.)

is traversed by the urethra. Its expanded hinder end is fixed to the perineal membrane which stretches between the sides of the pubic arch; its expanded anterior end, the *glans* (L. glans = an acorn), fits like a cap on the ends of the corpora cavernosa.

The redundant skin covering the glans is the foreskin or *prepuce*. The operation of circumcision consists in removing the prepuce.

The Scrotum is the bag of skin and subcutaneous tissue in which the testes lie. Like the penis it is free from fat.

Semen (L. = seed) is composed of spermatozoa suspended in the secretions of the ducts of the testes and of the accessory glands.

FEMALE GENITAL SYSTEM

The female reproductive organs are:

Ovary, Uterine Tube .... paired

Uterus, Vagina .... unpaired

The external genital parts include:

Clitoris

Pudenda (mons pubis, labium majus, labium minus, vestibule of vagina, bulb of vestibule, greater vestibular gland, vaginal orifice)

Rudimentary or vestigial structures:

Epoophoron and duct

Paroophoron

The Ovaries or female sex glands, one on each side, lie on the side walls of the

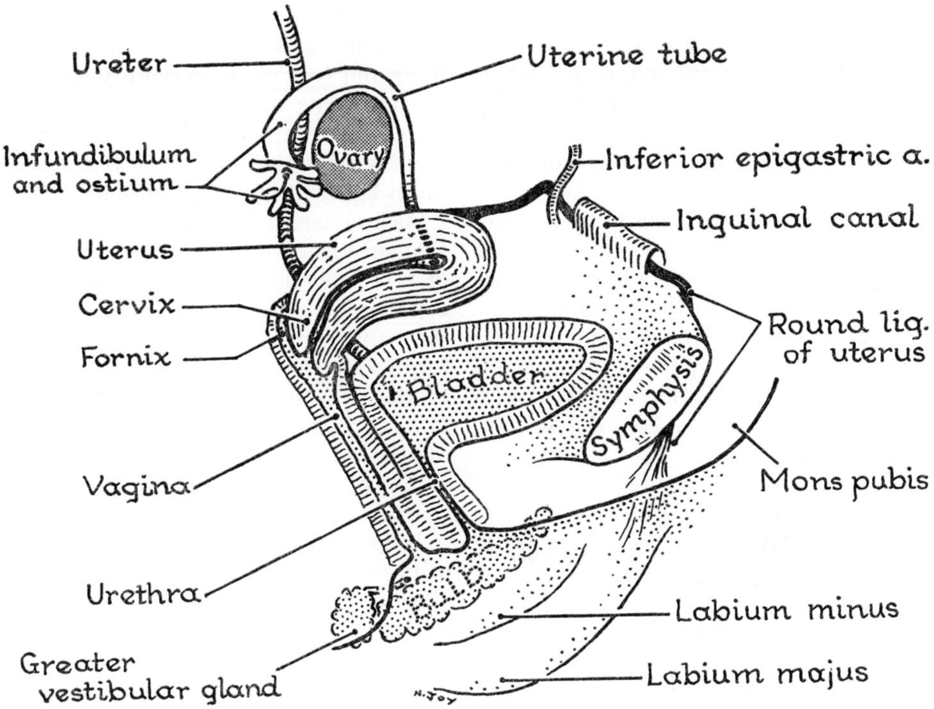

FIG. 51.1. The female pelvis and perineum, median section

pelvis (*fig. 381*). Each ovary is a solid body about half the size of a testis. It has an attached border; elsewhere it projects into the peritoneal cavity. It is covered, however, not with squamous peritoneal cells but with a cubical epithelium (germinal). Its surface is scarred and pitted due to the shedding of ova. At birth each ovary contains about 200,000 (immature) ova. From puberty to the end of the reproductive period (15th to 45th year) an ovum is shed into the peritoneal cavity about once a lunar month, and, having no motive power, there it lies at large. In all about 400 ova are shed; the rest are absorbed in the ovary.

The **Uterine Tube** (*fig. 51.1*) is about 4½″ long, is as large as a pencil, lies in the free edge of a fold of peritoneum, the *broad ligament*, and takes a twisted course from ovary to uterus. Its ovarian end is funnel shaped, the *infundibulum*, and at the bottom of the funnel is the abdominal mouth or *ostium* which lies open to the peritoneal cavity, beside the ovary. Its other end opens into the cavity of the uterus.

When an ovum is about to be shed the mouth of the tube is turned and likely applied to the ovary ready to receive the ovum. Peristaltic action propels it along the tube, the cilia perhaps helping, and the secretion of the tube nourishing. In the tube the ovum may be met and fertilized by a spermatozoon, which is able to propel itself through the uterus in about 6 hours.

The Uterus is a thick-walled, hollow, muscular organ placed near the center of the pelvis and projecting upward into the peritoneal cavity between the bladder and the rectum (see *fig. 379*). It is shaped like an inverted pear, somewhat flattened from before backward so that its cavity is collapsed, and is 3″ long. Above, a uterine tube opens into it on each side; below, it opens into the vagina. The upper 2″ are the *body;* the lower 1″ is the *cervix;* the part of the body above the entrance to the tubes is the *fundus.* The peritoneum covering the body and fundus stretches from each side of the uterus as a fold, the *broad ligament,* that rises from the pelvic floor, extends to the side wall of the pelvis, and contains the uterine tube in its upper free edge. Its function is to harbor a fertilized ovum for 9 months. During the first 2 months the ovum is in the indifferent or embryonic stage; during the last 7 it is in the formed or fetal stage.

The Vagina (L. = a sheath) is a relatively thin-walled collapsed tube, about 3½″ long. The cervix projects into its upper end; below, it opens into the vestibule.

Accessory Glands. THE GREATER VESTIBULAR GLANDS are paired like their homologues in the male, the bulbo-urethral glands, and like them have long ducts, well seen in figure 340.

External Genitalia

These (pudenda) have their homologous parts in the male, see pages 307–309.

Nerve Supply. See page 305.

SKIN AND ITS APPENDAGES AND THE FASCIAE

Functions; Dermis or Corium; Epidermis; Nails; Hairs; Arrectores Pilorum Muscles; Sebaceous Glands; Sweat Glands; Vessels; Nerves.

Superficial Fascia or Tela Subcutanea

Loose Areolar Tissue; Adipose Tissue.

Deep Fascia

The skin or cutis has four appendages:
hairs and nails
sweat glands and sebaceous glands

Do not misconceive the skin to be merely an envelope wrapped around our bodies like paper around a parcel. It is, indeed, a wrapping but it is more than a wrapping—it is one of our most versatile organs.

As an *envelope* it has admirable properties: being waterproof it prevents the evaporation and escape of tissue fluids; it becomes thick where it is subject to rough treatment; it is fastened down where it is most liable to be pulled off; it has friction ridges where it is most liable to slip; "—even with our ingenious modern machinery we cannot create a tough but highly elastic fabric that will withstand heat and cold, wet and drought, acid and alkali, microbic invasion, and the wear and tear of three score years and ten, yet effect its own repairs throughout, and even present a seasonable protection of pigment against the sun's rays. It is indeed the finest fighting tissue" (Whitnall).

As an *organ* it is the regulator of the body temperature; it is an excretory organ capable of relieving the kidneys in time of need; it is a storehouse for chlorides; it is the factory for antirachitic vitamin D (ergosterol) formed by the action of the ultraviolet rays of the sun on the sterols in the skin, and necessary for the mineralization of bones and teeth; and it is the most extensive and varied of the sense organs.

In an average adult man the skin covers a body surface of 1.7 sq. meters. At the orifices of the body it is continuous with the mucous membranes. The skin, somewhat modified, forms the conjunctiva and the outer layer of the ear drum.

The Skin has two parts (*fig. 52*): (1) dermis and (2) epidermis. (L. cutis and Gk. derma = skin; *cf.* the terms subcutaneous and hypodermic.)

The **Dermis or Corium** is of mesodermal origin. It is a feltwork of bundles of white fibers and of elastic fibers. Superficially the feltwork is of fine texture; deeply it is coarse and more open and its spaces contain pellets of fat, hair follicles, sweat glands, and sebaceous glands. It is in general 1 to 2 mm. thick, but is thicker on the palms and soles and back, and is thinner on the eyelids and external genital parts. The spaces in the feltwork are lozenge-shaped; hence, a puncture made with a conical instrument, such as a large needle, does not remain a round hole for the skin splits in the long axes of the lozenges. The long axes are differently directed in different parts, usually being parallel to the lines of tension of the skin. A cut across the long axes of these **Lines of Cleavage** (Langer's Lines) will gape. (Cox.)

It is due to the presence of elastic fibers that the skin, after being stretched or pinched into a fold, returns to normal. Dermis, when tanned, is called leather.

The **Epidermis** is a nonvascular stratified epithelium of ectodermal origin. The deeper

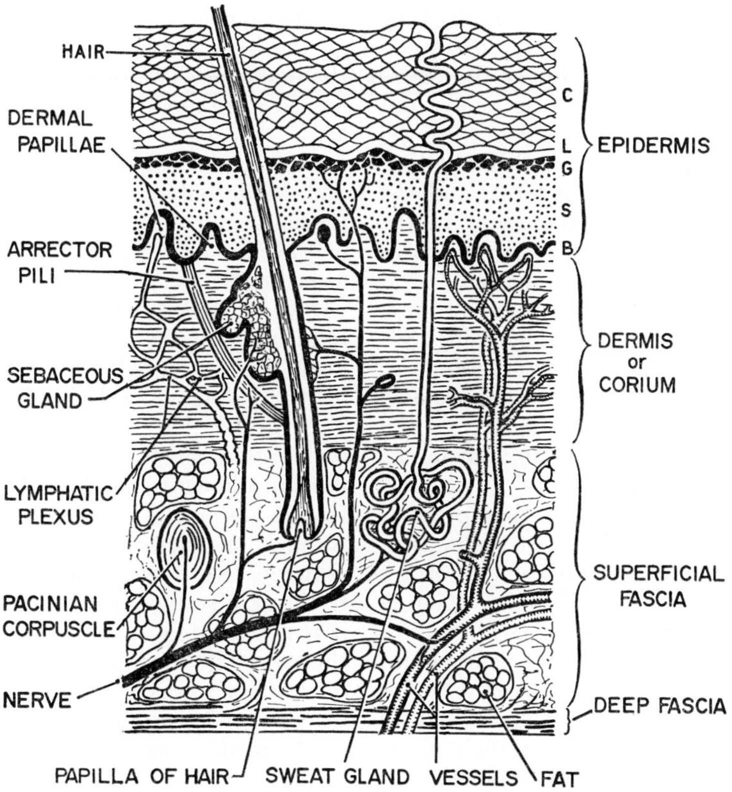

FIG. 52. Section of thick skin, superficial fascia, and deep fascia. (*C, L, G, S, B* = Strata Corneum Lucidum, Granulosum, Spinosum, and Basal layer, respectively.) (After Appleton, Hamilton, and Tchaperoff.)

layer, the *germinative layer*, is living. It consists of several strata of polyhedral cells resting on a single stratum of columnar (basal) cells. The superficial layer, the horny layer or *stratum corneum*, is dead. It consists of several strata of dry, flattened, scaly cells without visible nuclei. The surface cells are perpetually being rubbed away and are perpetually being replaced by cells of the germinative layer.

Ridges of dermis, which on section have the appearance of nipple-like processes or *papillae*, project into the epidermis (Ham and Leeson).

For *Finger Prints* see figure 141, and p. 145, and consult Cummins and Midlo.

The **Nails** are thickenings of the deeper layers of the stratum corneum. A nail has a free end which projects, a root which extends proximally deep to the overhanging nail fold, two lateral borders, a free surface, and a deep one. The white crescent appearing distal to the nail fold is the *lunule*. The deep surface rests on and adheres to the *nail bed*. This largely consists of white fibrous tissue which attach the dermis to the periosteum.

Growth takes place at the root and from the bed as far distally as the lunule; beyond this the nail probably slides distally on its bed, adhering to it. Poisons, formed during an acute illness, temporarily arrest the growth of the nails (as they do of the bones, see *fig. 15*) and a transverse ridge appearing on each nail when growth is resumed is evidence of a past illness. Seeing that the average rate of nail growth is 0.1 mm. a day or 3 mm. a month (i.e., about 1½″ a year) the date of a past illness can be estimated. The nail of digit III consistently grows fastest, that of digit V, slowest. Nails grow rapidly in "nail biters"; in immobilized limbs they grow slowly (Le Gros Clark and Buxton).

The **Hairs** are distributed over the entire surface of the body except the palms and soles, dorsum of the last segment of the digits of the hand and foot, red of the lips, and parts of the external genitals and the conjunctiva. They are also present in the vestibule of the nasal cavity and in the outer part of the external acoustic meatus.

Hairs may be short (a few mm.) or long. Long hairs are present in the scalp, eyebrows, margins of the eyelids, vestibule of the nose, outer part of the external acoustic meatus; and at puberty they appear on the pubes, external genitals, axillae, and in the male on the face.

A hair has a *shaft* or part that projects beyond the skin surface, a *root* that lies in a follicle of the skin, and at the end of the root there is a swelling, the *bulb*, which is moulded over a dermal papilla. The life of a hair on the head is about 2–4 years; of an eyelash about 3 to 5 months. Like the leaves of an evergreen tree, old hairs are constantly falling out and new ones taking their place.

The Arrectores Pilorum Muscles are bundles of smooth muscle that pass obliquely from the epidermis to the slanting surface of the hair follicles deep to the sebaceous glands. By contracting they cause the hairs to stand erect. In birds, by erecting the feathers, they increase the air spaces between them thereby preserving heat; hence, sparrows look plump in cold weather. In man, spasm of the Arrectores produces "goose skin."

Sebaceous Glands are simple alveolar glands, bottle-shaped, and filled with polyhedral cells which break down into a fatty secretion, called sebum, into the hair follicles. The glands develop as outgrowths of hair follicles into the dermis, one or more being associated with each hair. Commonly, the glands are largest where the hairs are shortest (e.g., end of nose, and outer part of the external acoustic meatus). They make the skin waterproof—"like water off a duck's back" is a common expression.

Fortunately there are no hairs on the palms and soles; neither are there sebaceous glands to make the surfaces greasy. Independently of hairs, sebaceous glands are present on the inner surface of the prepuce, on the labia minora, and on the areolae of the mammae. The tarsal glands of the eyelids also are modified sebaceous glands (*fig. 655*).

Boils (and carbuncles) start in hair follicles and sebaceous glands and are therefore possible, indeed common, in the vestibule of the nose and outer part of the external acoustic meatus.

Sweat Glands are present in the skin of all parts of the body (red of the lips and glans penis excepted), being most numerous on the palms and soles and in the axillae. They are simple tubular glands. The secretory part is coiled to form a ball (0.3 to 0.4 mm. in diameter) situated in the fat deep to the dermis. The duct runs tortuously through the dermis, enters the epidermis between two ridges and proceeds spirally to the skin surface. In the stratum corneum it is represented merely by a cleft between the cells. The resemblance to the "intestines of a fairy" was fancifully suggested by Oliver Wendell Holmes.

The ceruminous glands in the outer parts of the external acoustic meatus and the ciliary glands of the eyelids are modified sweat glands. In the axilla, about the external genitals, and around the anus are long, large (3 to 5 mm. in diameter) modified sweat glands that produce an odor. They are spoken of as "sexual skin glands."

Sweating lowers the temperature. In man at rest, sweating is observed to begin abruptly when the body temperature is elevated as much as 0.2 to 0.5°F. This is due to the action of the heated blood on the brain centers. Since the autonomic nerve fibers to sweat glands travel to the skin in the ordinary cutaneous nerves, if such a nerve is cut the area is not only deprived of sensation but it also cannot sweat.

Sweat glands are excretory organs—accessory to the kidneys. The salt taste of sweat is due to sodium chloride. The normal sweat secretion is important in keeping the thick horny layers of the palms and soles supple, and it increases the friction between the skin and an object grasped. In dogs, sweat glands are confined to the foot pads; so, being unable to sweat, dogs pant.

Vessels. The vessels for the supply of

the skin run in the subcutaneous fatty tissue. From these the dermis receives two arterial plexuses; one is deeply seated near the subcutaneous tissue, and the other is in the subpapillary layer. This sends capillary loops into the papillae. The returning blood passes through several layers of thin-walled subpapillary venous plexuses, thence through a deep venous plexus, and so to the superficial veins. Arterio-venous anastomoses, which are sometimes open and sometimes closed, connect some of these arterioles and venules.

The *lymph vessels* of the skin form a plexus at the junction of the dermis and the superficial fascia. This plexus receives blind finger-like vessels (or networks) from the papillae and it drains into lymph vessels that accompany the superficial arteries and veins.

Nerves. The cutaneous nerves have (1) *efferent* autonomic fibers for the supply of:

Smooth muscle.... { of hairs (Arrectores) / of blood vessels

Glands............ { sweat glands / sebaceous glands

(2) *afferent* somatic fibers of general sensation, namely touch, pain, heat, cold, and pressure (*fig. 43*, p. 41).

As figure 52 indicates, free fibers end between the cells of the germinative layer (hence, intra-epidermal injections may cause pain), and around the hair follicle and beside it (probably touch fibers); tactile corpuscles occupy occasional papillae (for touch); Pacinian corpuscles lie in the superficial fascia and are plentiful along the sides of the digits (for pressure).

Superficial Fascia or Tela Subcutanea

Superficial fascia is a subcutaneous layer of **loose areolar tissue** which unites the corium of the skin to the underlying deep fascia. It consists of (1) bundles of *white* or *collagenous fibers* which, by branching and uniting with other bundles, form an open webbing, filled with (2) *tissue fluid;* (3) a slender network of *yellow elastic fibers*, and scattered amongst all this lie (4) *connective tissue cells* (*fig. 53*).

When areolar tissue is exposed to the air, the tissue fluids rapidly evaporate with consequent drying and shrinking. Fortunately, the addition of an (antiseptic) saline solution will restore to areolar tissue its original fluffy texture.

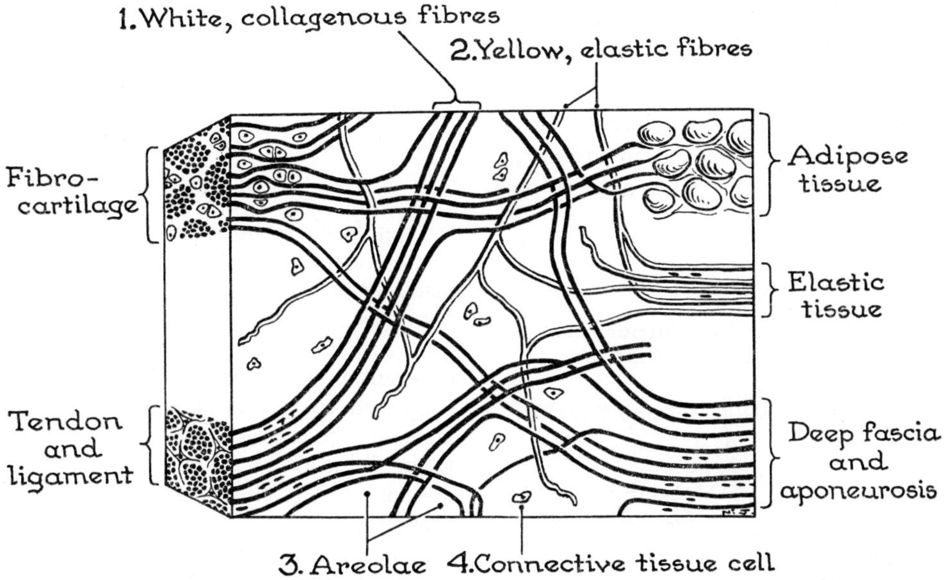

FIG. 53. Scheme to indicate that the four ingredients of areolar tissue (viz., collagenous fibers, elastic fibers, areolar spaces and cells), when blended in different proportions, form other tissues (e.g., adipose, elastic, collagenous, ligamentous, and fibro-cartilaginous) and that one may merge into another.

Areolar tissue is derived from those portions of mesoderm that remain after bones, ligaments, tendons, muscles, and vessels have taken form. It is, therefore, not confined to the superficial fascia but is diffusely spread; for example, it forms the sheaths of muscles, vessels, nerves, and viscera, and it fills up the spaces between them; it forms the basis of the mucous, submucous, and subserous coats of the hollow viscera; the serous membranes (i.e., peritoneum, pleura, pericardium, and tunica vaginalis testis) are but areolar membranes lined with flat mesothelial cells.

Areolar tissue is potentially **Adipose Tissue** or fat, and wherever areolar tissue occurs, there fat also may occur. The fat accumulates in the connective tissue cells. Fat is fluid at body temperature, but because each drop of fat is imprisoned in a cell, it does not gravitate to lower levels or flow from a wound.

Distribution. The superficial fascia almost everywhere contains fat—except in the eyelids, external ear, penis and scrotum, and at the flexion creases of the digits. In the palms and soles it forms a protective cushion; here and still more so in the breast and scalp it is loculated (*fig. 661*). It is most abundant in the buttocks.

In the female, fat is most extensively deposited in the gluteal and lumbar regions, front of the thigh, anterior abdominal wall below the navel, mammae, postdeltoid region, and cervico-thoracic regions.

Adipose or fatty tissue, as mentioned, is modified areolar tissue, and is notably present in the superficial fascia, the subserous layer of the abdominal wall and in the omenta and mesenteries. It covers parts of the urinary tract (e.g., kidney, ureter, sides of the bladder), but it leaves free the gastrointestinal tract, liver, spleen, testis, ovary, uterus, and lung. It is odd, then, that it should be present in the sulci of the heart. There is no fat within the cranial cavity to dispute possession with the brain, nor within the dura mater covering the spinal cord. The loose fatty tissue of the orbital cavity provides the eyeball with a soft and movable bed.

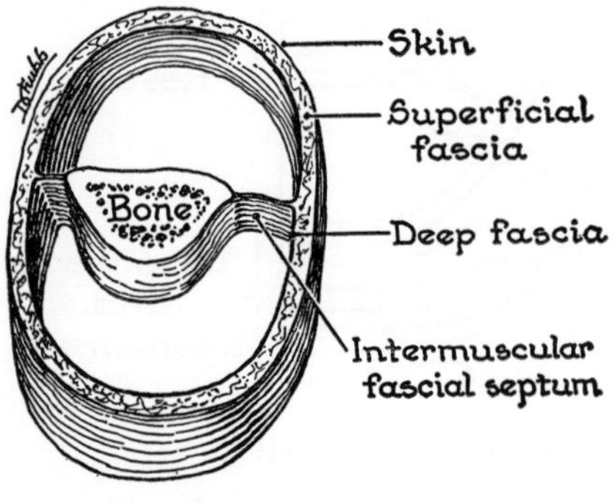

FIG. 54. An intermuscular septum passing from deep fascia to bone.

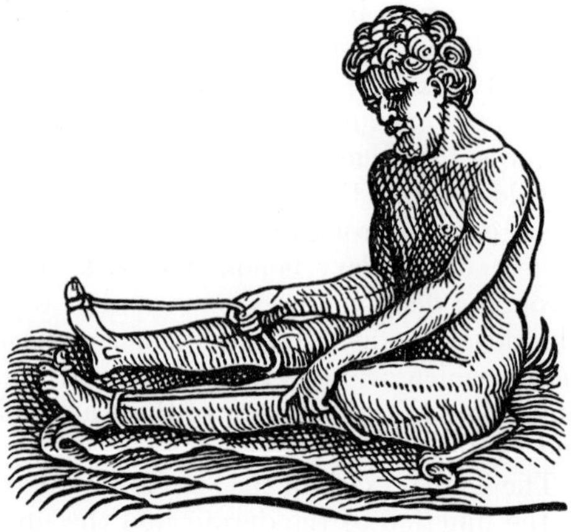

FIG. 55. Demonstrating the function of a retinaculum (anular ligament). (After Andreas Vesalius—De Humani Corporis Fabrica, 1568 edition: first published in 1543.) (By the courtesy of the Toronto Academy of Medicine.)

Subcutaneous Bursae. See page 24.

Deep Fascia

Deep fascia is the membranous investment of the structures deep to the superficial fascia (*figs. 53* and *54*). Like tendons, aponeuroses, and ligaments it contains the same four ingredients as areolar tissue, but in different proportions; and, like them, being subjected to tensile strains, the white collagenous fibers form parallel bundles; the tissue fluids are at a minimum, and the cells are flattened (stellate on cross-section) from pressure.

Deep fascia is best marked in the limbs and neck, where it is wrapped around the muscles, vessels, and nerves like a bandage, the fibers being chiefly circularly arranged.

Around the thorax and abdomen, which require to expand and contract, there may be a film of areolar tissue but there can be no true deep fascia; nor is it well developed over flat muscles (e.g., Gluteus Maximus, Pectoralis Major) since there it would have a restraining or ligamentous function; nor on the face, since the facial muscles, like the Platysma, are cutaneous muscles.

The deep fascia sends septa, *intermuscular septa*, between various muscles and groups of muscles (*fig. 54*) and usually blends with or attaches to periosteum (see *Axiom*). At the wrist and ankles there are exceptions to this generalization (pp. 164 and 402).

AXIOM. ***Where deep fascia encounters bone, it does not cross it, but attaches itself to it, for the simple reason that both have a common derivation; so, unless some muscle during development intervenes and detaches the fascia from the bone, the two remain attached.***

The deep fascia is thickened where muscles are attached to it, and the direction of its fibers takes the line of the pull of the muscles (e.g., Gluteus Medius, Biceps Brachii). It is also thickened about the wrist and ankle to form, as it were, bracelets and anklets, called *retinacula*, which prevent the tendons of muscles from bowstringing (*fig. 55*).

SECTION II

Upper Limb

CHAPTER 5

PECTORAL REGION AND AXILLA

INTRODUCTION

Man's upper limbs are free and are adapted to purposes of prehension and not of locomotion like the forelimbs of the quadruped. They articulate with the trunk at one small joint, the *sternoclavicular joint,* of their respective sides. They possess great range of movement. His lower limbs have no such freedom. They have to bear the weight of his body when he walks, runs, jumps, and stands. Accordingly, they are united behind to the vertebral column at the sacro-iliac joints, and in front to each other at the symphysis pubis. The security the lower limbs enjoy is in the upper limbs sacrificed to mobility. (See table 1.)

It is generally held that the upper and lower limbs are *serially* homologous, the thumb corresponding to the big toe, the radius to the tibia, the ulna to the fibula, and the humerus to the femur.

In prenatal life the thumb and the radius,

TABLE 1
Bones of Upper Limb

Region	Bones
Shoulder or Pectoral Girdle	Clavicle Scapula
Arm or Brachium	Humerus
Forearm or Antebrachium	Radius Ulna
Hand or Manus	Carpal bones Metacarpal bones Phalanges 1st or Proximal 2nd or Middle 3rd or Distal

and the big toe and the tibia, are situated on the cranial or head side of the central axis of the respective limbs and are said to be *preaxial*, whereas the 5th finger and ulna, and the 5th toe and fibula lie on the caudal or tail side of this axis and are said to be *postaxial*. The palms of the hands face each other, and so do the soles of the feet.

On assuming the **Anatomical Posture** (*fig. 1*), the upper and lower limbs undergo rotation but in opposite directions; the thumb by rotating laterally brings the palm of the hand to the front, while the big toe by rotating medially brings the sole of the foot to the ground. The thumb and forearm can voluntarily be caused to rotate medially, as, for example, when you let the palm of the hand rest on the knee. In this position the distal parts of the upper and lower limbs come to occupy equivalent positions, and it becomes apparent that the dorsum of the hand corresponds to the dorsum of the foot, the back of the forearm to the front of the leg, the elbow to the knee, and the back of the arm to the front of the thigh.

Mooring Muscles (*fig. 56*). The upper limb is moored to the head, neck and trunk by muscles, which may be likened to guy ropes.

Lines of Force Transmission. The following fundamental points should be verified by reference to the skeleton and figure 57.

The clavicle is a strut that thrusts the scapula laterally and backward. It does so through the medium of a strong ligament, the *coracoclavicular*. If this ligament holds the scapula (and the rest of the limb with it) away from the median plane, its fibers should pass downward and medially; and they do. The clavicle has an enlarged medial end which articulates with a shallow socket formed by the sternum and 1st rib cartilage. A strong ligament, in the form of an *articular disc*, prevents the clavicle from being driven medially on to the sternum. This is in virtue of its diagonal mode of attachment to the clavicle above and 1st rib cartilage below. The lateral end of the *clavicle* is not enlarged; it does little more than make contact with the *acromion*, the *coracoclavicular ligament* being the essential bond of union between the clavicle and the scapula.

At the shoulder joint the rounded head of the humerus makes side-to-side contact with the shallow glenoid cavity of the scapula. The overhanging coraco-acromial arch (i.e., acromion, coraco-acromial ligament, and coracoid process) forms a hood-like roof, which prevents upward dislocation of the humerus. The lower end of the humerus articulates with the ulna and the radius.

The ulna is enlarged above and tapering below; the radius is tapering above and enlarged below; and, the two are united by a strong *interosseous membrane*. Clearly,

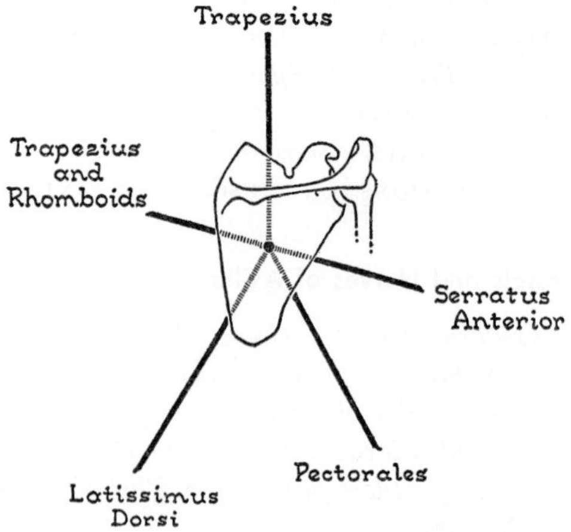

FIG. 56. The upper limb is moored to the body by muscles.

at the elbow joint the ulna is more important than the radius; at the wrist joint the contrary is true. The enlarged lower end of the radius articulates with the carpal bones, but the ulna does not.

From figure 57 observe that:

1. An impact, the result of, say, a fall on the palm of the outstretched hand, is transmitted by the scaphoid and lunate bones to the radius. The radius transfers part of the force directly to the humerus and part, via an interosseous membrane, to the ulna. To effect this transference of force the fibers of the membrane obviously must pass downward and medially from radius to ulna. Thence the force travels up the humerus (1) to the overhanging coraco-acromial arch against which the upper end of the humerus abuts and (2) in part across the glenoid cavity to the neck of the scapula, and up the coracoid process. If the force is sufficient to overcome the lower mooring muscles, the strut (i.e., the clavicle) may break.

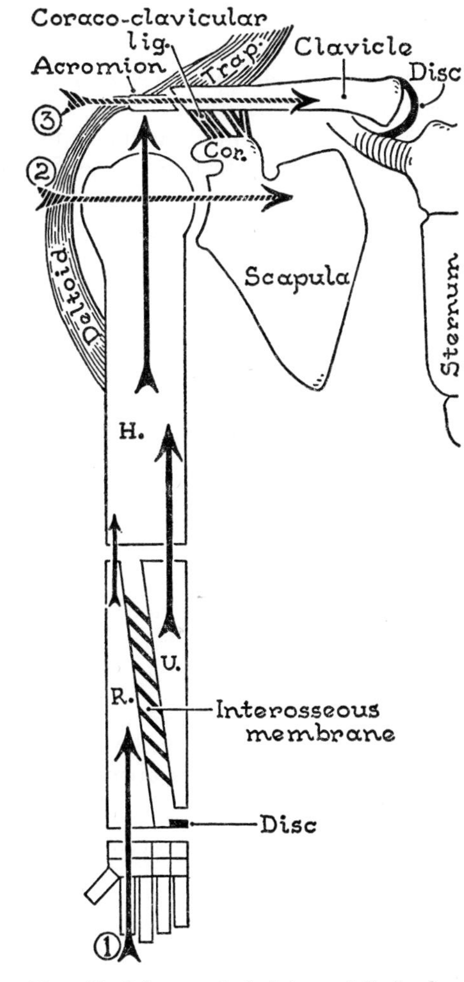

FIG. 57. Scheme of skeleton of limb showing lines of force transmission and ligaments that may transfer force as the result of a fall:
1. on the hand—interosseous membrane,
2. on the shoulder—coracoclavicular ligament,
3. on the acromion—articular disc.

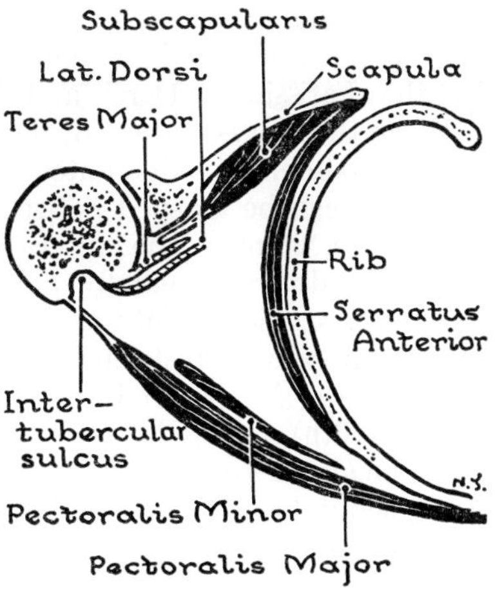

FIG. 58. Walls of axilla, on cross section

2. When force is applied to the side of the upper end of the humerus, the coracoclavicular ligament prevents the scapula from being driven medially. This it does in virtue of the direction of its fibers, which obviously must pass inferomedially.

3. The force of an impact on the acromion is transmitted along the entire length of the clavicle and may result in fracture of the clavicle or in dislocation of the acromioclavicular joint.

Definition and Boundaries. The **axilla** is the pyramidal space above the arm pit. It has four walls, an apex, and a base (*fig. 58*). *The anterior wall* is fleshy and is formed by the Pectoralis Major and two muscles that lie behind it enclosed in a sheet of fascia, called the *clavipectoral fascia.* [This wall is practically synonymous with the Pectoral Region, which, however, includes the medial part of the Pectoralis Major and the breast or mamma superficial to it.]

The posterior wall is formed by the scapula overlaid by the Subscapularis, and below this by the Latissimus Dorsi and Teres Major. When the arm is abducted, the thick fleshy lower borders of the anterior and posterior walls can be grasped between the fingers and the thumb. The anterior and posterior walls diverge medially and converge laterally; so, the medial wall is expansive and the lateral wall restricted.

The medial wall is formed by the upper ribs (2nd to 6th) covered with Serratus Anterior. The *lateral wall* is the intertubercular sulcus (bicipital groove) of the humerus. It lodges the long tendon of the Biceps, and its lips give attachment to muscles of the anterior and posterior walls.

The base is the skin and fascia of the arm pit. *The truncated apex* is the triangular space bounded by three bones—the clavicle, the upper border of the scapula, and the 1st rib.

The Contents of the Axilla (*fig. 65*). The great vessels and nerves of the upper limb pass through the axilla on their way to the distant parts of the limb—they are the chief contents. The other contents are: the two heads of the Biceps, the Coracobrachialis, and lymph nodes.

Landmarks, bony and muscular (*fig. 59*).

The *Sternum,* or breast bone, is a flat bone, shaped like a gladiator's sword. It consists of three parts: manubrium, body, and xiphoid process. The manubrium, or handpiece, meets the body at a slight angle, called the *sternal angle.* On each side the sternum articulates with a clavicle and seven costal (rib) cartilages. (For details see page 466.)

The *Coracoid Process* of the Scapula (Gk. Korax = a crow, i.e., a crow's beak) might more aptly be called the *digital process,* as figure 60 shows. (For attachments see *fig. 187.*) The *tip of the coracoid process* lies 1 inch below the clavicle under shelter of the anterior edge of the Deltoid.

To palpate this essential landmark in the living subject, place your index finger in the gap between the Deltoid and the Pectoralis Major, known as the infraclavicular fossa or *deltopectoral triangle,* and press firmly not backward, but laterally under the Deltoid's edge.

The **Clavicle,** or collar bone (*figs. 59* and *60.1*), is a long bone, curved concavo-convexly, and set nearly horizontally, the lateral end being directed laterally, backward, and

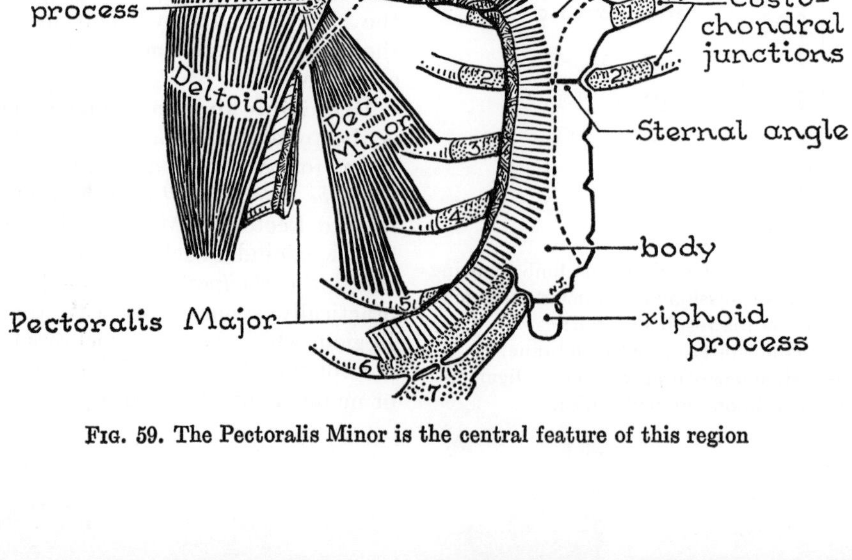

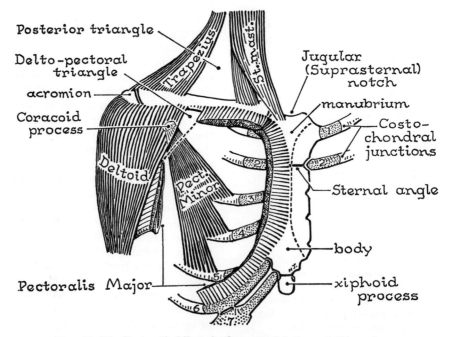

FIG. 59. The Pectoralis Minor is the central feature of this region

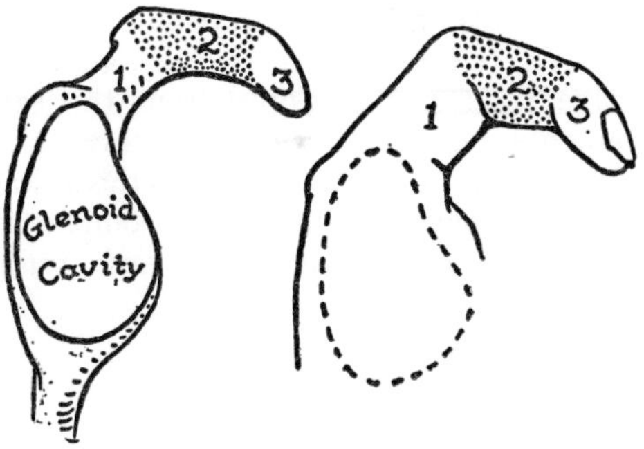

FIG. 60. The coracoid process of the scapula resembles a bent finger.

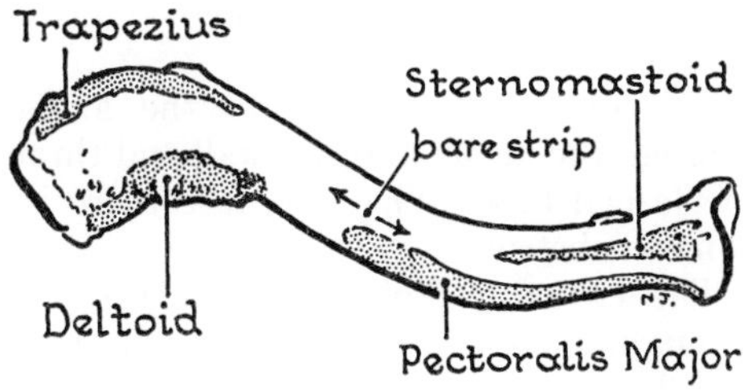

FIG. 60.1. The clavicle, showing attachments of muscles.

slightly upward. It has two parts: the part medial to the underlying coracoid process (medial three-fourths) is triangular on cross-section like long bones in general; but the part lateral to the process is flattened in conformity with the acromion with which it articulates lightly, as noted on page 76. This part is rough below for the ligaments that bind the scapula, via its coracoid process, to the clavicle (*fig. 60.2*).

The clavicle, although almost visible through the skin, is not merely subcutaneous but also subplatysmal; because a thin elastic sheet of muscle, the *Platysma*, descends from the neck to the level of the 2nd or 3rd rib and intervenes between the clavicle and the skin. It is the Platysma that allows the skin to move so freely over the clavicle, and its looseness and elasticity usually save a fractured clavicle from penetrating the skin. The Platysma is superficial even to the cutaneous nerves, the *supraclavicular nerves*, that cross in front of the clavicle (*fig. 61*) and descend to the level of the second intercostal space (*fig. 98*).

The clavicle is easily palpated from sternal end to acromial end because a bare, linear strip to which no muscle is attached extends the whole length of its superficial aspect. This strip lies between the attachments of the Sternomastoid and Trapezius above and of the Pectoralis Major and Deltoid below (*figs. 59 and 63*).

(The clavicle is described on p. 103.)

The posterior surface of the clavicle is smooth and almost bare; whereas the inferior surface of the medial part gives attachment to the finger-sized Subclavius.

The **Pectoralis Minor** (*fig. 59*), at present concealed by the Pectoralis Major, is the central feature of the pectoral region. It arises from the (2nd), 3rd, 4th, 5th, and (6th) ribs, where bone and cartilage join, and it is inserted into the medial border of the coracoid process near its tip. Of course, the insertion or apex of this triangular muscle is fibrous (tendinous or aponeurotic) (*fig. 61.1*).

AXIOM: When the site of insertion of a muscle is smaller than the site of origin, or of the cross-sectional area of the fleshy belly, that insertion must be fibrous, there being insufficient room for fleshy fibers.

In locating the origin of the Pectoralis Minor from the 3rd, 4th, and 5th ribs, remember that the only certain way of identifying any rib lies in reckoning from the *sternal angle* which is at the level of the

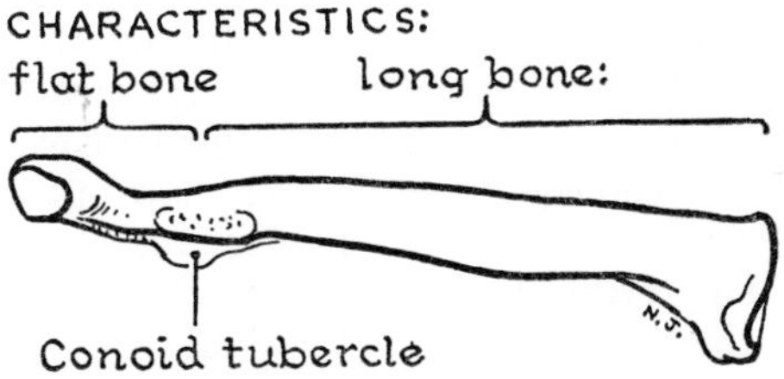

FIG. 60.2. The two parts of the clavicle

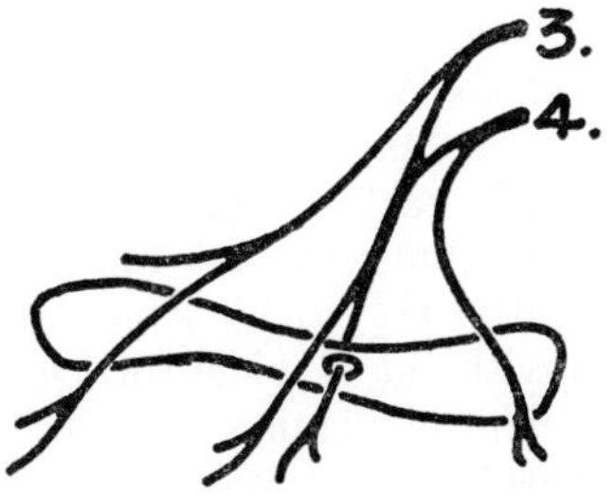

FIG. 61. The clavicle is occasionally pierced by a branch of the supraclavicular nerves.

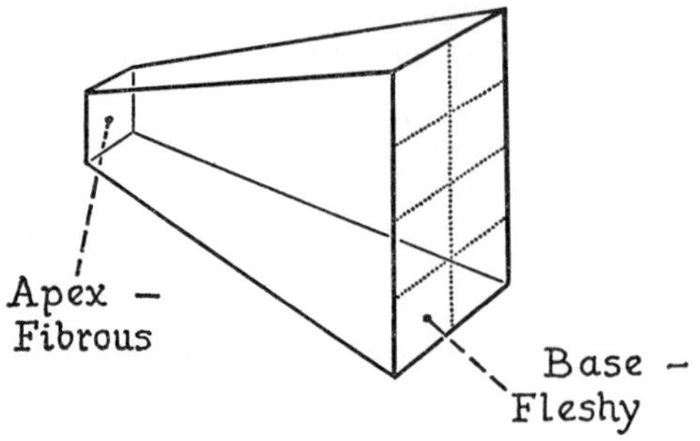

Fig. 61.1. A fibrous (tendinous) attachment conserves space.

2nd costal cartilages. Place therefore your index and middle fingers, one above the other, in the *jugular notch* (suprasternal notch) at the upper end of the sternum and run them down the middle line of the bone until, about 2″ below the notch, you encounter the transverse ridge which indicates where the manubrium and body of the sternum articulate with each other. This is the sternal angle. With one finger above the ridge and the other below, follow the ridge laterally to the 2nd costal cartilage. Employing the same two fingers you may readily palpate the 3rd, 4th, and 5th cartilages through the substance of the Pectoralis Major. Travel along what you estimate to be the length of the 3rd costal cartilage, say 2″, to the costochondral junction. By joining this point to the coracoid process you define the upper border of the Pectoralis Minor; similarly by joining the 5th rib near its cartilage, say 4½″ from the median plane, to the coracoid process you map out the lower border of this triangular muscle.

Two Triangles Separated by the Clavicle: At their attachments to the skull the Sternomastoid and Trapezius are continuous with each other, but below they diverge, leaving the middle third of the clavicle free. The triangular space so-formed is the *Posterior Triangle of the Neck*. In the same manner the Pectoralis Major and Deltoid are continuous with each other below at their humeral attachments, but above they diverge slightly (½ inch) from each other and form with the clavicle the *Deltopectoral Triangle*. The clavicular portions of these two muscles have a common action, namely that of flexing and adducting the shoulder as when raising the arm in boxing, pushing, or lifting the hand to the mouth; and, both derive their nerve supply from the same segments, namely the 5th and 6th cervical. The deltopectoral triangle allows the passage of the cephalic vein, its accompanying arterial twig (the deltoid), and lymph vessels.

WALLS OF AXILLA

From figure 58 and from the general description given on page 78, it is evident that one wall of the axilla is bony, one muscular, two consist of bone overlaid with muscle.

The obvious approach to the axilla is through the fleshy anterior wall and through the fascial base. Why? Because there is no bone to obstruct.

The **Anterior Wall** of the Axilla is formed throughout by Pectoralis Major, and behind this by Pectoralis Minor and Subclavius within their sheaths of clavipectoral fascia (*fig. 63*).

Pectoralis Major. This fan-shaped muscle has a clavicular and a sternal head of origin (*figs. 59, 63,* and *65*). The *clavicular head* arises in line with the Deltoid from the anterior aspect of the clavicle below the bare, linear strip. The *sternal head* meets its fellow of the opposite side along the midline of the body of the sternum; it curves upward and laterally across the manubrium sterni to the sternoclavicular joint where it meets the clavicular head; and it curves downward and laterally along the 5th (or 6th) costal cartilage.

The two heads have, therefore, a continuous curved fleshy origin from clavicle, joint, sternum, and underlying cartilages. The muscle increases its origin below, not by arising from rib or cartilage, for none is available (the Rectus Abdominis and Obliquus Externus Abdominis having monopolized them), but by gaining attachment to the External Oblique aponeurosis in front of the Rectus. Again, since the muscle meets its fellow in the median plane, it obviously could not—even if it would—increase its origin medially unless a bony keel were to develop from the sternum, as happens in birds of flight that have need of powerful wing muscles.

The Pectoralis Major is inserted by means of a trilaminar aponeurosis into the crest of the greater tubercle of the humerus (lateral lip of the bicipital groove). This lip extends upward from the deltoid tuberosity to the front of the greater tubercle (tuberosity) (*fig. 84*).

» The clavicular part of the muscle is inserted by means of an anterior lamina, which blends somewhat with the middle lamina behind it. The sternal part is folded upon itself to form a middle and a posterior lamina, continuous with each other below. Thus, the upper sternal fibers pass to the middle lamina; the lower sternal fibers and those from the External Oblique pass to the posterior lamina, the lowest fibers of origin becoming the highest fibers of insertion.

Actions. On considering its attachments it is obvious that all parts of the Pectoralis Major adduct the humerus (i.e., move it toward the median plane of the body) and rotate it medially (on its own long axis). If, while palpating your Pectoralis Major, you put the radial side of your closed fist under the edge of a heavy table and try to raise it, you will find that the clavicular part of the muscle comes into action. If, now, you put the ulnar side of your closed fist on the table and press downward, you will find that the sternal part comes into action. This indicates that the clavicular part aids in flexing the shoulder joint (i.e., raises the humerus forward, as in pushing), and that the sternal part aids in extending the joint (i.e., brings the flexed humerus downward and backward to the side).

The **cephalic vein** (*fig. 62*), which occupies the furrow between the Deltoid and the Pectoralis Major, may be followed through the delto-pectoral triangle, across the anterior aspect of the Pectoralis Minor, and through the costocoracoid membrane to its termination in the axillary vein. In following it, care need be taken of one structure only, the *nerve to the clavicular head of the Pectoralis Major*, for this nerve crosses either superficially or deep to the cephalic vein.

The Practical Significance of the cephalic vein is that a surgeon may pass a fine, pliable tube through it and the axillary and subclavian veins and on to the heart in order to withdraw samples of blood.

The **costocoracoid membrane** is so-called because it extends laterally from the 1st and 2nd costal cartilages medially, to the coracoid process. It is part of a larger fascial sheet, the **clavipectoral fascia** (*fig. 63*), which extends vertically from the clavicle above to the dome of the axillary fascia below.

This clavipectoral fascia splits below to

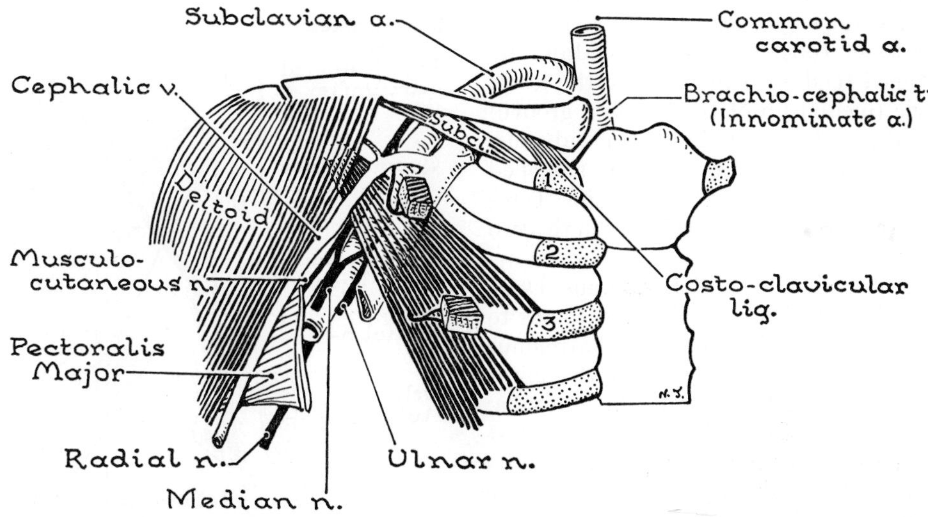

FIG. 62. The cephalic vein, as seen after removal of Pectoralis Major and costocoracoid membrane. (Note 2 "buttons" of Pectoralis Major with nerves attached.)

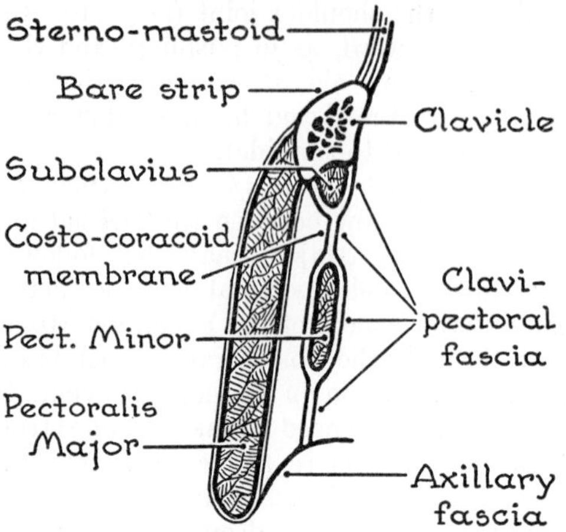

FIG. 63. The anterior wall of axilla (in sagittal section).

form a sheath for the Pectoralis Minor, and above to form a sheath for the Subclavius; it is to the portion between these two muscles that the term *costocoracoid membrane* is given. This fascia is responsible for the anterior and posterior sharp lines on the under surface of the clavicle that bound the fossa for the Subclavius.

The **Posterior Wall of the Axilla** is formed from above downward by the Subscapularis, Teres Major, and Latissimus Dorsi; the scapula being the background (*fig. 64*). These three muscles are attached to the humerus by tendons and, therefore, to bony elevations (*fig. 84*); the Subscapularis to the lesser tubercle; the Teres Major by a flattened tendon to the crest of the lesser tubercle (medial lip of the bicipital groove) which descends from the lesser tubercle; and the Latissimus Dorsi[1] by a flattened tendon immediately lateral to the Teres Major—a bursa intervening between the two glistening tendons.

Near its insertion the Latissimus Dorsi winds below the Teres Major and comes to lie in front of it. Although the Latissimus Dorsi forms the greater part of the lower border of the posterior wall of the axilla, it is the Teres Major that forms the most lateral part of this lower border because its insertion extends slightly below that of the Latissimus Dorsi.

[1] Actually the tendon of the Latissimus is inserted into the floor of the groove.

(For Origin of Latissimus from vertebral spines, iliac crest, and lower ribs see *fig. 77* and p. 94.)

During a dissection, the lower border of the Latissimus should be defined and cleaned early because it forms an important side of the "picture frame" of this region; and the nerve to the Latissimus Dorsi and its companion vessels should be identified, because they are in danger. They enter the deep surface of this large and important muscle ½ inch from its border at the mid-point between the chest wall and the abducted humerus.

If the Subscapularis be separated from the Teres Major, a long triangular space, whose lateral side or base is the surgical neck of the humerus, will be opened up. In its depths the long head of the Triceps Brachii will be seen. This head of the Triceps subdivides this long triangular space into a small, unimportant, medial *Triangular Space* and an important, lateral *Quadrangular Space* (*fig. 64* and p. 99).

The **Lateral Wall of the Axilla.** Since the three muscles of the posterior wall of the axilla are attached to the lesser tubercle of the humerus and to the crest that descends from it (*figs. 64* and *65*), and since the Pectoralis Major of the anterior wall is attached to the crest that descends from

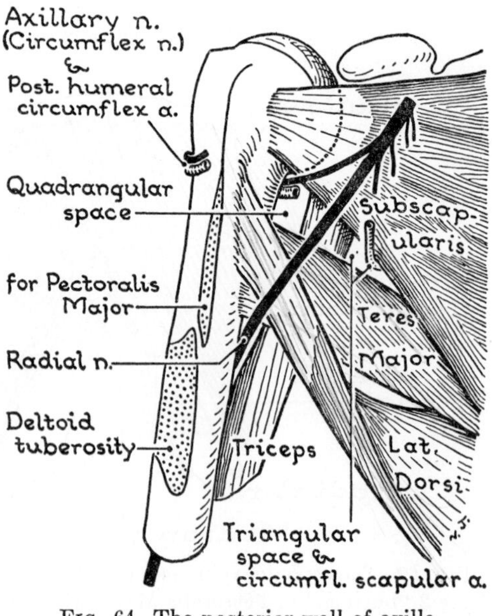

FIG. 64. The posterior wall of axilla

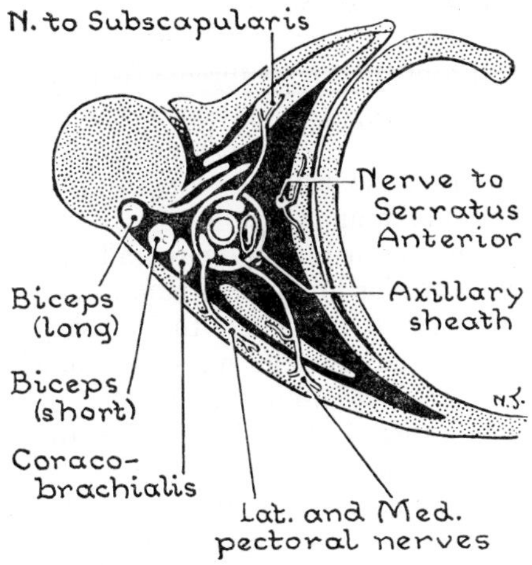

FIG. 65. The contents of the axilla, on cross section.

the greater tubercle, it follows that the lateral wall of the axilla is the narrow interval between these two crests, called the *intertubercular sulcus* (formerly the *bicipital groove* because it lodges the tendon of the long head of the Biceps).

The **Medial Wall of the Axilla** is formed by the ribs and intercostal muscles covered with Serratus Anterior. *The Nerve to the Serratus* (the long thoracic nerve) is one of paramount importance. It must not be damaged, for the Serratus is the chief muscle to protract or pull forward the scapula, as when pushing (*fig. 66*). If it is paralyzed, attempts to raise the arm in front of the body largely result in causing the inferior angle of the scapula to project from the back. The nerve is to be found running vertically a little behind the midaxillary line. It is directly applied to the Serratus Anterior and in its course it gives off twigs to it. (For attachments see p. 97.)

Observations on Muscles of Axilla

»» 1. The three largest and most important muscular constituents of the walls are Pectoralis Major, Latissimus Dorsi, and Serratus Anterior—each belongs to a different wall. The nerves to Latissimus and Serratus are in danger and therefore should be found early in a dissection.

2. A finger swept between Pectoralis Major and the clavipectoral fascia encounters the medial and lateral pectoral nerves and the pectoral branches of the thoraco-acromial vessels.

3. The long head of Biceps is applied to the lateral wall of the axilla, which is synonymous with the intertubercular groove of the humerus; and the insertion of Pectoralis Major prevents that head from being displaced laterally.

4. The combined tendon of the short head of Biceps and Coracobrachialis, which arises from the tip of the coracoid process, lies medial to the long head.

5. The Subscapularis passes under the arch formed by the coracoid process and conjoint tendon of Biceps and Coracobrachialis.

VESSELS AND NERVES OF AXILLA

The great axillary vessels and nerves are enveloped in a thin tube, the **axillary sheath**, derived from the fascia covering the Scalene muscles (*fig. 665*). In passing from the neck to the axilla they traverse a triangular space whose patency is maintained by three bones—clavicle, 1st rib, and upper border of the scapula. As they descend through the axilla they curve from the anterior part of its medial wall to the lateral part of its posterior wall.

The **Great Arterial Stem** of the limb (*fig. 67*) is called the *subclavian artery* until it reaches the lower border of the 1st rib. From there to the lower border of the Teres Major it lies within the axilla and is known as the *axillary artery*. On leaving the axilla

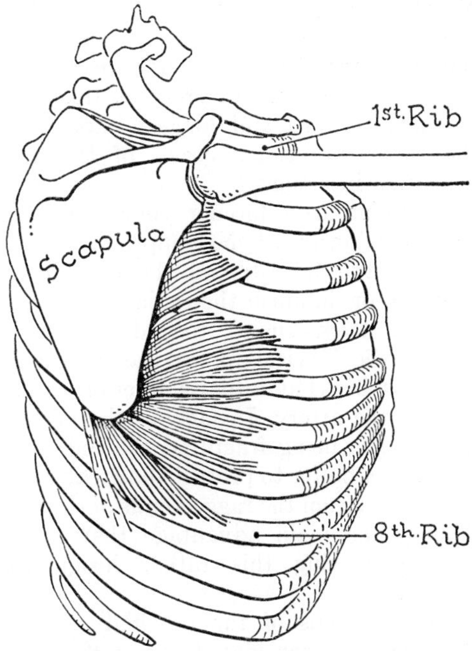

FIG. 66. The Serratus Anterior

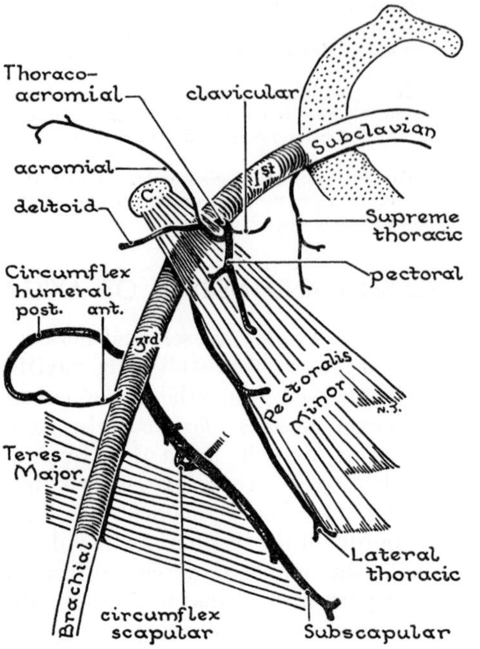

FIG. 67. The three parts of the axillary artery and its branches.

to enter the arm or brachium it becomes the *brachial artery* (p. 120).

The **Axillary Artery** is conveniently divided into three parts by the Pectoralis Minor (*fig. 67*). Of these, the 1st part traverses a fatty space; the 2nd lies close behind the Pectoralis Minor a finger's breadth from the tip of the coracoid process—this is important; the 3rd and longest part crosses the three posterior muscles of the axilla near their insertions.

On voluntarily forcing your arm backward and downward you compress the artery between the 1st rib and the clavicle and so arrest or diminish the radial pulse at the wrist—a trick known to old soldiers—or rather, the clavicle forces the Subclavius, which is inserted into its inferior surface, against the artery. In fact, in the event of the clavicle being fractured the Subclavius serves as a buffer to protect the great vessels and nerves from the ragged ends of the bone. This is the main advantage that accrues from possessing this rather insignificant muscle.

The relations of the brachial artery to the nerves are considered on page 86.

Branches. Branches arise from the three parts of the artery, as follows:

1. From the 1st—supreme thoracic.
2. From the 2nd—{thoraco-acromial, lateral thoracic.
3. From the 3rd—{subscapular, posterior humeral circumflex, anterior humeral circumflex.

Of these 6 branches, the subscapular is much the largest; the supreme thoracic and the anterior circumflex are small.

The supreme thoracic a. helps to supply the upper two intercostal spaces.

The thoraco-acromial a. arises at the upper border of the Pectoralis Minor, pierces the costocoracoid membrane, and divides into four branches which radiate in the plane between the clavipectoral fascia and the Pectoralis Major. Its main duty is, of course, to supply the Pectoral Muscles; accordingly, a large pectoral branch descends between the Major and Minor and supplies them.

The lateral thoracic a. follows the lower border of the Pectoralis Minor to the chest wall.

The three branches of the 3rd part of the axillary artery arise either singly or together about the level of the surgical neck of the humerus, in front of the quadrangular space (*fig. 64*).

» Emboli or blood clots expelled from the heart during life are apt to lodge at this site, because beyond it the main vessel is much reduced in caliber.

The subscapular a. is the artery of the posterior wall, and it follows the lower border of the Subscapularis to the medial wall. It sends a large branch, the *circumflex scapular a.*, to the dorsum of the scapula by way of the triangular space; other branches accompany the nerves to Subscapularis, Teres Major and Latissimus Dorsi, and the terminal branches end on the chest wall where they meet the nerve to Serratus Anterior (*fig. 68*).

It is through the anastomoses that this, the largest of all the branches of the axillary artery, makes on the chest wall and around the scapula that the circulation in the limb is maintained after the distal part of the subclavian a. or the proximal part of the axillary artery has been ligated (*fig. 79*).

The circumflex humeral arteries encircle the surgical neck of the humerus. The posterior artery accompanies the axillary nerve, and is large.

The Axillary Vein lies on the medial or concave side of its artery, but it overlaps and conceals the artery when the arm is abducted. It begins at the lower border of the Teres Major as the continuation of the basilic vein, and it ends at the lower border of the 1st rib as the *subclavian vein.* It has two or three bicuspid valves.

Tributaries. In addition to receiving tributaries corresponding to the six branches of the axillary artery, it receives the two *venae comitantes* of the brachial artery and the *cephalic vein.*

The Brachial Plexus is formed by the alternate union and bifurcation of nerves, thus: five ventral nerve *rami* unite to form three *trunks,* which bifurcate to form six *divisions,* which unite to form three *cords,* which bifurcate to form six *terminal branches* (*fig. 69*). Of these six terminal branches, two soon unite to form the median nerve; hence, the plexus may be said to begin as five ventral rami and to end as five nerves.

The brachial plexus is constituted as follows: The ventral rami of the 5th and 6th cervical nerves unite; the 7th cervical remains single; the 8th cervical and 1st thoracic unite. Each of the three trunks so-formed divides into an anterior and a posterior division.

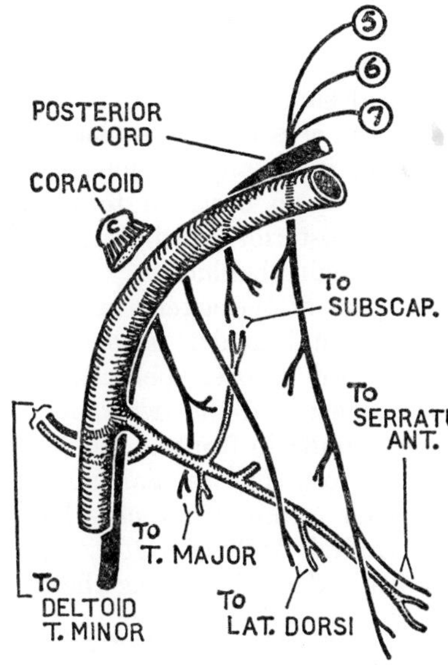

FIG. 68. Branches of the subscapular artery accompanying 5 motor nerves.

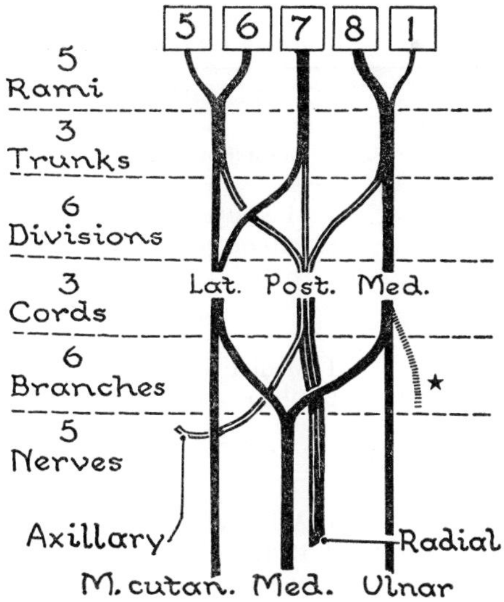

FIG. 69. Scheme of the brachial plexus. * Indicates the medial cutaneous nerve of the forearm.

The three posterior divisions unite together to form a single posterior cord.

Of the three anterior divisions, the lateral and intermediate unite to form the lateral cord, while the medial continues its course as the medial cord.

***AXIOM:** It is a fundamental truth that the nerves to the muscles on the original ventral and dorsal surfaces of the upper and lower limbs are derived from the anterior and posterior divisions respectively of the brachial and lumbosacral plexuses.*

Each of the three cords gives off one or more *collateral branches* and ends by dividing into two *terminal branches* (as shown in table 2 on p. 86), the lateral cord dividing into the musculocutaneous nerve and the lateral root of the median nerve, the medial cord into the ulnar nerve and the medial root of the median nerve, and the posterior cord into the radial and the axillary nerve (circumflex n.).

From a glance at figure 69 it should be clear that the musculocutaneous nerve and the lateral root of the median nerve can

TABLE 2

Derivatives of the Brachial Plexus within the Limits of the Axilla

Cords	Terminal branches	Collateral branches	
	Mixed (motor and sensory)	Motor	Cutaneous
Lateral	1. Musculocutaneous 2. Lateral root of median	1. Clavicular head of Pectoralis Major (and upper part of sterno-costal head)	
Medial	1. Medial root of median 2. Ulnar	1. Sterno-costal head of Pectoralis Major 2. Pectoralis Minor	1. Med. cutan. n. of arm 2. Med. cutan. n. of forearm
Posterior	1. Axillary 2. Radial	1. Subscapularis 2. Latissimus Dorsi 3. Teres Major	
From the musculocutaneous		1. Coracobrachialis	
From the radial		1. Triceps (long head) and	Post. cutan. n. of arm
From the 5, 6, and 7 roots of the plexus		1. Serratus Anterior	

derive fibers from the 5th, 6th, and 7th nerve segments; the ulnar nerve and medial root of the median nerve from the 8th and 1st; the median nerve itself and the posterior cord from each of the 5 segments.[2]

»» The medial and lateral cords might better have been called the "antero-medial" and "antero-lateral" cords in order to emphasize the fact that they supply all the muscles on the anterior or flexor aspect of the limb and that they supply no other muscles. The posterior cord is well named because it is destined to supply all the muscles on the posterior or extensor aspect of the limb from the axilla distally, and it supplies no other muscles. As to this fundamental fact you should be perfectly clear.

The rami and the trunks of the plexus lie in the neck, the divisions behind the clavicle, the cords above and behind the Pectoralis Minor, and the terminal branches distal to it.

Relation of Plexus to Artery. The brachial plexus (*fig. 70*) has now to be related to the axillary artery. Consider, the plexus emerges from the cervical portion of the vertebral column; the great artery arises almost directly from the heart. Clearly, then, the plexus should at first be above, behind, and lateral to the artery; and it is.

The three cords chance to be disposed around the second part of the axillary artery—the part behind the Pectoralis Minor—as their names suggest; that is to say, the posterior cord lies posteriorly, the lateral cord laterally, and the medial cord medially. Obviously, it can only be by crossing the 1st part of the artery that the medial cord can come to take up a position on the medial side of the 2nd part of the artery; and the crossing takes place behind the artery. It is equally obvious that the lateral cord has no occasion to cross the artery. The posterior cord takes origin behind and remains behind.

The 2nd part of the artery may be said to perforate the brachial plexus, because the medial cord crosses behind the 1st part of the artery and the two roots of the median nerve unite in front of the 3rd part.

Identification. The medial and lateral cords and their terminal branches have the form of a capital "M" (*fig. 70*). This fact should be utilized in identifying them.

»» Thus, pick up at random any large nerve below the level of the Pectoralis Minor; place a finger behind it; and run the finger upward till the cord of which it is a terminal branch is reached; then proceed to follow downward the other terminal branch of that cord. If for example, you happen to pick up the *median*

[2] In point of fact their origins are: musculocutaneous 5, 6, 7; ulnar (7) 8, 1; median (5) 6, 7, 8, 1; radial 5, 6, 7, 8 (1); axillary 5, 6.

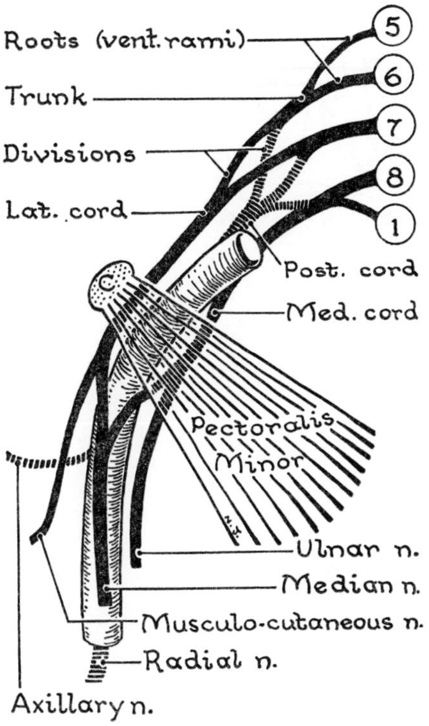

FIG. 70. The brachial plexus

nerve, your finger will be conducted by the medial root to the ulnar nerve and by the lateral root to the *musculocutaneous nerve,* which may then be followed downward. Similarly, if you happen to pick up the *ulnar nerve* it will lead to the medial root of the median nerve and so to the median nerve itself. So, by running the finger up and down behind the limbs of the M all three nerves, as well as the lateral and medial cords from which they arise, can be picked up and identified.

Two Cutaneous Branches also can be found. The larger of these is the *medial cutaneous nerve of the forearm.* It and the much smaller *medial cutaneous nerve of the arm* arise from the medial cord just before it bifurcates.

If the derivatives of the lateral and medial cords are held aside, the only remaining large nerve, namely, the *radial nerve,* will be identified by this process of exclusion.

Unless the foregoing procedure is followed, that is to say, unless the musculocutaneous, median, and ulnar nerves are first identified and held aside, the radial nerve may easily be mistaken for the ulnar nerve. (*See fig. 71.*)

The identity of the *radial nerve* should be confirmed by following it proximally to, or above, the lower border of Subscapularis, where it and the *axillary nerve* will be seen to be the two terminal branches of the posterior cord. All three lie behind the axillary artery.

»» Of the five terminal nerves of the plexus, the axillary nerve alone does not run longitudinally, but disappears into the quadrangular space. And, it is difficult to find access to it unless the arm can be brought well forward, that is to say, raised from the table, as by putting a block under the elbow. This simple act renders all the structures on the posterior wall accessible; and adducting the arm renders the great vessels and nerves lax.

Motor Nerves of the Axilla in Review (*figs. 171* and *172*). Because the two *Pectoral Muscles* belong to the anterior wall they must be supplied by anterior cords (i.e., lateral and medial). The branch from the lateral cord, the *lateral pectoral nerve,* supplies the upper half of Pectoralis Major. The branch from the medial cord, the *medial pectoral nerve,* pierces Pectoralis Minor and supplies it and the lower half of Pectoralis Major.

Just before the musculocutaneous nerve pierces *Coracobrachialis,* it supplies that muscle.

Because *Subscapularis, Teres Major,* and *Latissimus Dorsi* belong to the posterior wall of the axilla, they must be supplied by the posterior cord. Two (or more) branches reach Subscapularis high up; a third supplies its lower border and passes on to the Teres Major, which it reaches about 2″ from the humerus when the arm is abducted. The nerve to Latissimus Dorsi is readily found on everting the lower border of Latissimus, for it enters the axillary surface of the muscle ½″ from its border at a point midway between the chest wall and the humerus when the arm is abducted.

The nerve to *Serratus Anterior* takes origin in the neck from the roots (5, 6, 7) of the plexus, and because Serratus is developmentally a posterior muscle, this nerve descends behind the axillary vessels (*figs. 65* and *68*), and it is applied to Serratus Anterior throughout its entire length.

The only nerve to *long head of Triceps* arises, in conjunction with the *posterior cutaneous nerve of the arm,* from the back of the radial nerve just before that nerve leaves the axilla and while still resting on the flat tendons of Latissimus Dorsi and Teres Major.

A Typical Spinal Nerve (*fig. 72*) is a serially segmental structure which is at-

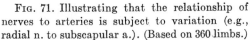

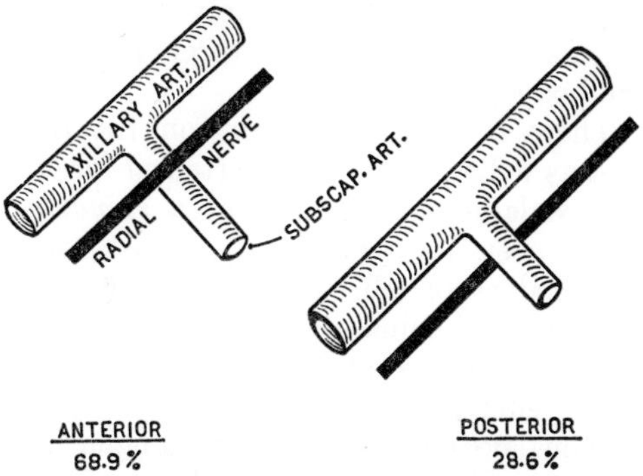

FIG. 71. Illustrating that the relationship of nerves to arteries is subject to variation (e.g., radial n. to subscapular a.). (Based on 360 limbs.)

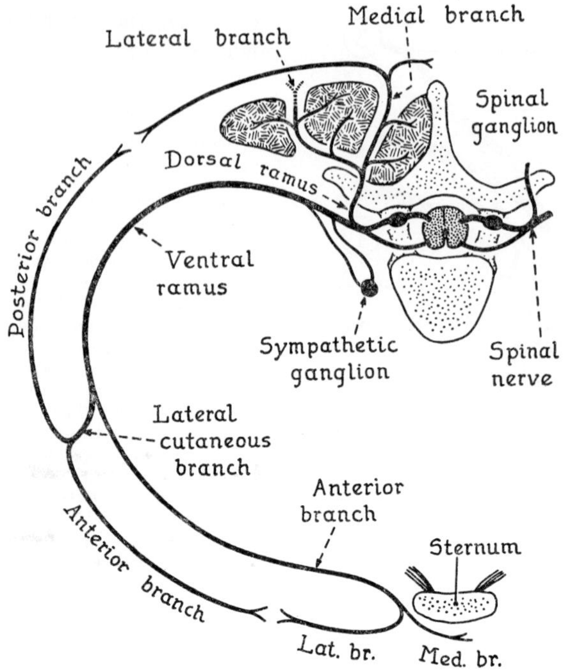

FIG. 72. A typical segmental nerve

tached to the spinal cord by *two roots*—a ventral (anterior) which is motor or efferent, and a dorsal (posterior) which is sensory or afferent. The two roots leave the vertebral canal through an intervertebral foramen and join immediately beyond it to form a *spinal nerve.* Having both motor and sensory fibers, the nerve is said to be mixed. After the course of a few millimeters the spinal nerve divides into a *ventral* and a *dorsal ramus.* Roughly, the dorsal rami supply the muscles of the back that act on the vertebral column and the skin covering them; whereas ventral rami supply the muscles and skin of the anterior three-quarters of the body wall.

There is an enlargement on the dorsal root as it lies in the intervertebral foramen. This enlargement, known as a *spinal ganglion* (post. root ganglion), consists of the cell bodies of all the afferent (sensory) fibers in that spinal nerve.

Spinal nerves and their branches also carry efferent fibers of the sympathetic nervous system. Sympathetic ganglia lie on the sides of the vertebral bodies in front of the spinal nerves to which they are connected by white and gray rami communicantes. White rami carry fibers from the spinal cord to the ganglia. Gray rami carry fibers from the ganglia, where their cell bodies are located, to the spinal nerves and thence to their branches. Thus, the white rami contain preganglionic fibers, the gray contain postganglionic fibers, and the ganglia are the site of transmission of impulses from one to the other. The fibers traveling along the peripheral nerves confine their attention to involuntary muscle and to glands (*fig. 43*), as follows:

Involuntary muscle { of blood vessels; of hairs }

Secretory glands { sweat; sebaceous }

The Cutaneous Nerves. The ventral rami of the thoracic nerves are usually called *intercostal nerves.* A typical intercostal nerve gives off a *lateral cutaneous branch* in the midaxillary line and ends, after piercing the Pectoralis Major at the side of the sternum, as an *anterior cutaneous branch* (*fig. 72*).

The lateral cutaneous branch divides into an anterior and a posterior branch which appear less than an inch apart between the digitations of the Serratus Anterior. The anterior branch runs forwards superficial to the Pectoralis Major; the posterior branch runs backward superficial to the Latissimus Dorsi.

Now, the *first three intercostal nerves* are atypical: the 1st in having neither a lateral nor an anterior cutaneous branch; the 2nd in sending its lateral branch across the dome of the axilla in the laminated fascia and then descending on the postero-medial aspect of the arm as the *intercostobrachial nerve* (*fig. 98*); and the 3rd in sending a small lateral branch to the medial side of the arm.

Explanation. In prenatal life, the ventral rami of nerves C. 5, 6, 7, 8, and Th. 1 are drawn out from the trunk into the developing limb to supply it with both motor and sensory fibers. They form the brachial plexus and their simple segmental arrangement is lost. Since these five rami (5, 6, 7, 8, and 1) send no cutaneous branches to the pectoral region, it becomes the duty of the supraclavicular branches of C. 3 and 4 to descend in front of the clavicle to the level of Th. 2 thereby closing the gap or hiatus thus occasioned. In consequence, a person whose spinal cord is injured due to a fracture of the 5th cervical vertebra might retain sensation to pinprick as low as the 2nd intercostal space (*fig. 97*).

The cutaneous supply to the limb draws upon more segments than the motor supply, for branches from C. 3 and 4 descend to the deltoid region; branches from Th. 2 and 3 descend to the medial side of the arm. This may be represented thus:

	Sensory	
	Motor	
3, 4	5, 6, 7, 8, 1,	2, 3

FASCIA, MAMMARY GLAND, LYMPH NODES, AND ANOMALIES

Fascia. If the chest were enveloped in a tough, dense fascia, respiration obviously would be interfered with. So, for this reason, if for no other, you might expect the investing fascia in this region to be thin and loosely woven. Indeed, the *deep fascia* here, as over flat muscles in general, is thin and areolar in nature. Where it forms the dome-shaped floor of the axilla, it is irregularly laminated.

The *clavipectoral fascia,* which is the sheath of Pectoralis Minor and Subclavius, acts as a suspensory ligament for the dome-shaped floor of the axilla.

You have seen that the great axillary vessels and nerves occupy a tubular sheath, the *axillary sheath.* This sheath is attached behind the Subclavius to the clavipectoral fascia; so, the vessels move with the clavicle.

The large quantities of very loose, moist, areolar tissue found between the various muscles of this region are necessary to allow the limb a wide range of movements.

The Mammary Gland or breast (*fig. 74*) lies in the superficial fascia. It is made up of 15–20 units of glandular tissue, whose lobules, enclosed in a fibro-areolar stroma, radiate from the nipple into the surrounding superficial fat, much as spokes radiate from the hub of a wheel. The periphery of the gland, or rim of the wheel, extends from the 2nd to the 6th rib in the vertical plane and from the side of the sternum to near the midaxillary line in the horizontal plane. Of the several tail-like processes it may possess, one runs upward along the lower border of the Pectoralis Major to the 3rd rib level.

About two-thirds of the gland overlies the Pectoralis Major; one-third the Serratus Anterior. Although easily separated from the fascia covering these muscles, the gland is firmly connected to the true skin by fibrous bands (*ligaments of Cooper*) that pass from its stroma between lobules of fat.

In the pinkish areola surrounding the nipple there is a number of nodular rudimentary milk glands, *the areolar glands,* and deep to the areola is some unstriped muscle, a lymph plexus, and an absence of fat.

Vessels and Nerves. *Nerves:* Intercostal nerves (2nd–6th), via lateral and anterior cutaneous branches. These or the vessels convey sympathetic fibers.

Arteries. Perforating branches (especially the 2nd and 3rd) of the *internal thoracic a.*

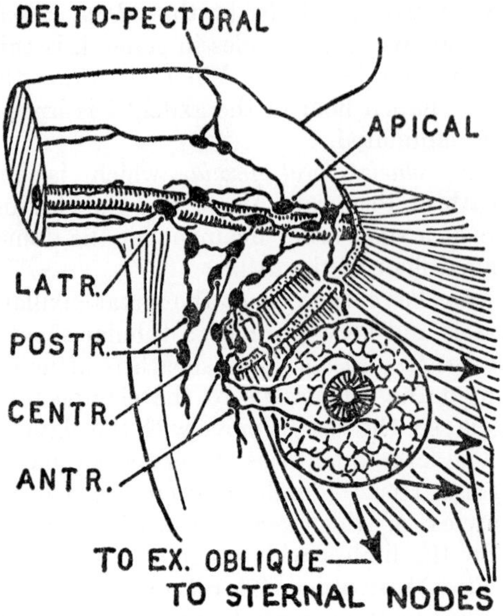

FIG. 73. Lymphatics of the breast and axilla (*sternal* nodes = *parasternal*). (After Poirier and Charpy.)

(internal mammary a.) and two branches of the *lateral thoracic a.* approach the gland from the sides, ramify on its superficial surface, send branches into it, and anastomose around the nipple. Twigs from the *intercostal aa.* may enter the deep surface of the gland.

For *Venous Connections* see page 570.

Lymphatics. The main lymph vessels of the mamma, like the ducts, converge on the nipple. Deep to the areola they form a subareolar lymph plexus (*fig. 73*). (1) From this plexus two or three distinct vessels course superficially to the pectoral lymph nodes. (2) From the medial border of the mamma, lymph vessels pass to the parasternal lymph nodes, which lie along the internal thoracic a. (3) From the deep surface of the mamma, lymph vessels pass through the Pectoralis Major to the interpectoral nodes, which lie superficial to the Pectoralis Minor and costocoracoid membrane, or passing through these end in the apical nodes.

The Axillary Lymph Nodes (Glands) (*fig. 73*) are arranged in several main groups: (1) *the lateral* nodes lie along the lower parts of the axillary vein. They receive the lymph vessels that ascend along the medial side of the arm and they empty into (2) *the apical* (*infraclavicular*) nodes that lie along the upper part of the axillary vein between the Pectoralis Minor and the clavicle. All the vessels of the limb, including those following the cephalic vein, drain either directly or indirectly into this group, and it in turn drains into *the subclavian lymph trunk* which ends in the right lymph duct or (left) thoracic duct. (3) *The pectoral* (*anterior*) nodes lie along the lower border of the Pectoralis Minor with the lateral thoracic vein. (4) *The subscapular* (*posterior*) nodes lie along the subscapular veins. (5) *The central* nodes lie between the layers of fascia

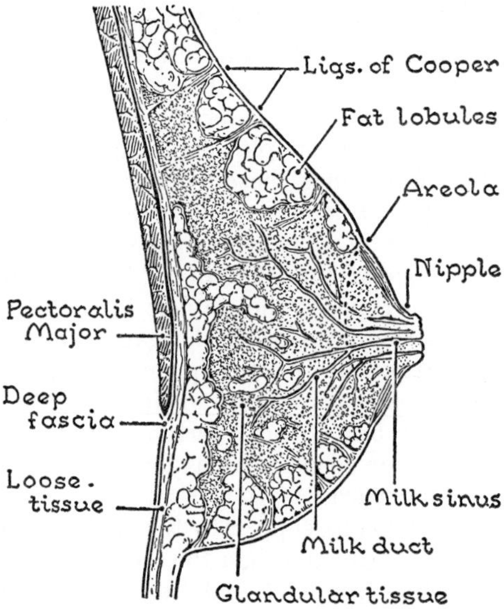

FIG. 74. The mamma on vertical section. (After Testut.)

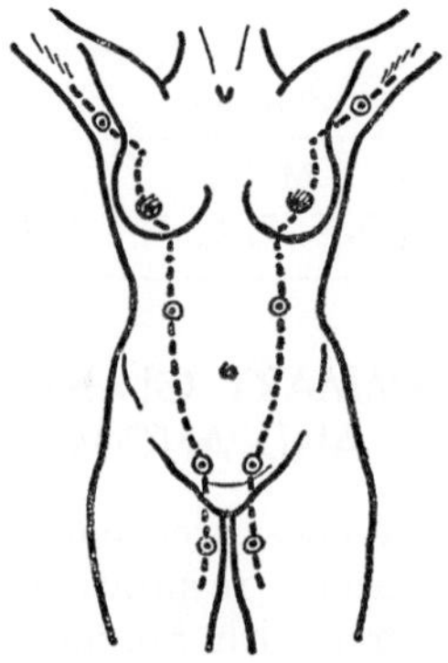

FIG. 75. Accessory nipples may appear on the milk line.

at the base of the axilla or in the fat deep to it. (6) Occasionally one or two small nodes occur along the cephalic vein in the *deltopectoral triangle.*

Anomalies. *Accessory Nipples* or even *Mammae* are occasionally found along the "milk line" (*fig. 75*).

Sternalis muscle. A band of muscle, ½″ to 1″ wide, lying in front of Pectoralis Major and in line with Sternomastoid and Rectus Abdominis, is commonly found.

Axillary Arch: a band of voluntary muscle, ½″ to 1½″ wide, that stretches across the base of the axilla from Latissimus Dorsi to Pectoralis Major or coracoid process.

Pectoralis Major: its sternal head may be absent.

The lateral root of the median nerve (or part of it) may travel with the musculocutaneous nerve far into the arm before joining the medial root.

CHAPTER 6

SCAPULAR AND DELTOID REGIONS

The Scapula is a flat bone with two surfaces, a *costal* and a *dorsal;* it is triangular in shape, having three borders and three angles; and it has two processes, the *coracoid process* and the *spine* which ends as the *acromion* (*fig. 76*).

The *spine* of the scapula crosses obliquely the medial four-fifths of the dorsal surface,

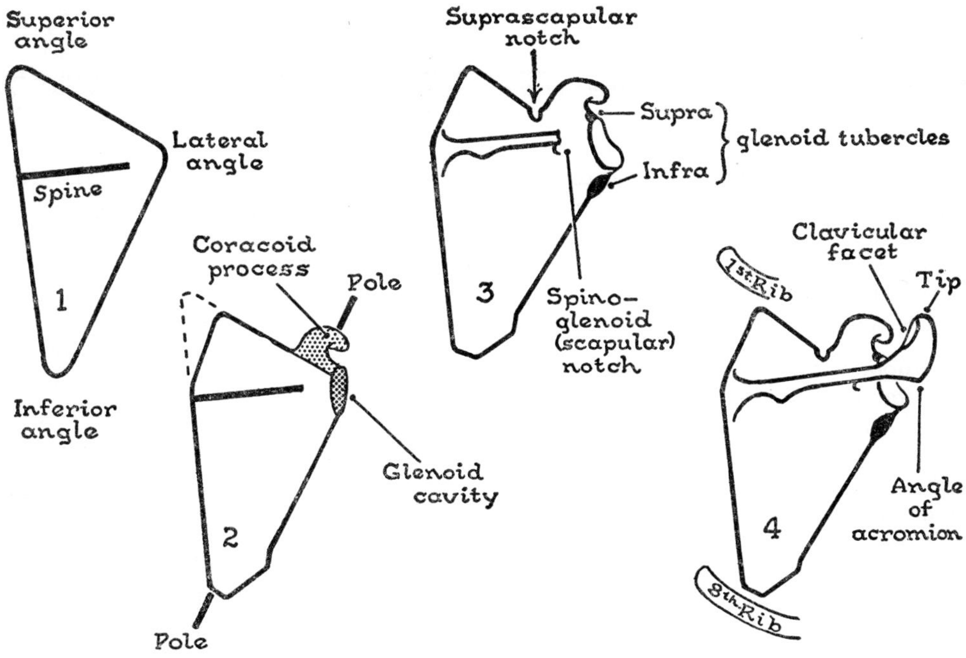

FIG. 76. The progressive stages in sketching a scapula, from behind

dividing it into a smaller *supraspinous* and a larger *infraspinous fossa.* These two fossae communicate with each other at the "*spino-glenoid notch*", which lies between the lateral border of the spine and the *glenoid cavity.* The posterior border or *crest of the spine*—often for the sake of brevity referred to as "the spine"—ends above the shoulder joint in a free, flattened and expanded piece of bone, the *acromion.* The acromion has on its medial border, very close to its tip, a small oval bevelled facet for articulation with the flattened acromial end of the clavicle.

Palpable Parts. The crest of the spine, the acromion, and the clavicle form a *bony arch* which you can palpate from end to end through the skin. This is possible because no muscle, save the Platysma, crosses any part of this arch.

The *acromioclavicular joint* is likewise subcutaneous. You can easily locate it by pressing medially with the fingertips because the acromial end of the clavicle is a little thicker than the acromion and it projects above it.

The *medial (vertebral) border* of the scapula is covered in its upper half with Trapezius, but you can easily palpate it from the *inferior angle* to the *superior angle.* The *lateral (axillary) border* you can trace with some difficulty. The inferior angle and the tip of the coracoid are, so to speak, at opposite "*poles*" of the scapula. By grasping the inferior angle with one hand and palpating the coracoid process with two fingers of the other, you can so manipulate the scapula that a fracture between the "*two poles*" would reveal itself.

Relations to Ribs and Vertebrae. The *medial border* is almost parallel to the spines of the vertebrae and is about 2″ distant from them. This border crosses 6 of the 12 ribs and leaves the other 6 uncrossed. And since the superior angle overlies the 2nd rib, it follows that the inferior angle overlies the 7th rib (or 7th interspace) and that there is one uncovered rib above the superior angle, and that there are five below the inferior angle.

The apex of the spine of the scapula lies at the level of the 3rd thoracic spine.

»» Although the 8th rib takes a downward slope, at the *inferior angle* of the scapula it is on practically the same level as the tip of the spinous process of the 8th thoracic vertebra. This is due to the fact that the spinous process also takes a downward slope.

The inferior angle of the scapula is a valuable practical guide to the upper limits of the diaphragm and liver and to the lower limits of the lung.

To measure the limb. *The angle of the acromion* is the usual point from which to measure the length of the limb, since it is readily found on drawing two fingers dorsally along the lateral border of the acromion and the thumb laterally along the lower lip of the crest of the spine until the three palpating digits meet at an angle.

(The scapula: for details see page 105.)

Cutaneous Nerves of the Back. The ventral rami of nerves C. 5, 6, 7, 8 and Th. 1, it will be remembered, take part in the brachial plexus, and send no cutaneous branches to the pectoral region. The dorsal rami of these same nerve segments have likewise a restricted distribution: the dorsal ramus of the middle nerve of the series, i.e., the 7th, has no cutaneous branch; of those on each side of it, the 6th and, sometimes, the 8th usually have none; while the 5th cervical and 1st thoracic have small cutaneous twigs. Therefore, both on the front of the girdle and on the back there is a break in the sequence of the cutaneous nerves.

A typical dorsal nerve ramus divides into a medial and a lateral branch (*fig. 72*). Both branches supply muscles, and one or the other of the branches becomes cutaneous. Above the midthoracic region it is the medial branches that become cutaneous, and they do so close to the median plane; below, the lateral branches become cutaneous at some distance from the median plane. The cutaneous branch of Th. 2 extends to the acromion and is the longest of the dorsal rami.

The area of skin supplied by a single dorsal (i.e., sensory) nerve root is called a *dermatome*. On the trunk the dermatomes form obliquely encircling bands (*fig. 43.3*).

First Layer of Muscles of the Back:

Latissimus Dorsi and Trapezius.

These are inserted into the upper limb.

Latissimus Dorsi. The Subscapularis, Teres Major, and Latissimus Dorsi have differentiated from closely related premuscle masses.

»» The facts (1) that the nerve to the Teres Major supplies a branch to the Subscapularis, (2) that the Teres Major and Latissimus describe complete half turns, and (3) that the Latissimus commonly has a slip of origin from the back of the inferior angle of the scapula in conjunction with the Teres Major bear evidence of this.

Origin. During development the Latissimus has evidently migrated farther than its two companion muscles, for its origin now extends in a fan-shaped manner from the 7th thoracic spine to the middle of the outer lip of the iliac crest. Between these two points its aponeurotic origin is attached to the lower 6 thoracic, the lumbar, and the sacral spines, to the supraspinous ligament, and to the posterior part of the outer lip of the iliac crest, largely through the medium of the thoracolumbar fascia (lumbar fascia). It also arises from the lower three ribs by fleshy fibers that interdigitate with the External Oblique of the Abdomen in series with those of the Serratus Anterior.

Insertion and Nerve Supply: see pages 82 and 87.

Actions and Functions. The Latissimus extends the humerus, rotates it medially, and adducts it. It brings the outstretched arm from above the head to behind the back. It is used in swimming, in raising the body when one hangs from a horizontal bar, in rowing, in pulling, in elbowing one's way through a crowd.

»» **Two Triangles associated with Latissimus** (*fig. 77*). The upper horizontal border of the Latissimus crosses the inferior angle of the scapula, and, carried medially, reaches the 7th thoracic spine. Bounded by this border of the Latissimus, the Trapezius, and the Rhomboideus Major is the *Triangle of Auscultation.* Its floor is the naked thoracic wall. It is formed by the 6th interspace and the ribs bounding it (*fig. 77*).

The anterior oblique border of the Latissimus often fails to meet the posterior border of the Obliquus Externus Abdominis at the middle of the iliac crest in which case another triangular area, the *Lumbar Triangle* is formed (*fig. 77*). Its floor is the Obliquus Internus Abdominis.

Trapezius. This is a triangular muscle. The Trapezii of the two sides together form a trapeze or table.

The *Origin* of the Trapezius extends from the skull above to the spinous process of the last thoracic vertebra below. As will be seen later, it arises from the medial third of the superior nuchal line of the occipital

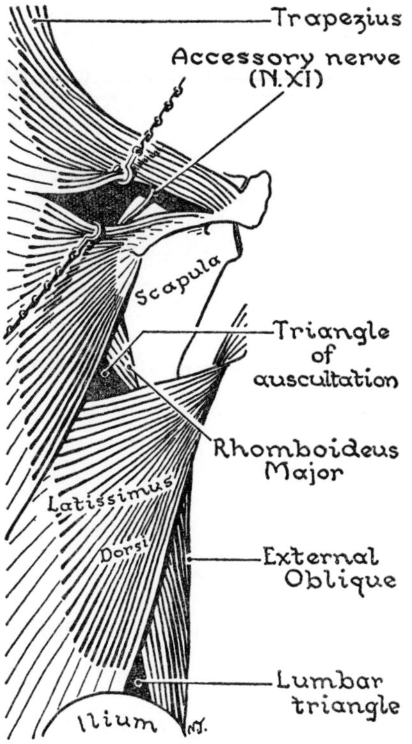

FIG. 77. Exposure of the superior border of the scapula. Two triangles.

bone, the inion, the tips of the spines of all the cervical and thoracic vertebrae, and the intervening supraspinous ligament. The attachment to the cervical spines is not direct but through the medium of the ligamentum nuchae.

Insertion. The upper fibers of the muscle pass inferolaterally to the posterior border and adjacent part of the upper surface of the flattened lateral third of the clavicle; the intermediate fibers pass horizontally laterally to the medial border and adjacent part of the upper surface of the acromion, as well as to the upper lip of the crest of the spine of the scapula; the lower fibers, that is to say, those arising below the level of the apex of the spine of the scapula, converge as they pass superolaterally and form an aponeurosis which is inserted into and accounts for the well marked tubercle on the lower lip of the crest of the spine. Note the direction of this tubercle.

Functions. The Trapezii are the suspensory muscles of the shoulder girdles. In health they hold the shoulders back and up, thus giving a "military carriage." Drooping or bottleneck shoulders indicate weakness of the Trapezii. The Trapezius comes into play, raising or steadying the shoulder girdle, whenever a weight is either supported on the shoulder or carried in the hand (*fig. 176*). The lower fibers are not necessarily antagonistic to the upper fibers. In fact, they assist the upper fibers to rotate the scapula, for when the upper fibers raise the point of the shoulder, the lower fibers by pulling on their tubercle of insertion depress the medial border. The middle, horizontal fibers form the thickest part of the muscle; they are used to moor the scapula, being particularly active during pulling.

If the muscle is paralyzed the normal concavity of the neck becomes an angularity, the point of the shoulder droops.

Nerve Supply. The Trapezius is supplied on its deep surface by (1) the accessory nerve (external branch), which arises from the upper five cervical nerve segments and takes a devious course (*fig. 764*), and (2) by the ventral rami of C. 3 and 4, which take a direct course, and are not purely sensory in man as they are in some species (Corbin and Harrison; Wookey).

The **Upper Border of the Scapula** lies deep to Trapezius and is the key to the suprascapular region. It extends from the superior angle, where the Levator Scapulae is inserted, to the upper part of the glenoid cavity where the long head of the Biceps arises from the *supraglenoid tubercle* (*fig. 76*). The medial part of this border is subjected neither to stress nor to strain, and as it affords attachment to only one muscle, the slender Omohyoid, it has no occasion to be other than thin and sharp. Laterally, it becomes abruptly deeper—the *scapular notch* (suprascapular notch). This notch is bridged by a sharp, taut band, the *transverse scapular ligament* (suprascapular lig.). Between the notch and the supraglenoid tubercle the border is drawn out into the stout *coracoid process.*

Ossification. The coracoid process fuses

with the rest of the scapula during the 15th year (*fig. 87*).

»» The upper border of the scapula cannot be seen from behind since, being concave, it is, of course, concealed by the upper border of the Supraspinatus which, being straight, rises above the concavity. With this in mind, pass the index finger over the upper border of the Supraspinatus and down its anterior surface till the sharp concave upper border of the bone is felt. Then, by sense of touch run the finger laterally along the upper border of the bone and of the transverse scapular ligament to the root of the coracoid (*fig. 78*). Do this in disregard of the unimportant Omohyoid which is attached near the notch. Thence run the finger up the coracoclavicular ligament to the clavicle, and then medially behind the bare posterior surface of the clavicle. With the aid of these fixed landmarks you can find your way about; without them you grope.

Suprascapular Vessels and Nerve. With a little blunt dissection the suprascapular vessels, crossing above the ligament, will be set free, and the suprascapular nerve, crossing below the ligament, can be picked up with a blunt hook. On the dorsum of the scapula the suprascapular vessels and nerve lie in contact with the bone. They pass from the supraspinous fossa through spinoglenoid notch to infraspinous fossa.

Distribution. The suprascapular nerve supplies the Supraspinatus and Infraspinatus, and it sends twigs to the shoulder joint. It has no cutaneous branches.

Second Layer of Muscles of the Back:

Levator Scapulae and Rhomboidei.

These are inserted into the upper limb.

When the Trapezius is thrown aside, the **Levator Scapulae** and the **two Rhomboids** are exposed. Together they occupy the whole length of the medial border of the scapula (*fig. 78*).

Origins. The *Levator Scapulae* arises from the posterior tubercles of the transverse processes of the upper four cervical vertebrae. The *two Rhomboids* arise from the lower part of the ligamentum nuchae and the tips of the spines of the last cervical and upper four thoracic vertebrae and the intervening supraspinous ligament.

Insertions. The *Rhomboideus Minor* finds attachment at the level of the apex of the spine; the *Levator Scapulae* is attached to the border above this level; and the *Rhomboideus Major* below it. The Levator Scapulae not only elevates the scapula, but, by

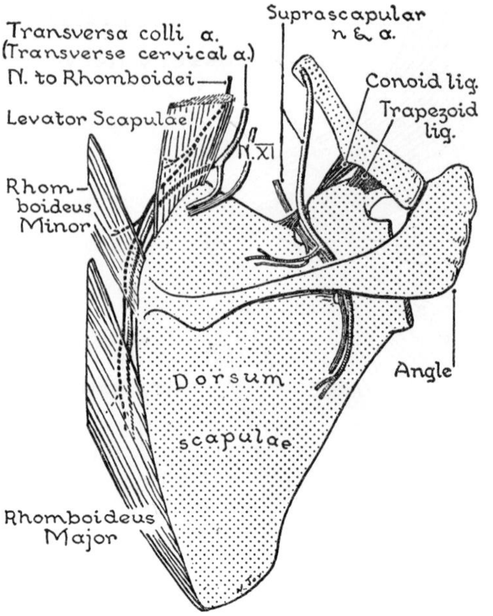

FIG. 78. The superior and medial borders of the scapula.

its pull on the superior angle, it helps to rotate the scapula so that the glenoid cavity turns downward. The Rhomboideus Major pulls on the inferior angle, for, as a little care will show, the upper part of the attachment of this muscle is not so much an insertion as an areolar connection.

Nerve Supply. Levator—C. 3, 4 and twigs from 5. Rhomboids—C. 5 (as dorsal scapular nerve).

Transversa Colli Artery. This artery [transverse cervical] runs backward on the floor of the posterior triangle of the neck till it meets the anterior border of the Levator Scapulae which, as it were, splits it into a superficial and a deep branch. The *superficial branch* accompanies the *accessory nerve* on the deep surface of the Trapezius, while the *deep branch* passes deep to the Levator Scapulae and Rhomboids and runs close to the medial border of the scapula in company with the *nerve to the Rhomboids*, also called the *dorsal scapular art. and nerve.*

The **Anastomoses on and around the Scapula** are very free. They bring notably the 1st part of the subclavian artery into communication with the 3rd part of the axillary artery on the body of the scapula,

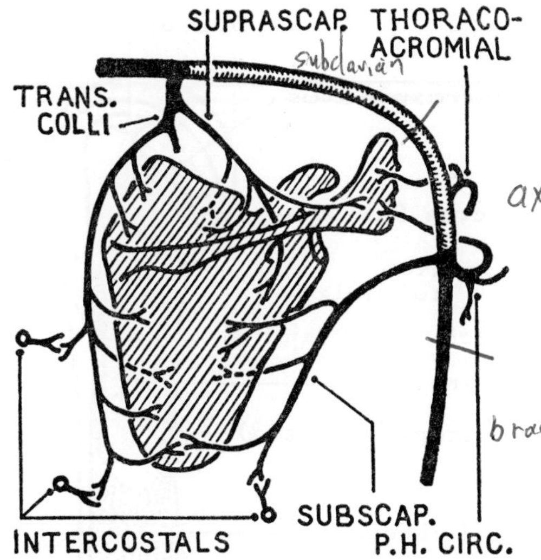

FIG. 79. Scheme of the anastomoses around the scapula.

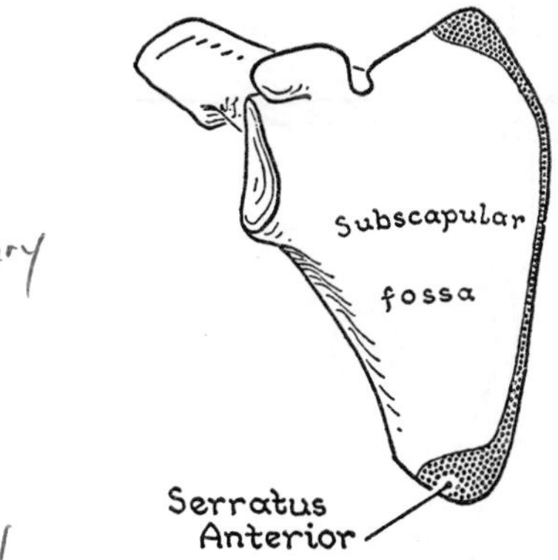

FIG. 80. The insertion of Serratus Anterior

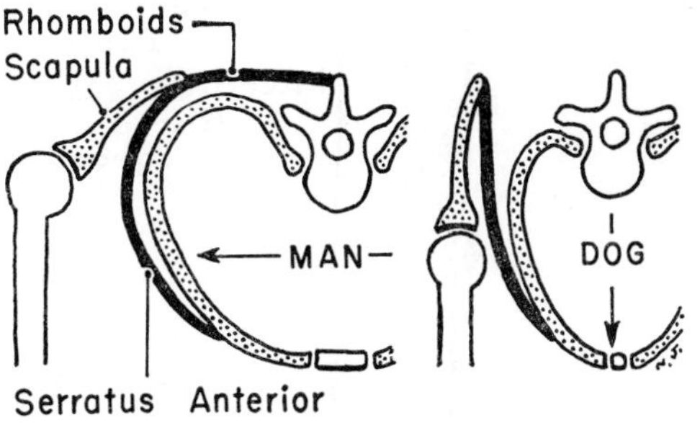

FIG. 81. To show that the Rhomboids and the Serratus together hold the medial border of the scapula applied to the thoracic wall. In the quadruped, the thorax is suspended by the Serrati.

on the acromion, and with intercostal arteries around the scapula, as shown in figure 79.

Serratus Anterior is interposed between the Subscapularis and the chest wall (*fig. 81*). Although it forms the medial wall of the axilla and its nerve was studied with the axilla, the muscle can be examined better now (*figs. 65* and *66*).

Origin. The Serratus arises from the outer surfaces of the upper eight ribs by a series of fleshy digitations: those arising from the upper four ribs are hidden by the Pectoralis Minor; those arising from the middle four ribs interdigitate with the upper digitations of the Obliquus Externus Abdominis.

Insertion. The Serratus is inserted (*fig. 80*) into the costal aspect of the medial border of the scapula by a linear attachment that enlarges into a small triangular area at the superior angle and into a large triangular area at the inferior angle. Only three ribs (1, 2, and 3) send digitations to the superior angle and medial border; while five ribs (4, 5, 6, 7, and 8) send converging digitations to the inferior angle. The reason for this distribution is apparent; the fibers are concentrated where they act to best advantage, which is at the end of a lever.

Functions. The lower digitations are required to steady or pull forward the inferior angle when the arm is raised either in front of the body or away to the side. The upper digitations draw the scapula forward, thereby increasing the reach of the outstretched hand.

During the excursions of the scapula, the Rhomboids and the Serratus Anterior together keep the medial border applied to the thoracic wall. If either be paralyzed, the medial border and inferior angle will project from the back; when prominent, the condition is known as a "winged scapula."

Upper Half of Humerus and Shoulder Region

Upper Half of the Humerus (*figs. 82, 83*, and *103*).

The **upper end** consists of: an articular portion, the *head*, which forms a third of a sphere, is covered with cartilage, and is directed medially, upward, and a little

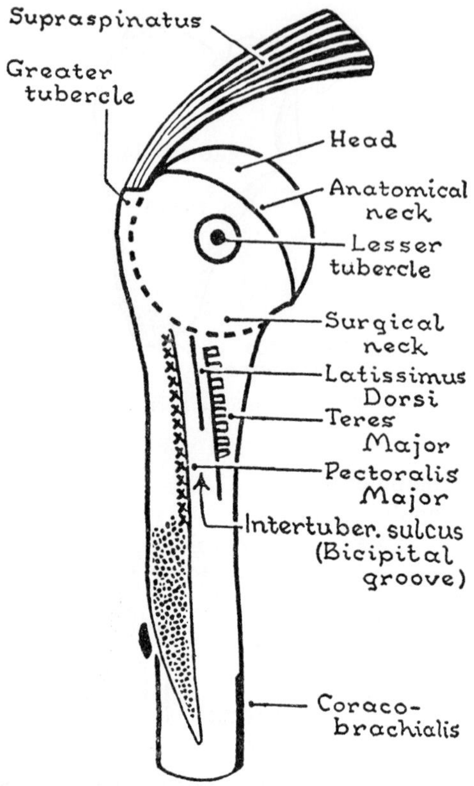

FIG. 82. Upper half of humerus (anterior view, schematic).

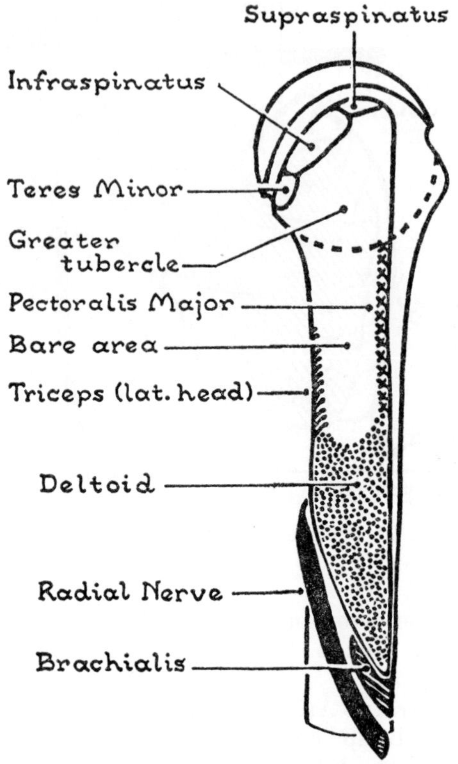

FIG. 83. Upper half of humerus (lateral view, schematic).

backward. Surrounding the articular cartilage is the *anatomical neck* to which the fibrous capsule of the joint is attached.

A mass of bone, affording attachment to the tendons of four muscles that retain the head in its socket, projects both in front and laterally (*fig. 182*). This mass is divided into two unequal parts, the *lesser* and *greater tubercles* (tuberosities), by a groove, the *intertubercular sulcus* (bicipital groove), wherein lodges the long tendon of the Biceps.

The prominent **lesser tubercle** (tuberosity) lies, so to speak, at the center of a circle, and is directed straight forward—when the limb is in the anatomical position. On rotating the humerus medially and laterally, it can be palpated through the Deltoid. It is situated $1\frac{1}{2}''$ inferolateral to the tip of the coracoid process. It gives attachment to the Subscapularis.

The less prominent, although larger, **greater tubercle** projects laterally beyond the acromion and so gives the shoulder its roundness. It too can be palpated through the Deltoid. It possesses three flat contiguous facets: a horizontal one above for the Supraspinatus, a vertical one behind for the Teres Minor, and joining these two an oblique one for the Infraspinatus. Its lateral aspect passes imperceptibly into the body or shaft of the bone below.

The tubercles are, then, separated from the head by the anatomical neck; from the body by the surgical neck; and from each other by the intertubercular sulcus.

The **surgical neck** is the zone between the head and tubercles above and the body below. It is completely encircled by the circumflex humeral vessels and partly encircled by the axillary nerve.

The surgical neck meets the anatomical neck medially, in the region of the quadrangular space; and slightly above the level of the surgical neck runs the epiphyseal line (*fig. 188*).

The **upper half of the body** is cylindrical in shape and, therefore, circular on cross-section. Its features are *two crests* and a *sulcus* on the anterior aspect, and a *tuberosity* for the insertion of the Deltoid on the lateral aspect.

Into the rugged *crest of the greater tubercle* (lateral lip of the bicipital groove) the Pectoralis Major is inserted; into the *crest of the lesser tubercle* (medial lip of the bicipital groove) the Teres Major is inserted, and into the *intertubercular sulcus* (bicipital groove), which descends between the two crests, the Latissimus Dorsi is inserted.

Deltoideus. This muscle, shaped like the Greek letter delta inverted, would form with the Trapezius a continuous muscular sheet, were it not that the clavicle and scapula intervened between them.

Attachments. The Deltoid arises from the anterior border of the flattened lateral third of the clavicle (where it is separated from the origin of the Pectoralis Major by the base of the deltopectoral triangle), also from the lateral border of the acromion, and from the whole length of the lower lip of the crest of the spine of the scapula. From this extensive linear origin the muscle descends to its restricted and, therefore, fibrous insertion into the *deltoid tuberosity* of the humerus.

The **deltoid tuberosity** is the rough elevation that spreads across the lateral surface of the bone and extends down to its midpoint (*fig. 83*). About 1½″ long, it also has the form of an inverted delta. The anterior side of this inverted delta, followed vertically upward, becomes the crest of the greater tubercle, which affords insertion for Pectoralis Major. The posterior side, followed obliquely upward, becomes the rough line of origin of the lateral head of the Triceps. These extensions of the delta bound a *bare area* on the lateral aspect of the humerus. Behind the tuberosity is a broad shallow groove, the (*spiral*) *groove* for the radial nerve.

Winding around the posterior border of the Deltoid below the middle of its length is the cutaneous branch of the axillary nerve, called the *upper lateral cutaneous nerve of the arm* (*fig. 98*).

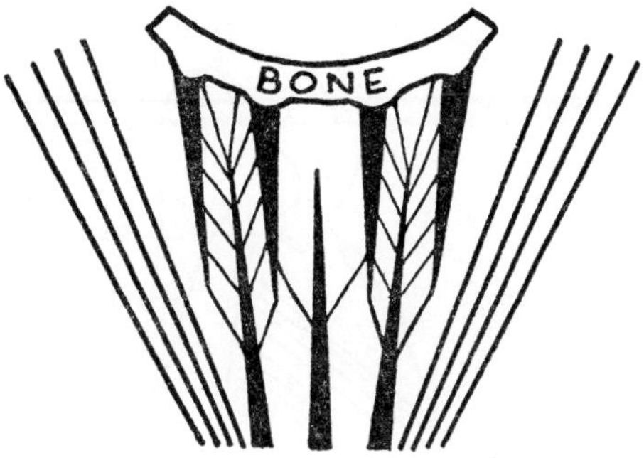

FIG. 84. Architecture or internal structure of Deltoid.

»» Detach the Deltoid from its origin and turn it downward and thereby expose the axillary nerve (circumflex n.), accompanied by the posterior humeral circumflex artery, which adheres to the deep surface of the Deltoid and supplies it (*fig. 86*). Follow the nerve and vessel to the quadrangular space. Also exposed is the greater tubercle and the bare area on the lateral aspect of the humerus.

Internal Structure of Deltoid. If the deep aspect of the Deltoid be examined, four tendinous septa will be seen to descend in its substance (*fig. 84*). These spring from four small tubercles on the lateral border of the acromion. The muscle fibers arising from the adjacent sides of two tendinous septa converge to be inserted into a third tendinous septum which ascends from the deltoid tuberosity to receive them.

This, the intermediate part of the Deltoid, is multipennate, the muscle fibers being very numerous but very short. On this account it is very powerful, but its range of action is very short. It abducts the shoulder joint.

The anterior and posterior parts of the Deltoid have a different internal structure; they are composed of long parallel fibers because they take part in the more extensive movements of flexion and extension of the shoulder.

With a little care, each of the three portions of the muscle, each with its own vascular and nerve supply, can be separated from the other two.

The Quadrangular Space is merely the lateral or basal portion of an *isosceles triangle* whose boundaries are: *above*, the lateral border of the scapula and the capsule of the shoulder joint; *laterally*, the surgical

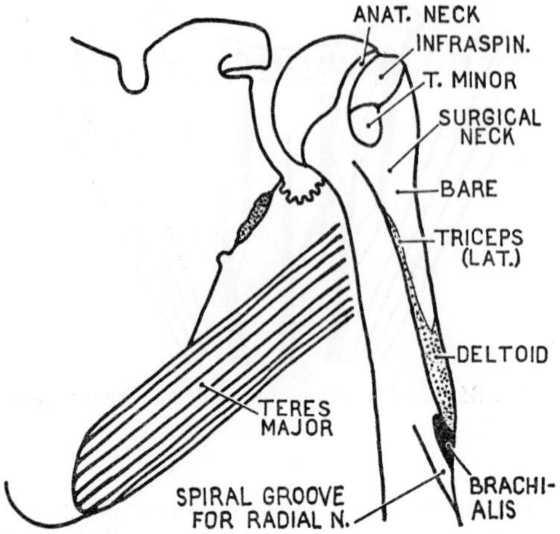

FIG. 85. Upper half of humerus (posterior view): The foundation of the quadrangular space.

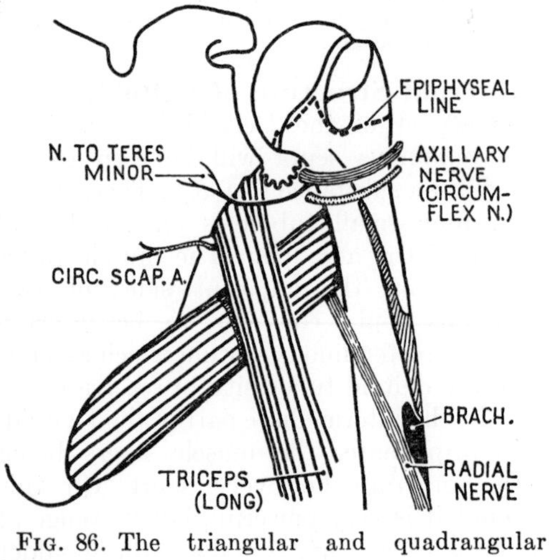

FIG. 86. The triangular and quadrangular spaces.

neck of the humerus; *below*, the Teres Major (*figs. 85* and *86*).

Since the lateral border of the scapula is clothed anteriorly with Subscapularis and posteriorly with Teres Minor, these two muscles assist in the formation of the upper boundary of the triangle; and, because their insertions into the humerus are far apart—the one to the lesser tubercle, the other to the lowest impression on the greater tubercle—it follows that the upper boundary of the triangle is very deep laterally.

The long or scapular head of the Triceps, arising from the rough triangular infraglenoid tubercle of the scapula, divides this triangle into an apical and a basal portion, known, respectively, as the *triangular* and the *quadrangular space*.

Entering the triangular space is a large anastomotic artery, the *circumflex scapular branch* of the subscapular artery, which, on its way to the infraspinous fossa, grooves the axillary border of the scapula. Passing through the quadrangular space are the *axillary nerve* and the *posterior humeral circumflex artery*.

Axillary Nerve (Circumflex N.) (C. 5 and 6). This nerve has two important relations:

1. The capsule of the joint above.
2. The surgical neck of the humerus laterally.

As the axillary nerve passes through the quadrangular space it sends twigs to the capsule of the joint; and, on leaving the space it supplies the Teres Minor. Thereafter, it supplies the Deltoid and the skin covering the Deltoid (*fig. 98*).

Distribution. This nerve, then, is distributed to the joint, to two muscles that act upon the joint, and to the skin covering the joint.

Surface Anatomy. The position of the axillary nerve is indicated on the skin surface by a horizontal line drawn 2 inches below the angle of the acromion.

Parts Covered by Acromion. When the Deltoid is thrown down, it is not the fibrous capsule of the joint that you see but the tough tendons of three dorsal scapular muscles—Supraspinatus, Infraspinatus, and Teres Minor—which conceal and adhere to the capsule. Between the acromion and the Supraspinatus tendon is the **subacromial bursa,** which functionally plays the part of an accessory joint cavity. It is large, extending beyond the acromion laterally deep to the Deltoid, anteriorly deep to the coraco-acromial ligament, and sometimes medially deep to the Trapezius (*fig. 183*).

The greater tubercle of the humerus projects beyond the acromion. It is evident that it is to this projection, and not to the Deltoid which covers it, that the roundness of the shoulder is due, for when the joint is dislocated the roundness is lost, the acromion becomes the most lateral bony point, and the shoulder appears square.

When the arm is abducted, the greater tubercle passes completely under cover of the acromion; hence, the necessity for an extensive subacromial bursa.

Since the shoulder joint has but two muscles lying above it, it can evidently possess but *two abductors:* they are the Supraspinatus and the intermediate fibers of the Deltoid. Each is supplied by the 5th and 6th cervical nerve segments, the one via the suprascapular nerve; the other via the axillary nerve.

The acromion is stronger than you might think, for the lateral border of the spine of the scapula, which bounds the spinoglenoid notch, is very stout and rounded—evidently with the object of buttressing and strengthening the acromion, on the under surface of which it fades away (*fig. 92*).

During the 15th year, when the *Coracoid Process* is fusing with the scapula (*fig. 87*), the acromial epiphysis begins to ossify. It fuses with the main mass of the acromion along a line that passes either through or just behind the facet for the clavicle (*fig. 88*). The acromial epiphysis commonly fails to fuse and on X-ray examination may simulate a fracture. (Age of maturation or complete fusion, see p. 108.)

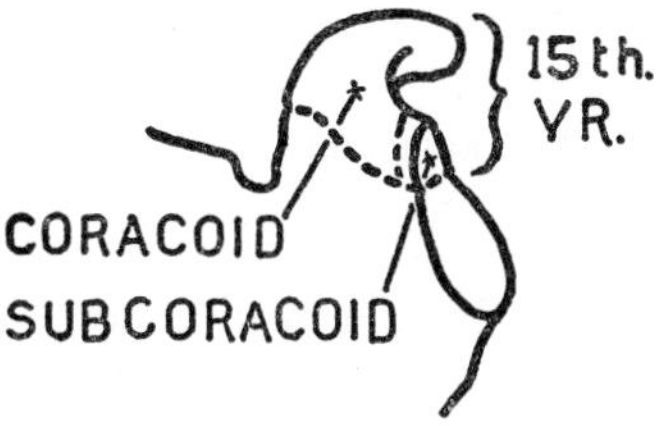

FIG. 87. Coracoid epiphyses

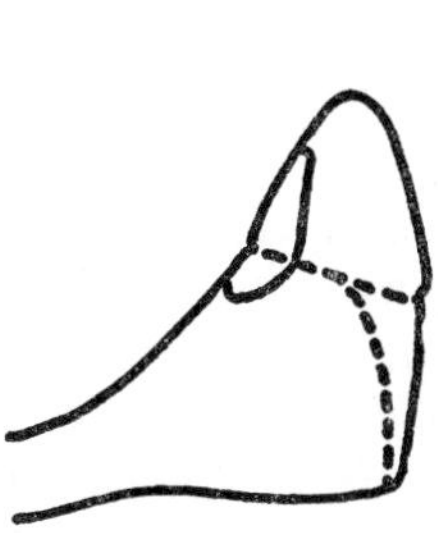

FIG. 88. Acromial epiphyses

»» Of less importance are three traction epiphyses, related to the pull of muscles that are too obvious to name: (1) along the vertebral border, (2) at the inferior angle, and (3) along the lateral border of the acromion.

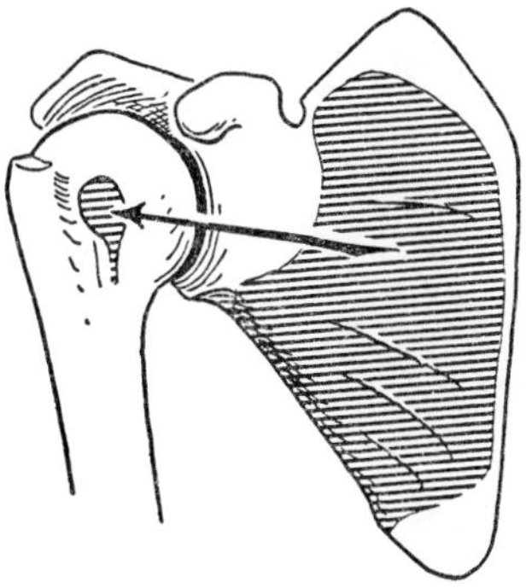

FIG. 89. The attachments of Subscapularis

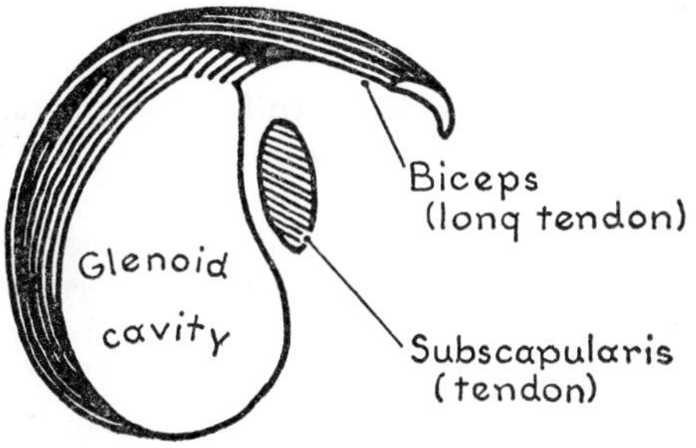

FIG. 90. Glenoid cavity, Biceps, and Subscapularis.

FIG. 91. The three muscles attached to the end of the lever.

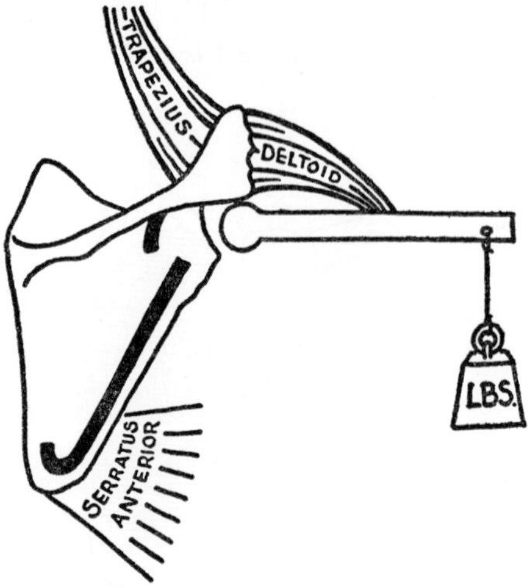

FIG. 92. The three chief muscles concerned in elevation of the limb: Two strengthening bars on the scapula.

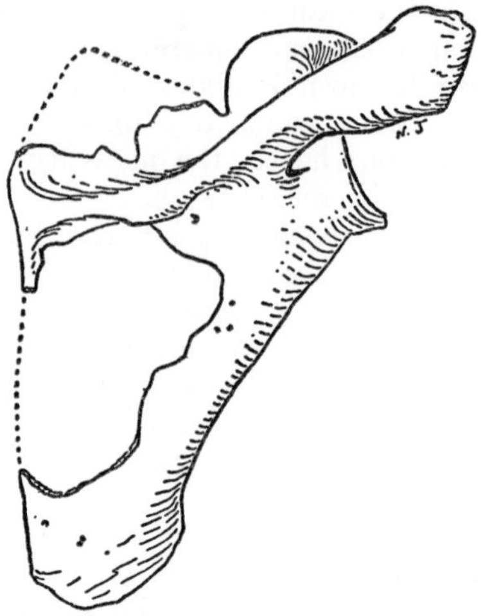

FIG. 93. The lateral or axillary border is the strong border; the others can be broken away with the fingers.

Subscapular Fossa and Subscapularis. The concave area on the costal surface of the scapula, the *subscapular fossa*, is crossed by three or four oblique lines that converge on the lesser tubercle of the humerus (*fig. 89*). These lines are the ossified bases of fibrous partitions that extend into the **Subscapularis** and afford it a multipennate origin, similar to that of the Deltoid.

The tendon of the Subscapularis, which is inserted into the lesser tubercle, grooves the anterior margin of the glenoid cavity and helps to give it a pear-shaped appearance (*fig. 90*). This feature distinguishes the anterior border of the cavity from the posterior.

Inferior Angle and Lateral Border of Scapula. The *Inferior Angle*, situated at the end of the lateral border where leverage is best, is thick and strong because three muscles act upon it: Serratus Anterior, Teres Major, and Rhomboideus Major (*fig. 91*).

The Lateral Border extends from glenoid cavity to inferior angle. At its upper end there is a rough, triangular area, the *infraglenoid tubercle*, from which the long or scapular head of the Triceps arises. Running parallel to this border on the costal surface is a strong, smooth bar of bone. Its purpose is to ensure that the lateral border

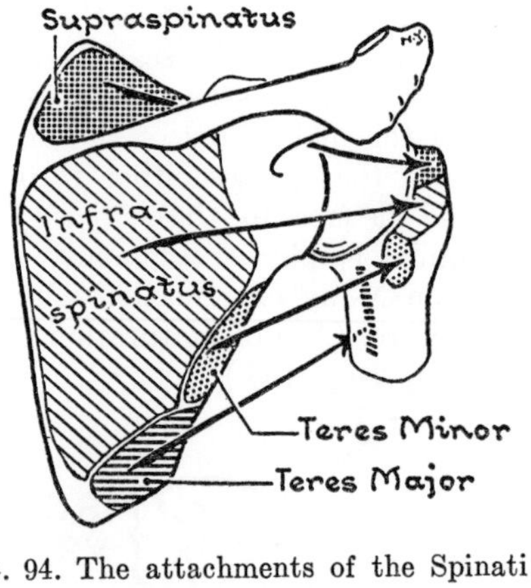

FIG. 94. The attachments of the Spinati and Teretes.

shall neither buckle nor break when the Serratus Anterior is steadying the inferior angle of the scapula or pulling it forward against resistance, as in raising a weight in front of the body or when pushing (*figs. 92* and *93*). The Serratus and the lateral border are similarly employed by a quadruped when on all fours (*fig. 81*).

Teres Muscles (teres, L. = round) (*fig. 94*). *Origins.* The *Teres Minor* arises from the dorsum of the lateral border of the scapula and from adjacent fasciae. The *Teres Major*, which is a very large muscle, arises from the large impression on the dorsum of the inferior angle and lateral border of the scapula and partly from the dense fascia covering the Infraspinatus.

Insertions. Both muscles are inserted into the humerus by tendon—the Minor into the lowest facet on the greater tubercle; the Major into the crest of the lesser tubercle.

Nerve Supply. Both muscles are supplied by nerve segments C. 5, 6, but via different nerves.

Actions. The Minor is a lateral rotator of the humerus; the Major is a medial rotator.

AXIOM: When muscle fibers contract they shorten by about a third or a half of their relaxed length, i.e., if a muscle is to move its insertion through 1″, its fleshy fibers must be 2 to 3″ long.

By applying a general rule (see *Axiom*), you could reason correctly and foresee that the origins of the Subscapularis, Supraspinatus, and Infraspinatus do not extend right up to the margin of the glenoid cavity but leave the neck of the scapula free. The **neck of the scapula** is the part encircled by a line drawn from the scapular notch (suprascapular notch) to the infraglenoid tubercle. The glenoid cavity and coracoid process are lateral to the neck.

»» **Observe** (1) that the long head of the Triceps passes between the Teres Major and Teres Minor, (2) that the Teres Major passes between the axillary and radial nerves; and (3) that the fibers of the Teres Major take a half spiral course, like those of the Latissimus Dorsi, and that the flat tendon of insertion of the Teres Major blends below with that of the Latissimus Dorsi, but is separated from it above by a bursa.

Spinatus Muscles. *Attachments* (*fig. 94*). The Supraspinatus and Infraspinatus *arise* by fleshy fibers from the respective supraspinous and infraspinous fossae of the scapula. They are *inserted* by tendon into the upper and middle facets on the greater tubercle of the humerus, the tendons fusing with the fibrous capsule of the shoulder joint.

Nerve Supply. They are supplied by the suprascapular nerve (C. 5 and 6).

Actions. See Muscle Force Couples, page 183.

BONES OF PECTORAL GIRDLE: IN DETAIL

Clavicle

In *type* the clavicle or collar bone is a long bone, and accordingly it has a shaft and two ends. It is *situated* at the antero-superior part of the thorax and there *articulates* with the sternum and 1st costal cartilage medially and with the acromion (and coracoid process) laterally.

It is *palpable* from end to end, and by palpation it is readily determined: (1) that the skin is freely movable over its entire length. This is due to the interposition of the Platysma; it is therefore subcutaneous or, better, *subplatysmal;* (2) that in *shape* its medial part is convex forward, its lateral part concave forward; and (3) that when it is in correct *orientation* it lies nearly horizontally with the lateral end directed laterally and backward; but, when the Trapezius, which suspends the lateral end, is vigorous, this end is slightly raised (as when the shoulders are shrugged).

Its *function* is to act as a strut holding the scapula and therefore the upper limb laterally, backward, and slightly upward. As a result, the limb hangs behind the line of gravity and by its weight helps in the maintenance of the erect posture. When the clavicle is fractured, the shoulder falls medially, forward, and slightly downward, as might be expected.

Animals such as the dog, ox and horse that use their forelimbs merely for support and locomotion (i.e., for forward and backward motions) have either no clavicles or only rudimentary ones; but primates, rodents, guinea pigs and bats that employ them for grasping, climbing, burrowing, or flying (i.e., for side to side motion as well) have clavicles.

To *identify the side* to which a detached clavicle belongs, so hold it (1) that the flattened part is lateral, (2) that the aspect with rough markings at both ends is inferior, and (3) that the forward convexity is medial and the forward concavity lateral (*fig. 94.1*).

The clavicle has two functionally distinct parts—one lateral to the coracoid process,

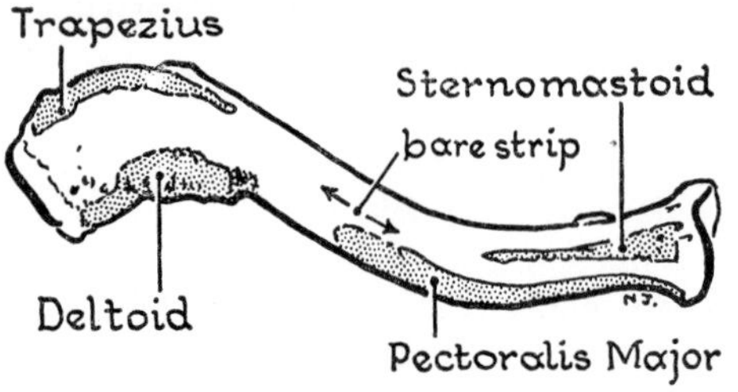

FIG. 94.1. Right clavicle from above—muscle attachments.

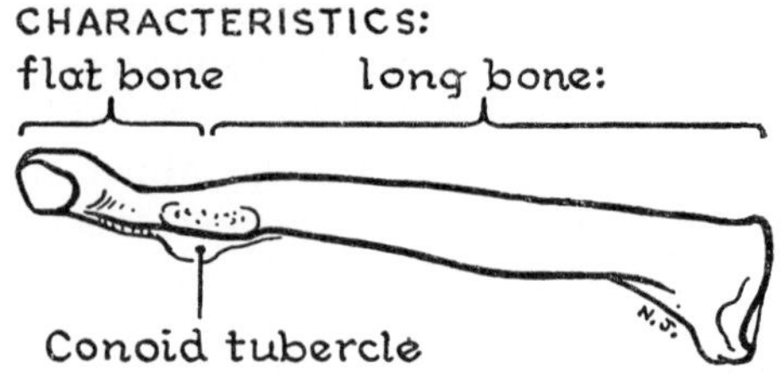

FIG. 94.2. Right clavicle from in front—its two parts.

the other medial. The lateral part is flattened and forms one-fourth to one-third of the bone; the medial part is prismatic, being triangular on cross-section, and forms two-thirds to three-fourths. The flattened part affords anchorage for the scapula; the prismatic part plays the role of a long bone.

Flattened Lateral One-Fourth. It is compressed from above downward and is united to the scapula both terminally and inferiorly, thus: (1) *Terminally*—there is a small, oval *articular facet* for the acromion of the scapula, so bevelled that in cases of dislocation the acromion is driven under the clavicle. The articular end is not enlarged like the ends of long bones in general, so the articulation depends for security upon the conoid and trapezoid portions of the coracoclavicular ligament. (2) *Inferiorly*—these unite the coracoid process of the scapula to the clavicle and are responsible for the following markings: a tubercle, the *conoid tubercle*, which is placed below the posterior border of the bone at the junction of the flattened and prismatic parts, and a rough line, the *trapezoid ridge*, which extends diagonally laterally and forward across the inferior surface from the conoid tubercle to the anterior end of the articular facet (*fig. 94.2*).

The Trapezius is partly inserted into the posterior border of the flattened part of the bone and into the adjacent part of the upper surface; the Deltoid partly arises from the anterior border of the flattened part of the bone and from the adjacent part of the upper surface.

Prismatic Medial Three-Fourths. Triangular on cross section like a typical long bone, accordingly, it has three surfaces separated by three borders. The *posterior surface*, continuous with the posterior border of the flattened lateral quarter, is concave, nearly vertical, and perfectly smooth and so it protects the subclavian vessels and the brachial plexus which pass behind it. A nutrient foramen opens on to this surface and by its direction indicates the sternal end to be the more actively growing one.

The *anterior surface*, continuous with the upper surface of the flattened part, faces antero-superiorly. Attached to its medial inch and a half in line with the insertion of the Trapezius is the clavicular head of the Sterno-(cleido-)mastoid; and arising from its whole length in line with the origin of the Deltoid is the clavicular head of the Pectoralis Major—an interval of an inch or less, representing the base of the delto-pectoral triangle, intervening. Between these 4 muscles lies the subplatysmal linear strip of the clavicle (*fig. 59*).

The *inferior surface*, continuous with the inferior surface of the flattened part, extends from the conoid tubercle to the medial end where there is a rough, half-inch-long depression (sometimes tubercular) for the costoclavicular ligament. The area between these points is fusiform, smooth, and gives insertion to the Subclavius. The sharp lines bounding it in front and behind (= anterior and inferior borders) give attachment to the clavipectoral fascia (*fig. 63*).

The inferior surface of the clavicle, then, is mainly for ligamentous attachments; the anterior (or antero-superior) is subplatysmal and palpable between 4 muscles; the posterior protects the great vessels and nerves entering the upper limb, and it also can readily be palpated, provided the Trapezius and Sternomastoid are relaxed as when leaning heavily on the arms of a chair.

The three borders need not trouble us.

THE MEDIAL (STERNAL) END of the bone is enlarged and triangular, its 3 margins corresponding to the 3 surfaces of the neighboring part of the bone. Of its 3 angles, the superior rises above the manubrium and thereby adds to the depth of the jugular notch; the inferior projects far back postero-inferiorly; the anterior is nondescript.

The end of the bone is covered with articular cartilage, and this extends on to the inferior surface; it is, however, separated from its socket, formed by the sternum and first costal cartilage, by a diagonally set articular disc. Crossing in front of this end of the bone is the flattened sternal head of the Sternomastoid. Crossing behind it are the common carotid and subclavian arteries, the vagus nerve, and the internal jugular vein; but these are separated from the bone by the Sternothyroid and Sternohyoid, the latter gaining part origin from the clavicle.

Variations. The clavicle varies more in shape than most other long bones. It is peculiar in having no medullary cavity. The right clavicle, though stronger than the left, is usually shorter. It may be perforated by one of the supraclavicular nerves (*fig. 61*).

Ossification. The clavicle is the first bone in the body to start to ossify, beginning during the 5th fetal week in membrane from two centers which are placed close together and which soon fuse. One represents the Trapezius-Deltoid end, the other the Sternomastoid-Pectoralis Major end. The two ends pass through a cartilaginous phase. A secondary center, which appears at the sternal end, forms a scale-like epiphysis which begins to fuse with the diaphysis between the 18th and 25th years, and is completely fused to it between the 25th and 31st years. (McKern and Stewart.) This is the last of the epiphyses of the long bones to fuse. An even smaller scale may be present at the acromial end.

Scapula

The scapula is in *type* a flat bone, and in *shape* it is triangular. It therefore possesses two surfaces, three borders, and three angles. From the bone there project two processes (1) the coracoid process, and (2) the spine, which terminates laterally in the acromion; so, the scapula may legitimately be called irregular.

It is *situated* behind the thorax where it partly covers 50 per cent of the 12 ribs, namely the 2nd–7th inclusive. Its *functions* are to give attachment to muscles, to form the socket of the shoulder joint, and by its free mobility to enhance the movements of the shoulder joint. All this it can do because its only bony connection with the trunk is through the clavicle. Its *articulations* are with the humerus at the glenoid cavity and with the clavicle at the acromion.

To *identify the side* to which a loose scapula belongs, place the spine posteriorly, the glenoid cavity laterally, and the acromion above the glenoid cavity. The cavity will then face the side to which the bone belongs.

Orientation (i.e., position in space): Since the scapula is applied to the upper part of the barrel-shaped thorax, its inferior angle lies behind the plane of the glenoid cavity, therefore the lateral (axillary) border is directed obliquely downwards and backwards as well as downwards and medially. The glenoid cavity faces laterally and slightly upwards and forwards.

Palpable parts. As the fingers run laterally along the subcutaneous strip on the clavicle, they cross the acromioclavicular joint and pass on to the acromion. The tip of this flat plate lies in front of the acromioclavicular joint. The tip, lateral border, angle, and posterior border of the acromion are readily felt. The acromion is continued medially into the crest (posterior border) of the spine of the scapula, and both are subcutaneous.

The inferior angle of the scapula can be grasped and the fingers passed between it and the chest wall when the subject's arm hangs by his side, but not when he stretches it in front of him, because the Serratus Anterior and Rhomboideus Major are then contracted. The medial (vertebral) border, which ascends from the inferior angle to the superior angle, can be palpated when the limb hangs by the side. The lateral (axillary) border can be palpated vaguely when the muscles are relaxed. The tip of the coracoid process is readily felt on pressing laterally 1″ below the clavicle in the deltopectoral triangle.

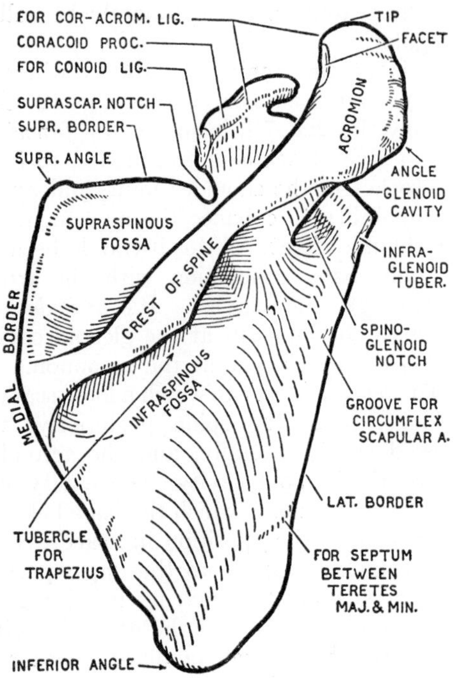

FIG. 94.3. Scapula—posterior aspect

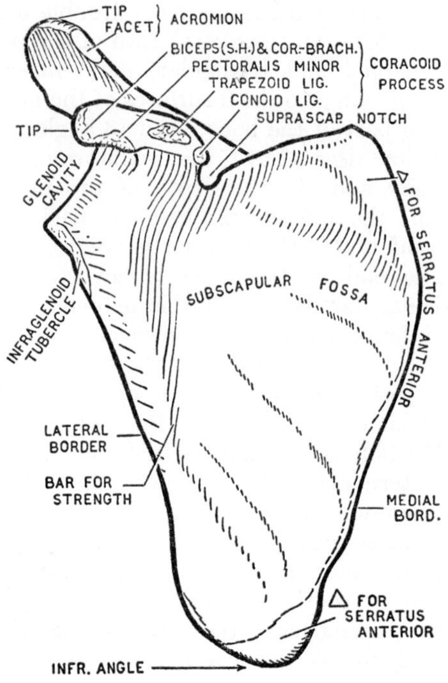

FIG. 94.4. Scapula—anterior aspect

Angles. The *lateral angle* is truncated (*fig. 94.3*). It is enlarged to form an articular socket for the head of the humerus. Because the socket is shallow it is called the *glenoid cavity* (Gk. glene = shallow). Its anterior margin is grooved for the Subscapularis tendon; this helps to give it a pear-shaped appearance. The coracoid process, which rises above it, represents the stalk of the pear. In the quadruped mammal the cavity faces the ground and rests upon the head of the humerus; in erect man the scapula is thrust backwards by the clavicle, so the cavity faces laterally—making side to side contact with the humerus—but with a slight upward and forward tilt.

The *inferior angle* is thick and rounded and gives attachment to three strong muscles (*fig. 91*). The *superior angle* is relatively thin and acute.

Borders. The *superior border* inclines laterally and downwards from the superior angle, where the Levator Scapulae is inserted, to the upper end of the glenoid cavity, where the long head of the Biceps arises from the *supraglenoid tubercle*. This border, not being subjected to stress or strain and not giving attachment to muscles —save the delicate Omohyoid—is thin and sharp. Laterally it becomes abruptly deeper, the (*supra-*)*scapular* notch, which is bridged in life by a ligamentous band, the suprascapular ligament, which converts the notch into a foramen. Between the notch and the supraglenoid tubercle the border is, so to speak, drawn out to form the *coracoid process* (*fig. 94.4*).

The *medial* (vertebral) *border* is arched and is thicker than the superior one, because it affords insertion to the 2nd layer of muscles of the back, namely, the Rhomboid Minor at the apex of the spine, the Levator Scapulae between the apex and the superior angle, and the Rhomboid Major between the apex and the inferior angle.

The *lateral* (axillary) *border* is thick and smooth. It extends from the inferior angle upwards, laterally, and forwards to the glenoid cavity. At its upper end it has a rough, triangular impression, the *infraglenoid tubercle*, for the long head of the Triceps.

Surfaces. The *costal* (ventral) *surface* is monopolized by the Serratus Anterior and Subscapularis. Thus: converging fibers of the Serratus pass to raised triangular areas at the superior and inferior angles, the inferior being the larger; diverging fibers pass to a line along the medial border which connects these triangles. The Subscapularis arises by fleshy fibers from the remainder of this surface, except near the glenoid cavity. It also arises from four fibrous septa which create sharp lines that run from the medial border obliquely upwards and laterally towards the glenoid cavity.

A smooth *strengthening bar*, running close to the lateral border, connects the glenoid cavity to the inferior angle (*fig. 92*). Between this bar and the Serratus insertion the surface is concave, the *subscapular fossa*, the concavity being deepest at the level of the glenoid cavity.

The *dorsal surface* (dorsum scapulae) is slightly arched from above downward, and near the lateral border it is corrugated longitudinally. It is divided by a triangular plate of bone, the *spine*, into a smaller, deep *supraspinous fossa* and a larger, shallow *infraspinous fossa.*

Spine. Its *apex* lies at the medial border of the bone and presents a smooth, triangular area across which aponeurotic fibers of the Trapezius play. The base or *lateral border* of the spine lies a finger's breadth from the midpoint of the posterior margin of the glenoid cavity. It is very stout and rounded and forms the medial border of the *spinoglenoid notch* through which the infraspinous branches of the suprascapular vessels and nerve pass from the superior to the inferior fossa. The *anterior border* is attached to the dorsum scapulae. The posterior border or *crest* is broad and flat, and has an upper and a lower sharp lip with a subcutaneous strip between them. The lower is for the Deltoid throughout. The lowest fibers of the Trapezius converge on the lower lip superficial to the Deltoid, and there create a downwardly directed *tubercle.* The upper lip lateral to the tubercle is also for the Trapezius.

Acromion (Gk. akros = a point; omos = the shoulder; cf. acropolis, acromegaly). The spine of the scapula is drawn out laterally into a flat, stout, triangular plate the *acromion,* which overhangs the glenoid cavity. It is greatly strengthened by the lateral border of the spine which fades away on its under surface. Due to this it can withstand the lateral thrust of the clavicle, the upward pull of the Trapezius, the downward pull of the Deltoid, and impacts from the humerus below.

The *upper surface* of the acromion (as you may determine on yourself by palpation) is subcutaneous and faces postero-superiorly. The *lateral border* of the acromion meets the lower lip of the spine at a right angle, the *acromial angle,* readily located with two fingers. This border of the acromion gives origin to the Deltoid and possesses four tubercles for the attachment of septa that descend into the Deltoid (*fig. 84*).

It is the *medial border* that troubles the student. This has an oval, *articular facet* for the clavicle; behind this the Trapezius is attached, in front the Deltoid; and the *tip* gives attachment to the apex of the coraco-acromial ligament under cover of the Deltoid.

Coracoid Process (Gk. korax = a crow). Shaped like a bent finger, it has two parts, a vertical and a horizontal. The *vertical part* is the upward continuation of the most lateral part of the superior border of the scapula. It is smooth and flattened from before backward.

The *horizontal part* is rounded and is directed forwards, laterally and downwards. Its tip is rough for the common tendon of the Biceps (short head) and Coracobrachialis; the anterior half of the medial border is marked for the tendon of the Pectoralis Minor, which occasionally crosses the upper surface (*fig. 178*), so only the posterior half of the upper surface is marked for the trapezoid ligament; a tubercle at the junction of the vertical and horizontal parts is for the conoid ligament, and also for the suprascapular ligament. The lateral border is marked throughout its length for the base of the coraco-acromial ligament; and approximately in line with the Pectoralis Minor the coracohumeral ligament arises from this border

Muscle Attachments. Levator Scapulae and Rhomboidei to the whole length of the medial border; long heads of the Biceps and Triceps to the supra- and infra-glenoid tubercles, the Biceps also gaining attachment to the posterior margin of the glenoid cavity (*fig. 90*); Serratus Anterior and Subscapularis monopolize the entire costal surface; Spinati and Teretes monopolize the entire dorsal surface; Trapezius and Deltoid are attached to opposite lips of the crest of the spine and to opposite borders of the acromion; Omohyoid to the upper border beside the notch; Pectoralis Minor, Coracobrachialis and Biceps (short head) to the coracoid process; Latissimus Dorsi may receive a few fibers from the inferior angle.

Ligamentous attachments: In addition to the capsular ligaments of the shoulder and acromioclavicular joints there are four scapular ligaments; and all four are attached to the coracoid process. They are: the coracoclavicular (conoid and trapezoid), coracoacromial, coracohumeral and suprascapular.

Medullary Foramina are small and numerous; a large one occurs on the dorsum just below the spine, and another large one about the corresponding point on the costal surface.

Ossification. The primary center appears at the 8th fetal week. Secondary centers: for the coracoid in the 1st year, and subcoracoid, including the upper end of the glenoid cavity, in the 10th year; these fuse with the scapula during the 15th year. About puberty two centers appear in the acromion and others in the medial border and inferior angle; these usually fuse with the scapula between the 18th and 20th years, and in all cases by the 23rd year. (McKern and Stewart.)

Anastomoses around the scapula (*fig. 79*).

Variations. The terminal *epiphysis* (metaphysis) of the acromion commonly fails to unite; the failure is usually unilateral; the epiphyseal line passing transversely through the hinder part of the oval, articular facet or just behind it (*fig. 88*). The portion of the *medial border* of the scapula below the level of the spine may be convex, straight, or concave. The *suprascapular ligament* may be ossified.

CHAPTER 7

CUTANEOUS NERVES AND SUPERFICIAL VEINS

CUTANEOUS NERVES

General; Dermatomes; Regional Supplies: pectoral, axilla, shoulder, brachium or arm, antebrachium or forearm, palm of hand, dorsum of hand; Variations in Pattern in Hand; Seeking Nerves.

SUPERFICIAL VEINS

Basilic Vein; Cephalic Vein; Median Cubital Vein; Relations; Anomaly; Venous Valves.

Superficial Lymph Nodes.

CUTANEOUS NERVES

GENERAL. The muscles of the upper limb are supplied by nerve segments C.5, 6, 7, 8 and Th. 1 by way of the brachial plexus. The cutaneous supply is more extensive: it draws not only on the plexus, but also on two additional cephalic and two additional caudal segments. It comes from segments C 3, 4——5, 6, 7, 8, 1——2, 3. T

The upper limbs make their appearance in the embryo on a level with the segments from which they derive their nerves, and like many other organs (e.g., heart, diaphragm, stomach, and sex glands) they descend, dragging their nerves after them. This explains the oblique, infero-lateral, course of the brachial plexus.

The limbs sprout and grow from the anterior or ventral half of the body; so, the brachial plexus of the upper limb and the lumbosacral plexus of the lower limb are derived from ventral nerve rami (*fig. 95*). And, it is probable that the anterior and posterior divisions and cords of the brachial plexus represent the anterior and posterior branches of lateral cutaneous nerves, shown in figures 72 and 95.

Initially the thumb and radius occupy the cephalic or *preaxial* border of the limb; the little finger and ulna occupy the caudal or *postaxial* border. Similarly, in the lower limb the big toe and tibia occupy the cephalic or preaxial border; the little toe and fibula occupy the caudal or postaxial border. Later the limbs undergo rotation in opposite directions with the result that the thumb and radius are carried laterally and the palm of the hand comes to face forward, while the

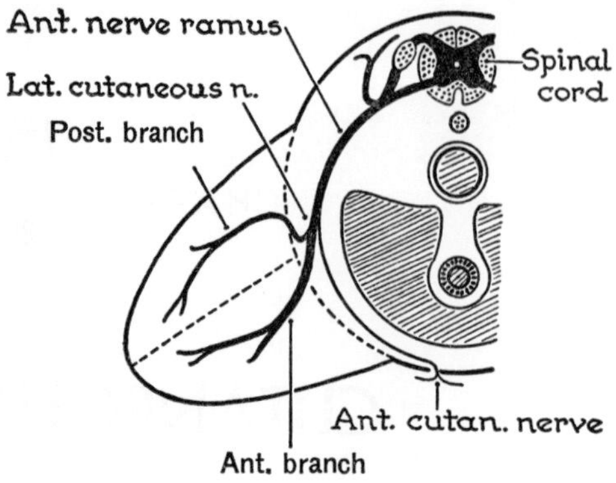

FIG. 95. Scheme of the developing limb bud. (After Patterson.)

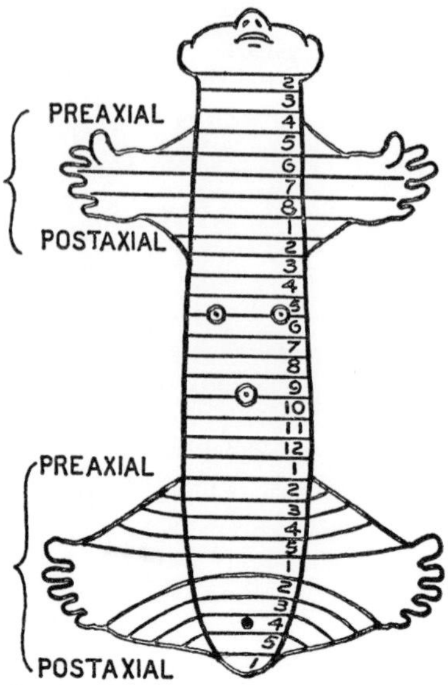

FIG. 96. Scheme of primitive segmental nerve distribution. (After Purves-Stewart.)

big toe and tibia are carried medially and the sole of the foot faces backward (or downward).

Authorities have long held that in the limbs the areas of skin supplied by individual dorsal nerve roots, i.e., **dermatomes,** were, so to speak, pushed out as loops over the expanding limb buds and that the nerve segments supplied the skin in orderly numerical sequence from the shoulder down the preaxial border of the limb to the thumb, from the thumb to the little finger, and from the little finger up the postaxial border to the axilla (*fig. 96*).

More recently, Keegan (*fig. 97*), having very extensive surgical (and experimental) experience with herniae of the intervertebral discs, assisted by Garrett, finds that individual nerve roots C. 6, 7, and 8 supply strips of skin that run from the vertebral column down the back of the limb and finally wrap around to the front to include the whole hand. C. 5 and Th. 1 dermatomes are confined to the front of the arm and forearm. (A similar arrangement of dermatomes occurs in the lower limb.)

The skin over the upper part of the pectoral and shoulder regions would seem to have been drawn down from the neck, as a sheet of rubber might be drawn down, bringing with it the *supraclavicular nerves* (C. 3, 4); similarly, the skin of the axilla and of the medial side of the arm would seem to have been pulled off the chest bringing the *intercostobrachial nerve* (Th. 2) and a branch from the lateral cutaneous

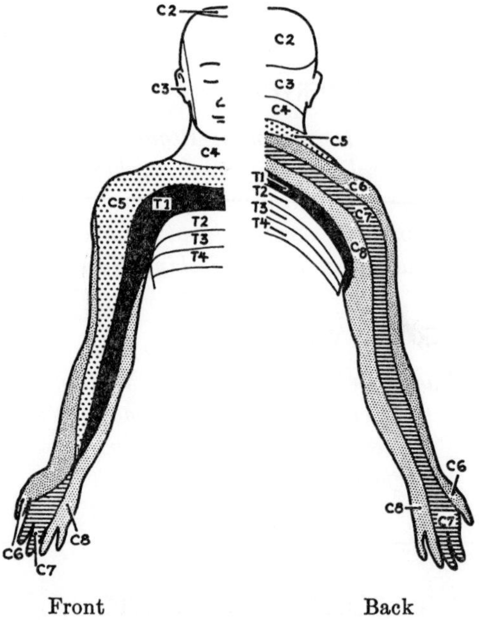

FIG. 97. The cutaneous distribution of the spinal nerves—dermatomes. (After Keegan and Garrett, modified.)

branch of the *3rd intercostal nerve* (Th. 3) with it.

(The scheme in figure 97.1 may be found helpful.)

Pectoral Region. Above the 2nd rib this region is supplied by the *supraclavicular*

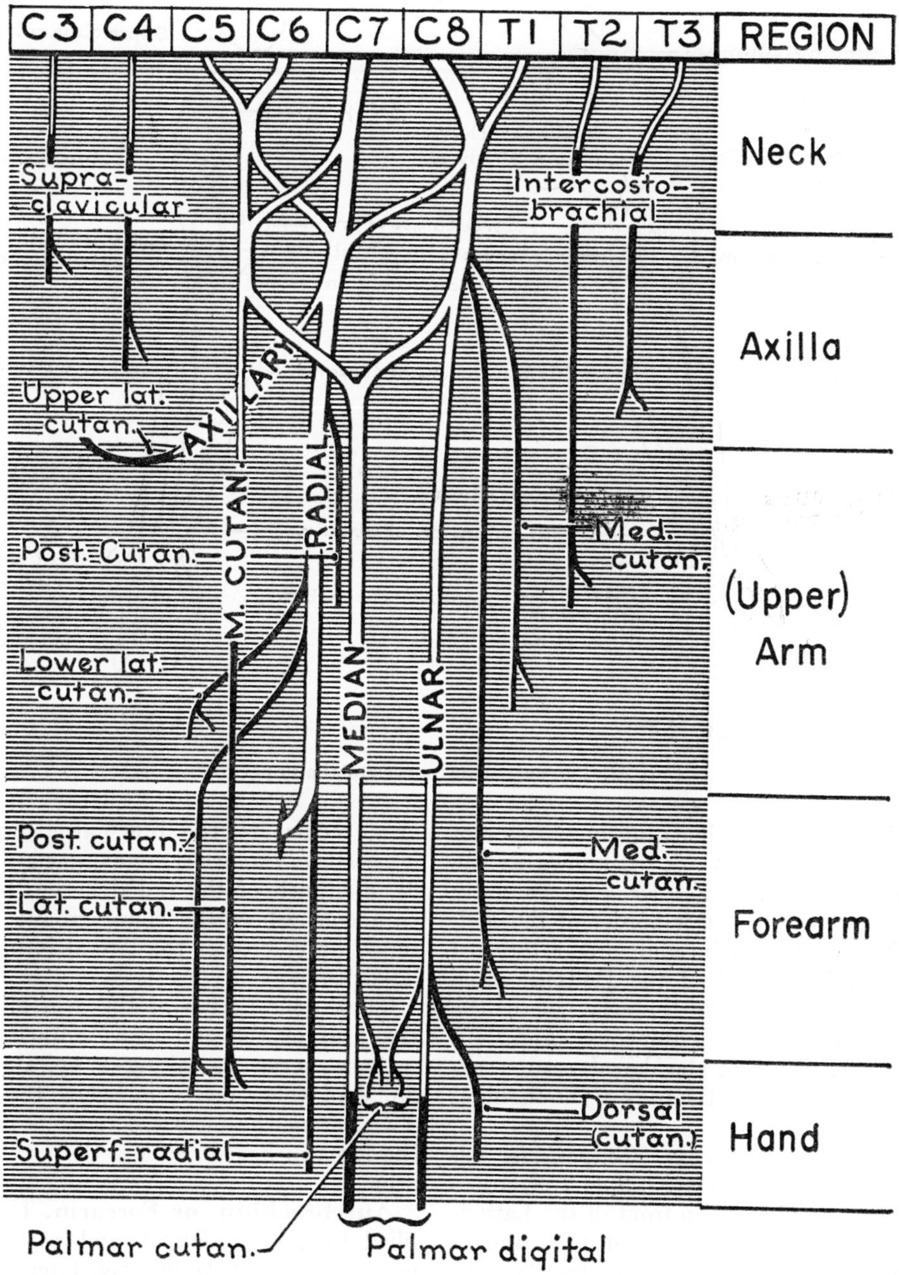

FIG. 97.1. Scheme of the cutaneous nerves of the upper limb (in black). It shows three features—their source, level of origin, and level of termination.

nerves (C. 3, 4); and below the 2nd rib by the *anterior cutaneous nerves* and anterior branches of the *lateral cutaneous nerves* (Th. 2–6).

Axilla. The *intercostobrachial* (Th. 2) and Th. 3 supply the skin at the base of the axilla.

Shoulder. *Supraclavicular nerves* (C. 3, 4) cross the clavicle and acromion deep to the Platysma and supply the upper half of

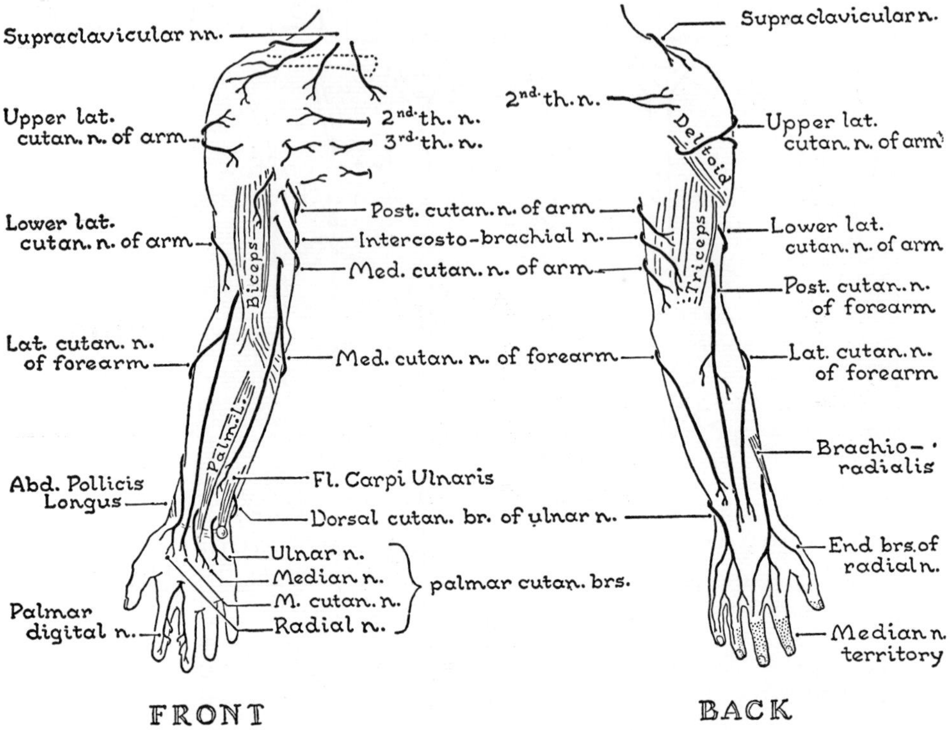

FIG. 98. The cutaneous nerves of the upper limb

the deltoid region. The cutaneous branch of the axillary nerve (C. 5, 6), known as the *upper lateral cutaneous nerve of the arm*, appears at the posterior border of the Deltoid below its midpoint and spreads forward over the lower half of the Deltoid; some twigs from the stem of the nerve pierce the Deltoid to become cutaneous. And, cutaneous branches of the dorsal rami, especially of Th. 2, reach the back of the shoulder (*fig. 98*).

Brachium or Arm. *The posterior cutaneous nerve of the arm* (C. 5, 6, 7, 8) arises from the radial nerve in front of the Latissimus Dorsi by a stem common to it and to the nerve to the long head of the Triceps. It becomes cutaneous below the insertions of the Latissimus and Teres Major. *The intercostobrachial nerve* (Th. 2), accompanied by a branch of the 3rd intercostal nerve, pierces the fascial floor of the axilla and becomes cutaneous. *The medial cutaneous nerve of the arm* (C. 8 and Th. 1) springs from the medial cord of the plexus and becomes cutaneous in the upper third of the arm, medial to the brachial artery. *The lower lateral cutaneous nerve of the arm* (C. 5, 6), a branch of the radial nerve, becomes cutaneous where the spiral groove for the radial nerve crosses the lateral intermuscular septum.

These four nerves of the arm all follow the lead of the cutaneous branch of the axillary nerve in taking a spiral course. None of them descends below the elbow. Twigs from the medial cutaneous nerve of the forearm help to supply the front of the arm.

Antebrachium or Forearm. It is supplied by *medial*, *lateral*, and *posterior cutaneous nerves of the forearm*. Each of these three cutaneous nerves is derived either directly or indirectly from the similarly named medial, lateral, and posterior cords of the brachial plexus. Each of the three outcrops on the surface above the elbow.

The medial cutaneous nerve of the forearm, a direct branch of the medial cord ((7) 8, 1), lying medial to the brachial artery, becomes cutaneous half way down the arm in the

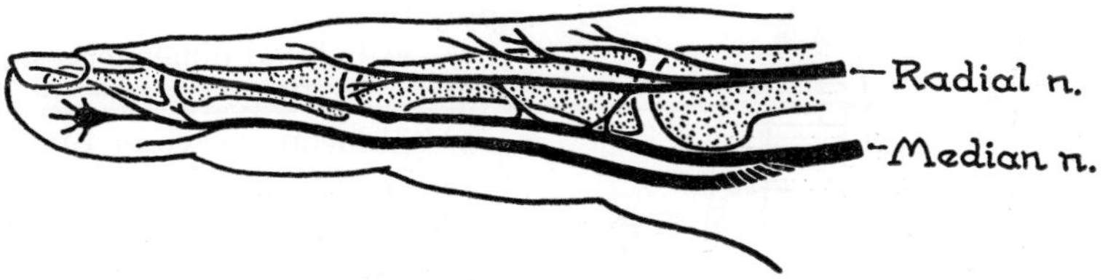

FIG. 99. Digital nerves of the index. (From a dissection by M. Wellman.)

company of the basilic vein. It divides into an anterior and a posterior branch, both of which pass in front of the elbow and then descend on the front and back of the ulnar side of the forearm as far as the wrist. Its branches pass either superficial or deep to the median cubital vein and other cutaneous veins at the elbow.

The lateral cutaneous nerve of the forearm is the end branch of the musculocutaneous nerve (C. 5, 6 (7)), and therefore of the lateral cord. It appears at the lateral border of the Biceps 1″ or so above the elbow and becomes cutaneous 1″ or so below the elbow. Like the medial cutaneous nerve it divides into anterior and posterior branches which pass in front of the elbow before descending on the front and back of the radial side of the forearm; the anterior branch to reach the ball of the thumb, the posterior branch to end at or beyond the wrist. At the wrist both the anterior and the posterior branch communicate with the (superficial) radial nerve and the anterior branch sends a twig to the radial artery.

The posterior cutaneous nerve of the forearm, a branch of the radial nerve and therefore of the posterior cord (C. 5, 6, 7, 8), becomes cutaneous along the line of the lateral intermuscular septum from 1″ to 3″ above the lateral epicondyle. It crosses behind the muscles arising from the lateral supracondylar ridge and descends in the midline of the back of the forearm to the wrist or beyond it.

Palm of the Hand. Of the five terminal branches of the brachial plexus all, except the axillary nerve, pass into the arm and each ultimately contributes a palmar cutaneous branch to the hand (*fig. 98*).

"The palmar cutaneous branch of the musculocutaneous nerve" (C. 6), via the lateral cutaneous nerve of the forearm, ends on the ball of the thumb.

The palmar cutaneous branch of the median nerve (C. 6, 7, 8) and the *palmar cutaneous branch of the ulnar nerve* (C. 8) becomes cutaneous proximal to the flexor retinaculum on the lateral side of Palmaris Longus and Flexor Carpi Ulnaris, respectively. *The palmar cutaneous branch of the radial nerve* (C. 6, 7) follows the anterior border of the Abductor Pollicis Longus on to the ball of the thumb.

Perhaps the most important cutaneous nerves of the upper limb are the **Palmar Digital Nerves.** There are 10 palmar digital nerves—one for each side of each digit. The lateral seven are branches of the median nerves; the medial three are branches of the ulnar nerve; that is, the median nerve supplies 3½ digits; the ulnar nerve 1½ (*fig. 100*). The palmar digital nerves furnish branches to the entire palmar surfaces of the digits, and to the distal parts of the dorsal surfaces including the subungual regions (i.e., deep to the nail) and to the local joints (*fig. 99*).

To expose a palmar digital nerve you should feel for the edge of a phalanx and make a longitudinal incision in front of it, because the nerves run on the sides of the flexor tendons in their fibrous sheaths anteromedial to their accompanying arteries. A longitudinal incision that strikes bone is behind the nerve and misses it (*fig. 156*).

Dorsum of the Hand. The dorsum is supplied by the radial, ulnar and median nerves. *The dorsal cutaneous branch of the ulnar nerve* (C. 7, 8) and *the superficial branch of the radial nerve* (C. 6, 7), after passing deep to the Flexor Carpi Ulnaris and Brachioradialis, respectively, outcrop on the surface at the posterior borders of these muscles from 1 to 4″ above the corresponding styloid process. The dorsal branch of the ulnar nerve reaches the dorsum of the hand by crossing the medial (ulnar collateral)

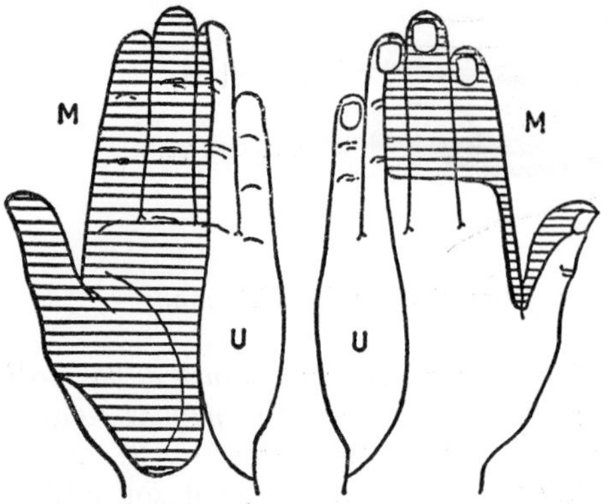

FIG. 100. Distribution of median and ulnar nerves in the hand. (After Stopford.)

ligament of the wrist; the superficial radial nerve by crossing the "snuff-box." On the back of the hand they communicate. As at the front so at the back, the ulnar nerve supplies one and one-half digits (*fig. 100*). The radial supplies the remainder, except for the distal parts of the lateral three and one-half digits, which the median nerve supplies. The radial nerve supplies twigs to the joints in its territory.

Variations in Pattern in the Hand (*fig. 101*).

Palmar Digital Patterns: The ulnar nerve commonly (14 per cent, Stopford) extends its territory to include the radial side of the ring finger; occasionally it includes the ulnar side of the middle finger and rarely the entire middle finger. Conversely the median nerve occasionally takes over the entire supply of the ring finger.

Dorsal Patterns (*fig. 101*): The cutaneous supply to the back of the hand varies, thus: (1) the radial and ulnar nerves may increase or diminish their territories; (2) the posterior cutaneous nerve of the forearm commonly invades the dorsum of the hand; (3) the dorsal branch of the lateral cutaneous nerve of the forearm may do so, even to the extent of completely replacing the cutaneous branch of the radial nerve; and (4) the radial nerve commonly supplies the subungual region of the thumb.

Seeking Nerves. There is too great a tendency to search for the cutaneous nerves of the limbs at prescribed horizontal levels. Most of the cutaneous nerves of the upper limb are constant in becoming cutaneous at the borders of muscles, which here run longitudinally, but the *level at which they become cutaneous varies* by as much as several inches; examples shown in figure 98 are:

»» The upper lateral brachial cutaneous n. at the posterior border of the Deltoid.

The lower lateral brachial cutaneous n. and

The posterior antebrachial cutaneous n. between the Triceps and Brachioradialis along the line of the lateral intermuscular septum.

The lateral antebrachial cutaneous n. at the lateral border of the Biceps.

The superficial branch of the radial n. at the posterior border of the Brachioradialis.

The palmar cutaneous branch of the median n. at the lateral border of the Palmaris Longus.

The palmar cutaneous branch of the ulnar n. at the lateral border of the Fl. Carpi Ulnaris.

The dorsal branch of the ulnar n. at the posterior border of the Fl. Carpi Ulnaris.

AXIOM: When seeking cutaneous nerves in the limbs, one should think vertically and act vertically—not horizontally—because the border is constant, whereas the level is inconstant.

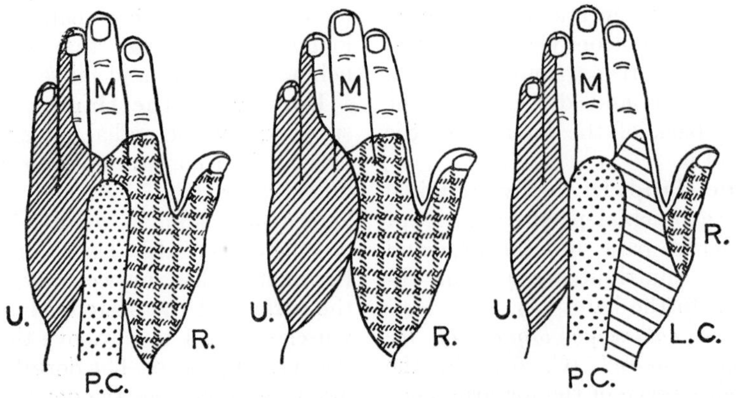

FIG. 101. Patterns of distribution of cutaneous nerves on dorsum of hand. (After Stopford.)

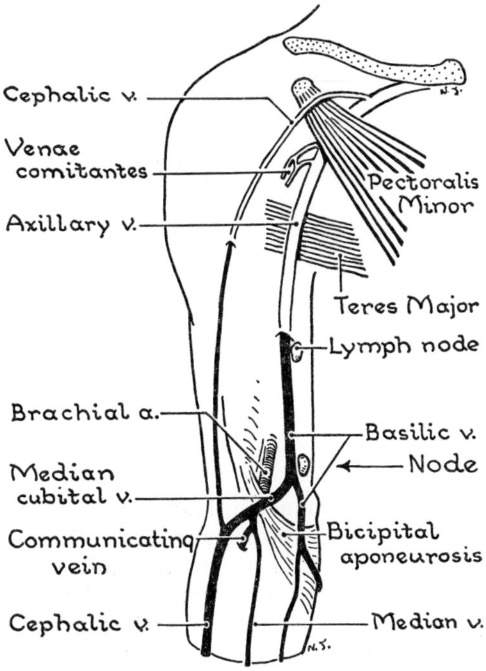

FIG. 102. The superficial veins of the arm

SUPERFICIAL VEINS

The superficial veins of the upper limb (*fig. 102*) are generally visible through the skin in the male; if not, they can readily be made so by swinging (circumducting) the arm vigorously at the shoulder joint, ending with the limb dependent and below the level of the heart.

The veins form many patterns. *The Dorsal Venous Arch* on the back of the hand receives *digital branches*. It ends medially as the basilic vein and laterally as the cephalic vein. The **Basilic Vein** ascends on the ulnar side of the forearm to the elbow and then in the medial bicipital furrow to the middle of the arm where it pierces the deep fascia. It then accompanies the brachial artery and its venae comitantes to the axilla and becomes the axillary vein.

The **Cephalic Vein** crosses "the snuff-box" (that is, the depression at the side of the wrist proximal to the base of the metacarpal of the thumb) superficial to the branches of the radial nerve. It ascends on the radial border of the forearm; in the lateral bicipital furrow of the arm; and in the cleft between the Deltoid and Pectoralis Major at the shoulder. It pierces the delto-pectoral triangle and, after crossing superficial to the Pectoralis Minor and costo-coracoid membrane, ends in the axillary vein. It passes either in front of or behind the lateral pectoral nerve (*fig. 102*).

In the embryo, the cephalic vein crosses in front of the clavicle and ends in the external jugular vein; it may continue to do so in postnatal life.

A small vein, the *median vein,* runs up the front of the forearm and, after communicating with a *deep vein*, bifurcates into a medial and a lateral branch, which join the basilic and cephalic veins respectively. This is the simple M-like pattern. More commonly, however, a large oblique vein, the **Median Cubital Vein,** placed in front of the elbow, joins the cephalic vein to the basilic vein.

»» The practitioner of today employs the median cubital vein in blood transfusion; the barber of former days employed it in blood-letting. Hence the barber's sign—red and white wound spirally on a pole and a brass dish hanging from the pole. The pole for the patient to grasp; white for the bandage; red for blood· the dish to catch the blood.

RELATIONS: The median cubital vein passes in front of the bicipital aponeurosis (lacertus fibrosus) which alone separates it from the brachial artery and median nerve; and it passes in front of (or between) the branches of the medial cutaneous nerve of the forearm.

Anomaly. Instead of descending deep to the muscles of the forearm, 3 per cent of ulnar arteries descend either deep to the deep fascia of the forearm or superficial to it. The pulse of such a **superficial ulnar artery** can be felt, but not if a tourniquet has been applied. It may then be mistaken for a vein—and with awkward consequences.

Venous Valves. To demonstrate the valves in the veins see page 33 and figure 38.

Lymph Nodes

The most distal superficial node in the upper limb is the *cubital* (*supratrochlear*) *node*, placed 2″ above the medial epicondyle. There may be a node where the basilic vein pierces the deep fascia (*fig. 102*). Though not palpable, these are tender when inflamed.

CHAPTER 8

ARM

LOWER HALF OF HUMERUS

The **Lower End** of the humerus has articular and nonarticular parts. The former is divided into two areas: the *capitulum* for the head of the radius and the *trochlea* for the trochlear (semilunar) notch of the ulna. One is spheroidal; the other is shaped like a spool (*fig. 103*). Immediately above and wide of these two condylar or knuckle-like articular areas are two projections, the *medial* and *lateral epicondyles*. The medial epicondyle can easily be grasped between the finger and thumb; the posterior surface of the less prominent lateral epicondyle is smooth, subcutaneous, and palpable.

There are also three depressions: two small ones in front, the *radial* and *coronoid fossae*, which receive the margin of the head of the radius and the tip of the coronoid process of the ulna when the elbow is fully flexed; and a large triangular one behind, the *olecranon fossa*, which receives the olecranon of the ulna when the elbow is extended.

The **Lower Half of the Body of the Humerus** is flattened from before backward and is divided by the medial and lateral supracondylar ridges into an *anterior* and a *posterior aspect*. The medial and lateral *supracondylar ridges* ascend from the epicondyles and afford attachment to the medial and lateral intermuscular septa. The lateral and more prominent ridge extends to a broad shallow groove, the *groove for the radial nerve* (spiral groove), which intervenes between the ridge and the *deltoid tuberosity*. But the groove is far too wide for the radial nerve, which runs along it. The medial ridge rises to approximately the same level as the lateral one, and there for an inch gives place to a linear roughness, the site of *insertion of the Coracobrachialis*.

Though the lower half of the humerus is flattened, it is nevertheless not flat. A rounded strengthening bar of bone extends from the interval between the radial and coronoid fossae to the anterior margin of the deltoid tuberosity. It is continuous in the upper half of the bone with the crest of the greater tubercle (lateral lip of bicipital

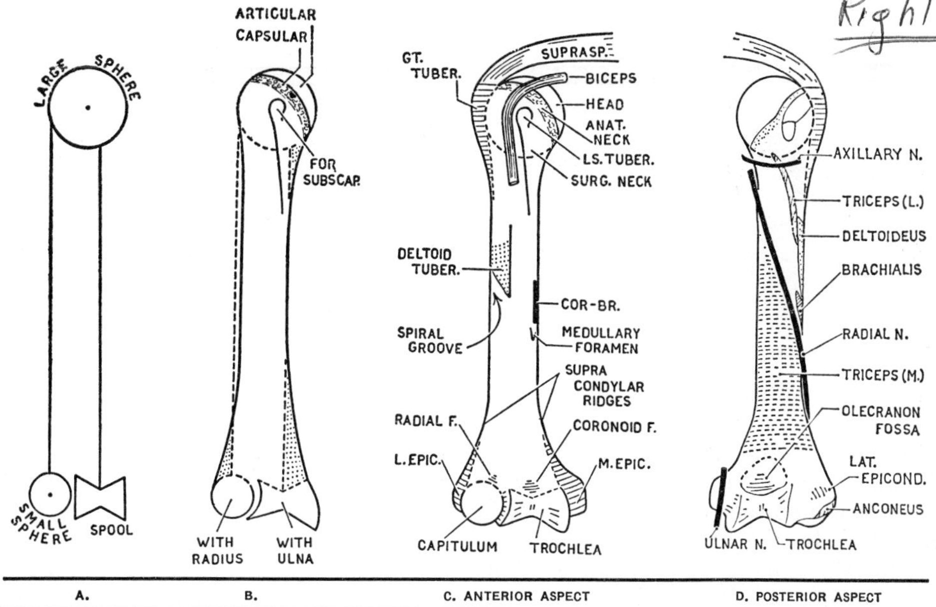

FIG. 103. *A*, *B*, and *C* represent progressive stages in sketching a humerus from the front. *D*, posterior aspect showing attachments of muscles and contacts with nerves.

FIG. 104. Cross-sections of humerus: the borders are indicated by letters.

groove), which extends from the deltoid tuberosity to the anterior part of the greater tubercle (*figs. 104 and 105*).

The smooth, rounded bar performs the same strengthening function as the smooth, rounded, lateral border of the spine of the scapula and the smooth, rounded bar running parallel to the axillary border of the scapula. Its presence causes the lower half of the humerus to be triangular on cross-section, and it subdivides the anterior aspect into a medial and a lateral surface. These surfaces are entirely devoted to fleshy fibers of the Brachialis; so, they are smooth.

The lower half of the *posterior surface* is entirely devoted to fleshy fibers of the medial head of the Triceps; so, it also is smooth.

FASCIAE and MUSCLES

Fascia. The muscles of the arm or brachium are enveloped in a sleeve of tough deep fascia whose fibers take a more or less

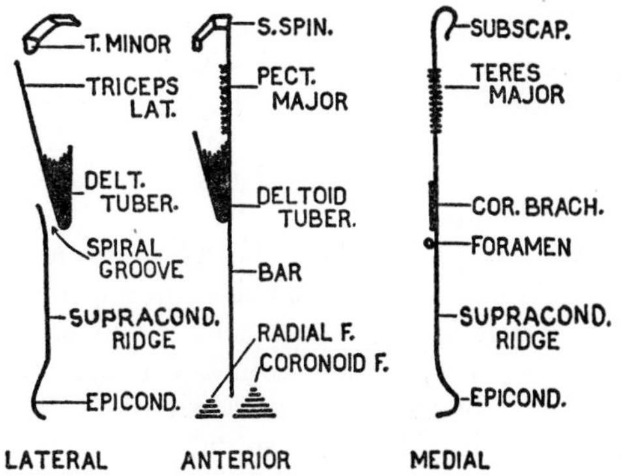

FIG. 105. The borders of the humerus

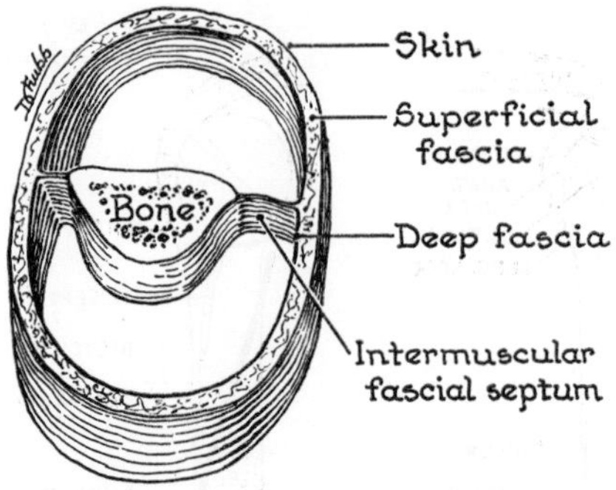

FIG. 106. The two compartments of the arm

circular course. This sleeve is divided into an anterior and a posterior compartment by the medial and lateral intermuscular septa which pass from the enveloping deep fascia to the supracondylar ridges (*fig. 106*).

Muscles. In the anterior compartment there are three muscles—Coracobrachialis, Biceps Brachii, and Brachialis. In the posterior compartment there is one muscle—Triceps Brachii.

The **Coracobrachialis** shares the tip of the coracoid process with the *short head of the Biceps;* so, both have tendinous origins. The roughness at the middle of the medial border of the humerus denoting the site of insertion of the Coracobrachialis has been observed.

The **Long Head of the Biceps** springs from the supraglenoid tubercle and posterior rim of the glenoid cavity (*fig. 90*). Its tendon curves across the front of the head of the humerus, as will be seen when the shoulder joint is studied, and then descends in the intertubercular sulcus, encased in a *synovial sheath* (i.e., a tubular bursa), continuous with the synovial cavity of the shoulder joint.

When the long head of the Biceps, accompanied on its medial side by the short or coracoid head, passes beyond the bony intertubercular sulcus, it comes to lie in front of the fleshy Brachialis and ceases to be tendinous.

The long and short heads unite about the middle of the arm. Their common tendon is inserted into the posterior, rough half of the tuberosity of the radius, which is situated just below the medial side of the neck of the radius (*fig. 107*); so, when the Biceps contracts, as when driving in a screwnail or corkscrew, it unrolls or supinates the radius. A *bursa* is required between the tendon and the smooth anterior part of the olive-shaped tuberosity. The Biceps is also inserted into the fascia covering the flexor muscles by means of a fibrous band, the *bicipital aponeurosis* (lacertus fibrosus).

The **Brachialis** arises from the entire breadth of the anterior aspect of the lower half of the humerus and from the intermuscular septa. The origin splits into two limbs at the insertion of the Deltoid. One limb largely fills the (spiral) groove for the radial nerve (*fig. 110*). Its origin is fleshy; so, the underlying bone is smooth. Its restricted and therefore fibrous insertion produces a rough elevation (tuberosity of the ulna) on the anterior aspect of the coronoid process of the ulna.

Actions. (1) The Coracobrachialis passes from scapula to humerus. It flexes and adducts the shoulder joint. (2) The Brachialis passes from humerus to ulna. It is the main flexor of the elbow joint. (3) The Biceps passes from scapula to radius. It can do by itself what the Coracobrachialis and Brachialis do together; moreover, as has just been explained, it is a powerful supinator of the radio-ulnar joints.

Nerve Supply. These three muscles, and these three only, are supplied by the musculocutaneous nerve (*fig. 172*).

The **Triceps Brachii:** Its *long* or scapular head, being tendinous, springs from a rough impression, the *infraglenoid tubercle,* situated on the lateral border of the scapula immediately below the glenoid cavity. This long head forms the medial boundary of the quadrangular space.

The Triceps has two humeral heads, a *medial* and a *lateral;* of these the medial head arises by fleshy fibers from the entire posterior surface of the humerus below the level of the (spiral) groove for the radial nerve and from the intermuscular septa (*fig. 103*). The lateral head is largely tendinous and is responsible for the line that ascends from the posterior margin of the deltoid tuberosity. It also arises from a fibrous arch that bridges the spiral groove.

The common tendon of insertion is attached to the posterior half of the upper surface of the olecranon, a *bursa* intervening

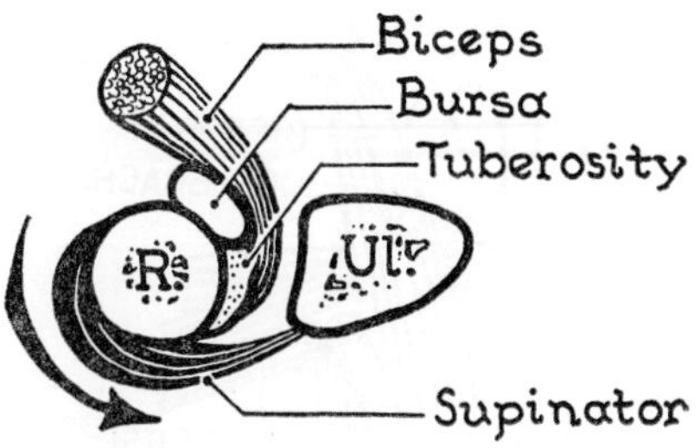

FIG. 107. The insertion of the Biceps. The Biceps supinates.

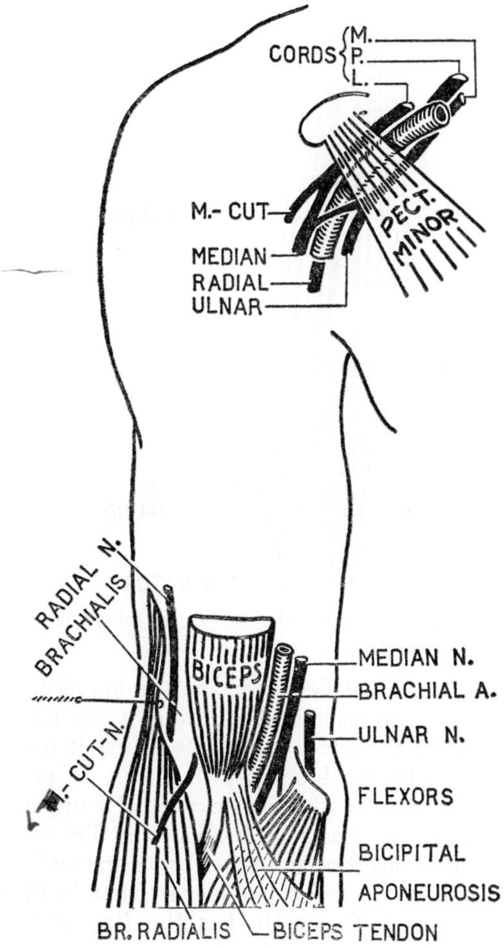

FIG. 108. Two key positions

between it and the capsule of the elbow joint. Some fibers sweep distally into the deep fascia that covers the Anconeus, thereby forming a *"tricipital aponeurosis"* (*fig. 113*).

Action and Function. The Triceps is the extensor of the elbow joint. Its chief function or use is to keep the extended elbow extended (i.e., to prevent it from flexing) when one is pushing an object.

Nerve Supply. All three heads are supplied by the radial nerve (*fig. 171*).

PALPABLE STRUCTURES AROUND ELBOW

Before studying the vessels and nerves of the arm, become familiar with the disposition of the structures around the elbow, for they assume a key position both to the front of the arm and to the front of the forearm (*figs. 108* and *109*). You can, therefore, at any time roll up your sleeve, palpate, and thereby refresh your memory.

Thus, when the elbow is flexed to a right angle and the forearm forcibly supinated (the palm of the hand then faces upward), the *Biceps tendon* and the *bicipital aponeurosis* stand out at the middle of the front of the elbow as a prominent central landmark, $\frac{3}{4}''$ in width. They can be grasped between the index finger and the thumb. When the Biceps is relaxed (rest forearm on the table) the pulsations of the *brachial artery* can be felt just medial to the Biceps tendon; and with the tips of the fingers the *median nerve,* which lies just medial to the artery, can be rolled on the Brachialis.

The *ulnar nerve,* lying behind the medial epicondyle, can be felt to slip from under the finger tips as they are drawn across it. It can be traced half way up the arm.

With the tips of two or three fingers the lateral supracondylar ridge can be traced to the spiral groove, and an endeavor made to roll the *radial nerve* against the bone. For success in this, it must be appreciated that

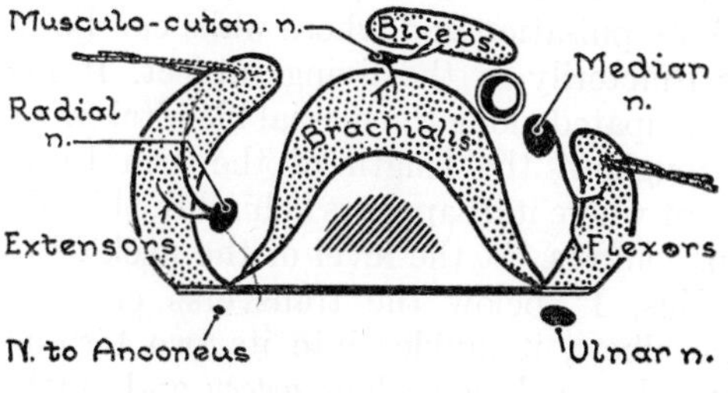

FIG. 109. Section showing nerves just above the elbow. Note their "sides of safety."

the course of the nerve is almost vertical. [The *musculocutaneous nerve* appears at the lateral border of the Biceps, 1 or 2″ above the bend of the elbow, as the lateral cutaneous nerve of the forearm. Though easily located, it cannot be palpated.]

With the elbow bent to a right angle and the palm of the hand facing the body (that is, midway between pronation and supination, as you would carry it loosely in a sling) the *two muscles* (Brachioradialis and Ex. Carpi Radialis Longus) that spring from the lateral supracondylar ridge can be grasped between fingers and thumb. If this fails to render them prominent, placing the radial edge of the closed fist under the edge of a heavy table and trying to lift it will cause the muscles to stand out. If you could open up the space between these two laterally lying muscles, on the one hand, and the Brachialis, which they overlap, on the other, you would see the radial nerve in the depths. The bicipital aponeurosis prevents the flexor muscles, which spring from the medial epicondyle, from being grasped.

ARTERIES AND NERVES OF THE ARM

Brachial Artery. The axillary artery, after crossing the Subscapularis, Latissimus Dorsi, and Teres Major, enters the arm as the brachial artery (*fig. 110*).

»» When the dispositions of the structures around the elbow are established in your mind, you may return to a former landmark, the *Pectoralis Minor* (*fig. 108*). Behind the Pectoralis Minor you saw the three cords of the brachial plexus—medial, lateral, and posterior—arranged around the **axillary artery** in accordance with their names. The *axillary vein*, which is the upward continuation of the basilic vein, lies medial to the artery, a finger's breadth from the tip of the coracoid process.

The **brachial artery** is the largest artery whose pulsation and whose walls can be felt satisfactorily in the living subject. It may be palpated along the medial bicipital furrow throughout the length of the arm to the point where it disappears behind the bicipital aponeurosis. At the level of the neck of the radius, 1″ below the transverse crease of the elbow, it divides into its two terminal branches, a larger *ulnar artery* and smaller *radial artery*. In the upper part of its subfascial course it lies medial to the humerus; therefore, to occlude it you must press laterally. In the lower part of its course it lies anterior to the humerus; therefore, to occlude it you must press backward. Its upper one-third has the long head of the Triceps and the insertion of the Coracobrachialis behind it; its lower two-thirds, that is 67 per cent of its length, has the Brachialis behind it.

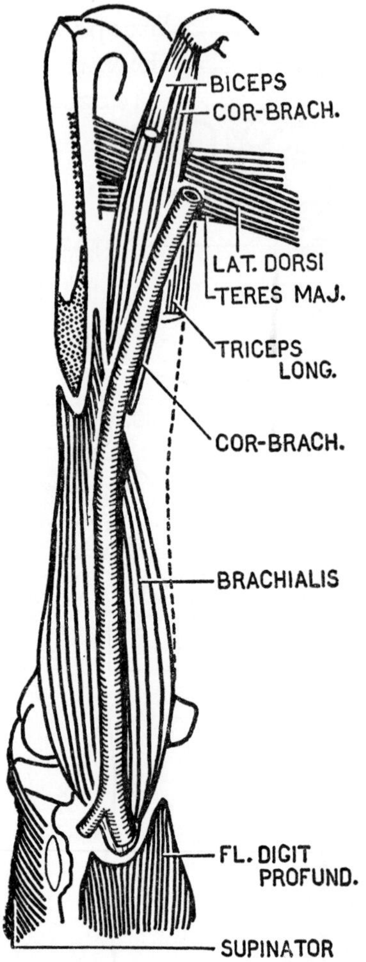

FIG. 110. Showing the posterior relations of the brachial artery.

Its *Collateral Branches* (*fig. 128*) are:
Profunda brachii a. (p. 123),
Superior ulnar collateral a. and
Inferior ulnar collateral a.
whose special interest lies in the anastomoses they effect at the shoulder and elbow.

Muscular branches, and
Nutrient a.
which enters the humerus beside the insertion of Coracobrachialis.

Venae comitantes accompany the brachial artery and make a very open network around it. They join the axillary vein.

Nerves. Of the five terminal nerves of the brachial plexus all, except the axillary nerve, leave the axilla to enter the arm (*fig. 108*). Indeed, you have already identified them around the elbow. They are: musculocutaneous, median, ulnar, and radial nerves. Also entering the arm here are: two collateral branches of the plexus, viz., medial cutaneous nerve of the arm and of the forearm (p. 112), and combined motor and cutaneous branch of radial nerve (p. 87).

At first, the terminal nerves, naturally, bear the same relation to the third part of the axillary and beginning of the brachial artery as the cords from which they spring bear to the second part of the axillary artery. The two roots of the median nerve, however, unite almost at once in front of (or rather toward the lateral side of) the artery.

The **Musculocutaneous Nerve** arises from the lateral cord of the plexus (5, 6, 7) and extends to the lateral border of the Biceps, an inch or more above the transverse crease of the elbow. It soon pierces the deep fascia as the *lateral cutaneous nerve of the forearm.* It, therefore, must course distally and laterally. It pierces the Coracobrachialis and continues between the Biceps and Brachialis; and it supplies these three muscles. It generally supplies and pierces the Coracobrachialis while in the axilla; therefore, though it lies lateral to the brachial artery, it is a short distance from it.

»» *Variations:* Commonly, many of the fibers that the lateral cord should contribute to the median nerve elect to travel with the musculocutaneous nerve for a variable distance, even as far as the lower third of the arm, before joining the median nerve (*fig. 172*).

Sometimes the musculocutaneous nerve does not pierce Coracobrachialis, but travels to the midarm with the median nerve.

The **Ulnar Nerve** arises from the medial cord of the plexus ((7), 8, 1) and extends to the back of the medial epicondyle, and onward into the forearm. It, therefore, must pass distally and medially. It is applied to the medial side of the great arterial stem till it reaches the middle of the arm. There it leaves the artery and passes behind the medial intermuscular septum into the posterior compartment of the arm, where it lies subfascially, applied to the medial head of the Triceps. You have palpated it in the distal half of the arm. Accompanying it behind the medial septum are the superior ulnar collateral artery and a nerve, called the *ulnar collateral nerve,* sent by the radial nerve to the medial head of the Triceps.

The ulnar nerve neither gives nor receives branches in the arm, but makes a "non-stop" journey through it.

The **Median Nerve.** Its two roots ((5), 6, 7, 8, and 1) unite a little below the Pectoralis Minor in front of—or rather to the lateral side of—the artery. You have rolled it on the Brachialis medial to the artery at the elbow; so, evidently it crosses the artery very obliquely. Does the crossing take place behind the artery or in front of it? Usually in front (in the ratio of 7:1) (*fig. 111*).

The median nerve gives off no branches in the arm—unless a muscular branch to the flexors arises unusually high. It commonly receives a large communication from the musculocutaneous nerve and occasionally it gives one to it; and, strictly speaking, the formation of the median nerve is not com-

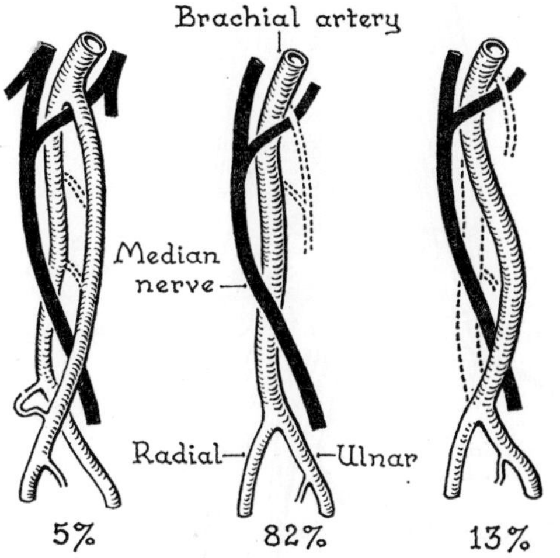

Fig. 111. Developmental explanation of the variable relationship of median nerve to brachial artery. (Based on 307 limbs.)

pleted until the last communication from the musculocutaneous has joined it. After crossing the artery in the middle of the arm, the median nerve assumes the position held by the ulnar nerve above this level.

The **Radial Nerve,** being a terminal branch of the posterior cord, (5, 6, 7, 8 (1)), lies behind the axillary artery and in front of the Subscapularis, Latissimus Dorsi, and Teres Major. On entering the arm, it still lies behind the main arterial stem and is in front of the long head of the Triceps.

You have now to trace the radial nerve through the posterior compartment of the arm. On leaving the long head of the Triceps, the nerve enters the wide, spiral groove of the humerus, but does not nearly fill it. This groove is converted into a tunnel by the lateral head of the Triceps and the lateral intermuscular septum. Within the tunnel, the radial nerve descends almost

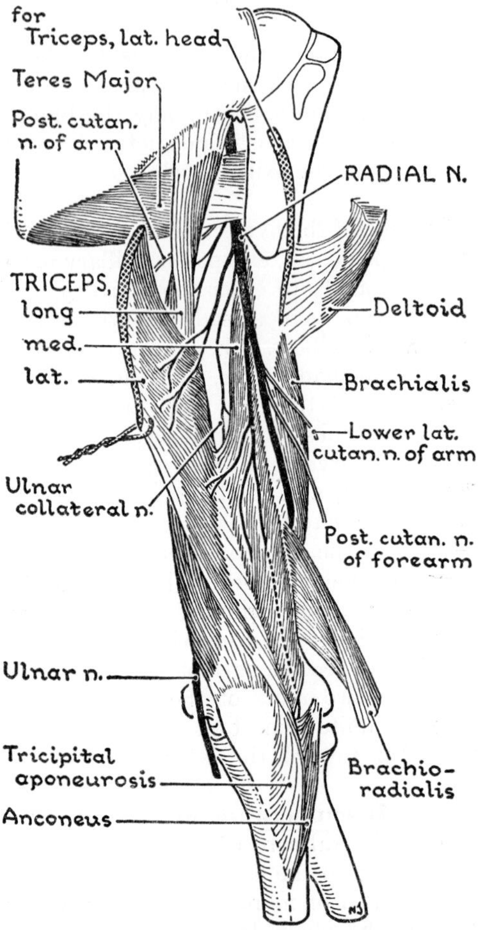

FIG. 113. The radial nerve and the Triceps

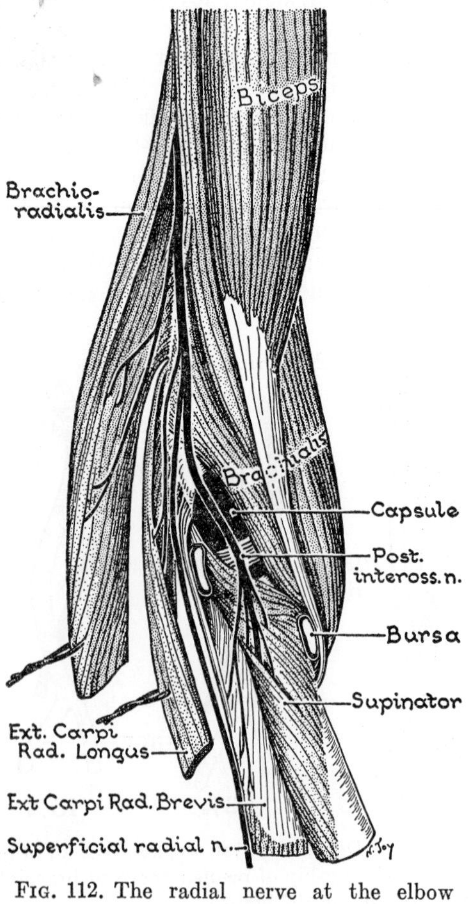

FIG. 112. The radial nerve at the elbow

vertically along the origin of the medial head of the Triceps, which lies medially (*fig. 113*) and the origins of the lateral head of the Triceps and the Brachialis, which lie laterally.

On escaping from the tunnel, the radial nerve enters the anterior compartment of the arm and continues its nearly vertical descent in the depths between the Brachioradialis and the Brachialis. Distal to this it lies on the capsule of the elbow joint and on the Supinator. At a variable point it divides into two terminal branches: (1) a sensory branch, the *superficial radial nerve,* and (2) a branch that is essentially motor, the *posterior interosseous nerve* (deep radial n.). The latter disappears into the substance of the Supinator just below the elbow (*fig. 112*).

»» *Warning.* It is common and dangerous to dissect for the radial nerve along the posterior border of the Deltoid, forgetting that the Brachialis extends well up the groove and largely fills it (*fig. 113*). Indeed, the radial nerve is a finger's breadth from the insertion of the Deltoid.

Collateral Branches (*figs. 113* and *112*). *In the axilla,* the branch to the long head of the Triceps arises with the posterior cutaneous n. of the arm.

At *the medial side of the arm,* high up, before the radial nerve enters its spiral groove, a branch to the medial head of the Triceps (ulnar collateral n.) arises and descends with the ulnar n. behind the medial intermuscular septum.

At *the back of the arm,* branches arise high up for the humeral heads of the Triceps and the Anconeus; the lower lateral cutaneous n. of the arm and the posterior cutaneous n. of the forearm arise lower.

At *the lateral side of the arm and front of the elbow,* branches pass from the radial and posterior interosseous nerves to four muscles—Brachioradialis, Ex. Carpi Radialis Longus, Ex. Carpi Radialis Brevis, and Supinator. The radial nerve usually supplies the proximal two muscles and the posterior interosseous nerve the distal two muscles.

»» Paradoxically, a twig passes to the lateral fibers of the Brachialis, which developmentally is a ventral muscle, but these fibers are evidently a detached part of the Brachioradialis. Brachioradialis is, in fact, commonly partly fused with Brachialis.

All muscles supplied by the radial n. and its branches belong developmentally to the back of the limb; and all muscles supplied by the musculocutaneous, median, and ulnar nerves belong developmentally to the front, as explained (page 109).

AXIOM: The level at which motor (and sensory) branches leave a nerve is variable, but the side from which they leave is constant; naturally, they leave from the side nearest the muscles to which they are distributed. Certain nerves have sides of safety and sides of danger; sides on which it is safe to dissect and sides on which it is dangerous.

The median nerve supplies flexors, therefore, its branches pass medially. The radial nerve supplies extensors; therefore, its branches pass laterally (*fig. 109*). It is, therefore, safe, or relatively safe, to dissect on the lateral side of the median nerve and on the medial side of the radial nerve.

The **Profunda Artery** arises from the brachial artery just below the Teres Major. It is the companion artery of the radial nerve. By its anastomoses it brings the axillary artery above into communication with the radial and ulnar arteries below. Thus:

Above, a *recurrent branch* (commonly present) ascends on the humerus between the Teres Major and lateral head of the Triceps and anastomoses with the posterior humeral circumflex art. (*fig. 114* and p. 96).

Below, it has *two terminal branches,* an anterior and a posterior. The anterior branch follows the radial nerve "through" the intermuscular septum and anastomoses with the radial recurrent artery; the posterior branch descends behind the septum to the back of the lateral epicondyle and anastomoses with the posterior interosseous recurrent artery and, across the posterior

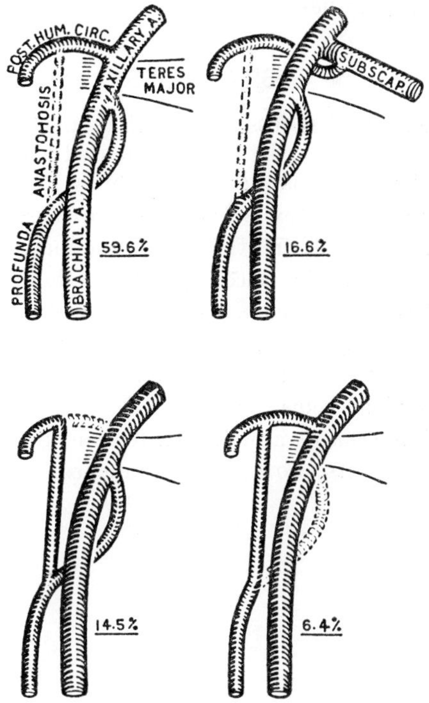

Fig. 114. Four types of variations in origin of the posterior humeral circumflex and profunda brachii arteries; in 2.9 per cent the arteries were otherwise irregular. Percentages are based on 235 specimens.

In 7.3 per cent of 123 specimens the profunda artery arose from the stem of the subscapular artery.

surface of the humerus, with the inf. ulnar collateral artery (supratrochlear a.) (*fig. 128*).

A *nutrient branch* is commonly given off, in which case there is a foramen in the spiral groove.

Features of Interest near Midarm, where Coracobrachialis is inserted:

1. Basilic vein pierces deep fascia to become deep.
2. Medial cutaneous nerve of the forearm pierces the deep fascia to become cutaneous.
3. A subcutaneous lymph node is not uncommonly present.
4. Median nerve crosses the brachial artery.
5. Ulnar nerve passes behind the intermuscular septum accompanied by the
6. Superior ulnar collateral artery and ulnar collateral nerve.
7. Nutrient artery enters the bone.
8. The lower or apical end of the deltoid tuberosity lies at this level.

CUBITAL FOSSA

The cubital fossa is the triangular space at the front of the elbow, bounded laterally by Brachioradialis and medially by Pronator Teres. The apex is below, where these two muscles meet, and the base is the imaginary line joining the epicondyles of the humerus.

Covering the fossa is deep fascia reinforced with Bicipital aponeurosis, superficial to which are cutaneous nerves (*fig. 98*) and superficial veins (*fig. 102*).

The contents are: Biceps tendon, brachial art. and its two terminal branches, median nerve, and (on retracting Brachioradialis) radial nerve (*figs. 108* and *112*).

The Floor is formed by Brachialis and Supinator (*fig. 123*).

Segmental Innervation of Muscles of Shoulder and Upper Arm Supplied by Brachial Plexus*

<table>
<tr><th colspan="2">C. 5</th><th colspan="2">C. 6</th><th colspan="2">C. 7</th><th colspan="2">C. 8</th><th colspan="2">Th. 1</th></tr>
<tr><td colspan="3">Teres Minor
Supraspinatus
Rhomboids
Infraspinatus
Deltoid</td><td colspan="7"></td></tr>
<tr><td colspan="4">Teres Major
Biceps
Brachialis</td><td colspan="6"></td></tr>
<tr><td colspan="6">Serratus Anterior</td><td colspan="4"></td></tr>
<tr><td colspan="8">Subscapularis</td><td colspan="2"></td></tr>
<tr><td colspan="10">Pectoralis Major</td></tr>
<tr><td colspan="2"></td><td colspan="6">Pectoralis Minor</td><td colspan="2"></td></tr>
<tr><td colspan="3"></td><td colspan="3">Coracobrachialis</td><td colspan="4"></td></tr>
<tr><td colspan="3"></td><td colspan="5">Latissimus Dorsi</td><td colspan="2"></td></tr>
<tr><td colspan="4"></td><td colspan="4">Anconeus</td><td colspan="2"></td></tr>
<tr><td colspan="4"></td><td colspan="5">Triceps</td><td colspan="1"></td></tr>
</table>

* Modified after Bing; and Haymaker and Woodhall.

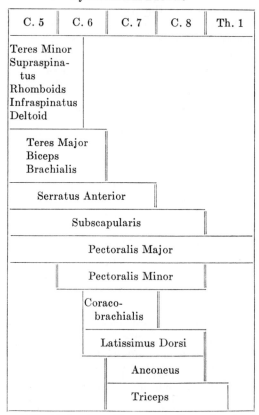

CHAPTER 9

FLEXOR REGION OF FOREARM

In constructing this region, you will find it profitable to erect the two bones as scaffolding, to build three layers of muscles on and around them, and, employing your knowledge of the palpable parts at the elbow and wrist, to install the vessels and nerves.

RADIUS AND ULNA

The **features of the ends** of these two bones are to be identified now, and the **flexor surfaces** of the bodies studied in detail (*fig. 115*).

The proximal end of the **radius** consists of: *Head, neck,* and *radial tuberosity* for the insertion of the Biceps.

The distal end of the radius consists of: *Lower articular surface, ulnar notch, styloid process,* anterior and posterior aspects. On the last are the *dorsal radial tubercle (of Lister)* and several grooves.

The proximal end of the **ulna** consists of: *Olecranon, coronoid process, trochlear notch, radial notch,* and *ulnar tuberosity* for the insertion of the Brachialis.

The distal end of the ulna consists of: *Head, styloid process, pit* for the attachment of the articular disc, and *groove* for Ex. Carpi Ulnaris.

The **body of the radius** is cylindrical and somewhat tapering above; the **body of the ulna** is cylindrical and somewhat tapering below. The expanded lower two-thirds of the radius and the expanded upper two-thirds of the ulna are triangular on cross-section.

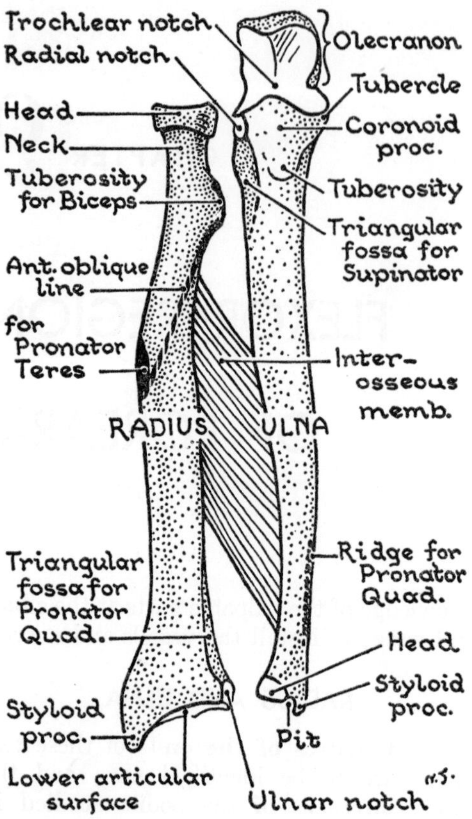

FIG. 115. The radius and ulna, anterior aspect

The two bones are united by an **interosseous membrane,** which, on account of the inferomedial direction of its fibers would seem able to transfer from radius to ulna the force of an impact received by the hand (*fig. 116*)—though recently Halls and Travill have shown experimentally that this is highly improbable. This strong membrane produces a sharp ridge on the radius and an equally sharp one on the ulna, known as their medial and lateral borders, respectively, or alternatively as their *interosseous borders.*

The medial or interosseous border of the radius may be traced proximally, from where the two lines bounding the ulnar notch unite above a *triangular fossa,* to the radial tuberosity.

The lateral or interosseous border of the ulna may be traced distally, from where the two lines bounding the radial notch unite below a *triangular fossa,* to the lateral side of the head of the ulna (*fig. 115*).

»» *Conventions in Terminology.* Typically, the bodies of long bones are triangular on cross-section, and their surfaces and borders are named by opposites (*fig. 117*). Therefore, as the radius has a medial border it must have a surface designated the lateral surface; and the ulna, having a lateral border, must have a surface designated the medial surface. Now, a glance at the skeleton will suffice to show that both the radius and the ulna have anterior and posterior surfaces and therefore, as a corollary, posterior and anterior borders.

It is well to reserve the term "*surface*" of a long bone for an area bounded by two specified borders; and to apply the term "*aspect*" to an area visible from a certain aspect or viewpoint, and perhaps embracing two surfaces: for example, the lower half of the anterior aspect of the humerus includes its medial and lateral surfaces as well as the anterior border between them (*fig. 104*).

At the summit of the convexity of the lateral surface of the radius there is a rough *area for the Pronator Teres.* This impression spreads right across the lateral surface; and from it two sharp lines, the *anterior* and

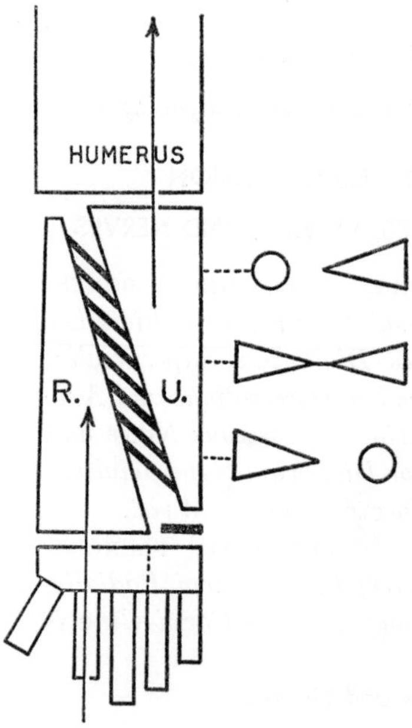

FIG. 116. Scheme of the radius and ulna

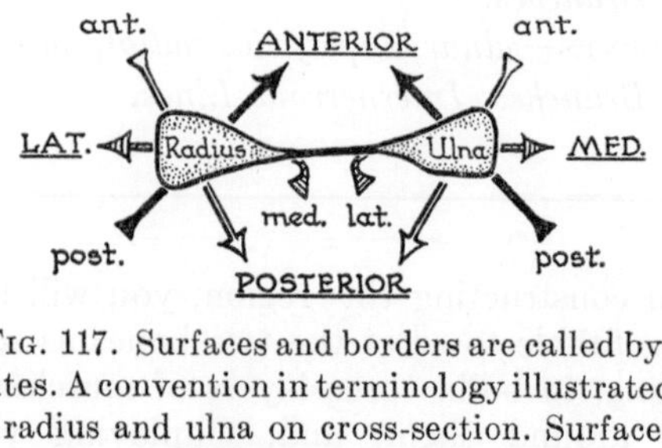

FIG. 117. Surfaces and borders are called by opposites. A convention in terminology illustrated by the radius and ulna on cross-section. Surfaces in large type; borders in small type.

posterior oblique lines, ascend across the anterior and posterior aspects of the bone to the radial tuberosity. These lines are the upper segments of the anterior and posterior borders.

The entire V-shaped area of the body of the radius between the anterior and posterior oblique lines is appropriated by the *Supinator*. The anterior border can be traced downward to the front of the styloid process; the posterior border to the dorsal radial tubercle.

The posterior border of the ulna extends from the apex of the posterior *subcutaneous surface of the olecranon,* on which lies the olecranon bursa, to the back of the styloid process. This border is sharp, subcutaneous, and always palpable from end to end; and when the forearm is raised in self-protection, it is liable to be struck and the bone fractured.

The anterior border extends from the tuberosity on the coronoid process, into which the Brachialis is inserted, to the front of the styloid process. It is smooth, except in its lower quarter where it forms a rough ridge, the *pronator ridge,* for the fibrous origin of the Pronator Quadratus. This smooth, rounded, anterior border of the ulna separates the anterior surface from the medial surface. It is a strengthening bar that fulfils the same function as the smooth, rounded, anterior border of the humerus (*fig. 118*). [The former gives origin to fleshy fibers of the Flexor Digitorum Profundus; the latter to fleshy fibers of the Brachialis.] Functionally, then, the anterior and medial surfaces of the ulna are parts of a single "flexor surface."

The posterior and lateral borders afford attachment to fibrous tissue and owe their sharp and rough qualities respectively to this fact.

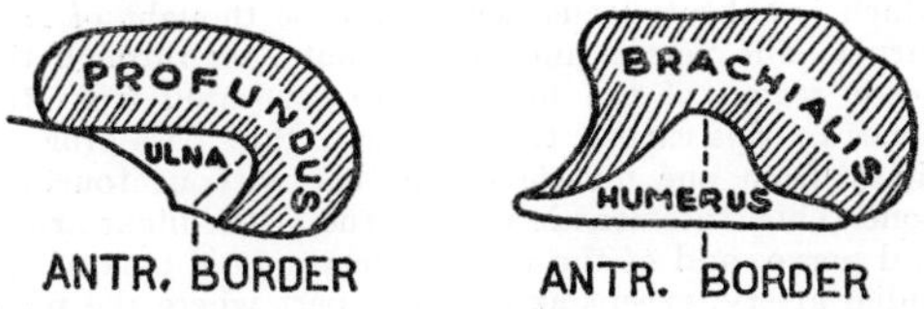

FIG. 118. Rounded borders are usually strengthening bars; sharp and rough borders give attachment to fibrous tissue. (See also scapula, *fig. 92.*)

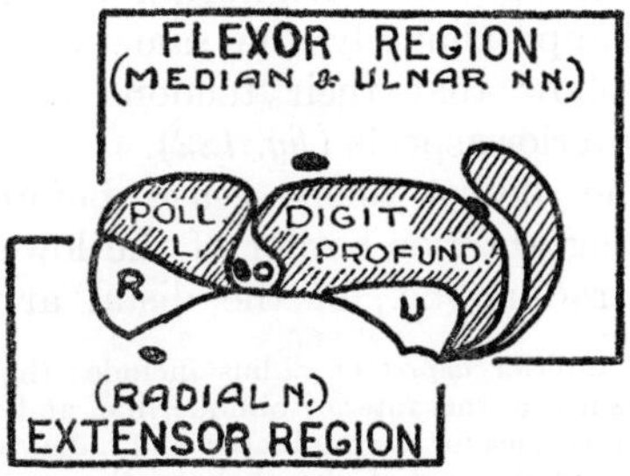

FIG. 119. Regions of forearm

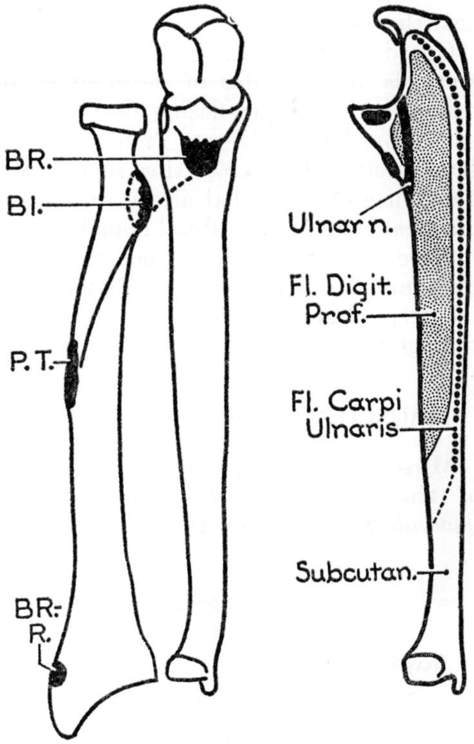

FIG. 120. Flexor aspect of the bones of the forearm. The four flexors of the elbow like sentinels guard the boundary between flexor and extensor territories.

Boundaries of Flexor Region (*fig. 119*). The flexor region of the forearm has as its basis the anterior surface of the radius and the anterior and medial surfaces of the ulna. Medially, it is marked off from the extensor region by the olecranon and the posterior border of the ulna, both of which are subcutaneous. Laterally, it is marked off from the extensor region by the anterior border of the radius, which is submerged except near the wrist.

Guarding the lateral boundary like four sentinels are the sites of insertion of the tendons of the four flexors of the elbow joint—Brachialis, Biceps, Pronator Teres, Brachioradialis (*fig. 120*). More superficially, the course of the radial artery serves as a practical guide to the lateral boundary.

Since neither the medial nor the lateral boundary line is crossed by a motor nerve, the deep parts of the limb may be explored through these internervous lines.

MUSCLES OF FLEXOR REGION

Muscles Clothing the Flexor Aspects of the Bones (*fig. 121*). The *Pronator Quadratus* arises from the pronator ridge of the ulna. It is inserted by fleshy fibers into the smooth, lower quarter of the anterior surface of the radius as well as into the triangular area above the ulnar notch. This is possible because the interosseous membrane follows the hinder of the lines limiting this triangular area.

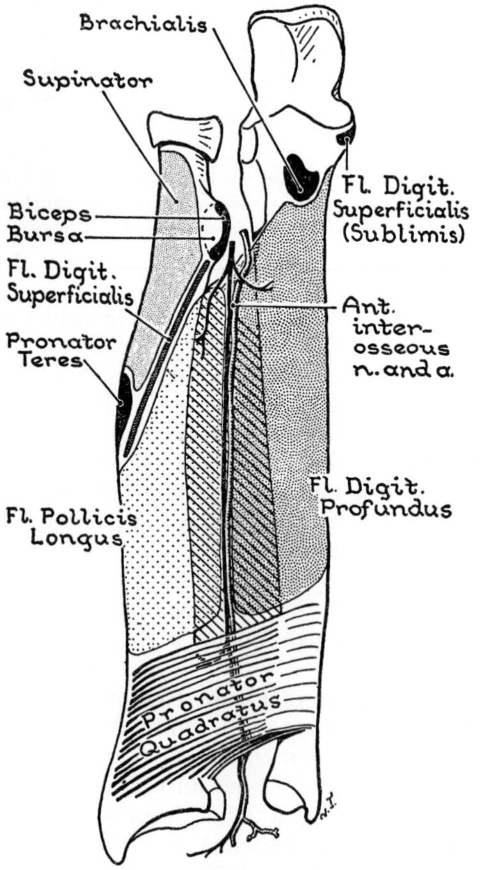

FIG. 121. The radius, ulna, and interosseous membrane, showing attachment of muscles; front view.

The *Flexor Pollicis Longus* arises from the smooth, anterior surface of the radius and adjacent part of the interosseous membrane from the level of the Pronator Quadratus below right up to the anterior oblique line from which the aponeurotic radial head of the *Flexor Digitorum Superficialis* for the 3rd digit arises. Above this level the *Supinator* has been seen to occupy the bone up to and beyond the insertion of the *Biceps* into the posterior, rough half of the radial tuberosity.

The *Flexor Digitorum Profundus* arises from the smooth anterior surface, smooth rounded anterior border, and smooth medial surface of the ulna, and adjacent part of the interosseous membrane from the level of the Pronator Quadratus right up to the insertion of the *Brachialis* anteriorly and up so as to cover the coronoid process and olecranon medially (*fig. 120*).

» *Note.* Between them, the seven foregoing muscles occupy all the available space on the anterior aspects[3] of the bodies of the radius and ulna as well as on the medial aspect of the ulna above its lower one-third, which is subcutaneous. They may be thought of as a carpet. The vessels and nerves that pass through the flexor region of the forearm are separated from the bones by this carpet; that is to say, they pass progressively from one muscle to another without touching bone. This statement is wholly true of the ulnar artery and nerve, and of the median nerve. It is true of the radial artery, except at its lower part where the pulse is felt. It is not true of the anterior interosseous artery and nerve, see page 129.

Observe: 1. Since the individual fleshy fibers of the deep digital flexors (i.e., Flexores Pollicis Longus and Digitorum Profundus) are of approximately the same length, it must follow that their tendons begin on their anterior aspects (*fig. 122*).

2. The fleshy fibers cease before the projecting anterior border of the lower end of the radius (i.e., of the distal articular

[3] The anterior *aspect* of radius includes the entire anterior surface, the anterior oblique line, and part of the lateral surface for the Supinator, and radial tuberosity. The medial *aspect* of ulna includes the medial surface, and the medial surfaces of the coronoid process and olecranon.

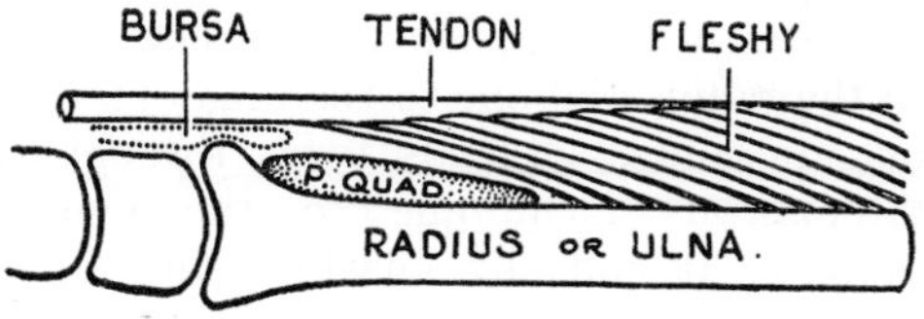

FIG. 122. Tendon of deep digital flexor (*see Axiom*).

surface) is reached and the tendons are enveloped in a synovial sheath.

AXIOM: Fleshy fibers cannot survive severe pressure or friction, and even a tough tendon requires a bursa or a synovial sheath where it rubs against bone or other resistant structures, e.g., fibrous sheath, other tendons.

3. The Pronator Quadratus is sheltered by the projecting anterior border of the lower end of the radius; the deep flexors bridge it and therefore do not hamper its action.

4. The five tendons of the deep digital flexors converge on the midline of the limb in order to enter the carpal tunnel (*fig. 144*). In doing so, the tendon of the Flexor Pollicis Longus must leave the lateral part of the Pronator Quadratus uncovered, thereby allowing the radial artery to come to lie on it (*fig. 123*); and, the Flexor Digitorum Profundus must leave the lower third of the medial surface of the ulna denuded, and, therefore, subcutaneous and palpable between the tendons of the Flexor and the Extensor Carpi Ulnaris (*fig. 120*). The five tendons of the deep digital flexors lie side by side as they pass through the carpal tunnel.

›› In lower primates there is a common deep digital flexor for the five digits, but in man the Flexor Pollicis Longus is an independent muscle and the deep tendon to the index acquires a certain independence in the forearm. The designer of the work glove (*fig. 123.1*) apparently recognized that the pollex and index are used in many fine movements and that digits 3, 4, and 5 are commonly used as a unit.

The **Anterior Interosseous Nerve and Artery** arise from the median nerve and common interosseous artery, respectively, an inch or so below the elbow, and pass to the interosseous membrane. Thereafter, the nerve and artery and their branches cling to, and never part from, the **"skeletal plane"**—i.e., bone, interosseous membrane, ligament, or capsule of joint.

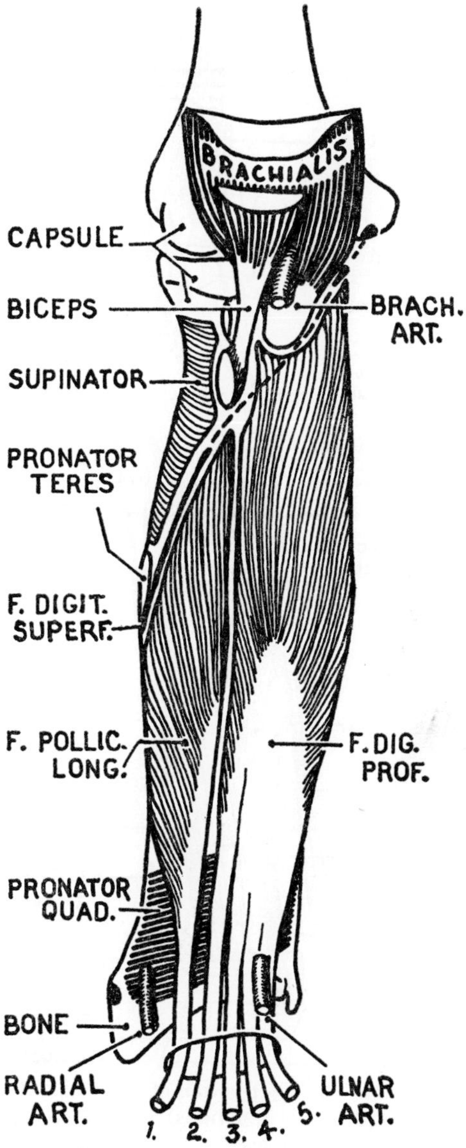

FIG. 123. The seven muscles clothing the flexor aspect of the radius and ulna.

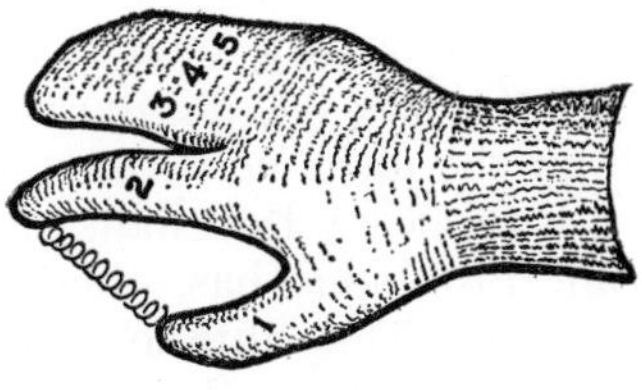

FIG. 123.1. See text

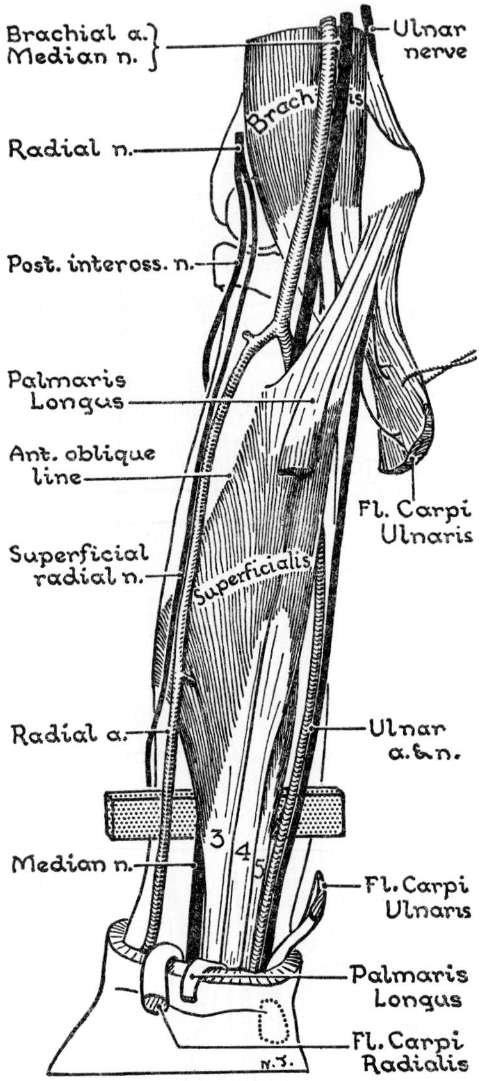

FIG. 124. The key position of the Flexor Digitorum Superficialis (Sublimis) with reference to the nerves and arteries.

The Nerve supplies the three deep muscles (Fl. Pollicis Longus, Fl. Digitorum Profundus, and Pronator Quadratus)—but not entirely: the branches it sends to the deep flexors control the tendons to the 1st, 2nd, and 3rd digits, leaving those to the 4th and 5th for the ulnar nerve to supply. This it does a little below the elbow. The Flexor Digitorum Profundus has, then, a double nerve supply. The anterior interosseous nerve ends by supplying the wrist and carpal joints.

The Artery supplies a nutrient branch to the radius and one to the ulna. Throughout its course it sends twigs through the interosseous membrane to the extensor muscles. It ends by anastomosing on the front and back of the wrist.

Flexor Digitorum Superficialis or Sublimis (*fig. 124*). This muscle occupies an intermediate position between the superficial and deep flexors. Developmentally, it is a delaminated portion of the deep flexors of the digits; and, it arises at their upper borders (*fig. 123*). Thus, it arises from: (1) the anterior oblique line of the radius between the attachments of the Flexor Pollicis Longus and the Supinator, (2) the anterior strong fibrous cord of the ulnar collateral ligament (medial lig.) of the elbow joint, and from the bone at each end of the ligament (viz., the medial epicondyle of the humerus and the tubercle on the coronoid process of the ulna), and (3) the intermuscular septa, especially the septum between it and the Fl. Carpi Ulnaris. It has, then, a humeral, an ulnar, and a radial origin.

A fibrous band bridges the interval between the ulnar and radial origins of Superficialis, and under the bridge run the median nerve and the ulnar artery. The median nerve supplies the Superficialis, including the proximal and distal bellies of the digastric parts, and it clings closely to its deep surface.

» Unlike the tendons of the Fl. Digitorum Profundus which lie side by side, those of the Fl. Digitorum Superficialis are "two deep", those for digits 3 and 4 being in front of those for digits 2 and 5; and all four are free in the forearm. The radial head belongs to digit 3; the fleshy bellies for digits 2 and 5 are interrupted about their middles by intermediate tendons; i.e., they are digastric muscles and each belly needs a nerve. As the tendons pass behind the flexor retinaculum they come to lie side by side.

Surface Anatomy of Front of Wrist (*fig. 125*). Like the structures about the elbow, those at the wrist must be identified by palpation in the living subject and confirmed by dissection.

The most distal *skin crease* at the wrist, slightly convex toward the palm, corresponds to the upper border of the flexor retinaculum (transverse carpal ligament). It crosses the two prominent proximal bony

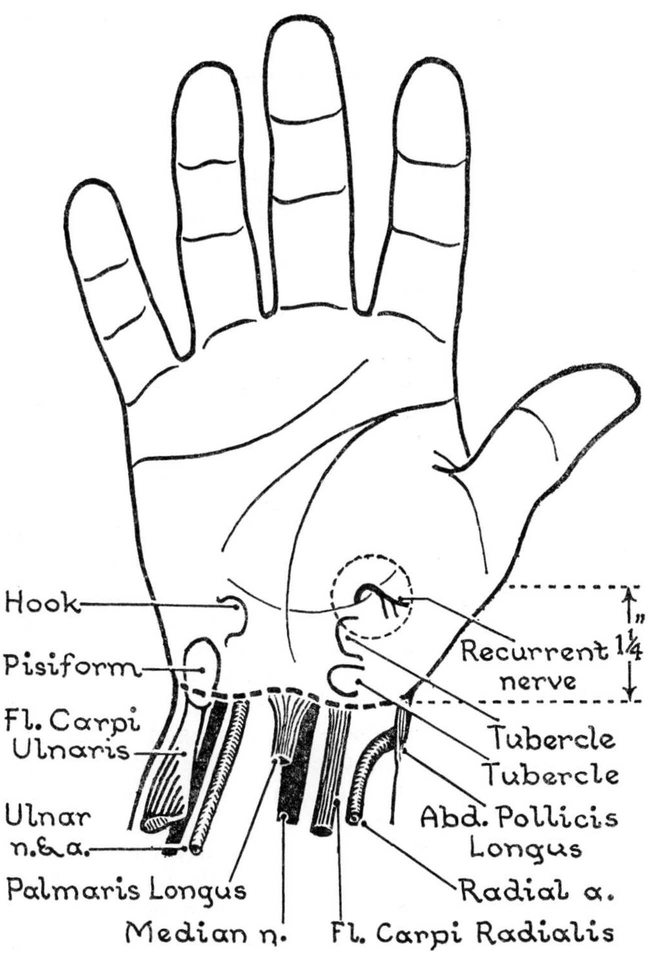

FIG. 125. Surface anatomy of the front of the wrist: a key position.

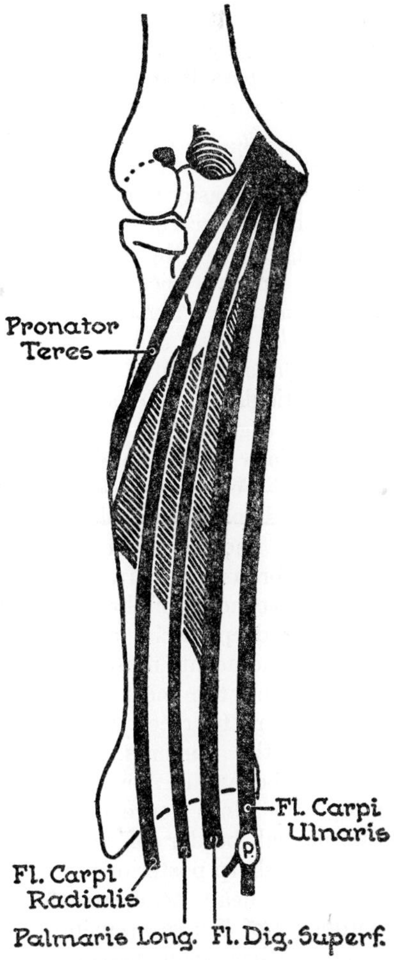

FIG. 126. The four superficial flexors and the Flexor Digitorum Superficialis.

pillars to which the retinaculum is attached, namely: the *tubercle of the scaphoid bone* laterally, the *pisiform bone* medially.

Where the prominent tendon of the *Flexor Carpi Radialis* crosses this skin crease at the junction of its lateral one-third with its medial two-thirds, it passes in front of the scaphoid tubercle and so serves as a guide to it. The Flexor Carpi Radialis is rendered very prominent when the clenched fist is fully flexed against resistance.

The tendon of the *Flexor Carpi Ulnaris*, the most medial of all the structures at the wrist, can be traced to the pisiform at the medial end of the crease.

The most lateral of all the structures are the tendons of the *Abductor Pollicis Longus* and *Extensor Pollicis Brevis*.

Bisecting the distal skin crease (i.e., at the middle of the front of the wrist) is the most important of all the structures—the *median nerve*. It cannot be palpated, but it is there. Two layers of fascia and the *Palmaris Longus* tendon lie in front of it. The Palmaris Longus is to be brought into prominence by fully flexing the closed fist and then applying resistance to it.

»» In a series of 379 subjects, Palmaris Longus was present on both sides in 80%, absent on both sides in 7%, absent on the right only in 7%, and absent on the left only in 6% (R. K. George).

The *radial artery* is to be felt pulsating

between the Fl. Carpi Radialis and the Abductor Pollicis Longus. The *ulnar artery* and *nerve* pass into the palm immediately lateral to the pisiform, which is protective to them (*fig. 144*). As, however, a strong band of fascia covers them, the pulse of this artery is not easily felt.

Finally, when the wrist is extended, a fullness, due to the *Fl. Digitorum Superficialis*, appears between the Fl. Carpi Ulnaris and the Palmaris Longus. The *lower end of the radius* can be grasped between the fingers and thumb. The anterior margin of its articular surface is surprisingly prominent and rugged.

The **Four Superficial Flexors** are the Pronator Teres, Flexor Carpi Radialis, Palmaris Longus, and Flexor Carpi Ulnaris (*fig. 126*). They have a common and, therefore, a fibrous origin from the front of the medial epicondyle of the humerus, from the investing deep fascia, and from the septa between adjacent muscles. The *Pronator Teres*, being the most lateral, is able by fleshy fibers to creep upward toward the shaft of the humerus. The *Flexor Carpi Ulnaris*, being the most medial, is able to bridge the ulnar nerve and to creep along the medial border of the olecranon and down the sharp posterior border to the ulna. This ulnar head, being attached to a sharp border, is of course aponeurotic. It cannot creep farther than three-quarters of the way down this border because its tendon of insertion has to reach the pisiform bone; so, it repeats the procedure of the Flexor Digitorum Profundus, and thereby leaves the lower one-fourth of the medial surface of the ulna denuded and subcutaneous (*fig. 120*).

The four superficial muscles spread out fanwise in an obvious sequence, and the tendons of all but the Pronator Teres have been recognized at the wrist. In order that the *Pronator Teres* may pronate (i.e., rotate medially) more effectively, it creeps on to the lateral surface of the radius, thereby invading extensor territory. It is inserted into the whole breadth of the lateral surface of the radius at its middle, and being fibrous it leaves a mark. It cannot be identified by palpation.

An insignificant fleshy bundle, the *deep head of Pronator Teres*, arises from the medial part of the coronoid process of the ulna.

ARTERIES AND NERVES OF FRONT OF FOREARM

Familiar with the surface anatomy of the structures at the elbow (*fig. 108*) and at the wrist (*fig. 125*), you cannot find it difficult to map out the general courses of:

Ulnar artery and nerve.
Radial artery and nerve.
Median nerve (and artery) (*fig. 127*).

You can postulate: (1) that the vessels and nerves cross superficial to the muscles that carpet the radius and ulna; (2) that the ulnar and superficial radial nerves together embrace their companion arteries (*fig. 127*); (3) that the median nerve crosses the ulnar artery; (4) that the median nerve and ulnar artery pass under the "Superficialis or Sublimis arch" which is specially designed for their passage (*fig. 124*); and (5) that the ulnar nerve passes under the bridge between the humeral and ulnar heads of the Fl. Carpi Ulnaris.

Surface Anatomy. Slightly curved lines, connecting the site where the brachial artery was observed to divide into the ulnar and radial arteries, 1″ below the skin crease at the elbow, to the points where these arteries were identified at the wrist, indicate the general directions of the two arteries.

Ulnar Artery. In its course through the forearm, the ulnar artery passes deep to the fibrous arch that connects the radial and humero-ulnar heads of the Fl. Digitorum Superficialis, because this is the purpose of the arch; therefore it passes deep also to the superficial flexors. Under this arch the median nerve must cross the ulnar artery from medial to lateral side, and it crosses superficially (the deep head of the Pronator Teres intervening).

Behind the ulnar artery are the muscles clothing the anterior aspect of the ulna, namely: Brachialis and Fl. Digitorum Profundus. The Pronator Quadratus is not an immediate posterior relation (*fig. 123*).

Its pulse is not readily felt at the wrist

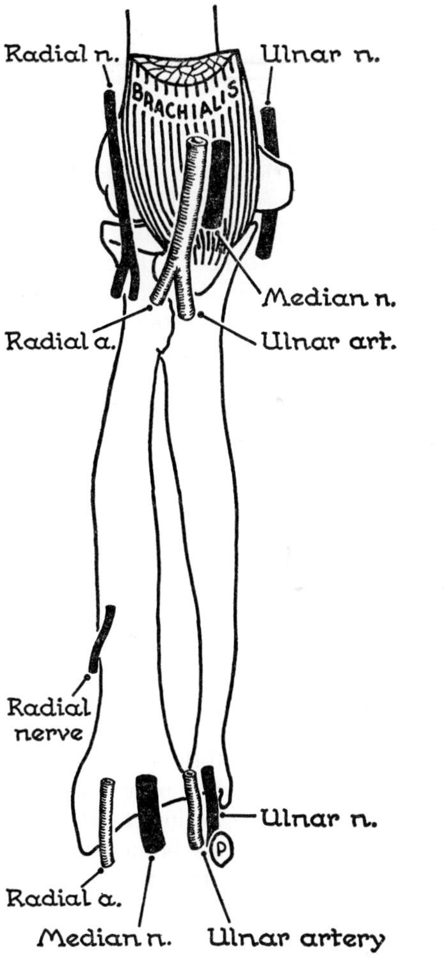

FIG. 127. The vessels and nerves of the forearm at key positions. Complete this picture by filling in the missing segments.

because it is there bridged by a taut band of deep fascia (the *volar carpal lig.*), which stretches from the Fl. Carpi Ulnaris to the trapezium (*fig. 145*).

AXIOM: Limbs being organs of prehension and locomotion require motors, that is, muscles, to move them. Accordingly, muscles make up the bulk of a limb and receive most of the blood delivered to the limb. That is to say, most branches of arteries are muscular branches and they are usually unnamed. Certain muscular branches anastomose, especially about joints; so do a few nonmuscular branches, and they are named. The branches to the skin, fat, fasciae, tendons and nerves are relatively small.

BRANCHES of ULNAR ARTERY given off in forearm:

1 and 2. *Anterior and posterior ulnar recurrent aa.* take part in the anastomoses around the medial epicondyle, the posterior artery following the ulnar nerve proximally (*fig. 128*).

3. *Common interosseous a.* is a short stem that passes to the upper border of the interosseous membrane and divides there into the anterior and posterior interosseous aa. Their branches are:

Anterior interosseous artery:
- Median, companion to median nerve.
- Nutrient, to radius and ulna.
- Muscular.
- Anterior communicating, anastomoses in front of the wrist.
- Terminal, anastomoses behind the wrist (*figs. 155* and *157*).

Posterior interosseous artery:
- Recurrent, anastomoses behind the lateral epicondyle.
- Muscular.
- Terminal, anastomoses behind wrist.

4. *Muscular branches.*

5, 6. *Palmar and dorsal ulnar carpal aa.* take part in the anastomoses around the wrist (*fig. 155*).

»» The *median artery* is of historical and practical interest. For a brief period in embryonic life it is the lineal successor to the anterior interosseous artery and, as the chief artery of the forearm and hand, it accompanies the median nerve through the carpal tunnel into the palm where it supplies certain digits until it disappears. Occasionally it persists.

Radial Artery. If in a dissected limb the muscular branches of the radial artery are severed, the vessel can be lifted right up from its bed, because like its parent, the brachial artery, it is not crossed by any muscle. Why then can the radial pulse not be felt throughout the entire course of the artery? Because the Brachioradialis is overlapping.

The radial artery lies between the extensor and flexor groups of muscles. So, no motor nerve crosses this artery. The Brachioradialis is lateral and overlaps it; the Pronator Teres is medial in its upper one-third; the Flexor Carpi Radialis is medial in its lower two-thirds.

Immediately behind it are the muscles

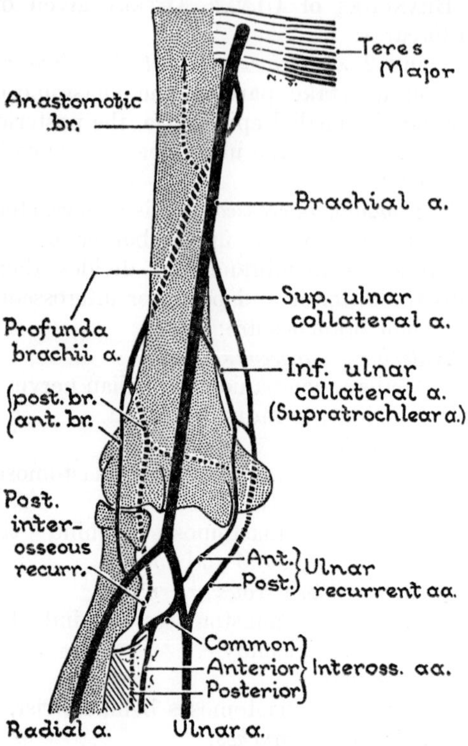

FIG. 128. The arterial anastomoses around the elbow.

that clothe the anterior aspect of the radius (*fig. 123*), namely, the Biceps, Supinator, Pronator Teres, radial head of Fl. Superficialis, Fl. Pollicis Longus, Pronator Quadratus—beyond these are the lower end of the radius and the capsule of the wrist joint. They occur in the sequence just given.

The artery gains the back of the wrist by passing below the styloid process and deep to the Abductor Pollicis Longus.

The superficial radial nerve accompanies the radial artery through the middle third of the forearm.

BRANCHES of RADIAL ARTERY given off in forearm:

1. *Muscular*.
2. *Recurrent*, follows the radial nerve proximally, and anastomoses with the profunda brachii a. in front of the lateral epicondyle (*fig. 128*).
3. *Palmar* (*anterior*) *carpal* (p. 156).
4. *Superficial palmar*, arises at the wrist and descends across the ball of the thumb to complete the superficial palmar arch (*fig. 148*). When large, its pulsations can be felt.

Ulnar Nerve. The ulnar nerve takes a straight course from the back of the medial epicondyle to the lateral side of the protective pisiform. It lies throughout on the Fl. Digitorum Profundus. The Fl. Carpi Ulnaris covers it proximally and overlaps it distally. Its artery approaches it, obviously from the lateral side, and is in contact with it in the lower two-thirds of its course.

BRANCHES (*fig. 172*). At the elbow the ulnar nerve supplies one and one-half muscles, namely: the Fl. Carpi Ulnaris and the medial half of the Fl. Digitorum Profundus —these are the only muscles it supplies above the level of the wrist—and it sends twigs to the elbow joint. Somewhat above the wrist its palmar and dorsal cutaneous branches arise (*fig. 98*).

If you sever the humeral origin of the Fl. Carpi Ulnaris, you can bring the ulnar nerve to the front of the elbow; and if you then flex the elbow joint, you shorten the course of the nerve by several inches.

Superficial Radial Nerve. This is the portion of the radial nerve distal to the origin of the posterior interosseous nerve. It is the last cutaneous branch of the radial nerve. To expose it, turn the Brachioradialis laterally (*fig. 112*).

After crossing the capsule of the elbow joint, the nerve descends along the anterior border of the Ex. Carpi Radialis Longus, passes backward between the Brachioradialis and Ex. Carpi Radialis Longus, and becomes cutaneous about 2″ above the styloid process of the radius.

The radial artery approaches the nerve from the medial side and accompanies it through the middle third of the forearm. Both the nerve and the artery pass to the extensor region of the limb, but at different levels and deep to different tendons (*fig. 124*).

Median Nerve. You have palpated it medial to the brachial artery at the elbow and you have located it where the Palmaris overlaps it at the midpoint of the wrist. It takes a straight course between these two points. It passes with the ulnar artery deep to the "Superficialis bridge" and therefore deep to four muscles (i.e., Pronator Teres, Fl. Carpi Radialis, Fl. Digitorum Superficialis and Palmaris Longus). It happens to cross superficial to the ulnar artery, (the slender deep head of the Pronator Teres intervening). Behind it are the muscles clothing the front of the ulna, namely, the Brachialis and Fl. Digitorum Profundus.

The median nerve, then, crosses anterior to the brachial artery in the arm and to the ulnar artery in the forearm.

BRANCHES (*fig. 172*). The median nerve supplies all the flexor muscles of the forearm, except the one and one-half supplied by the ulnar nerve. The branches to four of these, namely, the Pronator Teres, Fl. Carpi Radialis, Palmaris Longus, and Fl. Digitorum Superficialis, spring from the main stem, obviously from its medial side. They commonly arise above the level of the elbow.

Its obligations to the two and one-half deep muscles being discharged by its interosseous branch, the median nerve is free to adhere to the deep surface of the Fl. Digitorum Superficialis and to give it branches in its course through the forearm.

It also sends articular twigs to the elbow and wrist joints.

The median nerve is accompanied by the median artery, which, though usually a mere twig, may be a large vessel.

Internervous Lines. When a finger or the handle of an instrument is insinuated between the Fl. Carpi Ulnaris and Fl. Digitorum Superficialis and carried proximally, it is arrested by the common septum from which these two muscles spring. Now, the Fl. Digitorum Superficialis is supplied by the median nerve and the Fl. Carpi Ulnaris by the ulnar nerve; so, the septum marks an internervous line. This may safely be opened up, the two muscles pulled apart, and access gained to the deeper parts of the forearm without fear of damaging a motor nerve, until a point is reached about 2½″ below the medial epicondyle, for at this level branches of the ulnar nerve enter the Fl. Digitorum Profundus and Fl. Carpi Ulnaris.

Other Internervous Lines. The posterior border of the ulna marks the internervous line between the motor territories of the ulnar and radial nerves; similarly, the course of the radial artery marks the internervous line between the motor territories of the median and radial nerves.

CHAPTER 10

HAND

CARPAL BONES AND JOINTS

Carpal bones; Drawing Carpus; Distal Surface of Carpus and Bases of Metacarpals; Dorsal and Palmar Aspects; Flexor Retinaculum; Palpable Parts; "Snuff-box."
Midcarpal Joint; Joint Surfaces.
Striking a Blow; Intercarpal Ligaments.

METACARPAL BONES AND JOINTS

Bases; Bodies; Metacarpal of Thumb; Metacarpo-phalangeal Joints; Collateral Ligaments; Palmar Ligaments; Deep Transverse Metacarpal Ligaments; M-P Joint of Thumb.

PHALANGES AND INTERPHALANGEAL JOINTS

OSSIFICATION OF BONES OF HAND

PALM OF THE HAND

Finger prints; Skin Creases; Surface Anatomy; Digital Formula.
Definitions: Movements of Digits; Axial Line of Hand.
Carpometacarpal Joint of Thumb.
Flexor Retinaculum; Fl. Carpi Ulnaris.
THENAR MUSCLES—*Abductor Pollicis; Opponens Pollicis and Flexor Pollicis Brevis; Nerve Supply.*
HYPOTHENAR MUSCLES—*Nerve Supply.*
Adductor Pollicis; Opposition.
Ulnar Nerve in Hand; Palmaris Brevis; Median Nerve in Hand; Variations in Motor Distribution.
Palmar Aponeurosis; Structures Crossing Skin Crease at Wrist; Fibrous Sheaths of Digits; Insertions of Long Flexors; Lumbricals; Synovial Sheaths; Mesotendons; Common Carpal Synovial Sheath.
Palmar Spaces.
ARTERIES OF HAND—*Superficial Palmar Arch; Radial Artery; Deep Palmar Arch; Palmar Carpal Arch; Dorsal Carpal Arch.*

BONES OF CARPUS—IN SOME DETAIL

Scaphoid; Lunate; Triquetrum; Pisiform; Trapezium; Trapezoid; Capitate; Hamate.

»» There is little purpose in studying the bones of the hand individually before you are familiar with them collectively; so, we shall consider first the hand as a whole, and later attend to the notable features of the individual bones. And, because considerable areas of the different bones take parts in joints, we should find it difficult to avoid discussing the joints and ligaments with the bones.

When reading the following remarks, have beside you the bones of the hand, preferably strung on catgut. Do not omit also to make the suggested observations on your own hand.

The following comprise the skeleton of the hand:

1. The carpal bones, or bones of the wrist, or carpus.

2. The metacarpal bones, or bones of the palm, or metacarpus.

3. The phalanges, or bones of the digits.

The digits are numbered I, II, III, IV, V. The first digit is the thumb or pollex; the second, the forefinger or index; the third, the middle finger or digitus medius; the fourth, the ring finger or digitus anularis; and the fifth is the little finger, or digitus minimus.

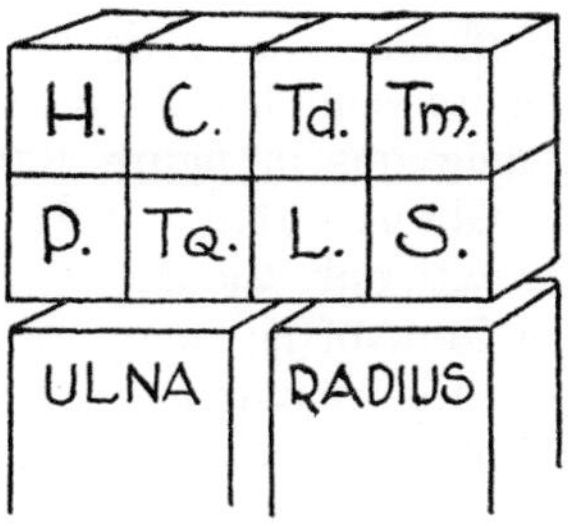

FIG. 129. The carpal bones as cubes

CARPAL BONES AND JOINTS

The carpal bones are short or cubical bones (p. 5). The only other short bones in the body are the tarsal bones. The metacarpals and phalanges are long or tubular bones.

Being cubical, the carpal bones have typically six surfaces. Of these, two surfaces, the *anterior* and *posterior*, are rough for the attachment of ligaments, while four surfaces articulate with adjacent bones and are, therefore, covered with cartilage. Obviously, the lateral surfaces of the lateral bones and the medial surfaces of the medial bones, otherwise known as the *marginal surfaces*, are not articular, but are rough for ligaments.

Cubical or short bones resemble the pressure epiphyses of long bones: (1) in structure —both being composed of cancellous tissue, which is completely encased within a shell of compact bone, which in turn is covered in part with hyaline cartilage, (2) in retaining red marrow for some years after it has disappeared from the bodies of long bones, and (3) in not starting to ossify until shortly before birth or within a few years after it.

The carpal bones, eight in number, are arranged in a proximal and a distal row, each of four bones. Their names express their general appearance. From radial to ulnar side they are:

Proximal row—*scaphoid*, *lunate*, *triquetrum*, and *pisiform*.

Distal row—*trapezium*, *trapezoid*, *capitate*, and *hamate*.

(Scaphoid = navicular, in B.N.A.
Trapezium = greater multangular,
Trapezoid = lesser multangular.)

It may be helpful first to picture these as eight uniform cubes arranged as in figure

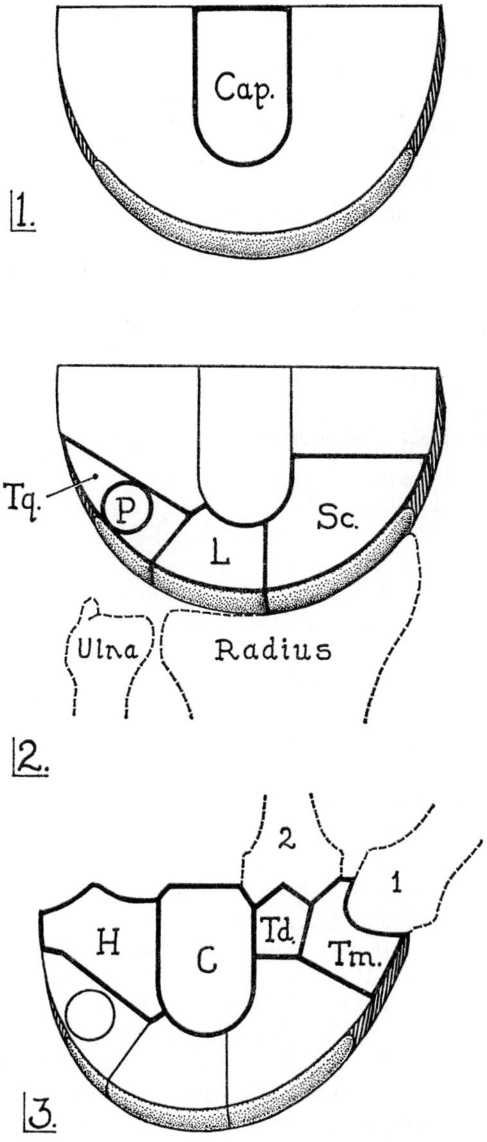

FIG. 130. Steps in drawing the carpal bones (see text).

129, but a glance at an articulated skeleton shows a more complex arrangement. The series of diagrams in figure 130 illustrates the plan. Observe that: (1) the pisiform articulates with only the triquetrum and lies entirely in front of it; therefore, (2) to the wrist joint the remaining three proximal bones present a common articular surface, which is a convex ovoid that allows movements in all directions (except rotation); (3) the capitate is the largest bone; it is centrally located and around it the others are organized; its caput or head fits into a concavity provided by the proximal row; (4) on the lateral side the scaphoid is elongated distally while the trapezium and trapezoid are relatively small; (5) the hamate reaches the lunate between the capitate and triquetrum, and so (6) the line of articulation between proximal and distal rows—called the midcarpal joint—is seen to be sinuous, having a very sharp "jog" laterally; this limits abduction and adduction between the two rows but allows flexion; (7) the trapezium has a saddle-shaped articular surface for the base of the first metacarpal, giving it great mobility (*fig. 131*); (8) the second metacarpal is deeply wedged and immobilized between the trapezium, trapezoid, and capitate; (9) the broad distal surface of the capitate articulates with the flat base of the third metacarpal; (10) the hamate has two adjoining concave surfaces for the concave base of the 4th and 5th metacarpals; these permit a slight degree of flexion; and (11) the sides of the bases of the metacarpals 2, 3, 4, and 5 articulate with each other.

Distal Surface of Carpus and Bases of Metacarpals. Neither have we here plane gliding surfaces, such as would allow the metacarpals to shift from side to side, and backward and forward. They are very irregular (*fig. 131*), and the irregularities are now to be accounted for. The metacarpal bones of the five digits (thumb and four fingers) have only four carpal bones with which to articulate. The articulated hand reveals that the bases of the 4th and 5th metacarpals articulate with the hamate. [In the more primitive carpus, e.g., that of the turtle, the *hamate* like its homologue in the foot, the *cuboid*, is represented by two bones.]

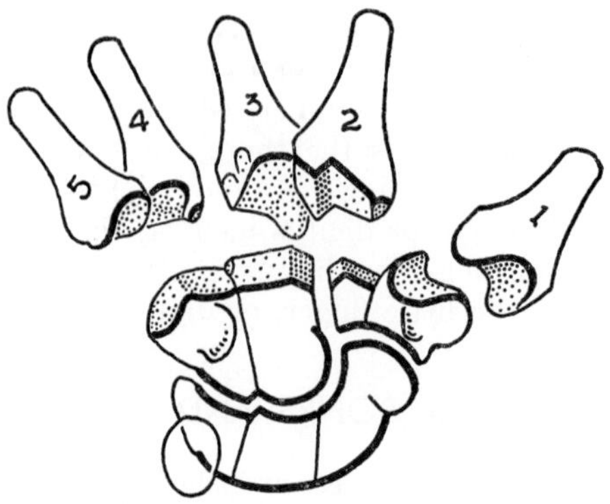

FIG. 131. The carpal bones and the bases of the metacarpal bones.

Grasp in turn the knuckles or heads of the metacarpals of your own fingers, noting that the 5th metacarpal can be moved freely backward and forward, that the 4th metacarpal can be moved to a less degree, and that the 3rd and 2nd metacarpals are almost immobile. Again, view the back of your knuckles as you tightly close your fist (*fig. 206*) and see illustrated the same fact: that the 5th and 4th metacarpals flex at their carpometacarpal joints while the 3rd and 2nd remain rigid and immobile. An examination of the carpus gives the reason: the 5th and 4th carpometacarpal joints are clearly hinge joints, the hamate presenting two concavities for the convex bases of the 5th and 4th metacarpals. [In the foot the corresponding articular surfaces of the cuboid for the 5th and 4th metatarsals are similarly fashioned.]

The capitate has an expansive plane surface for the base of the 3rd metacarpal. The trapezoid (lesser multangular) does not project so far distally as the carpals on each side of it; and in consequence, the base of the 2nd metacarpal is mortised between the capitate and trapezium (greater multangular), and in part articulates with them. The trapezoid, moreover, possesses an anteroposteriorly placed ridge which fits like a wedge into the guttered base of the 2nd metacarpal.

Although the metacarpal of the thumb or pollex can be flexed and extended, abducted and adducted, and rotated, it does not possess the spherical base you naturally look for,

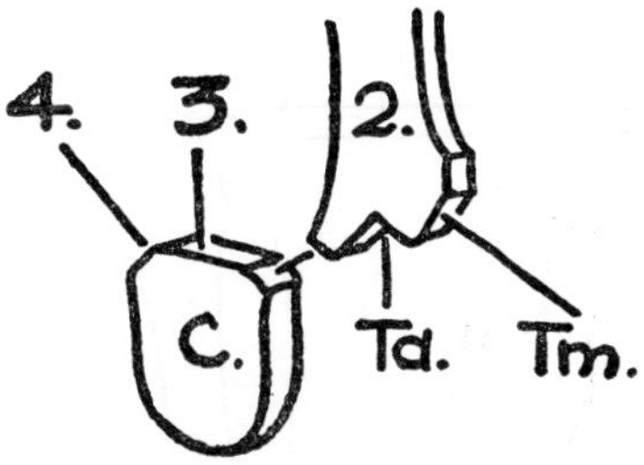

FIG. 132. The capitate articulates with three metacarpals. The 2nd metacarpal articulates with three carpals.

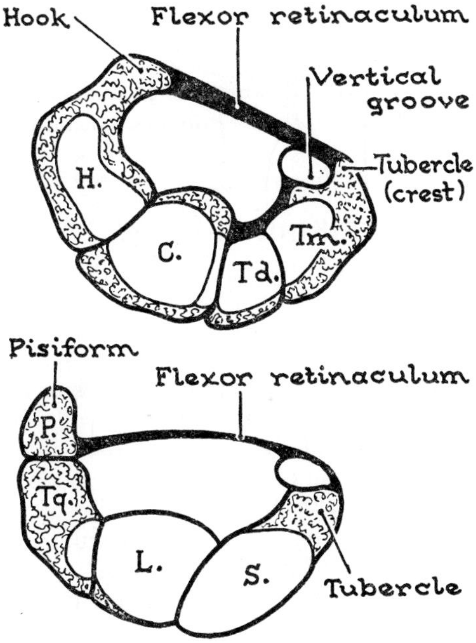

FIG. 133. The four marginal bones of the carpus give attachment to the flexor retinaculum.

but a saddle-shaped surface which fits on to the distal surface of the trapezium, which is reciprocally saddle-shaped. To allow these free movements the capsule around the carpometacarpal joint of the thumb must necessarily be slack.

It is instructive to note that the 2nd metacarpal articulates with three carpals, and that the stalwart capitate articulates with three metacarpals (*fig. 132*).

Dorsal and Palmar Aspects of Carpus. Observe that the dorsum of your wrist is transversely arched or convex, and that the dorsum of an articulated carpus likewise is transversely arched or convex. Its palmar surface is hollow or concave. The arched condition is maintained by a tie beam, the **flexor retinaculum** (transverse carpal ligament), which unites the marginal bones of the carpus. Its proximal part extends between two rounded prominences, namely, the *pisiform* and the *tubercle of the scaphoid* (*fig. 133*), whereas its distal part stretches between two crests, namely, the *hook of the hamate* and the *tubercle of the trapezium*. These crests, being the ossified ends of the distal half of the tie-beam, are directed toward each other.

The tubercle of the trapezium is also the lateral lip of a groove in which the tendon of the Flexor Carpi Radialis runs on its way to the base of the 2nd (and 3rd) metacarpal, where it is inserted. The groove is, therefore, placed vertically; and at its upper end is the prominent tubercle of the scaphoid which acts as a pulley over which the tendon plays.

Like the stones in an arch of masonry the carpal bones are broad on their convex or dorsal aspects, and narrower on their concave or palmar aspects, with the single exception of the lunate which is more expansive ventrally than dorsally. When the lunate becomes dislocated or dislodged, the displacement is usually forward. The trapezoid makes a very slight appearance on the front of the carpus.

(The Carpal Bones in detail, see p. 156.)

Palpable Parts. The lowest transverse skin crease at the front of the wrist has been seen to cross the pisiform and the tubercle of the scaphoid. The Flexor Carpi Ulnaris has been traced to the pisiform, and the Flexor Carpi Radialis to the tubercle of the scaphoid. The hook of the hamate can be palpated as a resistant structure infero-lateral to the pisiform, the interval between them being sufficient to allow the passage of the ulnar artery and nerve (*fig. 144*). Immediately below the tubercle of the scaphoid lie the groove and tubercle of the trapezium. The tubercle can be identified by its resistant feel. The scaphoid and the trapezium can also be palpated in the **"anatomical snuff-box"**, that is, the hollow at the lateral side of the wrist between the styloid process of the radius proximally and the base of the metacarpal of the pollex distally. Here the radial artery crosses them, and its pulse can be felt on employing light pressure.

» **Midcarpal Joint** (Transverse Carpal Joint). This joint lies between the proximal and distal rows of carpal bones (*fig. 134*). Here the trapezium and trapezoid together form a *small lateral unit* which presents a concave, oval surface for articulation with the convex, oval distal surface of the scaphoid. The capitate and hamate together form a *large medial unit*, which articulates with the concave socket formed by the scaphoid, lunate, and triquetrum. The midcarpal joint therefore is sinuous.

The capitate or bone with a head (L. caput = head) is the largest and most centrally placed of the carpal bones. Its medial surface is flat, faces the hamate (L. hamulus = hook), and is in part smooth and articular and in part rough for a ligament. Its rounded head excavates the two lateral bones of the proximal row of carpals, causing one to resemble a boat (Gk. skaphe = boat) and the other, a new moon (L. luna = moon). The tubercle of the scaphoid is the bow of the boat; the flat stern articulates with the lunate.

Joint Surfaces. When you close your fist or grasp an object, your wrist automatically becomes extended (*fig. 209*). Extension at the radiocarpal joint is more free than flexion; therefore, the articular cartilage covering the proximal surfaces of the scaphoid, lunate, and triquetral bones extends far dorsally. The greater part of the flexion that appears to take place at the radiocarpal joint actually takes place at the midcarpal joint.

When you touch the back of your right shoulder with the tips of your right digits, by raising your arm forward, you may be said to wind up your limb, by flexing the following joints: shoulder, elbow, radiocarpal, midcarpal, 1st, 4th, and 5th carpometacarpal (the 2nd and 3rd are immobile), metacarpo-phalangeal, and interphalangeal. One bony surface of each of these joints is necessarily concave; the other is convex.

Striking a Blow. You may crystallize your knowledge of the carpals by considering the mechanism involved in striking a blow. When you strike a blow with your fist, you instinctively employ the knuckles of the 2nd and 3rd metacarpals in preference to those of the 4th and 5th. Why is this? Because, (1) The 2nd and 3rd metacarpals are long, stout, and strong; whereas the 4th and 5th are shorter and more slender. (2) The bases of the 2nd and 3rd are individually equal in surface area to the combined bases of the 4th and 5th. (3) The 2nd and 3rd are rigid and immobile; whereas the 4th and 5th are not. (4) The line of force traveling along the 2nd and 3rd metacarpals is transmitted directly to the radius via the trapezoid and scaphoid, and via the capitate and lunate (*figs. 134* and *143*); whereas that traveling along the 4th and 5th is transmitted via the apex of the hamate to a linear facet on the lunate and so to the radius. Further, (5) The upper articular facet of the triquetrum, such as it is (*fig. 133*), is applied to the ulnar collateral ligament (medial lig.) of the wrist, except during adduction of the wrist when it moves into contact with the articular disc of the radiocarpal joint; so, the triquetrum and pisiform are not force transmitters.

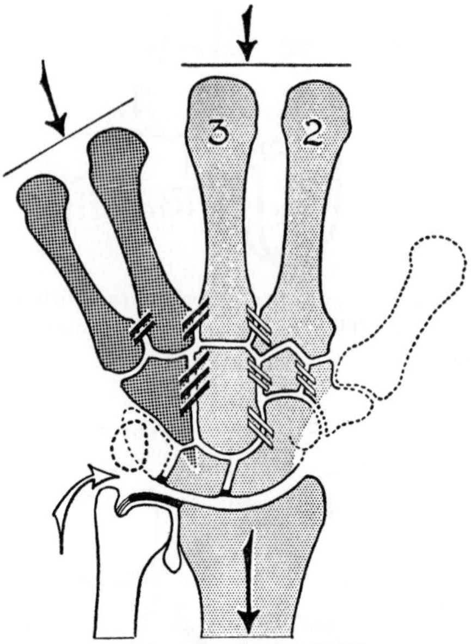

STRIKING A BLOW

FIG. 134. When striking a blow use the 2nd and 3rd knuckles. Observe that the ligaments take the directions of usefulness.

Ligaments. On striking with the 4th and 5th knuckles, the direction taken by the strong interosseous ligaments uniting the 4th to the 3rd metacarpal, and the hamate to the capitate, is such as to relieve the linear facet on the lunate of the brunt of the impact. And the small facet on the capitate for the 4th metacarpal takes some of the impact directly.

» **Intercarpal Ligaments.** The various carpal bones are bound to each other by dorsal and palmar bands which largely radiate from the capitate. The bones of the proximal row are further united to each other by interosseous bands which shut off the radiocarpal joint from the intercarpal joints. The bones of the distal row are united to each other by incomplete interosseous ligaments, of which the one between the hamate and capitate is very strong. No interosseous bands exist to hamper the movements between proximal and distal rows, where flexion is so surprisingly free. Between the individual bones of each row a slight amount of gliding can take place; that is to say, the joints are plane (arthrodial).

Observation: No muscle is inserted into any carpal bone. All muscles that cross the radiocarpal joint also cross the midcarpal and carpometacarpal joints, that is to say, they span the carpus, gain insertion to the metacarpals and phalanges, and control the joints they cross. Three short muscles of the thumb and three of the little finger, however, arise from the flexor retinaculum and from the four marginal bones united by it.

When saying no muscle is inserted into any carpal bone, one is regarding the pisiform as a *sesamoid bone* developed in the tendon of the Fl. Carpi Ulnaris and as being to the Fl. Carpi Ulnaris what the patella is to the Quadriceps Femoris. The pisometacarpal ligament, which passes from pisiform to the base of the 5th metacarpal may be likened to the lig. patellae (*fig. 145*).

Variants. Certain tendons (Abd. Pollicis Longus and Fl. Carpi Radialis) may send slips to the trapezium.

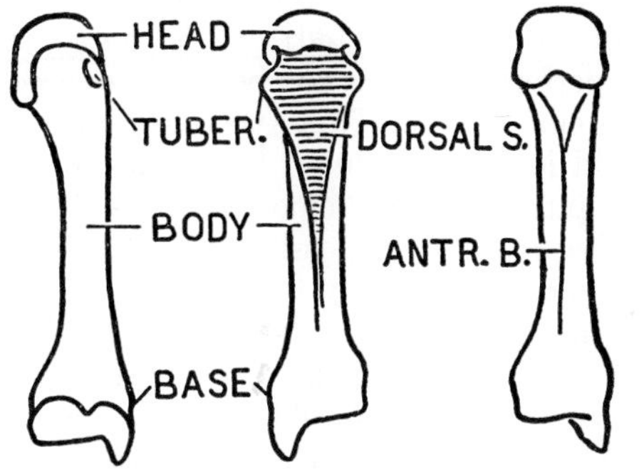

FIG. 135. A metacarpal bone

METACARPAL BONES AND THEIR JOINTS

The metacarpal bones are long bones, each having a body and two ends.

The **Proximal Ends or Bases** have articular facets which are counterparts of the distal surfaces of the carpals (*fig. 131*). They have been described. You will remember that the second metacarpal articulates with three carpals—the trapezium, trapezoid, and capitate; and that the capitate articulates with three metacarpals—the 2nd, 3rd, and 4th. The 1st, 3rd, and 5th metacarpals articulate with one carpal each, the 4th with two, and the 2nd with three. Further, the apposed surfaces of the bases of the 2nd, 3rd, 4th, and 5th metacarpals articulate with each other and, therefore, carry articular facets. The base of the 3rd metacarpal has a styloid process on its postero-lateral side, but nothing is attached to it. The base of the 5th metacarpal has a tubercle on its medial side for the insertion of the Extensor Carpi Ulnaris.

The **Bodies of the Metacarpal Bones of the Four Fingers** (*fig. 135*) are triangular on cross-section. Each has a rounded, anterior border which separates an anterolateral from an anteromedial surface. As the anterolateral and anteromedial surfaces approach the base of the bone they wind dorsally. In consequence of this encroachment, the dorsal surface is rendered triangular and its apex tapers proximally into a line. This surface is bare, flat, and palpable.

The **Metacarpal of the Thumb** is short, stout, and flattened from before backward. It is rounded posteriorly, like a

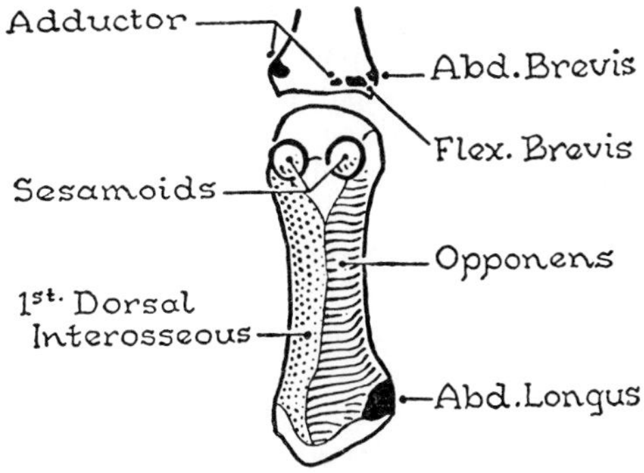

FIG. 136. Metacarpal of thumb, showing attachments of muscles, palmar aspect.

phalanx; ventrally it is divided, like any other metacarpal, into antero-lateral and antero-medial surfaces. Of these the antero-lateral, for the fleshy insertion of the Opponens, is greater than the antero-medial, which gives origin to the lateral head of the first Dorsal Interosseus. By this you can tell to which side a first metacarpal belongs (*fig. 136*). The base is saddle-shaped. The head is compressed antero-posteriorly; and, in front, a non-articular notch separates the facets on which the two sesamoid bones play.

The Metacarpo-phalangeal Joint. Observe on your own hand that your knuckles, i.e., the heads of the metacarpals of the fingers, are uncovered when the fingers are flexed, and that these uncovered heads are spheroidal. The bases of the proximal phalanges fit the metacarpal heads and, so, are concave.

The metacarpo-phalangeal articulations of the four fingers can be flexed and extended;

and, when the hand is open, they can also be abducted and adducted; that is to say, they can perform the four component movements of circumduction. They, therefore, are condyloid joints (Kondulos, Gk. = a knuckle). Manipulation will demonstrate that some passive rotation is possible too; but, little, if any, occurs actively.

When the joints are flexed, neither abduction nor adduction is possible; and, the reason for this is two-fold: (1) because the heads of the metacarpals, though rounded at their ends, are flattened in front; (2) because the **collateral ligaments,** though slack on extension, are taut on flexion, due to their eccentric attachments to the sides of the heads of the metacarpals. Look, therefore, near the posterior part of the side of the head of a metacarpal for an eccentrically placed *tubercle* and for a *pit* in front of it to which the collateral ligament is attached (*fig. 137*).

To allow flexion and extension the anterior and posterior parts of the capsule must necessarily be lax. Posteriorly there are no ligaments to these joints: the extensor (dorsal) expansions of the extensor muscles effectively serve the part. After all, when the hand is closed, it is grasping some object or, if not, the fingers close on the palm; but in neither case is strain put upon the back of the capsule.

Anteriorly, the capsule is replaced by a fibrocartilaginous plate, the **palmar ligament** or **plate** (volar accessory lig.). This plate is firmly united to the anterior edge of the base of the phalanx, and loosely attached to the metacarpal bone. In consequence, if a finger is wrenched off the hand, the plate-like palmar ligament will part from the metacarpal and remain attached to the phalanx. Fibers of the collateral ligaments radiate to the sides of this plate and keep it firmly applied to the front of the head of its metacarpal, visor-fashion (*fig. 137*).

The plate lies between the front of the head of a metacarpal and the flexor tendons; and, although known as the palmar ligament, it is not a bond of union between the two bones that it connects, but is part of the articular socket.

The sides of the palmar ligaments of the

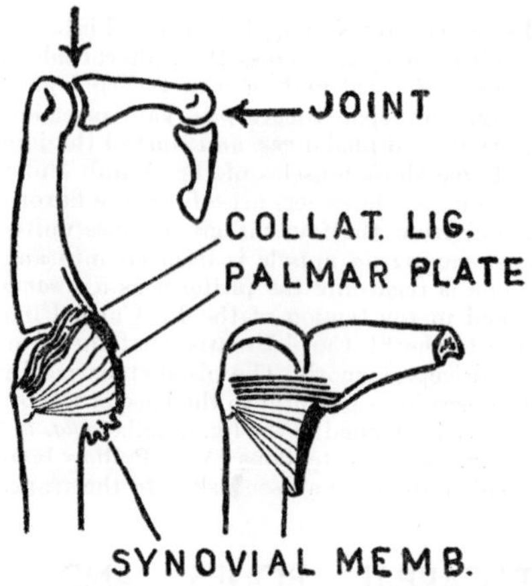

FIG. 137. Metacarpo-phalangeal and interphalangeal joints.

fingers are united to each other by three ligamentous bands, the **deep transverse metacarpal ligaments,** which help to prevent the metacarpals from spreading. They leave the thumb free (*fig. 170*). In front of the transverse ligaments pass the digital vessels and nerves and the Lumbricals; behind them pass the Interossei. Slips from the four digital bands of the palmar aponeurosis are attached to the transverse ligs. (*fig. 149*) in front; slips from the extensor expansions are attached to them behind.

The Metacarpo-phalangeal Joint of the Thumb. The head of the metacarpal is rounded and the base of the phalanx is concave. The movements allowed are: flexion and extension, some rocking from side to side, and some rotation.

PHALANGES AND THEIR JOINTS

The phalanges also are long bones, two for the thumb and three for each of the other digits. They are known as: the proximal or 1st; the middle or 2nd; and the distal or 3rd (*fig. 138*).

The distal ends of the distal phalanges have a smooth surface and a rough one. The fingernail overlies the smooth surface; the area for the finger-pad is rough owing to the attachment of fibrous bands that bind the skin to it.

The dorsal aspects of the proximal and

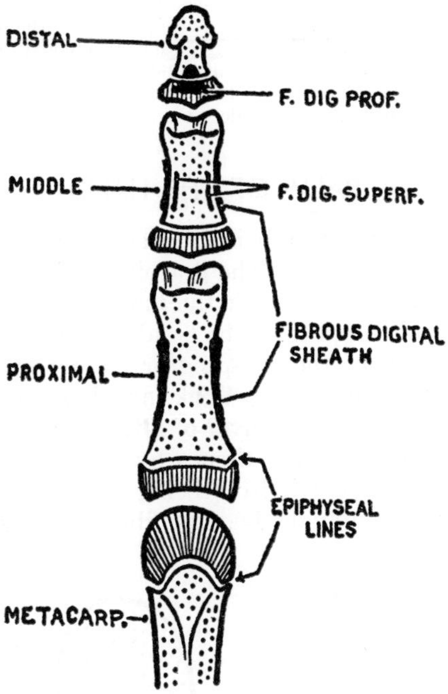

FIG. 138. Phalanges (palmar aspect) showing epiphyseal lines and attachments of fibrous sheath and flexor tendons.

middle phalanges are smooth, rounded and covered with the extensor expansion. The palmar surfaces take part in the floor of the osseofibrous tunnels (*fig. 150*) in which the flexor tendons glide. They are smooth and flat.

Each phalanx has a medial and a lateral border. The borders of the proximal and middle phalanges possess sharp crests for the attachment of the transverse, or rather arched, fibers of the fibrous digital sheath. Those of the middle phalanx are especially well marked because to them are also attached the slips of insertion of the Fl. Digitorum Superficialis.

When your hand is closed, the heads of the middle and proximal phalanges are uncovered. They have two little condyles. The bases of the distal and middle phalanges have two little depressions. The bases of the proximal phalanges articulate with the rounded knuckles and are concave.

The Interphalangeal Joints are constructed on the same plan as the metacarpophalangeal joints of the fingers. Each possesses collateral ligaments, a palmar fibrocartilage, and a loose dorsal capsule guarded by an extensor expansion. Their movements, however, are restricted to flexion and extension in consequence of the antero-posterior flattening of the ends of the bones. Patently, they are ginglymus or hinge joints.

OSSIFICATION OF BONES OF HAND

The bodies of the metacarpals and phalanges start to ossify during the 3rd prenatal month. The carpal bones, unlike the tarsal bones, have not started to ossify at the time of birth, although, in the female, centers may have appeared in the capitate and hamate. The carpals proceed to ossify in orderly spiral sequence, approximately in the following years: capitate and hamate 1st, triquetrum 3rd, lunate 4th, scaphoid 5th, trapezoid and trapezium 6th—and the pisiform 12th (*fig. 139*).

Epiphyses. Each of the long bones has one epiphysis: in the metacarpals these occur at the heads; in the phalanges at the bases—the metacarpal of the thumb is the exception, for it resembles a phalanx in that its epiphysis is at its base.

The epiphyses start to ossify in the 2nd to 3rd year and fuse in the 17th to 19th year. Epiphyses have been found at both ends of the 1st and 2nd metacarpals.

Radiograms (*fig. 140*). The hand and wrist are always accessible and they happen to be eminently suitable for X-ray photography, because the radiograms are sharp and clear. They impart information on the stage of ossification of no less than 29 bones.

Now, sex, stature, weight, and *chronological age* are usually known. And at any given time during the period of physical growth, which is from birth to about the

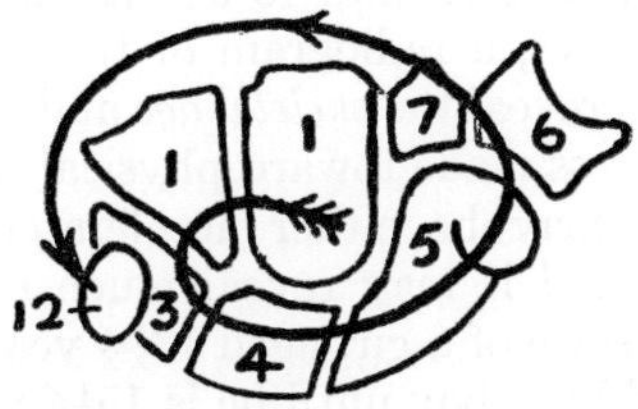

FIG. 139. Spiral sequence of ossification of carpals; approximate ages in years.

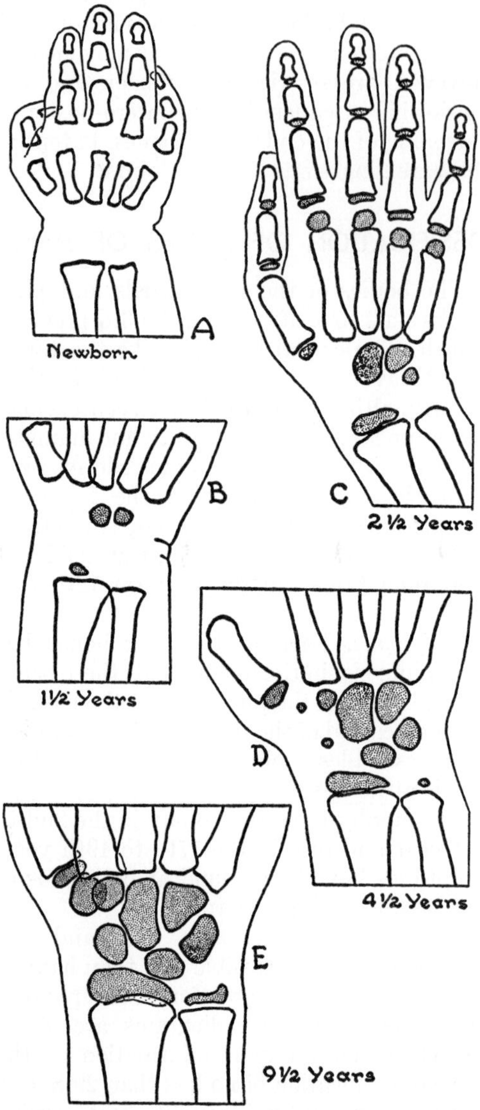

FIG. 140. Progressive ossification of the bones of the hand. (Courtesy of Dr. J. D. Munn, Hospital for Sick Children, Toronto.)

17th year in girls and to about the 18th or 19th in boys, a radiogram of the hand and wrist will reveal the *skeletal age* and therefore the progress made toward physical maturity —which may be either accelerated or retarded—and it may reveal much else. The skeletal state of a girl aged 13½ years is not achieved by a boy until he is 15½ years old (Greulich and Pyle).

» Garn *et al.* find that the hand alone cannot be used as a standard of skeletal development for the whole body, that all ossific centers do not have equal predictive value, and that a small number of centers of high predictive value in the hand and foot provide more useful information than does the entire number.

PALM OF THE HAND

The upper limb is used as a grasping or prehensile organ. The grasping is done with the hand, the rest of the limb being an adjustable support for the hand. In adaptation, the skin of the grasping or palmar surface of the hand is very thick, and it rests on a protective pliable layer of fat. It is anchored to the underlying tissues by fibrous bands, which prevent it from being drawn off as a loose glove might be. The fibrous bands are

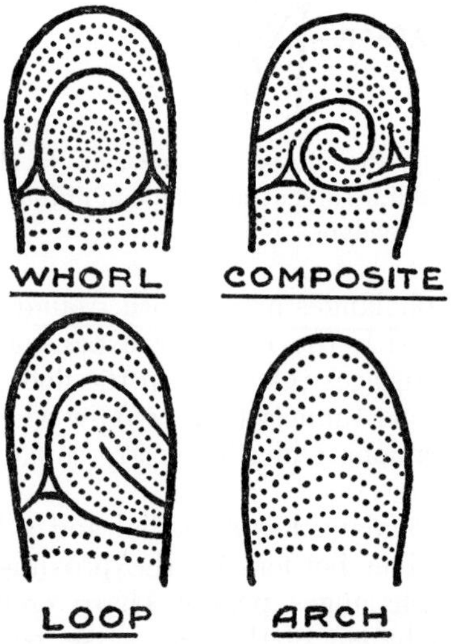

FIG. 141. Types of finger prints (After Wilder.)

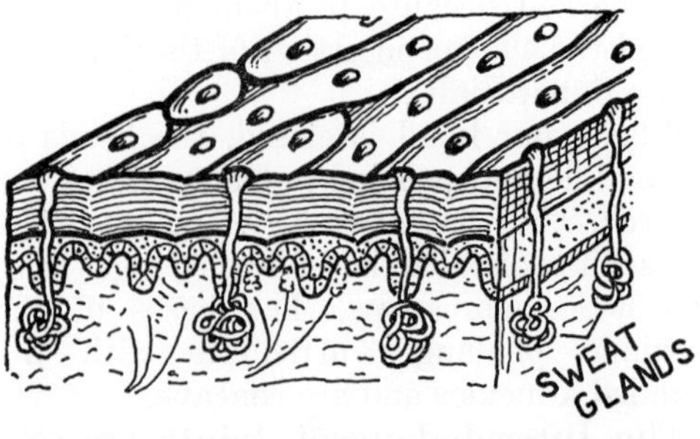

FIG. 142. Friction ridges and orifices of ducts of sweat glands on the fingers. (After Wilder.)

most dense at the pads of the fingers where they extend to the bone, along the sides of the fingers, and in front of the palmar aponeurosis. The fat, accordingly, tends to be imprisoned in loculi, as in the breast.

In order that the grip shall not slip, the skin is corrugated; it is ridged and furrowed, and there is a convenient absence of greasy, sebaceous glands. On the summits of the ridges the mouths of numerous sweat glands open. The disposition of the ridges in arches, loops, and whorls differs in detail from person to person; so does the spacing, the shape, and the size of the mouths of the sweat glands. The impressions left by the ridges and gland mouths are known as **Finger Prints** (*figs. 141* and *142*).

Permanent **Skin Creases** occur in the hand. On the digits they are transverse; in the palm they have the form of the letter M; the lowest of the three at the wrist is bowed. At the creases there is an absence of fat and the skin is bound to the underlying fibrous tissue. Movements of flexion and of opposition, as you can readily determine, are responsible for the creases. The relation of the creases to the joints is shown in figures 143 and 125.

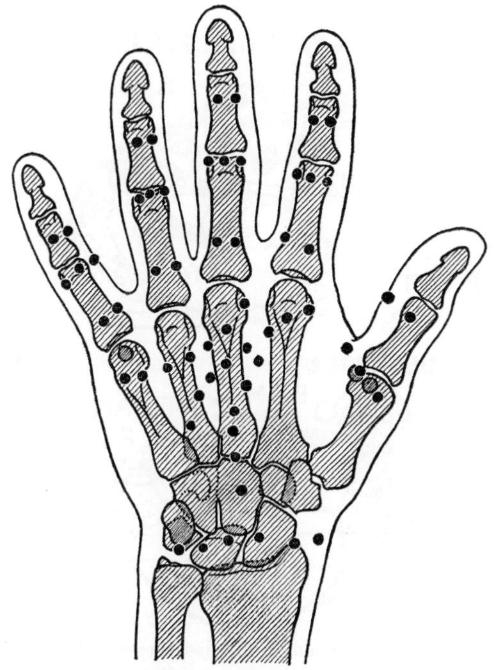

FIG. 143. Tracing of X-ray of hand. Shot was placed on the skin creases to show their relations to the joints (see *fig. 125*).

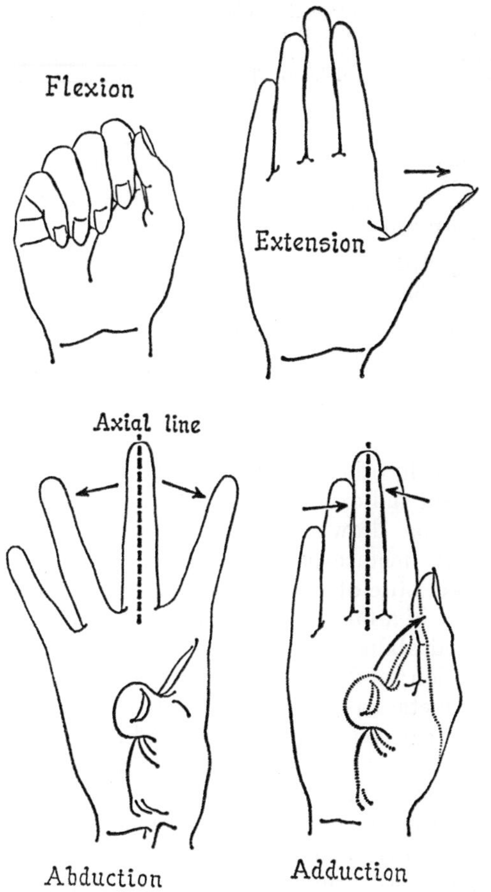

FIG. 143.1. Movements of fingers and thumb defined.

Surface Anatomy. Here are some points of significance: (1) The most distal skin crease at the front of the wrist represents (2) the proximal border of the flexor retinaculum. (3) Behind the midpoint of the skin crease the median nerve descends (*fig. 147*), and dorsal to this nerve lies (4) the lunate bone (*fig. 143*). Hence, (5) forward dislocation of the bone compresses the nerve against the retinaculum.

The folds of skin, called the *webs of the fingers*, are palmar structures and are not present on the dorsum.

»» The most projecting digit is the middle finger; next in order come the ring finger, index, little finger, and thumb, so the **Digital Formula** reads, 3 > 4 > 2 > 5 > 1 (Wood Jones). This is the primitive arrangement. It is common to apes and man including the N. American Indian. In 19 per cent of white people the index and ring project equally (3 > 4 = 2 > 5 > 1) and in 33 per cent the index exceeds the ring finger 3 > 2 > 4 > 5 > 1). Among white females the percentages are higher than among the males (George). A long index is characteristic of white races.

Definitions. Movement of Digits. Note that the thumb is set at right angles to the other digits; that, whereas the nails of the fingers of the open hand face backward, the nail of the thumb faces laterally; and that, on opening and closing the hand the fingers and thumb move on planes at right angles to each other. These are movements of flexion and extension.

A line drawn through the middle finger, middle metacarpal and capitate is called the **Axial Line of the Hand** (*fig. 143.1*). Movement of a finger away from this axial line is called abduction; movement toward it, adduction; and the movements take place at the metacarpo-phalangeal joints. The thumb also can be abducted and adducted; the movements take place, however, not at its metacarpo-phalangeal joint, but at its carpometacarpal joint; the movement forward (anteriorly) being abduction, and backward (posteriorly) adduction; that is to say, in the antero-posterior (sagittal) plane you flex and extend your fingers, abduct and adduct your thumb; whereas in the side-to-side (coronal) plane you abduct and adduct your fingers and flex and extend your thumb.

Carpometacarpal Joint of Thumb. Thus far the thumb appears in no way superior to a finger. Consider however its carpometacarpal articulation where, in addition to the movements of flexion–extension, and abduction–adduction, the extra movements of medial and lateral rotation are permitted. It is to these latter movements of rotation that the thumb owes its peculiar value, a value that exalts it above many fingers. The metacarpal of the thumb sits on the trapezium as though astride a saddle, enjoying all the movements of a ball and socket joint. Here, then, we are dealing with a multiaxial joint of the saddle variety (p. 21).

»» The capsule of the joint is necessarily slack. Now, there are in this loose capsule two ligamentous bands, called the anterior and posterior *oblique carpometacarpal ligaments*. These arise from the respective surfaces of the trapezium and converge to be inserted near each other on the ulnar side of the base of the 1st metacarpal. During the act of flexion, the posterior ligament becomes taut and forces the metacarpal into medial rotation; similarly, during the act of extension, the anterior ligament forces the metacarpal into lateral rotation. (Haines.)

Flexor Retinaculum. The dorsum of your wrist, like the dorsum of your foot, is transversely arched or convex. This arched condition of the wrist or carpus is maintained by a tie-beam, the *flexor retinaculum* (*fig. 144*). The retinaculum forms with the carpal bones an osseofibrous tunnel, the *carpal tunnel.* You can pass a finger through it but not a thumb.

The proximal part of the retinaculum stretches feebly between two rounded prominences, the *tubercle of the scaphoid* and the *pisiform;* the distal part stretches between two crests, the *tubercle of the trapezium* and the *hook of the hamate* (*fig. 149*). The crests may be regarded as the ossified ends of the retinaculum.

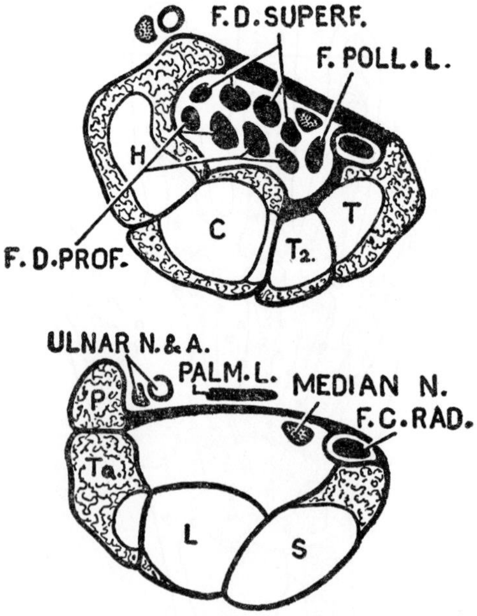

FIG. 144. Proximal and distal rows of carpal bones viewed from above (i.e., distal surfaces of the radiocarpal and midcarpal joints). The flexor retinaculum forming the osseofibrous carpal tunnel.

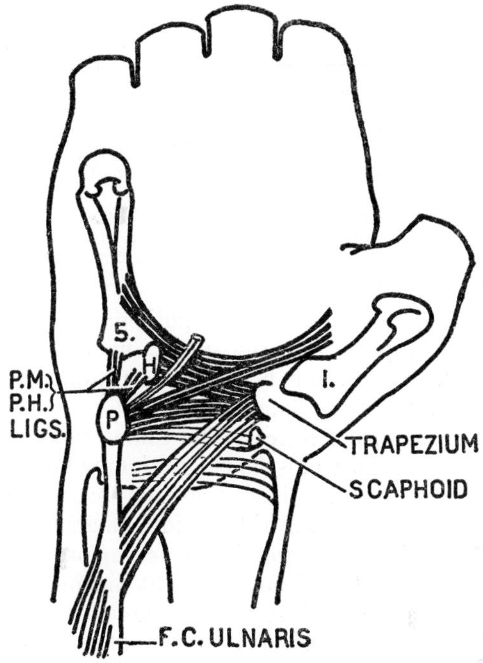

FIG. 145. The flexor retinaculum (P.M. = pisometacarpal; P.H. = pisohamate).

›› The distal band is always taut; but the proximal band, being attached to the movable pisiform, depends on the **Fl. Carpi Ulnaris** to steady it. Figure 145 is a detailed picture of the retinaculum. It depicts the scaphoid as affording the retinaculum but little attachment, the Flexor Carpi Ulnaris as extending its grasp to the trapezium, the upper border of the retinaculum as blending with the deep fascia of the forearm, and the lower border as concave owing to the attachments it gives to the short muscles of digits I and V.

Insertion. The tendon of the Flexor Carpi Ulnaris is relayed beyond the pisiform to the base of metacarpal V and to the hook of the hamate by the *pisometacarpal* and *pisohamate ligaments.*

Functions. The flexor retinaculum not only acts as (1) a tie beam; but also plays the part of (2) a restraining band that prevents the long flexors of the digits from "bowstringing" when the wrist is flexed; and (3) it affords chief origin to the thenar and hypothenar muscles.

The Three Thenar Muscles (MUSCLES OF THE BALL OF THE THUMB) arise together from the flexor retinaculum and its two lateral bony pillars (tubercle of scaphoid and tubercle of trapezium).

The most superficial of them, the *Abductor Pollicis Brevis,* is inserted into the lateral side of the base of the proximal phalanx of the thumb (*fig. 136*) and slightly into the tendon of the Ex. Pollicis Brevis. It is self-evident from its position and attachments that it draws the thumb forward (i.e., abducts it); and the movement takes place at the saddle-shaped carpometacarpal joint.

Reflexion of the Abductor uncovers a fleshy sheet (*fig. 146*) that extends obliquely inferolaterally to be inserted into the whole length of the anterolateral surface of the metacarpal of the thumb and adjacent part of the base of its proximal phalanx. This sheet resembles the Pronator Teres of the radius in direction and in action. On this account it might appropriately be called the "*Pronator Pollicis*". It pronates or medially rotates the thumb at its carpometacarpal joint, and flexes it at its metacarpo-phalangeal joint.

The portion inserted into the metacarpal is named the *Opponens Pollicis;* the portion into the phalanx, the *Flexor Pollicis Brevis* (*fig. 136*). To find the line of cleavage between them, you should expose the metacarpo-phalangeal joint and then, by working proximally, effect a separation of muscle fibers. Because there is little, if any, areolar

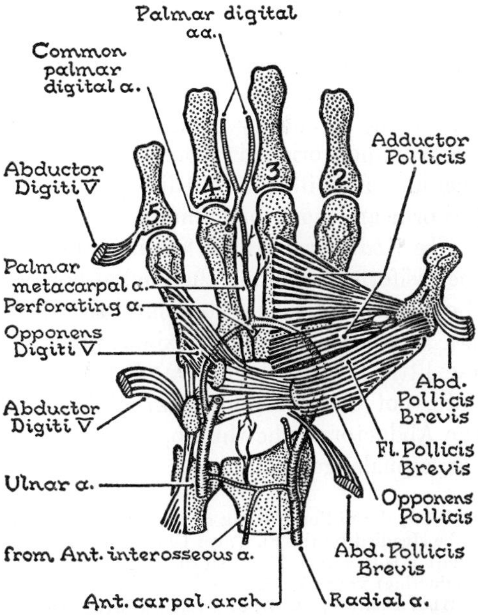

FIG. 146. Short muscles of thumb and 5th digit. Arteries of hand (semischematic).

tissue between the two portions, it is difficult to think that they do other than act and behave as one—opposition is always accompanied usefully by flexion.

The insertion of the Fl. Pollicis Brevis into the proximal phalanx is largely via the radial sesamoid embedded in the palmar ligament.

NERVE TO THE THREE THENAR MUSCLES. A branch of the median, it takes a recurrent course around the lower border of the retinaculum. It is to be found lying 1¼″ vertically below the point where the skin crease, corresponding to the upper border of the retinaculum, crosses the tubercle of the scaphoid (*figs. 147* and *125*). A small coin centered on this point will cover the nerve, whose importance is bound up with the importance of the thumb itself.

The deep fascia covering the thenar eminence is too thin to afford the nerve much protection, and for practical purposes it is subcutaneous. A cut or a puncture wound of the skin may easily damage the nerve. The superficial palmar branch of the radial artery usually lies along the medial side of the nerve, and, so, serves as a guide to it.

The Three Hypothenar Muscles (MUSCLES OF THE BALL OF THE LITTLE FINGER) are in most respects mirror images of the muscles of the thenar eminence. In number, in name, in origin, in insertion, and in action the similarity is almost complete. The common origin is from the flexor retinaculum and its two medial pillars—viz., pisiform and hook of hamate.

The Abductor Digiti V springs only from the pisiform, lies along the medial border of the hand, and is inserted into the medial side of the base of the proximal phalanx of the little finger, which it abducts. It acts, note, not on a carpometacarpal joint, like the Abductor of the thumb, but on a metacarpo-phalangeal joint.

»» Now, the pisiform, being a movable bone, requires to be steadied by the Fl. Carpi Ulnaris when the Abd. Digiti V is in action. This you can verify on spreading (abducting) your own fingers.

Abd. Digiti V, like Abd. Pollicis Brevis, is inserted slightly into an extensor expansion.

The Opponens Digiti V and *Flexor Digiti V*, like their namesakes of the thumb, arise from the flexor retinaculum and from a distal carpal bone (the hook of the hamate). Their insertions correspond exactly to those of the thumb. Their fibers run disto-medially.

The Flexor Digiti V appears to be a portion of the Abductor that has spread laterally in front of the Opponens. It is commonly absent.

The little finger cannot be opposed to the other fingers, because the degree of rotation permitted at its carpometacarpal joint is trivial. At this joint, however, flexion and extension take place, as described on page 138.

The Opponens and Flexor Digiti V flex the carpometacarpal joint of the little finger and, so, increase the hollow of the palm thereby adapting it for use as a drinking cup or to catching a ball.

Nerve Supply. The hypothenar muscles are supplied by the ulnar nerve (deep branch) as it runs between the pisiform and the hook of the hamate.

Adductor Pollicis. The thumb possesses a fourth short muscle, the Adductor Pollicis. It lies in the depths of the palm, arises from the palmar border of the middle metacarpal, from the corresponding carpal bone (the capitate), and from adjacent ligamentous material. It is inserted, via an ulnar sesamoid bone embedded in the palmar ligament into the base of the first phalanx of the thumb. It may also be inserted via the radial sesamoid (*fig. 146*). The deep palmar arch interrupts its origin, dividing it into a

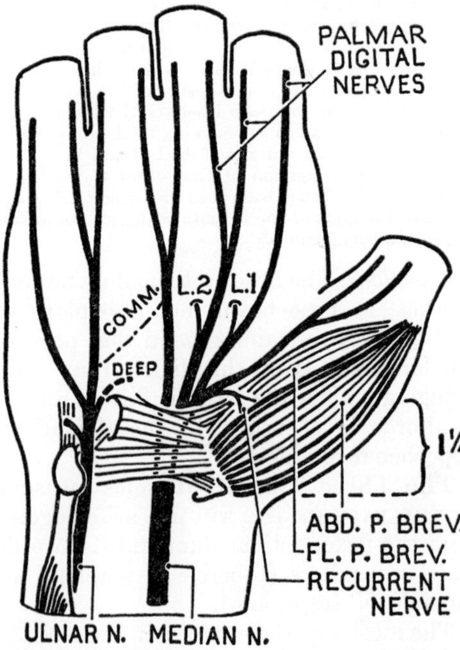

FIG. 147. Median and ulnar nerves and thenar muscles. (L. 1 and L. 2 = Lumbrical branches of median n.)

distal *transverse head* and a proximal *oblique head.*

The distal border of the Adductor is subcutaneous—or more accurately, it is subfascial—and is exposed by removing the skin at the cleft between the pollex and index, that is, at the distal end of the 1st intermetacarpal space. And, after removing the fascia at the cleft, the space between the Adductor and the 1st Dorsal Interosseus can be opened with the handle of a knife.

Actions. Obviously the Adductor draws the thumb across the palm and keeps it applied to the palm.

Nerve Supply. Contrary, perhaps, to expectation, it is supplied by the ulnar nerve.

Opposition is the bringing of the pad of the thumb to the pad of a finger and holding it there, as in pinching, writing, holding a cup by its handle, or fastening a button. Most delicate actions performed by the hand involve opposition.

As regards the thumb, the movements executed almost simultaneously are circumduction, rotation, and flexion. Rotation takes place principally at the metacarpo-phalangeal joint but also at the carpometacarpal joint, while the trapezium moves on the scaphoid and the scaphoid angulates forward (Bunnell).

The three joints of the opposing finger (or fingers) are flexed by the Profundus, the Superficialis, a Lumbrical, and two Interossei.

»» *Note.* Without two muscles supplied by the median nerve (Opponens and Flexor Pollicis Brevis), there would be no rotation. Without two muscles supplied by the ulnar nerve (Adductor Pollicis and an Interosseus), the grip would be weak. An Interosseus is required to steady (i.e., to prevent ulnar deviation of) the finger against which the Adductor Pollicis is exerting pressure. In the case of the index it is the 1st Dorsal Interosseus. Hence, ulnar paralysis results in weak opposition.

Ulnar Nerve. For reasons given, the ulnar nerve lies medial to its vessels. It enters the hand by passing vertically between the pisiform and the hook of the hamate (*figs. 147* and *148*) and therefore in front of the upper part of the flexor retinaculum and the pisohamate lig. It is covered first by a slip of deep fascia, and then by the **Palmaris Brevis** (*fig. 148*), which is a superficial sheet of muscle that passes from the retinaculum to the skin at the ulnar border of the hand. Between pisiform and hamate the nerve divides into a *deep* and a *superficial branch.*

Distribution. The superficial branch supplies cutaneous branches to the medial one and one-half fingers and the motor branch to the Palmaris Brevis, and it communicates with the median nerve. Twigs also pass to the joints of the fingers and to the local vessels.

The deep branch supplies the three muscles of the hypothenar eminence, and then curves around the lower edge of the hook of the hamate into the depths of the palm where it supplies all the short muscles of the hand, except the five supplied by the median nerve.

Median Nerve. After descending through the forearm, the median nerve crosses the midpoint of the skin crease of the wrist. It there lies medial to the Flexor Carpi Radialis tendon and under shelter of the Palmaris Longus tendon. It enters the palm through the carpal tunnel. In the tunnel, it adheres to the deep surface of the flexor retinaculum (*fig. 144*). It appears in the palm deep to the prolongation of the Palmaris Longus called the palmar aponeurosis, so it is fairly superficially placed. At once it begins to break up into "recurrent" and digital branches. These are distributed to five muscles and to the skin of the lateral three and one-half digits, to the joints of these digits and to the local vessels.

Motor Branches. The 5 muscles supplied by the median nerve are the three thenar muscles and the two lateral lumbrical muscles:

Abductor Pollicis Brevis }
Opponens Pollicis } by the recurrent branch
Flexor Pollicis Brevis }
and
1st Lumbrical }
2nd Lumbrical } by the palmar digital branches

These are shown in figure 147, and the "recurrent" branch is described on page 148.

»» *Variations in Motor Distribution.* The standard, or textbook, pattern of motor innervation to the hand just described, is commonly departed from either by the *ulnar nerve* encroaching on median nerve territory or vice versa. Thus, in 226 hands the ulnar nerve supplied Fl. Pollicis Brevis partially in 15 per cent and completely in 32 per cent; Abd. Pollicis Brevis in 3 per cent and all 3 thenar muscles in 2 per cent. Conversely, the *median nerve* supplied Add. Pollicis in 3 per cent,

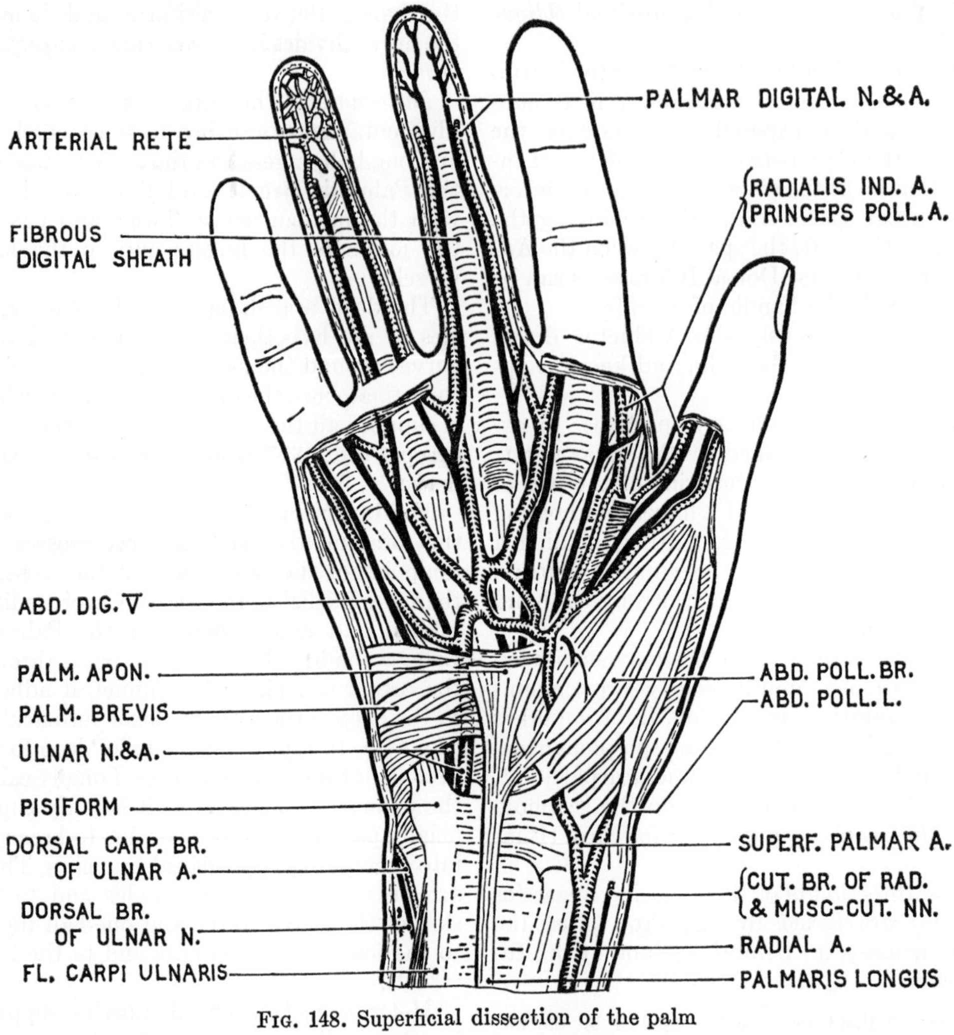

FIG. 148. Superficial dissection of the palm

and Add. Pollicis + first Dorsal Interosseus in 1 per cent. Neither the musculocutaneous nor the radial nerve has been proved to supply a thenar muscle (T. Rowntree, clinical observations).

The Palmar Digital Branches of the Median and Ulnar Nerves have been identified on the sides of the fibrous digital sheaths (p. 113). The palmar digital branches for the adjacent sides of the four fingers are derived from the three common palmar digital nerves that descend to the three interdigital clefts and after bifurcating become cutaneous at the webs of the fingers (*fig. 148*). These three nerves are protected by the tough palmar aponeurosis and are crossed only by the superficial palmar arch. Obviously, the branch to the radial side of the index and the branch to the ulnar side of the little finger do not bifurcate.

The two digital branches to the thumb descend in the furrow medial to the thenar eminence, where they lie first in front of the synovial sheath of the Flexor Pollicis Longus and thereafter along the sides of its fibrous digital (flexor) sheath.

»» The digital branches of the median and ulnar nerves to the ring finger communicate in the palm, and through this communication the ulnar nerve commonly extends its influence to median nerve territory and vice versa, varying the pattern (p. 114).

Palmar Aponeurosis. The Palmaris Longus tendon crosses in front of the flexor retinaculum, gains partial attachment to it, and in the palm divides into four broad, diverging bands of longitudinal fibers that descend to the roots of the four fingers, there to be lost in the subcutaneous tissues (*fig. 149*). Dorsal to each band runs a pair of long digital tendons (a Superficialis and a Profundus).

The Palmaris Longus has, then, an antebrachial portion and a palmar portion. The palmar portion is called the *palmar aponeurosis.* It receives an accession of fibers from the retinaculum; so, it is a stronger structure than the antebrachial portion, which may be missing.

In the distal half of the palm two parallel fibrous septa pass dorsally from each band to be attached to the palmar ligs. (plates) and to the sheet of fascia continuous with them that covers the deep muscles of the palm (Interossei and Adductor Pollicis) (*fig. 154*). Thus is the palmar aponeurosis anchored distally to the 1st phalanges and to the metacarpals.

» The longest and strongest of these anchoring septa lie on each side of the tendons passing to the middle finger. To display them make a longitudinal incision through the band that descends to the middle finger, turn the cut edges aside and with forceps reveal the sharp, curved, proximal margins of the septa.

The four diverging digital bands are united by transverse fibers. Lying deep to the transverse fibers are the digital vessels and nerves and the Lumbricals. Thus, in the palm there are alternate sets of tunnels deep to the palmar aponeurosis: (1) tunnels for long digital flexor tendons, and (2) tunnels for Lumbricals and digital vessels and nerves.

Structures Crossing the Skin Crease at the Wrist to Enter the Palm (*fig. 144*).

1. Those crossing superficially and not entering the carpal tunnel are:

a. The ulnar nerve and vessels.

b. The Palmaris Longus.

c. The superficial palmar branch of the radial artery (*fig. 148*).

d. The palmar cutaneous nerves derived from the ulnar, median, musculocutaneous, and radial nerves (*fig. 98*).

2. Those traversing the carpal tunnel are:

a. Flexor Pollicis Longus and Flexor Digitorum Profundus, lying side by side.

b. Flexor Digitorum Superficialis: tendons III and IV lie in front of II and V as they approach the tunnel, and lie between them, side by side, as they leave. Tendon V is very slender.

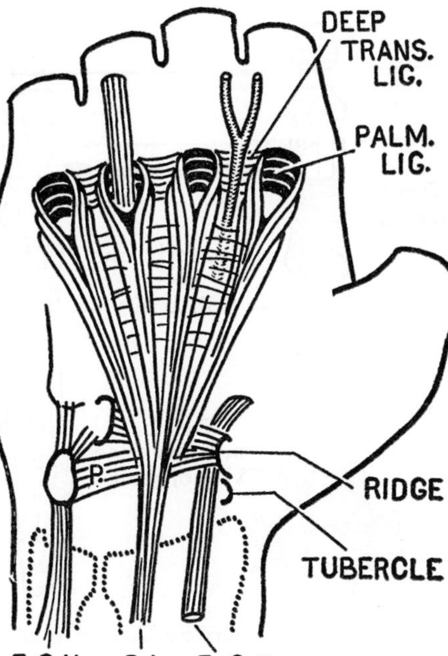

FIG. 149. The three flexors of the wrist. Palmar aponeurosis. Flexor retinaculum.
(*ridge of trapezium = tubercle*)

c. The median nerve (and artery when present) clinging to the posterior surface of the retinaculum.

d. Flexor Carpi Radialis, which on its way to its insertion into the base of metacarpal II, crosses in front of its elevated pulley, the *tubercle of the scaphoid*, and then sinks into the vertical groove on the trapezium. It is separated from the foregoing structures by a deep slip of the retinaculum; so, it occupies a private side tunnel (*fig. 144*).

The foregoing tendons and the median nerve converge from the forearm, traverse the carpal tunnel, and then diverge to the digits. The Flexor Pollicis Longus runs between the three thenar muscles and the Adductor Pollicis.

Fibrous Sheaths of the Digits. A pair of tendons, a *Superficialis* and a *Profundus*, descends deep to each of the four digital slips of the palmar aponeurosis. In front of the head of a metacarpal bone each pair

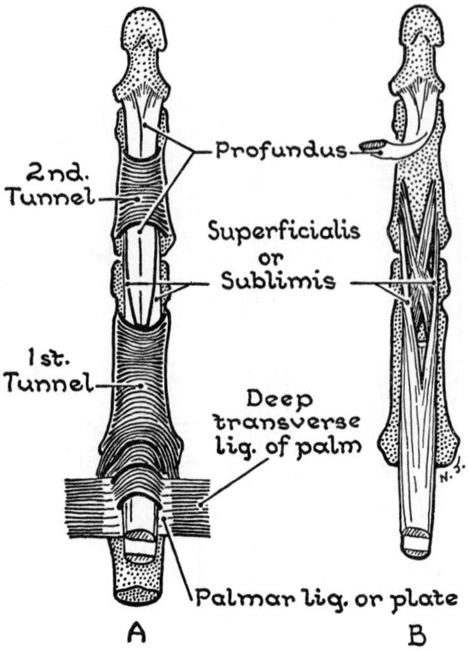

FIG. 150. *A*, a fibrous digital flexor sheath showing the two osseofibrous tunnels. *B*, mode of insertion of the long digital flexors.

enters a *fibrous digital sheath* (*fig. 150*). Each sheath extends from the palmar lig. (plate) of a metacarpo-phalangeal joint to the insertion of a Profundus tendon into the base of a distal phalanx. Each sheath, therefore, crosses 3 joints. In front of the joints the sheath, for mechanical reasons, must be pliable; here, then, it is thin and its fibers are arranged like the limbs of a St. Andrew's Cross. But in front of the bodies of the proximal and middle phalanges the fibers are transversely curved and are strong. With the phalanges they form osseofibrous digital tunnels which are comparable in structure and function with the osseofibrous carpal tunnel.

Insertions of Long Digital Flexors. Each Profundus tendon is inserted into the whole breadth of the anterior aspect of the base of a distal phalanx. Each Superficialis tendon splits in front of a proximal phalanx into medial and lateral halves (*fig. 150*). The two central quarters of the split tendon spread apart like the limbs of the letter V and find attachment to the proximal ends of the ridges on the margins of a middle phalanx; the two side quarters wrap round the sides of a Profundus tendon, decussate behind it like the letter X, and pass to the distal ends of the ridges on the opposite margins of the phalanx. As a result, the surfaces of each of the decussating parts of each Superficialis tendon are reversed. Each Profundus tendon passes through a perforation in a Superficialis.

»» You might think that a contracting Superficialis would grip the Profundus tendons and arrest them; but it is not so. If you cut across a Profundus tendon and withdraw it from the Superficialis, and then pull on the Superficialis, you will find that the intricate perforation remains so widely open that you can easily thread the Profundus tendon through it again.

The ridges on the margins of the proximal and middle phalanges give attachment to the transverse fibers of the fibrous digital sheath. Those on the middle phalanx are the better marked because they give attachment to a Superficialis tendon also.

The Lumbricals (*fig. 153*) are four muscles which in shape, size, and color resemble earthworms. They arise in the palm from the Profundus tendons. They lie behind the digital vessels and nerves, and they accompany them in front of the deep transverse ligaments of the palm to the radial side of the fingers, where they join the extensor (dorsal) expansions distal to the attachments of the Interossei (*figs. 165* and *170*). The Lumbricals to the index and middle fingers arise from the radial side only of the corresponding Profundus tendons, and like them they are supplied by the median nerve. The Lumbricals to the ring and little fingers take origin from the radial and ulnar sides of the adjacent tendons and like the corresponding Profundus tendons are supplied by the ulnar nerve.

Action (see page 167).

»» *Note.* By not giving origin to the 2nd Lumbrical' the Profundus tendon to the index enjoys a freedom denied to the other Profundus tendons.

Synovial Sheaths or **Vaginae Synovi-**

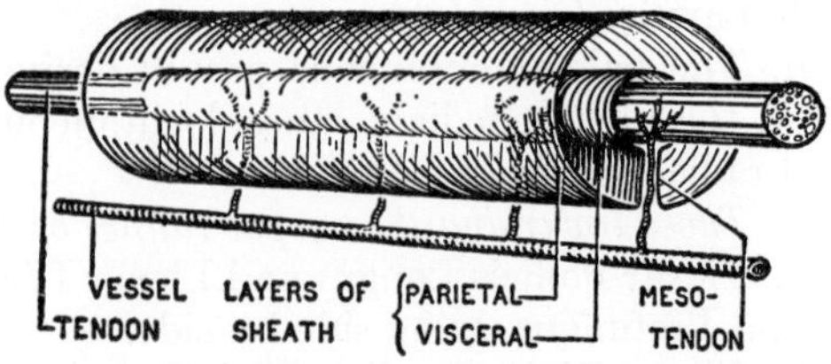

FIG. 151. Diagram of a synovial sheath

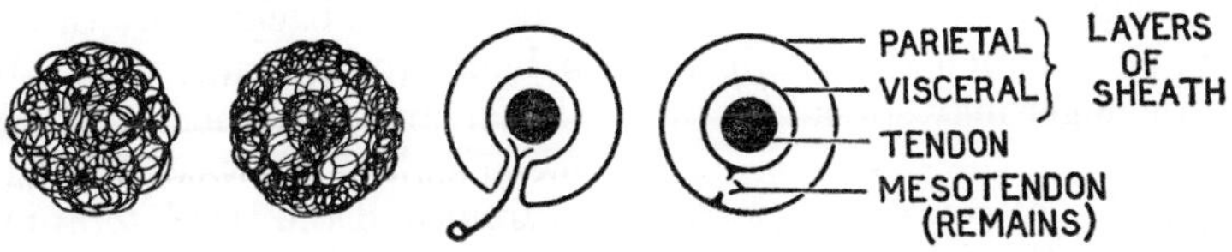

FIG. 152. Stages in the development of tendon, synovial sheath, and mesotendon

ales. A synovial sheath is a lubricating device. It is a bursa that envelops or ensheaths a tendon; so, it is of tubular form. Indeed, it is a tube within a tube, and the potential cavity between the inner and the outer tube is closed at both ends (*fig. 151*).

It is evident that during flexion of the wrist the long flexor tendons rub on the back of the flexor retinaculum and that during extension of the wrist they rub on the prominent anterior margin of the lower end of the radius and on the carpal bones. Bursae therefore are required both in front of these tendons and behind them. Under circumstances such as this, Nature provides tubular bursae called *synovial sheaths*. They are found only in the hands and feet and around the long tendon of the Biceps Brachii.

Every tendon lying within a synovial sheath has, or must at one time have had, a **mesotendon** (*fig. 152*). A mesotendon is analogous to a mesentery. It is a double layer of synovial membrane that attaches a tendon to the wall of its sheath and conveys vessels to it. It is attached to the side of the tendon least liable to friction.

»» On an average a synovial sheath extends 1 inch proximal to and 1 inch distal to the site of friction. But this depends upon the excursion the tendon makes: the greater the excursion, the greater the length of the sheath, and probably the greater the likelihood of the mesotendon disappearing.

Now, the long flexor tendons (Superficialis, Profundus, and Pollicis) require synovial sheaths first where they pass through the osseofibrous carpal tunnel and subsequently where they pass through the osseofibrous digital tunnels. They have, therefore, *carpal synovial sheaths* and *digital synovial sheaths*. Of all the digits, the thumb has obviously the freest range of movement, followed in order by digits V, IV, III, and II. This and the shortness of the metacarpals of the thumb and of digit V result in their carpal and digital sheaths coming into contact (*fig. 153*). Those of the thumb probably always unite; those of the little finger fail to unite in about 10 per cent of persons; those of digits II, III, and IV (always) remain discrete.

The carpal sheaths of the four Superficialis and four Profundus tendons usually become one, the **Common Synovial Sheath** of the digital flexors. The carpal sheath of the Flexor Pollicis Longus commonly joins the common flexor sheath. In such cases, fluid injected into the digital flexor sheath of the little finger flows into the common flexor sheath, thence to the "carpal" sheath of the

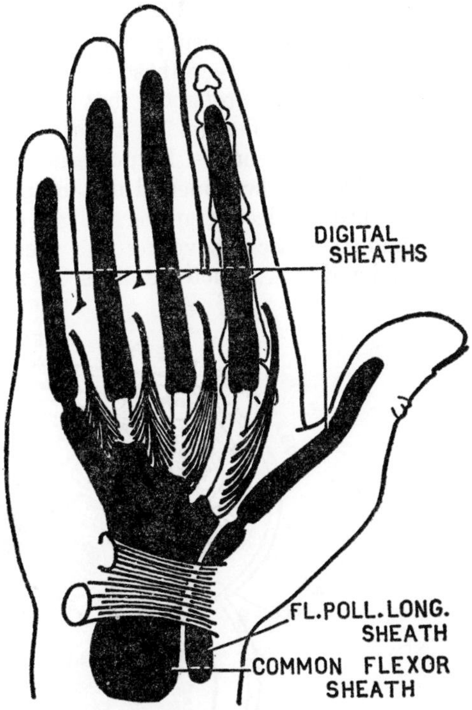

FIG. 153. Synovial sheaths or tubular bursae are required for the long digital flexor tendons at the osseofibrous carpal tunnel and at the osseofibrous digital tunnels. The Lumbricals are shown.

Flexor Pollicis Longus, and so to its digital sheath. Equally, an infection starting in the sheath of the little finger may spread by this route to the thumb.

The digital sheaths, of course, do not extend distally beyond the insertions of the Flexor Digitorum Profundus and Flexor Pollicis Longus, that, is, beyond the epiphyses of the terminal phalanges. A cut, therefore, over the diaphysis of a terminal phalanx will not enter a sheath.

The very end portions of the original mesotendons of the Flexores Superficialis, Profundus, and Pollicis Longus remain as triangular folds, the *vincula brevia*, and, several thread-like portions of the mesotendons of the Profundus and Superficialis persist in front of the proximal phalanges as *vincula longa*. The vincula convey blood vessels to the tendons. (The singular of vincula is *vinculum*.)

Palmar Spaces (*fig. 154*). There are in the palm four closed fascial spaces. The thenar muscles occupy one, the *thenar space;* the hypothenar muscles occupy another, the *hypothenar space*. Between these two there is a large triangular *central space* that contains the tendons of the fingers. Its anterior wall is the palmar aponeurosis. Its posterior wall is formed by the three medial metacarpals, the palmar and deep transverse ligs. (*fig. 149*), and the fascia covering the medial Interossei and the Adductor Pollicis. Its side walls are the backwardly turned edges of the palmar aponeurosis which fuse with the thenar and hypothenar fasciae. The fourth space is placed between the Adductor Pollicis in front and the two lateral intermetacarpal spaces behind.

»» In the distal half of the palm, the central space has eight subdivisions or tunnels: one being for each of the four pairs of long flexor tendons and one for each of the four Lumbricals and the companion digital vessels and nerves. The septa separating the tunnels are derived from the palmar aponeurosis. (See page 151.) The tendons of the Lumbricals prolong the spaces downwards on to the dorsum of the digits. It is by this lumbrical route that infection in the central palmar space may spread to the dorsum of the hand.

Arteries of the Hand, Palmar and Dorsal

The blood supply to the hand is derived from the ulnar and radial arteries. The supply is good and the anastomoses are excellent.

In the hand, four transversely placed arterial arches unite the ulnar and radial arteries to each other (*fig. 155*). In order of magnitude they are:

1. The superficial palmar arch lying deep to the palmar aponeurosis (*fig. 148*).
2. The deep palmar arch.
3. The dorsal carpal arch.
4. The palmar carpal arch (2, 3, and 4 lying on the skeletal plane, i.e., bone, ligament, or fibrous capsule).

The Superficial Palmar Arch is the largest, the most distal, and the only super-

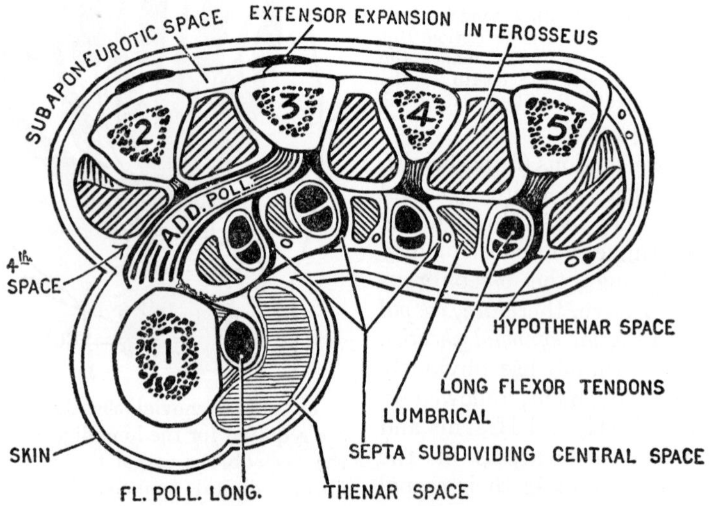

FIG. 154. The palmar spaces in cross section

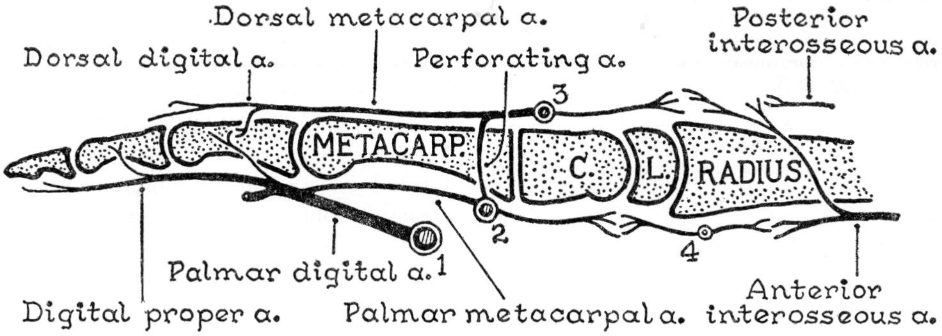

FIG. 155. Scheme of arteries of the hand: The four arches are numbered in order of size—three cling to the skeletal plane.

ficial arch. It is the continuation of the ulnar artery in the hand. It descends from the lateral side of the pisiform to the level of the web of outstretched thumb and there curves laterally to be completed by one of the following three branches of the radial artery: (1) superficial palmar, (2) digital branch to index or, (3) digital branch to thumb.

The superficial palmar arch lies immediately subjacent to the Palmaris Brevis and the palmar aponeurosis which alone separate it from the skin. Hence, it is properly called superficial.

As it enters the hand it descends between the pisiform and hamate bones and crosses in turn the upper band of the flexor retinaculum, the pisohamate lig., the Flexor and Opponens Digiti Quinti, the long flexor tendons, the lumbrical muscles, and the digital branches of the median nerve. The deep branch of the ulnar artery arises between the pisiform and hamate bones and accompanies the deep branch of the ulnar nerve.

Palmar Digital Arteries. The superficial palmar arch supplies the medial three and one-half digits, leaving the lateral one and one-half to the care of the deep palmar arch; it sends one digital branch to the medial side of the little finger and three common palmar digital branches, to the clefts between digits 5 and 4, 4 and 3, and 3 and 2, where they bifurcate into digital branches proper. The palmar digital branches to the lateral one and one-half digits arise from the deep palmar arch, which is the continuation of the radial artery into the palm.

Note that on the fingers the palmar digital arteries and nerves run on the sides of the flexor tendons in their fibrous sheaths, the nerve being antero-medial to the artery (*fig. 156*). To expose them, you should feel with your finger nail for the edge of a phalanx and make a longitudinal incision in front of it.

Radial Artery. After crossing the Pronator Quadratus, the radial artery comes into contact with the lower end of the radius. From there until, as the deep palmar arch, it unites with the deep branch of the ulnar artery, it lies in contact with the skeletal plane. Thus, after giving off the *palmar radial carpal* and *superficial palmar arteries*, it turns round the lateral border of the wrist and descends vertically through the anatomical snuff-box to reach the proximal end of the first intermetacarpal space.

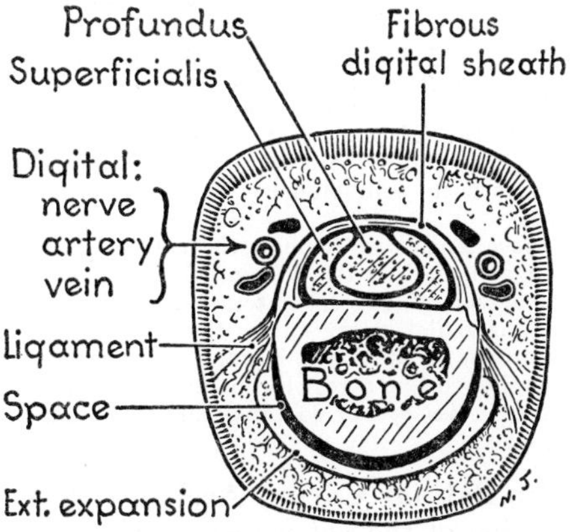

FIG. 156. Cross section through a proximal phalanx.

»» It crosses in turn the radial collateral ligament of the wrist, the scaphoid and trapezium; and, in turn it is crossed by the three tendons that bound the snuff-box, branches of the radial nerve to the thumb, and the dorsal venous arch.

While in the snuff-box the radial artery gives off the *dorsal radial carpal artery*, and sends small branches, *dorsal digital aa.*, to the sides of the lateral one and one-half digits, passes between the two heads of the First Dorsal Interosseus, and enters the palm to become the *deep palmar arch.*

The Deep Palmar Arch (*fig. 146*) is the radial artery continued into the palm. It is completed medially by the deep branch of the ulnar artery.

»» It crosses the metacarpals (2, 3, and 4) just distal to their bases. It interrupts the origin of the Adductor Pollicis, dividing it into a transverse and an oblique head. The deep branch of the ulnar artery, accompanied by the deep branch of the ulnar nerve, becomes deep by curving round the lower border of the hook of the hamate and in so doing it interrupts the origin of the Opponens Digiti Quinti.

The deep arch is the **great anastomosing artery** of the hand (*fig. 146*). Thus, it connects the radial artery laterally, the ulnar artery medially, the palmar carpal arch proximally, the palmar digital arteries distally, and the dorsal metacarpal branches of the dorsal carpal arch posteriorly.

Branches. On entering the palm, the radial artery becomes the deep palmar arch, which supplies: (1) *Palmar digital branches* to the lateral one and one-half digits (viz., princeps pollicis and radialis indicis aa.).

»» These vessels are larger than the dorsal digital branches. They descend between the Adductor Pollicis and the First Dorsal Interosseus, and then follow the sides of the digits in the usual manner. They may complete the superficial palmar arch. Its other branches are: (2) *three palmar metacarpal arteries* which run distally in the three medial intermetacarpal spaces to join the three common digital arteries; (3) *three perforating arteries* which pass between the heads of the 2nd, 3rd, and 4th Dorsal Interossei to join the three dorsal metacarpal arteries (*cf.*, the radial artery and the 1st Dorsal Interosseus); and (4) *Several recurrent branches* which run upwards to join branches of the anterior carpal arch.

Surface Anatomy. To map the course of the deep palmar arch, feel on the dorsum of your hand for the proximal end of the 1st intermetacarpal space, i.e., where the radial artery enters the palm. Relate this point to the front of the hand, and from it carry a slightly bowed line across the palm to the hook of the hamate. It lies ½″ or so proximal to the superficial palmar arch.

The Palmar Carpal Arch is formed by the union of the *palmar carpal branch of the ulnar artery* and the *palmar carpal branch of the radial artery.*

»» It lies in front of the lower end of the radius and the proximal row of carpal bones. It anastomoses with twigs of the anterior interosseous artery and with recurrent branches of the deep palmar arch to form a rete or network (*fig. 146*).

The Dorsal Carpal Arch is applied to the dorsal surface of the carpal bones. It is formed by the anastomosis of the dorsal carpal branches of radial and ulnar arteries. The terminal branches of both the anterior and the posterior interosseous arteries anastomose with it (*fig. 157*).

»» Its *branches* are: (1) a branch to the medial side of the little finger, and (2) three dorsal metacarpal arteries. The latter divide into dorsal digital aa. which end on the proximal phalanges. And, (3) three perforating arteries (in series with the radial artery itself), join the deep palmar arch.

BONES OF THE CARPUS—IN SOME DETAIL

Scaphoid Bone (Gk. skaphe = a boat). The hollowed out interior of the boat articulates with the side of the head of the capitate, and faces medially. Above this and also facing medially, a narrow, flat, crescentic surface for the lunate represents the stern of the boat. The smooth, rounded, exterior of the boat (it has no keel) is extensive, articulates with the radius, and faces superolaterally.

The prow, called the *tubercle*, lies inferolaterally at the front of the bone. The fo'c's'le (the distal surface) is convex and oval for the trapezium and trapezoid. Posteriorly, laterally, and anteriorly there are nonarticular areas, the anterior one being concave. Only through these areas can blood vessels supply the bone.

Surface Relations. Distally, the tubercle of the scaphoid is prominent and palpable behind the point where the Flexor Carpi Radialis tendon intersects the lowest skin crease at the front of the wrist (*fig. 125*). Proximally, the scaphoid extends a finger's breadth above the skin crease—in fact, up to the prominent, palpable, crest-like anterior border of the lower articular surface of the radius. Laterally, it is palpable in the anatomical snuff-box, especially during adduction of the hand.

The **Lunate Bone** lies behind the midpoint of the most distal skin crease at the

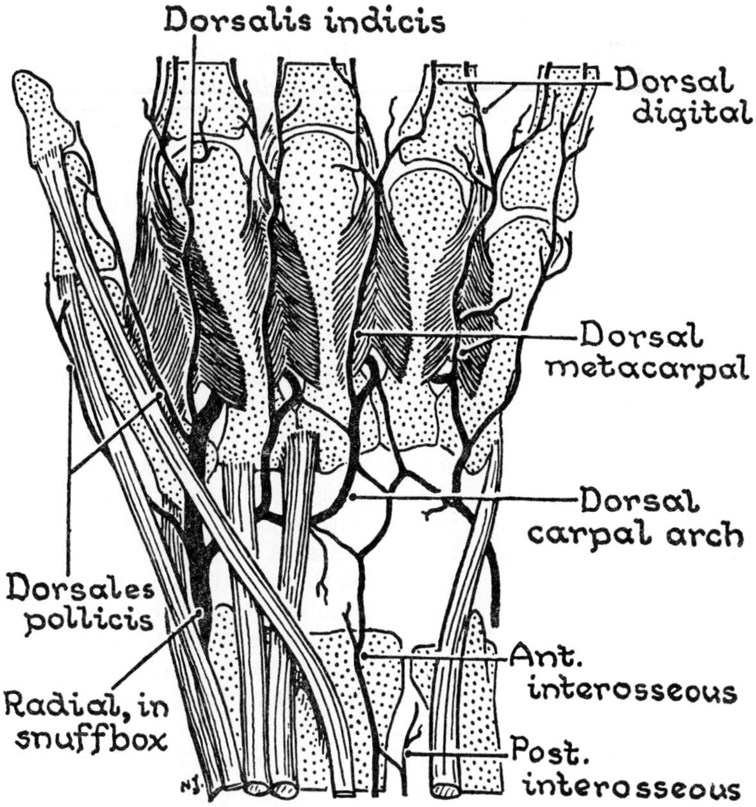

FIG. 157. The arteries of the dorsum of the hand

front of the wrist (*fig. 143*). It is semilunar or crescentic. The concavity faces distally, and with the concavity of the scaphoid forms a socket for the head of the capitate. The convexity faces proximally, articulates with the radius, and corresponds in shape and size to the radial surface of the scaphoid (*fig. 144*). Laterally, there is a narrow, flat crescent for the scaphoid. The medial surface is flat and square for the triquetrum. Between the triquetral and capitate surfaces there is an antero-posterior articular strip for the apex of the hamate. The nonarticular, anterior surface is much wider than the posterior.

The **Os Triquetrum** (L. = three cornered, triangular) is cuneiform. The base is flat, square, and faces laterally for the lunate. The apex points medially. The distal surface is sinuous for the hamate. The anterior surface is flat and rough and has a large, round (commonly raised) isolated facet for the pisiform. The postero-superior surface is convex and rough, save for a small facet—the end of an oval—for the articular disc of the wrist joint on full adduction (*figs. 130* and *134*).

The **Pisiform Bone** (L. pisum = a pea) is larger than the sesamoid bones of the big toe. It has only one facet and that is for the triquetrum. The facet is large and flat (or slightly concave) and on the posterior surface. It does not reach the most distal part of this surface. The lateral surface, beside which runs the ulnar nerve, is flatter than the medial one.

The other surfaces are rounded. The pisiform is crossed by the most distal skin crease at the wrist and the Flexor Carpi Ulnaris descends to it. When the fist is clenched and relaxed, the pisiform can be felt moving up and down. When the wrist is flexed and limp, the pisiform can be moved from side to side.

The **Trapezium** (Gk. trapeza = a table) (greater multangular) has distally a saddle-shaped facet for metacarpal 1, but this facet has a lateral tilt because the thumb is not in line with the fingers. The anterior, lateral, and posterior surfaces are rough; on the anterior surface there is a vertical groove for the Flexor Carpi Radialis tendon. On each side of the groove is a vertical ridge for the flexor retinaculum; the lateral is the more prominent (the *tubercle*) and is directed toward the hook of the hamate. The medial surface is a concave half-oval facet for the trapezoid; between this and the saddle, and in line with the vertical groove, is the small facet for metacarpal 2. The proximal surface is a concave half-oval facet for the scaphoid.

Surface Relations. The tubercle is continuous with the tubercle of the scaphoid and can be felt distal to the skin crease at the wrist. The trapezium is also palpable in the snuff-box at the base of metacarpal 1.

Trapezoid Bone (Gk. trapeza = a table; eidos = like). Next to the pisiform this is the smallest of the carpal bones. The posterior nonarticular surface is much larger than the anterior one. The medial surface is an oblong facet, concave antero-posteriorly for the capitate. The lateral surface is a convex half-oval facet for the trapezium. The proximal surface is a concave half-oval facet for the scaphoid. The distal surface fits like a wedge into the groove on the base of metacarpal 2.

The **Capitate Bone** (L. caput = a head) has at the proximal end a rounded head for the socket formed by the lunate and scaphoid, so this articular surface extends well on to the lateral aspect. Its posterior nonarticular surface is flattish, and is broader than the more rounded anterior one. The base (inferior surface) is flat for metacarpal 3, and has a linear strip laterally for metacarpal 2, and a small facet postero-medially for metacarpal 4. The medial surface is flat and resembles a judge's head and wig, the head being rough for the very strong interosseous ligament that joins the hamate to the capitate; the wig or posterior margin is articular. The lateral surface includes part of the head, as mentioned; distally it is convex antero-posteriorly for the trapezoid.

The **Hamate Bone** (L. hamatum = hooked) is a wedge-shaped bone with a hook. The anterior and posterior surfaces are rough and nonarticular; the hook curves laterally from the anterior surface and points towards the ridge on the trapezium, for both give attachment to the flexor retinaculum (*fig. 144*). The distal surface or base has two concave facets which allow metacarpals 5 and 4 to flex and extend; the medial one is somewhat triangular (or quadrate); the lateral one is quadrate (*cf.* the cuboid bone of the foot). The lateral surface is flat and partly articular for the capitate and partly rough for the strong interosseous ligament which unites it to the capitate. The superomedial surface is sinuous for the triquetrum. The hook is crossed by the ulnar nerve and artery, and its lower border is grooved by the deep branches of the ulnar nerve and artery. The hook is felt as a resistant surface on pressing deeply in the palm infero-lateral to the pisiform.

CHAPTER 11

EXTENSOR REGION OF FOREARM AND HAND

Boundaries; Tendons; Palpable Parts of Ulna; of Radius; Snuff-box and Three Dorsal Tendons; Internervous Line.
Supinator; Posterior Interosseous Nerve.

MUSCLES OF THE EXTENSOR REGION—*Lateral Superficial Group; Posterior Superficial Group; Deep Group.*

Posterior Surfaces of Ulna and Radius; Arteries: back of forearm, back of hand; Cutaneous Nerves; Deep Fascia; "Tricipital Aponeurosis;" Extensor Retinaculum.
Tendons at Back of Wrist; Extensor (Dorsal) Expansions: Lumbricals and Interossei.
INTEROSSEI—*attachments, course, insertions, nerve supply.*
Nerve supply to components of expansion; Fascial Spaces on Dorsum of Hand.

The muscles covering the lateral surface of the radius, as well as those on the back of the radius and ulna, are supplied by the posterior cord of the brachial plexus via the radial nerve itself or via its posterior interosseous branch; and, they belong developmentally to the extensor region of the limb (*fig. 158*).

Boundaries. No motor nerve crosses the boundary lines, which are: *medially*, the subcutaneous border of the ulna and the ulnar border of the hand, and *laterally*, the course of the radial artery in the forearm and the radial border of the hand.

Tendons (*figs. 158.1, 163,* and *164*). All tendons passing from the forearm to the back of the hand span the carpus and reach either the bases of the metacarpals or the bases of the phalanges. Those passing to the metacarpals are strong and rounded like flexor tendons; they help to steady the wrist. Those passing to the phalanges are weak, flattened aponeuroses resembling thick fascia; little is expected of them. They are not employed against resistance, but are used to open the hand preparatory to closing it in order to grasp an object. The metacarpals and phalanges are palpable through the flattened tendons.

As there are no fleshy muscle fibers on the dorsum of the hand, but only tendons, there is no occasion for motor nerves, and there are none.

Palpable Parts of Ulna (*fig. 159*): (1) The triangular posterior surface of the *olecranon*, which the subcutaneous olecranon bursa covers. (2) The *posterior border* of the

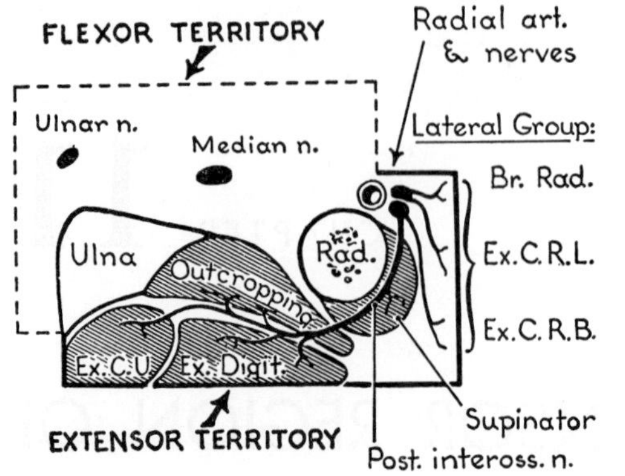

FIG. 158. The extensor region of the forearm, on cross-section.

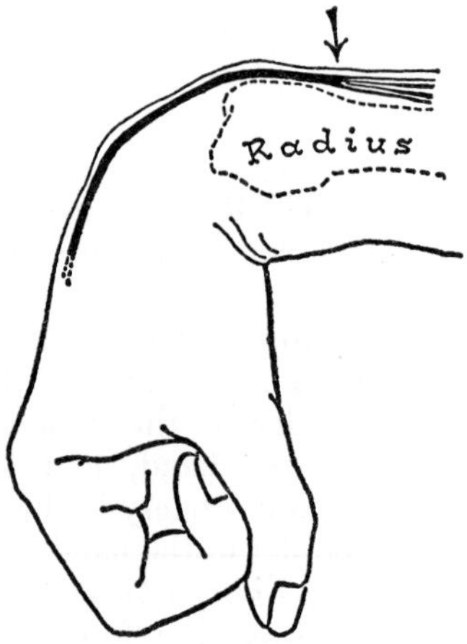

FIG. 158.1. Fleshy fibers must give place to tendon beyond the arrow at the lower end of the radius.

ulna; it extends from the apex of the posterior surface of the olecranon to the styloid process. It is sharp in its upper three-quarters because the aponeuroses of the Flexor and Extensor Carpi Ulnaris, which lie one on each side of it, arise from it. (3) The *subcutaneous lower quarter* of the medial surface; it is subcutaneous because neither the Flexor Digitorum Profundus nor the Flexor Carpi Ulnaris is able to utilize it (see p. 132). (4) The *head*, and (5) the *styloid process*. When you pronate your forearm in order to inspect the back of the hand, the lateral part of the rounded head of the ulna is brought into view, covered, however, with the capsule of the distal radio-ulnar joint. (6) The upper, lateral, and medial surfaces of the *olecranon* can be palpated through the muscles attached to them (Triceps, Anconeus, Profundus).

Palpable Parts of Radius: (1) The disc-like *head*. It lies immediately below the smooth posterior aspect of the lateral epicondyle. When the elbow is extended, the head lies at the bottom of a visible hollow in which its upper margin is easily felt on pressing firmly downward. When the elbow is flexed and the forearm alternately pronated and supinated, the head can be felt to revolve under the palpating fingers. It is covered by the common tendon of origin of the extensors and the anular ligament of the radius. (2) The *lower end of the radius* can be grasped between the fingers and thumb. The rough, crested, anterior margin of the lower articular surface is very prominent. (3) And the *dorsal radial tubercle* (*of Lister*) projects from the posterior aspect of the wrist, lateral to its midpoint. (4) The *styloid process* of the radius lies in the anatomical

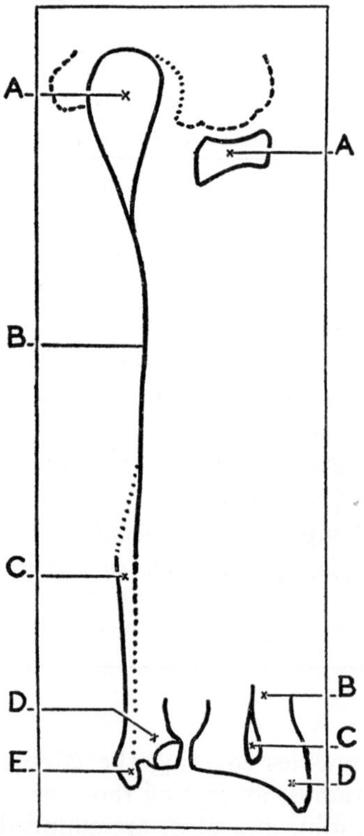

FIG. 159. Palpable parts of ulna and radius, from behind (see text).

snuff-box and is ½ inch below the level of the ulnar styloid process. In order to palpate the tips of these processes, grasp the sides of the wrist between your thumb and index, and press upward.

Snuff-Box and the Three Dorsal Tendons of the Thumb. When the thumb is fully extended, a hollow, called the **"snuff-box,"** can be seen on the dorsum of the wrist, at the root of the thumb. Bounding the snuff-box medially is the tendon of the Extensor Pollicis Longus. Bounding it laterally, and at the same time forming the lateral boundary of the wrist, are the tendons of the Abductor Pollicis Longus and Extensor Pollicis Brevis. These three tendons can be seen in the living subject and should be traced in the dissected limb distally to their insertions. One will be found attached to the base, which is also the epiphysis, of each of the three long bones of the thumb (*fig. 140 C*).

Crossing the snuff-box superficially are the beginning of the *cephalic vein* in the dorsal venous arch, and the *superficial radial nerve.* When these are displaced, the *radial artery* can be exposed crossing the snuff-box on the skeletal plane.

The Three Dorsal Tendons of Thumb Traced Proximally (*fig. 160*). First, follow the Abductor Pollicis Longus and Extensor Pollicis Brevis to the side of the radial styloid process, and the Extensor Pollicis Longus to the medial side of the dorsal radial tubercle; then, follow them upward into the lower third of the forearm to the site where they outcrop from the depths.

The furrow along which these three obliquely running muscles of the thumb emerge is to be opened up as far as the head of the radius. As this involves splitting the intermuscular septum [between the radial extensors of the wrist and the extensors of the digits] the point of a sharp knife must be used.

Perhaps the most important single observation for you to make on the back of the forearm is this: The line of the three outcropping muscles of the thumb is crossed by no nerve. It is an **internervous line.** This makes it the safest line of approach and entry to the deeper parts of the back of the forearm. Any other extensive intermuscular incision in this region will imperil a motor nerve. This is, therefore, *a line of safety* or of relative safety. It divides the superficial muscles of the extensor region into a lateral and a posterior group, each with its own nerve supply. On separating the two groups of muscles, the Supinator, which is one of the deep muscles, is seen wrapped around the upper third of the radius.

Supinator (*fig. 160*). This functional relation of Biceps arises from the lateral ligament of the elbow and from the anular ligament of the radius (*fig. 192*) but mainly from the supinator crest of the ulna (i.e., the prominent posterior side of the triangular area distal to the radial notch of the ulna (*figs. 107* and *189*)). Because it is a supinator of the forearm, its fibers take a

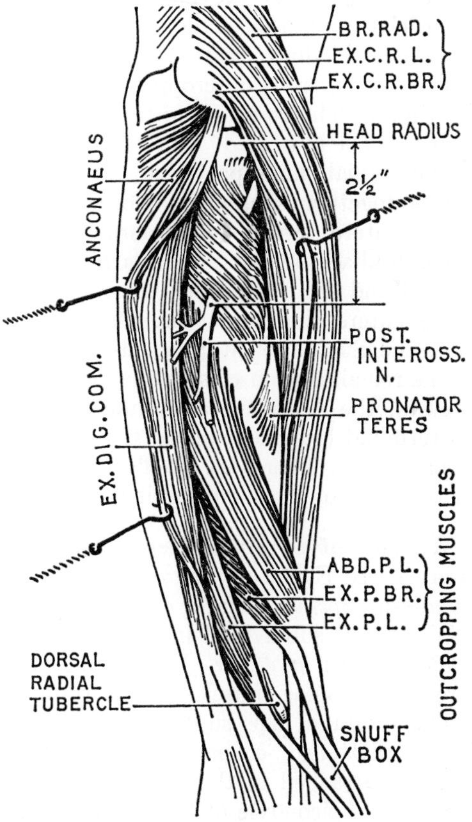

Fig. 160. The furrow of "the 3 outcropping muscles of the thumb" opened up—the line of relative safety.

direction antagonistic to those of the Pronator Teres. They are inserted into the body of the radius between the anterior and posterior oblique lines (*figs. 121* and *161*).

The **Posterior Interosseous Nerve** (DEEP RADIAL NERVE) is one of the two terminal branches of the radial nerve, the other branch being the superficial radial nerve. It arises from the radial nerve in front of the capsule of the elbow joint and under cover of the Brachioradialis. The superficial radial nerve (p. 134) is cutaneous and articular in its distribution; the posterior interosseous nerve is motor and articular.

The posterior interosseous nerve winds round the radius in the substance of the Supinator, which forms for it a fleshy tunnel. It emerges from the tunnel 2½″ or less below the head of the radius and finds itself under cover of the posterior group of superficial muscles. The fleshy tunnel, therefore, conducts the nerve across the furrow of the three outcropping muscles of the thumb. The roof of the tunnel is thin; so, it must be respected.

The radial and posterior interosseous nerves together supply the three muscles of the lateral group (Brachioradialis, Ex. Carpi Radialis Longus, Ex. Carpi Radialis Brevis) and the Supinator before the latter nerve enters the Supinator. On emerging from the Supinator, it proceeds to supply all the remaining muscles on the back of the forearm, the Anconeus as a rule excepted. Its terminal branches supply the wrist and carpal joints. There are no fleshy muscles on the back of the hand for it to supply.

Muscles of Extensor Region of Forearm. These Extensors are arranged in two layers—a *superficial* and a *deep*. The superficial layer is subdivided into two groups—a *lateral* and a *posterior*—by the line of the three outcropping muscles of the thumb.

The origin of the superficial muscles is from a flattened, *common extensor tendon*, which is attached to the anterior aspect of the lateral epicondyle of the humerus, from the investing deep fascia, and from intermuscular septa. The origin of the lateral group of muscles extends up the lateral supracondylar ridge as far as the (spiral) groove for the radial nerve. The common tendon crosses behind the humero-radial joint and the anular ligament, and therefore behind the head of the radius which is palpable through it.

Lateral Group of Superficial Extensors:

1. *Brachioradialis.*
2. *Extensor Carpi Radialis Longus.*
3. *Extensor Carpi Radialis Brevis.*

They are lateral to the line of the three outcropping muscles of the thumb.

Collectively these three lateral muscles are related to the lateral surface of the radius, being separated from it above by the Supinator, in the middle by the insertion of the Pronator Teres; while below they are in contact with the bone. The two radial extensors of the wrist are crossed by all

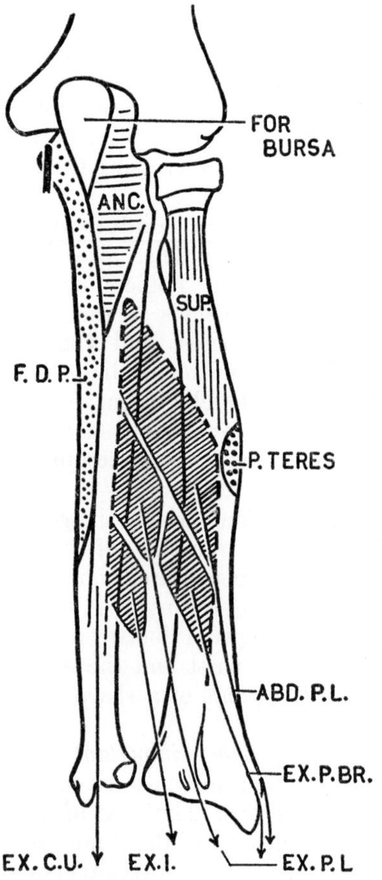

FIG. 161. Posterior aspect of ulna and radius, clothed.

three outcropping tendons of the thumb (*fig. 160*).

The Brachioradialis arises from the upper two-thirds of the lateral supracondylar ridge and lateral intermuscular septum. It bounds the cubital fossa laterally and shelters the radial nerve. Its tendon is inserted into the base of the styloid process of the radius. It is peculiar in having both origin and insertion at the distal ends of bones.

Bring your limb into the position in which you would carry it in a sling, i.e., the elbow flexed, forearm midway between pronation and supination, the palm facing the chest. Then flex the elbow against resistance, noting how powerfully the Brachioradialis stands out. Clearly, it acts as a flexor, though developmentally it belongs to the extensor group of muscles and is supplied by an "extensor" nerve.

The Extensor Carpi Radialis Longus arises from the lower one-third of the supracondylar ridge and lateral intermuscular septum.

The Extensor Carpi Radialis Brevis arises from the common tendon, the radial collateral lig. of the elbow, and the intermuscular septum between it and the Extensor Digitorum. The tendons of the two radial extensors occupy the broad sulcus on the lower end of the radius lateral to the dorsal radial tubercle (*fig. 164*). They cross the snuff-box and pass to the bases of the 2nd and 3rd metacarpals.

There is commonly a *bursa* at each end of the Ex. Carpi Radialis Brevis. The one lies between its tendon of origin and the anular ligament; it is said to be inflamed in "tennis elbow". The other lies between its tendon of insertion and the styloid process of the 3rd metacarpal; it is sometimes distended with fluid.

Surface Anatomy. While viewing your own wrist from the radial side, alternately clench and relax your closed fist, observing that the Ex. Carpi Radiales Longus and Brevis tendons spring backward as the fist goes into dorsiflexion (extension). Now, gently grasping your wrist anteroposteriorly, palpate these two tendons as they spring backward.

Posterior Group of Superficial Extensors:

1. *Extensor Digitorum (Communis).*
2. *Extensor Digiti Minimi or V.*
3. *Extensor Carpi Ulnaris.*
4. *Anconeus.*

The Three Extensors arise from the common tendon of origin, the deep fascia covering them, and the septa separating them from each other and from the Ex. Carpi Radialis Brevis.

The Ex. Digitorum (Communis) runs in the most medial groove on the back of the lower end of the radius; with it is the Ex. Indicis. The Ex. Digiti V runs alone behind the distal radio-ulnar joint. *Insertions* (see pages 166–167).

The Ex. Carpi Ulnaris plays in the deep groove between the head and styloid process of the ulna. It is inserted into the tubercle on the medial side of the base of metacarpal V. Just proximal to this, you can palpate its tendon from the medial side—particularly when the open hand is extended and adducted.

The Anconeus arises by tendon from the back of the lateral epicondyle. It is inserted by fleshy fibers into the posterior surface of the ulna above the oblique line and into the lateral surface of the olecranon (*fig. 161*). Developmentally, it is an extension of the Triceps. It is covered with a dense fascial expansion of the Triceps, and is supplied by a branch of the radial nerve that descends in the medial head of the Triceps. It can, therefore, be separated from the Ex. Carpi Ulnaris without damage to a motor nerve.

Deep Group of Extensor Muscles of Forearm:

1. *Abductor Pollicis Longus.*
2. *Extensor Pollicis Brevis.*
3. *Extensor Pollicis Longus.*
4. *Extensor Indicis.*
5. *Supinator* (considered on p. 161).

The three tendons to the thumb outcrop in the furrow between the two groups of superficial muscles (*fig. 160*). They are inserted into the epiphyses at the bases of the three long bones of the thumb: Abd. Longus to the front (not back) of the metacarpal (*fig. 136*) and Ex. Brevis and Ex. Longus to the backs of the proximal and distal phalanges (*fig. 157*). In their courses, the Abductor and the Brevis groove the radial styloid process, but the Longus is held away from these by a pulley (dorsal radial tubercle); hence the snuff-box.

Extensor Indicis joins the extensor expansion to the index.

To appreciate these muscles better some knowledge of the dorsal surfaces of the ulna and radius is required.

Posterior Surfaces of Ulna and Radius (*fig. 161*). The posterior surface of the ulna is crossed by an *oblique line* that passes from the radial notch to the bend on the sharp posterior border at the junction of the upper one-third and lower two-thirds of the bone. The area above this line belongs to the Anconeus.

The posterior surface of the radius also is crossed by an oblique line, the *posterior oblique line.* The area above this belongs to the Supinator.

From the oblique line of the ulna a *vertical line* descends and divides the posterior surface into medial and lateral halves. The medial half is smooth and bare; it leads to the groove between the head and styloid process of the ulna. The Ex. Carpi Ulnaris overlies the medial half and its tendon plays in the groove.

The lateral half of the posterior surface of the ulna below the oblique line and the whole width of the posterior surface of the radius below the oblique line, plus the intervening interosseous membrane, are utilized by the origins of four deep muscles, three being for the thumb, one for the index (*fig. 161*). They descend in oblique sequence to their insertions, and their tendons do not cross each other; so, there can be no alternative as to their arrangement.

Arteries. Back of the Forearm. The *Posterior Interosseous Artery* is the smaller of the two terminal branches of the common interosseous artery (*fig. 128*). It does not enter this region with the nerve of the same name, but by passing over the upper border of the interosseous membrane and between the contiguous borders of the Supinator and the Abductor Pollicis Longus. It descends between the superficial and deep muscles, supplies them, and takes part in the anastomoses at the elbow and wrist, thus:

At the elbow, the (*posterior*) *interosseous recurrent artery,* ascends under cover of the Anconeus and anastomoses with the posterior branch of the profunda brachii artery (*fig. 128*).

At the wrist, twigs join the *terminal branch of the anterior interosseous artery,* which pierces the interosseous membrane behind the Pronator Quadratus, and descends to anastomose with the dorsal carpal arch (*fig. 157*).

Back of the Hand. While the radial artery is crossing the snuff-box, it sends a dorsal carpal branch medially behind the carpal bones. This branch joins the dorsal carpal branch of the ulnar artery to form the *dorsal carpal rete* or *arch,* and from it branches, lying strictly on the skeletal plane, proceed as shown in figure 157.

Cutaneous Nerves (*figs. 98* and *101*).

Deep Fascia. For a few inches *below the elbow* the deep fascia gives origin to the extensor muscles; so, its fibers are strong and run vertically. Just as the fascia covering the flexor muscles receives an accession of fibers from the Biceps, called the bicipital aponeurosis, so the fascia covering the extensors receives an accession from the Triceps, which may be called the **tricipital aponeurosis.**

At the middle of the forearm the fibers are weaker and less definite in direction, and are attached to the subcutaneous posterior border of the ulna.

At the lower end of the forearm the fibers are required to retain the extensor tendons in place. They might, therefore, be expected to pass transversely between the subcutaneous parts of the lower end of the radius and ulna. But this could not be, because such a union between the two bones would effectively prevent pronation. This difficulty is overcome, and to advantage, in the following manner: (1) the more proximal fibers, violating the rule that deep fascia must be attached to all the exposed, subcutaneous, bony points it crosses, turn round the head of the ulna and become continuous with the deep fascia on the front of the forearm, thereby forming a sort of anular ligament for the head of the ulna (*fig. 162*); and (2) the more distal fibers pass obliquely downward and medially from the radius to the

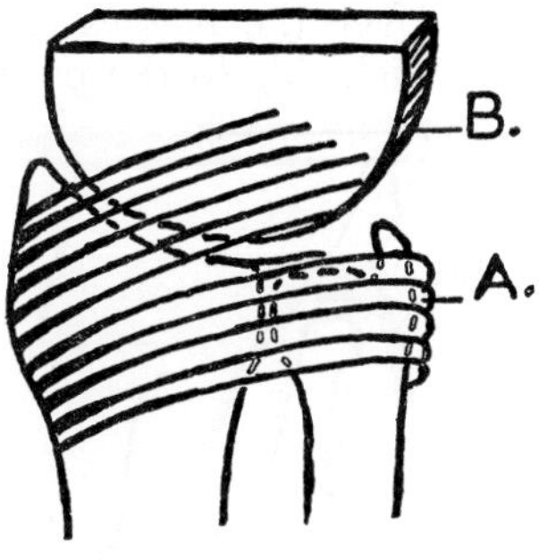

FIG. 162. The extensor retinaculum

medial carpal bones (pisiform, triquetrum, and hamate).

These strong obliquely set fibers, known as the **extensor retinaculum,** send septa to the radius and medial carpals thereby forming osseofascial tunnels for the tendons. There are six of these, each lined with a synovial sheath (*fig. 163*).

DORSUM OF WRIST AND HAND

Tendons at the Back of the Wrist (*fig. 164*). In placing these tendons in their appointed places, it is perhaps easiest to dispose first of the three thumb muscles, because they are conspicuous where they bound the snuff-box, then of the three carpal extensors, and lastly of the three digital extensors.

These nine tendons occupy six grooves, thus: (1) The *Ex. Pollicis Longus* lies in a narrow groove medial to its pulley, the easily palpated dorsal radial tubercle. (2) The *Abd. Pollicis Longus and Ex. Pollicis Brevis* lie in a broad shallow groove that completely covers the lateral side of the styloid process of the radius. (3) The *Ex. Carpi Radiales Longus and Brevis* groove the remaining part of the radius lateral to the dorsal tubercle. (4) The *Ex. Carpi Ulnaris* fills the groove between the head and styloid process of the ulna. (A fibrous band converts this groove into a tunnel at the proximal end of the main tunnel behind the carpal bones.) (5) The *Extensor tendons* and the *Ex. Indicis* groove the remaining part of the radius medial to the *Ex. Pollicis Longus.* (6) The *Ex. Digiti V* lies behind the distal radio-ulnar joint.

Extensor Expansions (DORSAL EXPANSIONS). The four flat tendons of the Ex. Digitorum (Communis) traverse the most medial tunnel at the back of the lower end of the radius and, diverging, pass to the four fingers. The common tendons of the index and little fingers are joined on their medial sides near the knuckles by their respective proper tendons—Ex. Indicis and Ex. Digiti V (*figs. 163* and *164*).

The Extensor Indicis tendon enters the hand in the same tunnel as the tendons of the Ex. Digitorum.

The Ex. Digiti V has a tunnel for itself

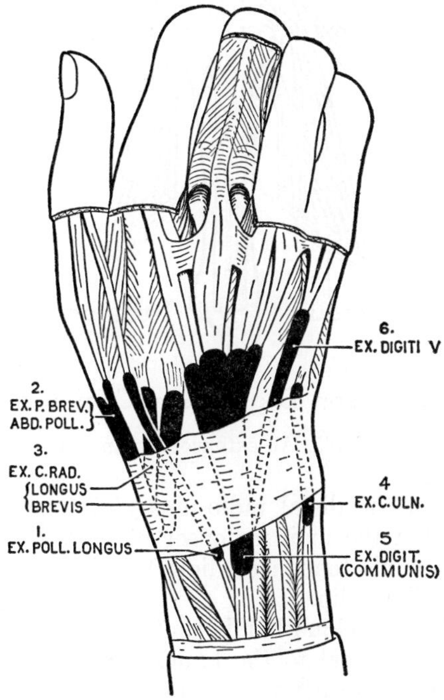

FIG. 163. The six synovial sheaths on the dorsum of the hand and a dorsal expansion—see also figure 164. (Dissection by C. P. Rance and J. W. Rogers.)

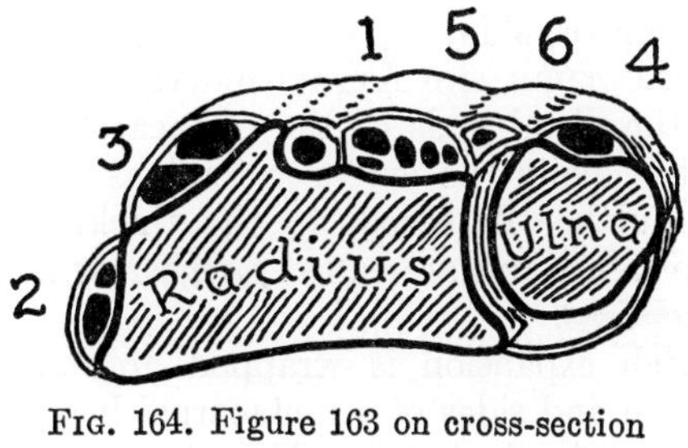

FIG. 164. Figure 163 on cross-section

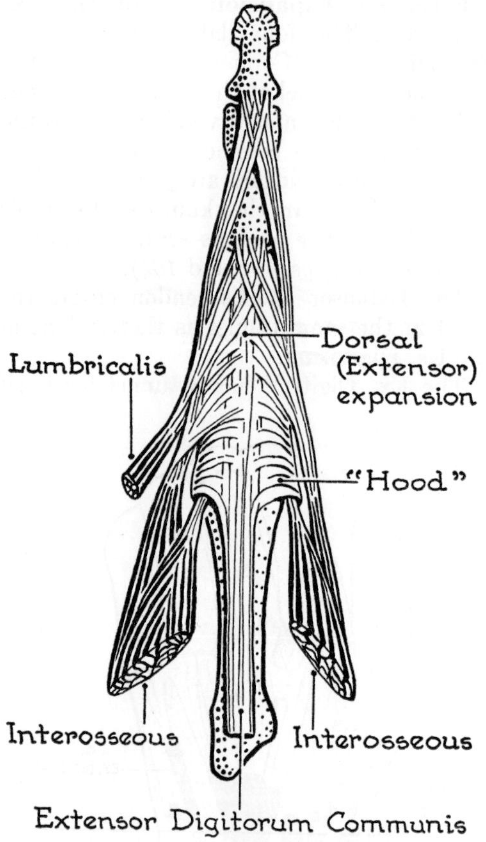

FIG. 165. An extensor expansion

behind the distal radio-ulnar joint, and it is often the main extensor of digit V, the Communis tendon of digit V being merely an oblique slip.

Three oblique bands unite the four tendons proximal to the knuckles. Hence, the independent action of your fingers is restricted, no one finger being able to remain flexed while the others pass into full extension. On flexing each of your fingers in turn, the tendons are seen to move sideways and the direction of the bands is discernible through the skin.

STRUCTURE AND ATTACHMENTS (*fig. 165*). On the distal ends of the metacarpals and on the digits the extensor tendons become still further flattened, to the thickness of deep fascia and are called *extensor* or *dorsal expansions.*

Each expansion is wrapped around the dorsum and sides of a metacarpal head and of a proximal phalanx. The *visor-like hood,* thus thrown over the metacarpal head, is anchored on each side to the palmar lig. or

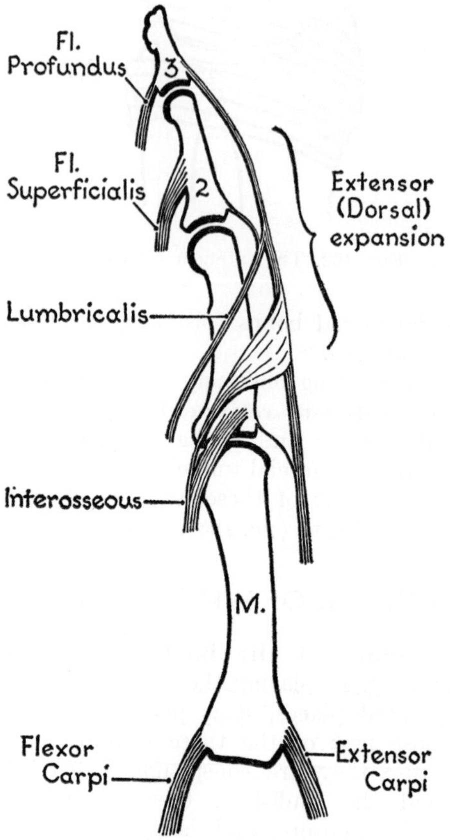

FIG. 166. The insertions of the tendons of a finger, side view.

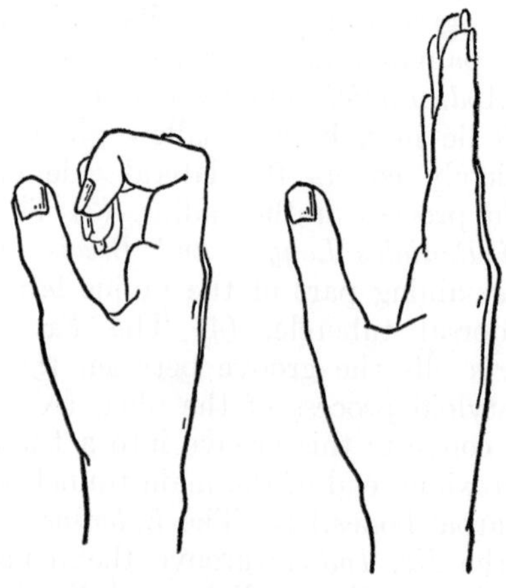

FIG. 167. *A,* long digital extensors extend metacarpo-phalangeal joints. *B,* Lumbricals and Interossei extend interphalangeal joints.

plate and thereby it serves to retain the extensor tendon in the midline of the digit. A broad *fibro-areolar ribbon* passes from the hood to the base of the proximal phalanx.

On the proximal phalanx the expansion divides into a *median band,* which passes to the base of the middle phalanx, and into *two side bands* which pass to the base of the distal phalanx.

The extensor tendon is inserted mostly via the median band and only slightly via the side bands.

Each side band is joined by half an Interosseus tendon and more distally, on

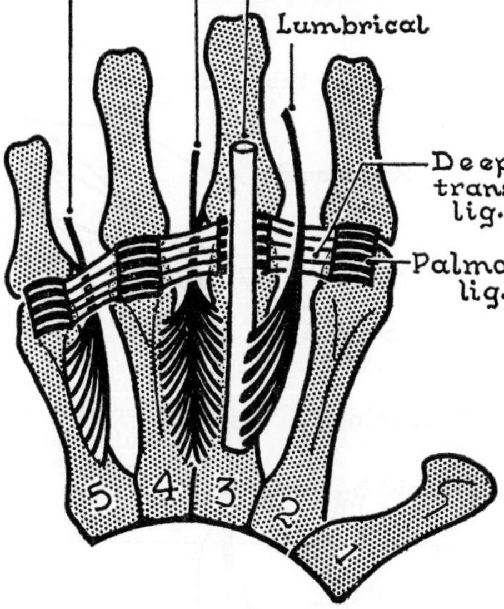

Fig. 170. The different relationships of Lumbricals and Interossei to the deep transverse metacarpal ligaments, palmar view.

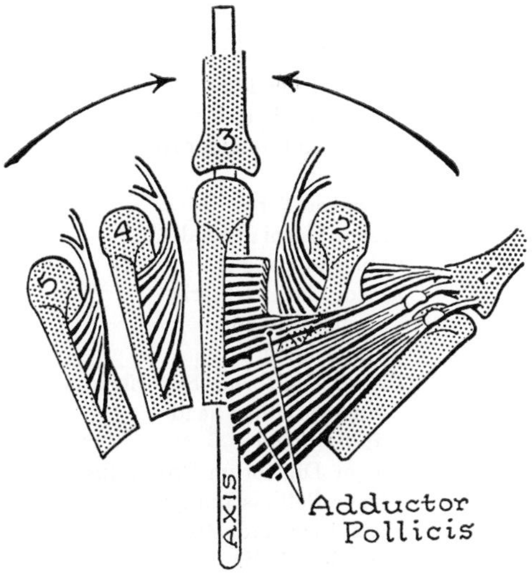

Fig. 168. Three Palmar Interossei

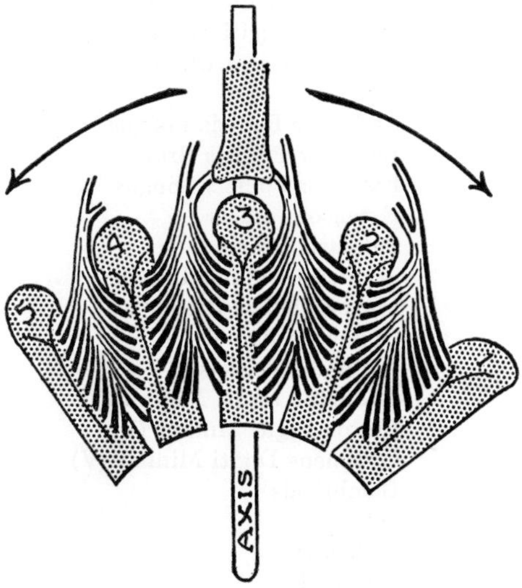

Fig. 169. Four Dorsal Interossei

the radial side, by an entire Lumbrical tendon. These tendons are united across the dorsum of the proximal phalanx by a sling of transverse fibers; and via the side bands they run to the bases of the 2nd and 3rd phalanges (*fig. 166*).

Actions. The extensor tendons extend the metacarpo-phalangeal joints.

Even after an extensor expansion has been cut across, dorsal to a proximal phalanx, traction on the corresponding extensor tendon still results in extension of the metacarpo-phalangeal joint due to the pull of the fibro-areolar ribbon attached to the base of the proximal phalanx.

The Interossei and Lumbricals flex the metacarpo-phalangeal joints. They do so by means of the arched fibers thrown across the proximal phalanges (*fig. 165*). In addition, they extend the interphalangeal joints (*fig. 167*) and impart side motion (abduction and adduction) to the fingers, provided the metacarpo-phalangeal joints are stabilized or steadied (by the long extensor tendons).

»» The action of the Lumbricals and Interossei in extending the interphalangeal joints is most powerful when the metacarpo-phalangeal joints are held fully extended, and the power diminishes progressively as these joints are flexed to a right angle. Indeed, when

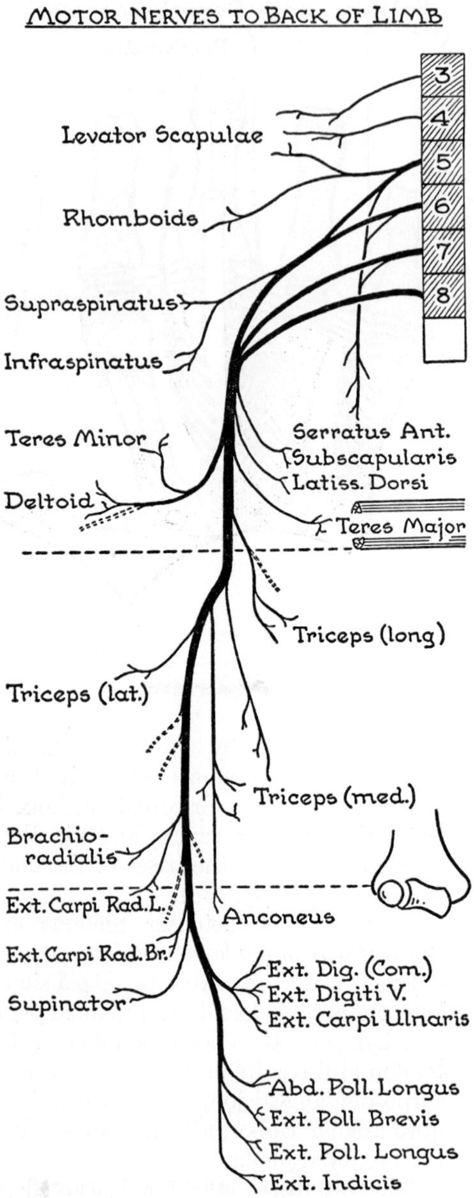

FIG. 171. The motor distribution of the nerves of the back of the limb.

A LIST OF THE MUSCLES OF THE UPPER LIMB
(This list may be found useful in review work)

Trapezius
Latissimus Dorsi
Levator Scapulae
Rhomboideus Major
Rhomboideus Minor
Pectoralis Major
  clavicular part
  sternocostal part
  abdominal part
Pectoralis Minor
Subclavius
Serratus Anterior
Deltoideus
Supraspinatus
Infraspinatus
Teres Minor
Teres Major
Subscapularis
Biceps Brachii
  long head
  short head
  bicipital aponeurosis
Coracobrachialis
Brachialis
Triceps
  long head
  lateral head
  medial head
  tricipital aponeurosis
Anconeus
Pronator Teres
Flexor Carpi Radialis
Palmaris Longus
Flexor Carpi Ulnaris
  humeral head
  ulnar head
Flexor Digitorum Superficialis
  humero-ulnar head
  radial head
Flexor Digitorum Profundus
Flexor Pollicis Longus
Pronator Quadratus
Brachioradialis
Extensor Carpi Radialis Longus
Extensor Carpi Radialis Brevis
Extensor Digitorum (Communis)
Extensor Digiti Minimi (V)
Extensor Carpi Ulnaris
Supinator
Abductor Pollicis Longus
Extensor Pollicis Brevis
Extensor Pollicis Longus
Extensor Indicis
Palmaris Brevis
Abductor Pollicis Brevis
Flexor Pollicis Brevis
Opponens Pollicis
Adductor Pollicis
Abductor Digiti Minimi (V)
Flexor Digiti Minimi (V)
Opponens Digiti Minimi (V)
Lumbricals
Interossei
  Palmar
  Dorsal

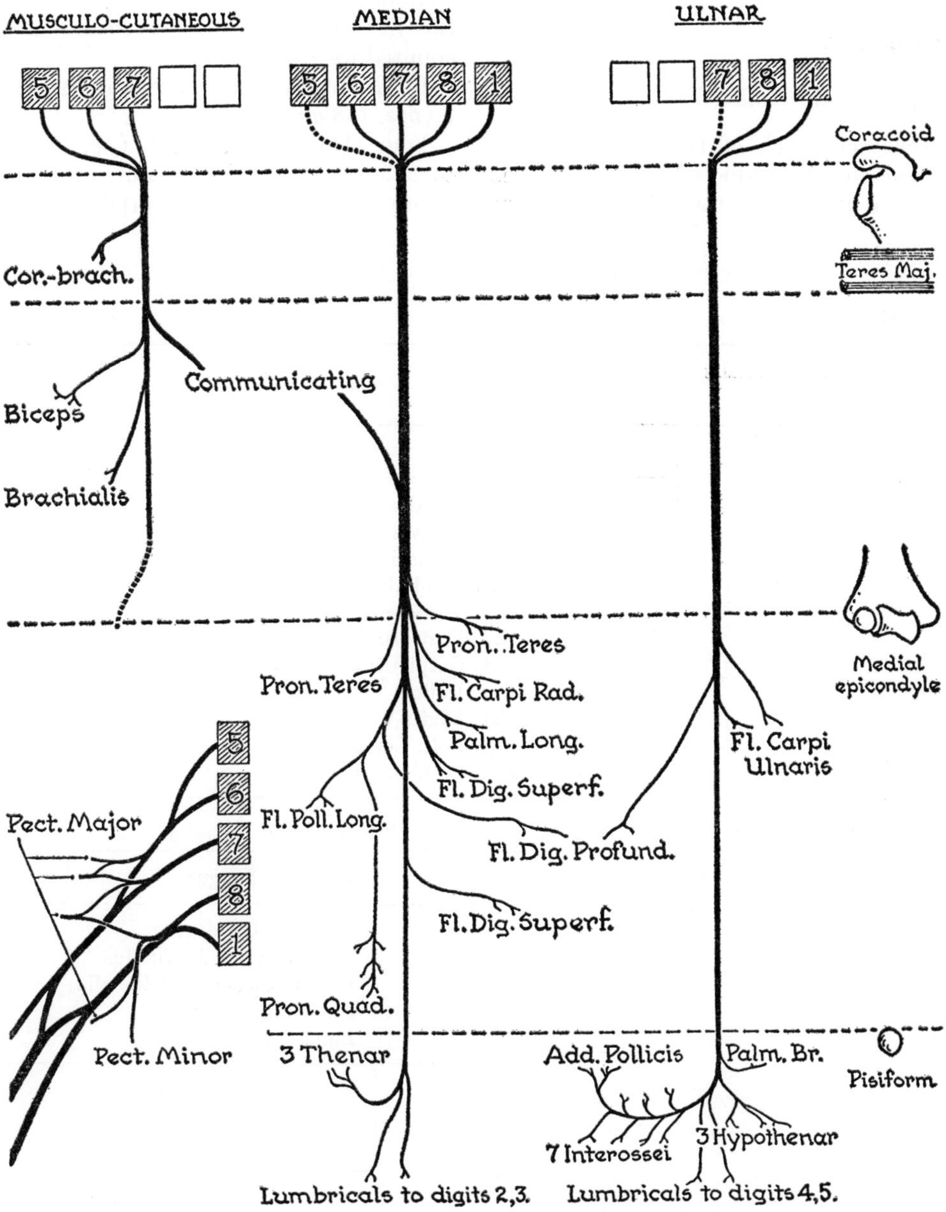

FIG. 172. The motor distribution of the nerves of the front of the limb. (You may find it profitable to compare the levels of origin of the branches in the limb you are dissecting with these average levels.)

the metacarpo-phalangeal joints are flexed to a right angle and the interphalangeal joints also are flexed, extension of the phalanges can be initiated only by the long extensor muscles (Bunnell).

The Interossei have the same functions as the Lumbricals, but they are stronger in all movements.

Origin of Lumbricals (see page 152).

Interossei. Each of the five digits can be abducted and adducted, that is, moved away from and moved toward a line passing through the middle finger, and called the *axial line of the hand*. For this, 10 muscles are required. The Adductor and Abductores Pollicis attend to the requirements of the thumb, and the Abductor Digiti V abducts the little finger; so 3 movements are accounted for.

Interossei account for the remaining 7 (*figs. 168 and 169*).

Four Dorsal Interossei (*fig. 169*) are conspicuous from the dorsum of the hand filling the four intermetacarpal spaces and

*Segmental Innervation of Muscles of Forearm and Hand**

<table>
<tr><th colspan="2">C.5</th><th colspan="2">C.6</th><th colspan="2">C.7</th><th colspan="2">C.8</th><th colspan="2">Th.1</th></tr>
<tr><td colspan="4">Brachioradialis
Supinator</td><td></td><td></td><td></td><td></td><td></td><td></td></tr>
<tr><td></td><td></td><td></td><td colspan="3">Pronator Teres</td><td></td><td></td><td></td><td></td></tr>
<tr><td></td><td></td><td></td><td colspan="4">Ext. Carpi Radialis
longus and brevis
Flexor Carpi Ulnaris
Flexor Carpi Radialis</td><td></td><td></td><td></td></tr>
<tr><td></td><td></td><td></td><td></td><td colspan="3">Ext. Digitorum
Ext. Carpi Uln.
Ext. Indicis
Ext. Digiti V
Ext. Poll. Longus
Ext. Poll. Brevis</td><td></td><td></td><td></td></tr>
<tr><td></td><td></td><td></td><td></td><td colspan="4">Abd. Poll. Longus</td><td></td><td></td></tr>
<tr><td></td><td></td><td></td><td></td><td></td><td colspan="4">Palmaris Longus</td><td></td></tr>
<tr><td></td><td></td><td></td><td></td><td></td><td colspan="5">Pronator Quadratus
Fl. Digitorum Profundus
Fl. Digitorum Superificialis
Fl. Pollicis Longus
Lumbricals</td></tr>
<tr><td></td><td></td><td></td><td></td><td></td><td></td><td colspan="4">Opponens Poll.
Abd. Poll. Br.
Flexor Poll. Br.</td></tr>
<tr><td></td><td></td><td></td><td></td><td></td><td></td><td></td><td colspan="3">Palmaris Brevis
Add. Pollicis
Fl. Digiti V
Abd. Digiti V
Opponens Digiti V
Interossei</td></tr>
</table>

* Modified after Bing; and Haymaker and Woodhall.

arising by double heads from the adjacent sides of the bodies of the five metacarpals. By exclusion there are three Palmar Interossei.

The three Palmar Interossei arise by single heads from the anterior borders of the metacarpals of the fingers with available borders, namely, 2nd, 4th, and 5th (*fig. 168*)—the 3rd anterior border is monopolized by the transverse head of the Adductor Pollicis. Moreover, each Palmar Interosseus arises from the metacarpal of the digit on which it acts.

Now, the index and ring fingers can be moved away (abducted) from the axial line and the middle finger can be moved to both sides of the line (radial and ulnar abduction); for these four movements the four Dorsal Interossei are employed.

The index, ring, and little fingers require to be moved toward the axial line (adducted); for these three movements the three Palmar Interossei are employed.

Course. The Interossei pass behind the deep transverse metacarpal ligaments (*fig. 170*); the Lumbricals and the palmar digital vessels and nerves pass in front.

Insertions. The sides of the fingers to which the Interossei must pass to perform these movements are apparent. Their insertions are partly into the bases of the proximal phalanges and partly into the extensor expansions.

» Salsbury points out (1) that the Palmar Interossei, except rarely, are inserted wholly into the extensor expansions; (2) that the 1st Dorsal Interosseus is always and only inserted into bone; (3) and that the 2nd, 3rd, and 4th Dorsal Interossei have variable insertions into the expansions and bone, each insertion generally arising from a separate fleshy belly. The 2nd Dorsal Interosseus has a greater bony insertion than the 4th, and the 4th than the 3rd.

Nerve Supply. All Interossei are supplied by the ulnar nerve.

» In 3 per cent of 100 limbs, however, the First Dorsal Interosseus was supplied exclusively by the median nerve. The radial nerve may send it fibers, which perhaps are sensory (Sydney Sunderland).

Nerve Supply of the Various Components of the Exterior Expansions.

Posterior interosseous nerve: Ext. Digitorum, Ext. Indicis, and Ext. Digiti V.

Ulnar nerve: Interossei (all seven), Lumbricals to digits 4 and 5, slip from Abd. Digiti V to Ext. Digiti V, and occasional slip from Add. Pollicis to Ext. Pollicis Longus.

Median nerve: Lumbricals to digits 2 and 3, and slip from Abd. Pollicis Brevis to Ext. Pollicis Longus.

» **Fascial Spaces.** If you plunge a needle through one of the flat extensor tendons on the dorsum of the hand and inject a fluid, (e.g., plaster of paris, or colored wax), you will reveal a subaponeurotic space (*fig. 154*). It is triangular, the apex being at the wrist, the base at the knuckles. Strong, thin, fibro-areolar membranes connect the expansions to each other and to the sides of metacarpals 2 and 5 which limit the space laterally and medially. The anterior wall is formed by metacarpals 2–5 and the fascia covering the three Interossei between them.

Similar closed spaces exist on the dorsum and sides of each proximal and of each middle phalanx (*fig. 156*).

Review of Nerve Supplies. The student will find figures 171 and 172 and the comprehensive tables on pages 124 and 170 useful for review.

CHAPTER **12**

JOINTS OF UPPER LIMB

JOINTS OF THE SHOULDER GIRDLE—*Sterno-clavicular Joint; Coracoclavicular Ligament; Acromioclavicular Joint; Movements of Shoulder Girdle.*

SHOULDER JOINT

The Ball and Socket; Movements; Fibrous Capsule and Ligaments: Coracohumeral and Glenohumeral; Long Head of Biceps; Strength of a Joint.

Four Short Muscles; Bursae: Subacromial Bursa; Coraco-acromial Arch.

Epiphyses; Orientation of Scapula and Humerus.

Muscles Acting on Shoulder Joint; Nerve Supply.

ELEVATION OF UPPER LIMB—*Muscle Force Couples.*

ELBOW JOINT

Bones Concerned: humerus, ulna, head of radius.

Proximal Radio-Ulnar Joint; Anular Ligament.

Ligaments and Capsule; Movements; Relations; Anastomoses.

Epiphyses (around elbow).

RADIO-ULNAR JOINTS

Intermediate Radio-Ulnar Joint

Interosseous Membrane; Oblique Cord.

Distal Radio-Ulnar Joint

Head of Ulna; Relations; Epiphyses; Movements and Observations; Nerve Supply.

WRIST OR RADIOCARPAL JOINT

Joint Surfaces; Movements of Wrist; Attrition of Disc and Ligaments.

Ligaments; Muscles; Nerve Supply.

Intercarpal, Midcarpal and Carpometacarpal Joints

Nerve Supply; Movements.

Intermetacarpal Joints

Metacarpo-phalangeal and Interphalangeal Joints

Movements of Fingers; Ligamentous Actions; Epiphyses of Upper Limb: Table of Chronology.

JOINTS OF THE SHOULDER GIRDLE

(Joints in which the clavicle takes part)

1. Sternoclavicular joint.
2. Coracoclavicular ligament.
3. Acromioclavicular joint.

The movements at these three joints augment those of the shoulder joint.

When you view the various ligaments attached to the clavicle, you are struck by their general *unity of direction*. But only among certain of them is there *unity of function*.

»» Unity of Direction. The Subclavius—a muscle rudimentary in man—passes from the first costal cartilage laterally and upward to be attached to the under surface of the clavicle between the costoclavicular ligament medially and the coracoclavicular ligament laterally (*fig. 173*). Indeed, these two ligaments have been regarded as the degenerated ends of the Subclavius, and all three take a common direction.

Unity of Function. It is practically the sole duty of the clavicle to thrust the scapula, and with it the arm, laterally and backward and to prevent it from being driven medially and forward when force is applied to the region of the shoulder. Since muscles can render the clavicle little aid in this, it places its reliance to some extent on the bony contacts it makes at its ends, but mainly on two structures, the *coracoclavicular ligament* laterally and the *articular disc* medially. From a consideration of the direction of the fibers of the ligament and of the sites of attachment of the disc, you will readily appreciate that between them and the clavicle there is singleness of function; so much so that a fall on the side of the shoulder must put a strain on the coracoclavicular ligament, on the portion of the clavicle medial to it, and on the articular disc (*fig. 174*).

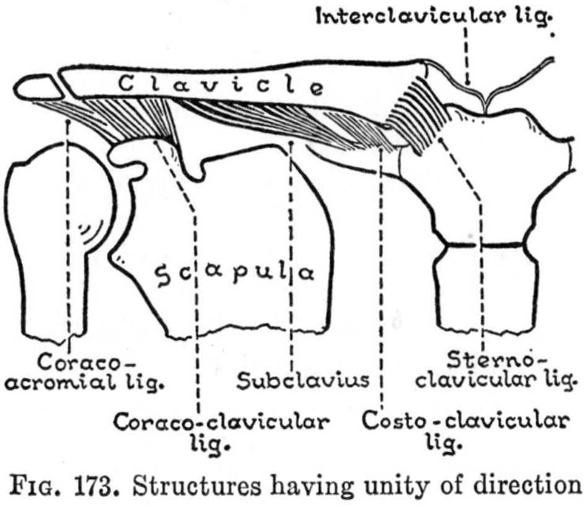

Fig. 173. Structures having unity of direction

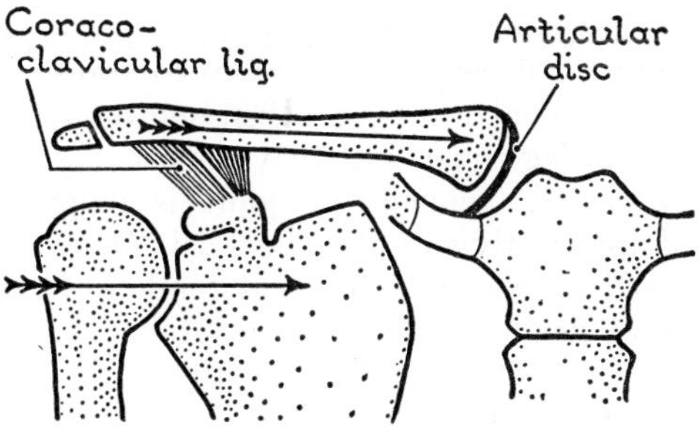

Fig. 174. Structures having unity of function

Sternoclavicular Joint

Structure. The enlarged sternal end of the clavicle articulates in the socket formed by the saddle-shaped facet at the upper angle of the manubrium and adjacent part of the 1st costal cartilage. The end of the clavicle rises above the manubrium, the two making an ill fit; but a strong, thick, *articular disc* of fibrocartilage divides the joint cavity into two and prevents medial displacement of the clavicle. This being so, its attachments must be to the clavicle above (actually above and posteriorly) and to the 1st costal cartilage below.

Strong *anterior* and *posterior ligaments*, to which the margins of the disc are attached, strengthen the joint.

Movements and Function. As you may discover by palpation, movements at this joint allow the scapula to choose its own position forward, backward, upward, or downward (i.e., circumduction), so long as it keeps its distance from the sternoclavicular joint. Also, it allows the clavicle to undergo axial rotation during elevation (p. 182).

The Costoclavicular Ligament passes from the 1st costal cartilage to a rough impression below the sternal end of the clavicle. Its anterior fibers, which pass upward and laterally, hide a strong layer of fibers which pass upward and medially.

When you stoop to lift a weight, the lateral end of the clavicle sinks and its medial part rests on the 1st costal cartilage, which, acting as a fulcrum, tends to cause the medial end of the clavicle to be levered out of its socket; this the disc and the ligaments resist.

The disc is not uncommonly found perforated, and yet its hold on the clavicle is not lost, for its anterior and posterior margins, not being subjected to compressive and frictional forces, are ligamentous (not fibrocartilaginous), and they persist.

Relations. Though the joint is palpable and apparently subcutaneous, it is in reality crossed anteriorly by the flat tendon of the sternal head of the Sternomastoid. Posteriorly, the Sternohyoid and Sternothyroid form a pad of muscle that separates the great vessels and the vagus nerve from the joint (*figs. 709 and 725.*)

»» A feeble band, the *interclavicular ligament*, perhaps homologous with the wishing bone of the bird, connects the two clavicles across the jugular notch (*fig. 173*).

Epiphyses. A scale-like epiphysis appears on the medial end of the clavicle. (Age of complete fusion, see p. 105.)

Nerve Supply. Supraclavicular nerves, and nerve to Subclavius.

Coracoclavicular Ligament

Here there are no articular surfaces—junction is effected by ligaments; so, the joint is a syndesmosis. The coracoclavicular ligament is in two parts, a conoid and a trapezoid.

»» 1. *The Conoid Ligament* is an inverted cone whose apex is attached to a roughness at the medial end of the coracoid process above the scapular notch (suprascapular notch). Its base is attached to the conoid tubercle at the back of the under surface of the clavicle where the lateral one-third of the bone, which is flattened, joins the medial two-thirds, which is triangular on section.

2. *The Trapezoid Ligament* is placed antero-laterally to the conoid ligament. It is three-quarters of an inch wide, and it extends from a rough line on the coracoid behind the occasional site of crossing of the Pectoralis Minor (*figs. 178* and *187*) to a rough line on the clavicle that runs antero-laterally from the conoid tubercle.

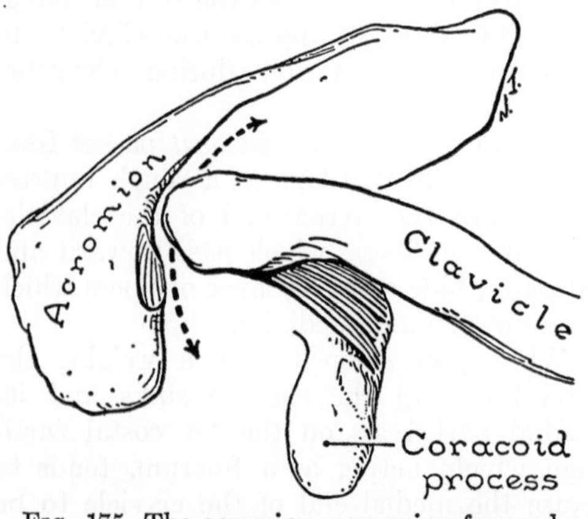

FIG. 175. The acromion may swing forward or backward, but, so long as the coracoclavicular ligament is intact, it cannot be driven under the clavicle.

Functions. (1) Owing to their medial (and downward) direction, the conoid and trapezoid ligaments prevent the scapula from being driven medially; in this, only the Serratus Anterior renders them aid. (2) They are the mainstay of the acromioclavicular joint, and so long as they remain intact, the joint may, indeed, undergo subluxation (partial dislocation), but the acromion cannot be driven under the clavicle (*fig. 175*). (3) With the aid of muscles they suspend the scapula.

Relations. The trapezoid band lies almost horizontally above the medial part of the coraco-acromial ligament.

Acromioclavicular Joint

The medial border of the acromion has near its tip a small oval facet which articulates with a similar small facet on the lateral end of the clavicle (*fig. 175*). The articular surfaces are so bevelled that an injury, resulting in dislocation, will drive the acromion below the clavicle. Strong parallel fibers form a complete capsule for the joint. A small *articular disc* hangs into the cavity from above.

Function. (1) This joint enables the scapula to move vertically on the chest wall when the pectoral girdle rises and falls (e.g., as when shrugging the shoulders). (2) It also enables the scapula (and with it the glenoid cavity) to glide forward and backward on the clavicle and so to face directions convenient to the head of the humerus (e.g., forward when striking a blow).[4] (3) Also, it is essential to free elevation of the limb (p. 182).

Epiphyses, page 181 and figure 188.

Nerve Supply. Axillary, suprascapular, and lateral pectoral nerves.

Relations. The joint is subcutaneous.

The end of the clavicle, being thicker than the acromion, is easily felt on pressing medially with a finger. It marks the site of the joint. Below lie the subacromial bursa and the Supraspinatus.

---

[4] The conoid lig. checks backward gliding of the acromion at the acromioclavicular joint and therefore widening of the angle between clavicle and scapula; the trapezoid lig. checks forward gliding.

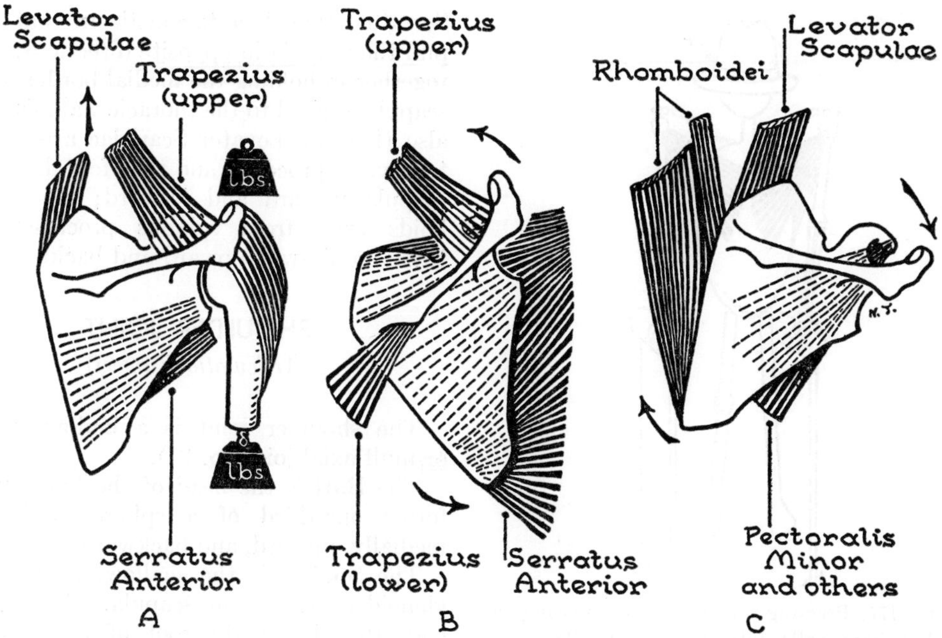

FIG. 176. *A*, simple elevation of the shoulder girdle. The suspensory muscles of the girdle. *B*, elevation of the girdle with upward rotation of the glenoid cavity. *C*, depression of the girdle with downward rotation of the glenoid cavity.

TABLE 3

*Muscles Acting upon the Shoulder Girdle**

Simple elevation	Simple depression	Elevation with upward rotation of glenoid cavity	Depression with downward rotation of glenoid cavity	Protraction or forward movement	Retraction or backward movement
Trapezius (upper) Lev. Scapulae Serratus Anterior (upper)	Pect. Minor Subclavius and Pect. Major Lat. Dorsi	Trapezius (upper) Trapezius (lower) Serratus Anterior	Lev. Scapulae Rhomboids Pect. Minor Trapezius (mid.) and Pect. Major Lat. Dorsi	Pect. Minor Lev. Scap. Serratus Anterior and Pect. Major	Trapezius (mid.) Rhomboids and Lat. Dorsi

* *Note.* Pectoralis Major and Latissimus Dorsi act on the girdle indirectly, through the humerus.

Movements of the Shoulder Girdle

1. *Simple elevation* of scapula: i.e., the scapula moves vertically upward. A low level of activity in Trapezius (upper), Levator Scapulae, and Serratus Anterior (upper) is sufficient to suspend the girdle; but when a weight is either supported on the shoulder or carried in the hand, these muscles contract vigorously (*fig. 176*). (See table 3.)

2. *Simple depression* is brought about by the weight of the limb. But as an active movement, e.g., pressing downward or resting on parallel bars, it calls into action the Pectoralis Minor, which acts on the girdle, and the Pectoralis Major and Latissimus Dorsi, which act on the humerus (*fig. 177*). The timely contraction of these muscles saves the clavicle from fracture, when one falls on one's outstretched hand (p. 77).

3. *Elevation with upward rotation of Glenoid Cavity*. In this movement the acromion rises, the superior angle of the scapula descends, and the inferior angle swings laterally. The Trapezius (upper), Trapezius

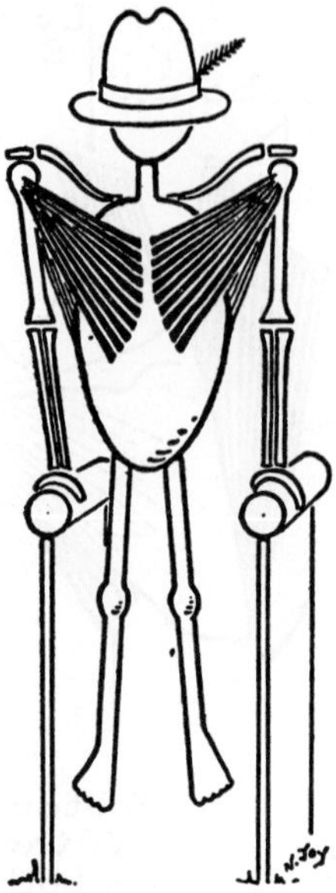

FIG. 177. Pressing downward or resting on parallel bars calls into action the Pectoralis Major and the Latissimus Dorsi.

(lower), and the Serratus Anterior combine in this rotation. This movement is almost always part of a larger movement involving either abduction or flexion of the shoulder joint, as when the hand reaches for some object above the head, i.e., the entire limb is elevated—see page 182.

4. *Depression with downward rotation of Glenoid Cavity*, that is, recovering from the last movement or overstepping the recovery, e.g. chopping wood (*fig. 176*). The Pectoralis Minor, Rhomboids, Levator Scapulae, and Trapezius (especially the middle portion) are called into play; and the Pectoralis Major and Latissimus Dorsi, which act indirectly through the humerus, give them powerful assistance.

5. *Protraction of the scapula* or forward movement, e.g., pushing. The Serratus Anterior, Pectoralis Minor, and Levator Scapulae act together with the Pectoralis Major.

6. *Retraction of the scapula* or backward movement, that is, recovering from the last movement or overstepping the recovery, e.g., pulling. The Trapezius (middle portion) and the Rhomboids act with the Latissimus Dorsi.

Observe that the Rhomboids and the Serratus, though antagonistic in that they pull the scapula in opposite directions, work together in holding the medial border of the scapula applied to the thoracic wall. Observe also that the Levator Scapulae arises from transverse processes and therefore draws the scapula upward and forward; the Rhomboids arise from spinous processes and therefore draw it upward and backward.

SHOULDER JOINT

(*Articulatio Humeri*)

The shoulder joint is a ball-and-socket or multiaxial joint (p. 21).

The **Ball** is the head of the humerus. It forms one-third of a sphere, and faces medially, upward, and backward.

The **Socket** is the shallow, pear-shaped glenoid cavity of the scapula. At its upper end, that is, at the root of the coracoid process, is the supraglenoid tubercle for the long head of the Biceps. At its lower end, that is, on the lateral border of the scapula, is the rough infraglenoid tubercle for the long head of the Triceps. The playing of the tendon of the Subscapularis across the front of the socket is responsible for the concavity that contributes largely to its pear shape. A strip of fibrocartilage, the *labrum glenoidale*, runs round the rim of the socket, deepens it somewhat, and makes a pliable elastic cushion for the ball to roll against, (*cf.* the cushion of a billiard table).

Movements. It is obvious that there is more freedom at the shoulder joint than at any other joint in the body. It is also obvious that the movements permitted are flexion and extension, and abduction and adduction—and, therefore, circumduction as well (p. xv). And, it is not difficult to satisfy oneself that the humerus can rotate medially and laterally on its own long axis. To demonstrate these movements of axial rotation, bend your elbow to a right angle (so that movements of the bones of the forearm shall not confuse), and keep the arm close to the side (so that the pectoral girdle shall remain stationary), then swing your hand first medially across your front and then laterally out to the side; and while doing so, palpate the epicondyles of your humerus noting that they rotate with the hand.

Fibrous Capsule and Ligaments. To allow such free movement, taut ligaments must surely be wanting and the capsule of the joint very loose. Such is the case. In fact, when the shoulder muscles are removed, leaving the humerus attached to the scapula only by the capsule and ligaments, the head of the humerus can be drawn ⅓″ away from its socket. However, in the adducted position the capsule becomes very tight superiorly, effectively preventing downward displacement of the humerus.

The *Fibrous Capsule* stretches as a loose tube from just proximal to the margin of the glenoid cavity of the scapula to the anatomical neck of the humerus. Inferiorly, however, it passes well down (½″) on to the surgical neck. When the arm is adducted, this lower part lies in folds (*fig. 183*).

The *Synovial Membrane* lines the fibrous capsule. Proximally, it is reflected from this capsule on to the glenoid labrum and there sends a fringe or fold dorsally into the joint cavity; distally, it is reflected along the anatomical (and surgical) neck as far as the hyaline cartilage of the head of the humerus, which is according to rule (*fig. 28*).

The **Coracohumeral Ligament** has been regarded as the divorced tendon of the Pectoralis Minor; and certainly a portion of that tendon at times passes over the coracoid process and blends with the ligament (*fig. 178*).

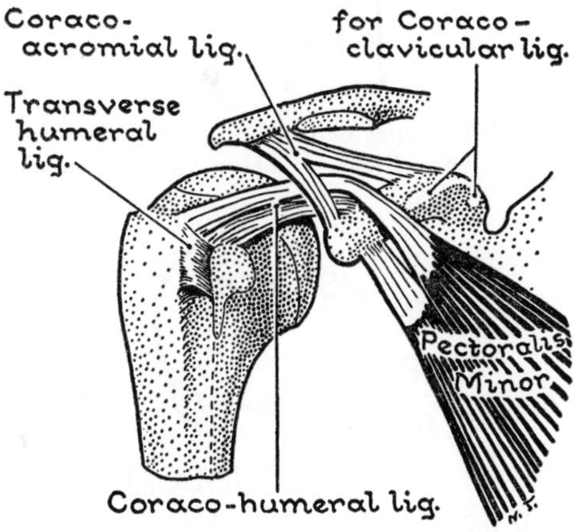

FIG. 178. *Variation:* Part of tendon of Pectoralis Minor augmenting the coracohumeral lig.

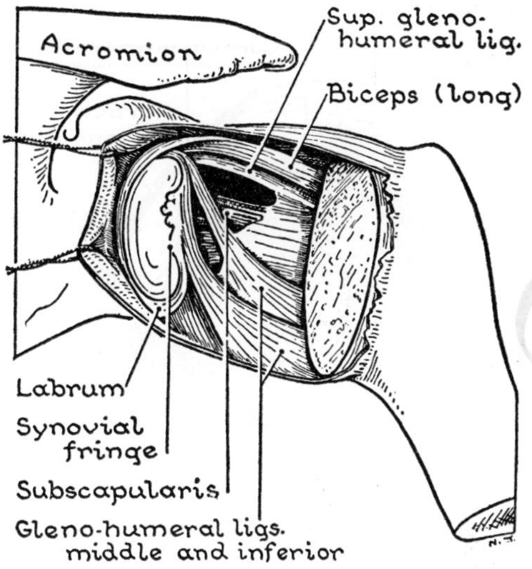

FIG. 179. Interior of shoulder joint (exposed from behind).

This remark is intended to suggest that the coracohumeral ligament is attached to the coracoid process approximately in line with the Pectoralis Minor. The ligament extends from the lateral border of the process to the anatomical neck of the humerus beside the lesser and greater tubercles—which are situated anteriorly and laterally—and its posterior fibers so blend with the capsule that the ligament can only be distinguished from the capsule when viewed from the front. Having these attachments, the ligament must resist lateral rotation and adduction.

Contrary to expectations, downward dislocation of the shoulder joint is not prevented by the vertically running muscles, e.g., Deltoid, Biceps, and Triceps. Normally it is prevented by a locking mechanism dependent on three factors: (1) the slope of the glenoid fossa, leading to (2) the tightening of the superior part of the capsule (including the coracohumeral ligament), and (3) the activity of the Supraspinatus muscle (and, to a lesser extent, the posterior fibers of Deltoid) (Basmajian and Bazant).

Interior of the Shoulder Joint. If the capsule of the joint is opened at the back [and, if necessary, the head of the humerus

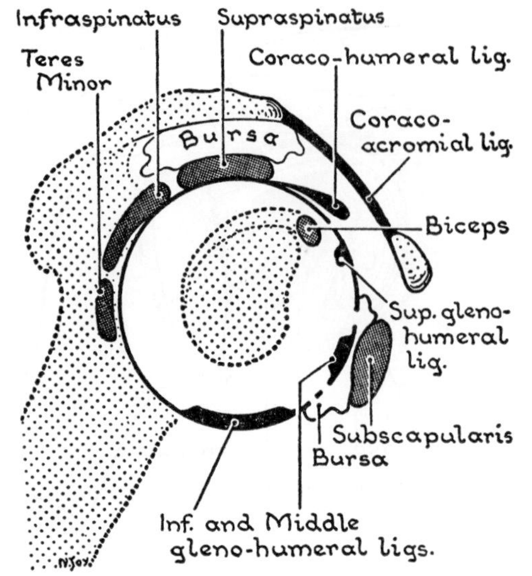

FIG. 180. Scheme of shoulder joint on sagittal section (lateral view).

removed], a view will be had of the synovial aspect of the anterior wall of the cavity, showing the structures labeled in figure 179. The three bands, called the superior, middle, and inferior glenohumeral ligaments, are thickenings of the fibrous capsule that stand out in relief.

The **Glenohumeral Ligaments** pass obliquely from the front and lower part of the anatomical neck of the humerus medially and upward to converge on the supraglenoid tubercle, the *inferior band* contributing fibers to the anterior part of the glenoid labrum en route. The *middle band* may stand out distinctly owing to the fact that the capsular wall has given way both above it and below and so brought the subscapularis bursa into communication with the joint cavity. In consequence, the *Subscapularis tendon* enters into this picture.

The *superior band* is slender and parallel to the Biceps tendon.

The **Long Head of the Biceps** may be followed from the intertubercular sulcus (which faces forward, *fig. 181*) across the front of the head of the humerus to its origin from the supraglenoid tubercle and posterior lip of the glenoid cavity where it constitutes the glenoid labrum (*fig. 90*). When the humerus is rotated laterally, the Biceps tendon is carried across the summit of the head of the bone. In this position it may play the part of an accessory ligament.

The long tendon, having lost its mesotendon, is free within the joint cavity; it is retained in the intertubercular sulcus by a band, the *transverse humeral ligament*, that spans the sulcus between the two tubercles (*fig. 181*).

The Strength of a Joint depends on three main factors:

1. Bony formation.
2. Ligaments.
3. Muscles.

It is evident that for strength the shoulder joint depends neither on its bony socket nor on ligaments, but on muscles. Now, of the muscles around the shoulder joint some are long; others are short. The long muscles perform movements; the short muscles—disposed closely around the head—have also the important function of retaining the head in its socket. In this they have the assistance of the overhanging coraco-acromial arch, which obviously prevents upward displacement of the humerus.

Four Short Muscles and the Immediate Relations of the Joint. The short muscles round the joint (*figs. 180* and *182*) are:

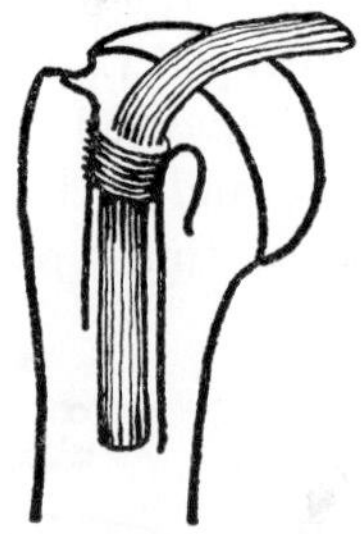

FIG. 181. Upper end of humerus (front view). Long tendon of Biceps and transverse ligament.

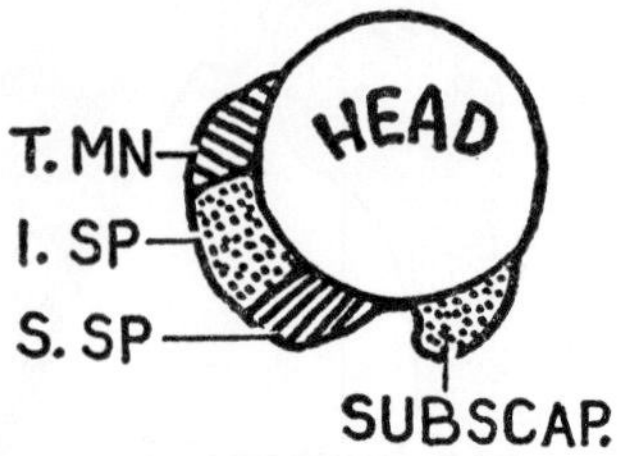

FIG. 182. Insertions of the four short muscles that act as "accessory ligaments" of the shoulder joint viewed from above.

Supraspinatus—above
Infraspinatus and Teres Minor—behind
Subscapularis—in front

The tendon of Supraspinatus fuses intimately and extensively (1″ in length) with the underlying fibrous capsule; posteriorly, the tendons of Infraspinatus and Teres Minor, and anteriorly, the tendon of Subscapularis fuse progressively less from above downward, the lowest fibers being fleshy and free.

The tendons of these four short muscles are in a sense *accessory ligaments*. They are, however, not passive ligaments, but ligaments active and alert in virtue of the fact that each has muscle fibers attached to its proximal end. They are "ligaments under control."

Below, there is no supporting short muscle—no alert ligament, but loose unsupported capsule and the quadrangular space. And through this space pass the axillary nerve (which supplies Deltoid and Teres Minor) and the posterior humeral circumflex artery.

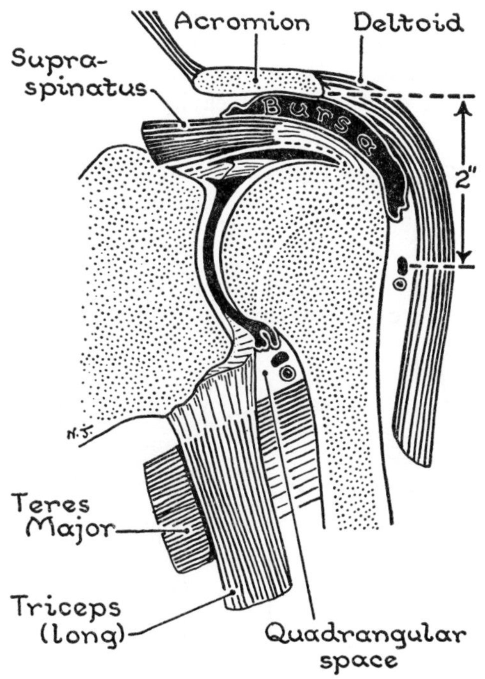

FIG. 183. Shoulder joint, on coronal section. Observe: (1) the upper epiphyseal plate of the humerus; (2) the axillary (circumflex) nerve in the quadrangular space and 2″ below the acromion; (3) the capsule in folds during adduction; and (4) the bursa which is both subacromial and subdeltoid.

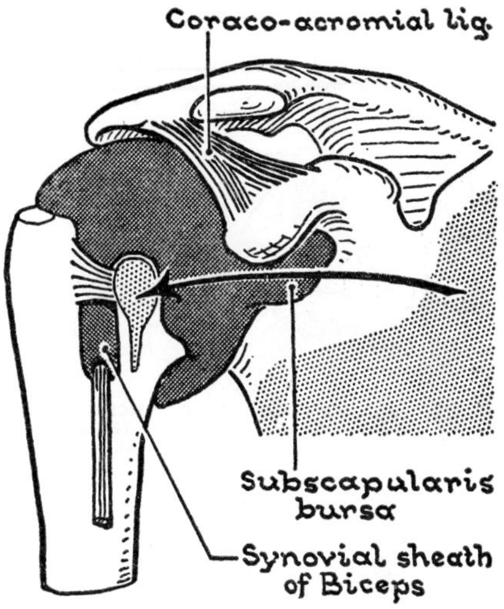

FIG. 184. Synovial capsule of shoulder joint and communicating bursae, distended.

When the humerus is abducted, the long head of the Triceps and the Teres Major come into contact with the capsule below.

»» Lying side by side on the insertion of the Subscapularis (*fig. 65*), close to the joint, are (1) the neurovascular bundle (i.e., the contents of the axillary sheath), (2) the Coracobrachialis, and (3) the short head of the Biceps, which in turn lies side by side with the long head.

Bursae. The tendon of the Subscapularis plays in its groove on the anterior border of the glenoid cavity, where it requires a bursa, the **subscapularis bursa,** to facilitate its play. Here, at the site of friction, bursal wall and joint capsule break down with the result that their cavities come into communication with each other above (and below) the middle glenohumeral band. This explains why the Subscapularis tendon can be seen when the joint is opened from behind.

The Biceps tendon requires a *tubular bursa,* or synovial sheath, to lubricate it where it plays in the upper 2″ of the intertubercular sulcus (*fig. 184*).

The **Subacromial Bursa** (*fig. 183*) lies between the acromion and the Supraspinatus tendon, and it extends downward between the Deltoid and the greater tubercle. How far down? As far as is necessary; i.e., far

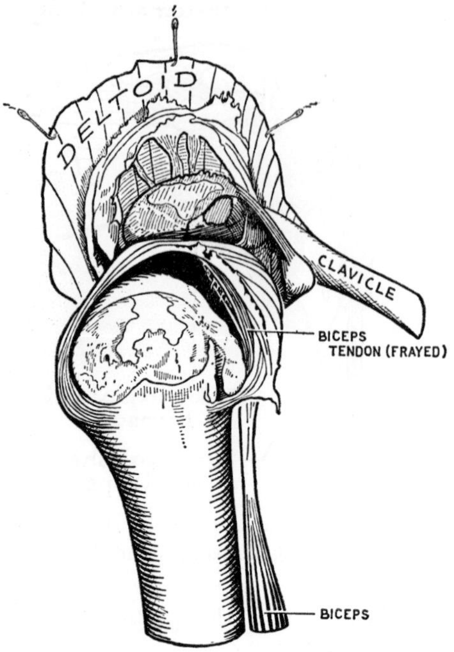

Fig. 185. The supraspinatus tendon and the underlying capsule are commonly worn through (see text).

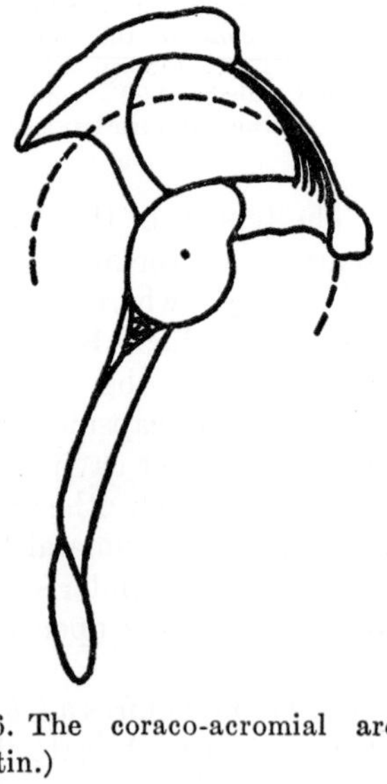

Fig. 186. The coraco-acromial arch. (After C. P. Martin.)

The **Coraco-Acromial Arch** is formed by the coracoid, the coraco-acromial ligament, and the acromion (*figs. 184* and *186*). The ligament is triangular; its apex is attached to the tip (and under surface) of the acromion anterior to the acromioclavicular joint; its base is attached to the lateral border of the coracoid process (*fig. 187*).

The arch, with the subjacent subacromial bursa, forms a resilient **secondary socket** for the head of the humerus, preventing its upward displacement. The coraco-acromial arch does not lie on the arc of a circle centered on the glenoid cavity but is farther enough to cover the part of the greater tubercle that passes under the acromion during abduction of the humerus.

» As the result of wearing away of the Supraspinatus tendon and underlying capsule, it is by no means uncommon for the subacromial bursa to be in wide open communication with the synovial cavity of the shoulder joint. Figure 185 represents an advanced stage of this condition. In the initial stages there is a nodular overgrowth of bone in the region of the greater tuberosity and an associated fraying of the capsule. Perforation follows. As the condition advances the soft tissues disappear from under the acromion; it becomes bare. Eburnation of the contact surfaces of humerus and acromion may follow. The intracapsular part of the long tendon of the Biceps becomes frayed —even worn away—leaving it adherent to the bicipital sulcus. Of 79 dissecting room specimens of proved age, none of the 16 under 50 years was perforated; but 3 of the 17 between 50 and 60 years, and 16 of the 46 over 60 were perforated. The condition is usually bilateral.

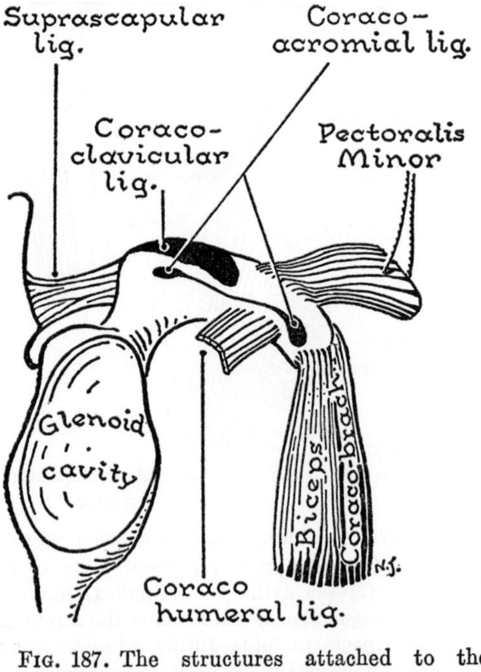

Fig. 187. The structures attached to the finger-shaped coracoid process. (See *fig. 60.*)

from it behind than in front (*fig. 186*). Now, when the arm is abducted to a right angle, the greater tubercle of the humerus impinges on the lateral edge of the coraco-acromial arch, and it is easily observed, by following the course of the lateral epicondyle, that on raising the arm still higher above the head, the humerus automatically rotates laterally. Thus is accommodation for the greater tubercle found under the acromion. It is to allow of this movement that the subacromial bursa is so extensive.

Epiphyses (*fig. 188*). The epiphyseal line of the **coracoid process** crosses the upper part of the glenoid cavity. Union occurs during the 15th year. The epiphyseal line of the acromion crosses the clavicular facet. If the epiphysis has not fused by the 23rd year, it will remain a separate bone (os acromiale).

The upper epiphysis of the **humerus** rests on the spike-like end of the diaphysis. The epiphyseal line lies at the upper limit of the surgical neck and enters the joint cavity medially. The upper epiphysis of the humerus is an amalgamation of three smaller epiphyses: a pressure epiphysis for the head which appears during the 1st year, and two traction epiphyses, one for the greater tubercle (3rd year), the other for the lesser tubercle (5th year). All three fuse together before the 7th year, and the resulting single mass fuses with the shaft completely by the 18th year in some cases and by the 24th year in all cases (McKern and Stewart).

»» **Correct Orientation of Scapula and Humerus.** ***The Humerus*** is to be held vertically, the lesser tubercle and the intertubercular sulcus facing forward, and the greater tubercle laterally.

The head of the humerus and the medial epicondyle face the same direction to within a few degrees. Hence, if the shoulder joint is dislocated, the epicondyle will indicate the position of the displaced head.

The Scapula, it must be remembered, is applied to the upper part of a barrel-shaped thorax. Hence, its lateral border slopes backward as well as downward and medially (*fig. 186*)—it is not vertical, as commonly depicted. The tip of the coracoid lies 1½″ supero-medial to the lesser tubercle of the humerus.

If you can orient these two bones correctly, you can understand: (1) how the Teres Major can act as an extensor, (2) why the head of a humerus, when it is dislocated, almost of necessity passes to the ventral aspect of the scapula, (3) why the coracohumeral ligament is taut in lateral rotation and in adduction, (4) why the long head of the Biceps can abduct only while the arm is laterally rotated, as only then does its tendon cross the summit of the head of the humerus.

Muscles Acting on Shoulder Joint. All muscles passing from the clavicle and scapula to the humerus must act upon the shoulder joint; and those passing from the trunk to the humerus must act on the shoulder joint and also on the joints of the clavicle (joints of the shoulder girdle). From your knowledge of the bony attachments of these muscles and of the correct orientation of the bones, you will find you are able without much difficulty to apportion to each muscle its proper actions or action and to gauge the relative importance of each. Test your knowledge of the actions of the muscles crossing the joint by entering their names in what you estimate to be the appropriate columns of the blank table 4; then compare your list with the one appended in table 5.

»» *Note.* The sternal fibers of the Pectoralis Major bring the humerus from the raised to the dependent position; the Teres Major is a powerful muscle—the sectional area of its fleshy belly is almost as large as that of the Biceps. The long head of the Triceps can extend the shoulder only when the arm is abducted, for when fully adducted its fibers are too slack; the Supraspinatus has not the power to raise the arm when the Deltoid is paralyzed.

Reference to table 5 makes it evident that the 5th and 6th spinal nerve segments control flexion, abduction, and lateral rotation, and that the 5th, 6th, 7th, 8th, and 1st control extension, adduction, and medial rotation. Therefore, if the 5th and 6th segments be paralyzed, the arm will come to occupy the extended, adducted, and medially

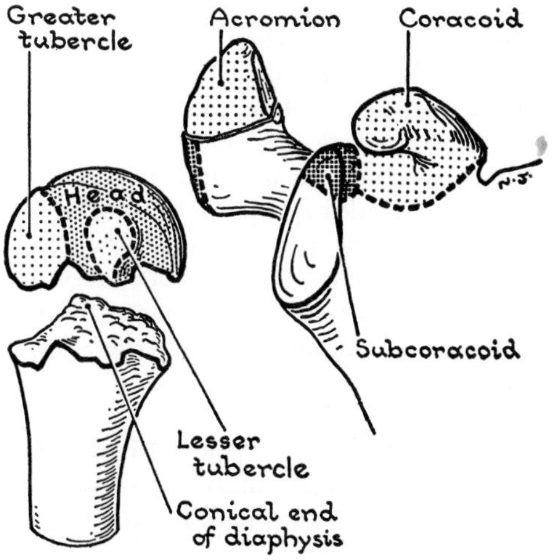

Fig. 188. Epiphyses about the shoulder joint

TABLE 4

Flexors	Extensors	Abductors	Adductors	Med. rotators	Lat. rotators

TABLE 5

Muscles Acting on the Shoulder Joint with Their Approximate Spinal Nerve Segments

Flexion		Extension		Abduction	
Deltoid (clav.)	5, 6	Deltoid (postr.)	5, 6	Deltoid (mid.)	5, 6
Supraspinatus	5, 6	Pect. Major (st.)	7, 8, 1	Supraspinatus	5, 6
Pect. Major (clav.)	5, 6	Teres Major	5, 6		
Biceps	5, 6	Lat. Dorsi	7, 8		
Coracobrachialis	7	Triceps (long.)	7, 8		
5, 6 (7)		5, 6, 7, 8, 1		5, 6	
Adduction		**Med. rotate**		**Lat. rotate**	
Deltoid (postr.)	5, 6	Deltoid (clav.)	5, 6	Deltoid (postr.)	5, 6
Pect. Major (cl.)	5, 6	Pect. Major (cl.)	5, 6	Infraspinatus	5, 6
Pect. Major (st.)	7, 8, 1	Pect. Major (st.)	7, 8, 1	Teres Minor	5, 6
Coracobrachialis	7	Subscapularis	5, 6		
Teres Major	5, 6	Teres Major	5, 6		
Lat. Dorsi	7, 8	Lat. Dorsi	7, 8		
Triceps (long.)	7, 8				
5, 6, 7, 8, 1		5, 6, 7, 8, 1		5, 6	

rotated position—described as the "position of a waiter taking a tip."

Nerve Supply of the Shoulder Joint. From C. 5 and 6 via the suprascapular, axillary, and lateral pectoral nerves, and posterior cord; also sympathetic fibers from the adventitia of the axillary artery (E. Gardner). Sensory (pain) fibers may accompany the sympathetic fibers, running back to the spinal cord through the sympathetic trunk.

Elevation of the Upper Limb. The free part of the upper limb moves through 180 degrees when it is raised from the dependent position to a vertical position above the head. This vertical position can be attained either through forward flexion or through abduction. In this movement the sternoclavicular, acromioclavicular, and shoulder joints take part simultaneously. Inman, Saunders, and Abbott have demonstrated that during the elevation through 180 degrees, the humerus and scapula move in the ratio of 2:1 from almost the beginning of the movement to the termination. Thus, in general, for every 15 degrees of elevation 10 occur at the shoulder joint and 5 are due to movement of the scapula.

As elevation progresses beyond shoulder level (90 degrees), the clavicle rotates backward on its own long axis and its lateral end rises. Without this clavicular movement, elevation above shoulder level is greatly restricted. If the scapula is held fixed, the humerus can move only through a right angle and the power of movement is greatly diminished. Therefore, in elevation of the limb the scapula must be free to rotate and it does so with the permission of the clavicular joints.

During the early phases of elevation, the sternoclavicular joint passes through its greatest range of movement, and in the terminal phase the acromioclavicular joint does so.

Muscle Force Couples. ***(1) Movements of the Humerus.*** The Supraspinatus and the Deltoid act together and progressively in elevating the arm. The Supraspinatus alone is unable to initiate abduction.

A study of action potential curves (p. 26) shows clearly that both muscles act together throughout the entire range of movement. These elevator muscles, however, are helpless to move the arm away from the side unless the three short depressors—Subscapularis, Infraspinatus, and Teres Minor—are in action. These two groups of muscles act as a force couple, the one elevating and the other depressing (*cf.* prime mover and antagonist).

(2) Movements of the Scapula. The upper parts of the Trapezius and Serratus Anterior (and the Levator Scapulae) constitute the upper component of the force couple necessary to the rotation of the scapula, whereas the lower parts of the Trapezius and Serratus Anterior constitute the lower component. The lower part of the Trapezius is more active in abduction; it relaxes gradually in flexion to allow the Serratus to draw the scapula forward.

The middle fibers of the Trapezius and the Rhomboids serve to steady the scapula during abduction.

ELBOW JOINT
(*Articulatio Cubiti*)

The elbow joint is a hinge or *ginglymus* joint, for it allows only flexion and extension (p. 21). With it the proximal radio-ulnar joint must be considered. There are, in fact, three joints with one synovial cavity—humero-ulnar, humero-radial, and proximal radio-ulnar joints (*fig. 191*).

The elbow joint being a hinge joint, the following general characters may reasonably be expected:

1. One bony surface will be convex, the other concave.
2. The muscles will be massed in front and behind in order to flex and extend.
3. The capsule will be loose in front and loose behind in order to permit flexion and extension.
4. Strong collateral ligaments will be required to prevent medial and lateral movements.
5. The medial and lateral bony surface will be palpable.

Bones. THE HUMERO-ULNAR PARTS.

Lower end of Humerus. This part is flattened from before backward and is set obliquely, being lower medially than laterally. It lies on a plane anterior to the body of the bone and possesses a spool-shaped pulley with sharp edges, the *trochlea.* The trochlea leads in front to a depression, the *coronoid fossa* and behind to a broad triangular hollow, the *olecranon fossa.*

Upper end of Ulna. Here we have a triangular bracket, the *coronoid process,* which projects forward (*fig. 189*). The portion of the ulna continued upward beyond

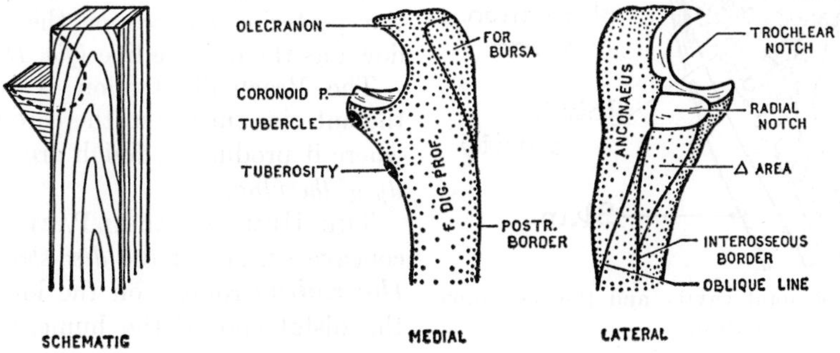

FIG. 189. Upper end of ulna

the level of the coronoid process is cubical, the *olecranon*. If there were no coronoid process, there would be no occasion to refer to the olecranon except as the upper end of the body.

Now, the anterior aspect of the olecranon and the superior aspect of the coronoid process articulate with the trochlea of the humerus; hence, they form not a right angled surface but a concavity, the *trochlear notch* (semilunar notch). This notch is reciprocally saddle-shaped for the trochlea of the humerus with which it articulates, being concave sagittally, and roughly convex from side to side (*fig. 192*).

A rounded ridge, which extends from the tip of the olecranon to the tip of the coronoid process, divides the notch into right and left portions; and nonarticular indentations, which in the intact joint are occupied by fat pads (see p. 20), partly divide the notch into upper and lower portions. Thus is the trochlear notch divided into four parts.

» The hinder part of the upper surface of the olecranon is commonly prolonged into a crest by the tendon of the Triceps.

Posteriorly, the olecranon presents a triangular, subcutaneous surface at the apex

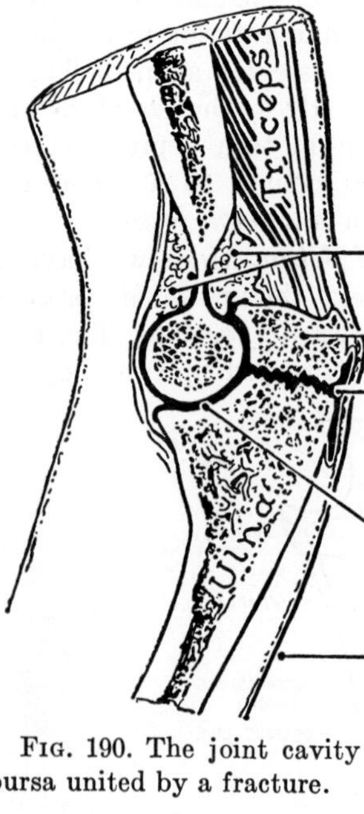

FIG. 190. The joint cavity and the olecranon bursa united by a fracture.

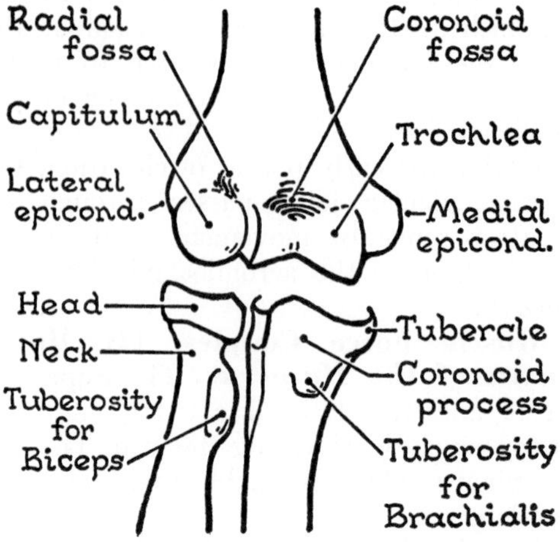

FIG. 191. The bony parts concerned in the elbow joint (front view).

of which the sharp, posterior border of the body begins. This surface is overlaid by the subcutaneous **olecranon bursa,** which might communicate with the joint cavity in the event of a fracture of the bone (*fig. 190*).

The medial surfaces of the coronoid process and olecranon merge into the medial surface of the body and like it afford fleshy origin for the Flexor Digitorum Profundus.

The lateral surface of the coronoid process is a concave facet, called the *radial notch* of the ulna. From the anterior and posterior ends of this notch two descending lines, meeting, become the interosseous border of the bone. The triangular depression, enclosed, accommodates the tuberosity of the radius and the Biceps tendon during full pronation of the forearm. The Supinator in part arises from this depression but mainly from the line or crest bounding it behind. The Anconeus is inserted into the lateral surface of the olecranon as well as into the posterior surface of the bone as far down as the oblique line (*fig. 189*).

The Brachialis tendon is inserted into the anterior surface of the coronoid process, where it produces a rough area, the *tuberosity of the ulna.*

THE HUMERO-RADIAL PARTS. The upper concave surface of the *disc-shaped* ***head of the radius*** rotates on the lower aspect of the distal end of the humerus during extension and on the anterior aspect during flexion. This demands the presence on the lower and anterior aspects of the distal end of the humerus of a rounded articular ***capitulum*** or little head. Posteriorly, the capitulum is nonexistent. Above and laterally, it merges with the lateral epicondyle. The rim of the upper surface of the disc-like head plays upon the lateral lip of the spool-shaped trochlea which, therefore, helps to prevent medial displacement of the radius (*fig. 191*). During full flexion the rim occupies the radial fossa of the humerus.

The Proximal Radio-ulnar Joint. The head of the radius is held in position by the **anular ligament,** which is attached to the ends of the radial notch of the ulna. The notch forms one-fourth of a circle; the ligament three-fourths.

The ligament is not strictly speaking ring-shaped, but rather it is cup-shaped, being of smaller circumference below than above (*fig. 192*). In consequence, the head of the radius cannot be withdrawn from the cup.

»» Before the age of seven, the head of the radius is hardly larger than the neck; so, sudden traction on a child's hand or forearm, as when pulling it out of the way of a passing motor car, may result in partial dislocation of the radius downward.

Ligaments and Capsule. The *Radial Collateral Ligament* (Lateral Lig.) of the elbow joint is fan-shaped. It extends from lateral epicondyle to the side of the anular ligament; so, indirectly it helps to retain the head of the radius in position. From it the Supinator and the Ex. Carpi Radialis Brevis in part arise.

The *Ulnar Collateral Ligament* (Medial

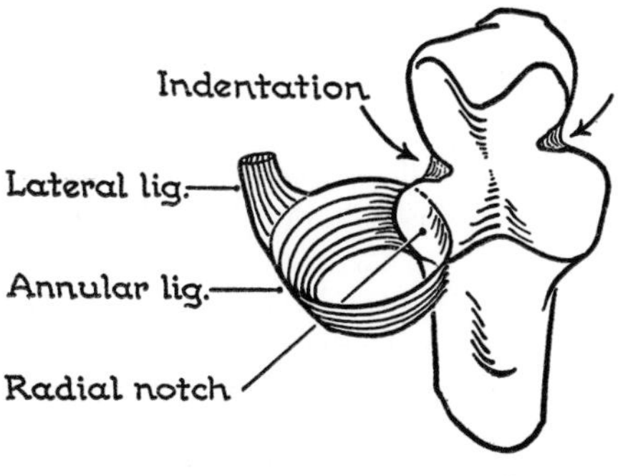

FIG. 192. Socket for head of radius (from above).

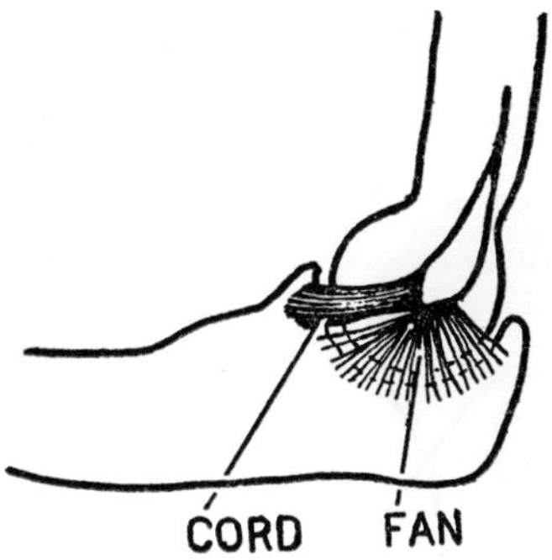

FIG. 193. Medial or ulnar collateral ligament of elbow joint.

Lig.) of the elbow joint extends in a fan-shaped manner from the lower part of the medial epicondyle to the medial margin of the trochlear notch. The humeral attachment is not quite centrally placed, but is so spread out that the posterior fibers are taut in flexion; the anterior in extension (*fig. 193*). The anterior fibers form a thick cord that is attached to a tubercle on the medial side of the coronoid. From this cord, as well as from the humerus at one end and the coronoid at the other, the Fl. Digitorum Superficialis in part arises. An oblique band of fibers serves to deepen the trochlear notch medially.

The Fibrous Capsule extends to the upper margins of the coronoid and radial fossae in front, but not quite to the top of the olecranon fossa behind. Below, it is attached to the margins of the trochlear notch except laterally where it is attached to the anular ligament.

The Synovial Capsule does not reach so high in the radial, coronoid, and olecranon fossae as the fibrous capsule. The intervals between the two capsules in these fossae are filled with fat, fluid at body temperature, and known as fat pads (Haversian glands).

Below, the synovial capsule bulges a quarter of an inch below the lower free margin of the anular ligament and surrounds the neck of the radius in a sac-like manner (*fig. 194*). This device obviously allows the radius to rotate without tearing the synovial membrane. Redundant *folds of synovial membrane* project into this joint—as they

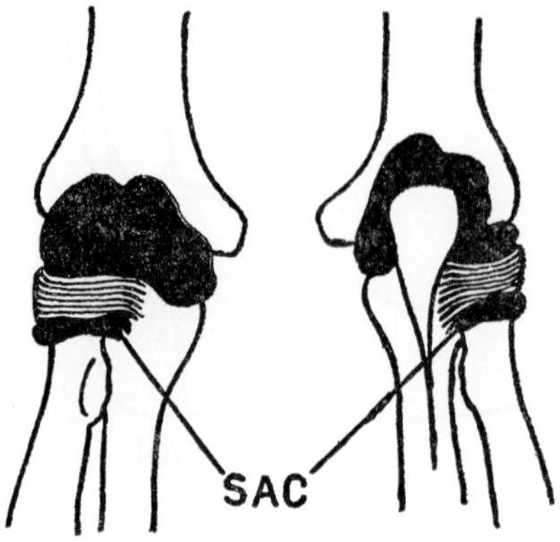

FIG. 194. Synovial capsule of elbow joint, distended.

do into other joints—and assist the fat pads to fill the unoccupied spaces.

»» Two of these synovial folds overlie the nonarticular indentations between the olecranon and the coronoid process; and an extensive crescentic fold occupies the angular interval between the head of the radius and the capitulum of the humerus. This fold, in fact, overlies the periphery of the upper surface of the head of the radius just as a semilunar cartilage overlies a condyle of the tibia.

Movements. *Bringing the Hand to the Mouth.* The medial lip of the trochlea of the humerus descends 5–6 mm. lower than the lateral lip; for the lower end of the humerus is oblique. On account of this obliquity you will observe that when your elbow is extended the humerus and ulna do not lie in line with one another but meet at an angle which opens laterally. This is known as *the carrying angle.*

The medial lip of the trochlea also projects forward about 5 mm. in advance of the lateral lip; therefore, though the humero-ulnar joint may be called a hinge joint, the ulna does not move on the trochlea like a door on a hinge, but rather it revolves on a cone. As a result the distal end of the ulna remains lateral to the axial line of the humerus in the flexed as well as in the extended position. Hence, in order to bring your hand to your mouth, you (fully) flex your elbow and either (1) medially rotate your humerus at the shoulder joint or (2) pronate your radius at the radio-ulnar joints.

Flexion is more powerful than extension in the ratio of 14:9.

Muscles. Of the three *flexors* (*fig. 120*) of the humero-radial joint two act also on the radio-ulnar joints; the *Biceps* acts as a supinator and the *Pronator Teres* as a pronator; but the *Brachioradialis* has no action on the radio-ulnar joints (Beevor). Each of the three is supplied by a different nerve (see table 6).

The Biceps, as a flexor of the elbow, acts best when the forearm is supinated, less well when semipronated, and not when pronated. As a supinator of the forearm, it does not act when the elbow is extended, unless against resistance. (Basmajian and Latif.)

The Brachioradialis, though supplied by the radial nerve, is a powerful flexor of the elbow, acting best during semipronation (and pronation) and poorly during supination. Its power is attributed to the fact that it creeps up the humerus almost to the insertion of the Deltoid and is therefore far removed from the axis of the joint (*fig. 195*). Even after the musculocutaneous and median nerves have been divided, the Brachioradialis is a useful flexor. But the Pronator Teres arises so close to the axis of the joint that in cases of musculocutaneous and radial nerve paralysis it is incapable of raising the hand to the mouth. For the same reason the muscles arising from the epicondyles have but little action on the elbow joint.

The chief flexor of the elbow joint is the *Brachialis.* Like the *Triceps* it acts upon the humero-ulnar joint.

The common use of the *Triceps* is not so much to extend the elbow as to prevent flexion of the elbow, or to regulate flexion, as in pushing a wheelbarrow. It is also an aggressive muscle, as in boxing.

TABLE 6

Muscles Acting on the Elbow Joint

Subdivisions of the joint	Flexors	Nerve segments	Nerve	Extensors	Nerve segments	Nerve
Humero-ulnar	Brachialis	5, 6	Musculocutan.	Triceps Anconeus	7, 8	Radial
Humero-radial	Biceps Brachioradialis Pronator Teres	5, 6 (5), 6 6	Musculocutan. Radial Median			

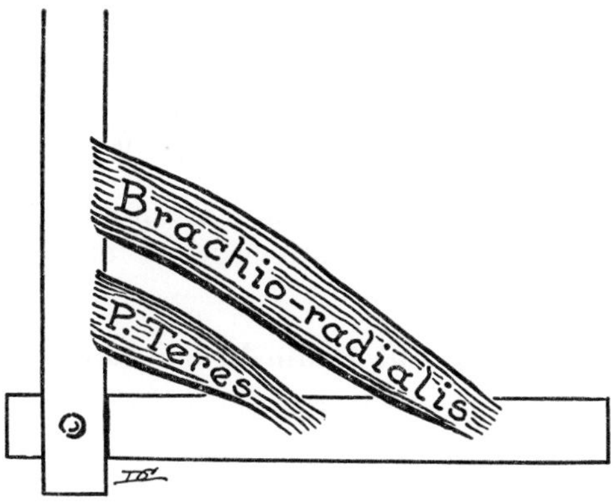

FIG. 195. As a flexor of the elbow joint, the Brachioradialis is more advantageously situated than the Pronator Teres.

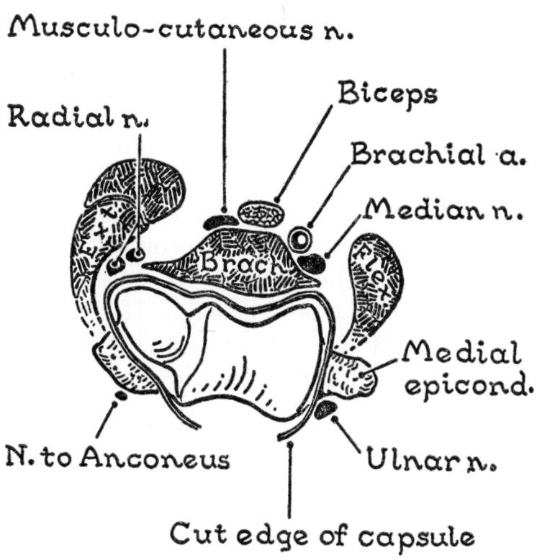

FIG. 196. Cross-section through elbow joint

Relations, particularly of five nerves (*fig. 196*). The Brachialis, though thick in the middle, is thin and attenuated at its edges. In consequence, the musculocutaneous nerve, which lies anterior to the middle of the muscle, is far removed from the joint; but the median nerve is separated from the capsule of the joint merely by the thinness of the medial edge of the Brachialis; the radial nerve (or its two terminal branches) is in direct contact with the capsule (*fig. 112*). The ulnar nerve is always in immediate contact with the ulnar collateral ligament and it is covered by Fl. Carpi Ulnaris. The nerve to the Anconeus crosses the capsule behind the lateral epicondyle.

Anastomoses around the joint. These are shown in figure 128.

Epiphyses. ***Humerus:*** The epiphyseal line separating the trochlea, capitulum, and lateral epicondyle from the diaphysis runs transversely just above the articular cartilage. It is, therefore, within the synovial capsule (*fig. 197*). This distal epiphysis is the first of all long bone epiphyses to fuse, synostosis being complete by the 17th or 18th year. The medial epicondyle fuses with a spur of bone that descends from the diaphysis and separates it from the lower epiphysis proper. Fusion may not be complete till the 20th year.

Ulna: The upper epiphysis is a traction epiphysis of the Triceps. It may be a mere scale or it may include the upper third of the olecranon.

Radius: The upper epiphyseal line lies just below the head except medially where it shaves it. It is altogether intrasynovial.

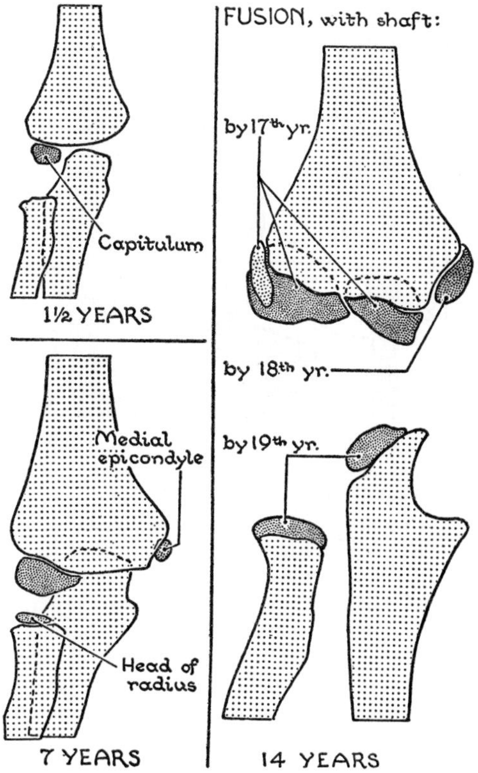

FIG. 197. Epiphyses about the elbow joint. (Courtesy of Dr. J. D. Munn, The Hospital for Sick Children, Toronto.)

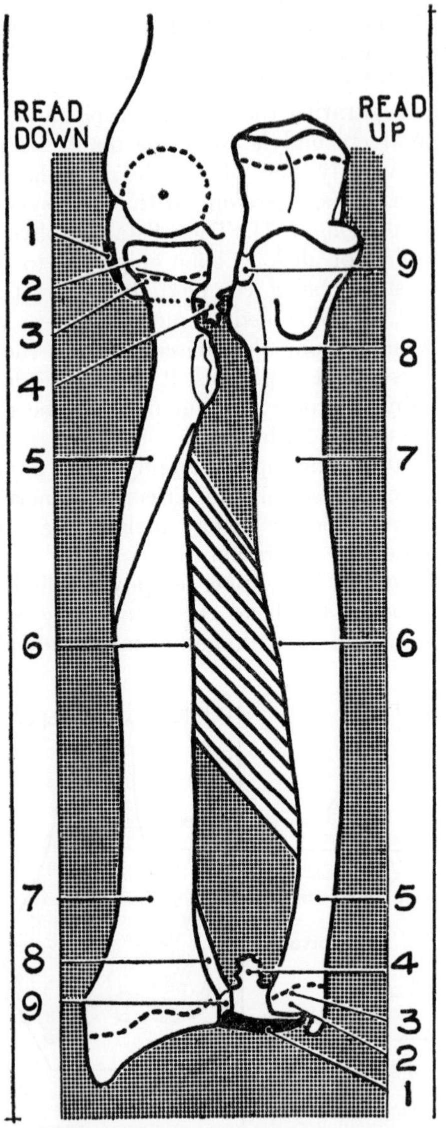

FIG. 198. Points of similarity between the proximal and distal radio-ulnar joints.

1. Anular ligament——Articular disc.
2. Circular head——Semicircular head.
3. Epiphyseal line enters the joint cavity.
4. Sacciform recess of synovial membrane.
5. The bone here circular on cross-section.
6. The interosseous border is here sharp.
7. The bone here triangular on cross-section.
8. Triangular fossa between border and notch.
9. Ulnar notch of radius——radial notch of ulna.

Nerve Supply. Each of the five nerves shown in figure 196, including the nerve to the Anconeus, sends a twig or twigs to the joint.

RADIO-ULNAR JOINTS

The two bones of the forearm are united at the proximal, "intermediate," and distal radio-ulnar joints.

Proximal Radio-Ulnar Joint

Considered with the elbow joint (p. 185).

Intermediate Radio-Ulnar Joint

The bodies of the radius and ulna are united to each other by three portions of fibrous tissue: (1) the *interosseous membrane,* (2) the oblique cord, and (3) the posterior layer of the fascia enveloping the Pronator Quadratus.

The **Interosseous Membrane,** being the medium that might transfer to the ulna the force of an impact travelling up the radius, must have its fibers directed infero-medially, and must be strong. It is best marked at the middle two-fourths of both bones. It is responsible for the sharpness of their interosseous borders. It is about equally taut in all positions—pronation, semipronation, and supination.

»» *The Oblique Cord.* This unimportant thickening in the fascia overlying the Supinator (Martin) extends from the tuberosity of the ulna inferolaterally to the radius, below its tuberosity.

The Posterior Layer of the Fascia Enveloping the Pronator Quadratus is much thicker than the anterior layer, but it has little strength. Above, it is continuous with the interosseous membrane. Below, it follows the hinder of the two lines into which the interosseous border of the radius splits above the ulnar notch.

Distal Radio-Ulnar Joint

This joint to some degree duplicates the design of the proximal joint (*fig. 198*) and understandably so, for these two joints are at opposite ends of the same pivot. Thus: (*1*) above, a circular band, the *anular ligament,* and, below, a triangular plate, the *articular disc,* holds (*2*) the circumference of the circular head of the radius, or of the semicircular head of the ulna, in (*9*) its socket, the *radial notch of the ulna,* or the *ulnar notch of the radius,* situated at the base of (*8*) the triangular fossa, the sides of which meet where (*6*) the interosseous border begins. Further, (*4*) a pouch of synovial capsule, enclosing the *sacciform recess*, is equally necessary above and below to prevent tearing during rotation. And (*3*) the epiphyseal line enters the joint cavity.

The **Head of the Ulna,** that is the articular part of the lower end (*fig. 115*), has a semicircular margin around which the ulnar notch of the radius rotates, and a semilunar or crescentic distal surface on which the articular disc plays. Within the concavity of the semilune, at the root of the styloid process, there is a *fovea or pit.* The apex of the disc is attached to the pit. The base is attached to the lower margin of the ulnar notch of the radius.

The disc is subjected to pressure and friction; therefore, it is fibrocartilaginous, but its two margins and its apex, not being so subjected, are ligamentous and pliable, and they are strong. The disc closes the joint cavity and separates it from the radiocarpal joint.

Relations. In front—Fl. Digitorum Profundus; behind—Ex. Digiti V.

Epiphyses. The distal epiphyseal plates of the radius and ulna lie on one and the same plane and cut into the distal joint cavity (*fig. 198*).

The lower or distal **radial epiphysis** appears before that of the **ulna** (*fig. 140*). Radiographically, these two epiphyses unite with the diaphyses about the 16th or 17th year in the female and the 18th or 19th in the male (see Greulich and Pyle). In the dry bones, however, complete union may be delayed until the 23rd year (McKern and Stewart).

Movements. The axis on which the radius revolves about the ulna during pronation and supination passes through the capitulum of the humerus and the pit at the lower end of the ulna to which the articular disc is attached (*fig. 198*). The whole articulation is a uniaxial joint of the trochoid or pivot variety (p. 21).

The value of the radio-ulnar joints depends upon the fact that the hand rotates with the radius following its excursions.

Muscles. See table 7.

»» **Observation.** When your elbow is flexed to a right angle and applied closely to the side of your body, so as to eliminate shoulder movements, your hand can be rotated through nearly two right angles. When your shoulder is abducted and your elbow extended, as in fencing, your hand can be rotated through nearly three right angles. The movements of pronation and supination of the radio-ulnar joints under these circumstances augment the axial rotation of the shoulder joint.

Nerve Supply: the proximal joint by the nerves to the lateral part of the elbow joint; the distal joint by the anterior and posterior interosseous nerves.

WRIST JOINT OR RADIOCARPAL JOINT

Observations. You can easily observe on your own limb that the movements permitted at the radiocarpal joint are: flexion, extension, adduction, and abduction. These together comprise the movement of circumduction. This, then, is a biaxial or ellipsoid articulation (p. 21).

»» Flexion at the radiocarpal joint would seem to be of greater range than extension, but this is a deception: extension is here more free than flexion. It is at the midcarpal joint that the greater part of the flexion often attributed to the wrist joint actually takes place.

Because the radial styloid process descends farther than the ulnar styloid process, abduction is more restricted than adduction.

TABLE 7

Muscles Acting upon the Radio-Ulnar Joints and Their Nerves and Nerve Segments

Pronators	Segment	Nerve	Supinators	Segment	Nerve
Pronator Quadratus	(7), 8, 1	Anterior Interosseous	Supinator	5, 6	Posterior Interosseous
Pronator Teres	6	Median	Biceps	5, 6	Musculocutaneous
Fl. Carpi Radialis	6	Median	2* dorsal muscles of the thumb	(6), 7, (8)	Posterior Interosseous

* The Ex. Poll. Brevis arises from the radius and therefore cannot assist in rotation.

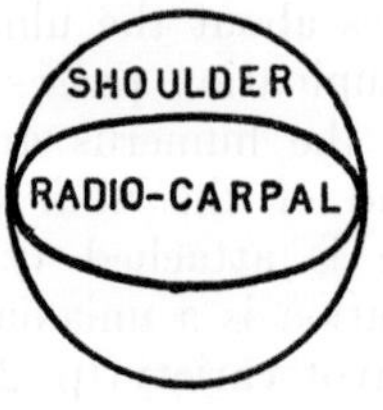

Fig. 199. Circle versus ellipse

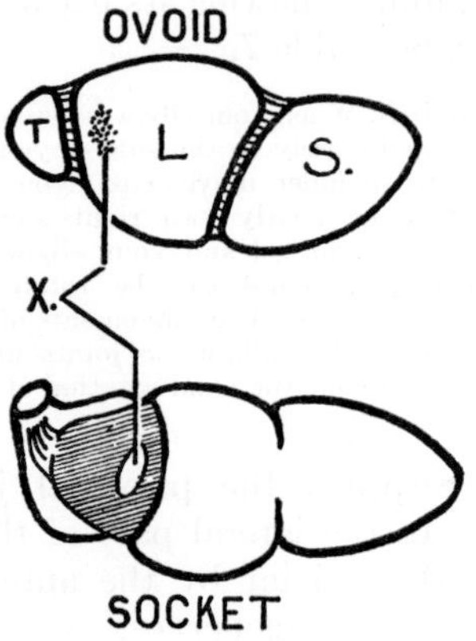

Fig. 200. "Ovoid" and socket of wrist joint. "X" marks the sites at which the disc is sometimes perforated and the lunate softened.

You have here to deal not with a "ball" and socket but with an "ovoid" and socket, for the articular surfaces are not circular in outline but ellipsoidal, the wrist being compressed from before backward (*fig. 199*). Accordingly, there can be no axial rotation here.

But, axial rotation (pronation and supination) does occur at the radio-ulnar joints. So, the circumduction at the wrist joint and the axial rotation at the joints of the forearm together duplicate the movements of the shoulder joint—and all is in the interest of the hand.

Joint Surfaces. The socket is formed by the lower articular surface of the radius plus the articular disc. The egg-shaped or ellipsoidal convex surface is formed by the proximal articular surfaces of the scaphoid, lunate, and triquetrum, plus the interosseous ligaments binding these three bones together. Figure 200 shows that the proximal bearing surfaces of the scaphoid and lunate are approximately equal in extent, and that that of the triquetrum is almost negligibly small. Figure 134 shows that, with the hand at rest, the facet on the upper surface of the triquetrum is in contact with the ulnar collateral ligament, and that the scaphoid and lunate alone transmit impacts from the carpus to the forearm.

When the radius and articular disc rotate about the ulna, they carry the hand with them. This is possible because the carpal bones do not articulate with the ulna but with the disc which excludes the ulna from the wrist joint. The articulation is, therefore, called radiocarpal and not radio-ulno-carpal.

In *Abduction* (radial deviation, *fig. 201*), which is more restricted than adduction because the styloid process of the radius interferes, the scaphoid rotates forwards, the lunate moves on to the articular disc,

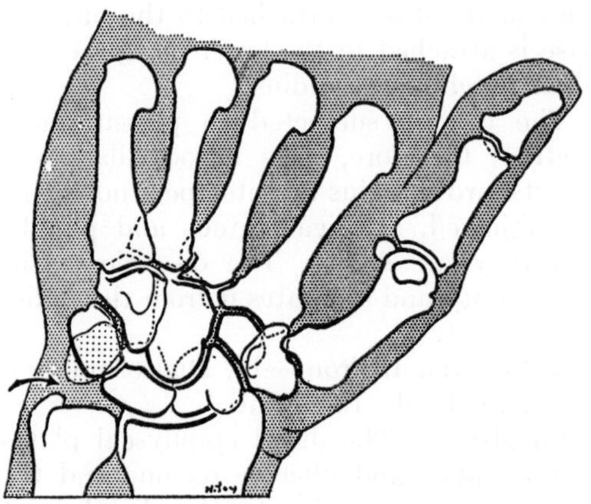

Fig. 201. Tracing of an X-ray of the wrist in abduction. (*Arrow* indicates a space, proximal to the triquetrum, present in abduction.)

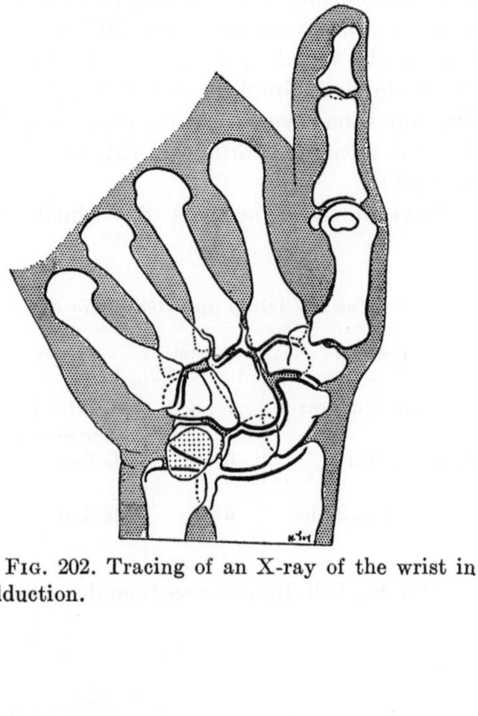

Fig. 202. Tracing of an X-ray of the wrist in adduction.

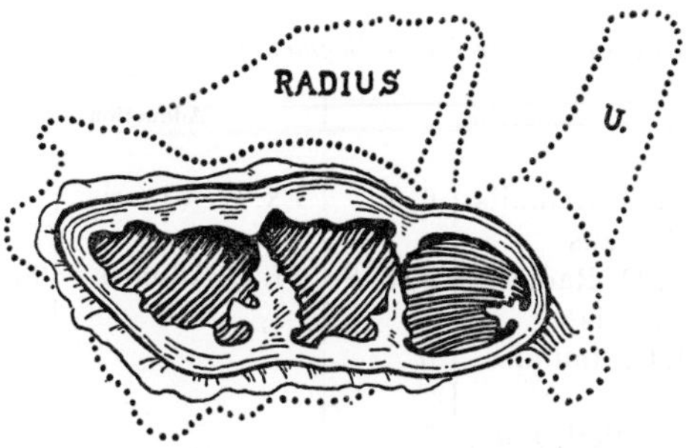

FIG. 203. Socket for proximal row of carpals. Note the transparent synovial fringes.

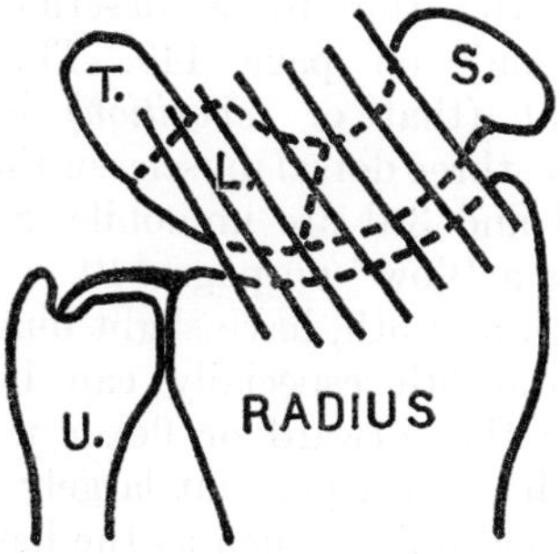

FIG. 204. Anterior (or posterior) radiocarpal ligament.

and the space between the triquetrum and the ulna is increased.

In *Adduction* (ulnar deviation, *fig. 202*) the scaphoid, lunate, and triquetrum move laterally, the lunate coming entirely on to the radius and the triquetrum making contact with the articular disc.

As to the *Distal Row of Carpals*, you may observe that in adduction the apex of the hamate comes into articulation with the lunate; the long axis of the capitate changes with reference to lunate and scaphoid; and the trapezoid and trapezium move medially on the scaphoid.

» **Attrition.** Commonly the articular disc and also both interosseous carpal ligs. that take part in the "ovoid and socket" of the wrist joint, shown in figure 200, are perforated. In consequence, the distal radio-ulnar joint is brought into communication with the wrist joint, and the wrist joint with the intercarpal joints. The perforation in the disc begins as an antero-posterior fissure, and in time it becomes a round hole. Further, the cartilage of the lunate opposite the hole is usually softened and unhealthy. To determine in a dissected specimen whether the interosseous ligaments are perforated or not, grasp the scaphoid, lunate, and triquetrum individually, and move them backward and forward on each other. The state of affairs will then reveal itself.

Ligaments. The fibers of the *palmar and dorsal radiocarpal ligaments* are so disposed that, during pronation and supination of the forearm, the radius shall drag the carpal bones, and with them the hand, after it. They, therefore, pass obliquely inferomedially from the front and back of the lower end of the radius to the front and back of the proximal row of carpal bones and to the capitate (*fig. 204*).

The extensor retinaculum, actually a thickened portion of the deep fascia (p. 164), may be regarded as a superficial layer of the dorsal radiocarpal ligament that has been detached through the interposition of the extensor tendons.

The radial and ulnar collateral ligaments (lateral and medial ligs.) extend from the styloid processes of the radius and ulna to the scaphoid and triquetrum, respectively.

Muscles. The muscles acting on the radiocarpal and midcarpal joints and their nerve segments are given in table 8 (p. 192).

Actions. The flexors and extensors of these joints are indicated in figure 205.

The Fl. Carpi Ulnaris, which is inserted into the front of the base of metacarpal V via the pisometacarpal lig. (and into the hook of the hamate via the pisohamate lig.), has a mechanical advantage over the Ex. Carpi Ulnaris, which is inserted into the tubercle on the side of the base of the same metacarpal. This is because the pisiform provides a raised moving pulley which advances it in front of the transverse axis of the joint.

The Fl. Carpi Radialis, inserted into the front of the base of metacarpal II, has a mechanical advantage over the Ex. Carpi Radialis (Longus et Brevis), which are inserted into the dorsal aspects of the bases of metacarpals II and III, because prior to

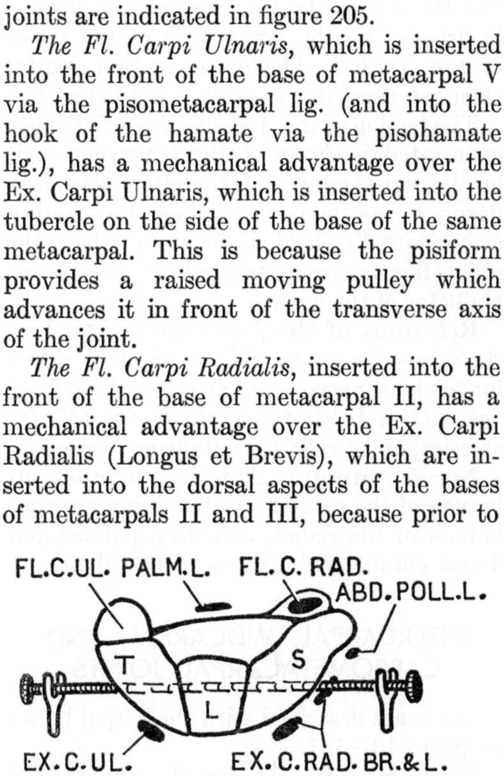

FIG. 205. The flexors and extensors of the wrist, on transverse section.

TABLE 8

Muscles Acting on the Radiocarpal Joint and Their Nerve Segments

Flexion		Extension		Abduction		Adduction	
Fl. C. Ulnaris	8, 1	Ex. C. Ulnaris	7	Ex. C. Radialis Longus	6, 7	Ex. C. Ulnaris	7
Fl. C. Radialis	6	Ex. C. Radialis Longus	6, 7	Ex. C. Radialis Brevis	6, 7, 8	Fl. C. Ulnaris	8, 1
Palm. Longus	7, 8, 1	Ex. C. Radialis Brevis	7	Fl. C. Radialis	6		
Abd. Poll. Long.	7			Abd. Poll. Long.	7		

occupying the vertical groove on the trapezium it crosses the tubercle of the scaphoid; this acts as a raised though fixed pulley, which advances it well in front of the joint.

The Palmaris Longus passes in front of the flexor retinaculum (trans. carpal lig.) and is therefore also far in advance of the transverse axis of the joint. It has no pulley.

The three important flexors are, therefore, more advantageously situated than the three important extensors which play in grooves on the lower ends of the bones of the forearm. Flexion is more powerful than extension in the ratio of 13:5 (Fick).

The tendon of the *Abductor Pollicis Longus* is inserted in front of the transverse axis of the wrist joint and therefore acts as a flexor. It has the power to raise the hand of a horizontally held limb even when the other flexors are paralyzed. It is also an abductor of the wrist.

Relations of the Joint are shown thus: *Anterior—figs. 123* and *125* which is a key for tendons, nerves, and arteries. *Posterior—figs. 163* and *164* for tendons; *fig. 157* for arteries; and *fig. 98* for cutaneous nerves.

Nerve Supply: Anterior interosseous branch of the median, posterior interosseous branch of the radial, and deep palmar and dorsal cutaneous branches of the ulnar.

INTERCARPAL, MIDCARPAL, AND CARPOMETACARPAL JOINTS

These are described with the carpal bones on pages 137–141.

Nerve Supply. As for the radiocarpal joints.

Movements at the carpometacarpal joints. The 1st (that at the saddle-shaped joint of the thumb) is described under "Opposition" on page 149. The reverse movement (that of *reposition*) is carried out by the three dorsal muscles of the thumb. The 2nd and 3rd are immobile. See under "Striking a Blow" on page 140.

The 4th and 5th, have slight hinge movements; the 5th especially can be flexed, and it is the forward or flexor movement of the 5th metacarpal that largely prevents a cylindrical object, such as the handle of a wheelbarrow or a garden rake, from slipping through the closed hand (*fig. 206*); similarly,

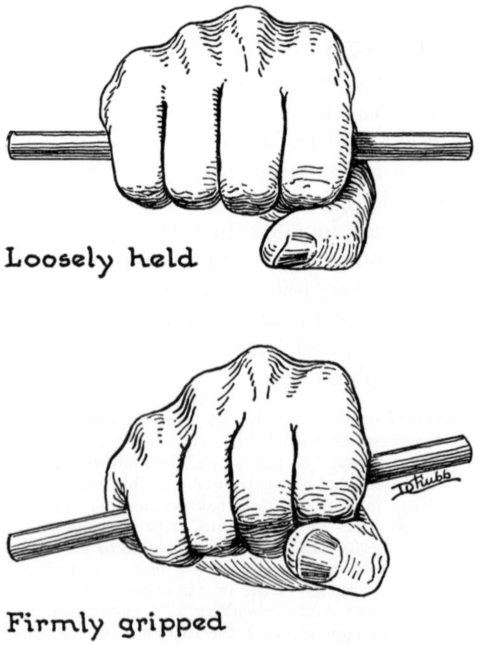

FIG. 206. Because the 4th and 5th carpometacarpal joints are hinge joints, the grip on a rod is more secure.

it helps when climbing or pulling a rope. The muscles here concerned are the Opponens Digiti V and the long digital flexors.

INTERMETACARPAL JOINTS

BASES. The apposed sides of the bases of metacarpals 2 and 3; 3 and 4; and 4 and 5 are contiguous. They have articular facets and their three joint cavities are continuous with the cavities of the carpometacarpal joints.

HEADS. Each head of a metacarpal is separated from its neighbor not only by adjacent collateral ligaments and Interosseus tendons but also by areolar tissue which commonly contains a **bursa**. The same arrangement obtains in the foot.

METACARPO-PHALANGEAL AND INTERPHALANGEAL JOINTS

Described with the metacarpal bones and phalanges on pages 141, 143.

NERVE SUPPLY: "It is quite evident from clinical observations that the digital nerves are the only important source of sensory fibers to the articulations of the digits." These are derived from the median, ulnar, and radial nerves. There is some variation in the number of joints each supplies, and this corresponds with the variations in the cutaneous distribution of these branches (*fig. 101*) (Stopford).

Movements of Fingers. Flex the fingers, one at a time, at the metacarpo-phalangeal and the proximal interphalangeal joints, noting that the pad of each finger strikes nearly the same point on the thenar eminence (*fig. 207*). Now flex the 2nd, 4th, and 5th digits, and lastly flex the 3rd, noting that it finds accommodation only by forcing the 2nd and 4th digits apart. From this you learn that flexed fingers are adducted fingers and that, when flexed and adducted, they steady each other.

The Fl. Digitorum Profundus flexes the distal interphalangeal joints; the Fl. Digitorum Superficialis flexes the proximal interphalangeal joints; and continuing to act, these two muscles flex the metacarpo-phalangeal, midcarpal, and radiocarpal joints; that is, they close the hand and curl it up.

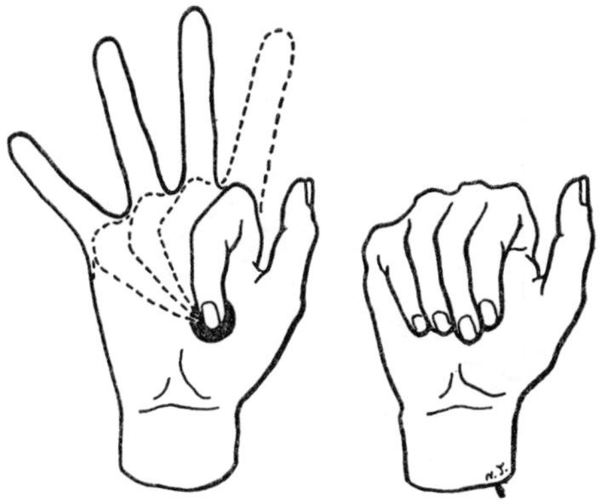

FIG. 207. To demonstrate that flexed fingers buttress each other.

When doing so, they draw together (adduct) the fingers.

Usually, when the hand is closed, the action of the Profundus and Superficialis on the wrist is opposed by the three extensors of the wrist (see table 8) which, acting as synergists, steady the wrist. If it is desired to flex the wrist with force or against resistance, the four flexors of the wrist (see table 8) are also called into action. Verify this by closing the hand, palm upward, and flexing the wrist; then, keeping it flexed, place the knuckles of the proximal phalanges under the edge of a table, and observe that the carpal flexors spring into prominence the moment the least resistance is encountered.

The Ex. Digitorum, Ex. Indicis, and Ex. Digiti V extend the metacarpo-phalangeal joints, and when so doing spread (abduct) the fingers. Their power to extend the interphalangeal joints is much restricted by their attachments at the bases of the proximal phalanges. The interphalangeal joints are extended by the Lumbricals, Interossei, and Abd. Digiti V through their attachments to the dorsal expansions.

»» The Interossei and Abd. Digiti V abduct and adduct the fingers at the metacarpo-phalangeal joints; this they can do while the palm lies flat on a table. Also, they can move each finger separately. These peculiarities distinguish Interosseus action (which is solely mediated by the ulnar nerve) from the abductor action of the long Extensors (mediated solely by the radial nerve) and adductor action of the long Flexors (mediated chiefly by the median), as stated above.

The Lumbricals, Interossei, and Abd. Digiti V flex the metacarpo-phalangeal joints of the fingers and they can, either separately or at the same time, extend the

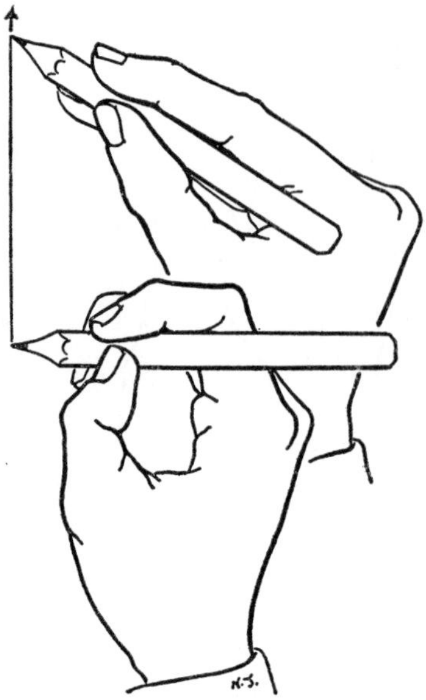

FIG. 208. The Interossei and Lumbricals making the upstroke in writing.

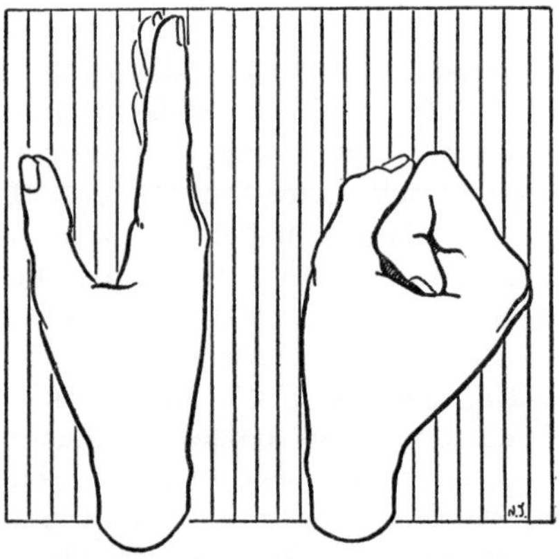

FIG. 209. The extensors of the wrist act synergically with the flexors of the fingers.

interphalangeal joints, as in making the upstroke in writing (*fig. 208*).

Synergists. The four flexors of the wrist acting as synergists, steady the wrist when the extensors of the fingers are in action; similarly, the three extensors of the wrist act synergically when the flexors of the fingers are in action (*fig. 209*). Indeed, you cannot clench your fist or grasp an object firmly unless you extend your wrist. And, it follows that the hand is rendered relatively useless if the extensors of the wrist are paralyzed (e.g., in lesions of the radial nerve).

Shortness of the Long Digital Tendons. You cannot fully flex your wrist while the hand is closed, but only when the fingers are extended; this is owing to the relative shortness of the extensor tendons. Similarly, it is not easy fully to extend your wrist while the fingers are extended; this is owing to the relative shortness of the flexor tendons.

Ligamentous Actions. If, beginning at the base of the 3rd or distal phalanx, you trace the free border (medial or lateral) of an extensor expansion proximally, you will be conducted by a narrow band of fibers to the corresponding border of the 1st phalanx and to its fibrous digital sheath (*fig. 210*). This component of the expansion is a ligamentous band, called the **retinacular lig.** (Landsmeer) or the *link lig.* (Haines). It spans the 2nd phalanx, crossing dorsal to the axis of the distal interphalangeal joint and palmar to the axis of the proximal joint.

Observations. 1. On flexing the distal joint (either passively in the cadaver or voluntarily in your own hand, through the action of the Fl. Profundus Digi-

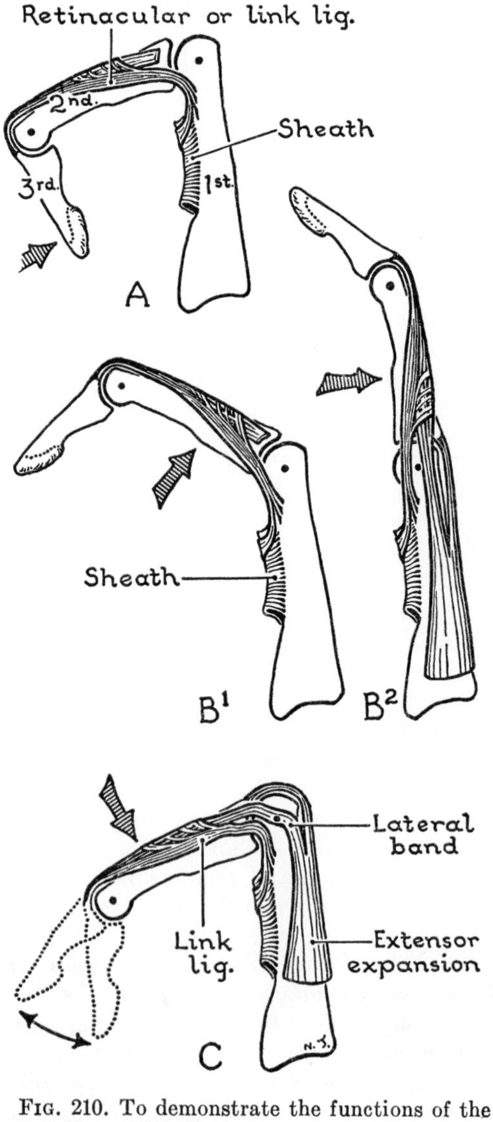

FIG. 210. To demonstrate the functions of the retinacular or link ligaments.

TABLE 9

Table of Appearance and Fusion Times of Epiphyses, Including Primary Centers for Carpus and Tarsus, in Years Unless Otherwise Stated

	Appears	Fuses
Scapula Acromion	15	19
Coracoid	1 }	15*
Subcoracoid	10 }	
Inf. Angle	15	22
Vertebral Border	15	22
Clavicle Sternal end	18+	22+
Humerus Head	Birth }	←with shaft→
Greater Tubercle	3 }	6 } 19*
Lesser Tubercle	5 }	
Medial Epicondyle	6	18
Lateral Epicondyle	12 }	
Capitulum	1 }	15 } 17
Trochlea	10 }	
Radius Upper end	7	19
Lower end	1	19*
Ulna Upper end	11	19
Lower end	6	19*
Scaphoid	6	
Lunate	5	
Triquetrum	4	
Hamate	½	
Capitate	½	
Trapezoid	6	
Trapezium	6	
Pisiform	12	
1st Metacarpal base	−3	19
2nd–5th Metacarpal heads	−3	19
Thumb, Proximal Phalanx base	2	18
Distal Phalanx base	−3	18
2nd–5th Fingers, Proximal Phalanx base	2	18
Middle Phalanx base	−3	18
Distal Phalanx base	−3	18
Sesamoids of thumb	−13	
Hip bone, three primary parts		16*
Ischium and Pubis		9
Ischial tuberosity	19	20
Iliac crest	16	22
Femur Head	1	18*
Greater Trochanter	−5	18*
Lesser Trochanter	−14	18*
Lower end	Birth	19*
Tibia Upper end	Birth	19
Lower end	2	18
Fibula Upper end	5	19
Lower end	2	18
Calcaneus—before birth	−30 week	
Tuberosity	11	17
Talus—before birth	−30 week	
Navicular	3	
Cuboid—before birth	+30 week	
1st Cuneiform	3	
2nd Cuneiform	−4	
3rd Cuneiform	1	
Great Toe Metatarsal base	−3	18
2nd–5th Metatarsal heads	−5	18
Great Toe, Proximal Phalanx base	−4	19
Distal Phalanx base	2	19
2nd–5th toes, Proximal Phalanx base	−5	19
Middle Phalanx base	−5	19
Distal Phalanx	−5	19
Patella	−5	
Sesamoids of great toe	−12	22+
Rib Head	15	As it ossifies
Tubercle	18	

Since the student will be concerned with the age periods at which he may reasonably be sure that fusion is complete, the *latest* times of fusion are given. Female bones fuse distinctly earlier.

* Asterisks denote times that are found to be quite constant. The table is a compilation from several authorities and is based on X-ray findings. It has been deemed advisable to give definite ages rather than a spread. Figures denote years unless otherwise stated.

+ = a later tendency. − = an earlier tendency.

torum) (*fig. 210A*) the retinacular lig. becomes taut and pulls the proximal joint into flexion.

2. Similarly, on extending the proximal joint (either in the cadaver or voluntarily), the distal joint is pulled by the retinacular lig. into nearly complete extension (*fig. 210B*).

3. While the proximal joint is fully flexed passively (e.g., by pressing on the 2nd phalanx) the 3rd phalanx cannot be extended voluntarily (actively), though it offers no resistance to passive extension. Indeed, it is flail. This is due to the fact that the lateral bands of the extensor expansion slip forward and hence are slack and ineffective (*fig. 210C*).

You will note, then, that the metacarpo-phalangeal joint of a finger can move independently of the interphalangeal joints whereas the interphalangeal joints are compelled by the retinacular or link ligs. to move together.

These and other points of interest are revealed by F. Braithwaite *et al.*, J. M. F. Landsmeer, and R. W. Haines.

SECTION III

Abdomen

CHAPTER **13**

ANTERIOR ABDOMINAL WALL AND SCROTUM

»» The abdomen is the region of the trunk between the diaphragm above and the inlet of the pelvis below. Its walls enclose and protect two hollow, tubular systems: (1) the gastro-intestinal canal and its two offshoots, the liver and pancreas, together with the spleen; and (2) the greater part of the urogenital system.

The different parts of the gastro-intestinal canal, being at one time full and at another time empty, require space in which to dilate, contract, and move about. This is afforded them by what is virtually an enormous bursa, called the *peritoneal cavity*, into which they project freely.

ANTERIOR ABDOMINAL WALL

When the physician examines a patient's abdomen, he inspects and palpates the anterior abdominal wall. When the surgeon

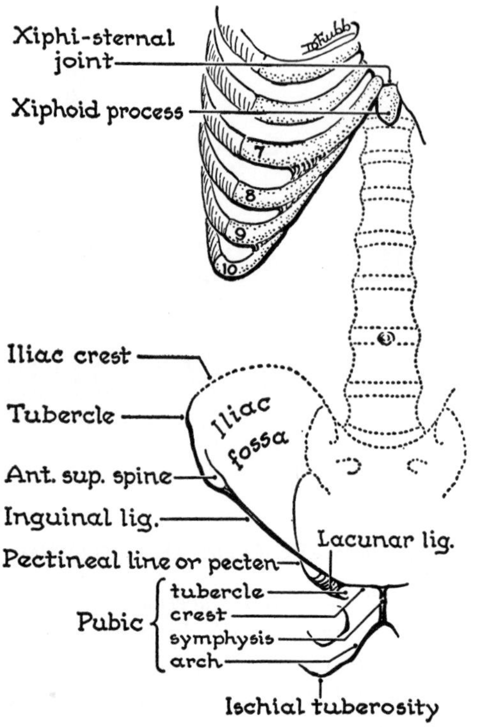

FIG. 211. Boundaries of the anterior abdominal wall.

operates on the abdomen, he cuts through the anterior abdominal wall. It is well, therefore, to have a knowledge of its structure.

Boundaries. The anterior abdominal wall is bounded above by the xiphoid process and the costal cartilages—not of the lower six ribs of each side, because the 11th and 12th costal arches are not long enough to reach the front, but—of the 7th, 8th, 9th and 10th (*fig. 211*). It is bounded below on each side by the portion of the iliac crest lying between the tubercle and the anterior superior spine, the inguinal ligament, the pubic tubercle, the pubic crest, and the upper end of the pubic symphysis.

The xiphoid process, note, lies at the bottom of the depression between the 7th costal cartilages. It varies in length and in shape. Its edges and tip afford attachment to the aponeurosis of the Transversus Abdominis; so, they are attenuated and not easily palpated, and the attempt to do so causes discomfort. Hence, the easily palpated lower end of the body of the sternum, at the xiphisternal joint, is preferred as a landmark.

Superficial Fascia. In the lower part of the abdominal wall, the superficial fascia is disposed in two easily separable layers: (1) an *adipose layer*, such as clothes the body generally, the fascia of Camper; and (2) a deeper *membranous layer* devoid of fat, the fascia of Scarpa.[5]

It is important to note that, if a horizontal incision be made through the fatty and membranous layers, the finger can be passed downward in a pocket between the membranous layer and the underlying aponeurosis of the External Oblique. In the region lateral to the pubic tubercle the finger will be arrested by the attachment of the membranous layer to the fascia lata (i.e., deep fascia of the thigh) a finger's breadth below the inguinal ligament (*fig. 212*); medial to the pubic tubercle it can be passed downward into the scrotum, for here the membranous layer is attached to the fascia lata along a line just lateral to the spermatic cord (p. 208) and, more caudally, to the pubic arch. In the median plane the finger is arrested by a mass of fibro-elastic tissue, *suspensory ligament of the penis* and scrotum, which is attached above to the symphysis pubis and lower part of the linea alba (p. 202); below, it forms a sling for the penis and sends fibers to end in the scrotum.

The cutaneous vessels and nerves lie in the superficial fatty layer of Camper (see pp. 203–204).

» **Deep Fascia,** such as is wrapped around the limbs, is made of the same stuff as tendons and ligaments and is practically inelastic. There can, therefore, be no deep fascia—in this sense—enveloping the abdomen and thorax. If there were, one would look forward with apprehension rather than with pleasure to the next meal and respiration would be impossible. All muscles, though, are surrounded with the areolar tissue in which they developed; for example, the Pectoralis Major, Latissimus Dorsi, Serratus Anterior, and the three flat muscles of the abdomen are covered with loose areolar tissue on both surfaces—but this is not deep fascia as usually understood. (See *Axiom.*)

AXIOM. The areolar tissue found between muscles affords them freedom of move-

[5] Tobin and Benjamin, whose interests are both anatomical and clinical, by studying cross sections and injections, find no independent membranous layer, but one layer of subcutaneous tissue composed of lobules of fat enclosed in bands or sheets of collagenous fibers.

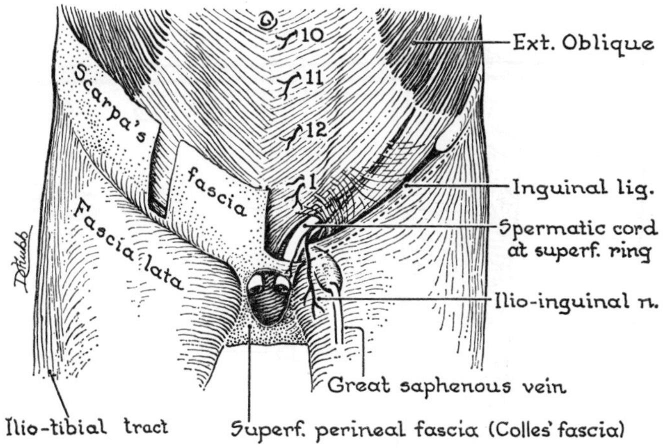

FIG. 212. The fasciae of Scarpa and Colles
(The penis and scrotum are cut away and the spermatic cords are cut across.)

ment, and its quantity varies with their range of independent contraction.

Muscles of the Anterior Abdominal Wall. On each side, they are:

Rectus Abdominis, and Pyramidalis, and

Three flat muscles { Obliquus Externus Abdominis, Obliquus Internus Abdominis, Transversus Abdominis.

The Rectus Abdominis and Its Sheath. The Rectus Abdominis (*fig. 213*) is a long strap-like muscle. It runs at right angles to the three flat muscles, and it obtains a certain freedom to contract by lying within a sheath. The sheath (*fig. 214*) is formed by the splitting of the aponeurosis of the Internal Oblique into an anterior and a posterior lamina. The anterior lamina is reinforced by the aponeurosis of the External Oblique; the posterior lamina by the aponeurosis of the Transversus.

When the anterior wall of the sheath is incised longitudinally, it is found that transverse *tendinous intersections* in the Rectus, indicative of its segmental origin, adhere to the anterior wall of its sheath at the levels of the umbilicus and xiphoid process, and midway between these two levels.

Attachments. The Rectus is attached horizontally above to the front of the xiphoid process and to the cartilages of the 7th, 6th, and 5th ribs. This upper attachment is three times as broad (3″) as the lower attachment to the front of the symphysis and body of pubis just below the crest. As would be expected, the thoracic attachment is fleshy; the pubic attachment is tendinous.

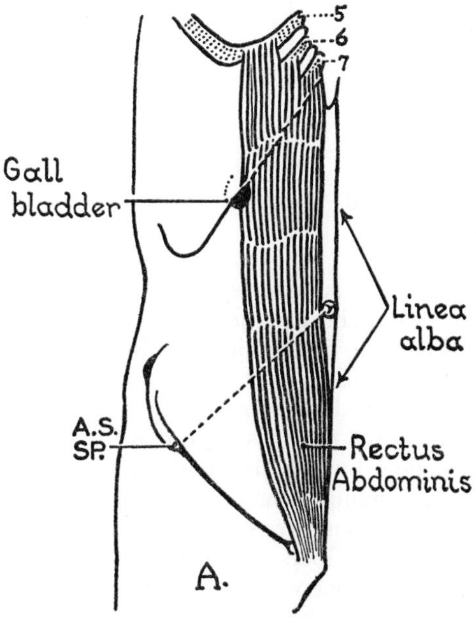

FIG. 213. *A*, The Rectus Abdominis

Surface Anatomy. The *lateral border* of the Rectus curves from the pubic tubercle, across the middle point of the line joining

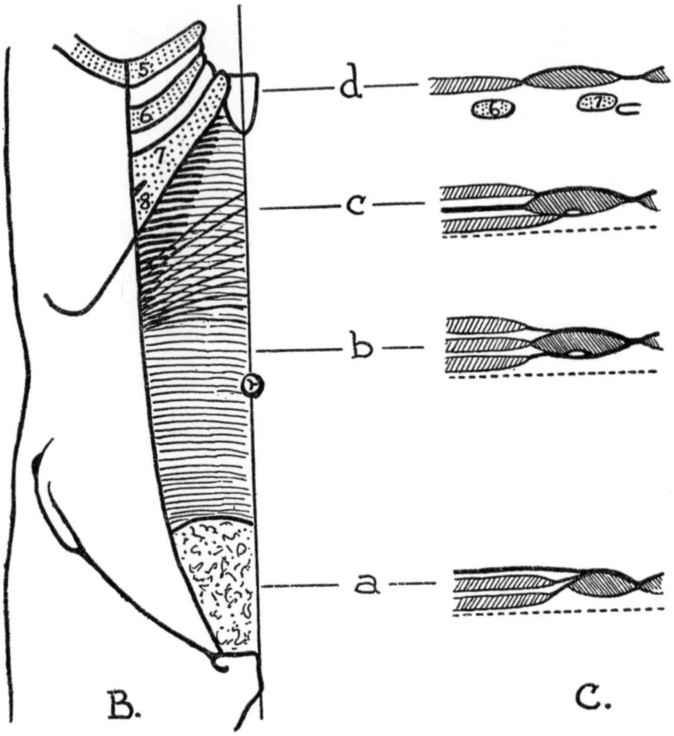

FIG. 214. *B*, The posterior wall of the Rectus sheath. *C*, Transverse sections of the sheath at four levels.

the anterior superior spine to the umbilicus, across the chest margin where, 3″ from the middle line, it overlies the tip of the 9th costal cartilage, and on to where the 5th cartilage and rib meet.

Its *medial border* is separated from that of its fellow by the **linea alba;** that is, the line extending between the xiphoid process and the symphysis pubis in which the aponeurotic fibers of the three flat muscles decussate. Below the umbilicus the linea alba is truly linear, the two Recti being practically in contact with one another; but above the umbilicus it forms a band, ½ inch or more wide.

Small gaps may be present between the decussating fibers of the linea alba through which herniae of extraperitoneal fat protrude.

Actions. When, on awakening in the morning, one rises from the recumbent to the sitting posture, the Sternomastoids raise the head and flex the cervical vertebrae; the Recti Abdominis approximate xiphoid process to pubis and flex the thoracic and lumbar vertebrae, and the Iliopsoases flex the hip joints.

The Recti can by contracting break the force of a blow and so protect the abdominal viscera from injury.

POSTERIOR WALL OF RECTUS SHEATH. At four different levels four different tissues lie in contact with the posterior surface of the Rectus (*fig. 214*). From below upward they are: (*a*) areolar, (*b*) aponeurotic, (*c*) muscular, and (*d*) cartilaginous.

»» First, consider level *b:* here the posterior layer of the aponeurosis of the Internal Obliques, reinforced by the aponeurosis of the Transversus, extends from about 3″ above the pubis to about 3″ below the xiphisternal junction, and constitutes the posterior layer of the true or fibrous sheath of the Rectus; its lower free edge is the *arcuate line.*

Below this, (level *a*) the aponeuroses of all three flat muscles pass in front of the Rectus, leaving its lowest 3″ in contact posteriorly with the areolar fascia transversalis through which extraperitoneal fat is visible.

Above, (level *c*) the Internal Oblique does not extend, with the result that the 3″ of the Rectus just below the body of the sternum come into contact with practically the whole breadth of the narrow upper end of the Transversus including its fleshy costal origin. This

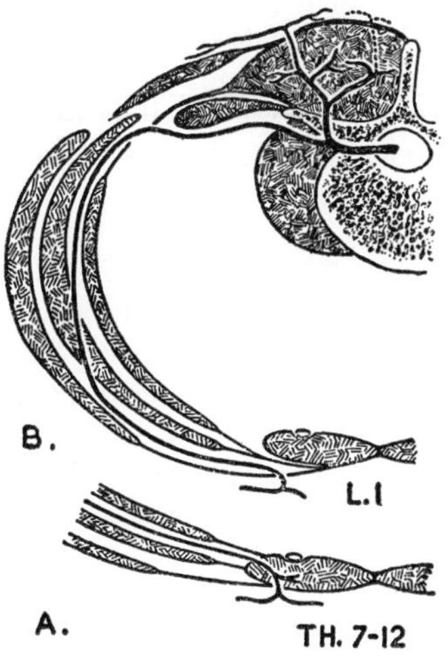

FIG. 215. The course of a ventral nerve ramus in the abdominal wall. *A*, lower thoracic. *B*, 1st lumbar.

fleshy origin is seen shining through the film of areolar tissue that covers it.

Above the chest margin, (level *d*) the Rectus lies in front of costal cartilages.

ANTERIOR WALL OF RECTUS SHEATH. This wall is aponeurotic throughout, but the aponeurosis has three different thicknesses—above the costal margin (and for 3″ below the xiphisternal junction) it is formed by External Oblique aponeurosis; to this in the intermediate part is added the anterior layer of the Internal Oblique aponeurosis while the lowest 3″ includes all three aponeuroses.

»» It is because the External Oblique alone of the three flat muscles extends above the chest margin that its aponeurosis alone forms the front of the Rectus sheath at level d. And, from its upper border the Pectoralis Major partly arises.

Pyramidalis. This thin triangular muscle (commonly absent) lies in front of the lower part of the Rectus Abdominis. It arises from the front of the body of the pubis below the attachment of the Rectus, and it is inserted into the linea alba below the umbilicus. A twig from Th.12 nerve supplies it.

Contents of the Rectus Sheath:
Muscles: Rectus Abdominis, Pyramidalis.
Nerves: ventral rami of Th. 7–12.
Vessels: superior and inferior epigastric.

Nerves. THE VENTRAL RAMI of the *lower six thoracic nerves* run between the Internal Oblique and the Transversus and they are guided by these muscles to where their aponeuroses blend behind the lateral margin of the Rectus (*fig. 215*). Thereupon, they pierce every structure intervening between them and the skin (i.e., the posterior lamina of the Internal Oblique, the Rectus, the anterior wall of the Rectus sheath) and ramify in the subcutaneous tissues, as anterior cutaneous nerves.

The ventral ramus of the *1st lumbar nerve* divides far back into two: the *ilio-hypogastric* and *ilio-inguinal*. Both of these branches run forward between the Internal Oblique and the Transversus until they pass the ant. superior spine when, at variable points, they pierce the Internal Oblique and then continue medially between the Internal and External Obliques, and they are guided by these muscles to the front of the Rectus; hence, they require to pierce only the External Oblique aponeurosis, or its tubular prolongation, the *external spermatic fascia*, to become cutaneous. The iliohypogastric nerve pierces the aponeurosis an inch or so above the superficial inguinal ring; the ilioinguinal nerve passes through the ring and pierces the external spermatic fascia.

Distribution (*fig. 216*). Of these nerves

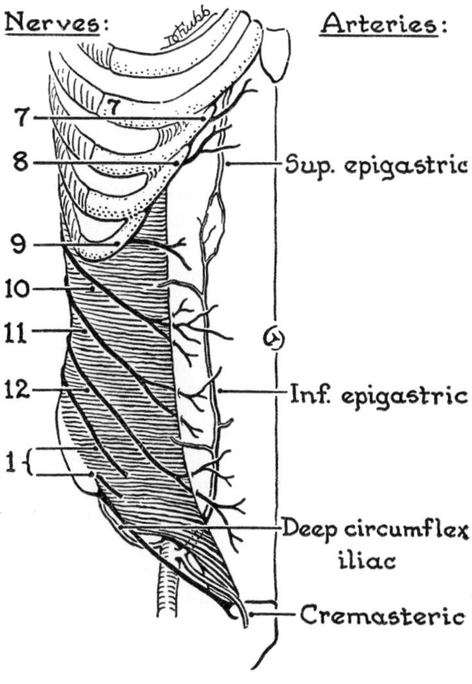

FIG. 216. The nerves and arteries within the rectus sheath.

Th.10 supplies the skin around the umbilicus, leaving three nerves (9, 8 and 7) to supply the region above the umbilicus, and three (11, 12, and 1) to supply the region below the umbilicus (*fig. 212*).

»» The ilio-inguinal nerve supplies the skin at the root of the penis, anterior part of the scrotum, and adjacent part of the thigh.

While these nerves (Th.7–L.1) are running between the Internal Oblique and the Transversus, they supply them, 12 and 1 being the most important because they control the vital lower part of the abdominal wall (*fig. 218*).

Those nerves that pierce the Rectus (Th.7 to 12, but not L.1) also supply it; and to sever any one of them results in paralysis of that segment of the Rectus for which it is responsible, with resulting weakness of the abdominal wall.

The Lateral Cutaneous Branches of the lower six thoracic and first lumbar ventral rami arise and become cutaneous in front of the midlateral line half way around the body (*fig. 72*). They appear between the digitations of the Serratus Anterior or External Oblique according to their level.

The lateral cutaneous branches of Th.7, 8, 9, 10, and 11 send: (a) branches forward as far as the lateral border of the Rectus where they meet the anterior cutaneous branches of their respective segments—it is from the stems of these branches that the External Oblique receives its nerve supply—and (b) branches backward across the Latissimus Dorsi for a short distance.

»» The lateral cutaneous branches of Th.12 and L. 1 cross the iliac crest in front of the tubercle and behind it, respectively, and ramify above the level of the greater trochanter of the femur, as the *iliac branches of the subcostal and iliohypogastric nerves.*

Epigastric Arteries (*fig. 216*). *The Superior Epigastric Artery* enters the Rectus sheath behind the 7th costal cartilage and anastomoses with the much larger *Inferior Epigastric Artery* which enters the Rectus sheath in front of the arcuate line. Thus, vessels to the upper and lower limbs are brought into communication with each other—for the superior epigastric artery is one of the two terminal branches of the internal thoracic (int. mammary) branch of the subclavian artery, and the inferior epigastric artery is one of the two collateral branches of the external iliac artery. Being the only two arteries in this region, the two epigastric arteries must supply everything in the region.

Branches. Their branches accordingly are *cutaneous*, *muscular*, and *anastomotic.*

The inferior epigastric artery has in addition two branches of some importance: (1) a *cremasteric branch* which supplies the covering of the spermatic cord and anastomoses with the testicular artery (*fig. 227.1*), and (2) a *pubic branch* which anastomoses on the back of the pubic bone (see p. 333).

The lateral border of the Rectus is a nearly bloodless line, because very few branches of the epigastric arteries cross it and anastomose with the intercostal and lumbar arteries.

Other Vessels in the Anterior Wall: *Intercostal and Lumbar Arteries* accompany nerves T.11, 12, and L.1 and their lateral branches.

The Deep Circumflex Iliac Artery ramifies between the Internal Oblique and the Transversus (p. 210), as do twigs of the musculophrenic artery (p. 472).

The Three Superficial Inguinal Arteries spring from the femoral artery and run in the superficial fascia, thus: (1) the *superficial epigastric a.* runs toward the navel; (2) the *external pudendal a.* crosses in front of the spermatic cord to supply the scrotal wall; and (3) the *superficial circumflex iliac a.* runs below the lateral half of the inguinal ligament.

The Three Superficial Inguinal Veins end in the great saphenous vein.

The superficial epigastric and lateral thoracic veins anastomose, thereby uniting the veins of the upper and lower halves of the body. Everyone is familiar with this conspicuous anastomosis in the flank of the horse.

The Superficial Lymph Vessels of the anterior abdominal wall above the level of the navel pass to the axillary nodes, those below to the inguinal nodes.

The Three Flat Muscles of the Abdomen—Obliquus Externus, Obliquus Internus, and Transversus—are the prototype of "three ply" wood, for the general directions of their fibers are, respectively, downward and medially, upward and medially, and transversely. Though the majority of the fibers of the three muscles take these *three general directions*, you will find that below the level of the anterior superior iliac spine all the fibers of all three muscles take *one particular direction*—downward, forward, and medially. These lower fibers, though in the minority, happen to be the most important fibers of the muscles; and, their attachments are complicated by the fact that before birth the testis in the male (round ligament in the female) descends from the abdomen into the scrotum (labium majus in the female) carrying before it a covering from each of the three flat muscles.

Obliquus Externus Abdominis. The External Oblique *arises from* the lower eight ribs a hand's breadth from the costal margin. (The 11th and 12th ribs, being very short, it arises from the ends of their cartilages.) The origin is by means of fleshy digitations that interlock with similar digitations of the Serratus Anterior and Latissimus Dorsi.

The External Oblique is fleshy above and laterally; elsewhere it is aponeurotic (*fig. 217*). The dividing line between the fleshy and aponeurotic portions curves from the anterior superior spine (more precisely, from a point 1″ behind it) upwards and medially to the costal margin, which it meets at the lateral border of the Rectus Abdominis.

The uppermost fibers of the External Oblique are nearly horizontal, and they end in an aponeurosis from which the Pectoralis Major in part arises. Its most posterior fibers are fleshy and nearly vertical, and they fail to meet those of the Latissimus Dorsi at the midpoint of the outer lip of the iliac crest by 1″, more or less, thereby forming the *lumbar triangle* (*fig. 77*).

INSERTION. Between its upper horizontal and posterior vertical borders the fibers of the External Oblique spread out fanwise:

A. The *fibers of the upper half* of the muscle help to form the front of the Rectus sheath, decussate in the linea alba, and cross the median plane from xiphoid to symphysis. The lowest of these decussating fibers strike the front of the body of the pubis of the opposite side. They are referred to as the *reflex inguinal ligament;* occasionally they extend to the pecten pubis.

B. The *fibers of the lower half* of the muscle find attachment between the lumbar triangle and the symphysis pubis as follows: (1) to the outer lip of the iliac crest from its midpoint to the anterior superior spine by fleshy fibers. (2) From the anterior superior spine to the pubic tubercle, the muscle has a free, lower, aponeurotic border, known as the **inguinal ligament** (Poupart's lig.). The inguinal ligament bridges the muscles, vessels, and nerves passing from the abdomen to the front of the thigh; and it is convex toward the thigh due to the pull of the

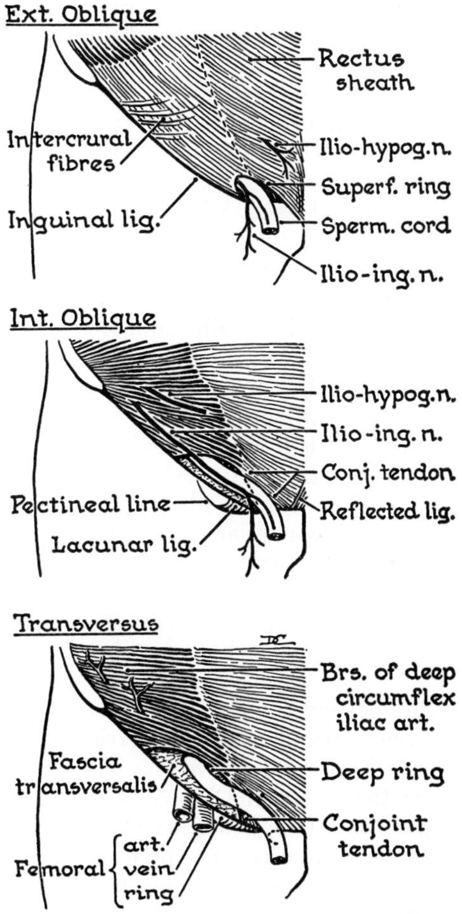

FIG. 217. The three flat muscles below the level of the anterior superior spine—the walls of the inguinal canal.

attached fascia lata. (3) Some fibers of the inguinal ligament pass beyond the pubic tubercle to the front of the body of the pubis; others, failing to reach the tubercle, are attached to the pecten pubis (pectineal line) as the **lacunar ligament** (*fig. 211*). It will be seen when the muscle is reflected (p. 207). (4) Between tubercle and symphysis the aponeurosis is attached to the front of the pubis, below the origin of the Rectus. This part is largely ballooned out to cover the testis and is known as the *external spermatic fascia.* The mouth of the balloon is the *superficial inguinal ring.*

Superficial Inguinal Ring. This oblique, triangular opening is 1″ long. Its center lies above the pubic tubercle; its apex is superolateral to the tubercle; its base, formed by the lateral half of the pubic crest—not the whole crest—is medial to the tubercle. The two sides of the ring, known as the *upper and lower crura* (L. crus = a leg) are diverging portions of the External Oblique aponeurosis. The lower crus is thick and rounded; figure 399 shows why.

A superficial sheet of curved fibers, the *intercrural fibers,* lying lateral to the ring, blends with the aponeurosis and prevents the crura from spreading (*fig. 212*). The medial continuation of this same sheet covers the ring, is attached to the margins of the ring, and, as the *external spermatic fascia,* is evaginated to cover the testis and spermatic cord. It is thin and areolar.

Obliquus Internus Abdominis. The direction of the muscle fibers that form the floor of the lumbar triangle may be observed to pass anterosuperiorly, at right angles to those of the External Oblique. Since these fibers belong to the Internal Oblique, it follows that the attachment of the Internal Oblique to the iliac crest must extend dorsally beyond the External Oblique for at least the width of the lumbar triangle, i.e., 1″ behind the midpoint of the iliac crest.

Like the External Oblique, the Internal Oblique has a free, posterior oblique border except when its origin creeps upward on to the underlying posterior aponeurosis of the Transversus (*fig. 308*).

Origin. The Internal Oblique, then, arises from more than the anterior half of the intermediate strip of the iliac crest, from more than the lateral half of the inguinal ligament, and commonly from the posterior aponeurosis of the Transversus.

Insertion. (1) Its most posterior fibers ascend to the cartilages of the lower four ribs (12, 11, 10, and 9). The next fibers necessarily miss the costal margin altogether. They become aponeurotic as they pass the 9th cartilage, and continuing obliquely superomedially, they split at the lateral border of the Rectus, contribute to the formation of the anterior and posterior walls of its sheath, and so reach the linea alba; there they decussate, 2 or 3″ below the xiphisternal junction. (2) The fibers that proceed from the anterior superior spine pass horizontally; (3) those from the inguinal ligament curve downward and medially to contribute to the falx inguinalis or conjoint tendon, described below.

Transversus Abdominis. The Transversus has a pelvic, a lumbar, and a costal origin. The *pelvic origin* is fleshy from the inner lip of the iliac crest and from the inguinal ligament. Its attachment to the iliac crest is almost co-extensive with that of the Internal Oblique, but it extends to the lateral third only of the inguinal ligament. The *costal origin* is by fleshy slips that spring from the inner surface of the lower six costal cartilages where they interdigitate with fleshy slips of the Diaphragm. Between its iliac and costal origins, it arises from the tips of the transverse processes of the *lumbar vertebrae* through the medium of an aponeurosis (*fig. 323*, and pp. 287–288).

From these three sites its fibers pass transversely forward to decussate in the linea alba, those above the arcuate line passing behind the Rectus, those below passing in front. Its uppermost fibers have been seen to form a posterior fleshy relationship for the Rectus. The fibers arising from the lateral third of the inguinal ligament join the conjoint tendon. *The xiphoid process* may be regarded as an ossification extending from the body of the sternum into the aponeurosis of the Transversus.

Falx Inguinalis or **Conjoint Tendon.** The inguinal parts of the Internal Oblique and Transversus join to form a common aponeurosis which becomes part of the lower end of the Rectus sheath; and, though not

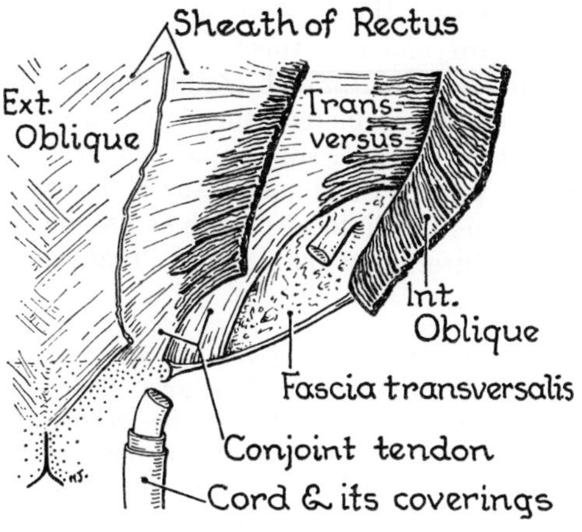

FIG. 217.1 Dissection to show what the conjoint tendon is.

fused with the External Oblique aponeurosis at this level, it is attached with it to the linea alba and to the body of the pubis. The common aponeurosis is prolonged laterally, beyond the pubic tubercle and, therefore, behind the superficial inguinal ring, as a delicate membranous sickle-shaped band which is attached to the medial half inch or more of the pecten pubis (*fig. 217.1;* also p. 317). The aponeurosis and the band constitute the *conjoint tendon.*

On pulling on the fleshy fibers of the Internal Oblique and Transversus, it becomes evident that both contribute to the aponeurosis, and that the Transversus alone becomes the sickle-shaped band. The band usually blends with the underlying fascia transversalis (Anson and McVay; and Chandler).

Both the lacunar lig. and the conjoint tendon are attached to the pecten pubis. The former, which represents Ext. Oblique, naturally is anterior to the latter, which represents Int. Oblique and Transversus.

The Nerve Supply to the fleshy fibers is from L. 1, via the ilio-inguinal and genitofemoral nerves (*fig. 218*).

Cremaster Muscle. This is the covering that the Internal Oblique and Transversus together give to the testis and spermatic cord. It is derived in the same manner as the external spermatic fascia (p. 206). It is, therefore, attached to the medial half of the inguinal ligament and to the pubis. It fills the concavity formed by the arching fibers of the two flat muscles, and in the scrotum its individual fleshy fibers form elongated loops separated widely from each other by areolar tissue.

Its Nerve is the genital branch of the genitofemoral (L. 1, 2).

Its Artery is the cremasteric branch of the inferior epigastric a.

Its Action is to retract or draw up the testis, and stroking the skin of the thigh supplied by the ilio-inguinal nerve (L. 1) reflexly brings about this retraction.

Functions of the Three Flat Muscles. The Internal Oblique is thicker than the External Oblique, and each of these is much thicker than the Transversus which, in fact, is uniformly thin. The Oblique muscles are much thicker in the flanks than in front. They are the chief lateral flexors of the trunk, and they give the Recti help in forward flexion. The External Oblique fibers of one side and the Internal Oblique fibers of the other, being parallel, act together in rotation of the trunk.

All three flat muscles help to maintain the intra-abdominal pressure. This pressure is much more important than ligaments and mesenteries in retaining the viscera in place.

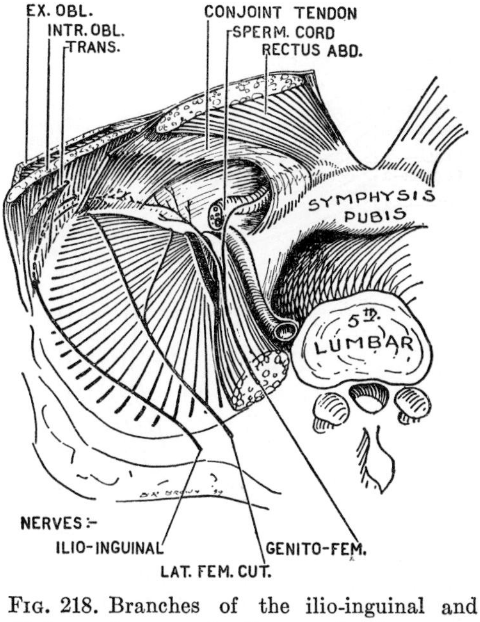

FIG. 218. Branches of the ilio-inguinal and genitofemoral nerves to the muscle fibers controlling the conjoint tendon. (Dissection by Dr. R. G. MacKenzie.)

The three flat muscles (1) by contracting alternately with the diaphragm as antagonist, help to bring about the expiratory act during forced breathing, and they are necessary to the abdominal form of respiration; (2) by contracting simultaneously with the diaphragm, they aid in expelling the contents of the abdominal organs (in micturition, defecation, vomiting, and parturition) and in driving on venous blood to the heart. They contract vigorously during coughing.

Above the Level of the Anterior Superior Spine the fibers of the three flat muscles run more or less at right angles to each other. A sufficient quantity of areolar tissue therefore is required between them to allow them to play across each other unimpeded.

AXIOM. On cutting through the abdominal wall, the encountering of a layer of loose areolar tissue is a signal that a change in direction of muscle fiber is imminent.

The lower six thoracic nerves cling to the deep surface of the Internal Oblique. Their direction in the abdominal wall is apparently decided by the direction of their respective costal cartilages (*fig. 216*); i.e., the 7th and 8th nerves incline upward; the 9th passes

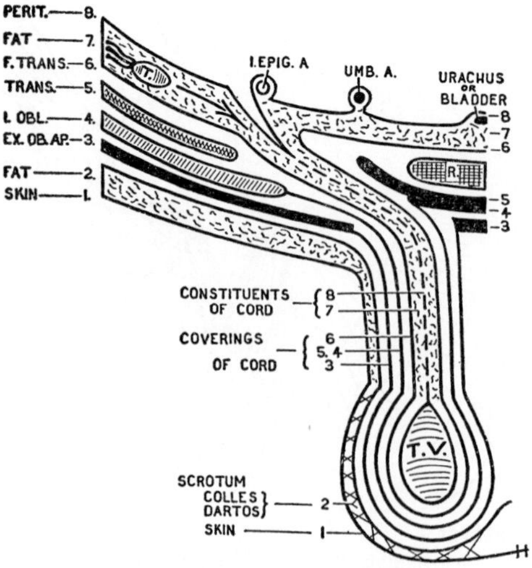

FIG. 219. Scheme: The inguinal canal, and the layers of the anterior abdominal wall prolonged into the scrotum. (See table 10.) (In this cross section the scrotum is supposed to be raised to the horizontal position.)

horizontally; the subsequent ones incline downward; and all of them pierce the Rectus.

The ascending branch of the *deep circumflex iliac artery* pierces the Transversus 1″ medial to the ant. sup. spine; the terminal branch pierces the Transversus 1″ lateral to the spine. Both branches then ascend between Internal Oblique and Transversus (*fig. 217*).

AXIOM. Above the level of the ant. sup. spine, the direction of muscle fibers, the presence of areolar tissue, the presence of nerves and of branches of the deep circumflex iliac artery all indicate the depth or layer at which you have arrived.

Below the Level of the Anterior Superior Spine the anterior abdominal wall deserves careful attention.

The 8 Layers of the Anterior Wall.

Lateral to the Rectus the abdominal wall consists of eight layers, each of which has a tubular evagination; of these, the outer two form the scrotum, whereas the inner six are contained within the scrotum (*fig. 219*). In table 10 the names of the layers of the abdominal wall and the corresponding layers found in the scrotum are set out in parallel columns.

Let it be understood that the testis, like other abdominal organs (e.g., kidney and ureter; bladder and urachus; the great vessels—but not the spinal nerves), develops in layer 7, that is to say, between the peritoneum and the fascia lining the abdominal muscles (e.g., Transversus, Ilio-Psoas, Diaphragm) (*fig. 220*). A month or so before birth the testis makes a descent through the abdominal wall. In descending it encounters the outer six layers of the wall and carries before it a tubular prolongation from each. Layers 1 and 2 form the *scrotum;* they do not envelop the testis and cord so snugly as layers 3–6, which are known as the *coverings of the cord.*

The testis drags after it its duct, arteries, veins, lymph vessels, and nerves, a quantity of the extraperitoneal tissue from layer 7 in which it develops, and a tube of peritoneum, called the *processus vaginalis,* belonging to layer 8. These constitute the **spermatic cord.** The passage through the abdominal wall is called the *Inguinal Canal.*

TABLE 10

The layers of the abdominal wall	The corresponding layers in the scrotum	
1. Skin	1. Skin	Scrotum
2. Superficial fascia (a) fatty (Camper); (b) membranous (Scarpa)	2. Dartos muscle and fascia	
3. External Oblique (aponeurotic)	3. External spermatic fascia	Coverings of the cord
4. Internal Oblique (fleshy)	4. Cremaster muscle	
5. Transversus (fleshy)	5. Cremaster muscle	
6. Fascia Transversalis (lining abdominal cavity in this region)	6. Internal spermatic fascia	
7. Extraperitoneal fatty tissue (layer inhabited by organs)	7. Areolar tissue with localized collections of fat	Two of the constituents of the cord
8. Peritoneum	8. Processus vaginalis	

»» The foregoing is a simplified description. In reality, the testis is not the active agent in producing the tubular prolongations within which it is later contained. The scrotum and the coverings of the cord are formed early, even before the abdominal muscles differentiate, and, as Curl and Tromly properly point out, there is a definite inguinal canal in the male fetus before the testis passes through the abdominal wall, and in the female it is just as definite. Originally, the inguinal canal is an almost straight anteroposterior passage through the abdominal muscles; subsequently, during the process of growth it becomes more oblique.

Inguinal Canal. The first of the six layers of the abdominal wall that the testis encounters during its descent is, of course, the fascia lining the Transversus, known appropriately as the *fascia transversalis.* The tubular covering provided is the *internal spermatic fascia.* The mouth of this tube, called the *deep inguinal ring,* is the entrance to the inguinal canal. It lies a finger's breadth above the midpoint of the inguinal ligament and immediately lateral to the stem of the inf. epigastric artery (*fig. 217*).

The tube derived from the Ext. Oblique aponeurosis is called the *external spermatic fascia.* Its mouth, called the *superficial (subcutaneous) inguinal ring,* is the exit from the inguinal canal.

Between the deep and the superficial inguinal ring the Transversus and Internal Oblique together contribute a tubular muscular covering, the *Cremaster,* which, as you would expect, lies in a layer of *cremasteric fascia.*

The Inguinal Canal extends from the deep inguinal ring to the superficial inguinal ring and is 1½ inches long. (1) The *anterior wall* is formed throughout by the External Oblique aponeurosis, as figures 217 and 219 show. (2) The *posterior wall* is formed throughout by the fascia transversalis. (3) Between these two are the Internal Oblique and the Transversus. Their fleshy fibers lie in front of the most lateral part of the canal and arch over it, and as the conjoint tendon or falx, they lie behind its most medial part, i.e., they lie in front of the deep ring and behind the superficial ring.

»» More precisely, the Internal Oblique almost always arises from more than the lateral half of the inguinal lig., and therefore covers the deep ring and takes part in the anterior wall of the canal. But the origin of the Transversus is very variable; rarely does it extend to the deep ring and take part in the anterior wall; indeed in 26 per cent of 110 regions its origin did not extend below the level of the anterior superior spine (Anson and McVay). As conjoint tendon (falx inguinalis) both muscles lie behind the superficial ring and there help to form the lowest part of the sheath of the Rectus and find attachment to the body of the pubis.

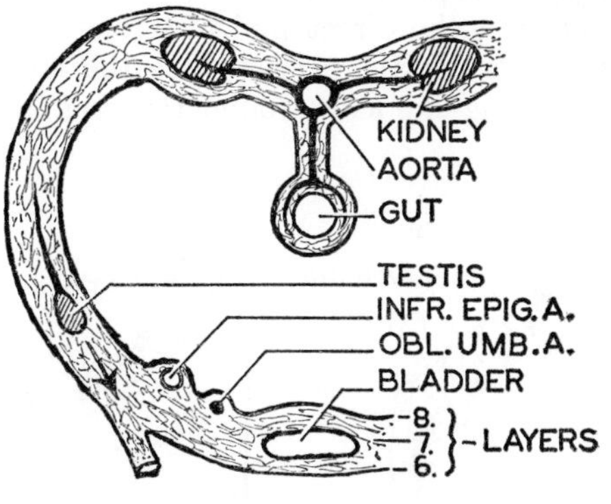

FIG. 220. The testis making its descent in layer number 7—i.e., the layer in which the organs and great vessels reside.

But, the Transversus makes the greater contribution, since it alone extends laterally, beyond the pubic tubercle, to be attached to the pecten pubis.

The tendon of the Rectus Abdominis, lying behind the medial half of the ring, is an important part of the posterior wall.

Running behind the posterior wall in the extraperitoneal fat are the inferior epigastric and the obliterated umbilical arteries. The inferior epigastric artery lies at the medial boundary of the deep ring and here the ductus deferens takes a recurrent course lateral to it. (4) The *floor of the canal* is formed by the grooved surface of the inguinal ligament and by the lacunar ligament (p. 206).

What control has one over his canal: How is it closed? Your conception of the canal may be helped by likening it to an arcade of three arches formed by the Transverse and the two Oblique muscles (*fig. 221*). The contraction of the External Oblique approximates the anterior wall to the posterior wall. During standing there is continuous contraction of Internal Oblique and Transversus in the inguinal region. During coughing and straining the vigorous contraction of the arched fleshy fibers of the Internal Oblique and Transversus, which form the roof of the canal, cause them to become lower, straighter, and taut. The action is that of a half-sphincter. This is one factor in a mechanism not well understood. For example, Lytle, and later Patey, concluded from dissections and stimulation studies that active elevation of the deep ring laterally is of prime importance. Closing of the canal results from the direct pull of Transversus on the transversalis fascia where the latter forms a sling-like loop around the ring.

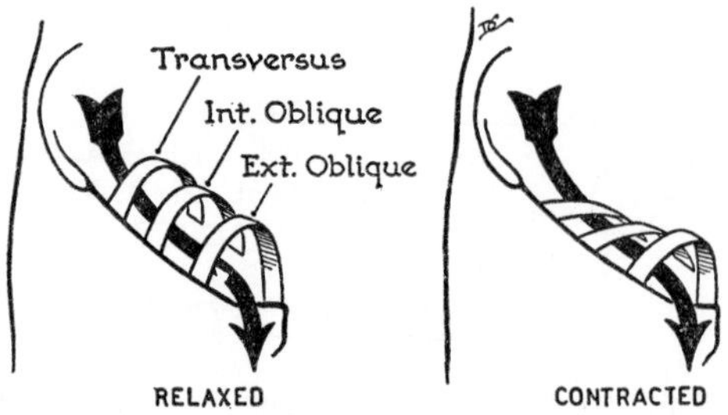

FIG. 221. "The inguinal arcade." The inguinal canal likened to an arcade of three arches traversed by the spermatic cord.

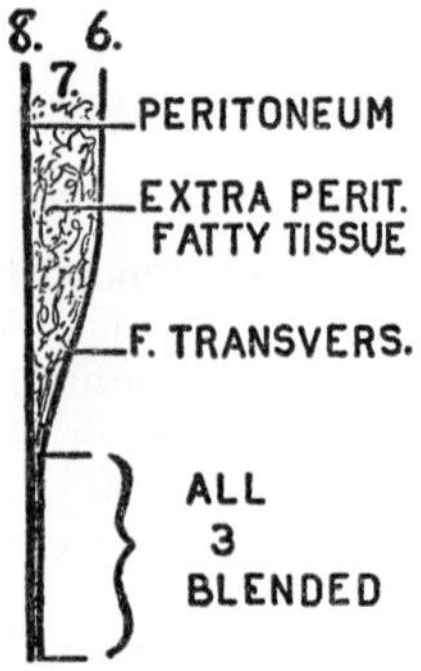

FIG. 222. In the absence of fat the inner three layers of the abdominal wall blend to form a single layer.

Observations:

1. The inguinal fibers of the Internal Oblique and Transversus, having a common origin, a common direction, and a common insertion, behave as one muscle. There is, therefore, no occasion for areolar tissue between them and, as none is present, it is often difficult to separate them.

2. The areolar lining of the Transversus, called the *fascia transversalis*, being relatively thick here, strengthens the inguinal region.

3. In spare subjects the extraperitoneal layer of fat is reduced to an areolar framework. In the absence of fat the three innermost layers of the abdominal wall—namely, the fascia transversalis, the areolar framework devoid of fat, and the peritoneum—blend to form a single areolar sheet; and you should not expect to be able to identify three (*fig. 222*). This is important. You may easily incise what you take to be fascia transversalis and find that you have opened into the peritoneal cavity.

4. Just before piercing the Internal Oblique the *ilio-inguinal nerve* sends branches forward to supply those fleshy fibers of the Transversus and Internal Oblique that control the conjoint tendon; the genitofemoral nerve also may send them a twig (*fig. 218*).

5. After piercing the Internal Oblique, the ilio-inguinal nerve, now purely sensory, runs less than a finger's breadth above the inguinal lig., and emerges through the superficial ring lateral to the spermatic cord, but it may be anterior, or medial, or posterior to it. The iliohypogastric nerve runs at a higher level (*fig. 217*).

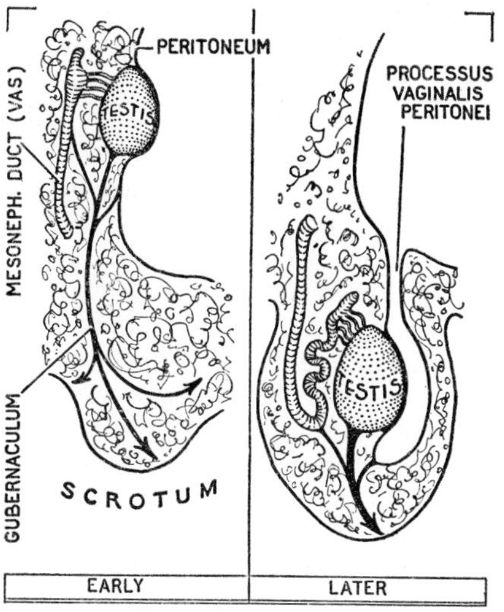

FIG. 223. Descent of the testis, processus vaginalis peritonei, and epididymis (side view—diagrammatic).

Inferior Epigastric and Deep Circumflex Iliac Arteries. These arise from the external iliac artery just before it passes behind the inguinal ligament to become the femoral artery. The one ends within the Rectus sheath; the other between the Transversus and the Internal Oblique.

»» To reach these destinations each must leave the extraperitoneal fatty layer in which it takes origin and pierce the fascia transversalis. *The Inferior Epigastric Artery* does not require to pierce the posterior wall of the fibrous sheath of the Rectus, because for about 3″ above the pubis this is wanting. It is only necessary for it to pass in front of the arcuate line to find itself within the sheath (p. 204). *The Deep Circumflex Iliac Artery* follows the inguinal lig. laterally and, after piercing the fascia transversalis, divides into the ascending and terminal branches, noted on page 208.

TESTIS, SPERMATIC CORD, AND SCROTUM

Descent of the Testis. The testis develops from the mesothelium covering the medial part of the mesonephros. In early fetal life a cord of spindle-shaped cells, called the **gubernaculum testis,** pushed before it into the scrotum the layers of the growing abdominal wall, and evaginated them as though they were so many sheets of rubber.

The upper end of the gubernaculum was attached (1) to the testis, (2) to the adjacent part of the peritoneum, and (3) to the mesonephric duct (later the epididymis and ductus deferens) (*figs. 219* and *223*). These it dragged after it, or at least it constrained them to follow in its wake. As a result, the peritoneum was drawn out into a blind tube, the **processus vaginalis peritonei,** and the testis, which was adherent to the outer surface of the tube, was drawn with it into the scrotum. The lower end of the epididymis was drawn down too. (It is a common error to suppose that the testis drops into the tubular processus vaginalis like a bucket lowered by a rope into a well.)

The testis descended to the iliac fossa during the 3rd prenatal month, traversed the inguinal canal during the 7th prenatal month, and reached the bottom of the scrotum after birth.

Variations. The testis sometimes fails to leave the abdomen, an *undescended testis,* or it may be out of place, an *ectopic testis,* and the scrotum empty. This may be the result of hormonal insufficiency (L. J. Wells).

Comparative Anatomy. In the elephant the testis is retained in the abdomen; in certain rodents it descends periodically and then returns to the abdomen; in the pig it descends to the perineum; and in the marsupials it becomes prepenile.

»» **To Display the Testis and Spermatic Cord** an incision, extending from the superficial inguinal ring to a point half way down the scrotum, should be carried through skin, Dartos, and fascia. The external pudendal vessels, which cross in front of the cord on their way to supply the front of the scrotum, must be cut. The testis and cord in their three coverings are then to be shelled out of the scrotum; but it will be found that this cannot be done until a band of tissue that anchors the coverings over the lower pole of the testis to the scrotum is first snipped through. The band is perhaps a remnant of the gubernaculum. In it are some small veins.

Scrotum is the name of the bag of skin and subcutaneous tissues in which the testes lie. It consists of representatives of the outer two layers of the abdominal wall. The scrotum has a bilateral origin. It is derived

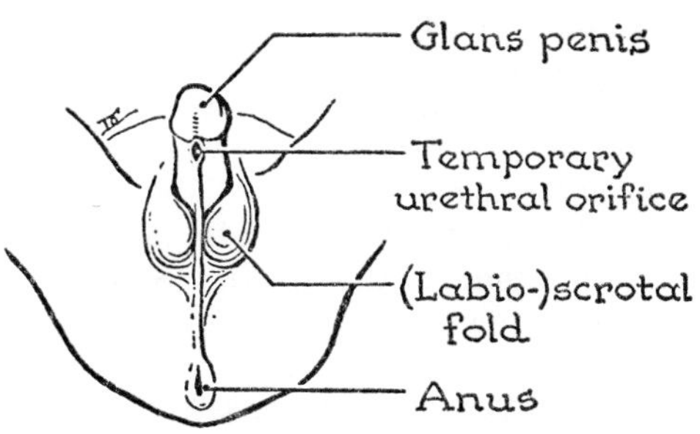

FIG. 224. The scrotum has a bilateral origin

from the right and left labioscrotal folds. In the female these folds remain discrete as the labia majora; in the male they fuse behind the penis to form the scrotum (*fig. 224*).

The skin of the scrotum forms a single pouch; the subcutaneous tissues of the scrotum form a right and a left pouch with a common median partition. The subcutaneous tissue is continuous with the fatty and membranous (Camper and Scarpa) layers of fascia on the abdomen, and with the fatty and membranous (Colles) layers of fascia in the perineum. It is, however, devoid of fat. It is laminated and it contains a sheet of involuntary muscle, the **dartos muscle.** The fibers of the Dartos adhere to the skin and cause it to wrinkle when cold. Sympathetic fibers supply the Dartos.

NERVES. The 1st lumbar segment, via the ilio-inguinal nerve, supplies the ventral part of the scrotum and the root of the penis; the (2nd), 3rd, and 4th sacral segments, via the posterior scrotal nerves and perineal branch of the posterior femoral cutaneous nerve, supply the perineal part of the scrotum. Here, then, segments L. 2, 3, 4, 5, S. 1, (2) are not represented (*fig. 336.1*). There is, in fact, a hiatus or break in the numerical sequence of the cutaneous nerves which corresponds to the segments from which the lower limb derives its nerves (*fig. 43.3*).

»» This is comparable to the hiatus on the front of the chest where segments C. 3 and 4 meet segment Th. 2 owing to the withdrawal of segments C. 5, 6, 7, 8 and Th. 1 to form the brachial plexus.

VESSELS. The scrotum is supplied by the ext. and int. pudendal arteries and veins. The lymph vessels pass to the superficial inguinal nodes (*fig. 399*).

Three Coverings of Testis and Spermatic Cord. These are continuous with the External Oblique aponeurosis at the superficial inguinal ring, with the fascia transversalis at the deep inguinal ring, and with the fleshy fibers of the Internal Oblique and Transversus between the two rings. The outer and inner coverings are known as the external and internal spermatic fasciae, and between them is the middle covering or cremaster muscle. These tubular coverings tend to form a single areolar membrane in which the fibers of the Cremaster are spread out in loops, but in a well preserved and muscular subject three layers can be dissected.

Supply. The Cremaster is supplied by segments L. 1 and 2 (via genitofemoral n.) and by the cremasteric branch of the inf. epigastric artery.

Spermatic Cord (cont'd). The spermatic cord consists of representatives of the inner two layers of the abdominal wall, viz., peritoneum and extraperitoneal fatty-areolar tissue; and in the fatty-areolar tissue are the structures running to and from the testis.

These constituents of the cord assemble at the deep inguinal ring lateral to the inferior epigastric artery, pass through the inguinal canal, and descend in the scrotum to the testis.

Observe: (1) that the cord lies behind the Internal Oblique laterally, and in front of it medially where it forms the conjoint tendon, and here the cord rests on the lacunar lig. (*fig. 217.1*); and (2) that, as the cord emerges from the superficial inguinal ring, it rolls over the pubic tubercle and covers it. So, in order to palpate the tubercle, it is necessary first to displace the cord either medially or laterally, which is easy to do.

The Constituents of the Cord are:

1. Representatives of the inner two layers of the abdominal wall:
   a. Processus vaginalis peritonei.
   b. Areolar tissue continuous with the extraperitoneal fatty areolar tissue.
2. Structures pertaining to the testis:
   a. Ductus deferens.
   b. Vessels (artery, veins, and lymphatics) and nerves of the testis.
   c. Vessels and nerves of the ductus deferens and epididymis.

The Processus Vaginalis Peritonei is the tube of peritoneum behind which the testis follows the gubernaculum into the scrotum. Its upper part lies in front of the ductus deferens, and is normally obliterated before birth (or within a month after birth) and becomes a fibrous thread, the *funicular process of peritoneum.* When it remains patent, it leads to congenital inguinal hernia. Its lower part remains patent, is invaginated from behind by the testis, and is known as the **tunica vaginalis testis.**

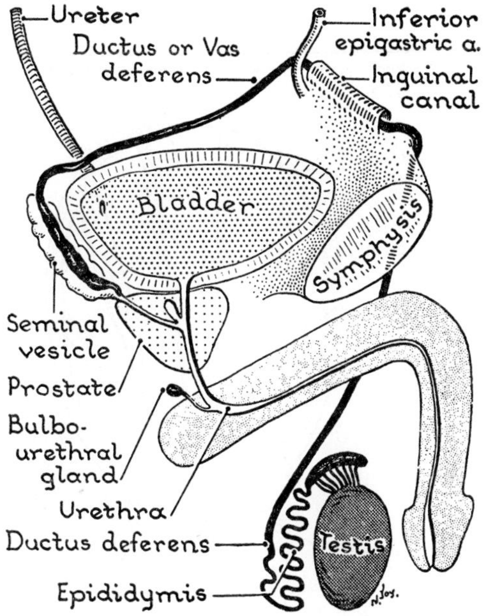

FIG. 225. Diagram of the ductus (vas) deferens.

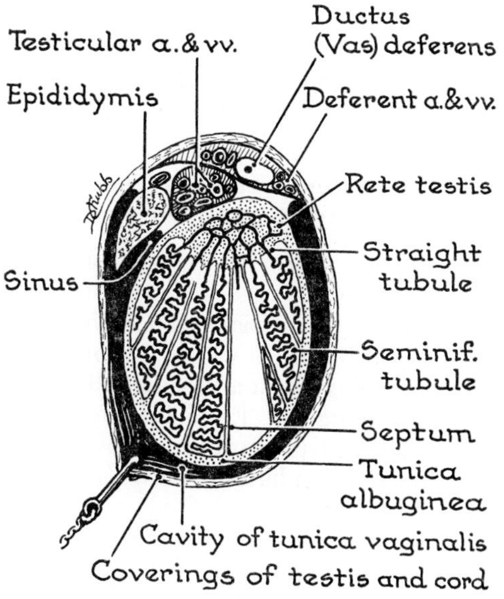

FIG. 226. Right testis in transverse section

Areolar Tissue surrounds the structures passing to and from the testis. In it are commonly found circumscribed *areas of fat,* which may attain the size of a pigeon's egg.

The **Ductus Deferens** (Vas Deferens) (*fig. 225*) is the duct that conveys spermatozoa from the testis to the urethra. It is the continuation of the canal of the epididymis. In length it equals the femur or the spinal cord. Developmentally, it is subperitoneal throughout its course (p. 311).

Except at its two extremities, which are dilated and thin walled, it has a thick muscular coat and a capillary lumen; hence, it feels firm like a whip cord. It first ascends behind the testis along the medial side of the epididymis; it continues through the scrotum and inguinal canal as the posterior constituent of the spermatic cord; it then hooks around the lateral side of the inferior epigastric artery and descends subperitoneally to the posterolateral angle of the bladder and thence to the urethra (*fig. 225*).

Testis (*fig. 226*). THE TESTIS is an ovoid gland measuring $1\frac{1}{2} \times 1 \times \frac{3}{4}''$. It is enveloped in the *tunica vaginalis testis* except where the epididymis and the structures of the spermatic cord are attached to its upper pole and posterior border. It has a tough, fibrous, white, outer coat, the *tunica albuginea,* which is comparable to the sclerotic, white, outer coat of the eyeball. Posteriorly the outer coat is thicker and less dense and is known as the *mediastinum testis.*

Areolar *septa* extend from the mediastinum to the tunica albuginea and divide the testis into about 250 elongated pyramidal compartments. Each contains a lobule formed from two or more *seminiferous tubules.* Being two feet long they are closely packed and convoluted, except at the apex of the compartment where they join together and take a short, straight course, the *straight tubules.*

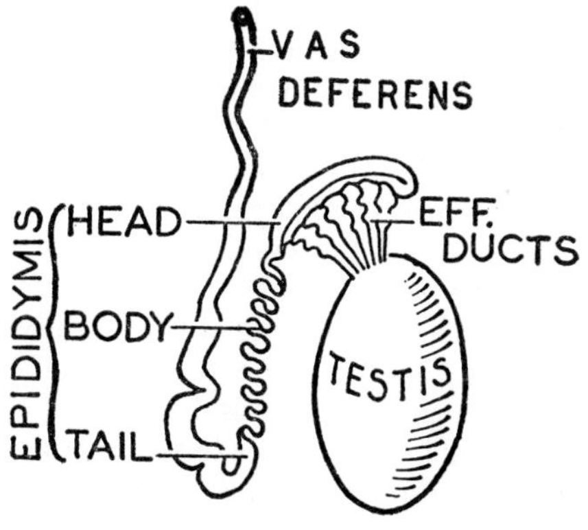

FIG. 227. The testis and epididymis

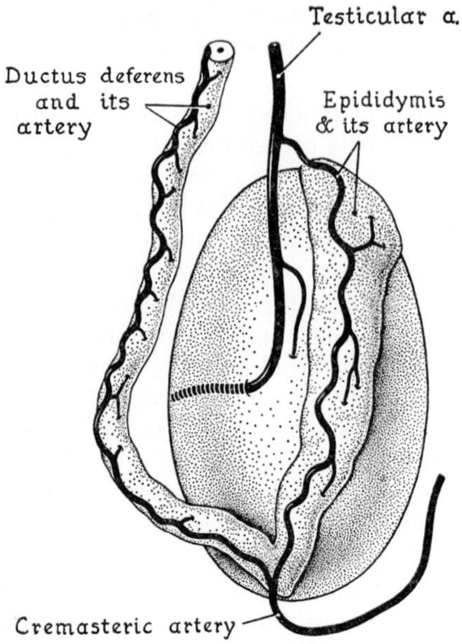

FIG. 227.1

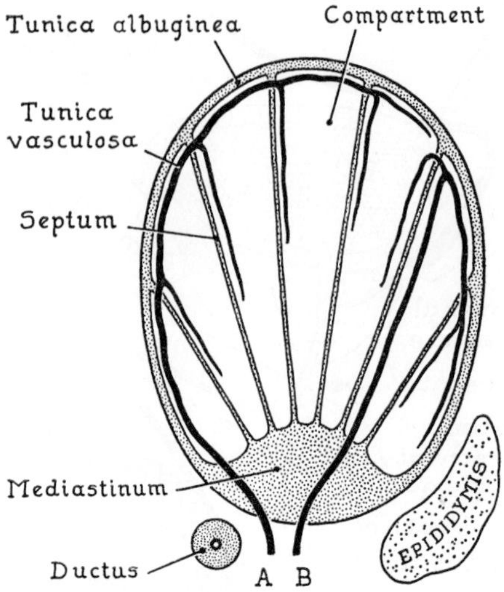

FIG. 227.2

FIGS. 227.1 and 227.2. The testicular artery and its anastomoses. This pattern is typical of 25 specimens in which the deferent artery was successfully injected with colored latex. By retrograde flow the testicular and cremasteric arteries were filled in all cases. (Courtesy of Dr. Neil Watters.)

In the mediastinum the straight tubules anastomose to form a network, the *rete testis.*

From six to a dozen fine ducts, the *efferent ductules*, connect the upper part of the rete testis with the head of the epididymis (*fig. 227*).

Epididymis. The epididymis is applied to the upper pole and posterior border of the testis. It is somewhat larger in diameter than a lead pencil. It tapers from above downward. It is subdivided into a *head* or upper part, a *body* or intermediate part, and a *tail* or lower part. It has an attached, slightly concave, testicular surface, and a free rounded posterior surface which is largely covered with tunica vaginalis (formerly peritoneum, *fig. 223*). A pouch of the tunica vaginalis, the *sinus of the epididymis*, dips in between the lateral side of the testis and the body of the epididymis, forming a canoe-shaped recess. The ductus deferens ascends on the medial side of the epididymis.

Structure. Each of the 6 to 12 efferent ductules of the testis coils to form a cone-shaped lobule. The lobules together comprise the head of the epididymis. They open into the duct of the epididymis. The duct of the epididymis forms the body and tail of the organ. It is greatly twisted and folded upon itself, and when unraveled it is as long as the small intestine (about 20 feet). The tail is continued as the ductus deferens.

Vessels and Nerves of Testis, Epididymis, and Ductus

Arteries: The *testicular artery*, a branch of the aorta, pierces the mediastinum testis as (1), 2, (or 3) divisions. These break up into over 50 branches which, by branching and rebranching, form a vascular coat lining the tunica albuginea. From this coat recurrent twigs turn backward in the interlobular septa, but some radiate forward. (*figs. 227.1 and 227.2.*)

The *deferent artery*, a branch of the inf. vesical artery, arises in the pelvis and clings to the ductus throughout, as do also its veins and nerves.

The *cremasteric artery* is a branch of the inf. epigastric artery.

Veins: Up to a dozen veins from the region form an anastomosing plexus, the *pampiniform plexus*, which ascends in three groups: (1) around the testicular artery, (2) with the ductus, and (3) alone. These become

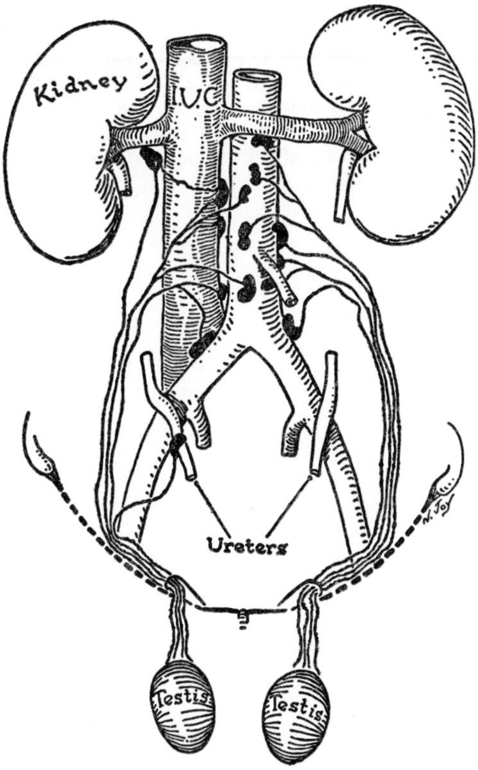

FIG. 228. The lymph drainage of the testes. (After Jamieson and Dobson.)

reduced to two or three veins and ultimately to one, which on the right side joins the inf. vena cava and on the left side, the left renal vein. The deferent veins end in the vesical plexus.

The testicular veins may become dilated and tortuous, a condition called varicocele (p. 281).

Lymphatics: The lymph vessels of the testis, like those of the ovary, end in nodes situated between the common iliac vein and the renal vein (*fig. 228*). Do not misconceive them to drain with the lymph vessels of the scrotum and penis into the inguinal nodes.

Nerves: Of testis—Th. (6, 7, 8, 9, and) 10. Of epididymis—Th. 11, 12, and L. 1, via the inf. hypogastric plexus (Mitchell).

»» **Development** (*fig. 229*). *The duct system of the testis* is of three-fold origin: (1) The seminiferous and straight tubules and the rete testis are developed from anastomosing cords of cells in the genital ridge between vertebral segments L. 4——S. 2. (2) The efferent ductules and the lobules in the head of the epididymis are formed from the six or more mesonephric tubules that succeed in establishing connections between the rete testis and the duct of the epididymis. (3) The duct of the epididymis and the ductus (vas) deferens are derived from the mesonephric duct, that is to say, from the duct of the primitive kidney.

Rudimentary Structures about the testis and epididymis are five in number. Of these, two are brought into view when the tunica vaginalis is opened. They

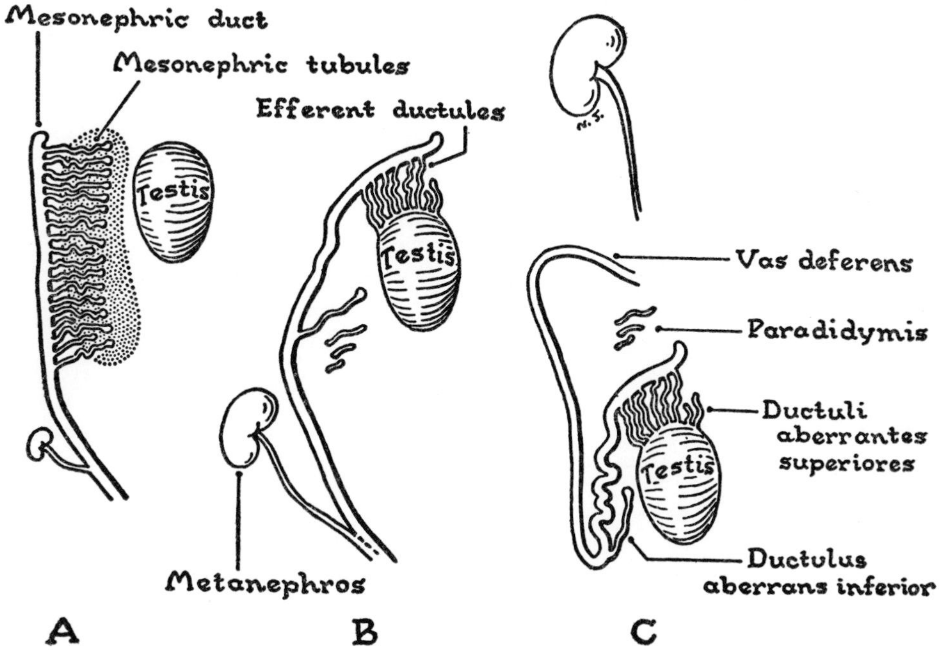

FIG. 229. Some mesonephric tubules become the efferent ductules; others persist as rudimentary or vestigial structures.

are little bodies attached to the upper pole of the testis and head of the epididymis. They probably represent the cranial ends of the paramesonephric (Mullerian) and mesonephric (Wolffian) ducts and are known as the *appendix of the testis* and the *appendix of the epididymis*, respectively.

The three other rudiments are revealed only when the epididymis is unraveled. They are the remains of mesonephric tubules. The *ductulus aberrans superior* is a tubule that has joined the rete testis but not the duct of the epididymis; the *ductulus aberrans inferior* is a tubule that has joined the duct of the epididymis but not the rete testis; and the *paradidymis* is a collection of tubules that has joined neither. It forms a little body in the spermatic cord above the testis. These embryological remains may become cystic.

When the testis descends, a fragment of spleen is rarely, a fragment of adrenal gland is occasionally, carried down with it.

CHAPTER **14**

ABDOMINOPELVIC CAVITY

Subdivisions; Planes: Transpyloric and Transumbilical; Midinguinal Point.
Protection of Viscera; Definitions (of parts of peritoneum).
Identification of Viscera.
Parts of Gastro-intestinal Canal: General Disposition; Large Intestine (parts).
EXAMINATION OF G.I. TRACT—*Stomach; Duodenum; Jejunum and Ileum; Features of Large Intestine; Cecum; Appendix; Colon.*

Upper Abdominal Viscera and Their Connections

Liver; Gall Bladder; Epiploic Foramen (Mouth of Lesser Sac).
Peritoneal Attachments of Spleen; Pedicle of Spleen; Omental Bursa (exploration).
PERITONEAL ATTACHMENTS OF LIVER—*Falciform Ligament; Round Ligament; Ligamentum Venosum.*
Lesser Omentum; Triangular Ligaments; Coronary Ligaments; Epiploic Foramen (cont'd); Caudate Lobe of Liver.
SPLEEN *(cont'd) –Surfaces; Borders; Surface Anatomy; Development; Variations.*
EVER CHANGING POSITIONS OF VISCERA—*Body Types or Bodily Habitus; Details of Changing Positions of Various Organs; Features of Hypersthenic and Asthenic Habitus.*

UMBILICUS

Development: Urachus; Umbilical Artery and Vein; Changes at Birth; Meckel's Diverticulum.

PERITONEUM

PERITONEAL FOLDS –*Those Containing and Not Containing Tubes; Fossae, Recesses, and Gutters; Notes on Development Explaining Relationships of Abdominal Structures.*
Afferent Nerves of Peritoneum.
OBLITERATION OF PERITONEAL CAVITY.

Subdivisions. Before your studies of the abdomen have proceeded far, you will find it necessary to relate the various viscera and other structures to each other and to the surface of the body. This you can do readily and most satisfactorily if you employ the vertebral column of the individual in ques-

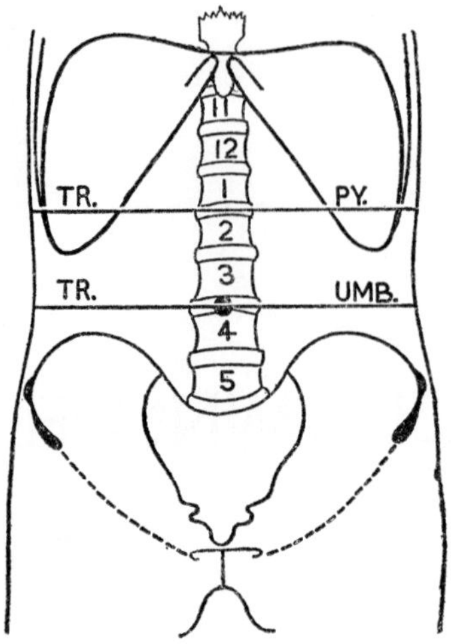

FIG. 230. Horizontal planes with the vertebral column as a measuring rod.

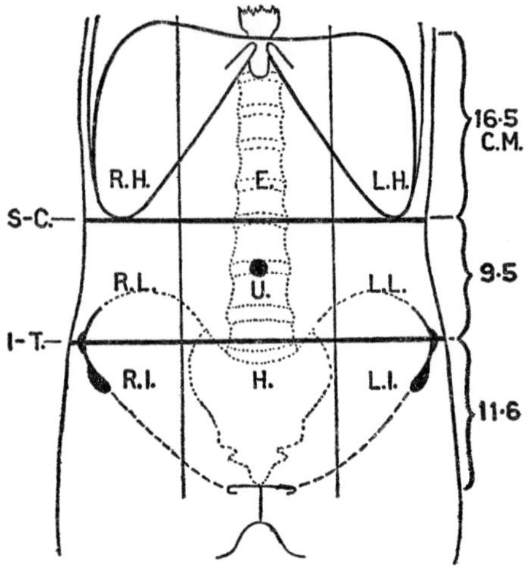

FIG. 231. The nine regions of the abdomen. *RH*, *LH* = right and left hypochondriac. *RL*, *LL* = right and left lateral or lumbar. *RI*, *LI* = right and left inguinal or iliac. E = epigastric. U = umbilical. H = suprapubic or hypogastric.

tion as a scale and refer structures to their vertebral levels. Instead of thinking in inches and centimeters *think in terms of vertebral heights.*

Obviously you will make use of the median plane to divide the body into right and left halves. Two horizontal planes are guides to the vertebral levels. **The transpyloric plane** bisects the line joining the top of the sternum to the top of the symphysis pubis, and lies at the level of the disc between the 1st and 2nd lumbar vertebrae (*fig. 230*). **The transumbilical plane** passes through the umbilicus, or navel, and lies at the level of the disc between the 3rd and 4th lumbar vertebrae. It is true that the level of the umbilicus varies somewhat with age, sex, obesity, and posture, but it is, for all that, a valuable landmark.

To remember the *vertebral levels* of these two planes—between 1 and 2, and between 3 and 4—should not tax the memory unduly (*fig. 230*).

»» For purposes of elaborate topographical work it is customary to divide the abdomen proper into three sections (upper, middle, and lower) by means of two horizontal planes; and to subdivide each section into three by means of two sagittal planes; making nine regions in all (*fig. 231*).

The upper horizontal plane lies at the level of the lowest points of the chest wall seen from the front. These points are on the 10th costal cartilages, and not on the 12th or 11th which are too short to reach the front. The lower horizontal plane lies at the level of the highest points on the iliac crests seen from the front. These are at the sites of the tubercles. The names of these planes are: subcostal and intertubercular.

The right and left sagittal or "vertical" planes are erected on the midpoint of the line joining the corresponding anterior superior spine of the ilium to the top of the symphysis pubis. This point is known as the **midinguinal point.**

Since the middle or umbilical section diminishes when you sit down and disappears entirely when you bend forwards, the subdivisions of the abdomen should be plotted out with the subject either fully recumbent or else erect. The upper section rises to the diaphragm and is subdivided into epigastric and right and left hypochondriac regions; the middle section is subdivided into umbilical and right and left lateral or lumbar regions; and the lower section is subdivided into suprapubic and right and left inguinal or iliac regions.

Protection to Viscera. The abdominal viscera lie largely "within" the thorax and pelvis. Of course, the viscera are not within the thoracic cavity, for they are situated below the diaphragm; but, since the diaphragm rises to the level of the 5th rib in the midclavicular line, the upper abdominal viscera are certainly well ensconced within the bony thorax. The lower abdominal viscera lie within the pelvis major protected behind and at the sides by the ilia. In the flanks only the breadth of two fingers separates the 11th ribs from the iliac crests. The ventral aspect of the abdomen, being within the field of vision, can be defended by the upper limbs and can be protected by bending forward or by curling up; so, it is in less need of bony protection.

Definitions. By *"abdominopelvic cavity"* is meant the space enclosed by the bones, muscles and fasciae of the abdominal and pelvic walls from the diaphragm cranially or above to the pelvic diaphragm caudally or below.

This cavity is divided at the pelvic inlet into the abdominal cavity (proper) and the pelvic cavity. These two divisions are set nearly at right angles to one another (*fig. 232*).

The Peritoneum is an areolar membrane covered with a single layer of squamous cells, the areolar membrane being to the cells what a wall is to the wallpaper covering it—necessary for its support.

The Peritoneal Cavity is a complicated sac, lined everywhere with peritoneum, and moistened with serous (watery) fluid. The cavity is a potential cavity; it is completely empty, except when air is admitted at operation or when fluid collects in persons suffering from dropsy. Accordingly, each part of its free surface is in contact with, and rubs against, some other part of its free surface. In the female, the peritoneal cavity communicates with the exterior through the uterine tubes, uterus, and vagina.

The portion of peritoneum lining the walls or parietes of the peritoneal cavity is called the *parietal layer* of peritoneum; that covering the organs or viscera is the *visceral layer*. The peritoneum forms certain folds and double layers. A double layer con-

FIG. 232. The abdominopelvic cavity

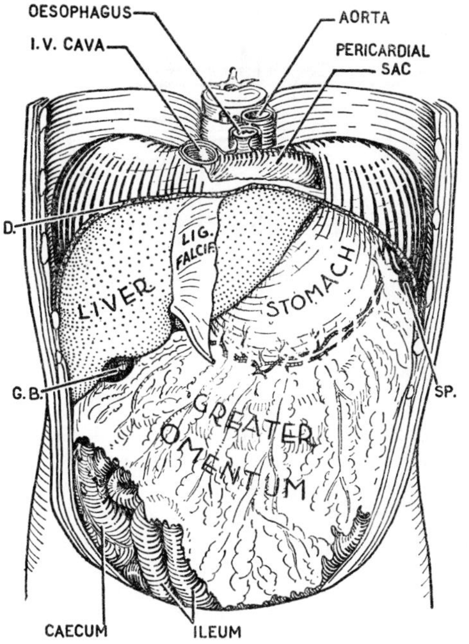

FIG. 233. Abdominal contents undisturbed. *G.B.* = gall bladder; *Sp* = spleen; *D* = cut edge of diaphragm.

necting the stomach to another structure is called an *omentum*. Of these there are two: (1) *the lesser omentum* which is attached to the lesser curvature of the stomach, and (2) *the greater omentum* which is attached to the greater curvature. A fold connecting the intestine to the posterior abdominal wall and conveying vessels and nerves to it is a *mesentery*. All other folds are called *ligaments*. The distinction, however, between the three terms is not one of importance.

»» **Identification of Viscera.** At this stage *let the following structures* (*fig. 233*) *be identified:* The *diaphragm,* which forms the roof of the abdomen; the *liver,* lying above and mainly on the right side, is divided into a right and a left lobe by the *falciform ligament* which connects the liver to the diaphragm and anterior abdominal wall in the median plane; the *gall bladder,* lying on the under surface of the right lobe of the liver reaches to or beyond its sharp, inferior border; the *stomach,* above and to the left; the *spleen,* behind the stomach and in contact with the diaphragm. Then let the *greater omentum,* which hangs like an apron from the greater curvature of the stomach, be thrown upward over the costal margin when the *small intestine,* surrounded by the *large intestine,* as though by a picture frame, will be seen. The apron-like part of the *greater omentum,* called the *gastrocolic ligament,* may now be followed to the portion of the large gut called the *transverse colon;* the broad, conspicuous *transverse mesocolon,* passing from transverse colon dorsally to the *pancreas,* is readily observed,

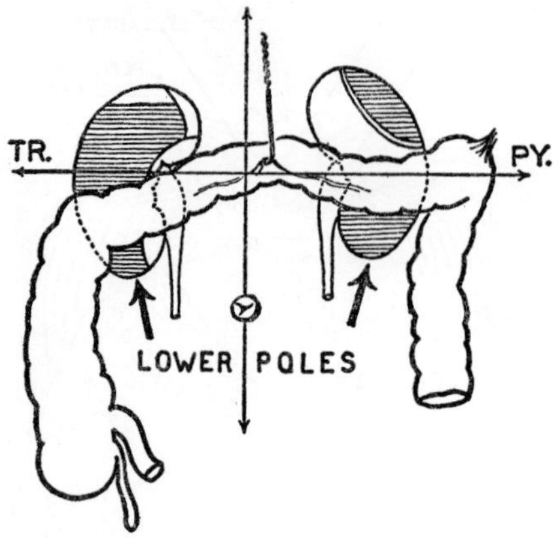

FIG. 234. The shaded parts of the kidneys are covered with peritoneum and are palpable when the peritoneal cavity is open.

although the pancreas cannot be identified at this stage. The rounded lower poles of the right and left *kidneys* can and should and indeed must be palpated in the upper angles of the intestinal "picture frame" (*fig. 234*). It may, however, first be necessary to steady the kidney by placing the unoccupied hand behind the lumbar region and pressing ventrally, below the last rib. The lateral convex border of each kidney should be traced above the colic flexure and part of the anterior surface palpated. The empty *urinary bladder* lies behind the pubis; the *rectum* lies in front of the sacrum.

Parts of the Gastro-intestinal Canal. *General Disposition* (*fig. 235*). The digestive passage extends from the mouth to the anus. It is divisible into the following parts: mouth, pharynx, esophagus, stomach, small intestine, and large intestine.

The stomach and intestines (i.e., from stomach to anus inclusive) are collectively called the **gastro-intestinal canal.** The last inch of the esophagus and the gastro-intestinal canal are situated within the abdomen and pelvis.

The *esophagus* pierces the diaphragm less than an inch to the left of the median plane and ends at the cardiac or esophageal orifice of the stomach. The *stomach* lies to the left of the median plane. Its exit, the *pylorus*, lies less than an inch to the right of the median plane in the transpyloric plane. It is succeeded by the *small intestine or gut*, which is subdivided into three parts: duodenum, jejunum, and ileum.

The *duodenum* is the horseshoe-shaped portion of the small intestine that has lost its primitive mesentery. It begins at the pylorus and ends at the *duodenojejunal junction*, an inch to the left of the median plane just below the transpyloric plane, i.e., about 2″ from where it begins. Having no mesentery, the duodenum adheres to the structures on the posterior wall of the abdomen. On

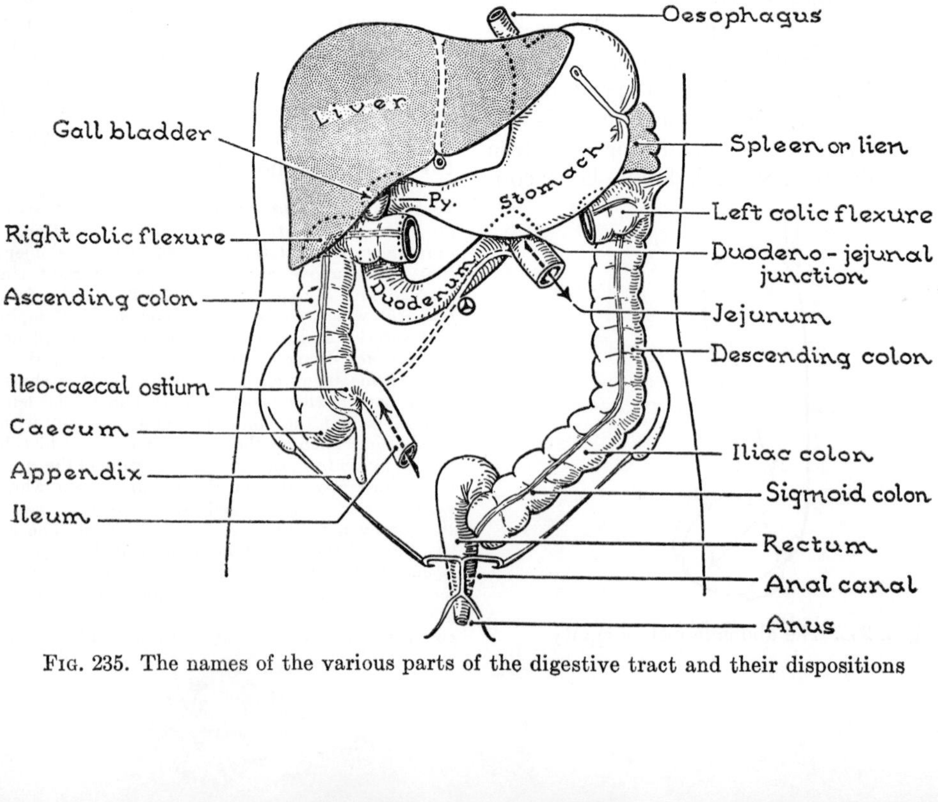

FIG. 235. The names of the various parts of the digestive tract and their dispositions

this account and because the transverse colon crosses in front of it and adheres to it, it is not conspicuous. The *jejunum* and the *ileum* are the two parts of the small gut that retain their mesenteries. They extend from the duodenojejunal junction to the right iliac fossa where the ileum opens into the large gut. The opening is called the *ileocecal orifice.*

The large intestine is subdivided into: vermiform appendix, cecum, ascending colon, right colic flexure, transverse colon, left colic flexure, descending colon, sigmoid colon, rectum, anal canal, and anus.

The *cecum* is the blind cul-de-sac situated below the ileocecal orifice. The worm-shaped *appendix* opens into the cecum less than an inch below the ileocecal orifice. The *ascending colon* ascends from the right iliac fossa, across the iliac crest, to the under surface of the liver where, in front of the kidney, it makes a bend, the *right colic* (*or hepatic*) *flexure*, and becomes the *transverse colon*, which extends across the abdomen to the under surface of the spleen where, in front of the left kidney, it bends again to become the *left colic* (*or splenic*) *flexure.* From here the *descending colon* descends to the pelvic brim where it becomes the *sigmoid* (pelvic) *colon.* As sigmoid colon it passes to the middle of the sacrum where it becomes the *rectum.* The lower portion of the rectum and the anal canal passes through the floor of the pelvis and in the perineum opens on to the surface at the *anus.*

Examination of Gastro-intestinal Canal. *By inspection and by handling one may examine the abdominal portions of the alimentary canal.*

The last inch of the *esophagus* lies in a groove on the posterior aspect of the attenuated left lobe of the liver.

The **Stomach** has entrance and exit: the one, the *cardiac* (or esophageal) *orifice*, is situated an inch to the left of the median plane behind the 7th costal cartilage; the other, the *pyloric orifice*, is situated an inch or less to the right of the median plane on the transpyloric plane. The two borders of the stomach extend between these two orifices. The *lesser curvature* is short and concave and, with the first inch of the duodenum, gives attachment to the *lesser omentum.* The *greater curvature* is long and convex and, with the first inch of the duodenum, gives attachment to an extensive double layer of peritoneum, the *greater omentum.* The greater omentum is divisible into three parts: (1) a lower apron-like part, the *gastrocolic lig.*, (2) a left part, the *gastrolienal lig.*, and (3) an upper part, the *gastrophrenic lig.* (*fig. 235.1*). These are attached to the transverse colon, lien (spleen), and diaphragm, respectively.

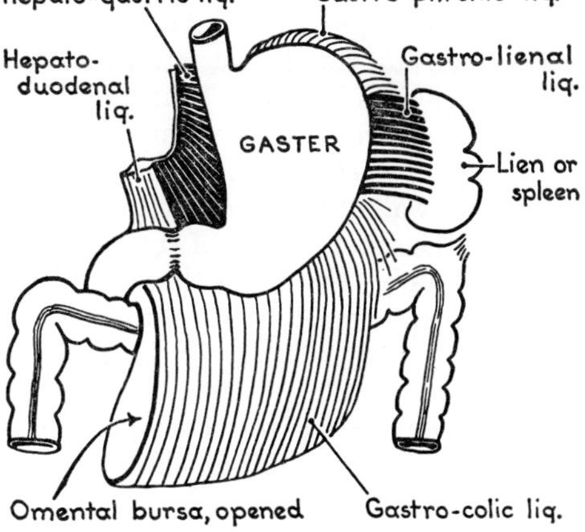

FIG. 235.1. Diagram of the two parts of the lesser omentum and of the three parts of the greater omentum.

The stomach is subdivided thus: a line drawn horizontally at the level of the cardiac orifice separates the *fundus* from the *body* (*fig. 236*). An oblique line joining an indentation on the lesser curvature (incisura angularis) to the greater curvature separates the body from the pyloric part of the stomach.

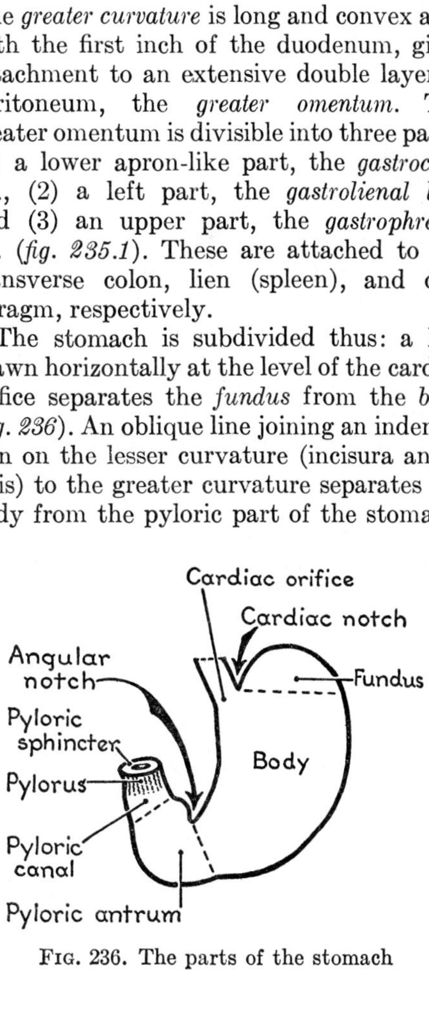

FIG. 236. The parts of the stomach

Another oblique line passing from an indentation on the greater curvature (sulcus intermedius) to the lesser curvature subdivides the pyloric part into a large chamber, the *pyloric antrum*, and a more tubular portion, the *pyloric canal*. By invaginating the anterior wall of this canal with the index finger and the anterior wall of the duodenum with the thumb, the tips of these two digits can be made to meet in the lumen of the *pylorus* and the thickness of its sphincter gauged.

The **Duodenum** is the fixed part of the small gut or the part that has lost its primitive mesentery. Though 10″ in length its two ends are but 2″ apart, for it begins at the pylorus, which lies on the transpyloric plane less than an inch to the right of the median plane, and ends at the duodeno-jejunal junction, where it is continuous with the jejunum, an inch to the left of the median plane and a little below the transpyloric plane. It is molded around the head of the pancreas and is horseshoe-shaped (*fig. 291*). Later (p. 260), we shall see that it is divided into four parts, and that the 2nd part is largely concealed by the transverse colon which crosses it and adheres to it.

The **remainder of the small gut** retains its mesentery and extends from the duodeno-jejunal junction to the ileocecal orifice, which is situated in the right iliac fossa where intertubercular and "vertical" planes intersect. Though a distance of but 6″ to 8″ separates these two points, the gut, under dissecting room conditions, steers a varying course of 20 odd feet between them. The root of the mesentery of the gut is attached diagonally across the posterior abdominal wall between the two points; accordingly, it likewise is 6″ to 8″ long, whereas its intestinal border is elaborately ruffled and frilled to accommodate the gut.

»» The small intestine is so convoluted and mobile that you can pass many feet of it through your hands without being able to decide whether it is leading you to its duodenal end or to its cecal end. But, by the simple device of placing a hand on each side of the mesentery and drawing the fingers forward from root to intestinal border, the convolutions are locally untwisted and the direction of the gut or intestine rendered quite obvious.

The *first coil of the jejunum* and the *last coil of the ileum* are parallel to each other; the former passes downward and to the left in front of the left kidney, the latter passes upward and to the right out of the pelvic cavity (*fig. 235*).

Jejunum Contrasted with Ileum. The upper two-fifths of the free part of the small gut are called jejunum, and the lower three-fifths ileum. The jejunum has a greater digestive surface than the ileum, because (1) its *diameter* is greater; (2) its spirally arranged folds of mucous membrane, called *plicae circulares* (p. 259), are bigger and more closely packed; and (3) the minute finger-like projections of its mucous membrane, called *villi*, are larger and more numerous. Hence, its wall feels thick and velvety, whereas the wall of the smaller calibered ileum with its fewer plicae and villi may be almost parchment-like in thinness.

The extraperitoneal *fat*, normally present in the mesentery, creeps along the vessels on to the ileal wall but fails to reach the jejunal wall; hence, there are translucent "windows" in the mesentery at the edge of the jejunum. Further, on holding the gut and mesentery to the light, the disposition of the *vessels* is seen to become progressively more complex from the beginning of the jejunum to nearly the end of the ileum; thus, the *vasa recta* or straight terminal vessels to the upper quarter of this section of the gut spring from a system of arcades, which become more complex from the beginning of the jejunum to nearly the end of the ileum (see Arcades, p. 256). (See also

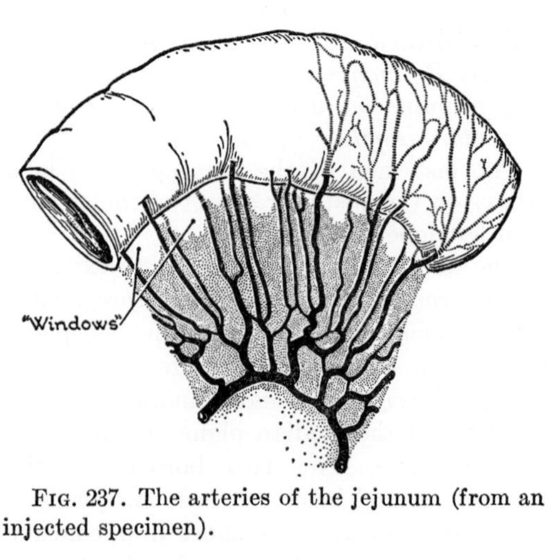

FIG. 237. The arteries of the jejunum (from an injected specimen).

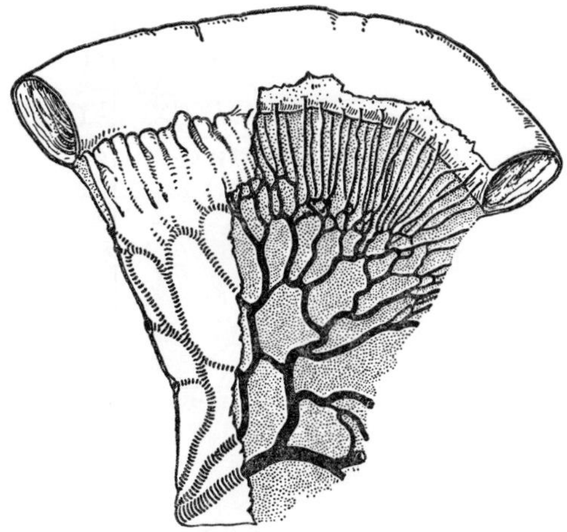

FIG. 238. The arteries of the ileum (from an injected specimen).

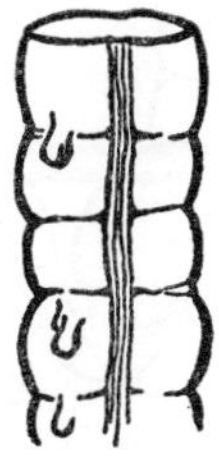

FIG. 239. Segment of large intestine showing one of the three teniae, sacculations, and appendices.

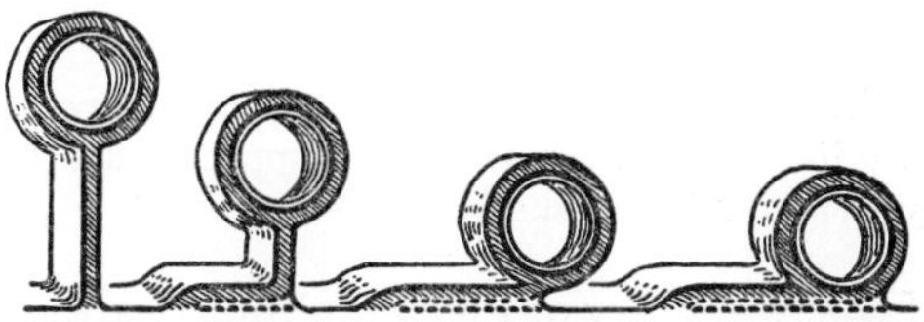

FIG. 240. Primitive mesentery of the large gut in various stages of absorption.

Michels.) At the same time the vasa recta become progressively shorter (*figs. 237* and *238*).

Features of the Large Intestine. The *large gut* forms three and one-half sides of a square around the small gut; so, by their relative positions the one may be told from the other. The outer longitudinal muscle coat of the large gut does not form a complete coat, as in the small gut, but it is arranged in three narrow bands, the *teniae coli*, which, being shorter than the gut itself, cause it to be gathered up into *sacculations*. As evidence of this, observe that if the teniae are cut the sacculated form is lost.

Peritoneal bags of fat, *appendices epiploicae*, hang from the large gut throughout its whole length (*fig. 239*). Those from the appendix, cecum, and rectum generally contain no fat.

Size alone does not necessarily distinguish large gut from small gut, the descending colon commonly having a *caliber* less than that of the small gut.

The primitive mesentery, possessed by the large gut during prenatal life, is constantly retained by the transverse and sigmoid colons, while the appendix acquires a mesentery, and the cecum is free. The extent to which the ascending and descending colons lose their primitive mesenteries varies (*fig. 240*): the mesentery may persist (1) wholly, or (2) in part; but usually the loss is complete, the colon being either (3) surrounded with peritoneum on all sides, or (4) surrounded on three sides and bare posteriorly.

The **cecum** is free and commonly lies in the right iliac fossa below the intertubercular plane and lateral to the "vertical" plane. Its rounded lower free end commonly hangs over the pelvic brim. The cecum may have a short mesentery or even two mesenteries, a medial and a lateral, with a cul-de-sac, the *retrocecal fossa*, extending upward between them. When present, this fossa usually contains the appendix. An extensive retrocecal fossa (i.e., one extending upward behind the ascending colon) is, of course, a *retrocolic fossa*.

The **vermiform appendix** in fetal life opened into the apex of the cecum; now it opens into the cecum an inch or less below the ileocecal junction. Like the hands of a clock, the appendix may be long or short, and may occupy any position consistent with its length (*fig. 241*).

»» In 10,000 cases Wakeley found it to be either retrocecal and retrocolic in 65.28 per cent; pelvic (on the Psoas, near or hanging over the pelvic brim) in 31.01 per cent; and rarely elsewhere; i.e., subcecal, pre-ileal, post-ileal, or ectopic, e.g., in a hernial sac.

A triangular fold of peritoneum, known as the *meso-appendix*, attaches the appendix to the terminal part of the left (lower) layer

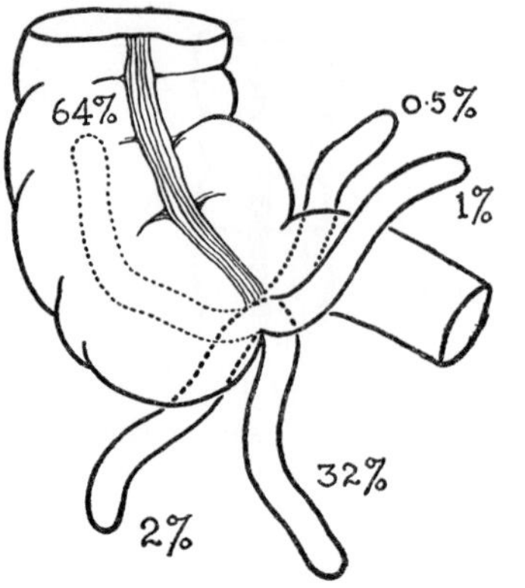

FIG. 241. The various sites assumed by the vermiform appendix and their approximate frequencies. (After Wakeley.)

of the mesentery of the ileum; but retrocecal and retrocolic appendices commonly lose their mesenteries and adhere to the posterior abdominal wall or to the cecum.

The appendix has a uniform external coat of longitudinal muscle fibers. At its root these fibers separate into the three teniae coli which remain discrete till they reach the rectum when they form for it a nearly uniform coat again.

Colon. The *ascending colon*, like the cecum and appendix, lies ventral to the fascia iliaca in the iliac fossa (*fig. 242*); it crosses the iliac crest and ascends in front of the Quadratus Lumborum and Transversus Abdominis to the under surface of the liver where, in front of the lower pole of the right kidney, it makes a right angle bend, the *right colic flexure*, and becomes the *transverse colon*.

Resting on the transverse colon are (*fig. 235*): the right lobe of liver, the body of the gall bladder, the quadrate lobe of the liver, and the greater curvature of the stomach. The lower border of the transverse colon is attached to the greater curvature of the stomach by the gastrocolic lig. (part of the greater omentum) (*figs. 248* and *282*). The upper border is slung from the anterior aspect of the body of the pancreas by a semilunar, double layer of peritoneum, called the *transverse mesocolon*.

The right extremity of the transverse colon crosses and adheres to the anterior aspects of: the right kidney, the second part

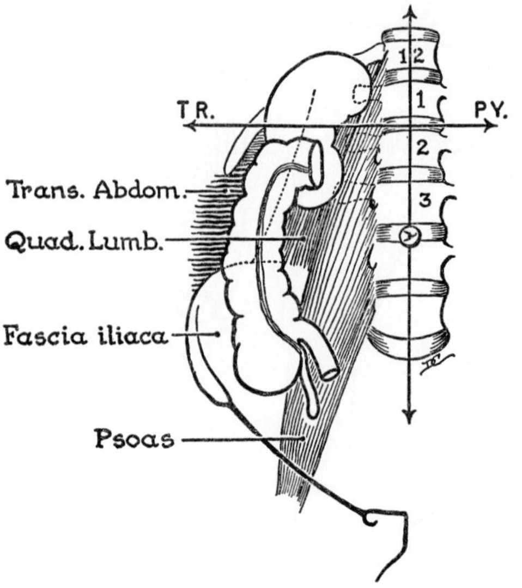

FIG. 242. The ascending colon

of the duodenum, and head of the pancreas (*fig. 243*). Thus, the right extremity is fixed; the remainder is free and hangs down for a varying distance but ascends again in front of the descending colon, and makes with it an acute angle at the left colic flexure.

The *left colic flexure* is attached to the diaphragm below the spleen, and therefore at the level of the 11th rib (*fig. 254*), by a bloodless fold of peritoneum, the *phrenico-colic ligament*.

The *descending colon*, often much reduced in caliber, descends, crosses the iliac crest, and proceeds across the iliac fossa to the pelvic brim where it becomes the sigmoid (pelvic) colon (*fig. 235*).

The *sigmoid colon* has a mesentery, the *sigmoid mesocolon*, whose root runs a Λ-shaped course: (1) upward along the pelvic

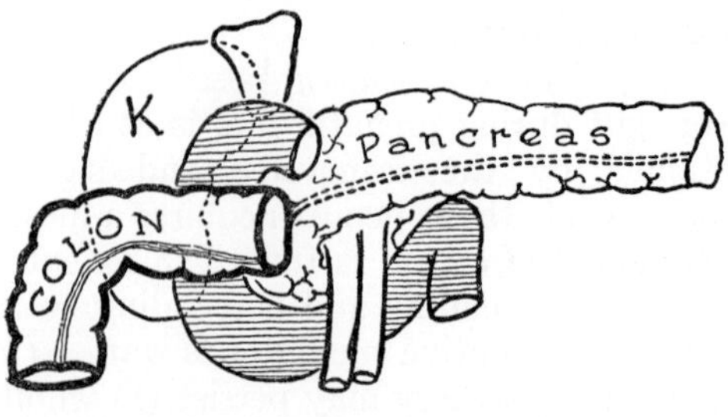

FIG. 243. The attachment of the transverse mesocolon (shown by *dotted lines*).

brim (actually, along the medial border of the Psoas) and then (2) downward in front of the sacrum as far as its middle or third piece. Its appendices epiploicae are very long fatty tags. The sigmoid colon may be of the short or long type—8 to 18″.

»» The long type crosses to the right of the pelvis and returns before taking the restricted course of the short type. The long type may be regarded as the short type to which a loop has been added. The long loop type is apt to rotate and become twisted on itself, thereby causing intestinal obstruction.

Where the sigmoid mesocolon ceases, there the *rectum* is said to begin; usually this is at the 3rd piece of the sacrum. The rectum lies in the pelvis and it will be studied with the pelvic organs.

UPPER ABDOMINAL VISCERA AND THEIR CONNECTIONS

Liver (hepar, L.). The liver is a soft, pliable organ weighing about 3 pounds. Molded by its surrounding structures, it owes to them its ever changing form. The hardened liver is shaped like an oblong block bisected diagonally and with its inferior surface whittled away posteriorly (*fig. 244*). This being so, the inferior surface must face downward, to the left, and backward. It is covered with peritoneum. Being in contact with viscera, it is irregular and is called the *visceral surface*.

The remainder of the liver is in contact with the anterior abdominal wall and the diaphragm, which make it smooth and round. It is called the *diaphragmatic surface*. Its anterior, superior, and right aspects are covered with peritoneum. The posterior aspect also is in contact with diaphragm, but it cannot be seen just now (see p. 250).

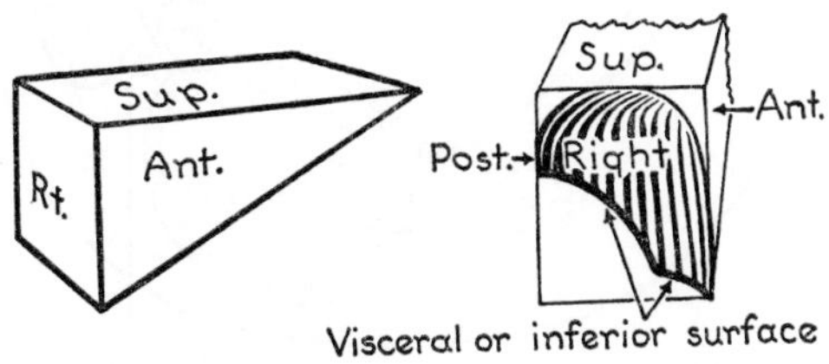

FIG. 244. The general shape of the liver

The liver, then, is described as having two surfaces: visceral and diaphragmatic; these are separated from each other (except behind) by the sharp, *inferior border*.

Far back on the visceral surface there is a deep transverse fissure, 2″ long, the **porta hepatis.** It is the door through which vessels, nerves, and ducts enter and leave the liver. To its lips the right half of the lesser omentum is attached.

(Cont'd on pp. 227–229 and 249–252.)

Gall Bladder. This pear-shaped vesicle, about 3 inches long and holding about 1½ ounces, is divided indefinitely into—*fundus*, *body*, and *neck*. The fundus of the gall bladder projects beyond the sharp, inferior border of the liver and comes into contact with the anterior abdominal wall where the lateral border of the Rectus crosses the costal margin (*fig. 213*). The body and neck are adherent to the sloping inferior surface, so, as they run backward to the right end of the porta hepatis, they also run upward (*fig. 245*).

Relations. You have seen that the transverse colon crosses the second part of the duodenum (*fig. 243*). Note that the gall bladder rests on the duodenum and on the colon (*fig. 245*); and that a gall stone could penetrate its way through the walls of the gall bladder (1) upward into the liver substance, or after traversing the peritoneal cavity, (2) downward into the duodenum, or (3) into the colon, or (4) forward through the anterior abdominal wall. These four structures are the immediate relations of the gall bladder (*fig. 245*).

»» *Comparative Anatomy.* A gall bladder is present in most species of fish and in orders of vertebrates higher than fish. It is curious that it should be present in most

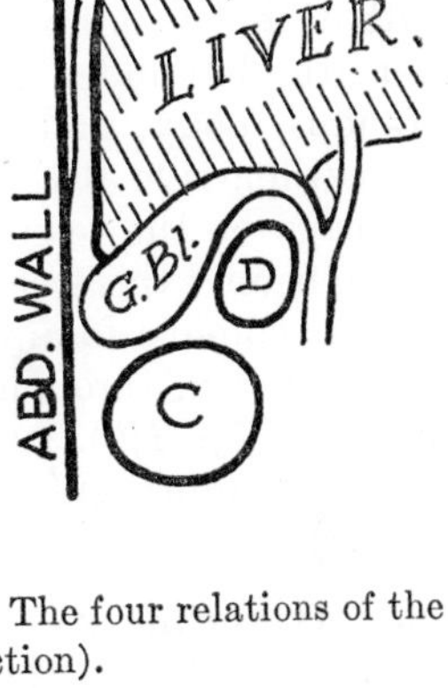

FIG. 245. The four relations of the gall bladder (sagittal section).

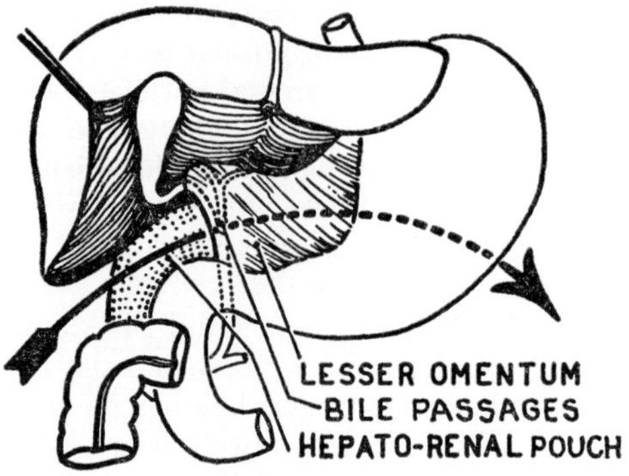

FIG. 246. Showing why the gall bladder serves as a guide to the epiploic foramen.

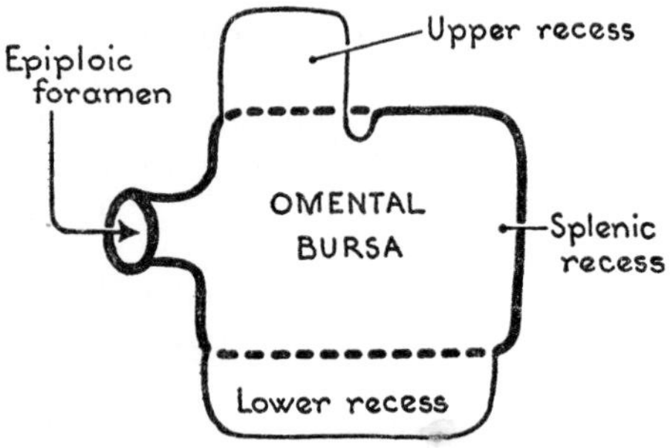

FIG. 246.1. Scheme of omental bursa

species of birds but absent in the pigeon; present in the ox, sheep, goat, and pig, but absent in the horse and deer; present in the guinea pig and rabbit but absent in the white rat; and generally absent in the cetaceae.

Epiploic Foramen (Mouth of the Lesser Sac). The gall bladder serves as a guide to the mouth of a diverticulum of the general peritoneal cavity, called the *omental bursa* (lesser sac of peritoneum). This is because the *cystic duct*, which drains the gall bladder, lies in the free edge of the lesser omentum; and the mouth of the sac lies behind this free edge. If, then, the left index finger follows along the fundus, body, and neck of the gall bladder, it will arrive at the cystic duct and the free edge of the lesser omentum; and, on slipping behind this free edge, it will pass through the epiploic foramen and into the omental bursa (i.e., through the mouth and into the sac) (*fig. 246*). In shape, this sac is not unlike an empty, rubber hot water bottle (*fig. 246.1*).

Peritoneal Attachments of Spleen (Lien, L. = Spleen). To find the spleen you should stand on the right side of the body, as so doing will allow you to thrust your right hand above the phrenicocolic ligament into the left hypochondrium and with the backs of your fingers to follow in comfort the diaphragm round to the back. The spleen will then lie within your palm. You have, so to speak, scooped it into your hand. It is situated farther back than you perhaps thought. Adhesions that can be broken down with the fingers sometimes cause the spleen to adhere loosely to the diaphragm.

After consulting figure 247, verify that in the foregoing maneuver your fingertips passed from the diaphragm across the anterior surface of the *left kidney* until arrested by a double layer of peritoneum, the *lienorenal ligament*, which, as its name implies, passes from spleen to kidney. It is also known as the phrenicolienal ligament. A second double layer, continuous with the gastrocolic lig., passes from the greater curvature of the stomach to the spleen; this is the *gastrolienal* (*gastrosplenic*) *lig.* These two ligaments suspend the spleen between the kidney and the stomach, and form a stalk or pedicle for it. Vessels run between their layers.

Pedicle of the Spleen; Omental Bursa (The Lesser Sac of Peritoneum). While still standing on the right side of the body, run your right middle finger upward between the kidney and the spleen, and your right index finger upward between the stomach and the spleen. The "pedicle or stalk" of the spleen now lies in the cleft between these

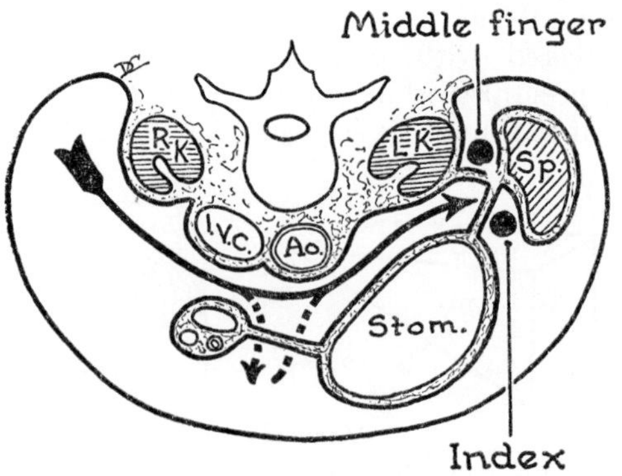

FIG. 247. Palpating the hilus of the spleen while its pedicle is clamped between two fingers of the right hand.

two fingers as though in a clamp. The pedicle has a free lower border (and a free upper border) or you could not grasp it as you are doing. Its linear site of attachment to the spleen is around the hilus.

Clamped between your index and middle fingers are four layers of peritoneum (*fig. 247*). Satisfy yourself of this by passing your left index finger through the epiploic foramen and across the abdomen, behind the stomach, till it touches the spleen between your two right fingers which are clamping the "pedicle." If your left index will not reach all the way, pass it as far as it will go, tear through the lesser omentum over its tip, withdraw the finger, and re-insert it at the half-way opening just made. The hilus of the spleen, which you are palpating, is situated at the left limit of the omental bursa (lesser sac).

To Explore the Lower Recess of this bursal sac (*fig. 248*), pass your left index through its foramen and downward behind the stomach and anterior two layers of greater omentum and in front of the pancreas, transverse mesocolon, transverse colon, and posterior two layers of the greater omentum. If the lower limits of the sac are shut off from the main portion, they can be investigated after snipping through the anterior two layers of the greater omentum below the stomach.

To Explore the Upper Recess of the bursa, pass the right index through its foramen and upward in the median plane between the liver and the diaphragm (*fig. 251*).

Peritoneal Attachments of the Liver

The free edge of the **falciform ligament** of the liver extends from the umbilicus to the sharp inferior border of the liver. Developmentally, it is "the mesentery of the vein" that before birth returned purified blood from the placenta of the mother to the liver of the fetus. After birth, this vein, the *umbilical vein*, becomes a fibrous cord, the *round ligament of the liver or lig. teres* (*figs. 249* and *269*). Accordingly, the falciform ligament has the round ligament in its free border; its convex border is attached to the anterior abdominal wall and diaphragm in the median plane; and its concave border is attached to the convex surface of the liver—not in the median plane but—as far to the right of the median plane as the ligament is wide. Hence, the ligament prevents displacement of the liver to the right.

Pass a hand backward on each side of the falciform ligament to where the peritoneum is reflected from the superior aspect of the liver on to the diaphragm, and follow the

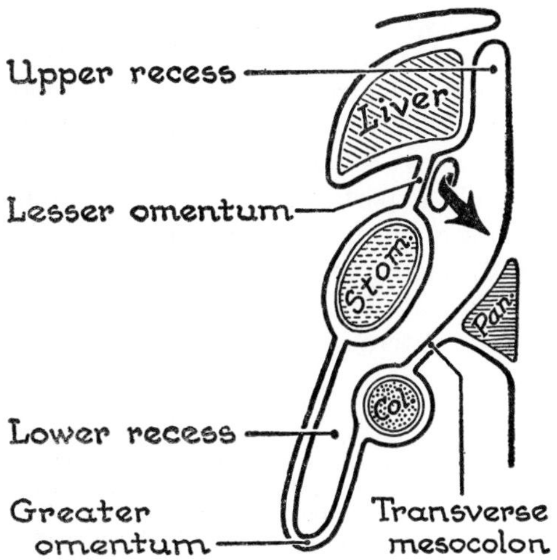

FIG. 248. Showing the vertical extent of the omental bursa (lesser sac). The *arrow* passes through the epiploic foramen (mouth of the lesser sac).

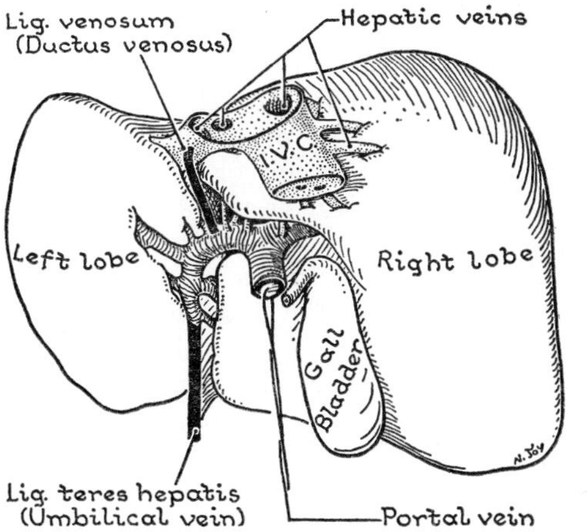

FIG. 249. The portal vein, the hepatic veins, and two obliterated veins, called ligaments. (Postero-inferior view.)

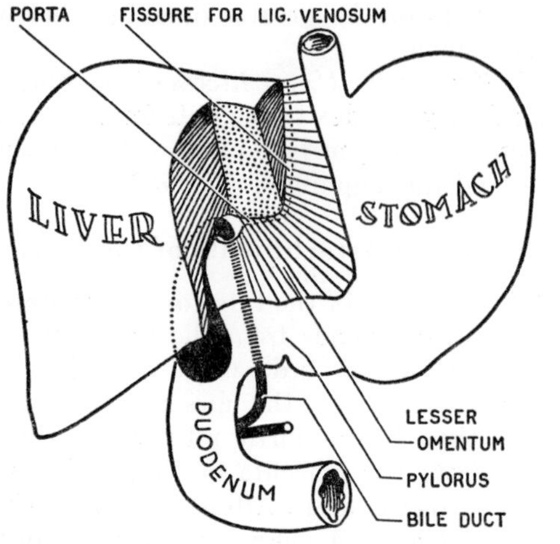

FIG. 250. The attachments of the lesser omentum. (A section has been taken from the liver to show the fissure for the lig. venosum.)

reflection to right and left to the respective triangular ligaments, to be described in a moment (*fig. 251*).

The *umbilical vein* of prenatal life—which becomes the **round ligament of the liver** [lig. teres hepatis] of postnatal life—extends in the free edge of the falciform ligament from the umbilicus to a notch on the sharp inferior border of the liver; thence it runs sagittally at the bottom of a fissure, the *fissure for the round lig.*, on the inferior surface of the liver to the left end of the porta.

Before birth the left umbilical vein opened for a short time into the left portal vein and, so, poured its blood into the liver. But the necessity for sending through the liver blood that had already been purified in the placenta was overcome by the development of another vein, the *ductus venosus*, which serves as a short circuit or bypass. It connects the left portal vein to the inferior vena cava, just below the diaphragm (*fig. 249*).

The ductus venosus is obliterated after birth and becomes the **ligamentum venosum.** It continues the sagittal course of the umbilical vein, at the bottom of a fissure, the *fissure for the lig. venosum*, on the posterior aspect of the liver. The fibrous remains of these two obliterated veins can be dissected when the liver is removed.

For descriptive purposes, these three ligaments—falciform, round, and venosum—divide the liver into a right and a left lobe.

The **lesser omentum** extends from the lesser curvature of the stomach and first inch of the duodenum to the fissure for the lig. venosum and to the porta hepatis (*fig. 250*).

The **triangular ligaments** are the sharp, bloodless, peritoneal folds at the extreme right and left limits of the attachment of the liver to the diaphragm (*fig. 251*). They lie at the (diagonally) opposite ends of the posterior aspect of the liver. The *left triangular ligament* is an extensive fold. (Actually, it is attached far back on the upper surface of the left lobe.)

The *right triangular ligament* is less well marked. It is attached to the right inferior end of the posterior aspect of the right lobe. Its two layers at once diverge and, as the upper and lower layers of the **coronary ligament,** limit the bare area on the back of the liver above and below. The upper layer of the coronary ligament is reflected from the right lobe of the liver on to the diaphragm. It is continuous with the right layer of the falciform ligament. The lower layer is reflected from the posterior aspect of the liver on to the right kidney (*fig. 251*), so it is synonymously called the *hepatorenal ligament*, but observe that it is also attached to the diaphragm, right suprarenal, and i.v. cava.

Below, or caudal to, the hepatorenal ligament there is a peritoneal space, the *hepatorenal recess* (*figs. 246* and *307*). This pouch is bounded ventrally by liver and dorsally by the kidney, as its name implies, and caudally by colon and duodenum. It is surgically important: (1) the omental bursa (lesser sac) opens into it; (2) the gall bladder and (3) duodenum may rupture into it; and (4) fluid traveling from a ruptured appendix upward, lateral to the ascending colon, could enter it.

»» *A Second Way to Find the Epiploic Foramen.* If you run your left index finger along the hepatorenal ligament (lower layer of the coronary lig.) to the left—the finger keeping contact with the liver— it will slip along the caudate process, above the 1st part of the duodenum, and behind the free edge of the lesser omentum, through the epiploic foramen into the omental bursa. Even though you make allowance for the forward curvature of the vertebral column, your finger may catch on the inferior vena cava, which forms the posterior relation of the foramen (*fig. 247*). Previ-

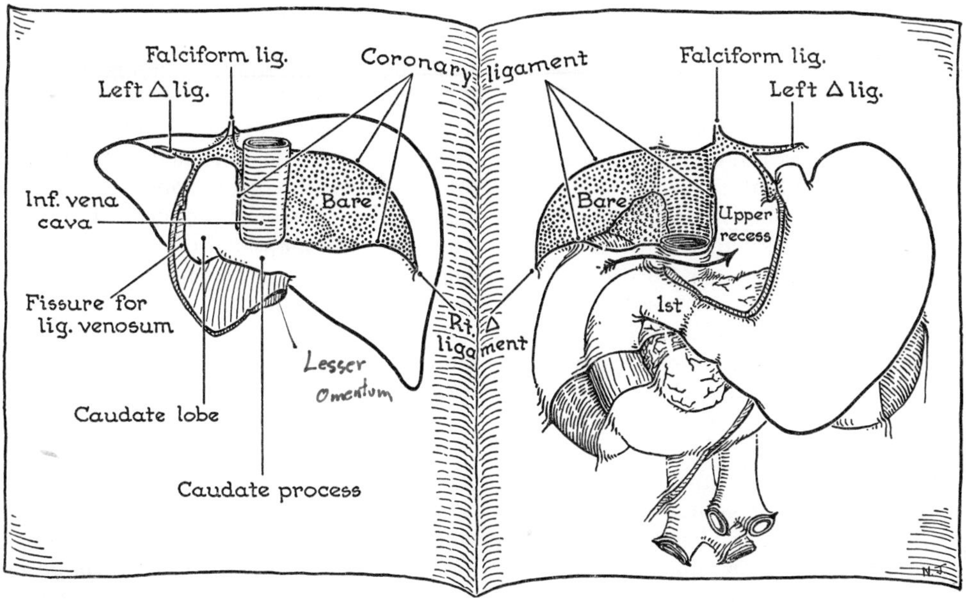

FIG. 251. The coronary and triangular ligaments of the liver. (The attachments of the liver are cut through, and the liver is turned to the left, as you would turn the page of a book. Hence, the posterior aspect of the liver is revealed on the left page and its posterior relations on the right page. The *arrow* passes through the epiploic foramen.)

ously (page 226) the gall bladder was your guide to the epiploic foramen.

Pass now the right index finger through the epiploic foramen and upwards in the median plane between diaphragm and liver. The finger is in the **upper recess of the omental bursa**—actually, in the posterior part of the recess. A glance at a cross-section (*fig. 252*) shows that the caudate lobe, growing from the right lobe, has invaginated the recess in the same manner as the testis has invaginated the cavity of the tunica vaginalis (*fig. 226*), and the lung the pleural cavity (*fig. 561*). The recess, which is wide enough to admit two fingers, is limited *above* near the falciform ligament (*fig. 251*); *on the right* by inf. vena cava; *on the left* by esophagus; *posteriorly* by diaphragm; and *anteriorly* by lesser omentum.

The inf. vena cava occupies the left or basal part of the bare area of the liver, and the peritoneum, there applied to the i.v. cava (*fig. 251*), is the left side or base of the coronary ligament, the right triangular lig. being the apex. The corona limiting the bare area (i.e., the area devoid of peritoneum) is, therefore, not circular but is triangular.

The **caudate lobe** is the lobe with a tail, the tail or **caudate process** being the narrow isthmus of liver that bounds the epiploic foramen above and connects the caudate lobe to the visceral surface of the right lobe (p. 250).

(The liver is continued on p. 249.)

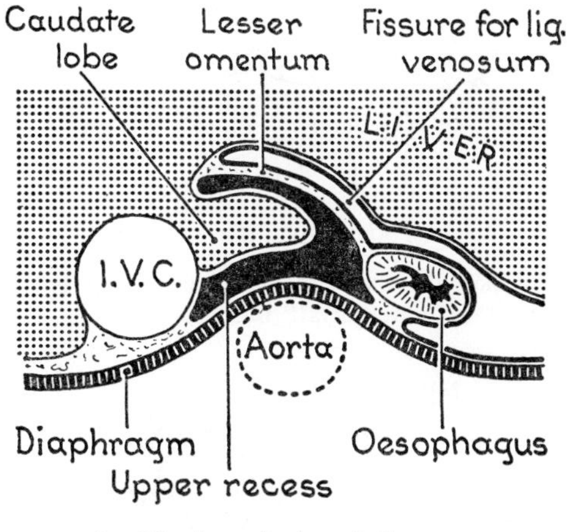

FIG. 252. The boundaries of the upper recess, viewed from below.

Spleen or **Lien** (cont'd. from p. 226). A thin peritoneal-covered, and easily torn capsule encases the soft, vascular spleen, which is molded by the structures in contact with it. The size of a small fist after death, it is much larger in life.

It has a parietal surface in contact with the *diaphragm* and therefore convex; and a visceral surface shared unequally by *stomach*, *kidney*, and *colon*, and therefore subdivided into three concave areas, varying in shape and extent with the degree of distension of these organs, and separated from each other by three rounded radiating borders (*figs. 253* and *253.1*).

The *hilus* is situated on the gastric surface; vessels and nerves penetrate the hilus; the tail of the *pancreas* abuts against it and is thereby rendered blunt.

The most pronounced feature of the spleen is the notches on its superior border. This *notched superior border* is part of the general or "peripheral" border that separates the parietal from the visceral surface.

Structure. The spleen has a capsule of white fibers, elastic fibers and smooth muscle fibers which allow it to expand and contract. Supporting *trabeculae* of the same materials spread inward from the capsule. The spaces between the trabeculae contain a supporting *sponge work* of reticular fibers and reticulo-endothelial cells and are filled with blood. About one-sixth of the total volume of blood in the body can be stored in the spleen, which accordingly varies greatly in size.

Function. The spleen is the largest of the lymphocyte-producing organs. It is the main storehouse of blood. It is the chief depot of reticulo-endothelial cells, which break down the hemoglobin of effete red cells and in so doing produce bile pigment, they also rid the blood of other debris, and they are concerned with resistance to disease and with immunity.

The spleen is not essential to life; in fact, in certain conditions its removal may be advisable.

Surface Anatomy. The spleen lies deep to the 9th, 10th, and 11th left ribs. Its long axis follows the 10th rib and extends from, or almost from, the suprarenal gland to the midaxillary line. Separating it from the ribs are the peritoneal cavity, the diaphragm, and the pleural cavity; in its upper half the left lung also intervenes (*fig. 254*).

Development (*figs. 269–271*). The spleen develops in the left layer of the primitive dorsal mesogastrium and draws upon the nearest artery to the stomach for its blood supply. This artery becomes the splenic artery of adult anatomy.

»» ***Variations.*** *Accessory Spleens,* the size of large lymph nodes (and very small ones), having a peritoneal covering, are common on the course of the splenic artery and its left gastro-epiploic br. and elsewhere. In performing splenectomy to relieve certain disorders of the blood, all accessory spleens must be removed if recurrence of the disorder is to be avoided (Curtis and Movitz; Halpert and Eaton).

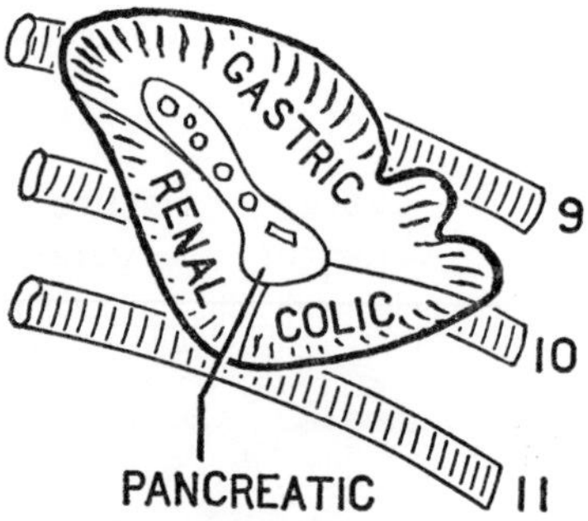

FIG. 253. The visceral surface of the spleen and its "circumferential" border.

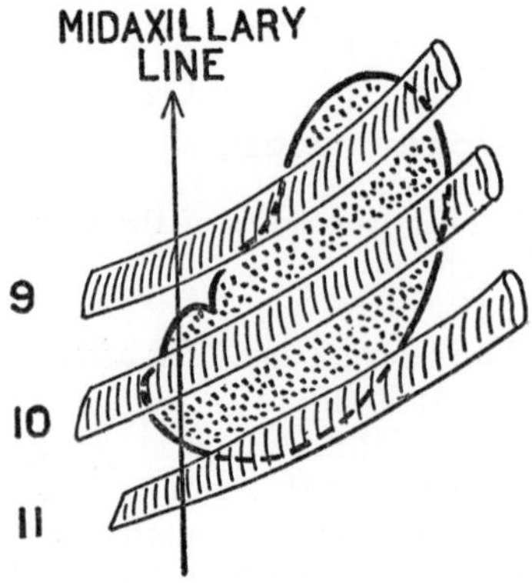

FIG. 253.1. The parietal (diaphragmatic) surface of the spleen.

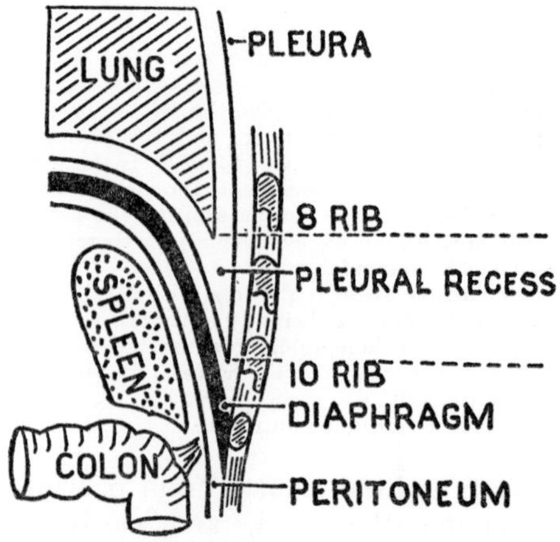

FIG. 254. Coronal section in the midaxillary line, to show the parietal relation of the spleen.

Notches: there are usually two notches on the superior border of the spleen, but there may be more or none. *Fissures* on the inferior border and on the diaphragmatic surface occur very commonly.

EVER CHANGING POSITIONS OF VISCERA

The positions of the various abdominal viscera vary considerably from subject to subject, depending largely upon the body build—upon whether the subject is of the broad type (when, characteristically, they are placed high in the abdomen) or of the intermediate and slender types (when they are placed lower).

Body Types or Bodily Habitus. Mills, as a radiologist working with large numbers of persons, recognized that healthy human beings differ from each other not only in outward appearance, form, and size, but also inwardly. He described two extreme physical types, the *hypersthenic* and the *asthenic* (*figs. 254.1* and *254.2*) which are the antitheses of each other, and two intermediate types, the *sthenic* and the *hyposthenic;* and these have their subdivisions.

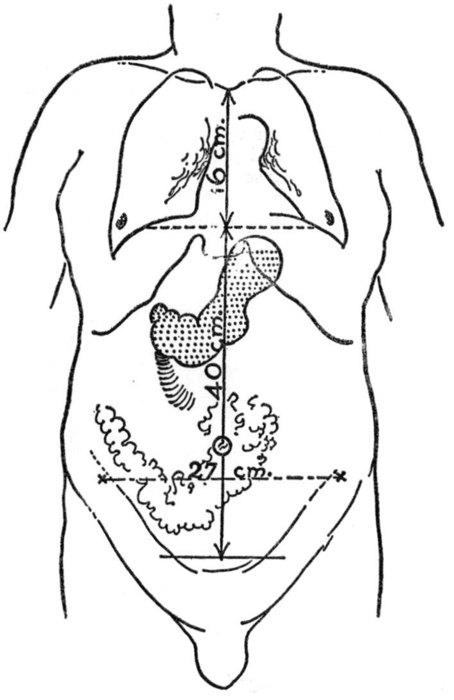

Fig. 254.1. Hypersthenic habitus

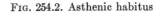

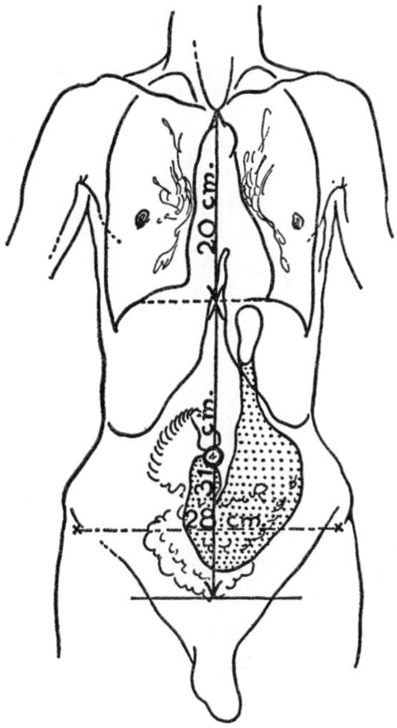

Fig. 254.2. Asthenic habitus

All four types occur in healthy persons—in normal persons, if you wish.

He noted (1) that there are variations in general bodily physique and in the relative capacities of the thorax, upper abdomen, lower abdomen and pelvis; (2) that there are variations in the form, position, tone and mobility of the viscera; and—which is still more important—(3) that there are constant relationships between (1) and (2); that is, between physical types and visceral types. For example, a powerful, heavily built individual with short thorax and long abdomen has a wide lower thorax and upper abdomen and a small pelvis occupied with much fat. In such an individual (hypersthenic) the gastro-intestinal tract is placed high (*fig. 254.3*), the stomach being nearly horizontal, a condition that never obtains in those of slender physique (asthenic).

Now, in life the viscera are not stationary, as after death, but are ever changing both their shapes and their positions. They move with the movements of the diaphragm and of the anterior abdominal wall. They move when the posture alters, being highest when

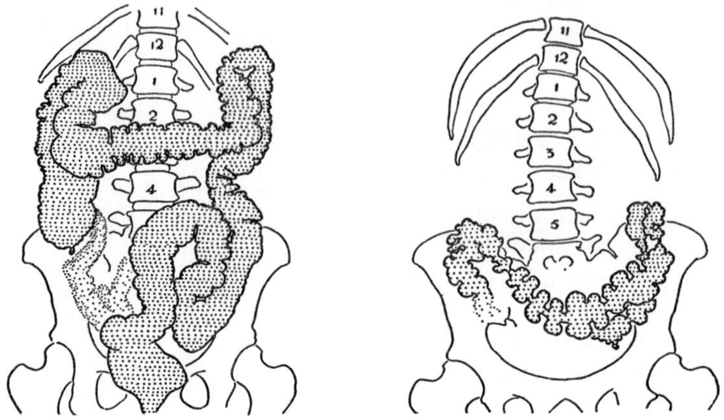

FIG. 254.3. *Left,* hypersthenic type. *Right,* asthenic type

the subject is recumbent, lower when he stands, and still lower when he sits—the Transversus Abdominis being then less active (*fig. 255*). They rise when the anterior abdominal wall is voluntarily retracted. The sizes of the hollow organs (e.g., stomach, intestines, bladder, and uterus) vary as they fill and empty, and they vary with the tone of their muscle coats (e.g., fear and other emotions result in relaxation of the stomach so that the greater curvature suddenly falls). The shapes of the so-called solid organs, particularly the liver and spleen which are virtually soft sponges filled with blood, depend largely upon the degree of distension of the contiguous hollow organs.

»» The following data are submitted for your appreciation—*not for you to memorize.* They are based largely upon extensive radiological work done by Moody and van Nuys on healthy adult male and female students.

The Stomach. The *Cardiac Orifice* of the stomach, being relatively fixed by the diaphragm, is nearly stationary. The lowest point on the *Greater Curvature* of the empty stomach, in healthy male students when erect, varies in level from vertebra L. 1 to S. 1, and when supine from Th. 12 to L. 5 (*fig. 256*). In any subject it is lowest in the erect posture, and on an average it rises the height of a vertebra on assuming the prone posture (face down), and of another vertebra on assuming the supine (face up). The position of the stomach when lying down is no indication of its position when standing up; it moves from 1 to 16 cm.

Similarly, the position of the *Pylorus* ranges from the level of L. 2 to L. 5 in the erect posture, and from Th. 12 to L. 4 in the supine (*fig. 256*), and horizontally, it ranges between 7 cm. to the right of the median plane and 5 cm. to the left. In any subject, on changing from the erect posture to the supine, it moves from 2 to 10 cm. (usually 6 to 8 cm.). On changing from the erect posture to the prone, and again from the prone to the supine, it moves upward and to the right (e.g., in the erect posture 34 per cent of pylori are to the left of the median plane, but in the supine only 8 per cent). The greater curvature and the pylorus are usually lower in the female than in the male.

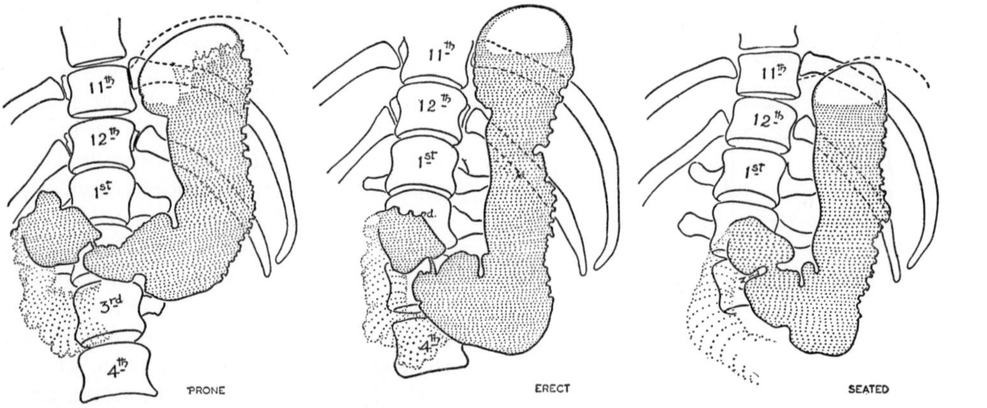

FIG. 255. Tracings of radiograms of the stomach of a healthy female, aged 30 years (Radiograms by Dr. Keith Bonner).

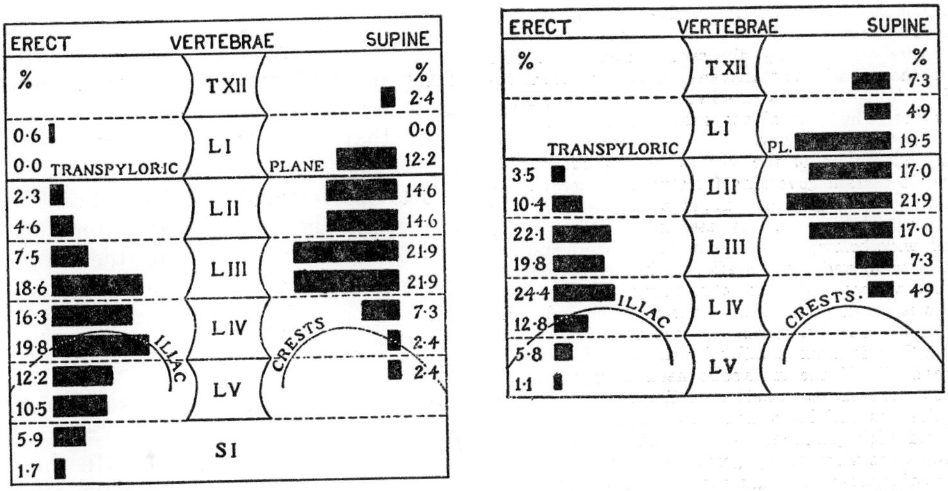

FIG. 256. *Left,* frequency distribution (in percentages) of the relation of the lowest part of the greater curvature of the empty stomach to the vertebral column in healthy adult males (172 erect, 41 supine). *Right,* frequency distribution (in percentages) of the relation of the pylorus to the vertebral column in healthy adult males (86 erect, 41 supine). (Based on the work of Moody, van Nuys, and Kidder.)

The neck of the pancreas is held firmly between the celiac and sup. mesenteric aa.

The Duodenum and the *Head of the Pancreas* are suspended from the liver by the bile passages, hepatic a., and portal vein. They can, however, slide downward on the areolar bed behind them, provided the liver adjusts its shape (*fig. 302*).

The Cecum in fetal life lies below the right lobe of the liver; thence it descends to the right iliac fossa. This descent may be incomplete; on the other hand, in 91 per cent of students the lowest part of the cecum is below the iliac fossa.

The Transverse Colon, in the erect posture, is most commonly U- or V-shaped, its lowest point most often being 3 to 4″ below the interiliac line (i.e., a line joining the highest points on the iliac crests).

The Liver and Spleen also vary in position. The greatest height of the right lobe of the *liver* in the erect posture varies from 15.5 to 25.5 cm. (average 20 cm.). In 50.2 per cent of males and 34 per cent of females the lower end of the right lobe lies below the interiliac line, as much as 5.0 cm. The average excursion made by this lower end, on changing from the erect posture to the supine, varies from 0 to 10.9 cm. (average 2.5 cm.). In the cadaver the lower limit of the *spleen* usually reaches the level of vertebra L. 1; but in the living of both sexes when erect it varies from L. 1 to L. 5 (average L. 3). The spleen is smaller after death, after exercise, and after hemorrhage or after giving blood for transfusion.

The Kidneys. The commonest position of both kidneys in both sexes is opposite the upper four lumbar vertebrae, when the subject is erect; and opposite the 12th thoracic and upper three lumbar vertebrae, when the subject is supine.

With the subject supine, the caudal pole of the right kidney is below L. 3 in 38 per cent of the men and in 48 per cent of the women; whereas this pole of the left kidney is below L. 3 in 17 per cent of the men and only 9 per cent of the women.

The excursion of the kidneys due to forced respiration varied from 0.1 to 6.5 cm.

In addition to an upward and downward movement of the kidneys, there is a movement of the poles (one or other, or both) to or from the median plane of the body, ranging from 1 to 25 mm.

FEATURES OF THE HYPERSTHENIC HABITUS:

1. A powerful and massive *physique,* great body *weight,* and heavy *bony framework.*

2. The *thorax* is short, deep, and wide; the *abdomen* is long and of great capacity in its upper zone. The *subcostal angle* is very obtuse, and the xiphoid process is broad.

3. The *lungs* are wide at their bases, and contracted at their apices which project but little above the clavicles.

4. The long axis of the *heart* is nearly transverse.

5. The *gastrointestinal tract* is high. The stomach is of the bull horn type, the pylorus being the lowest, or nearly the lowest, part of the stomach. The entire colon is short; the cecum is well above the iliac basin even when the subject is standing; the transverse colon is short, actually transverse, and high; consequently the descending colon is long, it is also straight. The relative proportions of the colon are characteristic, so are its fine, numerous haustrations. The gastric motility is fast; there is marked tone and rapid motility of the colon. Defecation takes place 2 to 3 times a day.

FEATURES OF THE ASTHENIC HABITUS:

1. Frail and slender *physique,* light body *weight,* and delicate *bony structure.*

2. The *thorax* is long and narrow; the *abdomen* is short. There is disproportion between the *pelvic capacity* and that of the upper abdomen, the false pelvis being often as wide and capacious as that of a hypersthenic subject of twice the weight. The *subcostal angle* is narrow.

3. The *lungs* are widest above, and their apices reach well above the clavicles.

4. The long axis of the *heart* is approximately in the median plane.

5. The *gastrointestinal* tract is low. The stomach is atonic and largely pelvic when the subject is standing. The entire colon is long; the cecum is capacious and low in the pelvis; the transverse colon dips down toward, or into, the pelvis; the haustrations of the colon are coarse. The tone of the gastrointestinal tract is poor and its motility slow.

The characters of the viscera can apparently be related to certain governing factors: (1) general body architecture; a high, wide upper abdomen is a long abdomen and is necessarily associated with a short thorax, wide below; hence, the lungs are short and the heart is wide, and room is afforded highly placed abdominal viscera. (2) The alimentary tone in such persons is good; consequently, the stomach is hypertonic and nearly horizontal and the transverse colon is high. This is made possible by the capacious upper abdomen. (3) If the metabolic need is great, much food is consumed; so an active, motile digestive system is required, essential to which are good gastrointestinal tone and high position. (4) The state of nutrition influences the visceral topography by the presence or absence of space-occupying abdominal fat. (5) Strength and good tone in the skeletal muscles aids greatly in the hypersthenic habitus.

UMBILICUS

When the umbilicus or navel is examined from its peritoneal aspect, four fibrous cords are seen radiating from it. They are the obliterated remains of four tubes which in fetal life traversed the umbilical cord (*fig. 257*). The tubes are: the urachus, the right and left umbilical arteries, and the umbilical vein. Each of the four may produce for itself a peritoneal fold or mesentery; but whether occupying peritoneal folds or not, they are all situated in the extraperitoneal fatty-areolar layer (layer 7) of the anterior abdominal wall, and it would be to no purpose that you search for them in other layers (*figs. 219* and *260*).

The Obliterated Allantoic Duct or *Urachus* ascends in the median plane from the apex of the urinary bladder to the umbilicus. [In the embryo chick the allantoic duct leads to a collapsed, vascular, respiratory sac, the *allantois* (*fig. 258*), which lines the egg shell.]

On each side of the urachus an *Obliterated Umbilical Artery* proceeds from the internal iliac artery to the umbilicus. [In the chick embryo these arteries supply the allantois; so, they are called the allantoic arteries.] In the human embryo the allantois is rudimentary; its duties are assumed by the placenta; and the allantoic aa. serve as placental aa. (*fig. 259*). After birth the umbilical cord is cut and the arteries thereafter become the obliterated umbilical arteries. Hence, the adjectives—allantoic, placental, and obliterated umbilical—record stages in the evolutionary history of these arteries. (Wide of these on each side an inf. epigastric artery passes from the ext. iliac artery to the rectus sheath, occasionally in a pronounced fold.)

The Obliterated Umbilical Vein. Before birth the *umbilical vein* returns purified blood from the placenta to the heart via the liver. It runs upward and backward

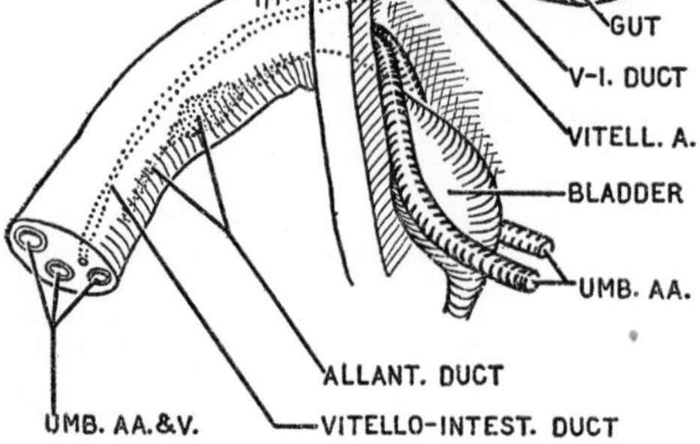

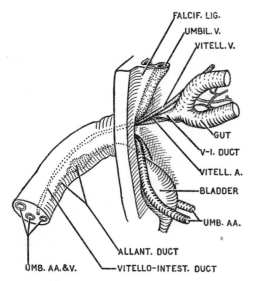

FIG. 257. Structures in the umbilical cord. (After Cullen.)

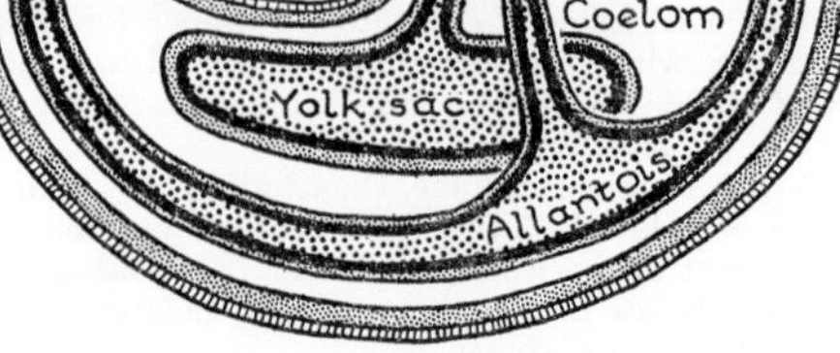

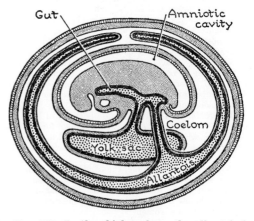

FIG. 258. In the chick embryo the allantois is an enveloping respiratory sac. (After Paterson.)

from the umbilicus, past the sharp inferior border of the liver, to the porta hepatis, and it occupies the lower free border of the falciform ligament, which indeed is its "mesentery." After the cord is cut at birth, the umbilical vein becomes obliterated and is thereafter known as the lig. teres hepatis or *round ligament of the liver* (*fig. 249*).

If at birth the cord is cut very short (1) urine will escape from the umbilicus, if the urachus is patent; (2) feces, if the vitello-intestinal duct is patent; and (3) the peritoneal cavity will be opened, if the extra-embryonic celom is patent.

Meckel's Diverticulum (*fig. 259.1*). The vitello-intestinal duct persists in 2 per cent of persons as a patent appendage of the gut, springing from the ileum within 5½ feet of the cecum (Jay *et al.*).

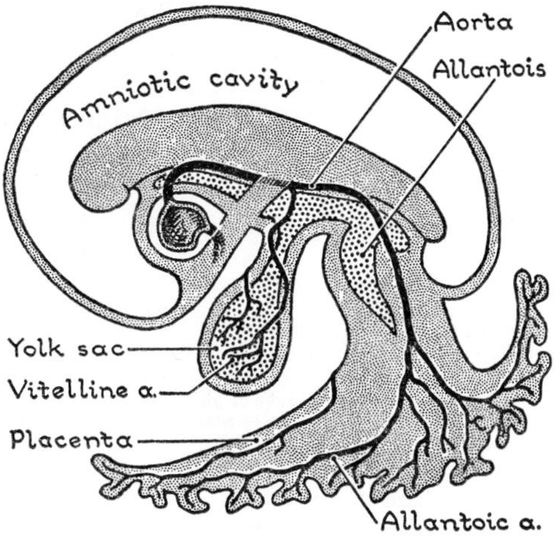

FIG. 259. In the human embryo the allantois is superseded by the placenta. (After Paterson.)

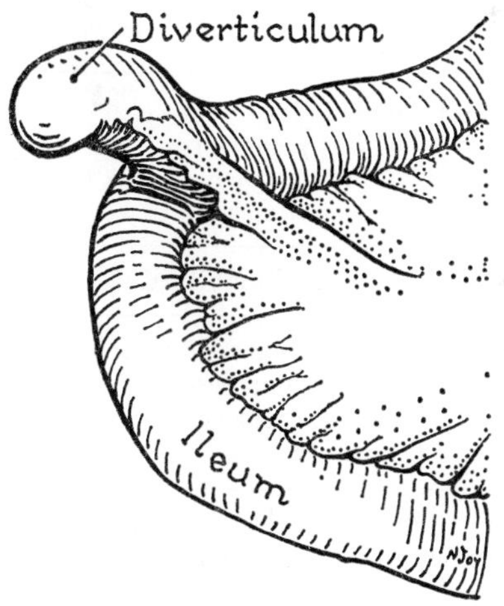

FIG. 259.1. Diverticulum ilei (of Meckel)

PERITONEUM

Peritoneal Folds. Peritoneal folds are so commonly "*the mesenteries*" of tubes that they should be treated on the suspicion that they conceal a tube in their free edges. The tubes may be ducts, veins, or arteries; they may be patent or obliterated.

SIXTEEN FOLDS CONTAINING TUBES are represented in figure 260 and table 11.

FOLDS NOT CONTAINING TUBES are indicated alphabetically in figure 260.

A. Left triangular lig. of the liver.
B. Right triangular lig. of the liver.
C. Phrenicocolic lig.
D. "Supporting lig. of liver."
E. Acquired folds lateral to the ascending and descending colons.
F. Fold guarding inf. duodenal fossa.
G. Inf. ileocecal fold (bloodless fold) (*fig. 261*).
H. Ligament of the ovary.

Peritoneal Fossae, Recesses, and Gutters occur as follows:

1. *Omental Bursa* (p. 226).
2. *Above the greater omentum:* The right and left *Subphrenic Spaces* lie between diaphragm and liver, one on each side of the falciform ligament. The *Hepatorenal Recess* or *Pouch* lies between the right lobe of liver, right kidney, and right colic flexure. When the subject is supine, this is the lowest part of the peritoneal cavity, above the pelvic brim (*fig. 262*). Hence, free fluid (e.g., from a ruptured gallbladder, duodenum, or appendix) will gravitate here—if the subject is supine.
3. *Below the greater omentum* are the following fossae and gutters:

Duodenal Fossae: The superior duodenal, inferior duodenal, paraduodenal, and retroduodenal fossae have a cruciate arrangement. Their mouths face each other and open on the left of the duodenojejunal junction. One or more of these is commonly present.

Cecal Fossae: The superior ileocecal, infe-

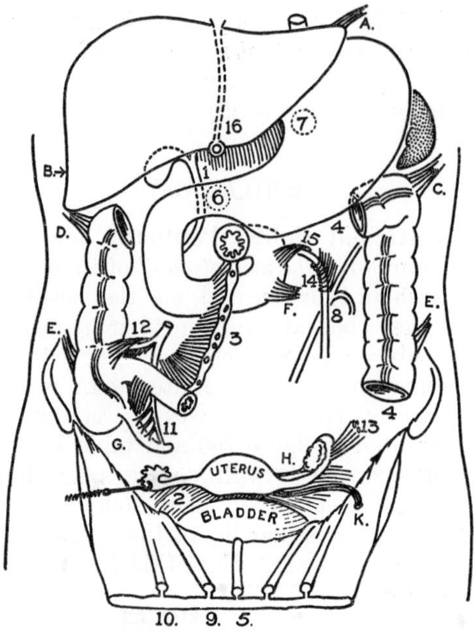

FIG. 260. Peritoneal folds acting as "mesenteries" of tubes (see table 11).

rior ileocecal, and retrocecal fossae are related to the cecum (*fig. 261*). An extensive retrocecal fossa is a retrocolic fossa.

An Intersigmoid Fossa is sometimes present. Its mouth opens at the apex of the $\wedge$-shaped root of the sigmoid mesocolon, where the left ureter crosses the common iliac vessels. A pencil can be pushed up the fossa for one or more inches in front of the ureter.

4. *Pelvic Fossae:* In the male the rectovesical fossa lies between rectum and bladder. In the female the uterus and its broad ligaments divide the rectovesical fossa into vesico-uterine and recto-uterine fossae.

5. *The "Retro-Omental"* or *Paracolic Gutters* (*fig. 262.1*)*:* The root of the mesentery and the ascending and descending colons project from the posterior abdominal wall under partial shelter of the greater omentum. As a result there are four gutters: (1) The right lateral gutter is placed lateral to the ascending colon and cecum. (2) The left

TABLE 11

Peritoneal Folds Acting as "Mesenteries" of Tubes

Nature of tube	Patent or obliterated	Name of fold	Name of tube of which the fold is a mesentery	Number on figure 260
Duct	Patent	The lesser omentum	The bile passages	1
		The broad ligament of uterus	The uterine tube	2
		The mesentery	The small intestine	3
		The mesocolon	The large intestine	4
	Obliterated	The median umbilical ligament	The urachus (Allantoic duct)	5
Artery	Patent	The right gastropancreatic fold	The hepatic a.	6
		The left gastropancreatic fold	The left gastric a.	7
		The fold of the paraduodenal fossa	The asc. branch of left colic a. sometimes	8
	Obliterated	The medial umbilical ligament	Obliterated umbilical a.	9
Artery and Vein	Patent	The lateral umbilical ligament	Inferior epigastric vessels	10
		The mesentery of the appendix	Appendicular vessels	11
		The superior ileocecal fold	Anterior cecal vessels	12
		The suspensory lig. of ovary	Ovarian vessels	13
Vein	Patent	The fold of paraduodenal fossa	Inferior mesenteric vein	14
		The fold of sup. duodenal fossa	Inferior mesenteric vein	15
	Obliterated	Falciform ligament of the liver	Lig. teres hepatis (Obliterated umbilical vein)	16

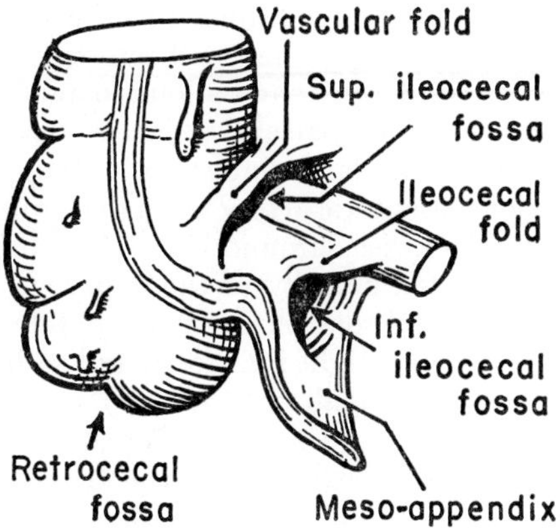

FIG. 261. Peritoneal folds and fossae about the cecum.

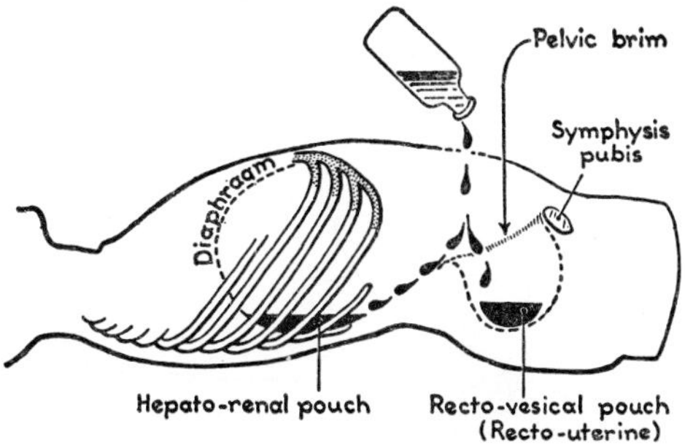

FIG. 262. Two pouches which are the lowest parts of the peritoneal cavity when the subject is supine.

lateral gutter is placed lateral to the descending and sigmoid colon. (3) The right medial gutter lies between the root of the mesentery and the ascending colon. (4) The left medial gutter lies between the root of the mesentery and the descending colon.

Of these, the right medial is closed above and below. The three others lead directly to the pelvis. The right lateral gutter is the only gutter open above. It would conduct fluid from the hepatorenal pouch and right subphrenic space past the appendix and into the pelvis—if the subject is sitting.

Notes on Development Explaining Relationships of Abdominal Structures

1. The abdomen may be said to exist in order to accommodate two tubular systems: (*a*) *The Gastro-intestinal Tract* and its two derivatives, the *liver* and *pancreas*, with

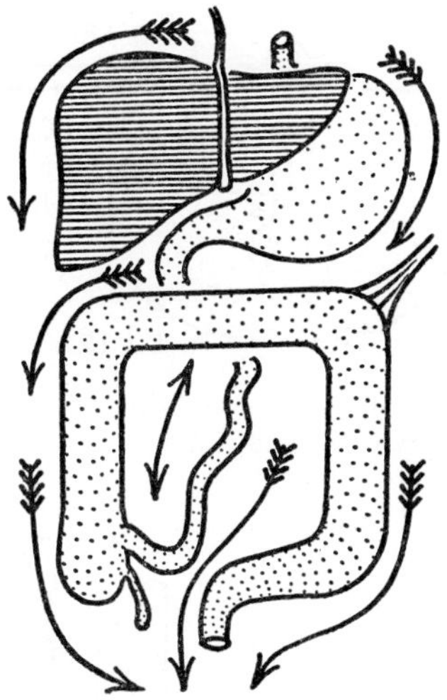

FIG. 262.1. The four retro-omental or "paracolic" gutters and three "supra-omental spaces."

which is associated the *spleen*. These you should regard collectively as "the gastro-intestinal tract and the three unpaired glands" or even, if it gives emphasis to the idea of a united system, as "*The G. I. Tract & Co.*" (*b*) *The Right and Left Urogenital Tracts*, and their two paired glands, the *kidneys* and *sex glands* (testes or ovaries) with which are associated the right and left *suprarenal glands*. These you may refer to collectively as the urogenital tracts and the three paired glands; or as "the three paired gland system" or even as the "*The U. G. Tracts & Co.*"

2. During embryonic life the "three paired glands" lie on each side of the aorta, covered with peritoneum of the posterior abdominal wall. [A comparable condition is found in the adult frog.]

3. At the same early period the gastro-intestinal canal was a straight tube of uniform caliber, slung from the front of the vertebral column and aorta by a mesentery, the *primitive dorsal mesentery* (*fig. 263*).

4. Three unpaired branches of the abdominal aorta, named the celiac trunk and superior mesenteric and inferior mesenteric arteries, supplied the gastro-intestinal tract and its three unpaired glands (*figs. 263* and *264*). The superior mesenteric artery continued as the *vitelline artery* through the umbilicus to supply the yolk sac (*fig. 259*).

4a. The portal vein is formed by three

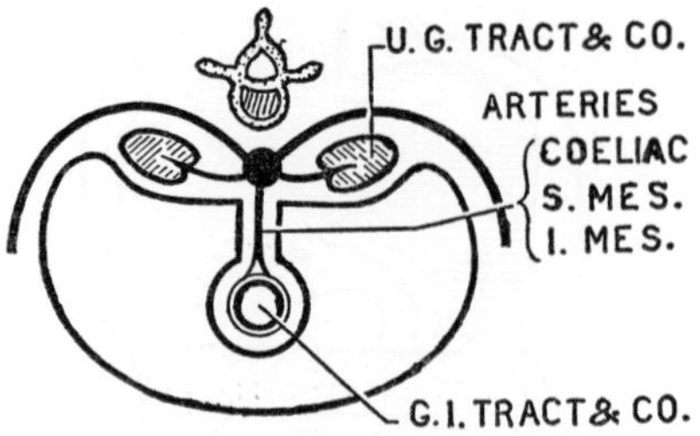

FIG. 263. Transverse section of the abdomen of an embryo (schematic).

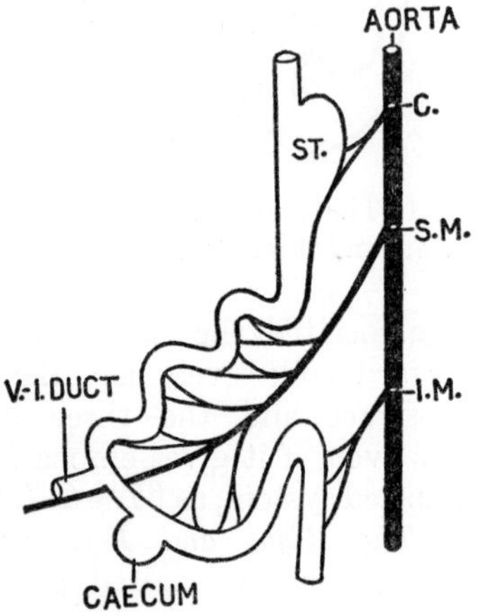

FIG. 264. The three unpaired arteries of the "G. I. Tract & Co." in the primitive dorsal mesentery.

unpaired veins, named the splenic (= the celiac), superior mesenteric, and inferior mesenteric veins; so, it returns to the liver the blood that the celiac, superior mesenteric, and inferior mesenteric arteries conveyed to the G. I. Tract and its unpaired glands, the liver, of course, excepted. The portal vein, therefore, receives all the blood returning from the "G. I. Tract & Co." and it receives no other blood (*fig. 265*).

5. The diaphragm is supplied by cervical segments 3, 4, and 5 by way of the phrenic nerves. It developed in the neck. With the advent of lungs, the diaphragm descended, pushing the stomach and celiac trunk before it and dragging the phrenic nerves after it.

6. The adult intestinal canal may reach 20 feet in length, but the abdominal cavity is less than 2 feet long. A time, therefore, must come in fetal life when the gut ceases to be a straight tube confined to the median plane of the body. The small intestine then becomes convoluted; and a long loop of gut, involving the cecum and adjacent parts of the small and large intestine, taking the superior mesenteric artery as an axis, rotates counterclockwise around it. This brings the cecum temporarily to the under surface of the liver. From there it ultimately descends into the right iliac fossa and so helps to encircle the small gut (*fig. 266*).

7. Thereafter, the mesenteries of the ascending, the beginning of the transverse, and the descending colon, together with any branches of the mesenteric vessels they may contain, adhere to the posterior abdominal wall (*fig. 267*).

The remainder of the transverse colon and the sigmoid colon alone retain mesen-

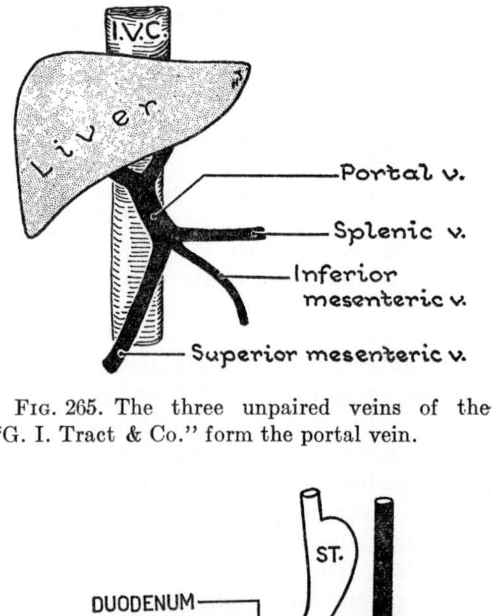

FIG. 265. The three unpaired veins of the "G. I. Tract & Co." form the portal vein.

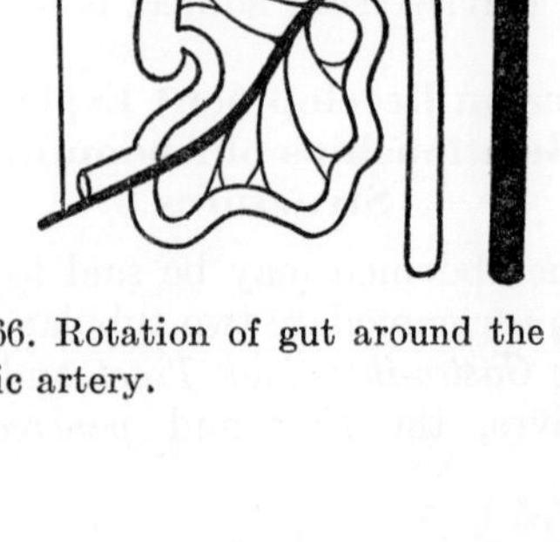

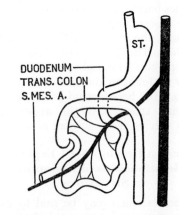

FIG. 266. Rotation of gut around the superior mesenteric artery.

teries. The rectum and the anal canal retain their primitive median positions.

8. Just as page 2 and 3 of an open book, on falling to the left or right, must come to lie in front of page 1 or page 4, so every part of "the G. I. Tract & Co." that falls to the left or right must come to occupy a position ventral to anything and everything pertaining to "the U. G. Tracts & Co." it happens to cross. That is, if it crosses any of the following structures, it will cross ventral to them; suprarenals, kidneys, testes or ovaries; suprarenal, renal, testicular, or ovarian vessels; and ureters, deferent ducts or uterine tubes (*fig. 268*).

9. The counterclockwise rotation of the gut must bring some part of the large intestine in front of the "superior mesenteric arterial axis" and some part of the small intestine behind it. The respective parts happen to be the transverse colon and the 3rd part of the duodenum (*fig. 266*). When the beginning of the transverse colon loses its mesentery, it adheres to the 2nd part of the duodenum and head of the pancreas (*fig. 243*).

It should now be quite evident that in order to free or mobilize a portion of the colon without damage to its vessels, the peritoneum must be torn through on the outer "rim" of the gut, for the vessels pass from aorta to colon as spokes radiate to the rim of a wheel. In mobilizing, you partially restore the gut to its former embryological state, giving it back its primitive mesentery. For example, to expose the posterior aspect of the 2nd part of the duodenum, you may safely pull the right colic flexure and the transverse colon downward, and swing the duodenum forward and medially, without damage to vessels or nerves (*fig. 302*).

10. The transverse colon would seem to have forced the entire duodenum (save its first inch) and the pancreas, which lay in the mesoduodenum, against the posterior abdominal wall, for the duodenum has lost its mesentery.

11. In addition to the primitive dorsal mesentery, which may be subdivided into as many parts as is found convenient (e.g., mesogastrium, mesoduodenum, mesojejunum, and the various mesocolons), there is a *primitive ventral mesentery*. It exists only above the umbilicus and first inch of duodenum, so it is better called the *ventral mesogastrium*. The liver divides it into two portions, the falciform ligament and the lesser omentum. The umbilical vein lies in the free edge of the one, the bile passages in the free edges of the other; so, the two portions may be regarded as "the mesentery of the umbilical vein (lig. teres)" and "the mesentery of the bile passages," respectively (*fig. 269*).

The liver, then, divides the *ventral mesogastrium* into (1) Falciform ligament and (2) Lesser omentum.

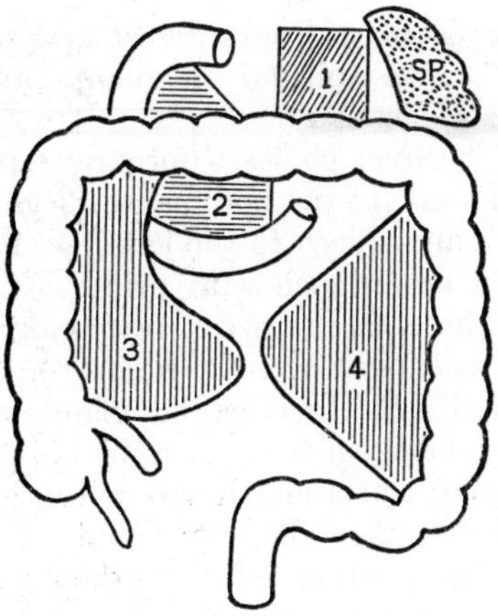

FIG. 267. Sites where primitive mesenteries adhere to the posterior abdominal wall, obliterating the peritoneal cavity: (*1*) dorsal mesogastrium, (*2*) mesoduodenum, (*3*) mesocolon of ascending colon and right colic flexure, (*4*) mesocolon of descending colon.

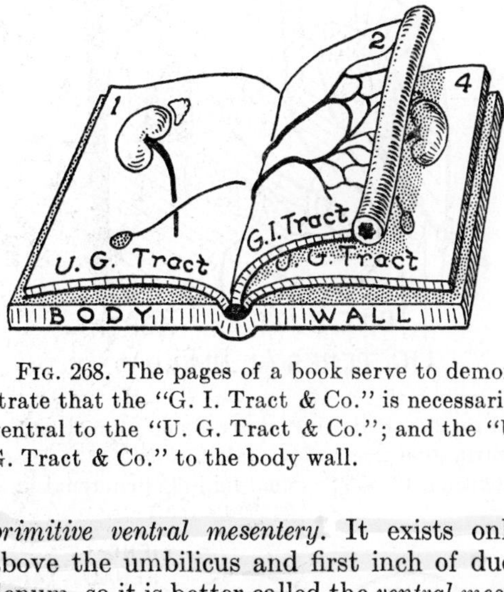

FIG. 268. The pages of a book serve to demonstrate that the "G. I. Tract & Co." is necessarily ventral to the "U. G. Tract & Co."; and the "U. G. Tract & Co." to the body wall.

The spleen divides the *dorsal mesogastrium* into (1) Gastrolienal ligament, and (2) Lienorenal ligament.

12. The liver comes to occupy especially the right side of the body, and relegates the stomach and spleen to the left (*figs. 270* and *271*). In accordance with principles stated above, these three organs, belonging to the G. I. Tract and Co., must lie in front of the right and left three paired gland system; the liver being in front of right kidney and suprarenal; the stomach and spleen in front of the left kidney and suprarenal.

13. The portion of the dorsal mesogastrium passing between spleen and aorta (it might be called lieno-aortic ligament) is forced against the posterior abdominal wall; and the epithelium lining the apposed surfaces is absorbed, leaving two areolar layers of peritoneum free to adhere to each other between the median plane and the front of the left kidney. In view of this new attach-

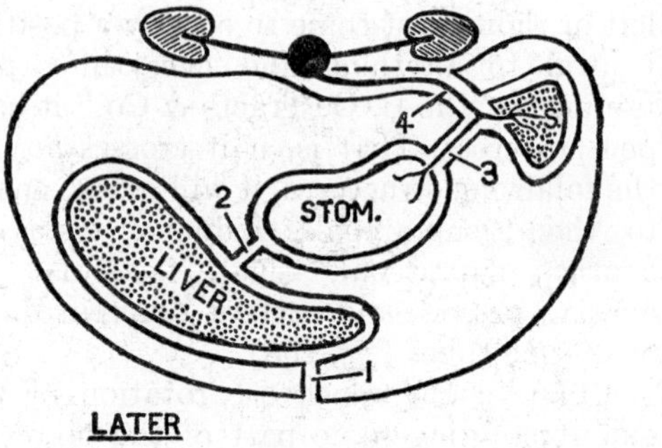

FIG. 271. A later stage than figure 270. Partial absorption of dorsal mesogastrium; the unabsorbed part is the lienorenal lig.

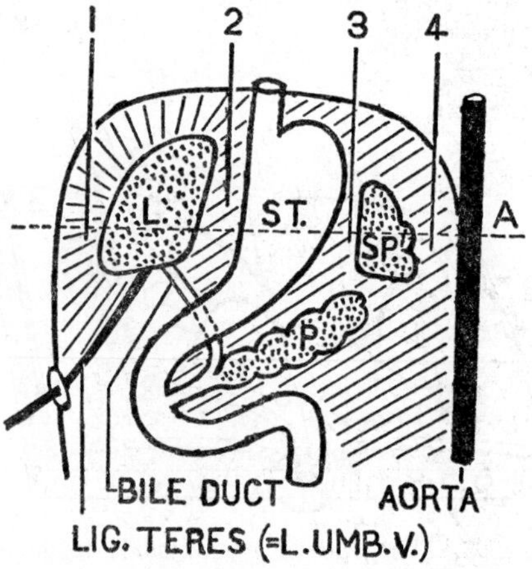

FIG. 269. Primitive ventral and dorsal mesogastria give rise to: (*1*) falciform lig., (*2*) lesser omentum, (*3*) gastrolienal lig., (*4*) lienorenal lig.

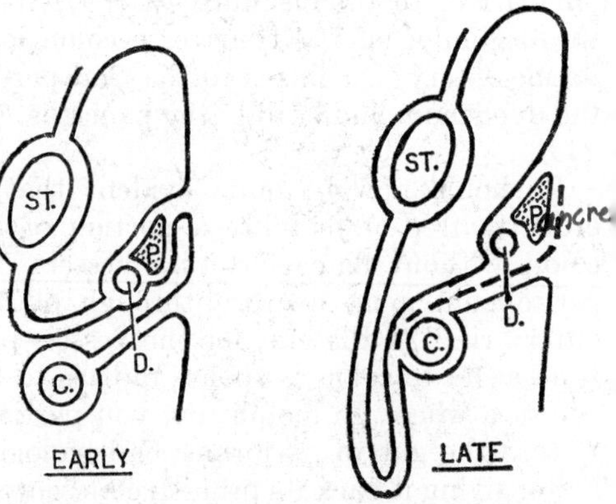

FIG. 272. Development of the greater omentum

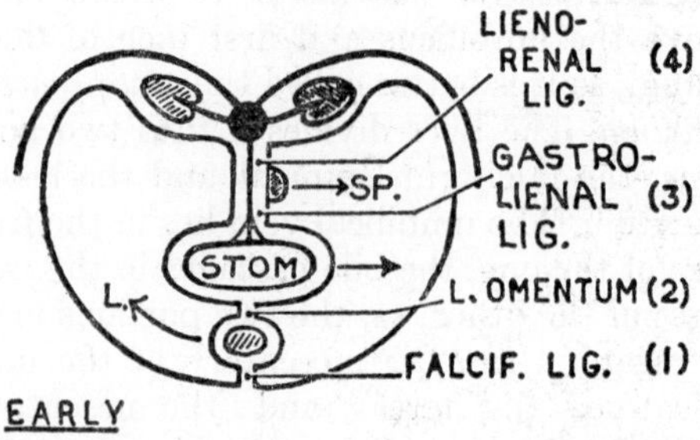

FIG. 270. Transverse section of abdomen of embryo at *level A*, figure 269, indicating that the liver moves to the right; the stomach and spleen to the left.

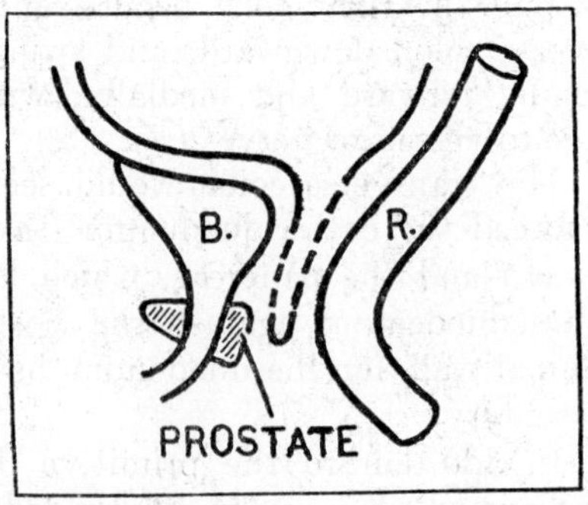

FIG. 273. The posterior aspect of the prostate was formerly subperitoneal. Obliteration of the "rectoprostatic" peritoneal fossa takes place along the broken line.

ment the "lieno-aortic" ligament becomes the *lienorenal ligament.* If you wish to free or mobilize the spleen, you may open up the *dotted line* in figure 271 and restore the entire "lieno-aortic" ligament without damage to the splenic vessels or to any other structures.

14. The omental bursa (lesser sac). When the stomach and spleen moved to the left, dragging their peritoneal attachment after them, the omental bursa took form. The duodenum, by losing its mesentery and adhering to the posterior abdominal wall, limited the epiploic foramen (mouth of the sac) below; the liver, by enlarging, encroached on the mouth, narrowing it from above; and the bile passages, passing from liver to duodenum in the free edge of the lesser omentum, limited the mouth in front.

15. The primitive omental bursa was at first limited below by the dorsal mesogastrium, but in time it bulged downward in front of the transverse mesocolon and transverse colon, and adhered to them, thereby forming the gastrocolic portion of the greater omentum. Developmentally, therefore, the transverse mesocolon is four layers thick (*fig. 272*).

16. The portion of the peritoneal cavity between the base of the bladder and prostate anteriorly and the rectum posteriorly underwent obliteration. And, it is safe to open it up (*fig. 273*).

17. When the stomach moved to the left, it underwent a rotation on its long axis. As a result, its original left surface became the ventral surface; the original right surface, the dorsal surface.

Afferent Nerves of the Peritoneum. These travel as follows: (1) from the *central parts of the diaphragm* via the phrenic nerve (C. 3, 4, 5); direct mechanical stimulation of this area causes pain referred by the supraclavicular nerves (C. 3, 4) to the lower part of the anterior border of the Trapezius; (2) from the *peripheral parts of the diaphragm* via the intercostal and subcostal nerves (Th. 7–12); here stimulation causes pain referred through these same nerves to the skin of the abdominal wall; (3) from the *parietal peritoneum* again via these same nerves (Th. 7–12) and L. 1; here stimulation is correctly localized at the point stimulated; (4) the mesenteries of the small and large intestines are sensitive from their roots to near the intestine, whereas the *greater omentum* and the *visceral peritoneum* are insensitive to mechanical stimulation (Morley).

In the mesentery, free endings of myelinated nerves persist after section and degeneration of vagus and splanchnic fibers. Evidently these endings are responsible for the sensitivity of the mesentery, and presumably they are derived from the somatic nerves supplying the parietal peritoneum (Sheehan).

Obliteration of Peritoneal Cavity

»» Peritoneum is an areolar membrane covered with a single layer of flat (mesothelial) cells. It may be likened to a painted wall; the paint may wear off (cells may die and not be renewed), but the wall (areolar membrane) endures. At sites where two denuded membranes are applied to each other, they cohere, obliterating locally the peritoneal cavity (*fig. 267*). The surfaces are, so to speak, only gummed together (no vessels, nerves or other structures pass between them)—they may be separated with impunity and restored to their embryological state; and of this the surgeon takes advantage.

The chief *sites of obliteration* of the peritoneal cavity are:

1. The portion of the dorsal mesogastrium between the aorta and the middle of the left kidney (*fig. 271*).
2. The mesoduodenum, including the part containing the pancreas (*fig. 272*).
3. The ascending and descending mesocolons (*fig. 267*).
4. The right portion of the transverse mesocolon adheres to the right kidney, 2nd part of the duodenum, and head of the pancreas (*fig. 307*).
5. The greater omentum adheres to transverse colon and mesocolon (*fig. 272*).
6. The walls of the greater omentum commonly cohere, thereby obliterating the lower recess of the omental bursa.
7. The pouch between the prostate and rectum is obliterated (*fig. 273*).
8. The processus vaginalis peritonei is obliterated in part (*fig. 223*).

CHAPTER **15**

STOMACH, LIVER AND RELATED STRUCTURES

LESSER OMENTUM, BILE PASSAGES, CELIAC TRUNK

Lesser Omentum and Bile Passages

The **lesser omentum** extends from the lesser curvature of the stomach and first inch of the duodenum to the fissure for the ligamentum venosum and to the porta hepatis (*fig. 250*), and in its free edge runs the cystic duct.

The **cystic duct** is to be traced from the neck of the gall bladder to a point 1.0 cm.

above the first part of the duodenum where it unites at an acute angle with the common hepatic duct to form the bile duct. Later the bile duct may be followed behind the first part of the duodenum and the head of the pancreas to the second part of the duodenum which it enters 3″ from the pylorus (*fig. 274*).

The **common hepatic duct** is formed in the porta hepatis by the union of the right and left hepatic ducts, and is bound to the cystic duct by a tough areolar web. Medial to these ducts lies the hepatic artery; and behind the ducts and artery lies the thin walled portal vein. Accompanying these are lymph vessels and branches of the vagal trunks and of the celiac plexus.

While cleaning these structures, a finger, or as a substitute a roll of paper, may be passed through the **epiploic foramen** to guard the i. v. cava which is the immediate posterior relation; below is the first part of the duodenum; above is the caudate process of the liver.

Lying between the two layers of the lesser omentum along the lesser curvature of the stomach are the right and left gastric arteries with their accompanying veins, lymph vessels, lymph nodes, and the anterior and posterior vagal trunks.

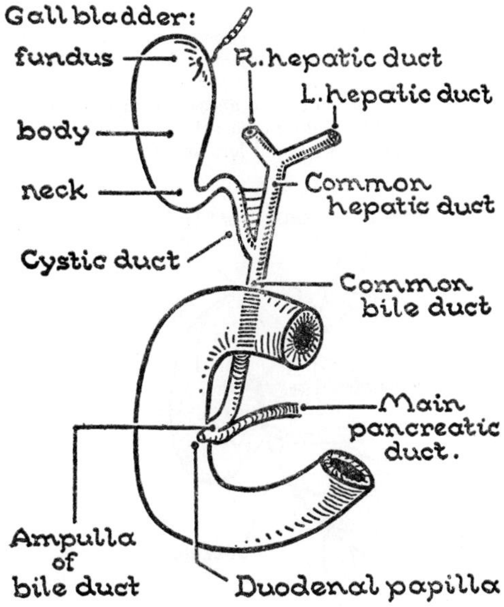

Fig. 274. The bile passages
The average lengths of the cystic, common hepatic, and (common) bile ducts are 3.4, 3.2, and 6.5 cm., respectively.

Celiac Trunk

The celiac trunk is the first of the three unpaired arteries that supply the gastro-intestinal tract (*fig. 264*).

Access to the celiac trunk, pancreas, and other structures behind the omental bursa may be had via 3 routes—by cutting through: (1) the lesser omentum or (2) the transverse mesocolon or (3) the greater omentum (*fig. 248*).

By way of *the lesser omentum* access is somewhat limited; by way of the *transverse mesocolon* it is good, but the middle colic artery, which runs in the mesocolon, must first be identified and preserved; by way of the *greater omentum* access is excellent—the cut should be made 1 inch below the greater curvature thereby avoiding the gastro-epiploic vessels, though severing their epiploic (omental) branches. Since the transverse mesocolon is applied to the greater omentum, the middle colic artery is in danger even by this route.

Surface Anatomy and Relations. The celiac trunk springs from the aorta between the crura of the diaphragm which, so to speak, sit astride it. The pancreas lies below it. Now, the diaphragm happens to descend in the median plane posteriorly to the level

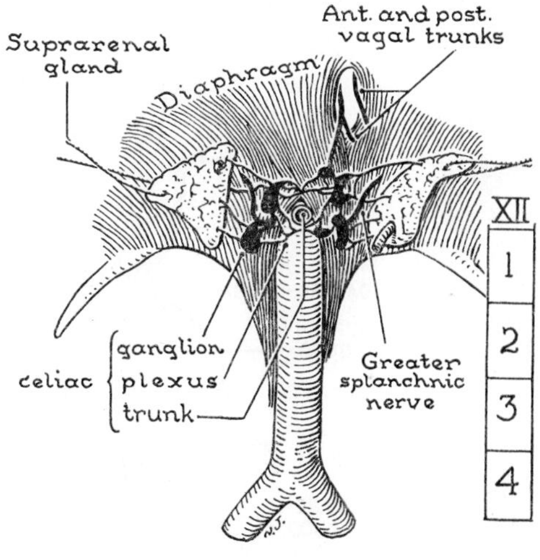

Fig. 274.1. The relations of the celiac trunk and its vertebral level. (Glands are retracted.)

of the disc between the last thoracic and the first (abdominal) lumbar vertebra. On the surface of the body this point is, of course, the depth of a vertebra and disc (say $1\frac{1}{2}''$) above the transpyloric plane; and it also marks the celiac trunk.

The celiac trunk or artery is ½ inch long. It is surrounded by the celiac plexus of nerves, wide of which are the tough, nodular, celiac ganglia; wide of these are the suprarenal glands (*fig. 274.1*).

A stout and strong branch of the posterior vagal trunk, containing fibers from both vagi, descends along the left gastric a. to the celiac plexus.

Later, the greater and lesser splanchnic nerves will be seen piercing the crura of the diaphragm to reach the celiac ganglia (pp. 284–285).

Distribution and Branches. It is the duty of the celiac trunk to supply the stomach, the adjacent parts of the esophagus and duodenum, and the three unpaired glands—liver, pancreas, and spleen (*figs. 275* and *276*). It has three branches:

1. Left Gastric:
    - esophageal
    - gastric
    - (aberrant left hepatic)
2. Splenic:
    - pancreatic
    - splenic
    - short gastric
    - left gastro-epiploic
3. Hepatic:
    - gastroduodenal:
        - supra- and retroduodenal
        - post. sup. pancreaticoduodenal
        - ant. sup. pancreaticoduodenal
        - right gastro-epiploic
    - right gastric
    - right hepatic and cystic branch
    - left hepatic

The **Left Gastric Artery** is the smallest of the three branches of the celiac trunk and the largest of the five arteries to the stomach. It ascends on the diaphragm toward the esophageal hiatus or orifice and, when a little short of it, arches forward to reach the lesser curvature of the stomach. In so doing, it drags downward a fold of peritoneum (the left gastropancreatic fold) as a "mesentery." Finding itself between the layers of the lesser omentum, it descends along the lesser curvature of the stomach, commonly as two closely applied stems, and anastomoses with the right gastric artery.

»» *Branches.* Its branches are *gastric,* of which four or five are distributed to the upper two-thirds of the anterior surface and four or five to the upper two-thirds of the posterior; and *esophageal,* which runs upward through the esophageal hiatus in the diaphragm to anastomose with the esophageal branches of the thoracic aorta.

Variation. Aberrant left hepatic arteries arise from the left gastric a. in one subject in four. Michels found aberrant left hepatic aa. in 23 per cent of 200 cadavera. Of these, 11.5 per cent were accessory to (partially replaced) normal left hepatic aa.; the other 11.5 per cent completely replaced normal left hepatic aa.

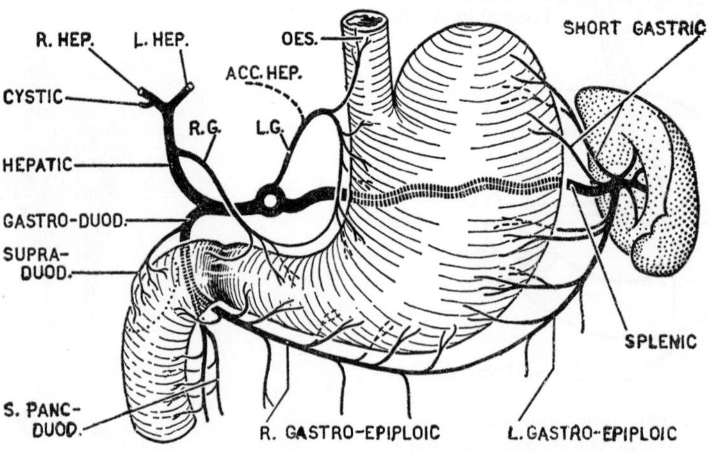

Fig. 275. Distribution of the celiac trunk or artery

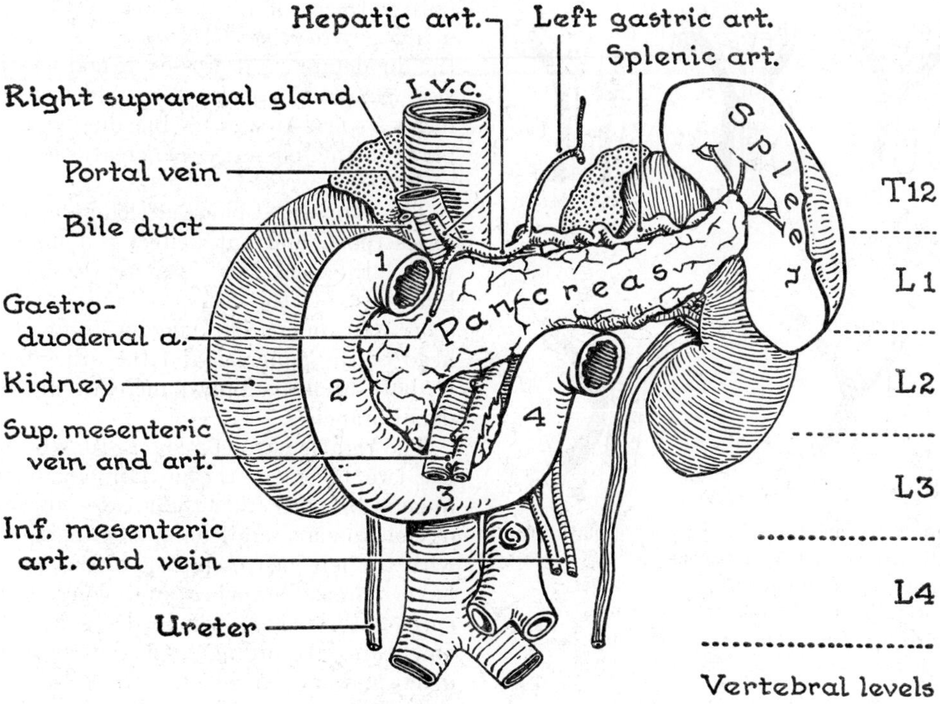

FIG. 276. Abdominal viscera and vessels—The key picture (For greater clarity, you may consider coloring it.)

The **Splenic Artery** is the largest branch. It takes a serpentine course to the left along the upper border of the pancreas. It crosses in turn the left crus of the diaphragm, the left suprarenal gland, and half the breadth of the left kidney. It then passes between the layers of the lienorenal ligament to the hilus of the spleen, which it enters as several branches.

Branches. It sends *pancreatic branches* to the body and tail of the pancreas; several *short gastric branches,* which pass by way of the gastrolienal ligament to the fundus and greater curvature of the stomach; and the *left gastro-epiploic branch,* which also passes by way of the gastrolienal lig. into the gastrocolic lig. (both being parts of the greater omentum) and gradually approaches the greater curvature of the stomach along which it runs, but never closer than a finger's breadth to it. As its name indicates, it sends *gastric* branches to the stomach and *epiploic* (omental) branches to the greater omentum.

The **Hepatic Artery** takes a more sober course to the right along the upper border of the pancreas and, like the left gastric artery, creates for itself a little "mesentery" (the right gastropancreatic fold), which conducts it to the front of the portal vein. There, like the stem of the letter T set on its side, it divides into two limbs, an ascending and a descending. The ascending limb is the continuation of the main artery upward within the lesser omentum, in front of the portal vein, and on the left side of the bile passages (*fig. 276*). The descending branch is the *gastroduodenal a.*

Terminal Branches. In the porta, the hepatic artery ends by dividing into the right hepatic a. and the left hepatic a. These enter the corresponding lobes of the liver. The right hepatic a. crosses the common hepatic duct, either in front or behind, to reach the porta (*fig. 277*).

The **cystic artery** arises from the right hepatic a. and divides into two branches, of which one ramifies on the free surface of the gall bladder and the other on the attached surface. It is an end-artery.

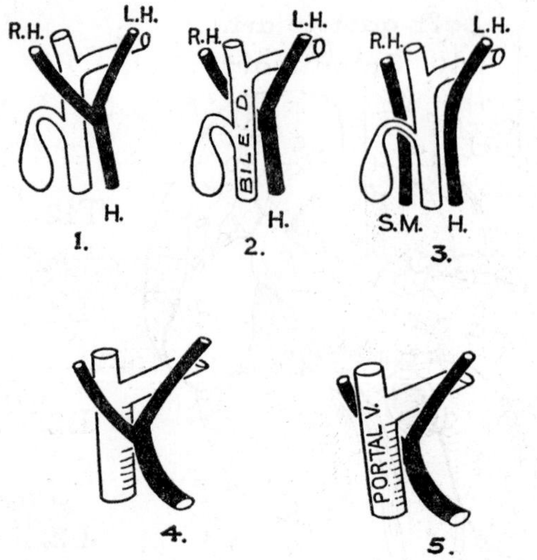

FIG. 277. Variations in the course of the right hepatic artery in 165 specimens:

1. anterior to bile duct	24%	100%
2. posterior to bile duct	64%	
3. arising from superior mesenteric artery	12%	
4. anterior to portal vein	91%	100%
5. posterior to portal vein	9%	

»» *Important to the Surgeon* are the following: The cystic a. usually arises in the angle between the common hepatic duct and the cystic duct. Its two branches anastomose with each other, supply the gall bladder, and send twigs to the liver.

Variations. In about 25 per cent of cases the two branches arise independently, i.e., there are two cystic arteries. The cystic a. may arise from any nearby artery. When it arises to the left of the common hepatic duct, it must cross that duct to reach the gall bladder, and the crossing usually takes place in front of the duct. (Daseler, Anson, Hambley, and Reimann.)

Collateral Branches of the Hepatic A. (1) The *right gastric artery* arises in front of the portal vein at some distance above the duodenum and, so, requires to make with the main artery a "hair pin" bend in order to descend to the lesser curvature of the stomach. (2) The *gastroduodenal artery* takes origin in front of the portal vein. It passes downward between the first part of the duodenum and the pancreas, where, after a course of ½–1″, it divides into the *right gastro-epiploic* and the *ant. sup. pancreaticoduodenal artery*.

The gastroduodenal a. gives off an end-artery, the "*supraduodenal a.*" (Wilkie), to the upper border and adjacent parts of both surfaces of the first part of the duodenum, *retroduodenal twigs* to the back of the duodenum as it crosses it, and the *post. sup. pancreaticoduodenal a.*, which usually forms a spiral around the bile duct and takes part in the posterior pancreaticoduodenal arch.

The superior pancreaticoduodenal arteries (post. and ant.) effect a double arch with the inferior pancreaticoduodenal branches of the superior mesenteric a. (*fig. 300*), one arch lying in front of the head of the pancreas and the other behind it; both arches supply pancreatic and duodenal branches.

The right gastro-epiploic a. runs between the two layers of the greater omentum, a finger's breadth from the greater curvature of the stomach, and commonly anastomoses with the left gastro-epiploic a. Both vessels have *gastric* branches and long slender *epiploic* branches, which descend in the omentum. Accordingly, if the gastroduodenal a. were named after its full distribution, it would read: gastro(*epiploicopancreatico*)duodenal artery.

»» **Collateral Circulation about the Liver.** To deprive the liver altogether of its arterial blood is usually fatal. There is however a *collateral anastomosis*. Thus: (1) the larger branches and the precapillaries of the right and left hepatic aa. anastomose so well both in the fissures of the liver and deep to the capsule that fluid injected into the one artery flows from the cut end of the other. The deep intrahepatic aa., however, are end-arteries. (2) If the common hepatic a. is ligated, the arterial supply to the liver may yet be assured in those 12 per cent of persons in whom the right hepatic a. arises from the superior mesenteric a. (*fig. 277*). (3) It may also be assured in the 11.5 per cent in whom a "replaced left hepatic a." springs from the left gastric a.; and perhaps in some of those in whom an accessory left hepatic a. does so (p. 244). (4) If the hepatic artery is obstructed gradually on the aortic side of the origin of the right gastric a., the circulation is maintained by the anastomosis the right gastric a. effects with the left gastric a. (5) The inferior phrenic, the cystic, and the superior epigastric aa. send fine twigs to the liver, the last *via* the falciform lig.

PORTAL VEIN

The portal vein drains all, and drains only, the gastro-intestinal tract and its unpaired glands, the liver of course excepted. It returns to the liver the blood delivered by the celiac, superior mesenteric, and inferior mesenteric arteries to these parts.

COURSE. The portal vein is formed between the head and neck of the pancreas by the union of the splenic (which represents the celiac artery), the sup. mesenteric, and the inf. mesenteric veins. It ascends to the right end of the porta where it divides into the right and left portal veins. The right vein enters the right lobe; the left vein passes transversely to the left end of the porta and supplies the caudate, quadrate, and left lobes (*fig. 249*, p. 227).

There are no functioning valves in the portal system.

RELATIONS. The portal vein ascends behind the neck of the pancreas, first part of the duodenum, and the gastroduodenal a. It then enters the lesser omentum, where the bile passages and hepatic artery lie in front of it.

Behind the portal vein lies the i. v. cava—but intervening are: (1) at the epiploic foramen—two layers of peritoneum (*fig. 247*), (2) below the foramen—two areolar membranes, one covering the i. v. cava, the other covering the portal vein (*fig. 302*), and (3) above the foramen—the caudate process of the liver.

During dissection, these membranes are the salvation of the i. v. cava; for they make separation without injury feasible.

TRIBUTARIES: Splenic, sup. mesenteric and inf. mesenteric veins, also left gastric, right gastric and post. sup. pancreaticoduodenal veins.

The ligamenta teres and venosum are attached to the left portal vein at the left end of the porta (*fig. 249*).

Portacaval Venous Anastomoses. When the portal vein is slowly obstructed, as a result of disease of the liver or from other causes, the portal blood may enter the inf. vena cava by way of certain anastomotic veins, which then become dilated and varicose—and they may burst.

»» They are as follows (*fig. 278*):

1. At the upper end of the gastro-intestinal tract: the esophageal branches of the left gastric vein anastomose with esophageal branches of the azygos veins. (When varicose they are called esophageal varix.)

2. At the lower end of the gastro-intestinal tract: the superior rectal vein anastomoses with the middle and inferior rectal veins and, most important of all, with the *pelvic venous plexuses* (p. 333). (When varicose, the rectal or hemorrhoidal veins are called hemorrhoids.)

3. Fine *para-umbilical veins* run with the round lig. of the liver from the left portal vein to the umbilicus where they anastomose with the superficial and deep epigastric veins.

4. Twigs of the colic and splenic veins anastomose in the extraperitoneal fat with twigs of the renal vein and with veins of the body wall. Here may be included twigs from the bare area of the liver.

Since the anastomotic veins seldom possess valves, they can conduct blood equally readily in either direction depending on whether the obstruction is in the portal vein or in the inferior vena cava (E. A. Edwards).

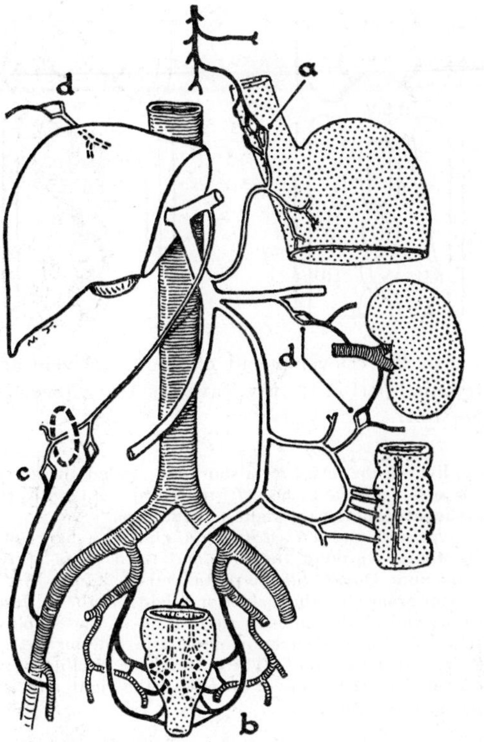

FIG. 278. Diagram of the chief portacaval anastomoses (see text).

Development of the Portal System. In prenatal life the *right* and *left vitelline veins* from the yolk sac and the *right* and *left umbilical veins,* originally from the allantois but later from the placenta, opened independently into the common sinus venosus of the heart (*fig. 279*) until the developing liver intercepted them and broke them up into the anastomosing sinusoids of the liver. Thereafter, the prehepatic parts of the right umbilical, left vitelline, and left umbilical veins disappeared, leaving only the prehepatic part of the right vitelline to conduct blood from the liver to the heart. [Prehepatic = cephalad to the liver; posthepatic = caudad to the liver.] Definitively, this prehepatic part of the right vitelline vein becomes the terminal segment of the i. v. cava (*fig. 316*).

The posthepatic part of the right umbilical vein disappeared, leaving the corresponding part of the left umbilical vein to bring from the placenta to the liver blood revived with oxygen and laden with products of digestion elaborated by the mother. Apparently, it was unnecessary that these should circulate through

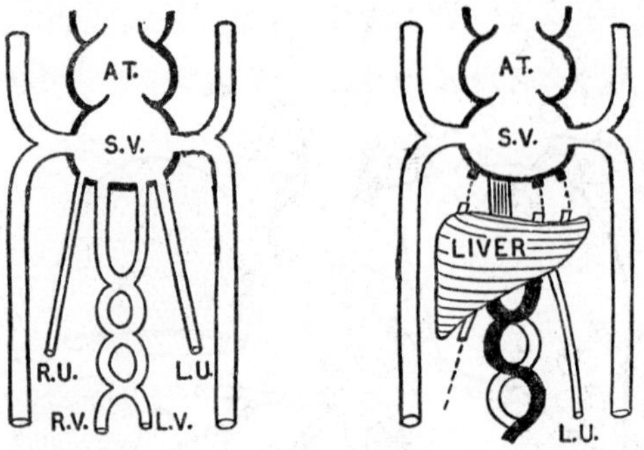

FIG. 279. Development of the portal vein and terminal part of the i. v. cava (see text). (See also *fig. 316*.)

the liver of the fetus, for a short cut, called the *ductus venosus*, connected the left umbilical vein with the prehepatic part of the right vitelline vein.

The right and left vitelline veins made a figure-of-8 anastomosis around the first and third parts of the duodenum. Out of this the portal vein took form by the disappearance of the posterior (right) limb of the 8 below and of the anterior (left) limb of the 8 above. It is joined by the superior mesenteric, inferior mesenteric, and splenic veins. The parts of the vitelline veins cephalad to the figure-of-8 became the right and left portal veins (*fig. 292*).

STOMACH

The stomach (Gk. gaster; L. venter) has two orifices, two surfaces, and two borders or curvatures. The left two-thirds are the fundus and body, the right one-third the pyloric antrum and pyloric canal (*figs. 235* and *236*). Attached to the lesser curvature and first inch of duodenum is the lesser omentum; attached to the greater curvature and first inch of duodenum is the greater omentum (i.e., gastro-colic, -lienal, and -phrenic ligs.).

A subserous vein, the *prepyloric vein*, marks the site of the pylorus in front.

Surface Anatomy. The *cardiac* or *esophageal orifice* is situated 1″ to the left of the median plane deep to the 7th costal cartilage at the level of the body of the 10th thoracic vertebra or 9th thoracic spine. The *pylorus* in the cadaver lies in the transpyloric plane 1″ or less to the right of the median plane. The *shape* and *position*, however, as learned from x-ray pictures, are in health highly variable (*fig. 256*). The esophageal or cardiac end is fixed to the diaphragm; the pylorus, duodenum, and head of the pancreas can slide extensively on the subjacent areolar sheet—provided the pliable liver, from which they are suspended by the bile passages, hepatic artery, and portal vein, by altering its shape, permits (*fig. 302*).

STRUCTURE. The coats of the stomach are: serous, subserous, muscular, submucous, and mucous.

»» *The muscular coat* has three layers—an outer longitudinal, a middle circular, and an inner oblique (*fig. 280*). *The longitudinal fibers* are continuous with those of the esophagus; they are best marked along the curvatures; at the pylorus they dip in to join the sphincter and only a few are continuous with those of the duodenum.

The *circular fibers* are present everywhere except at the fundus, and they are greatly increased at the pylorus to form a sphincter. At the pylorus and anus powerful sphincters are required to keep the contents from escaping from the stomach and rectum.

Anatomically the presence of a sphincter at the esophageal or cardiac end of the stomach is disputed; perhaps the diaphragm suffices. Physiologically, however, there is a cardiac sphincter which opens on stimulation of the vagus and closes on stimulation of the sympathetic.

The *oblique fibers* form ∩-shaped loops that extend over the fundus and down both surfaces of the stomach to the pyloric antrum, the cardiac notch forming their medial limit.

The mucous membrane is rugose when the stomach is empty and three or four uninterrupted ridges lie

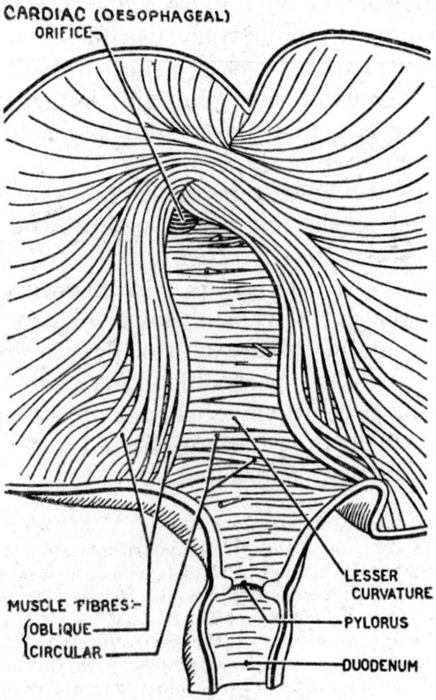

FIG. 280. The muscular coat of the stomach seen from within. (The stomach was opened along the greater curvature and the mucous and submucous coats were removed.)

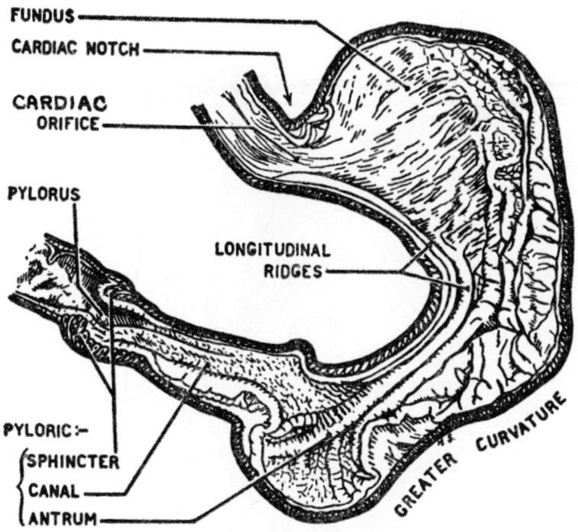

FIG. 281. The mucous coat of the posterior half of the stomach.

along the lesser curvature from esophagus to pylorus forming a gutter (*fig. 281*).

THE ARTERIES of the stomach are derived from the celiac trunk. The right and left gastric aa. form an arch close to the lesser curvature; the right and left gastro-epiploic aa. usually form a feeble arch at some distance from the greater curvature, the left artery recedes from the stomach as it is traced to the left. Three or four short gastric aa. pass to the greater curvature at the fundus via the gastrolienal ligament (*fig. 275*).

»» All arterial branches supplying the stomach penetrate the muscular coats and enter the submucosa where they form a very extensive network of comparatively large vessels. From this network in the submucosa two systems of branches are given off. Of these, one turns back to the muscular coats; the other continues to the mucosa. The branches to the mucosa usually divide twice, run spirally toward the muscularis mucosae, and pierce it to enter the mucosa where they suddenly become smaller by giving off end-branches (i.e., vessels connected only by means of a capillary network). Each end-artery continues to run a spiral course, and supplies an area of mucosa of about 2.5 mm. in diameter. The submucous network on the lesser curvature is made up of long parallel vessels which are smaller, make fewer anastomoses, and run more than twice the distance of similarly sized vessels in other parts of the stomach (Reeves).

LYMPHATICS OF THE STOMACH, p. 295 and *fig. 327.1*.

NERVES OF THE STOMACH. *Distribution of Vagal Trunks within the Abdomen.* Due to the anticlockwise rotation undergone by the stomach during development, the anterior vagal trunk (left vagus) enters the abdomen in front of the esophagus and the posterior vagal trunk (right vagus) behind it. Either trunk is occasionally in two or three branches. Both trunks, each carrying fibers from both vagi, run close to the lesser curvature and send gastric branches to the respective anterior and posterior surfaces of the stomach as far as the pyloric antrum.

The *Anterior Vagal Trunk* sends *hepatic branches* curving upward in the lower part of the lesser omentum to the porta hepatis, and it is through *pyloric branches* descending from these that the pyloric antrum, pylorus and first part of the duodenum are supplied.

From the *Posterior Vagal Trunk* a branch descends along the stem of the left gastric artery to the *celiac plexus* whence its fibers, in company with sympathetic fibers, are distributed along the branches of the aorta to the abdominal viscera, e.g., intestines (proximal to the left colic flexure), pancreas, and spleen. This is the only connection these organs have with parasympathetic nerves (*figs. 274.1* and *282*).

Sympathetic fibers, both afferent and efferent, from cord segments Th. 6, 7, 8, 9, and (10) via the splanchnic nerves and celiac ganglia, pass to the stomach along the blood vessels.

RELATIONS OF THE STOMACH. Antero-superiorly are: the left lobe of the liver, diaphragm, and anterior abdominal wall. The diaphragm separates it from the left lung and pleura and apex of the heart.

Postero-inferiorly, the omental bursa intervening, is **the stomach bed** formed to the extent shown in figures 282 and 297 by:

1. *"G. I. Tract and Co."*—Transverse colon, transverse mesocolon, pancreas, spleen, celiac trunk and its three branches.
2. *"U. G. Tracts and Co."*—L. suprarenal gland and kidney, celiac plexus, and celiac ganglion. (See *fig. 313*.)
3. *Abdominal wall.*—Diaphragm.

LIVER

(Continued from pp. 225, 227–229.)

The inferior or visceral surface faces downward, to the left, and backward. It is covered with peritoneum of the greater sac and bears

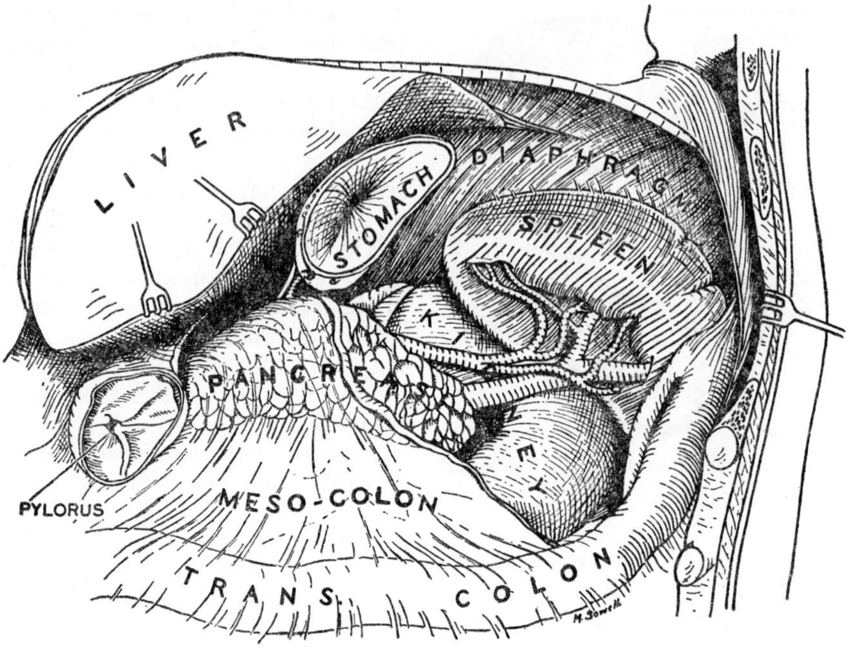

FIG. 282. The stomach bed. (The pancreas is unusually short; the left suprarenal gland, the left gastric artery and the branch of the posterior vagal trunk to the celiac plexus are not labeled.)

the imprint of the viscera that are everywhere in contact with it. The posterior aspect of the diaphragmatic surface is but indistinctly separated from the inferior surface.

An **H-Shaped Group of Fissures and Fossae** subdivides these two surfaces into four combined areas. The crossbar of the H is the *porta hepatis;* the quadrilateral area in front of it is the *quadrate lobe;* the quadrilateral area behind it is the *caudate lobe* (*figs. 251* and *283*).

The left sagittal limbs of the H are deep fissures containing the obliterated umbilical vein (lig. teres hepatis) and the obliterated ductus venosus (lig. venosum). The fissures in which these two veins lie join the left extremity of the porta. They separate the left lobe of the liver from the quadrate and caudate lobes (*fig. 249*, p. 227).

The right sagittal limbs of the H are fossae for the lodgment of the gall bladder and i. v. cava. Since the duct of the gall bladder occupies the right, free margin of the lesser omentum, it is but natural that the fossa for the gall bladder should lead to the right extremity of the porta. The fossa for the i. v. cava, however, fails to meet the porta by the width of the roof of the epiploic foramen, i.e., the caudate process or tail of the caudate lobe. The caudate process is bounded by the portal vein anteriorly and by the i. v. cava posteriorly; it connects the caudate lobe to the inferior surface of the right lobe.

The **Posterior Aspect** cannot be seen until the liver has been removed from the body. On the left, it is covered with peritoneum of the greater sac and is grooved by the esophagus. In the median plane, it forms the caudate lobe, which is covered with peritoneum of the upper recess of the omental bursa (lesser sac), and it is separated from the last two thoracic vertebrae by the diaphragm and thoracic aorta. Hence, this is the most deeply excavated area of the liver.

On the right, it is destitute of peritoneum and bare. This *bare area* is bounded by the three layers (upper, lower, and left) of the coronary ligament. The i. v. cava occupies the leftmost portion of the bare area; the

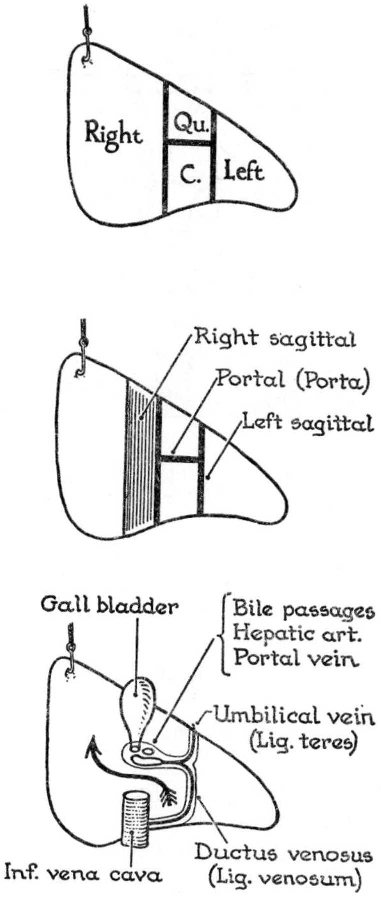

FIG. 283. Diagrams of the liver, hooked upward to show (1) the H-shaped fissure on the inferior and posterior surfaces, (2) the subdivisions of this fissure, and (3) their contents.

right kidney and suprarenal gland encroach on the bare area from below (*fig. 283.1*).

Visceral Surface of the Liver. Aided by figures 283.1 and 251, place the viscera methodically, thus:

Parts of G.I. Tract & Co.
esophagus—duodenum—stomach—colon

Parts of Three Paired Glands
right kidney, right suprarenal gland

»» The esophagus is in contact with the attenuated posterior aspect of the left lobe and the junction of 1st and 2nd parts of the duodenum is in contact with the inferior surface of the right lobe beyond the neck of the gall bladder. Obviously the intervening space between these two points must be occupied by the body of the stomach, the pyloric antrum and canal, the pylorus, and the 1st part of the duodenum. You have seen that the 1st part of the duodenum lies beneath the gall bladder (*fig. 245*); but the duodenum

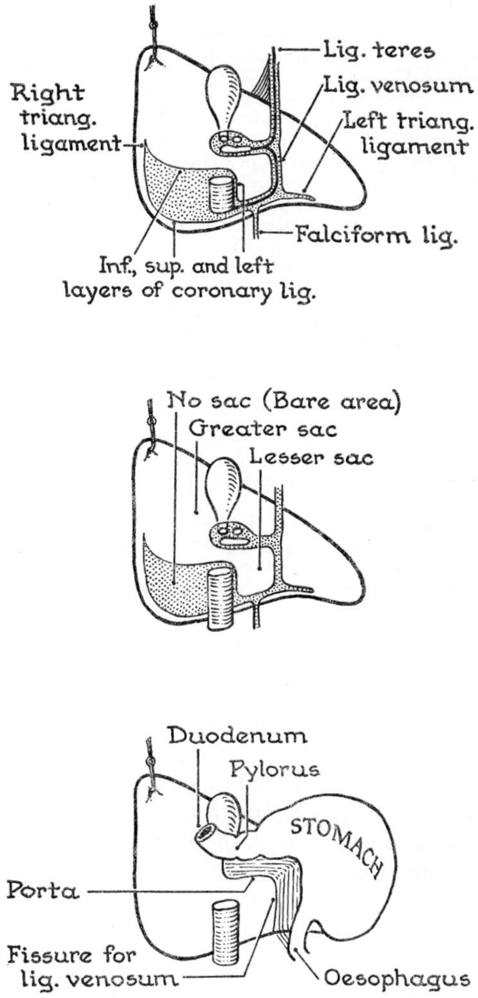

FIG. 283.1. Peritoneal attachments of the inferior and posterior surfaces of the liver.

is not nearly as wide as the gall bladder is long; so, it cannot conceal the entire bladder from below, nor the entire quadrate lobe.

2. The transverse colon, which you have seen in front of the 2nd part of the duodenum (*fig. 243*), runs from right to left behind the sharp, inferior margin of the liver as far as the median plane, and leaves its impress on the right lobe, gall bladder, and quadrate lobe.

3. Behind these intestinal areas the right lobe is hollowed for the right kidney and suprarenal, but is separated from these two glands by the peritoneum of the hepatorenal pouch (*fig. 246*). The upper ends of these two glands usually extend above the hepatorenal ligament (i.e., lower layer of the coronary lig.) and, so, come into direct contact with the bare area of the liver.

4. A portion of the left lobe of the liver (tuber omentale) fits into the lesser curvature of the stomach. It abuts against the lesser omentum which intervenes between it and the pancreas.

Note in Review that:

1. One-half of the lesser omentum is attached to the fissure for the lig. venosum; the other half to the porta hepatis (*fig. 250*).
2. Obliterated fetal veins occupy the fissures for the lig. teres and lig. venosum. The latter can be traced above the caudate lobe to the i. v. cava (*fig. 249*).
3. Of the three layers of the coronary ligament, the upper and left layers are reflected directly from the liver on to the diaphragm, whereas the lower layer (hepatorenal lig.) is largely reflected on to the kidney, suprarenal, and i. v. cava (*fig. 251*).
4. The tail or caudate process of the caudate lobe is the narrow stalk between the i. v. cava and the portal vein; it joins the caudate lobe to the under surface of the right lobe and forms the upper boundary of the epiploic foramen (*fig. 251*).
5. If you care to follow the line of reflexion of the peritoneum from the liver, you will find it to be a continuous line. If there were no bare area, i.e., if the layers of the coronary ligament were approximated to form an extensive right triangular ligament, much of the complexity associated with the peritoneum would disappear.
6. There are, indeed, three bare areas: (1) bounded by the coronary ligament, (2) the fossa for the gall bladder, and (3) where the two sheets of the falciform ligament diverge posteriorly on the upper aspect of the liver.

Surface Anatomy of the Liver (*fig. 233*). From the Front.

1. *The base* or right lateral aspect extends from near the right iliac crest (above or below) in the midlateral line, across ribs (11), 10, 9, and 8, up to rib 7.
2. *The upper limit*, of course, is the same as the upper limit of the diaphragm: it crosses the xiphisternal joint in the median plane and rises to the 5th rib in the right midclavicular line; *the apex* or leftmost part fails by an inch to reach the left midclavicular line and lies in the 5th intercostal space 1″ inferomedial to the left nipple.
3. *The sharp inferior border*, of course, connects in wavy fashion the lower limit of the base to the apex. It overlies the pylorus and, therefore, crosses the transpyloric plane about an inch to the right of the median plane.

The position of the **gall bladder** varies with that of the liver. Its fundus typically lies at the lateral border of the Rectus Abdominis somewhat below the costal margin (*fig. 213*).

»» From Behind. For nipples substitute inferior angles of the scapulae (they are on the same level as the nipples but medial to them) and for xiphisternal joint substitute the spine of Th. vertebra 8 (i.e., body of 9th Th. vertebra). The lower border follows the 11th or 12th rib.

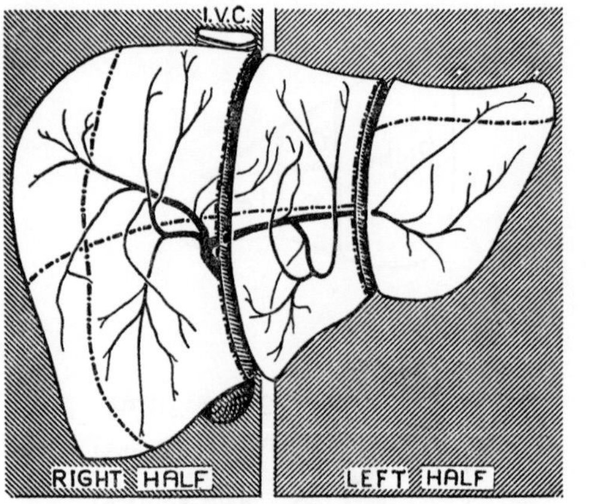

Fig. 284. The segments of the liver, according to the biliary drainage. (After Healey, Schroy and Sorensen.)

Lobes and Segments of Liver (*fig. 284*). *Descriptively*, the liver is divided into unequal right and left lobes by the falciform lig., the fissure for the round lig., and the fissure for the lig. venosum; i.e., by an anteroposterior plane passing through the left sagittal fissures.

Structurally, however, the right and left portal veins, hepatic arteries, and hepatic ducts serve approximately equal halves of the liver. The plane between the two halves (structural lobes) run anteroposteriorly through the fossa for the gall bladder and the fossa for the inf. vena cava; i.e., through the right sagittal fossae, and between the right and left groups of vessels and ducts in the porta.

The entire quadrate lobe and half the caudate lobe are served by left vessels and ducts. And, according to the prevailing pattern, no branches of the portal vein, hepatic artery or hepatic duct cross this right sagittal plane.

»» According to the biliary drainage, the left half of the liver is divided by the plane of the left sagittal fissures into a medial and a lateral segment; whereas the right half is divided by an oblique plane into an anterior and a posterior segment. Each of these four segments is subdivisible into an upper and a lower area, as in figure 284. (Healey, Schroy and Sorensen; and Hjortsjo.)

As shown in figure 249, (1) a large right hepatic vein and a less large left hepatic vein join the inf. vena cava just below the diaphragm, within an inch of the heart. (2) Between these two large veins is a third large vein. It helps to drain the left half of the liver and usually joins the left vein. But, being capricious, it may join the inf. vena cava as in figure 249, or the right vein, and it may drain both halves of the liver. (3) Several small hepatic veins constantly join the inf. vena cava at a lower level.

Bile Passages and Gall Bladder

»» STRUCTURE. *The Intrahepatic ducts* begin as intralobular ductules which are merely clefts between cords of contiguous liver cells. These are continued as interlobular ducts which are lined with cubical cells, and which accompany the branches of the portal vein and hepatic artery (*fig. 46*). *The Extrahepatic ducts* (viz., right and left hepatic, common hepatic, cystic, and bile) are fibrous tubes containing many elastic fibers and lined with columnar epithelium, but without a muscular coat, except at the lower 5–6 mm. of the bile duct where there is a strong and effective submucous sphincter. The end of the pancreatic duct has a feeble sphincter; the duodenal papilla (or the ampulla) also has a sphincter. In the cystic duct there is a spiral fold (valve) which probably serves to keep the duct patent (*fig. 284.1*).

The inner surface of the *Gall Bladder* is covered with small polygonal compartments, opening on to the interior and resembling the cut surface of a honeycomb. Like villi, these greatly increase the absorptive surface. The wall of the gall bladder has: a single, inner layer of columnar cells, a tunica propria, a muscular coat of decussating fibers, a subserous coat, and a serous coat (except where the bladder is applied to the liver).

FUNCTION. The function of the gall bladder is to concentrate and store the bile brought to it from the liver via the cystic duct between meals and to discharge it into the intestine via the cystic duct during meals.

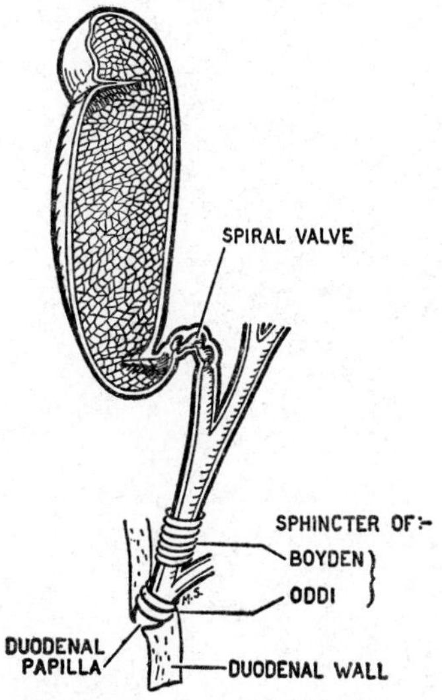

FIG. 284.1. The mucous membrane of the gall bladder and extrahepatic bile passages. The two sphincters are shown diagrammatically. This bladder happened to have a folded fundus.

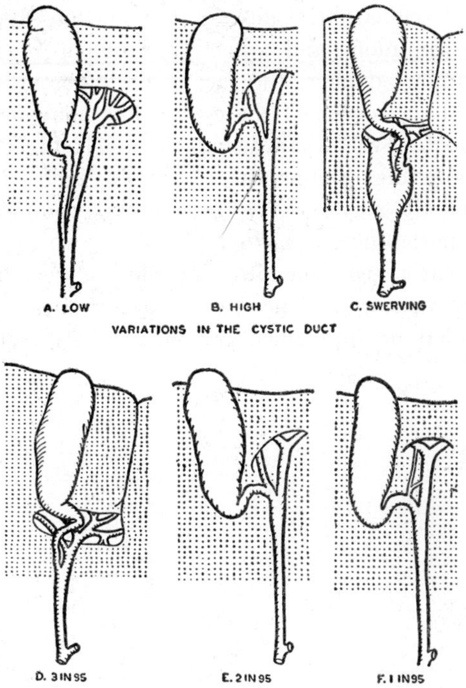

FIG. 285. Variations of the bile passages

A, *B*, and *C* = variations in length and course of cystic duct. *D*, *E*, *F* = accessory right hepatic ducts. (Of 95 gall bladders and bile passages injected in situ with melted wax and then dissected, seven had accessory hepatic ducts in positions of surgical danger. Of these, four joined the common hepatic duct near the cystic duct (*D*), two joined the cystic duct (*E*), and one was an anastomosing duct (*F*).

THE VESSELS AND NERVES of the gall bladder. *The Cystic Artery* (see p. 245). *The Cystic Veins* mostly plunge through the fossa for the gall bladder into the liver substance and behave like branches of the portal vein. *The Lymph Vessels* pass to the cystic node at the neck of the bladder and thence downward along the biliary chain. *The Nerves* are derived from the anterior vagal trunk (p. 249), and from cord segments Th. (6), 7, 8, 9, (10) via the celiac plexus.

VARIATIONS. The bile duct developed as an outgrowth from the duodenum (*fig. 293*). It branched and rebranched more or less dichotomously. One of the main branches, the *cystic duct*, instead of branching gave rise to a blind vesicle, the *gall bladder*.

Irregular branching of the bile passages is common, and when the branch is in surgical danger, the fact is of importance. Thus (*fig. 285A*) the cystic duct may end much lower than usual or much higher, sometimes joining the r. hepatic duct (*B*), and it may swerve across the common hepatic duct (*C*). When there are two right hepatic ducts, the lower is erroneously called an *accessory hepatic duct*—it is not an additional or supplementary duct, but merely one that arises unusually early (*fig. 285,D, E*, and *F*).

»» The gall bladder is rarely *absent* (unless, like an offending appendix, it has been removed). It is rarely *buried* in the liver, but occasionally it is suspended from the liver by an *acquired mesentery*. It is commonly attached to the transverse colon or to the duodenum by a *peritoneal fold*. Occasionally, it has a *sacculation* at its neck (Hartman's pouch), and occasionally the fundus is *congenitally folded* upon itself within its serous or peritoneal coat (*fig. 303*), or the folding may include the serous coat. Although *bilobed* gall bladders are very common in domestic animals, in man they are rare [17 cases of double bladder, however, each with a separate cystic duct, have been reported (Boyden)].

CHAPTER 16

MESENTERIC VESSELS DUODENUM, AND PANCREAS

MESENTERIC VESSELS

The Superior Mesenteric Artery supplies the small and large intestines from the 2nd part of the duodenum to the left colic flexure. For embryological reasons already given (*fig. 266*), this artery crosses in front of the 3rd part of the duodenum, and there you can pick it up as it enters the root of the mesentery. For embryological reasons to be given (*fig. 294*), it passes between the head and neck of the pancreas, and later you can follow it upward between them to its origin from the aorta close below the origin of the celiac trunk.

With the body of the pancreas you should associate the transverse mesocolon, which is attached to the pancreas anteriorly, and the splenic vein, which occupies a gutter in the pancreas posteriorly. These associated structures, being the three anterior relations of the s. mesenteric artery, must be raised when tracing the artery to its origin.

Clamped between the origin of the artery and the aorta, like a nut in nutcrackers, is the left renal vein (as you will see later), and lower is the third part of the duodenum (*fig. 285.1*). Pressure here may retard the flow of renal blood to the right and of duodenal contents to the left.

Having located the superior mesenteric a. in front of the duodenum (*fig. 291*), follow it caudally, in the root of the mesentery and applied to the inferior vena cava,

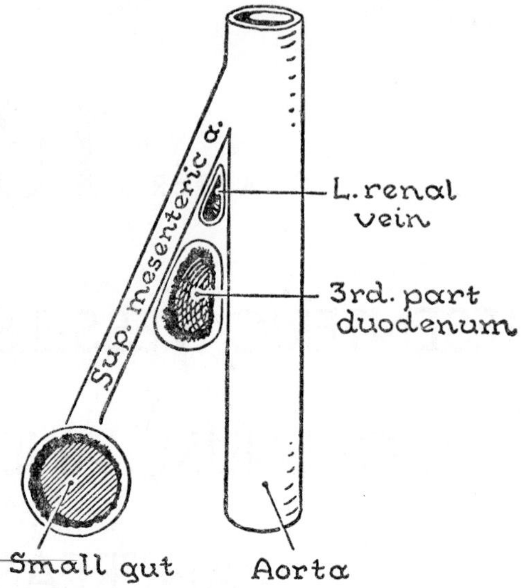

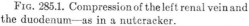

FIG. 285.1. Compression of the left renal vein and the duodenum—as in a nutcracker.

to a point beyond the origin of its ileocolic branch; there it turns into the mesentery, between whose layers it curves to the right until it reaches the ileum 6″ from the ileocecal junction. There it ends by forming an arch with one of its own branches—the ileal branch of the ileocolic artery.

Branches:

1. To the small intestine: inferior pancreaticoduodenal, jejunal and ileal.
2. To the large intestine: ileocolic, right colic, middle colic.

The **inferior pancreaticoduodenal arteries** (*fig. 300*). These two arteries, an anterior and a posterior, arise at the lower part of the head of the pancreas; with the corresponding superior pancreaticoduodenal arteries, an anterior and a posterior, they form two anastomotic arches, one in front of the head of the pancreas and the other behind it.

Each arch gives branches to the head of the pancreas and sends a row of straight terminal vessels, the *vasa recta*, to the 2nd and 3rd parts of the duodenum. Between the two rows of vasa the bile duct descends. These two arches link the superior mesenteric a. to the celiac trunk (*fig. 300*).

The **jejunal and ileal arteries,** 18 or so, fan out from the left side of the artery into the mesentery where they unite to form loops or arches from which straight terminal branches, *vasa recta,* tend in the main to pass alternately to opposite sides of the jejunum and ileum. The vasa recta do not themselves anastomose but pass to the submucous plexus where they ramify (*fig. 238*) and the ramifications anastomose freely. (Benjamin and Becker.)

Arcades. The number of tiers of arcades varies from subject to subject and from area to area, the heaviest concentration generally being in the second quarter of the length of the small intestine. In the first quarter there are 2–4 tiers (average, 2); in the second quarter, 3–5 (average, 4); in the third quarter, 2–4 (average, 2); and in the last quarter, 0–4 (only one in the majority of cases) (Michels *et al.*).

THE THREE COLIC BRANCHES of the s. mesenteric a. arise from its right border (*fig. 286*); frequently the right colic a. arises by a common stem from the main artery with either middle colic or ileocolic artery. Each, covered only with parietal peritoneum, bifurcates and joins the artery on each side of it to form loops or arches at a very variable

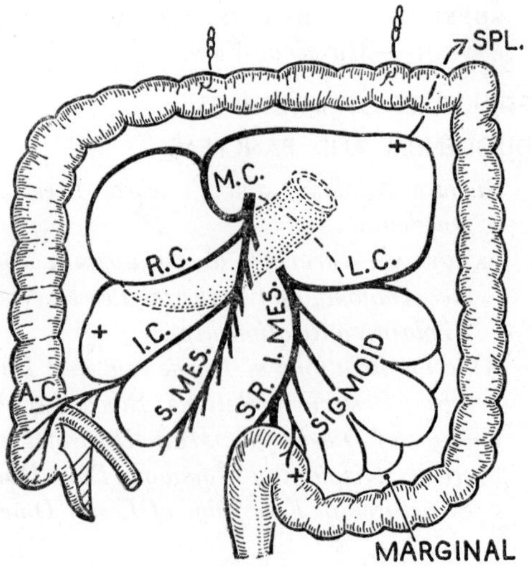

FIG. 286. The superior and inferior mesenteric arteries. (+ denotes three weak points in the marginal anastomosis: between ileocolic and right colic, between middle colic and left colic, between lowest sigmoid and superior rectal.

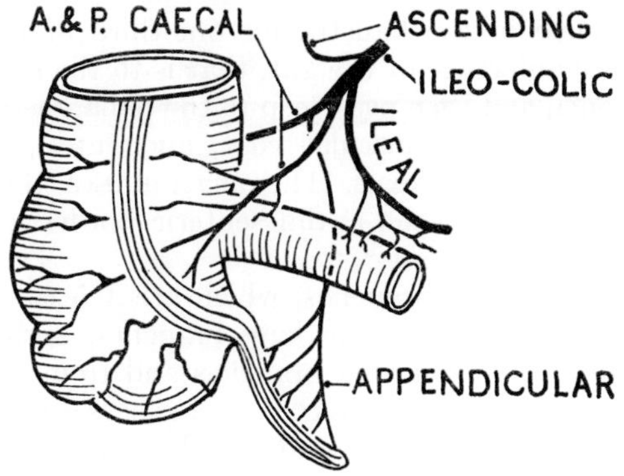

FIG. 287. The branches of the ileocolic artery

distance (0.5–8 cm.) from the colon. The colic branches of the inferior mesenteric a. run similar subperitoneal courses to the left and bifurcate similarly to form loops, and the result is a series of anastomosing links called "the **marginal artery**", which extends from the beginning of the ascending colon to the end of the sigmoid colon (*fig. 286*). The terminal branches to the colon proceed from "the marginal artery" as described on page 258.

The **ileocolic artery** descends subperitoneally toward the ileocecal region, crossing the i. v. cava and ureter, and then dividing into an ascending or colic and a descending branch.

The descending branch divides into—anterior cecal, posterior cecal, appendicular, and ileal branches. Of these, the *anterior cecal branch* passes in the vascular cecal fold (sup. ileocecal fold) (*fig. 261*) of peritoneum to the front of the cecum and ramifies there. The *posterior cecal branch* ramifies on the back of the cecum. The *ileal branch* anastomoses in the mesentery with the end of the superior mesenteric a. to form a single, or sometimes double, tier of arches from which vasa recta proceed to the last 6″ of the ileum (*fig. 287*).

The *appendicular branch* descends behind the end of the ileum and runs in the free edge of the mesentery of the appendix.

»» *Variations.* In 30 per cent of 60 specimens the appendix is supplied by two arteries: one from the anterior cecal a. and one from the posterior cecal a., or both from the posterior cecal a., or both from the anterior cecal a. (Shah and Shah).

The **right colic a.** crosses the same structures as the ileocolic a. (except when it arises higher than usual and crosses the duodenum) and divides into a descending and an ascending branch: the latter crosses the lower pole of the right kidney.

Very commonly its place is taken by branches of the middle and ileocolic aa.

The **middle colic a.** arises at the lower border of the pancreas. It curves downwards in the right half of the transverse mesocolon and divides into a right and a left branch.

»» It is in great danger of being cut when the right gastro-epiploic artery is being cleaned, as only two layers of peritoneum and a potential space (the omental bursa) separate the two vessels. When the greater omentum and the transverse colon are thrown upward, the artery then curves upward in the right half of the transverse mesocolon.

The Inferior Mesenteric Artery supplies the large gut from the left end of the transverse colon to the lower end of the rectum. It arises from the front of the aorta $1\frac{1}{2}''$ above its bifurcation (therefore, $\frac{3}{4}''$ above the umbilicus, and therefore in front of the third lumbar vertebra), where the lower border of the duodenum overlaps it (*fig. 291*). It descends retroperitoneally on the aorta and the psoas fascia, crosses the left common iliac artery, and enters the pelvis as the superior rectal (sup. hemorrhoidal) a.

Branches:

1. left colic (upper left colic),
2. sigmoid (lower left colic).

The **left colic artery** arises 1–2″ along the stem of the i. mesenteric a. and passes retroperitoneally to the left across the i. mesenteric vein, ureter, and testicular vessels, and divides into an ascending and a descending branch. Of these, the ascending branch crosses the lower pole of the left kidney.

The **sigmoid arteries** are generally 2–4 in number (*fig. 288*). The first commonly arises from the left colic artery; the lowest from the upper end of the superior rectal artery. The upper branches cross the structures in front of the Psoas (viz., inf. mesenteric vein, ureter, and testicular vessels). The lower branches cross the common iliac vessels and enter the horizontal part of the sigmoid mesocolon where they form two or three tiers of arches.

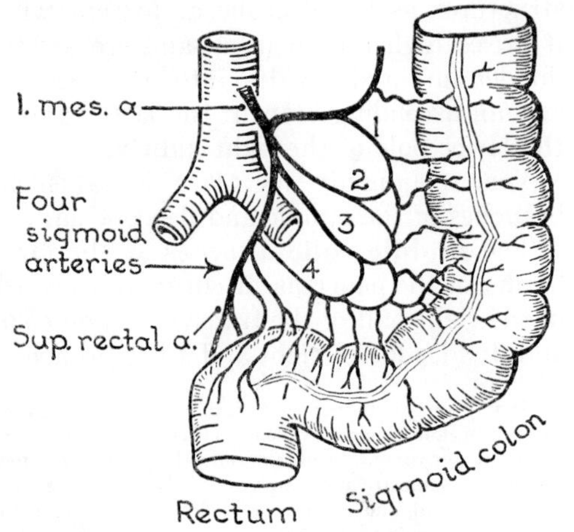

FIG. 288. The branches of the inferior mesenteric artery.

Marginal Artery (of Drummond). The colic arteries form a series of anastomosing loops which extend from the end of the ileum to the end of the sigmoid colon. The loops are for the most part single, though at places—notably at the right colic flexure and at the diagonally opposite sigmoid colon—they commonly form double or even triple tiers. The result is a continuous marginal artery situated from 0.5 to 8.0 cm. from the wall of the large gut. It is closest along the descending and sigmoid colons.

Long and short terminal branches proceed from "the marginal artery" to the colon (*fig. 289*). The long branches bifurcate near the mesenteric border into anterior and posterior branches which run a subserous course in the haustra for one-third of the circumference of the gut, that is to the next tenia, and then pass deep to the tenia, pierce the circular muscular coat, and enter the submucous plexus. The anastomoses they effect across the antimesenteric border are meager. (Ross.)

The short branches, which are 4–5 times as numerous as the long branches, spring both from the long branches and from the marginal artery directly. They pass to the mesenteric border and to the mesenteric two-thirds of the circumference. Like the long branches they pass to the submucous plexus after a short tortuous subserous course. The muscular coats are mainly supplied by recurrent branches from the submucous plexus.

»» VARIATIONS. (1) In about 5 per cent of 100 specimens the marginal artery is discontinuous, due to the ileocolic a. failing to anastomose with the right colic. (2) The right colic a. very commonly takes origin either from the middle colic or the ileocolic artery. (3) The middle colic a. commonly has an accesory left branch. (4) The left colic a. supplies the left end of the transverse colon in about two-thirds of cases, and in one-third it fails to reach the left colic flexure. (5) The middle colic and left colic aa. probably always anastomose, although the portion of the marginal artery so-formed is long and usually single. (6) A large branch (the arc of Riolan) not rarely connects the stem of the s. mesenteric a. with the left colic a. on the posterior abdominal wall. (7) Occasionally a branch connects the left colic a. with the splenic a. (8) The marginal artery does not link up the lowest sigmoid a. with the superior rectal a.—except occasionally and feebly—so, if the superior rectal a. is obstructed beyond the origin of the lowest sigmoid a., there is little chance of an effective collateral circulation being established (*fig. 286*) (Steward and Rankin; Basmajian; and Michels *et al.*).

The Superior Mesenteric Vein lies on

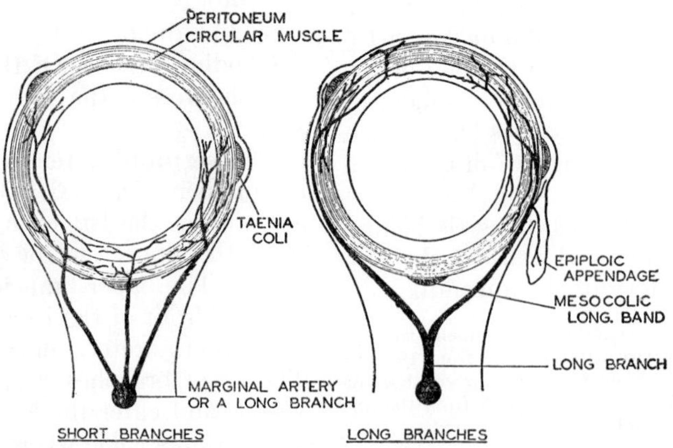

FIG. 289. The blood supply of the colon. (After Steward and Rankin.)

the right side of its artery. This you might expect from the facts (1) that the artery arises from the aorta which occupies the median plane, and (2) that the vein ends in the portal vein which, as you have seen, ascends in front of the i. v. cava—a structure situated to the right of the median plane.

The Inferior Mesenteric Vein is the continuation of the superior rectal vein (sup. hemorrhoidal vein). It begins in front of the left common iliac artery and ascends retroperitoneally on the psoas fascia between its artery, which lies medially, and the ureter which lies laterally. (It occupies the free edges of the para- and superior duodenal folds, when these are present.) It ends either in the splenic vein, which is embedded in the posterior surface of the pancreas, or curving medially behind the 4th part of the duodenum and in front of the stem of the sup. mesenteric a., it ends at or near the angle of union between the sup. mesenteric and splenic veins. The branches of the left colic and sigmoid arteries necessarily cross it, optionally in front or behind; the testicular artery and the genitofemoral nerve also cross it, but without option; they, of course, cross behind.

A Marginal Vein, which is effective, accompanies the marginal artery. Hence, if the inf. mesenteric vein be obstructed near its termination, its blood will reach the portal vein via the middle colic vein.

STRUCTURE OF INTESTINES

When the gut is opened, folds of mucous membrane, the *plicae circulares*, are seen running transversely for variable distances around the gut wall and commonly branching. Unlike the folds or rugae in the stomach, these are permanent; they contain a skeleton of areolar tissue derived from the submucous coat; and they greatly increase the absorptive surface of the gut. They begin in the duodenum, 1″ to 2″ from the pylorus, and end beyond the middle of the ileum. In the duodenum and upper part of the jejunum they are high (about 6 mm.) and closely set; lower down they gradually become smaller and more widely separated.

»» Toward the middle of the ileum small collections of lymphoid tissue, *solitary lymph follicles*, 2–3 mm. in diameter, appear and are present throughout the remainder of the small and large guts. On holding the otherwise translucent gut to the light, they appear as dark patches.

Also in the ileum, at the antimesenteric border, are 20 or more *aggregated lymph* follicles (Peyer's patches); they are oblong, ½″ wide by 1″ or more long, the long axis being in the long axis of the gut. Lymphoid tissue being a tissue of youth, these follicles are not commonly seen in dissecting-room subjects.

Finger-like projections, *villi* (0.5 to 1.5 mm. long) cover the mucous surface from pylorus to ileocecal orifice. They are best seen under water with a lens. They, too, greatly increase the absorptive surface of the gut.

The Ileocecal Orifice and Valve. Here the circular muscle of the small gut, covered with mucous membrane, pouts into the large gut. In the dried inflated specimen, the orifice is a transverse slit; its upper lip overhangs the lower and, so, directs issuing contents downward into the cecum. From each angle (anterior and posterior) of the orifice a fold, the *frenulum*, extends transversely. In life and in hardened specimens, the orifice is circular (*fig. 290*).

The Appendix opens into the cecum ½ to 1½″ below the ileocecal valve. Its mouth may be guarded by a semilunar fold of mucous membrane.

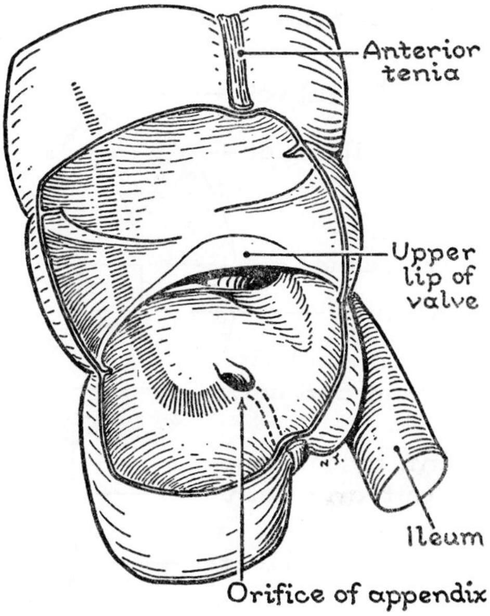

FIG. 290. The ileocecal valve, as seen on opening a dried cecum.

The sacculations or *haustra* of the cecum and colon are produced by the teniae coli acting as elastic bands; on nicking the teniae, the gut may be lengthened and the sacculations disappear.

The mucous and submucous coats of the gut are readily peeled off the circular muscular coat, and the vessels entering the submucosa are then seen.

DUODENUM AND PANCREAS

»» The word *Duodenum* is a Latin corruption of the Greek word dodekadaktulos, meaning 12 fingers (cf. the 12 islands in the Levant called the Dodecanese Islands). About 300 B.C., Herophilus of Alexandria gave the name dodekadaktulos to the first part of the intestine before it is thrown into folds. It was so-called from its being as long as 12 fingers are broad in those animals in which it was first described (Finlayson).

In man the duodenum is the part of the small intestine that has lost its dorsal mesentery. Ten inches long, it is molded around the head of the pancreas in horseshoe fashion and is divided into four parts (*fig. 291*):

1st or superior—2″ long.
2nd or descending—3″ long.
3rd or horizontal—4″ long.
4th or ascending—1″ long.

Surface Anatomy of Duodenum: Vertebral Levels. The duodenum begins at the pylorus in the transpyloric plane an inch to the right of the median plane, and ends at the duodenojejunal junction slightly below the transpyloric plane an inch to the left of the median plane. The ends of the horseshoe are, therefore, 2″ apart. Where the 3rd part of the duodenum crosses the median plane, it overlaps the origin of the inf. mesenteric artery—a fact of little importance in itself, but a noteworthy aid to surface anatomy and vertebral levels (*fig. 291*).

»» Thus: The umbilicus lies at the level of the disc between the 3rd and 4th lumbar vertebrae, and is midway between the origin of the inferior mesenteric artery and the aortic bifurcation. The bifurcation takes place ¾″ below the umbilicus, and therefore in front of L. 4; whereas the artery arises ¾″ above the umbilicus, and therefore in front of L. 3, and there the duodenum crosses it. With this information and knowing the vertebral level of the transpyloric plane, it becomes a simple matter to map out the duodenum on the surface of the body and to relate it to the vertebrae.

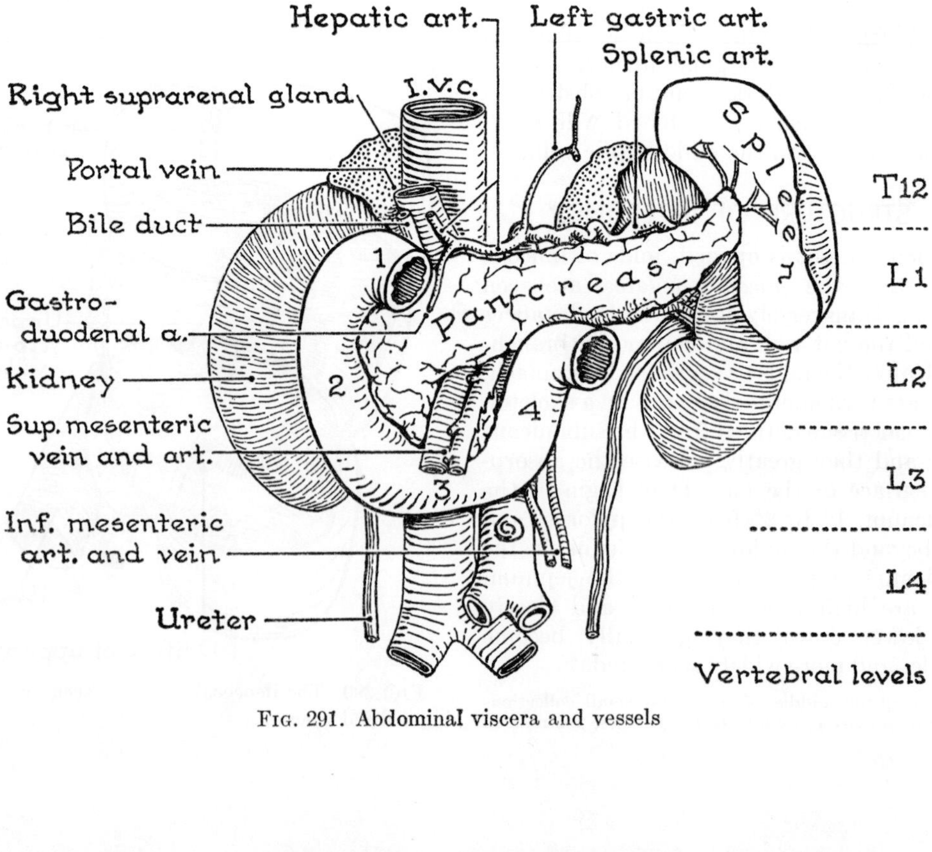

FIG. 291. Abdominal viscera and vessels

The Pancreas (Gk. Pan = all; kreas = flesh) resembles the letter J, or better a retort, set obliquely. The bowl of the retort, known as the *head* of the pancreas, lies within the concavity of the duodenum whilst the stem of the retort, divided indefinitely into *neck*, *body*, and *tail*, slants obliquely across the abdomen. The tip of the tail abuts against the spleen and lies above the level of the head. A small piece of the head projects medially, behind the superior mesenteric vessels; it is the *uncinate process* (*fig. 291*).

The pancreas is about 5 or 6 inches long and weighs about 3 ounces (170 grams) in the adult.

The celiac trunk, with the crura of the diaphragm astride it, lies at the upper border of the pancreas and sends its hepatic branch to the right along the upper border of the neck and head of the pancreas, and the splenic branch to the left along the upper border of the body and tail of the pancreas.

The **main duct** of the pancreas runs near the posterior surface of the gland and should be dissected from behind. It resembles a herring bone, in that small ducts spring from the main duct which is straight. This duct empties the *exocrine secretion* of the pancreas into the second part of the duodenum where it acts as a ferment upon carbohydrates, proteins, and fats.

The *endocrine secretion* is formed by tiny clusters of cells, the *islets of Langerhans* which manufacture *insulin*, a hormone concerned with carbohydrate metabolism.

Surface Anatomy of Pancreas (*fig. 291*): **Vertebral Levels.** With these facts, and recalling that the diaphragm descends in the median plane to the level of the disc between Th. 12 and L. 1, it becomes a simple matter to map out the pancreas on the surface of the body and to relate it to the vertebrae. Thus: The head lying within the concavity of the duodenum lies in front of vertebra L. 2; the body rises to the level of the celiac trunk and, therefore, is in front of vertebra L. 1; while the upwardly sloping tail is at the level of vertebra Th. 12.

Notes Explaining Relationships:

1. During early prenatal life, the intestines undergo rotation, counter clockwise, on the axis of the superior mesenteric artery, in consequence of which the stem of the artery comes to lie in front of the 3rd part of the duodenum and behind the transverse colon (*fig. 266*). Thereafter, the *duodenum* is thrust by the transverse colon against the structures lying on the posterior abdominal wall, and it loses its dorsal mesentery; that is, the right layer of its mesentery adheres to the structures on the posterior wall of the abdomen. The *pancreas*, which lies between the two layers of the dorsal mesentery, likewise loses the layer of peritoneum that formerly clothed its right surface—now its posterior surface. The *transverse colon* in turn loses its mesocolon where it crosses the 2nd part of the duodenum and the head of the pancreas, but retains it where it lies in front of the body of the pancreas (*figs. 272* and *298*).

2. The right and left vitelline veins returning blood from the yolk sac, are so united to each other below the liver as to suggest that the upper and lower limbs of the duodenum are held in venous manacles (*fig. 292*). The veins twine about the duodenum in figure-of-8 fashion. The splenic vein comes to open into the intermediate part of this figure-of-8. The portions of the 8 anterior to the 1st part of the duodenum and posterior to the 3rd part disappear with the result that the superior mesenteric, splenic and portal veins of adult anatomy take form.

3. The ducts of the liver and pancreas arise as two outpouchings or hollow buds, a dorsal and a ventral, of the endoderm

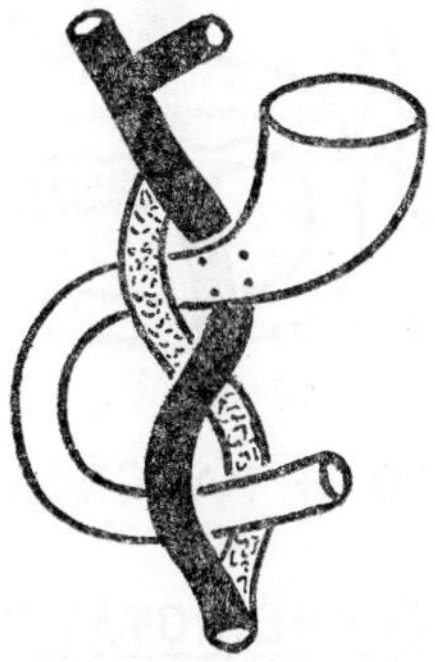

FIG. 292. Showing how the portal vein develops from a figure-of-8 anastomosis around the duodenum.

of the duodenal wall. The glandular tissue of the liver and pancreas develops from the ends of the ducts; the remainder is of mesodermal origin. One endodermal bud grows from the dorsal border of the duodenum into the dorsal mesoduodenum. It is the rudiment of the pancreatic duct around which the neck, body and tail of the pancreas develop. From the ventral border of the duodenum, and at a lower level, an endodermal bud grows into the ventral mesoduodenum (or mesogastrium) (*fig. 293*). It is the rudiment of the bile passages and of the liver and also of the pancreatic duct around which the head of the pancreas develops.

4. The 2nd part of the duodenum undergoes partial rotation to the right on its own long axis, due to the fact that different parts of its wall grow unequally. As a consequence, the opening of its upper or accessory duct, which was formerly posterior, is now carried to the front; and the duct that was originally anterior and lower is carried posteriorly to the concave border (*fig. 294*). This explains why the (common) bile duct passes upward behind the accessory pancreatic duct and 1st part of the duodenum. (See *fig. 296*.)

For descriptive purposes, the head of the pancreas may be regarded as swinging around behind the junction of the splenic, superior mesenteric, and portal veins, thereby causing them to occupy a position between it and the neck of the pancreas. The pancreas seems to close on these veins much as a book might close on a bookmark.

5. The tail of the pancreas, growing between the layers of the dorsal mesoduodenum, ultimately abuts against the spleen which develops from the left layer of the dorsal mesogastrium (*figs. 269* and *270*).

» 6. The primitive dorsal and ventral pancreatic ducts remain separate in 9 per cent of 200 specimens (*fig. 295*). In the remaining 91 per cent a communication is established between the two ducts, whereupon the left, or splenic, section of the dorsal duct, the con-

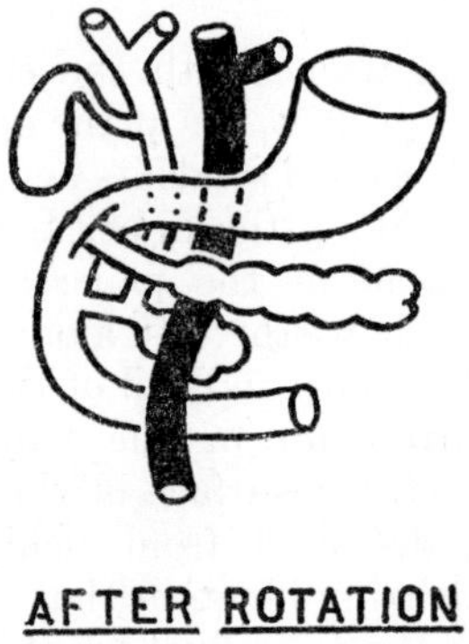

FIG. 294. The two rudiments of the pancreas close on the portal vein (or s. mesenteric vessels) like a book on a bookmark.

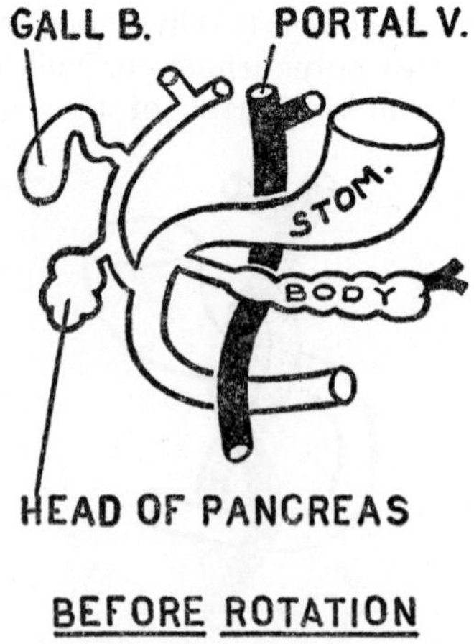

FIG. 293. The rudiments of the liver and pancreas arise as outpouchings of the duodenum into the ventral and dorsal mesogastria.

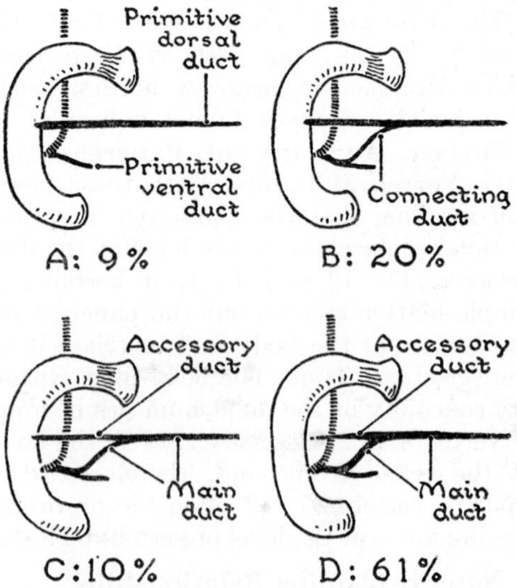

FIG. 295. Varieties of pancreatic ducts (see text, item 6).

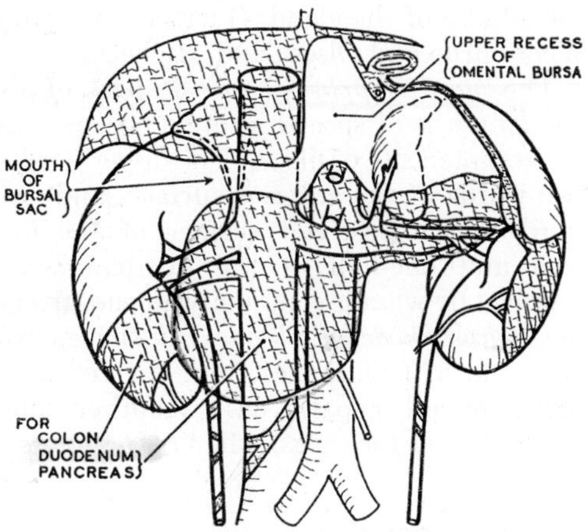

Fig. 296. Especially to show the extent of the duodenum and pancreas.

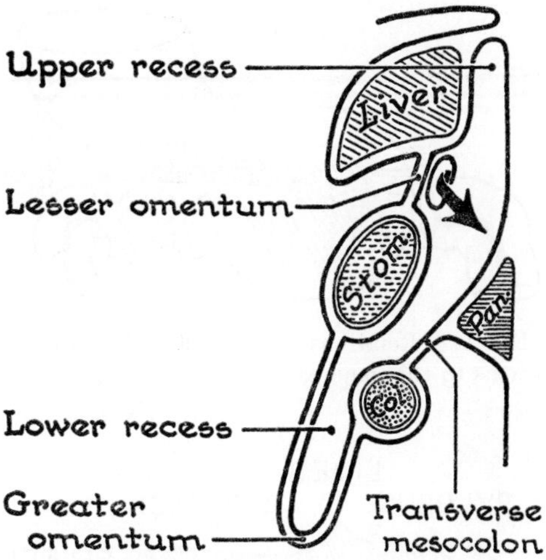

Fig. 297. Diagram of the stomach, omental bursa, and stomach bed, on sagittal section.

necting duct and the right, or duodenal, section of the ventral duct become the main duct; whereas the right, or duodenal, section of the dorsal duct becomes the accessory duct. Now, the accessory duct remains large enough to function as the chief duct in 20 per cent of specimens; it remains reasonably large but tapering in 10 per cent; and it either ceases to open into the duodenum or is of negligible size in 61 per cent.

Again, the (common) bile duct and the main pancreatic duct open separately into the duodenum, one above the other in 5 per cent of 200 cases. (These data after Millbourn should be appreciated but not memorized.)

Anterior Relations of Duodenum and Pancreas. The *Duodenum* was defined above as the part of the small gut that had lost its mesentery. This is not true of the first inch of the duodenum, for it has two mesenteries—the lesser omentum, which is attached to its upper border, and the greater omentum, which is attached to its lower border. They allow the first inch to move freely with the stomach.

You have seen that the gall bladder rests on the 1st part of the duodenum and on the transverse colon (*fig. 245*). Now, the 1st part of the duodenum is longer than the gall bladder is wide; so, it must come into contact with the liver on each side of the gall bladder. Hence, its anterosuperior relations are: quadrate lobe, neck of gall bladder, and right lobe (*fig. 283.1*).

The transverse colon is the direct anterior relation of the 2nd part of the duodenum (*fig. 298*).

The superior mesenteric vein and artery cross anterior to the 3rd part of the duodenum in the root of the mesentery; and clinically they appear at times to constrict the duodenum. Indeed, in the dissecting rooms, the duodenum is commonly found to be dilated before the site of crossing and contracted beyond. Coils of jejunum lie in front of the remainder of the duodenum.

The **Pancreas** has two aspects, an *anterior* and a *posterior*. The transverse colon is attached to the anterior aspect of the head by areolar tissue and is suspended from the anterior aspect of the body and tail (*fig. 243*) by the transverse mesocolon. When the surrounding hollow viscera are distended, the body of the pancreas is triangular on cross-section, and the line of attachment of the transverse mesocolon becomes the *anterior border* (*fig. 297*). Above the border, the pancreas is obviously covered with peritoneum of the omental bursa; whereas below the border, it is covered with peritoneum of the greater sac. The tip of the tail extends into the lienorenal ligament and abuts against the spleen.

The pancreas is surrounded by various portions of the gastro-intestinal tract (*figs. 298* and *299*) and these come to overlie it as shown in figure 291.

»» To be more precise, the 1st part of the duodenum overlaps the front of the head of the pancreas; its 2nd and 3rd parts are overlapped by the head (*fig. 291*).

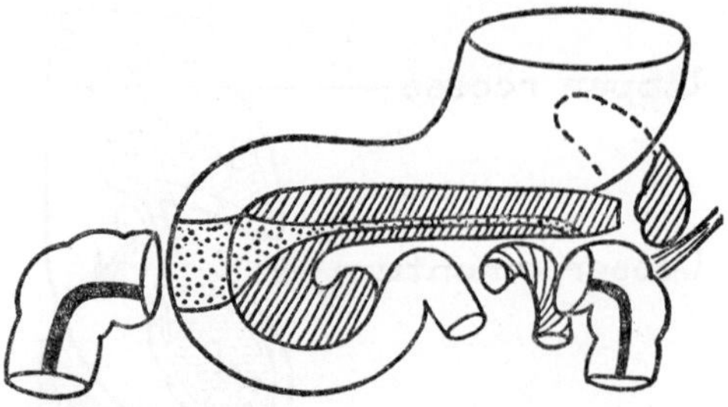

FIG. 298. Relations of the gastro-intestinal apparatus to the pancreas.

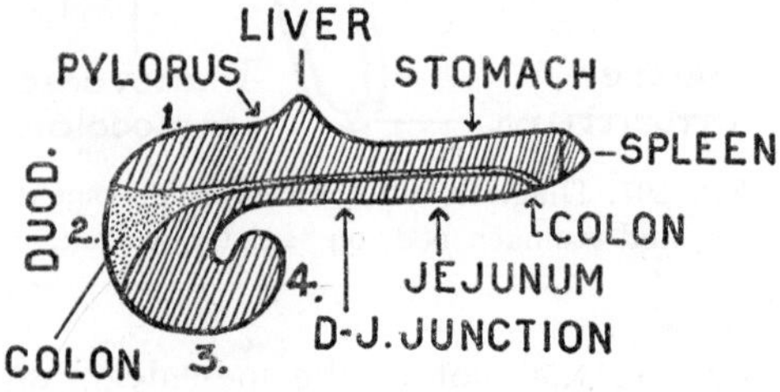

FIG. 299. Key to figure 298

Posterior Relations of Duodenum and Pancreas (*fig. 296*). These relations are the structures that lie in front of the posterior abdominal wall from the level of the celiac trunk above to the inferior mesenteric artery below; and, from the hilus of the right kidney to half way across the anterior surface of the left kidney, where the tail of the pancreas enters the lienorenal ligament and touches the spleen. These structures belong to the "three paired gland system" and to the great vessels.

Blood Supply of Duodenum and Pancreas (*fig. 300*). The duodenum and the head of the pancreas are situated at the site of union of the celiac and superior mesenteric arterial systems, and are supplied largely by the superior and inferior pancreaticoduodenal arteries.

The body and tail of the pancreas are supplied by two constant arteries: (1) the *splenic artery*, which runs behind the upper border of the gland, and (2) the *inferior pancreatic artery*, commonly derived from the celiac a., which runs behind the lower border to the tail. Inconstant arteries also supply the gland. The various arteries anastomose freely to form a network around the lobules of the gland. (Pierson; Wharton; Woodburne and Olsen; and Michels.)

The *blood supply of the 1st part* of the duodenum is of special interest because this is a common site of ulcers. The upper border, two-thirds of the anterior surface, and one-third of the posterior surface of the first inch and one-half of the duodenum are supplied by what is commonly an end-artery, the "*supraduodenal*" *branch* of the gastroduodenal a. (sometimes from the common, right, or left hepatic aa.). Another independent twig (or twigs), the "*retroduodenal*"

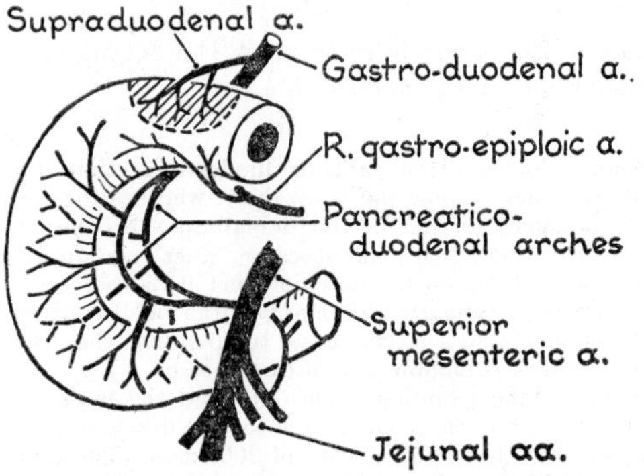

FIG. 300. The blood supply of the duodenum

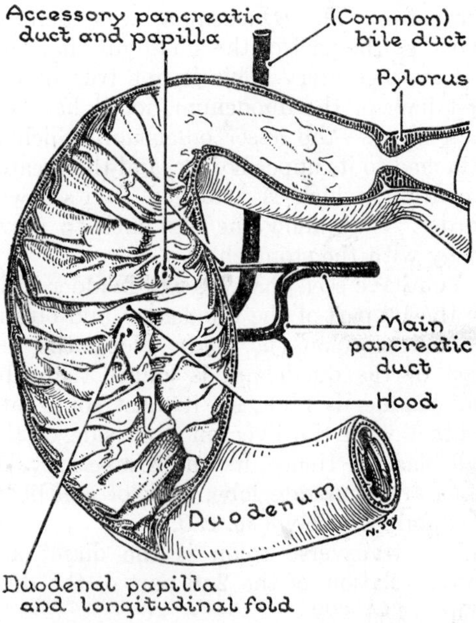

FIG. 301. The interior of the duodenum. The pancreatic ducts.

branch of the gastroduodenal a., helps to supply the posterior wall. The right gastro-epiploic a. supplies the inferior border; the right gastric a. may supply a twig to the upper border.

Interior of the Duodenum (*fig. 301*): (1) The first 1 or 2″ of the duodenum are smooth; beyond this, *plicae circulares* of mucous membrane are large and numerous; (2) the conjoint bile and pancreatic duct (sometimes dilated to form an *ampulla*, 5 mm. long, as it traverses the duodenal wall) opens on to the (*major*) *duodenal papilla*, which is situated on the concave side of the duodenum 3″ from the pylorus; (3) from the papilla a *plica longitudinalis* descends, and over the papilla a semicircular *hood-like fold* is commonly thrown; (4) the accessory pancreatic duct opens into the duodenum on a *minor or accessory papilla*, ¾″ antero-superior to the major duodenal papilla.

The **main duct of the pancreas** runs near the posterior surface of the gland and should be dissected from behind. It resembles a herring bone, in that small ducts spring from the main duct which is straight.

In displaying the (**common**) **bile duct** you should make use of your embryological knowledge and reopen obliterated portions of the peritoneal cavity (*fig. 302*).

1. First, pull the transverse colon downward off the front of the 2nd part of the duodenum and head of the pancreas. When done, note that the posterior aspect of the transverse colon is covered with a smooth areolar membrane and that the bared parts of the duodenum and pancreas are similarly covered. These are the areolar layers of peritoneum from which the squamous cells have been absorbed. In short, you have restored to the right end of the transverse colon its primitive mesocolon.

2. Then raise the duodenum and head of the pancreas, and swing them forward, as though on a hinge, toward the median plane. Note that their posterior surfaces are covered with a smooth areolar membrane and that the anterior surfaces of the kidney, renal vessels, and i. v. cava, from which they have been raised, are similarly covered. You have restored in part the mesoduodenum.

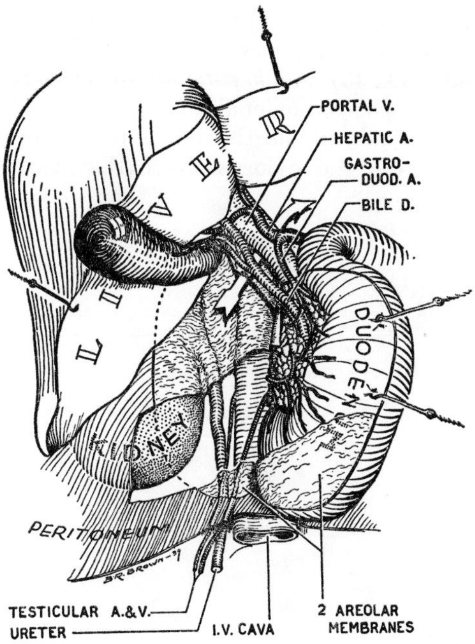

FIG. 302. Display of the bile duct by the embryological approach—see text. (*Arrow* passes through the epiploic foramen.)

3. You can now follow the bile duct downward behind the 1st part of the duodenum and head of the pancreas, and between the two rows of vasa recta duodeni that proceed from the anterior and posterior arches of the pancreaticoduodenal vessels, and so to its junction with the main pancreatic duct 3″ from the pylorus. Below the epiploic foramen the bile duct is separated from the i. v. cava by two areolar membranes, the posterior row of vasa recta, and commonly a portion of the head of the pancreas.

Warning instruction. To expose the (common) bile duct from the front is destructive: the transverse colon must be pulled down, the first part of the duodenum cut across, the anterior row of vasa recta and the accessory pancreatic duct cut across, in order that the head of the pancreas may be separated from the 2nd part of the duodenum.

Observation. Trace downward the *three chief structures in the free edge of the lesser omentum* noting their different relationships to the head of the pancreas. Thus: (1) the (*common*) *bile duct* passes behind the head;

(2) the *portal vein*, prolonged as the superior mesenteric vein, passes between the head and neck. (3) The *hepatic artery*, prolonged as the gastroduodenal artery, passes between the head and the duodenum, ¾ of an inch from the pylorus. Note that two of these, the bile duct and the portal vein, are important anterior relations of the i. v. cava. Both are separated from the i. v. cava by two areolar membranes; the bile duct is also separated from it by a row of vasa recta.

CHAPTER 17

THREE PAIRED GLANDS

SUPRARENAL, RENAL, AND GENERATIVE OR SEX GLANDS

Migrations during Development; Testicular Vessels—anterior relations, posterior relations, testicular veins contrasted; Ovarian Vessels; Ductus (Vas) Deferens.

SUPRARENAL GLANDS—*Structure and Development; Surface Anatomy; Relations; Vessels; Nerves.*

KIDNEY AND URETER

General; Surface Anatomy; Anterior Relations; Posterior Relations; Structure; Vessels and Nerves; Arterial Segments; To Explain Variations; Anomalies.

SUPRARENAL, RENAL, AND GENERATIVE OR SEX GLANDS

These three paired glands together with their ducts, vessels, and nerves may be referred to collectively as the three paired gland system.

Migrations. All three glands developed in the retroperitoneal tissue, and retroperitoneal they remain, save where parts of the gastro-intestinal system "fall" in front of them and, owing to obliteration of the peritoneal cavity in between, adhere to them (*figs. 268* and *296*). The suprarenal glands developed in situ. That the testes (and ovaries) descend is common knowledge; that the kidneys ascend is equally true.

As the testis and kidney migrate, their paths cross and in crossing one obviously must pass in front of the other (*fig. 305*). The testes ultimately lie in the ventral region of the body; the kidneys in the dorsal. This happens to be the relationship of the one gland to the other where their paths cross.

The ascending kidney dragged its duct after it and picked up new vessels during its ascent. The descending testis (or ovary) dragged after it not only its duct but also its artery, vein, lymph vessels, and nerves. And it dragged them in front of the path of the kidney and ureter. Definitively, the testicular (or ovarian) vessels and nerves cross the ureter in the abdomen; the deferent duct (or uterine tube) crosses it in the pelvis.

It is now evident why the lymph nodes that drain the testis (and ovary) are to be sought not in the groin but in the abdomen (*fig. 228*).

»» During its ascent in prenatal life the kidney or metanephros climbed, as it were, up an arterial ladder the rungs of which passed from the aorta to the mesonephros (or middle kidney) which was atrophying. If the kidney fails to let go its hold of one or more of the lower rungs after it has grasped one or more of the upper ones, then the adult kidney will possess more than one renal artery. It is on this basis that accessory renal arteries are explained (*fig. 311B*).

Testicular Vessels. The testicular artery, one on each side, arises from the aorta just below the renal artery and descends in the retroperitoneal tissue to the deep inguinal ring.

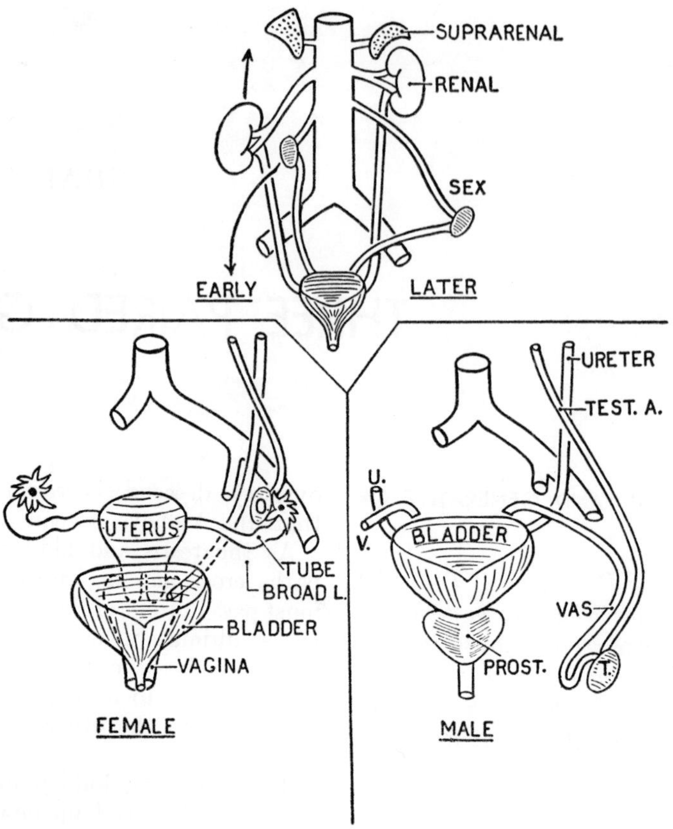

FIGS. 303, 304, and 305. The migrations of the kidneys and sex glands

Definitively the ovarian vessels and the uterine tube in the female bear the same relationships to the ureter as do the testicular vessels and the ductus (vas) deferens in the male.

Anterior Relations. The testicular artery adheres to the peritoneum, except where crossed by the following parts of the gastro-intestinal system: *on the right,* by the 3rd part of duodenum, the right colic and ileo-colic vessels, and the end of the ileum or the cecum; *on the left,* by the 4th part of the duodenum, the inf. mesenteric vein, the left colic and sigmoid vessels and the sigmoid colon.

Posterior Relations. The testicular artery descends on the psoas fascia, crosses the ureter and, at the deep inguinal ring, it lies in front of the external iliac artery. The right artery in addition crosses the i. v. cava (*figs. 313* and *318*).

The right testicular vein ends in the i. v. cava; *the left vein* in the left renal vein.

Ovarian Vessels. In their abdominal course, the ovarian vessels duplicate that of the testicular until they cross the external iliac vessels, ½″ in front of the ureter, and plunge into the pelvis (*fig. 381*).

Ductus Deferens (Vas Deferens). This duct runs a short subperitoneal course in the abdomen. From the deep inguinal ring it curves round the lateral border of the inf. epigastric artery and, crossing the ext. iliac vessels, enters the pelvis.

SUPRARENAL GLANDS (Adrenal Glands) (*fig. 306*).

These paired endocrine glands overlap the upper ends of the kidneys. They are crescentic in shape and very friable. The glands are situated one on each side of the celiac trunk, and, as the celiac ganglion alone intervenes, they are less than an inch from the trunk; indeed, their medial borders are exactly 2″ apart. A peak added to the right gland converts its crescentic form into a triangular one.

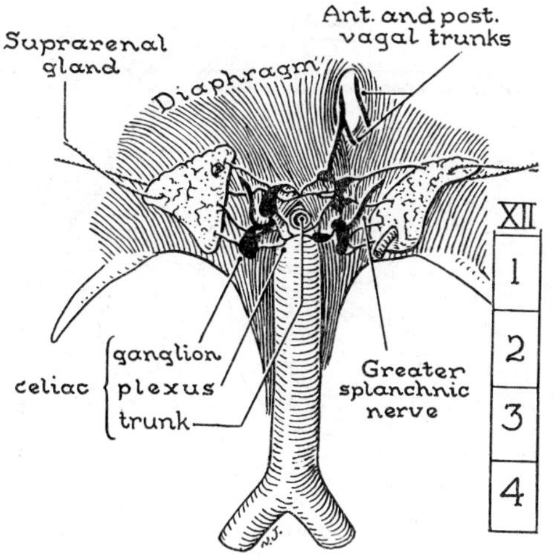

FIG. 306. The celiac plexus and the suprarenal glands (retracted). Note vertebral levels.

Structure and Development. Each gland is composed of two parts: an outer golden cortex and an inner vascular medulla. The cortex is of mesodermal origin; the medulla is of ectodermal. Originally, the gland consisted of cortical material only; later, sympathetic nerve cells and nerve fibers, derived from the celiac ganglion, traveled along the suprarenal vessels, penetrated the cortex, and gave rise to the medulla.

At birth the suprarenal gland covers nearly the upper half of the kidney; in the adult it lies at the upper pole and along medial border above the hilus, some fat intervening.

The suprarenal does not require to follow the excursions of the kidney. In fact, its association with the kidney is accidental.

Surface Anatomy. A methodical way to find the glands is: (1) to locate the celiac trunk between diaphragm and pancreas, (2) next to trace the fibers of the celiac plexus from the celiac trunk, which they encircle, to the tough, nodular celiac ganglion on each side of the trunk, and (3) then to follow the slender nerve fibers from the ganglion to the suprarenals (*fig. 306*). Further, it will assign the ganglion and the suprarenals to the level of the celiac trunk (i.e., the height of a vertebra and disc above the transpyloric plane).

Relations. Behind, lie the crura of the diaphragm. *In front,* lie portions of the gastro-intestinal canal and its three unpaired glands. Thus (*fig. 307*): The *Left Suprarenal* is crossed below by the pancreas and the splenic artery, elsewhere it is separated from the stomach by the omental bursa.

The Right Suprarenal is covered either directly or indirectly by the liver. Now, embedded in the bare area of the liver is the inferior vena cava, which covers the right celiac ganglion and overlaps the medial part of the right suprarenal gland (*fig. 307*). The gland, however, extends below the bare area of the liver and there, lying at the epiploic foramen, is separated from the inferior surface of the liver by peritoneum of the hepatorenal pouch.

Vessels. Numerous tenuous twigs from three arteries converge on each gland—(1) from the suprarenal artery proper, which springs from the aorta, (2) from the (inferior) phrenic artery above, and (3) from the renal artery below.

A single large suprarenal vein leaves the anterior surface of each gland: the right vein ascends to the i.v. cava; the left vein descends to the left renal vein.

Nerves. The greater and lesser splanchnic nerves pierce the crus of the diaphragm and pass to the celiac ganglion or an off-shoot of it. A branch of the posterior vagal trunk, containing fibers from both vagi, divides and passes to the ganglion (*fig. 306*).

From the ganglion, the half dozen nerve filaments that pass to each suprarenal gland are probably derived from the lesser and lowest splanchnics; other filaments from the 1st (and 2nd) lumbar sympathetic ganglia pass to the gland.

KIDNEY AND URETER

The kidneys (L. ren; Gk. nephros) are paired (*fig. 313*). Each kidney is about 4½″ long and weighs about 4½ oz. It possesses *two surfaces,* an anterior and a posterior, separated from each other by a "circumferential" border. In reality the anterior and posterior surfaces face anterolaterally and posteromedially, because the kidneys are applied to the muscles covering the sides of the vertebral bodies.

The circumferential border may be subdivided into two borders, a medial and a lateral, and *two poles*, an upper and a lower. The upper pole is generally a little thicker and nearer the median plane than the lower; so, the long axis of the gland is directed inferolaterally.

The intermediate third of the medial border presents a cleft, the *hilus* or door, which leads into a cavity, the *renal sinus*. Passing through the hilus into the sinus are the *pelvis* or expanded upper end of the ureter, the renal vessels and nerves, and some fat.

Above the hilus, the suprarenal gland is in contact with the medial border and upper pole; below the hilus, the ureter is close to the medial border.

Like other abdominal organs, the kidney lies in the extraperitoneal fatty tissue. In the midst of this fatty tissue there is a tough areolar membrane, the *renal fascia*, which splits to enclose the kidney and a certain quantity of fat, the *perinephric fat* or *fatty capsule*. The two layers of fascia do not blend below, so, the kidneys can move downward with the diaphragm during inspiration; neither do they blend medially but pass in front of and behind the renal vessels, aorta, and inferior vena cava to unite indefinitely with the respective layers of the opposite side. Above and laterally the two layers of fascia blend and fade away.

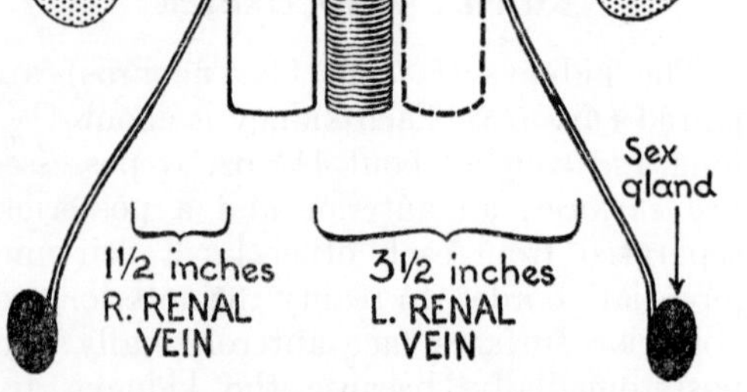

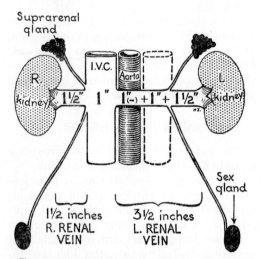

FIG. 306.1. The left renal vein, so-called, is in reality the vein of the three left paired glands, and it is longer than the right vein.

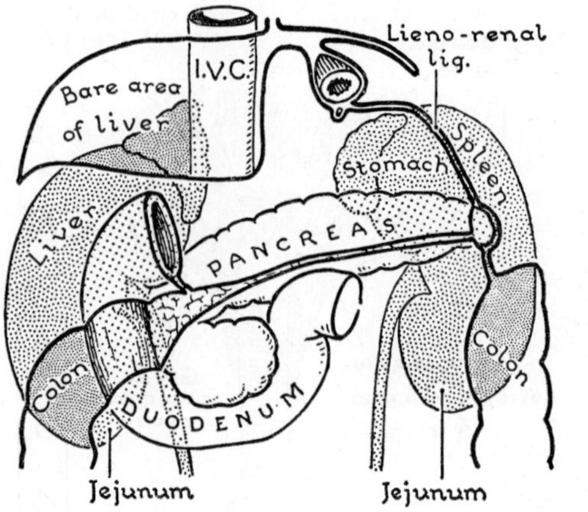

FIG. 307. The anterior relations of the kidneys and suprarenal glands. (The duodenum and pancreas are drawn in situ; the other relations are indicated by name.)

Surface Anatomy of the Kidney. The right kidney does not rise quite so high as the left kidney. Apparently, the presence of the liver is responsible for arresting the upward migration of the right kidney just as it arrests the downward expansion of the right lung.

The *lower poles* of the kidneys lie an inch or less above the transumbilical plane, which is at the level of the 3–4 intervertebral disc. The kidneys are 4½″ long; so, their *upper poles* must lie about 5½″ above the transumbilical plane. If you will measure, you will find these points to be behind the 7th costal cartilages.

The *suprarenal gland*, which caps the kidney and lies along its medial border, has its center at the level of the celiac trunk and, therefore, at the disc between the 12th thoracic and 1st lumbar vertebrae. It follows that the kidney extends from the level of the 3rd lumbar vertebra upward beyond the 2nd and 1st lumbar vertebrae to the level of the 12th thoracic vertebra, and, therefore, beyond the 12th rib.

Its *medial border* lies from the median plane nearly as far as the length of the right renal vein (1½″) + the breadth of the i. v. cava (1″) + half the breadth of the aorta (½″) = 3″ in all (*fig. 306.1*). But, when allowances are made for the obliquity of the vessels and the depression of the

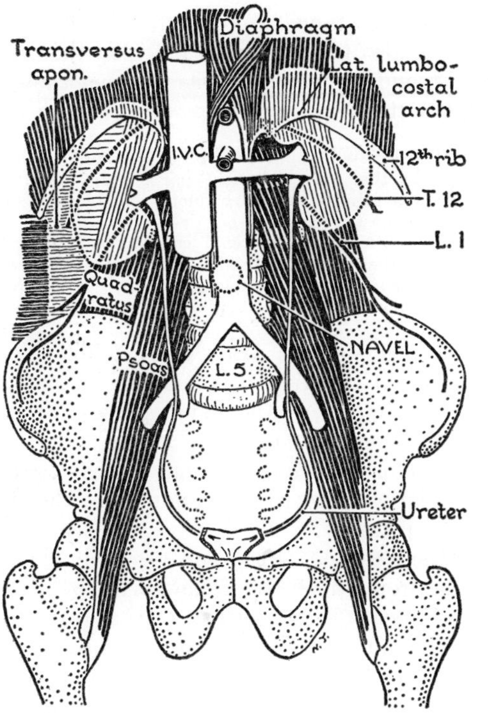

FIG. 308. The posterior relations of the kidneys. The course of the ureters.

renal hilus, the distance from the median sagittal plane will be seen to be less than 2″. The transpyloric plane crosses the upper part of the hilus (*fig. 291*).

At the back, the kidney extends from a point one or two fingers' breadth above the highest part of the iliac crest, which is on a level with the spine of the fourth lumbar vertebra, upward to or almost to the 11th rib.

(For vertebral levels see *fig. 291*.)

Anterior Relations (*fig. 307*). The kidneys are in direct contact with some structures and indirectly in contact with others.

The Direct Contacts are:

1. The 2nd part of the duodenum and the tail of the pancreas at the hili.
2. The right and left colic flexures.
3. Suprarenal glands.
4. Bare area of liver (on right side only).

The Indirect Contacts are:

1. Coils of jejunum.
2. Liver at the hepatorenal pouch on the right side.
3. Spleen on the left side.
4. Stomach on the left side.

Posterior Relations. Behind the kidney are parts of the roof and posterior wall of the abdomen (*fig. 308*). Thus:

1. Muscles and Bones: The diaphragm, together with the medial and lateral arcuate ligs. (lumbocostal arches) from which it arises; the Psoas and Quadratus Lumborum and, in the angle between them, the uncovered tips of the transverse processes of the 1st, 2nd, and (3rd) lumbar vertebrae; and, which is most apt to be forgotten, the posterior aponeurosis of the Transversus Abdominis, which arises from these transverse processes (*fig. 323*).

2. Nerves and Vessels: Theoretically, branches of nerves Th. 12 and L. 1, 2, and 3 might pass posteriorly because the kidney lies abreast of the corresponding vertebrae, but the only branches that actually do so are from Th. 12 (subcostal nerve) and L. 1 (iliohypogastric and ilio-inguinal nerves). Branches from L. 2 and 3 descend with a more vertical trend and lie medial to the normally placed kidney.

Structure of the Kidney. The kidney has a *fibrous capsule* which is easily stripped

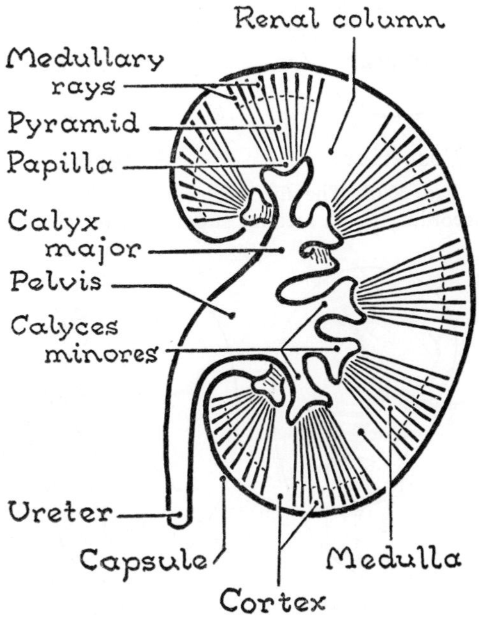

FIG. 309. The macroscopic structure of the kidney (seen on longitudinal section).

off. When a kidney is divided with a sharp knife into anterior and posterior halves, its cut surface is seen to possess six or more smooth, darkish, longitudinally striated, triangular areas known as the pyramids (*fig. 309*).

Each *pyramid* is seen to have a free, rounded apex or *papilla* (L. = nipple) which projects into the renal sinus, a *body* or main portion, and from the *base* of the body radiations, the *medullary rays*, occupy the cortex of the kidney and extend to the surface. A papilla, a body, and a series of medullary rays constitute a complete pyramid.

The outer or surface layer of the kidney is the *cortex*. It is the part that lies superficial to the bases of the pyramids and it comprises the entire outer one-third of the kidney substance. It looks granular. Cortical tissue also fills the areas between the pyramids and is there known as the *renal columns* (of Bertin).

»» The striated appearance of a pyramid is due to the fact that its component parts [loops of Henle, collecting tubules, papillary ducts, and blood vessels] converge on the papilla.

The cortex and the renal columns look granular because they are composed of structures [glomeruli, convoluted tubules, and blood vessels] cut across in various planes.

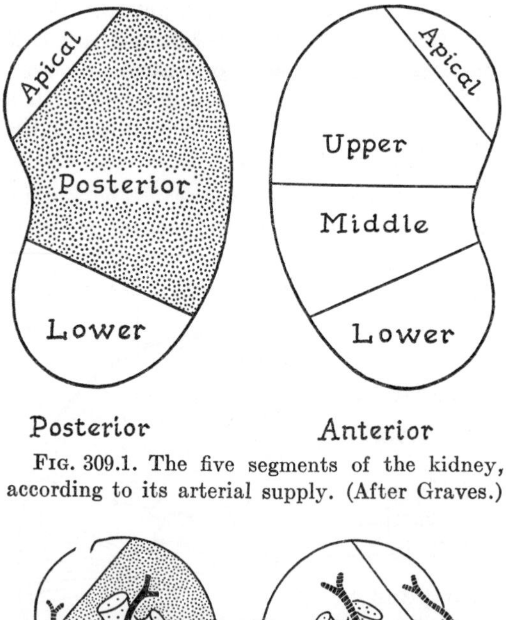

FIG. 309.1. The five segments of the kidney, according to its arterial supply. (After Graves.)

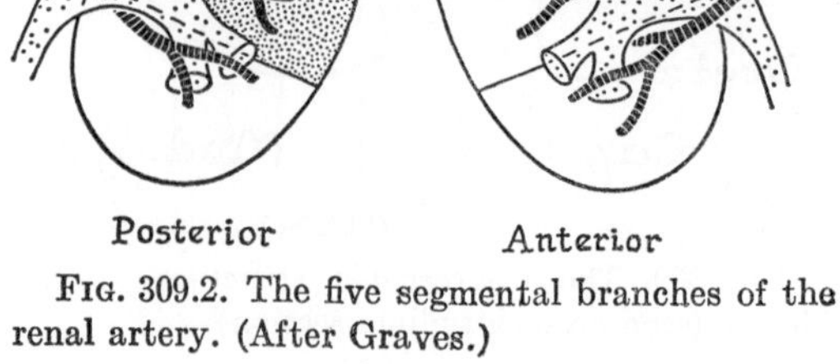

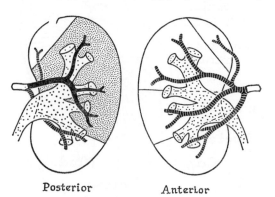

FIG. 309.2. The five segmental branches of the renal artery. (After Graves.)

Renal Vessels and Nerves. The blood supply of the kidney is peculiar in that all, or almost all, of the blood passes through the glomerular capillaries where it is purified before it passes through a second set of capillaries from which it nourishes the kidney substance.

The Renal Arteries, one for each kidney, arise from the sides of the aorta ¼″ below the superior mesenteric a. (See also p. 60.)

The immediate *anterior relations* of the renal arteries are the renal veins, and on the right side, the i.v. cava is also anterior—all covered in front with an areolar sheet (*fig. 302*). Anterior to these, on the *right side*, are the head of the pancreas and the 2nd part of the duodenum; on the *left side*, the body of the pancreas in which are embedded the splenic a. and v. The *posterior relations* of each renal artery are the crus of the diaphragm and the Psoas.

Arterial Segments of the Kidney. According to the distribution of the branches of the renal artery, the kidney has five segments (*fig. 309.1*).

Typically, the artery divides into an anterior division which enters the renal sinus in front of the pelvis, and a posterior which enters behind it. The anterior division has four relatively constant branches (*fig. 309.2*)—apical, upper, middle, and lower—which though variable in origin are fairly constant in distribution. The apical and the lower supply the whole thickness of the kidney; whereas the others (upper, middle, and the posterior division) confine themselves to their respective halves.

Between the five branches there are no anastomoses. The veins, however, anastomose freely (R. T. Graves).

The Renal Nerves are probably derived from segments T. 12, L. 1 and 2. (For details see p. 61.)

Pelvis of the Kidney (Pelvis of the Ureter) (*fig. 310*). The pelvis is the expanded, funnel-shaped, upper end of the ureter. It lies partly within the renal sinus and partly outside it. Traced toward the kidney it is seen to divide into two stalks, the *cranial and caudal calices majores,* with sometimes a third or middle calix. Each major calix divides into several goblet-shaped *calices minores* into each of which one or more papillae project. A dozen or more papillary ducts open on to each papilla.

To Explain Variations

»» The primitive ureter bifurcates to form a cranial and a caudal calix major. These continue to bud and divide progressively, the terminal branches being the collecting tubules in the pyramids of the renal medulla.

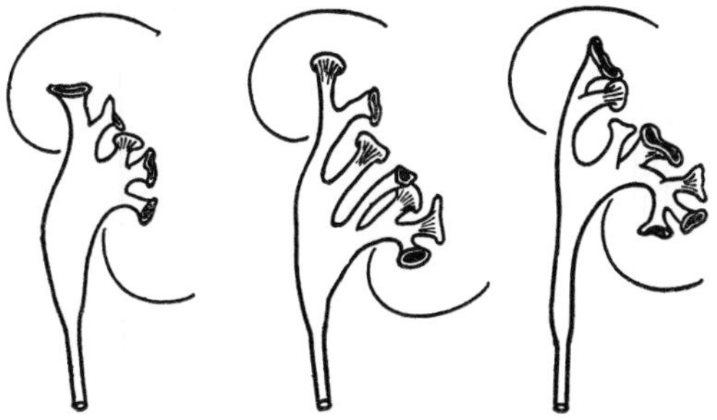

FIG. 310. Sketches of casts of the renal pelvis

The medulla is composed of seven pairs of pyramids (seven being ventral and seven dorsal) of which three pairs are connected with the cranial calix and four with the caudal (*fig. 310.1*).

The papillae of the pyramids become crowded at the two poles of the kidney (especially the upper pole), with the result that groups of two or more papillae fuse to form compound papillae (*fig. 310.1*). Accordingly, the maximal number of papillae is 14 and the average is 9.

Commonly there is a third calix major, the *middle calix,* which receives the fourth and fifth pairs of papillae, leaving only the sixth and seventh for the caudal calix (F. Lofgren).

Ureter

The Ureter or duct of the kidney is 10″ long. Its upper half is in the abdomen; its lower half is in the pelvis; its terminal part pierces the posterolateral angle of the bladder.

Its abdominal part extends almost vertically from the lower part of the hilus of the kidney (less than 2″ from the median plane) to the bifurcation of the common iliac artery (one-third of the distance from aortic bifurcation to the midinguinal point) where it crosses the external iliac vessels and enters the pelvis.

The ureter lies in the subperitoneal areolar tissue and adheres to the peritoneum. When the peritoneum is mobilized, the ureter is in danger of injury, for it moves with it.

In embryonic life the ureter was subperitoneal from end to end. When the testis (or ovary) descended, it drew its vessels across the front of the abdominal part of

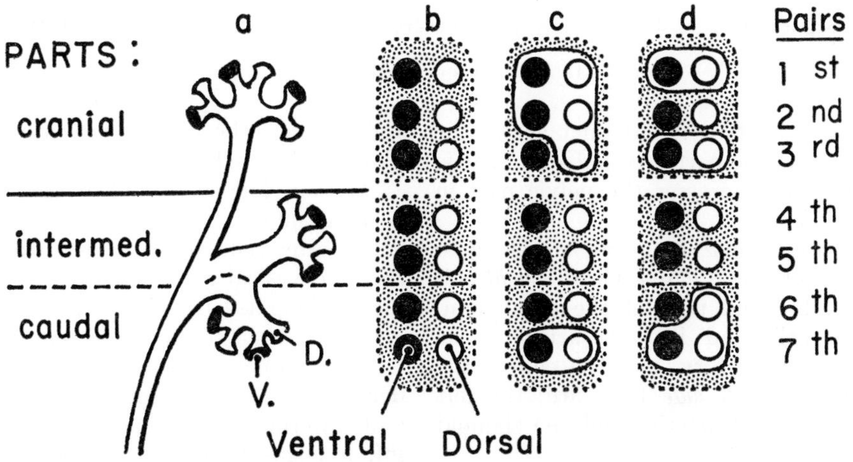

FIG. 310.1. An explanation of the variation in the number of individual pyramids and calices minores. The maximum number of 14 is almost always reduced through a variety of fusions.

An intermediate (middle) calix may appear due to early splitting of the caudal calix (After Lofgren.)

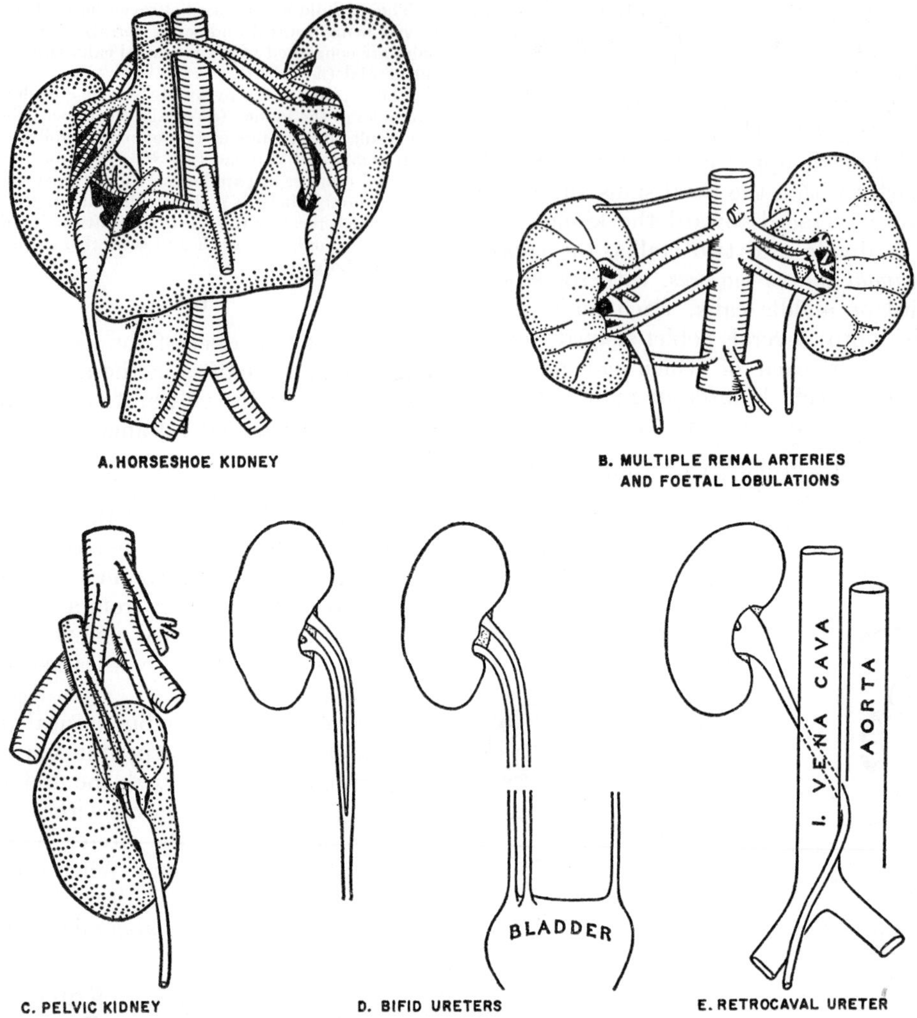

FIG. 311. Anomalies of the kidneys and ureters

the ureter and its deferent duct across the front of the pelvic part (*fig. 305*). (Similarly, the uterine tube crosses the pelvic part in the female.)

Otherwise its *anterior relations* belong to the gastro-intestinal canal. On the *right side* they are: the 2nd part of the duodenum, the right colic and ileocolic arteries, the root of the mesentery, and the end of the ileum. On the *left side* they are: the left colic and sigmoid arteries and the sigmoid mesocolon.

The ureter descends on the Psoas fascia and crosses the genitofemoral nerve. The i. v. cava is close to the medial side of the right ureter; the inferior mesenteric vein is close to the medial side of the left ureter.

Arteries. The pelvis and the ureter possess a longitudinal anastomosing network of arteries derived from the renal artery above and the vesical artery below. This is reinforced along its length by an aortic or testicular (ovarian) or common iliac branch.

Nerves. Like the arteries, the nerves are derived from nearby sources, i.e., the renal and intermesenteric plexuses above, the inf. hypogastric plexus (pelvic plexus) below; and the testicular and sup. hypogastric plexuses in between. As for the kidney, the cord segments are Th. 12, L. 1 and 2.

Anomalies (*fig. 311*). Much the commonest gross anomaly of the urinary tract is a *bifid ureter* and pelvis, the result of premature division of the ureteric bud in the fetus. The condition is generally incomplete and unilateral and the ureter is commonly constricted at the point of fission. When completely bifid, one of the ipsilateral ureters may open into other parts of the U. G. tract, e.g., the floor of the urethra, or roof of the vagina or seminal vesicle.

About 3 per cent of kidneys have *two renal arteries* arising from the aorta, of which one usually goes to the upper or lower pole. *Fused kidneys:* in 1 in 700 persons the right and left kidneys are fused, generally at their lower poles, and form a horseshoe kidney. The ascent may be arrested by the inferior mesenteric a. crossing in front of the isthmus. *Congenital absence of kidney and ureter* or *rudimentary kidney with ureter* occur with the same frequency as horseshoe kidney.

The kidney on one side may be *double* with independent ureters and vessels. One or other kidney may migrate across the median plane. A *pelvic ectopic kidney* is one that, failing to ascend, remains lodged in the pelvis and is supplied by arteries of low origin. The *fetal lobulation* present at birth (and well seen in the cow) is commonly retained. The *anterior lip of the sinus* is often undeveloped. A *congenital cystic kidney* results when the secreting parts of a kidney and their ducts fail to unite.

A retrocaval ureter is a ureter that winds spirally around the inf. vena cava (Pick and Anson).

CHAPTER 18

POSTERIOR ABDOMINAL STRUCTURES

GREAT VESSELS OF THE ABDOMEN

The great vessels are the abdominal aorta, the inferior vena cava, and the com-

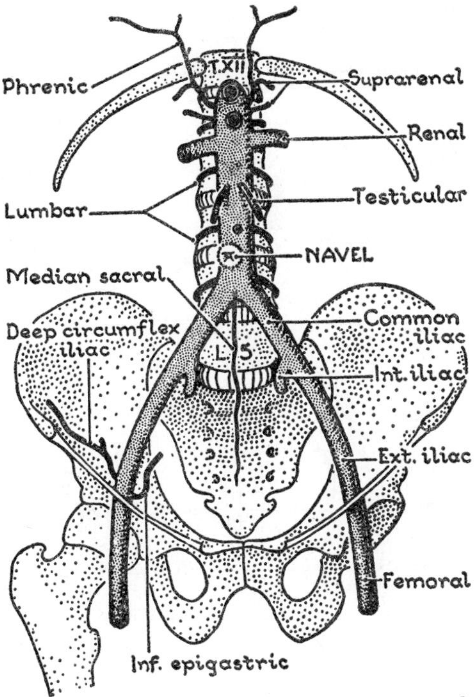

FIG. 312. The abdominal aorta and its branches —collateral and terminal.

mon, external, and internal iliac arteries and veins.

Abdominal Aorta. It is remarkable that this great vessel and its "continuation," the *median sacral artery,* should lie in contact with and beat against the bare vertebral column without any soft fatty or fleshy cushion intervening; but such is the case.

The aorta enters the abdomen in the median plane by passing behind the diaphragm at the level of the disc between vertebrae T. 12 and L. 1, which is, of course, the height of a vertebra above the transpyloric plane. It ends in front of L. 4, after crossing 3½ vertebrae and discs, by bifurcating into the right and the left common iliac artery (*fig. 312*). On each side of the aorta stretch the legs or crura of the diaphragm, the right crus descending to the 3rd lumbar vertebra and the left crus to the 2nd.

Each common iliac artery bifurcates into an internal iliac and an external iliac artery. The course of the common and external iliac arteries is indicated on the skin surface by a curved line joining the site of the aortic bifurcation to the midinguinal point. The upper third, or 2″, of this line marks the common iliac artery; the lower two-thirds, or 4″, the external iliac artery. It is at the junction of the upper one-third with the lower two-thirds that the bifurcation into external and internal iliac arteries takes place. At this point the ureter crosses the external artery and enters the pelvis in front of the internal artery.

Common and External Iliac Arteries. These two vessels curve from the aortic bifurcation across the front of the body of the 5th vertebra, along the medial border of the Psoas, and finally along the front of the Psoas to the midinguinal point where the name changes to femoral artery. The veins and arteries are loosely bound together in the extraperitoneal tissue.

The Veins lie within the bifurcation of the arteries, as shown in figure 313. The common iliac veins join to form the i. v. cava behind the right common iliac artery, in front of vertebra L. 5.

BRANCHES. Two branches arise from the external iliac artery just before it passes behind the inguinal lig. (*fig. 312*)—the *inferior epigastric* and *deep circumflex iliac arteries.*

Collateral Branches of the Abdominal Aorta:

A. Celiac trunk S. mesenteric a. I. mesenteric a.	To the G.I. canal and the 3 unpaired glands.
B. Suprarenal aa. Renal aa. Testicular aa.	To the 3 paired glands.
C. (Inf.) Phrenic aa. Lumbar aa. Median sacral a.	To the roof and walls of the abdomen.

These arteries, like the structures they supply, occupy three planes (*A*, *B*, *C*) as shown in figure 314 which makes it evident that vessels *A* ("gastro-intestinal plane") always remain ventral to vessels *B* ("three paired glands plane") and that these in turn remain ventral to, or within the embrace of, vessels *C* ("body wall plane").

A. The 3 arteries to the gastro-intestinal plane arise from the front of the aorta

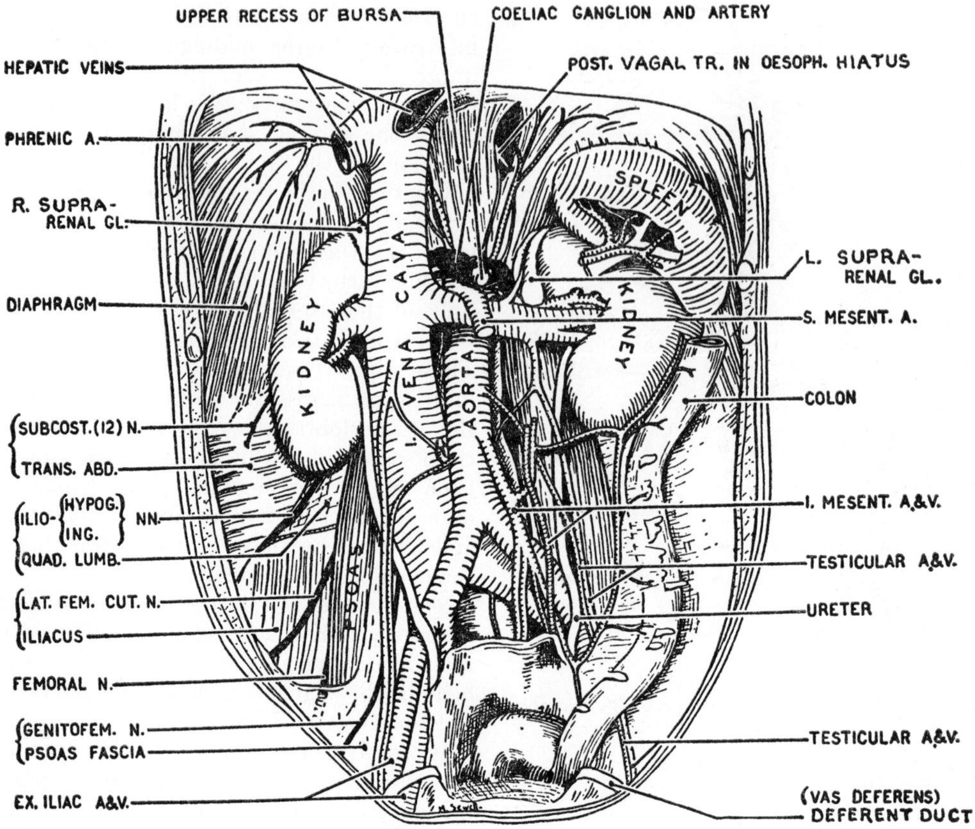

Fig. 313. Primary retroperitoneal structures, also spleen and colon

and are unpaired. Projecting forward like pegs, they prevent upward and downward displacement of certain structures that cross the median plane (*fig. 315A*).

The Celiac Trunk or Artery originally arose at the level of the 7th cervical vertebra, but when the lungs developed and depressed the diaphragm, the diaphragm in its turn forced the stomach and the celiac trunk caudally, so, now the median arcuate ligament, which unites the two crura of the diaphragm, rests upon the celiac trunk and the crura are astride it (*fig. 315*). Its level is, therefore, that of the disc between 12th thoracic and 1st lumbar vertebrae, which is a segment above the transpyloric plane. The trunk may be regarded as preventing ascent of the pancreas, which crosses below it.

The Superior Mesenteric Artery takes origin just below the celiac trunk, and therefore behind the neck of the pancreas, and

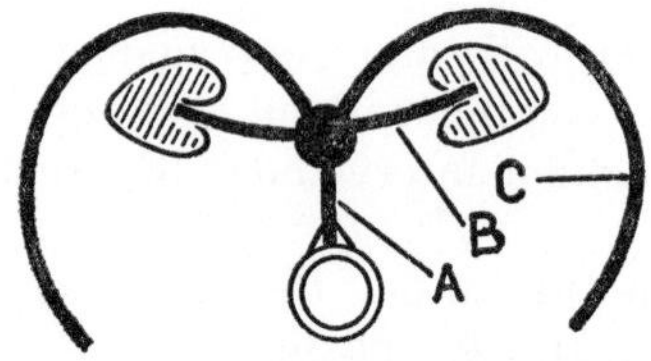

Fig. 314. "The three vascular planes" (Cross section, see *fig. 315*.)

therefore behind the splenic vein, which is embedded in the pancreas. It would prevent ascent of the left renal vein, which crosses the aorta close below it. The left renal vein may, indeed, be regarded as clamped between the root of the sup. mesenteric a. and the aorta like a nut within nut crackers (*fig. 285*). The artery descends ventral to the left renal vein, the uncinate process of the pancreas, and 3rd part of the duodenum and enters the root of the mesentery.

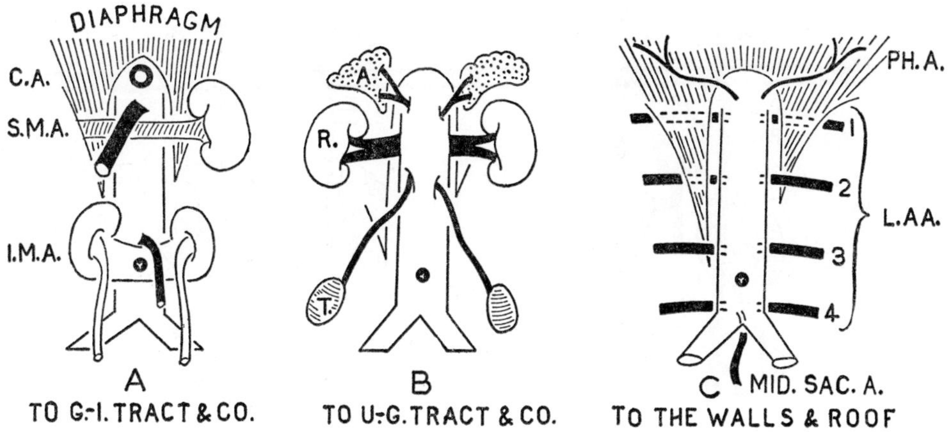

FIG. 315. The branches of the abdominal aorta arranged according to the planes they occupy

The Inferior Mesenteric Artery takes origin 1½″ above the aortic bifurcation, and ¾″ above the umbilicus, and therefore in front of the 3rd lumbar vertebra. It would arrest the ascent of a horseshoe kidney. Its origin is overlapped by the 3rd part of the duodenum (*fig. 291*).

B. The arteries to the 3 paired glands arise close together (*fig. 315B*):

The Renal Artery runs behind the renal vein and, therefore, arises just below the superior mesenteric artery.

The Suprarenal Artery arises just above the renal artery.

The Testicular (or *Ovarian*) *Artery* arises just below the renal artery.

C. From their inception the phrenic, lumbar, and median sacral arteries are part either of the roof or of the wall of the abdomen, no organ, vessel, or nerve intervening (*fig. 315C*).

The (*Inferior*) *Phrenic Artery* arises beside the celiac trunk and passes at once to the diaphragm, which it never leaves. Though but a small vessel, it attempts much; not only does it assist in supplying the diaphragm, which is the most important voluntary muscle in the body; it also sends branches to the suprarenal gland and esophagus and twigs to the liver.

The Lumbar Arteries. There is a pair of lumbar arteries for each of the five lumbar segments, but only four pairs succeed in arising from the aorta since it ends at the 4th lumbar vertebra. The 5th pair, called the *iliolumbar arteries*, spring from internal iliac arteries. The lumbar arteries, hugging the bodies of the vertebrae, pass dorsally medial to the sympathetic trunk and Psoas. The upper ones pass behind the crura also, and on the right side all pass behind the i. v. cava.

The Median Sacral Artery, the continuation of the aorta, descends in the median plane in contact with the 5th lumbar vertebra and sacrum and, therefore, behind the left common iliac vein. In lower mammals, as the anterior caudal artery, it supplies the tail.

Inferior Vena Cava

This, the largest vein in the body, begins in front of the 5th lumbar vertebra, below and to the right of the aortic bifurcation, where it is crossed anteriorly by the right common iliac artery. Above, it pierces the central tendon of the diaphragm at the level of the 8th (or lower) thoracic vertebra, which on the surface corresponds to a point on the right 6th costal cartilage, ½-inch from the side of the sternum. One-half inch higher it joins the right atrium of the heart. It extends, therefore, across eight vertebrae and is much longer (8½″ long) than the abdominal aorta which crosses only three and a half.

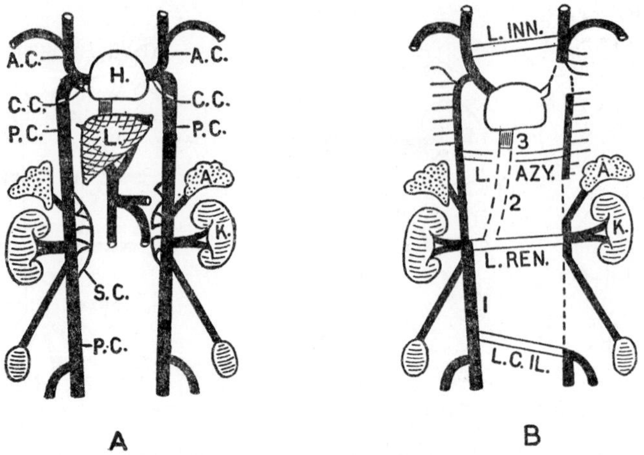

FIG. 316. Development of the inferior vena cava
(*A*): *A.C.*, *P.C.*, *S.C.*, *C.C.* = anterior, posterior, sub-, and common cardinal veins.
(*B*): *1* = postrenal segment of inf. vena cava; *2* = new connection; *3* = preheptatic segment.

The external and common iliac veins lie within the fork of the corresponding arteries. The internal iliac veins ascend out of the pelvic cavity behind their arteries.

DEVELOPMENT (*figs. 316* and *317*). The inferior vena cava is a composite vein of complex origin. Its course, relations, and tributaries, however, are rendered simple by reference to the elementary facts of its development; otherwise they are meaningless.

The outstanding features are these: a longitudinal vein, the *posterior cardinal vein*, appears on each side of the vertebral column and travels through the abdomen and thorax to join with the similar vein, the *anterior cardinal vein*, from the head, neck, and upper limb, to form the *common cardinal vein* (duct of Cuvier) which ends in the sinus venarum of the heart. In addition to receiving the *somatic segmental veins* (lumbar and intercostal) from the body wall, the posterior cardinal vein receives the *veins from the three paired glands*, but it does not receive the veins from the *gastro-intestinal tract* and its three unpaired glands, nor has it anything to do with them. They return their blood via the portal vein to the liver, and from the liver by the persisting right vitelline vein, which definitively becomes the terminal part of the inferior vena cava, to the heart, as described above (*fig. 279*, p. 248).

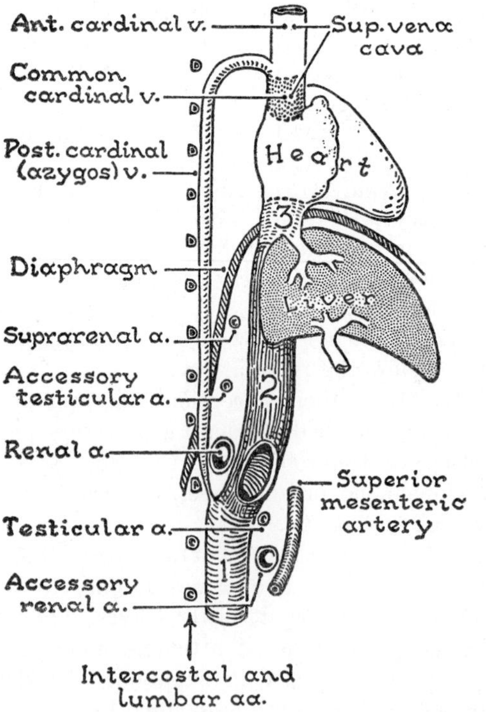

FIG. 317. Scheme of the development of the inferior vena cava, explaining its relationship to the arteries that cross it, side view.

Two cross-communications, of which one is the *left common iliac vein*, the other the *left renal vein*, divert the blood from the left posterior cardinal vein across the front of the aorta or its continuation, the median sacral artery, into the right posterior cardinal vein. The segment of the left posterior cardinal vein between the left common iliac and left renal veins is thereby rendered superfluous. It ceases to exist (*fig. 316B*), but it sometimes persists as the postrenal portion of a left inferior vena cava. Several cross-communications connect the *left lumbar veins* across the back of the aorta to the right posterior cardinal vein (*fig. 611*).

From the foregoing remarks you will appreciate that while the veins of the three right paired glands join the right post. cardinal vein independently, those of the three left paired glands join it collectively through the newly formed cross-communication. Now, though this communication is referred to in postnatal anatomy as a portion of the left renal vein, you must think of it as *"the vein of the three left paired glands"*; for such it properly is.

A newly formed vessel sprouts from the right posterior cardinal vein about the level of the right and left renal veins, and connects it with the right vitelline vein behind the liver (*fig. 316B, broken lines*).

Thereafter, the long route to the heart via the prerenal (thoracic) portion of the right posterior and common cardinal veins is almost abandoned in favor of the shorter route via the newly formed connection and the prehepatic part of the right vitelline vein. These three—(1) the right cardinal vein as far as the entrance of the renal veins, (2) the new connection, and (3) the terminal or prehepatic portion of the right vitelline vein—are the essential parts of the (right) inferior vena cava.

It is important to recognize that (1) the postrenal segment of the i. v. cava lies on a posterior plane—the plane of the three paired glands, that (3) the prehepatic segment lies on an anterior plane—the plane of the gastro-intestinal tract and the three unpaired glands, and that (2) the new connection connects the two planes.

»» If you will pull forward the right kidney, you will see a small vein, about the size of a lumbar vein, leave the back of the i. v. cava, at or just caudal to the site of entrance of the renal veins, and pass headward through the right crus of the diaphragm. This is a vestige of the prerenal portion of the right post. cardinal vein. In the thorax it largely becomes the azygos vein. The point to determine is that it lies on the same posterior plane as the postrenal portion of the i. v. cava for the simple reason that it was originally its headward continuation. Similarly, a vestige of the corresponding left post. cardinal vein passes from the back of the left renal vein through the crus and joins the hemiazygos vein.

Actually, the posterior cardinal vein is one of a series of three longitudinal intercommunicating veins (the posterior cardinal, supracardinal, and subcardinal) related to the primitive kidneys. Part of the supracardinal vein may be, and part of the subcardinal vein is, incorporated in the i. v. cava. Much academic interest has centered on these veins.

Tributaries of the Inferior Vena Cava. These fall into the same three groups as the branches of the abdominal aorta:

A. *The Blood from the Gastro-intestinal Canal* and from its three associated glands passes through the portal vein to the liver, and, after circulating in the liver, leaves it via the hepatic veins to enter the i. v. cava. When the liver is removed from the body, the open mouths of three large hepatic veins, issuing from the right and left lobes, are seen pointing upward as though ready to disgorge their contents through the last inch of the i. v. cava into the heart. And, when the portion of the i. v. cava embedded in the liver is slit up, the orifices of six or more small hepatic veins are seen.

B. *Veins of the Three Paired Glands:* On the right side the suprarenal, renal, and testicular (or ovarian) veins enter the i. v. cava separately; on the left side they unite to form a common trunk, the so-called left renal vein, which crosses in front of the aorta immediately or slightly below the origin of the superior mesenteric artery and, therefore, behind the pancreas and splenic (artery and) vein.

»» VARICOCELE, i.e., varicose testicular veins (p. 215), is a condition almost restricted to the left testicular (or ovarian) vein. In explanation of this, three mechanical reasons are advanced: (1) that the *left testicular vein* has less competent valves than the right vein—but this is not so, each having from one to three bicuspid valves in their abdominal portion (George); (2) that the adrenalin-laden blood issuing from the *left suprarenal vein* bathes the mouth of the left testicular vein causing it to contract—this explanation is ingenious; (3) that the *left "common" renal vein* is clamped between the root of the s. mesenteric artery and the aorta like a nut within nutcrackers; hence, in the erect posture, the intestines dragging on the sup. mesenteric artery apply pressure; this retards the flow in all three veins, viz., left testicular, left suprarenal, and left renal "proper"—this explanation has precedent, for the s. mesenteric artery (or root of the mesentery)

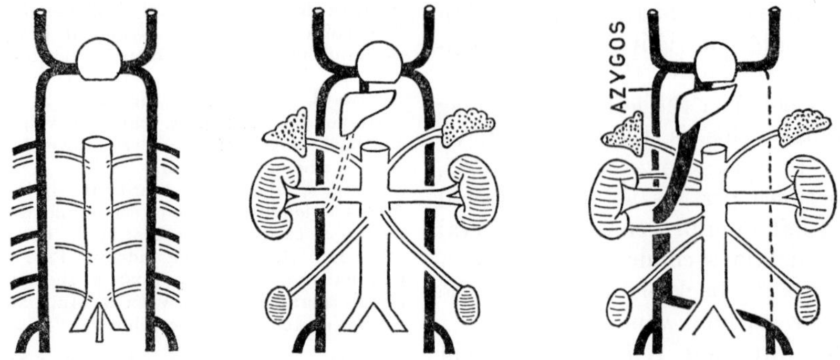

SOMATIC BRANCHES AND POST CARDINAL VEINS
A

LATERAL VISCERAL BRANCHES AND POST CARDINAL VEINS
B

LATERAL VISCERAL BRANCHES AND INF. VENA CAVA
C

FIG. 318. Explaining the relationships of the branches of the aorta to the cardinal veins and subsequently to the i. v. cava. In *C* note the relations of the accessory renal arteries to the i. v. cava.

has been shown by Hyde and others to be capable of obstructing the duodenum (*fig. 285*).

C. *Of the Veins of the Body Wall* the right and left (inferior) phrenic veins enter the i. v. cava; the left vein, however, commonly ends in the left renal vein.

The lumbar veins accompany their arteries. Those of both sides end in the i. v. cava or in some derivatives of the cardinal system of veins, the left ones crossing behind the aorta.

The right and left iliolumbar veins, which are the veins of the 5th lumbar segment, end in the right and left common iliac veins.

The median sacral vein ends in the left common iliac vein.

The lumbar veins, on each side, are linked together by an **ascending lumbar vein,** which lies in front of the lumbar transverse processes (*fig. 677*). This vein begins caudally at the common iliac vein and ends cranially at the azygos (or hemiazygos) vein. Commonly a link is missing, as is also the case between the two hemiazygos veins (*fig. 641*). The right and left ascending lumbar veins are (1) accessory to the i. v. cava, and (2) they are to be classified with the vertebral venous system (p. 569).

Relationships of the Branches of the Aorta to the I. V. Cava are explained on a developmental basis in figures 317 and 318.

A shows that the somatic segmental arteries (lumbar, iliolumbar, and intercostal) pass behind the cardinal veins in the embryo and, therefore, behind the inferior vena cava in the adult.

B shows that the arteries to the three paired glands pass in front of the cardinal veins. The (inf.) phrenic artery, being originally a branch of a suprarenal artery, does likewise.

C shows the relations that the arteries to the three right paired glands bear to the composite vessel called the i. v. cava—those crossing its postrenal segment pass in front; those crossing its prerenal segment pass behind. So, the right testicular (or ovarian) artery passes in front; whereas the right renal and suprarenal arteries pass behind, but of course they all cross on a plane anterior to the right posterior cardinal vein.

Accessory right renal arteries arising from the aorta below the renal vein usually cross in front of the i. v. cava; whereas accessory right renal and testicular arteries arising above the renal vein usually cross behind the i. v. cava.

All arteries and branches of arteries to the gastro-intestinal canal and its three unpaired glands that pass to the right of the median plane must cross in front of the i. v. cava, e.g., the hepatic, gastroduodenal, right colic, ileocolic, and the superior mesenteric artery itself where it lies in the root of the mesentery.

TABLE 12

The Relations of the Great Vessels—in Review

<table>
<tr><th></th><th colspan="4">Anterior Relations</th><th>Posterior Relations</th></tr>
<tr><th>Vessel</th><th colspan="2">G. I. canal, 3 unpaired glands their vessels and ducts</th><th>3 paired glands, their vessels and ducts</th><th>Other structures</th><th>Mainly parts of the body wall</th></tr>
<tr><td>Abdominal Aorta</td><td colspan="2">Stomach
(lesser sac intervening)
Pancreas (body)
splenic vein
transverse colon and mesocolon
Duodenum (3rd part)
Root of mesentery
Jejunum and ileum
(greater sac intervening)</td><td>Left renal vein
draining 3 left paired glands</td><td>Celiac and other preaortic plexuses</td><td>3½ vertebral bodies, discs and anterior longit. lig.
Left lumbar veins</td></tr>
<tr><td>C. Iliac A.</td><td>Right</td><td>Left
Inf. mesenteric vessels
Sigmoid aa. and veins</td><td></td><td>Branches joining aortic to hypogastric plexus</td><td>5th lumbar body and ala of sacrum
Sympathetic tr.
Lumbosacral tr.
Iliolumbar a.
Obturator n.
also on right side
I. vena cava</td></tr>
<tr><td>Ex. Iliac A.</td><td>End of Ileum
? Appendix
? Cecum</td><td>Sigmoid colon and mesocolon</td><td>Ureter
(male)
Deferent duct
Testicular a. and v.
(female)
Lig. teres uteri
Ovarian a. and v.

Genitofemoral n.</td><td></td><td>Psoas and its fascia</td></tr>
<tr><td>I. V. Cava</td><td>Liver (bare area)
Epiploic foramen
Duodenum (1st)</td><td>Portal vein
Hepatic and gastroduodenal a.
Bile duct</td><td>R. testicular (ovarian) a.</td><td>R. common iliac a.</td><td>Above renal vein
Diaphragm
Adrenal gland
Arteries to body wall and to 3 paired glands

Below renal vein
Psoas Crus
Vertebrae
Sympathetic tr.
Arteries to body wall</td></tr>
<tr><td></td><td colspan="2">Pancreas (head)
Bile duct
Accessory and main pancreatic ducts
Duodenum (3rd part)
Mesentery root and branches of s. mesenteric vv.
Small intestine
(greater sac intervening)</td><td></td><td></td><td></td></tr>
</table>

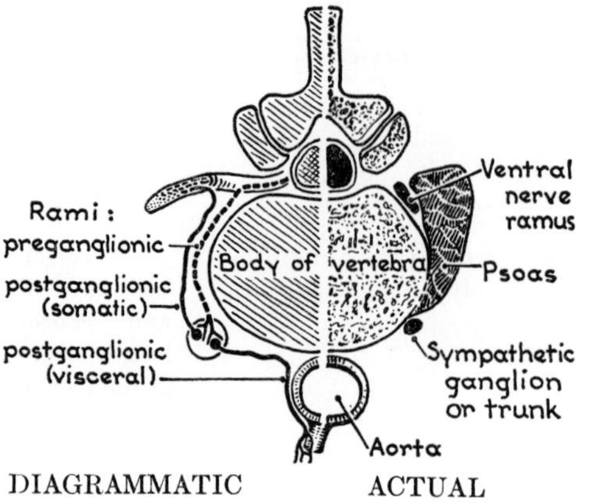

FIG. 319. Pre- and postganglionic fibers of a sympathetic ganglion.

Relationships. It would be folly to commit to memory the relationships of the great vessels when they can be arrived at by systematically passing in review the different parts of the G. I. tract and Co., U. G. Tract and Co., Body Wall, and other possible structures, as is done in table 12.

ABDOMINAL AUTONOMIC NERVES

The autonomic nervous system within the abdomen is represented by:

1. The sympathetic trunks, white and gray rami communicantes, lumbar splanchnic nerves, and thoracic splanchnic nerves.
2. The prevertebral plexuses—celiac, intermesenteric, and superior hypogastric.
3. Parasympathetic nerves—vagus and pelvic splanchnic nerves.

Sympathetic Trunk (*fig. 324*). In the abdomen the sympathetic trunk follows faithfully the anterior border of the Psoas. It descends, therefore, on the bodies of the vertebrae and the intervertebral discs, the transversely running lumbar vessels alone intervening. It enters from the thorax with the Psoas behind the medial arcuate lig. (lumbocostal arch) and it passes into the pelvis behind the common iliac vessels.

The *right trunk* is concealed by the i. v. cava, and crossed by the right renal artery. The *left trunk* is crossed by the left renal vessels, the left testicular and the inf. mesenteric artery.

As a rule each trunk has four ganglia —not five—two probably having fused.

CONNECTIONS. Each trunk receives a *white ramus* from each of the upper two (or three) lumbar nerves and sends one or more *gray rami* to each of the five lumbar nerves to be distributed with nerves to somatic structures. These white and gray rami curve backward and laterally on the sides of the vertebrae either with the lumbar vessels or independently (*fig. 319*). Four rami, the *lumbar splanchnic nerves,* run medially to the intermesenteric and superior hypogastric plexus to be distributed largely with blood vessels to viscera.

Celiac Plexus. The *celiac ganglia* (*fig. 306*) are tough, nodular masses connected to each other by fibers that encircle the celiac trunk, the whole being known as the *celiac plexus,* or as the *solar plexus,* because its branches radiate like the rays of the sun.

Each ganglion lies behind the peritoneum, between the celiac trunk and the suprarenal

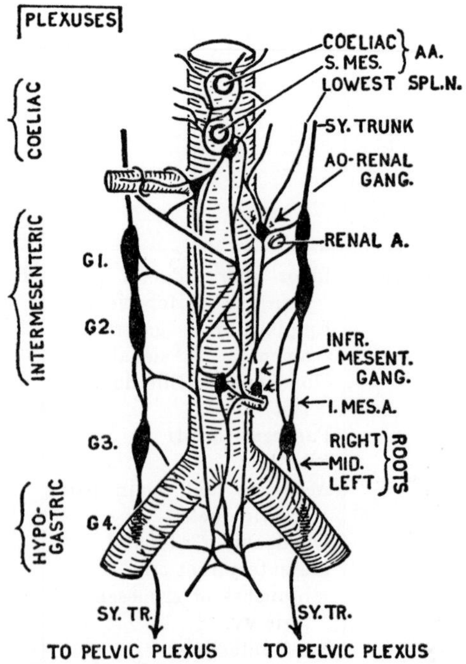

FIG. 319.1. The intermesenteric and sup. hypogastric plexuses. (Dissection by K. Baldwin.)

gland and, therefore, on the crus of the diaphragm. The i. v. cava largely conceals the right ganglion; the pancreas and splenic artery the left one.

The celiac plexus extends down the front of the aorta and is reinforced by the lumbar splanchnic nerves to form the **intermesenteric and superior hypogastric plexus.** The intermesenteric lies in front of the aorta; the hypogastric lies within the bifurcation of the aorta and therefore in front of the left common iliac vein and the 5th lumbar vertebra and disc (*fig. 319.1*).

From the celiac plexus fine branches stream into the suprarenal gland (*fig. 306*).

Sympathetic Connections. The greater splanchnic nerve is the size of a palmar digital nerve. It pierces the crus abreast of the celiac trunk and at once joins the celiac ganglion; the lesser splanchnic nerve pierces the crus just below and laterally and also joins the ganglion; the lowest splanchnic nerve also pierces the crus and joins an offshoot of the celiac plexus, called the *renal plexus.*

Parasympathetic Connections. Fibers of both *vagus nerves*, via a large branch of the posterior vagal trunk, pass through the celiac plexus (*fig. 306*) to be distributed with arteries (celiac, sup. mesenteric, and ? renal) to the abdominal viscera.

Fibers of both *pelvic splanchnic nerves* ascend from the pelvis in the hypogastric plexuses to be distributed with the inferior mesenteric artery to the gut.

The vagi control the gut as far as the left colic flexure; the pelvic splanchnics beyond it (*fig. 44.2*).

POSTERIOR WALL OF ABDOMEN PROPER

»» The gastro-intestinal apparatus is necessarily dissected before the three paired gland apparatus and the three paired gland apparatus before the posterior abdominal wall. It is, however, by reconstructing from behind forward that you best appreciate posterior relationships. Hence, when reviewing, it is well to read the sections on the posterior abdominal wall, diaphragm, and great vessels before studying the three paired glands, and to read the section on the three paired glands before studying the pancreas and duodenum.

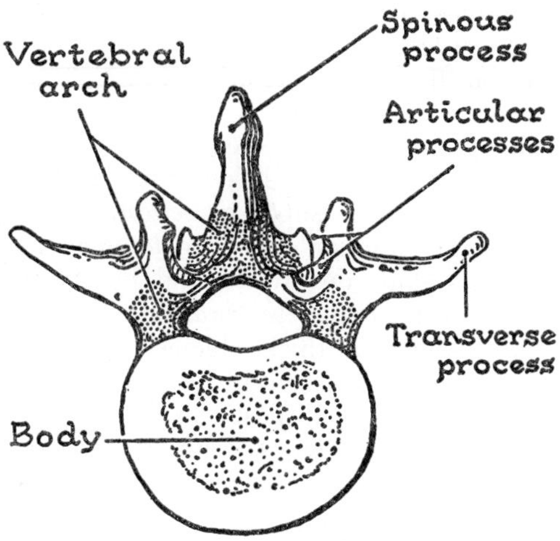

FIG. 320. A lumbar vertebra from above

Bony Parts

In the median plane are the bodies, intervertebral discs, and transverse processes of the five lumbar vertebrae; laterally the wall extends from the 12th rib above to the pelvic brim below, and it is divided into upper and lower parts by the iliac crest. The *bodies* of the lumbar vertebrae increase in height and width from 1st–5th; so do the discs. The *discs* bulge, and the student commonly mistakes them for bodies until he happens to stick the point of his knife into them. The *transverse processes* project laterally at the levels of the upper halves of the bodies. The 3rd projects farthest; those above and below it project progressively less. The 5th is stout and conical and it projects upward, backward, and laterally. The *12th rib*, variable in length, curves downward and laterally to about the level of the 2nd lumbar disc. The *iliac crest* curves upward and laterally to the level of the middle or lower part of the 4th lumbar vertebra (*fig. 323*).

The region of the abdomen between the iliac crests and the pelvic brim is the *pelvis major*. It includes the alae of the sacrum and the iliac fossae described on page 315.

The Lumbar Vertebrae (*fig. 320*). The *body* is large, kidney-shaped, and flat above and below. The 1st is always deeper behind than in front, so is the 2nd as a rule, the 3rd is transitional (either deeper or less deep), but the 4th is always deeper in front, and the 5th is much deeper in front.

The *pedicles* are directed backward and laterally. Above and below each pedicle, there is a small superior *vertebral notch* and a large inferior one. The *laminae* are thick and slope downward and backward, enclosing a triangular *vertebral foramen.*

The *spine* is a thick oblong plate that projects nearly horizontally backward and ends in a thickened posterior border.

The *transverse processes* each spring from the junction of pedicles and laminae and have a wide spread, the 3rd having the widest (*fig. 323*). They act, or function, as ossifications extending into the posterior aponeurosis of the Transversus Abdominis and as such they are thin and band-like; and, conforming to the shape of the rounded abdominal wall, they are directed slightly backward. Their ends give attachment to the Transversus Abdominis aponeurosis (ant. lamina of the thoracolumbar fascia) and to the Quadratus Lumborum. Owing to the topographical position of the 5th vertebra, its processes extend on to the body and are conical (p. 320).

The superior *articular processes* spring from the pedicles and, facing medially, grasp the inferior processes of the vertebra above, which spring from laminae and face laterally. The directions, however, gradually change, the inferior articular processes of the 5th lumbar vertebra facing nearly forward.

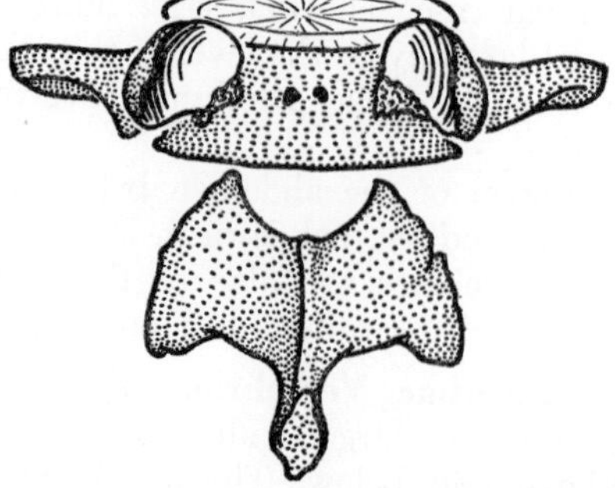

FIG. 321. The 5th lumbar vertebra is in two pieces in 5 per cent of individuals, rendering them liable to a deformity called spondylolisthesis.

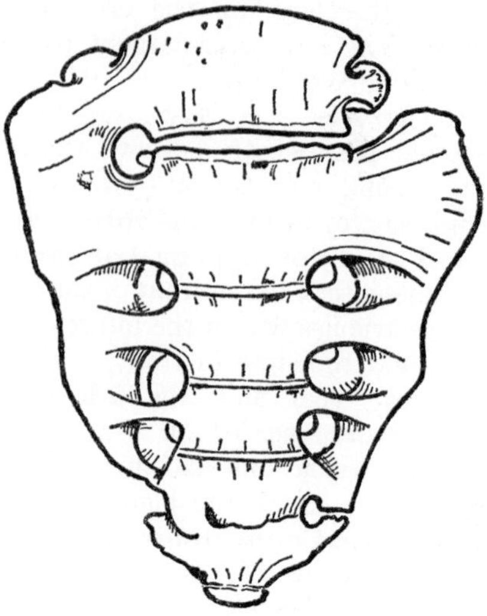

FIG. 322. The 5th lumbar vertebra is commonly partly sacralized.

Variations (racial, sexual, and chronological).

1. In 6.4 per cent of 1952 adult white males, one of the lower vertebrae is a *Bipartite Vertebra*, having a so-called "separate neural arch"—the spine, laminae, and inferior articular processes being detached (*fig. 321*). This is probably the result of fracture.

»» The bodies, losing the restraining influence of the inferior articular processes, tend to slip forward (spondylolisthesis). Now, this condition is twice as common in white people as in Negroes; it is three times as common in the male as in the female, and the incidence is unchanged between the ages of 20 and 80 years. The flaw is unilateral in one-sixth of cases and bilateral in five-sixths. Vertebra L. 5 is the defective vertebra in 85 per cent of instances, and L. 4 in 9 per cent. (Roche and Rowe.) The condition was found in 10 per cent of 162 Japanese and in 27 per cent of 350 Eskimos (T. D. Stewart).

2. The 5th lumbar vertebra is commonly partly sacralized (*fig. 322*).

3. The two sides of the vertebral arch of the lower (or of any) vertebrae may fail to meet (spina bifida).

Muscles and Fascia

Muscles. Iliacus, Psoas, Psoas Minor, Quadratus Lumborum, Transversus Abdominis, and Intertransversarii (*fig. 324*).

The **Iliacus,** like the iliac fossa from which it arises, is fan-shaped. Since the iliac fossa is smooth and devoid of any roughness or ridge, it follows that the origin is fleshy, but it does not include the lower one-third of the fossa because this is too close to the insertion (*axiom*, p. 103).

The fleshy fibers of the Iliacus are inserted into the lateral and anterior aspects of the Psoas tendon, and below the tendon a few of them pass directly to the femur.

The Iliacus and Psoas are referred to collectively as the Iliopsoas.

The **Psoas** is the part of the Iliacus that has migrated above the iliac crest. It takes fleshy origin from the sides of the bodies and intervertebral discs of all the lumbar vertebrae and Th. 12, the attachments extending backward on to the transverse processes and forward as far as the sympathetic trunk.

The ventral rami of the upper four lumbar nerves plunge into the substance of the Psoas when they emerge from the intervertebral foramina, but the 5th ventral ramus escapes under the medial margin of the muscle. On the sides of the vertebral bodies, which are constricted like a waist, the lumbar vessels and the rami communicantes of the sympathetic trunk run dorsally protected by sheets of fascia which bridge them and afford the Psoas an uninterrupted origin (*fig. 324*).

The Psoas ends in a tendon which is inserted into a traction epiphysis—the lesser trochanter of the femur. The Psoas plays in the groove between the anterior inferior iliac spine and the iliopubic eminence prior to crossing the middle of the front of the hip joint. Its tendon therefore must lie posterior to its fleshy portion and it must be separated from the bony groove and the capsule of the hip joint by a bursa, the *psoas [iliopectineal] bursa* (p. 433).

The Psoas assists the Rectus Abdominis to flex the lumbar segments of the column, and it assists the Iliacus to flex the hip joint.

»» The **Psoas Minor** is either absent (50 per cent) or insignificant. It arises from vertebral bodies Th. 12 and L. 1. Its flat tendon runs downward in front of the Psoas, blending with and strengthening the Psoas fascia through which it can be traced to a prominent ridge on the iliac portion of the pelvic brim.

Comparative Anatomy. In some lower mammals the Psoas Minor is larger than the Psoas itself. As a flexor of the pelvis on the spine, its value to the rabbit when running and to the ape when brachiating is apparent.

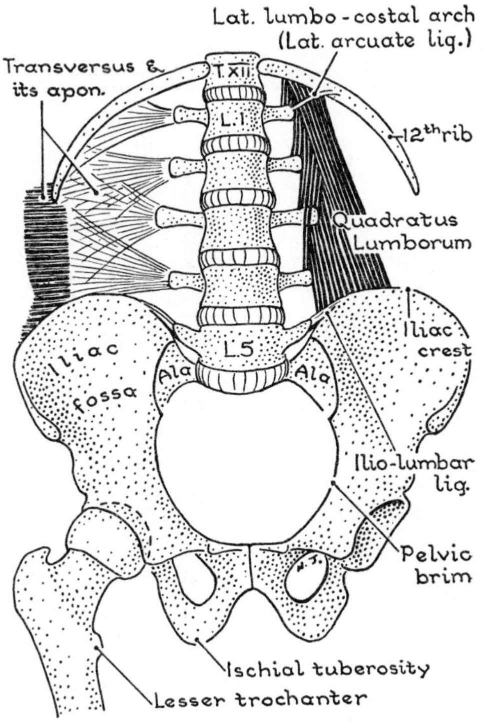

FIG. 323. The skeleton of the posterior abdominal wall.
The Transversus Abdominis and its aponeurosis.
The Quadratus Lumborum.

The **Quadratus Lumborum** is quadrate but not rectangular, for its lateral border is oblique (*fig. 323*); and this oblique border is a landmark when exposing the kidney from behind (*fig. 308*).

The Quadratus arises from the posterior 2″ of the part of the inner lip of the iliac crest that bounds the iliac fossa. It runs obliquely superomedially to be inserted into the medial 2″ of the lower border of the last rib. Also, it gives slips to the tips of the lumbar transverse processes and it receives slips from them.

The thin fascial covering ventral to this rhomboidal muscle is slightly thickened above to form the *lateral arcuate lig.* (lumbocostal arch)—which gives origin to the diaphragm—and greatly thickened below to form the important *iliolumbar ligament* (p. 320).

The **Transversus Abdominis** helps to form a sheath for the Rectus Abdominis in front and for the deep muscles of the back

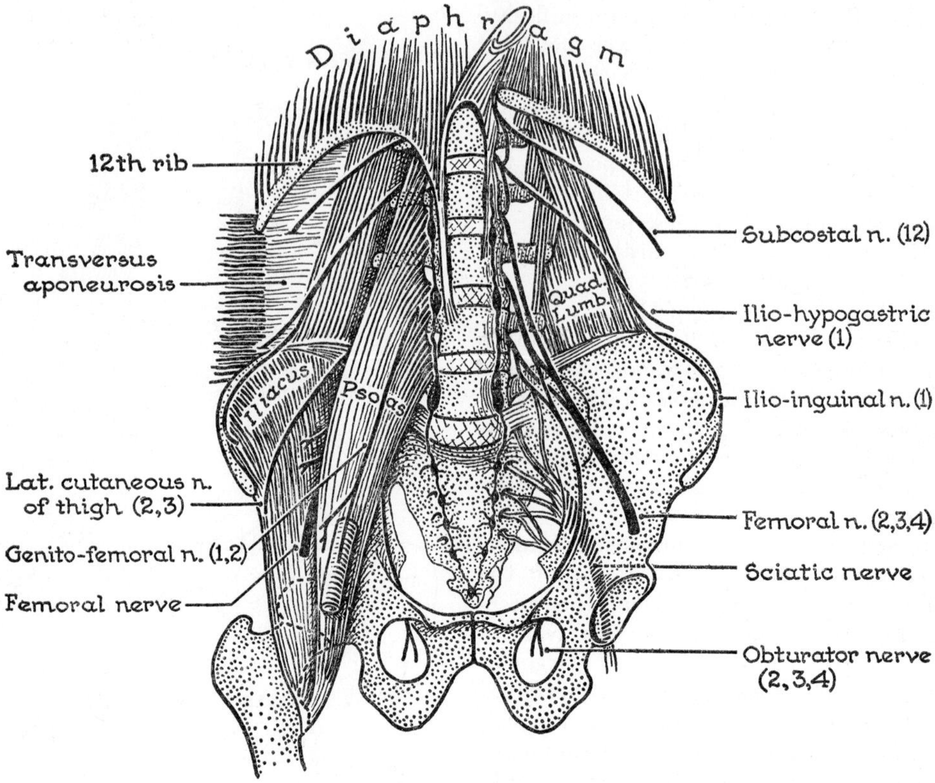

FIG. 324. The lumbar plexus and the muscles of the posterior abdominal wall

behind (*fig. 215*). Near the lateral border of the Quadratus it becomes aponeurotic. This posterior aponeurosis divides into two layers, the anterior and posterior layers of the thoracolumbar fascia. Of these, the posterior passes to the tips of the lumbar spines and supraspinous lig., whereas the anterior passes behind the Quadratus and attaches itself to the tips of the lumbar transverse processes (*fig. 323*), the last rib above and the iliac crest below.

The **Intertransversarii** are strong fleshy bands that pass between adjacent borders of transverse processes.

The **Fascia Iliaca** is a part of the general fascia that lines the muscles that enclose the abdominal cavity. This strong fascial sheet covers the Iliacus and the Psoas, and inferomedially it is separated by a partition from the fascia covering the Pectineus. It exemplifies the rule that fasciae do not cross exposed areas of bone but unite with them and, if strong, create lines or ridges.

In accordance with this rule, it is found that:

1. *Above and laterally*, the fascia iliaca is attached to the sharp, inner lip of the iliac crest.

2. *Medially*, reinforced by the tendon of Psoas Minor, it crosses the Psoas and gains attachment to the iliac part of the pelvic brim. Superiorly, and still following the medial border of the Psoas, it crosses the ala of the sacrum obliquely (and is there pierced by iliolumbar vessels, obturator nerve, and descending half of the ventral ramus of nerve L. 4) but, being weak, it makes no line on the ala. The ventral ramus of nerve L. 5 emerges from the intervertebral foramen below the origin of the Psoas and its fascia. The genitofemoral nerve pierces the Psoas fascia (sometimes as two roots).

3. *Below*, it is carried downward in front of the Iliacus and Psoas into the thigh. As the fascia covering the Iliacus is passing

behind the inguinal lig., it adheres to it and to the fascia transversalis; and in the thigh it lies deep to the fascia lata. But, the part covering the Psoas (and also the pectineal fascia) is separated from the inguinal ligament, fascia transversalis, and fascia lata by the femoral artery, femoral vein, and deep inguinal lymph vessels which here descend into the thigh wrapped around in extraperitoneal areolar tissue, called the femoral sheath (*fig. 401*).

4. The fascia iliaca is carried *upward*, above the iliac crest, in front of the Psoas as the Psoas fascia.

The Psoas Fascia is thickened above to form the medial arcuate lig., which gives origin to the diaphragm. Laterally, it blends with the Quadratus Lumborum fascia and is attached to the tips of the first three lumbar transverse processes, which project slightly beyond the Psoas (*fig. 324*). Medially, it is attached to the bodies of the lumbar vertebrae and to their discs. The attachment is, however, interrupted where the lumbar vessels and rami communicantes pass backward on the sides of the bodies.

The Iliopsoas, then, lies in an osseofascial pocket; hence, the contractions of this muscle disturb to a minimum the viscera (e.g., appendix, cecum, and colon) that lie in front of it.

Nerves

»» **The Lumbar Nerves.** The ventral and dorsal roots of each of the five lumbar nerves unite in the intervertebral foramen, below the vertebra with which they correspond numerically, to form a lumbar nerve. Each mixed nerve so formed at once divides into a ventral and a dorsal ramus. The *dorsal rami* are small. Each of them at once curves backward, lateral to a superior articular process and medial to an Intertransverse muscle.

The *ventral rami* are large, and they increase in size from the 1st to the 5th. Each of the five receives one or two gray rami communicantes from the sympathetic trunk; each of the upper two (or three) sends a white ramus communicans to the sympathetic trunk; most of the lumbar nerves supply the Psoas, Quadratus Lumborum, and Intertransversarii. Each of the five continues downward across the front of the root of the transverse process of the vertebra next below, the 5th crossing the ala of the sacrum (*fig. 324*). The ventral rami form the *lumbar plexus* (see below) and *lumbosacral trunk.*

LUMBAR PLEXUS

The lumbar plexus is formed by the ventral rami of the upper three and one-half lumbar nerves. The first ramus is joined by a branch of the 12th thoracic ramus. [The lower half of the 4th ramus joins the 5th ramus near the anterior border of the ala of the sacrum to form the *Lumbosacral Trunk*.] The branches of the plexus encounter the Psoas and pass among its posterior fibers.

With the exception of two branches, the *genitofemoral* and *obturator*, the plexus remains outside the fascial lining of the abdomen and pelvis. Its largest and most important branches are the *femoral* and *obturator nerves*, both of which spring from the segments L. 2, 3, and 4.

The **Obturator Nerve** courses to the upper part of the obturator foramen. It, therefore, appears from under cover of the medial border of the Psoas, where it pierces the psoas fascia. It then crosses the sacroiliac joint (but not in contact with it), and, as it passes lateral to the internal iliac vessels and ureter, it enters the pelvic cavity.

The **Femoral Nerve** courses to the lateral side of the femoral sheath and enters the thigh behind the inguinal ligament. It, therefore, appears at the lateral border of the Psoas, and runs downward in the angle between the Psoas and Iliacus. Being extrafascial, it cannot enter the femoral sheath, which encloses the femoral vessels (*fig. 412*). It supplies the Iliacus.

»» It is of interest to observe that though the femoral nerve supplies the muscles on the front of the thigh, its three roots arise behind the three roots of the obturator nerve, which supplies the muscles on the medial aspect of the thigh. The explanation is that during development the limb undergoes medial rotation whereby the femoral nerve region, originally behind, is brought to the front; and the obturator nerve region is carried from the front to the medial side. The femoral nerve may be compared to a posterior division of the brachial plexus; the obturator nerve to an anterior.

In addition to the femoral nerve, four other nerves appear at the lateral border of the Psoas. In ascending order they are:

1. *The Lateral (femoral) Cutaneous Nerve,* which arises from L. 2 and 3 either directly or else indirectly as a branch of the femoral nerve. It descends across the Iliacus and enters the thigh by passing behind the inguinal ligament anywhere between the anterior superior spine and the femoral nerve.

2. and 3. *The Ilio-inguinal* and *Iliohypogastric Nerves,* which arise either singly or together from L. 1, enter the abdomen behind the medial arcuate lig., and cross in front of the Quadratus.

The *ilio-inguinal nerve* is directed toward the anterior superior iliac spine. It pierces the Transversus about an inch behind the spine and the Internal Oblique about an inch in front of it, and then continues its course deep to the External Oblique aponeurosis less than a finger's breadth above the inguinal ligament.

The *iliohypogastric nerve,* commonly containing fibers from Th. 12 as well as L. 1, follows a similar course at a higher level. It pierces the Transversus aponeurosis just beyond the Quadratus, and the Internal Oblique in front of the anterior superior spine. The lateral cutaneous branch of the iliohypogastric nerve crosses the iliac crest behind the tubercle, and descends to the level of the greater trochanter of the femur (*fig. 425*).

4. *The Subcostal Nerve* (*ventral ramus of Th. 12*) is not a branch of the lumbar plexus, but it enters the abdomen behind the lateral arcuate lig. and, therefore, in front of the Quadratus Lumborum. Unlike an intercostal nerve, it sags below its rib. It pierces the Transversus aponeurosis, and then runs between the Transversus and Obliquus Internus, which guide it ultimately to the Rectus sheath which it enters. Its lateral cutaneous branch crosses the iliac crest behind the anterior superior spine and descends to the level of the greater trochanter (*figs. 324* and *216*).

The Genitofemoral Nerve (L. 1 and 2) comes to lie within the fascial lining of the abdomen and, to do so, pierces the Psoas and the psoas fascia. It divides at a very variable level into two branches, *femoral* and *genital,* which descend in front of the Psoas toward the midinguinal point. The *femoral branch* is the cutaneous nerve of the femoral triangle. To reach the triangle it requires to pierce the fascia a second time. It does so in several branches which run lateral to the femoral artery, behind the inguinal ligament, and through the fascia lata. The *genital branch* supplies the cremaster muscle and traverses the inguinal canal to end in the skin of the scrotum. In its course it passes in front of the end of the external iliac artery and pierces the coverings of the spermatic cord, one by one.

»» **Variations.** A considerable and variable interchange of fibers takes place in the abdominal wall between the iliohypogastric, ilio-inguinal, lateral femoral cutaneous, and genitofemoral nerves, in consequence of which the territory each supplies is variable.

An *Accessory Obturator Nerve* commonly arises from L. 3 and 4. It is a small nerve which, when present, adheres to the psoas fascia along the medial border of the Psoas. It crosses the superior ramus of the pubis and sends branches to the Pectineus and hip joint.

DIAPHRAGM

The diaphragm (Gk. dia = through, across; phragma = a partition) is the musculo-aponeurotic partition between the thorax and the abdomen. It has a rounded cupola on each side below the lungs, and a depressed median portion on which the heart lies (*fig. 326*). The median portion rises to the level of the xiphisternal joint which corresponds behind to the body of the 9th Th. vertebra or 8th spine (*fig. 548*).

The right cupola rises to the 5th rib, ½ inch below the right nipple; the left cupola rises to the 5th interspace, an inch below the left nipple. These correspond on the posterior surface of the body to points ½″ and 1″ below the inferior angles of the scapulae, and lateral to them.

Attachments and Marginal Gaps. The diaphragm is attached on each side by fleshy digitations to the back of the xiphoid process, to the inner surfaces of the 7th to 12th costal cartilages, and to the vertebral column. The costal slips interdigitate with slips of the Transversus Abdominis. Of the vertebral attachments or *crura,* the more powerful right crus is attached to the bodies of the upper three

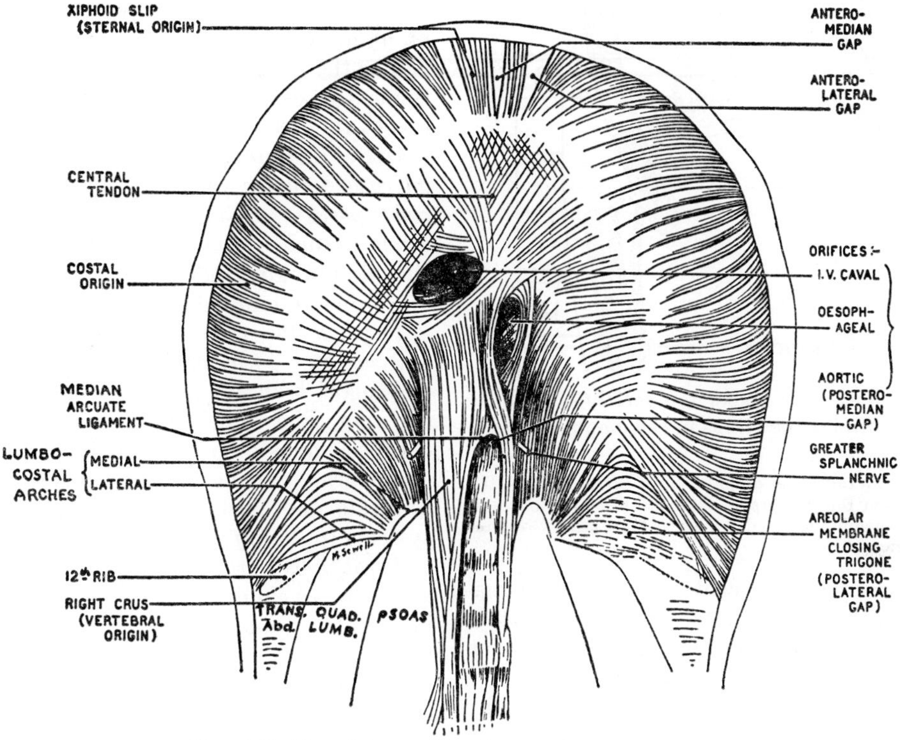

FIG. 325. The abdominal surface of the diaphragm. (*Lumbocostal arches* = *Arcuate ligaments*)

lumbar vertebrae; the left to the bodies of the upper two.

Anteriorly, in the median plane, there is a slight gap between the right and left xiphoid slips.

Posteriorly, in the median plane, there is a large gap between the two crura; through this the aorta passes. The medial parts of the crura are fibrous, and they join in front of the aorta immediately above the celiac trunk to form the fibrous *median arcuate ligament.*

Anteriorly, on each side, between the xiphoid slip and the slip from the 7th c. cartilage, the superior epigastric vessels pass into the rectus sheath.

Posteriorly, on each side, between the crus and the slip from the 12th rib, the pleural and peritoneal cavities are continuous with each other in prenatal life until crural fibers migrate laterally across the space toward the 12th rib, and as a rule succeed in reaching it, thereby closing the space and separating the two cavities (*fig. 325*). Sometimes they fail; a triangular gap, the *vertebrocostal trigone* (lumbocostal trigone), above the medial half of the 12th rib is the result. The areolar and muscular fibers closing the space find attachment to the fascia covering the Psoas and Quadratus Lumborum, which in response becomes thickened and strengthened to form the *medial* and *lateral arcuate ligs.* (lumbocostal arches). Of these, the medial ligament bridges the Psoas and extends from the lateral border of the crus to the transverse process of the 1st lumbar vertebra; the lateral ligament bridges the Quadratus and extends from the latter point to the middle of the 12th rib. In consequence, the upper ends of the Psoas and Quadratus lie within the thorax.

»» *Anomaly.* In cases where the pleural and peritoneal cavities remain in open communication through the vertebrocostal trigone, some of the abdominal contents may come to occupy the pleural cavity; that

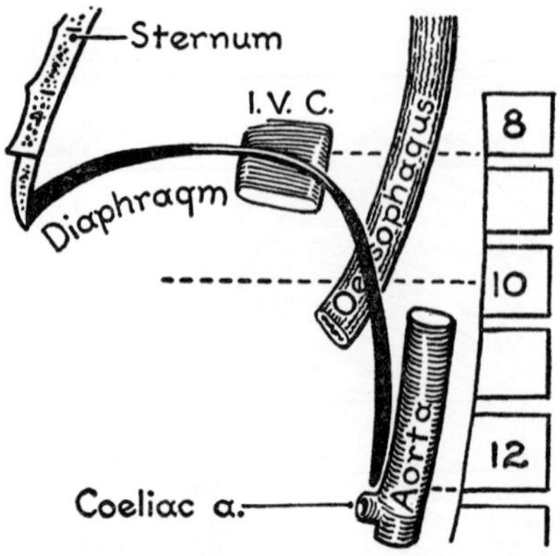

FIG. 325.1. The higher the vertebral level, the more ventral is the hiatus in the diaphragm.

is to say, a *congenital diaphragmatic hernia* results. But even when the diaphragm fails to close the space, an areolar membrane usually does so. The kidney overlies the trigone.

Structure. The central part of the diaphragm is called the *central tendon*. It is composed of decussating and interwoven tendinous fibers, and it has the shape of a trefoil or clover leaf. The peripheral fleshy fibers converge on it.

Structures Piercing (*fig. 325.1*). *The I. V. Cava* pierces the central tendon at the level of the 8th Th. vertebra. Its orifice enlarges during inspiration due to the pull of the surrounding fleshy fibers, and its contents are hurried on to the heart.[6]

The Esophagus pierces the decussating fibers of the right crus at the level of the 10th vertebra. These fibers appear to act as a sphincter for the cardiac end of the stomach and prevent its contents from returning to the esophagus, but recent studies appear to deny this role (Mann, Greenwood, and Ellis).

The Aorta does not pierce the diaphragm but passes behind the median arcuate ligament at the level of the 12th vertebra. It is not affected by the contraction of the diaphragm.

The vertebral levels, then are 8, 10, and 12.

[6] In some animals there is a certain degree of constriction of the i. v. cava during strong contraction of the diaphragm, as revealed by X-ray following injections of thorotrast; and it is not agreed by all that in man the i. v. caval opening in the diaphragm does enlarge during inspiration (Franklin).

Of the three large orifices in the Diaphragm, the aortic hiatus is in the median plane; the caval foramen is an inch to the right; the esophageal hiatus is an inch or less to the left.

Other Structures Piercing. *Through the caval foramen* pass some branches of the *right phrenic nerve*. The left phrenic and other branches of the right phrenic pierce the diaphragm independently to spread out on its abdominal surface.

Through the esophageal hiatus pass the *anterior and posterior vagal trunks* and the *esophageal branches of the left gastric artery and vein*. The vein is of special importance, because, anastomosing, as it does, with esophageal branches of the azygos veins, it connects the portal and systemic venous systems (p. 247; *fig. 278*).

Through the aortic hiatus passes the *thoracic duct* [also a vein connecting the right ascending lumbar vein to the azygos system] (*fig. 677*).

The phrenic nerves and the vagal trunks are not the only nerves to pass through the diaphragm, for on each side the three *splanchnic nerves* (greater, lesser, and lowest) pierce the crura to end in the celiac (and aortico-renal) ganglia.

Nerve and Blood Supply (*fig. 326*). The diaphragm is supplied by (1) the phrenic nerve (C. 3, 4, and 5) which is both motor and sensory, and by (2) the lower intercostal nerves, which are sensory to the peripheral parts.

»» The greater part of the diaphragm developed in the neck, but descended before the expanding lungs,

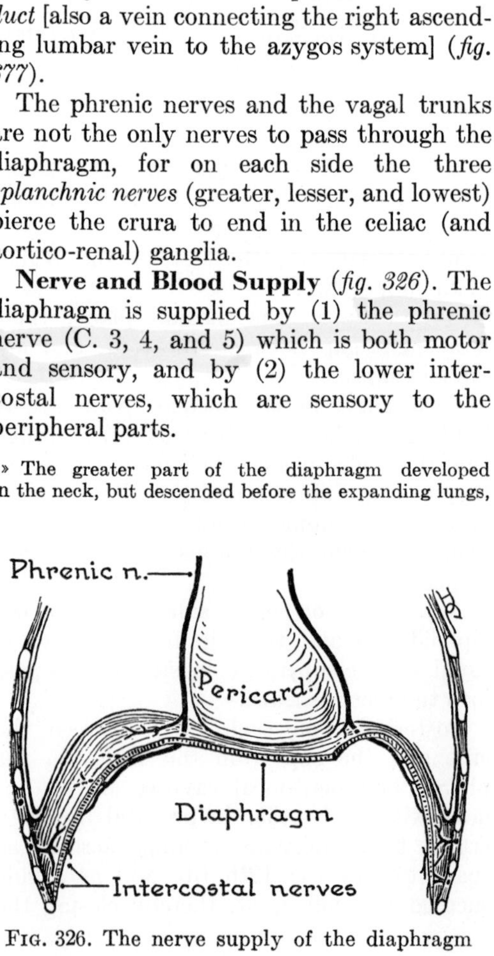

FIG. 326. The nerve supply of the diaphragm

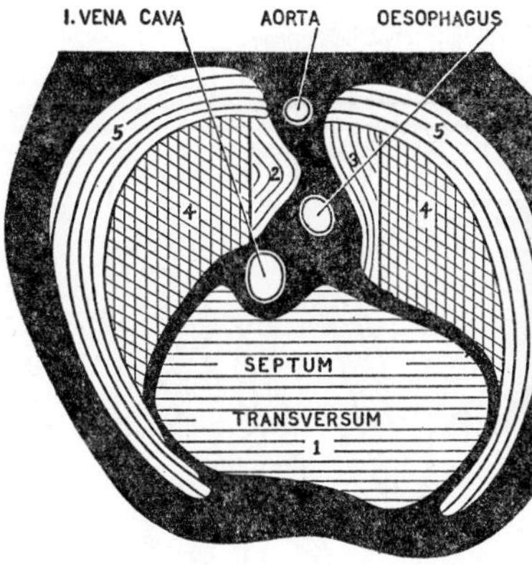

FIG. 326.1. The elements from which the diaphragm is developed.

1 = septum transversum; *2*, *3* = dorsal mesentery;

4 = pleuroperitoneal membrane; *5* = body wall. (After Broman.)

drawing the phrenic nerves after it. The phrenic nerve is the only motor nerve to the diaphragm. If cut (in the dog) the diaphragm atrophies and becomes fibrous up to the median plane.

Arteries. Pericardiaco-phrenic and musculo-phrenic aa. (from int. thoracic a.) and intercostal, sup. phrenic and inf. phrenic aa. (from the aorta).

Relations. *The abdominal relations* are: the liver, stomach, and spleen; the celiac ganglion, suprarenal glands, and kidneys. *The thoracic relations* are: the heart and pericardium, the lungs and pleurae, the pleural recesses and below the recesses are the lower intercostal spaces and ribs, the thoracic aorta and the esophagus (*figs. 233* and *313*).

Development. The fully formed diaphragm is derived from a mesodermal partition of composite origin (*fig. 326.1*). The anteromedian part arose from the septum transversum; the posteromedian part arose from the primitive dorsal mesentery; the lateral parts were, so to speak, dissected off the body wall by the developing lungs; the gap, the *pleuroperitoneal canal*, on each side between the posteromedian and the lateral part is closed by a membrane, the *pleuroperitoneal membrane*.

In the young embryo the hinder part of this composite partition lies at the level of vertebra C. 2; but it has a long descent to make for ultimately, as the crura of the diaphragm, it gains attachment to vertebrae L. 2 and 3. On passing vertebrae C. 3, 4, and 5, portions of the myotomes of these segments, supplied by the phrenic nerve, extend into it and pervade it, thereby forming the muscular diaphragm. Wells points out that the primitive tissues that finally form the diaphragm are not widely separated, but, in fact, they are parts of a single entity even from their earliest appearance.

THE SEPTUM TRANSVERSUM is the thick mesodermal mass that surrounds the vitelline veins (also the common cardinal veins) prior to their entering the sinus venarum of the heart. At a certain period this septum projects horizontally backward from the anterior body wall to meet the dorsal mesentery at the level where the duct system of the liver (of endodermal origin) buds from the duodenum.

Ultimately, the septum separates into three layers: (1) the upper layer forms part of the pericardium; (2) the intermediate layer forms part of the diaphragm; (3) the lower layer forms the connective tissue stroma of the liver.

The enlarging peritoneal cavity, by extending into the septum transversum between layers 2 and 3, "dissects" the liver from the diaphragm—but not entirely. Thus, "dissection" is practically complete on the *left side*, except for the left triangular ligament; in the *median plane*, except for the falciform ligament; and on the *right side*, except for the bare area bounded by the coronary ligament—here liver and diaphragm remain loosely connected. By this provision, during respiration, the contracting diaphragm can glide unhampered on the liver.

ABDOMINAL LYMPHATICS

Lymph capillaries, lymph vessels, and lymph nodes occupy areolar and fascial planes, e.g., the deep fascia, and the submucous and subserous coats of viscera. Lymph capillaries form networks which drain by the nearest issuing lymph vessels. Retrograde flow is prohibited by numerous valves. It is fundamental to recognize that if one group of vessels is obstructed, the lymph escapes into the next nearest issuing vessels, like water from a marsh.

After a meal the intestinal lymph vessels contain emulsified fat; and, since this is white like milk, the vessels are called *lacteals.*

The external and common iliac chains of nodes (*fig. 396*) continue upward along the sides of the aorta and around it as the *right* and *left aortic* or *lumbar chains of nodes.* They open by means of a *right* and a *left lumbar lymph trunk* into a tubular sac, called the *cisterna chyli.* The inf. vena cava runs through the right chain making it less accessible than the left.

These chains receive (1) lymph already filtered through nodes and coming from the lower limbs, lower part of the anterior abdominal wall, external genitals, perineum, and pelvis; (2) lymph vessels that follow the lumbar arteries and drain the posterior abdominal wall; (3) the vessels from the three paired glands—suprarenal, kidney, and testis (the ovary, upper part of the uterus, and the uterine tube in the female), and (4) the part of the gastro-intestinal tract supplied by the inferior mesenteric artery drains into the left aortic chain, but the parts supplied by the celiac and superior mesenteric arteries drain by means of a

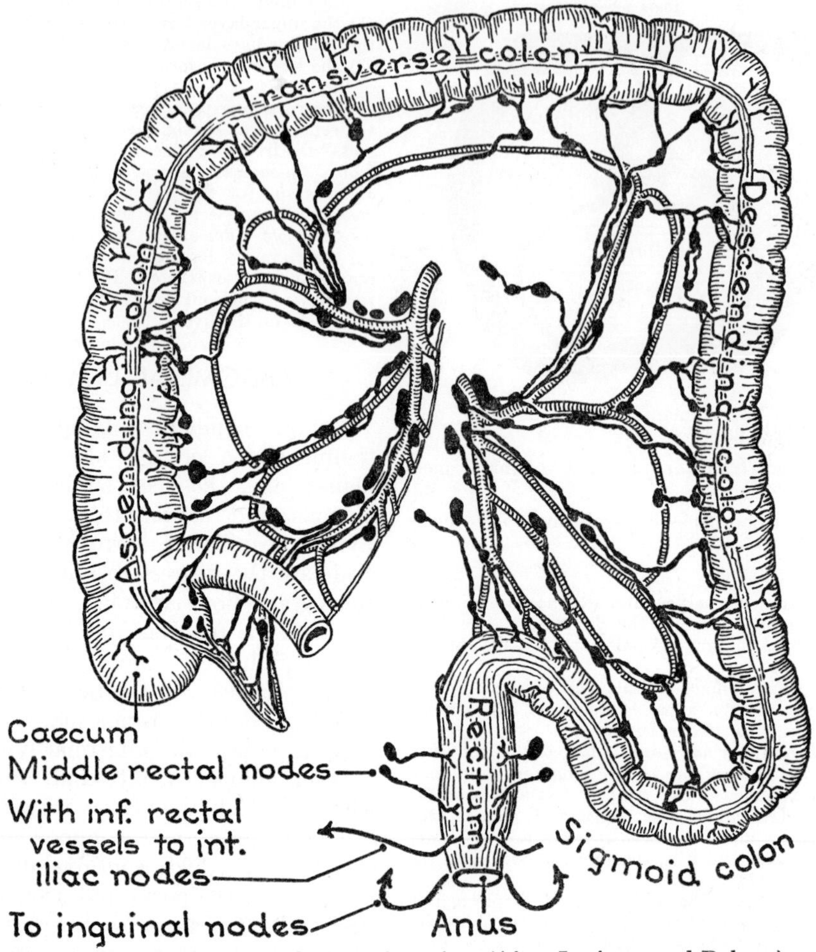

Fig. 327. The lymphatics of the large intestine. (After Jamieson and Dobson)

gastro-intestinal trunk into the cisterna chyli.

The cisterna chyli will be described now and the drainage of the gastro-intestinal canal and of the three unpaired glands (liver, pancreas, and spleen) will be considered.

The Cisterna Chyli resembles a 2″ segment of a vein, but it is white. Its diameter is less than that of a lead pencil, but it may be irregularly dilated. It lies between the aorta and the right crus of the diaphragm. It receives five or more trunks, namely, the *right* and *left lumbar trunks*, the *gastro-intestinal trunk*, and a *pair of vessels* that descend from the lower intercostal spaces. On passing through the aortic hiatus it becomes the thoracic duct.

Lymphatic Drainage

Intestine. The nodes of the *large intestine* are numerous and are roughly divisible into three groups: (1) *paracolic nodes* on the marginal artery close to the gut wall, (2) *intermediate nodes* on the stems of the colic arteries, and (3) *main nodes* near the roots of the colic arteries, beside the aorta. Also, there are a few very small *epicolic nodes* applied to the surface of the colon.

The lymph vessels from the intestine follow the blood vessels fairly closely and each vessel is interrupted by one or more groups of nodes (*fig. 327*). The lymph vessels from the segment of the large gut between

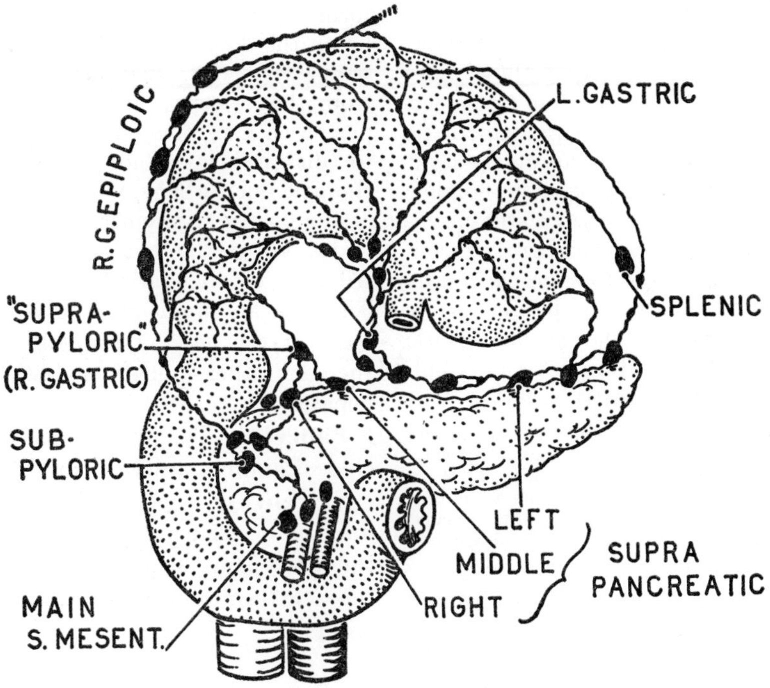

FIG. 327.1. The lymphatics of the upper abdomen and stomach

the appendix and the left colic flexure follow the branches and stem of the superior mesenteric artery and, joining those of the small gut, form the *intestinal trunk.* Those from the left colic flexure and remainder of the large gut follow the branches of the inferior mesenteric artery and end among the nodes of the left lumbar (aortic) chain.

There may be an appendicular node in the mesentery of the appendix; there are many nodes clustered in the ileocolic angle; the vessels from the transverse colon have the longest distance to travel; those at the left colic flexure communicate with the splenic nodes, traveling probably along the route of the occasional artery described on page 258.

The Small Intestine is drained through numerous nodes divisible like those of the large intestine into three groups. Ultimately a channel, the *intestinal trunk*, emerges and, by joining the *gastric trunk,* forms the *gastro-intestinal trunk* which opens into the cisterna chyli.

Pancreatic Group of Nodes. (Celiac and Superior Mesenteric Nodes, figure 327.1.) Along the upper border of the pancreas there are *middle, right, and left suprapancreatic groups* of nodes related to the celiac artery and to its hepatic and splenic branches. A *subpyloric* group is applied to the front of the head of the pancreas below the pylorus. A *left gastric chain* lies on the course of the left gastric artery. A *biliary chain* extends along the bile passages from the porta hepatis above, through the lesser omentum, and behind the first part of the duodenum and head of the pancreas, to the second part of the duodenum below. And, there is the *main group of sup. mesenteric nodes* at the root of the mesentery.

Stomach. The lymph vessels from the part of the stomach that lies to the left of a vertical line dropped through the esophagus pass with the left gastro-epiploic and short gastric arteries through the gastrolienal and the lienorenal ligaments to the suprapancreatic nodes; some, however, pass to a necklace of nodes that encircle the cardiac orifice.

Of the lymph vessels to the right of this vertical line, (1) those from the upper two-thirds of both surfaces of the stomach run to the left to nodes placed on the left gastric artery at the left end of the lesser curvature of the stomach and are there in part intercepted; but some vessels pass by these nodes to more distant ones on the stem of the left gastric artery, and so to suprapancreatic nodes. (2) The lower vessels run to the right to nodes placed on the right gastro-epiploic artery at the right end of the greater curvature, thence to the subpyloric group, from which they are dispersed to suprapancreatic nodes and to the main group of superior mesenteric nodes. (3) At the extreme pyloric end of the lesser curvature several lymph vessels follow the right gastric artery.

»» The lymph plexuses of the stomach communicate freely with those of the esophagus; but only feebly, if at all, with those of the duodenum. This is due to: the connective tissue septum in the submucous coat at the pyloric sphincter, to discontinuity of the circular muscle fibers, and to indipping of the longitudinal muscle fibers.

Liver. Lymph vessels from the upper surface of the liver pass through the falciform ligament to retrosternal nodes, which lie on the diaphragm and discharge into the parasternal (int. mammary) chain; some from the interior, following hepatic veins, pass with i. v. cava through the diaphragm to diaphragmatic nodes, thence to the thoracic duct; others, following the branches of the portal vein, emerge at the porta and travel down the biliary chain to be distributed to the various pancreatic nodes. There is an intercepting gland, the *cystic node*, at the neck of the gall bladder, and there are other "hepatic nodes" in the porta hepatis.

Pancreas. The lymphatics of the pancreas drain into adjacent nodes.

Spleen. The lymphatics of the spleen drain into splenic nodes situated where the tip of the pancreas abuts against the spleen; these in turn drain into the suprapancreatic group.

SECTION IV

Perineum and Pelvis

CHAPTER **19**

PERINEUM

Definition; Developmental Considerations; Definitions of: urogenital diaphragm, perineal membrane or inferior fascia of u.g. diaphragm, superficial perineal fascia and pouch, deep pouch, perineal body, anococcygeal raphe.

Anal Region

Sphincter Ani Externus; Ischiorectal Fossae; Contents; Vessels and Nerves.

Urogenital Region in the Male

SUPERFICIAL PERINEAL POUCH AND CONTENTS.

PENIS—*Parts; Skin; Suspensory Ligament; Vessels and Nerves; Erectile Tissue; Lymphatics.*

SUPERFICIAL PERINEAL MUSCLES.

DEEP PERINEAL POUCH AND CONTENTS.

INTERNAL PUDENDAL VESSELS AND NERVES—*Vasomotor Nerves.*

EXPOSURE OF PROSTATE.

Female Perineum

Comparisons (between female and male).

PERINEUM

The perineum is the region round about the outflow from the rectum and bladder. It is a diamond-shaped space at whose angles are the arcuate (inferior) pubic ligament, the tip of the coccyx, and the ischial tuberosities (*fig. 328*). The pubic arch and the sacrotuberous ligaments form its sides. The sacrotuberous lig., however, is hidden by the lower border of the Gluteus Maximus. The ischial tuberosities bear the weight of the body when sitting; so, they are covered with a mass of tough, stringy, fibrous tissue in which a bursa may be buried.

The anterior half of this diamond is the *urogenital region* (*triangle*); the posterior half is the *anal region* (*triangle*).

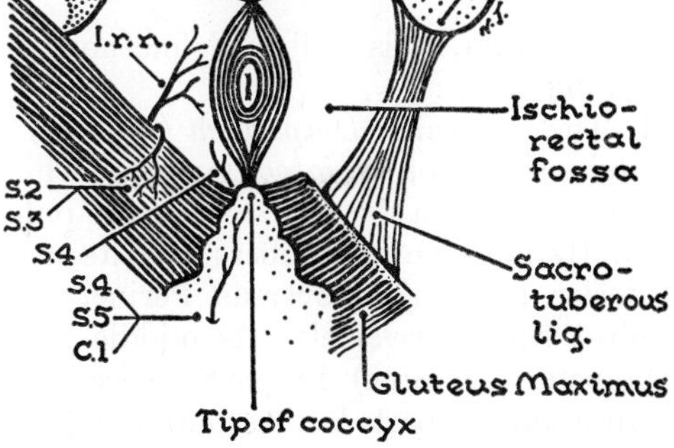

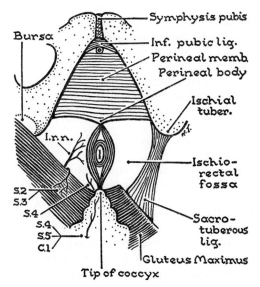

FIG. 328. Boundaries and subdivisions of the perineum. (*Inf. pubic lig. = Arcuate lig.*)

Developmental Considerations. In the embryo the endodermal-lined alimentary canal ends in a blind receptacle, the *cloaca,* shaped somewhat like a coffee pot, the spout being the *allantoic diverticulum,* definitively the *urachus* (*figs. 329 and 330*).

The *mesonephric duct* (definitively the *ductus deferens* in the male) grows caudally and opens into the anterior part of the cloaca. The *ureter* develops as an outgrowth from the mesonephric duct, and the two have for a period a common terminal duct. This common duct is absorbed subsequently into the posterior wall of the bladder and prostatic urethra with the result that the ureter and ductus deferens come to have independent openings.

In reptiles and birds the cloaca opens on to the skin surface through an orifice, guarded by a sphincter of striated muscle, the *cloacal sphincter.* In mammals, including man, a septum of mesoderm, the *urorectal septum,* divides the cloaca into (1) an anterior or urogenital part, and (2) a posterior or intestinal part. The cloacal sphincter also divides into anterior and posterior parts: the posterior part becomes the Sphincter Ani Externus; the anterior part becomes the other perineal muscles (p. 305).

From these considerations you will understand why on a single nerve, the *pudendal n.,* falls the onus of supplying all the muscles into which the cloacal sphincter divides, as well as the skin of the region, and why its companion artery, the *internal pudendal a.,* nourishes the entire territory; also why the bladder and rectum have a common nerve supply (pelvic splanchnic n. and hypogastric plexus).

Definitions. It is well to define now the following terms:

1. The *Urogenital Diaphragm* (*fig. 331*) is a thin sheet of striated muscle which stretches between the two sides of the pubic arch. Its most anterior fibers and its most posterior fibers (Transversus Perinei Profundus) run transversely. Its middle fibers (Sphincter Urethrae) in part encircle the urethra, and in part decussate and embrace it.

Like other muscles, the urogenital diaphragm is enveloped in areolar tissue, and because the diaphragm is flat, its envelope forms two sheets, *the inferior and superior fasciae of the urogenital diaphragm.*

Perineal Membrane is a shorter name for the inferior fascia of the u.g. diaphragm.

2. *The Superficial Perineal Fascia of Colles* is the fascia of Scarpa continued into the perineum. It is laminated like Dutch pastry and, therefore, absorptive as a sponge. Its attachments are to: the fascia lata, the pubic arch, and the base of the perineal membrane (*fig. 331*). In front it is prolonged over the penis and scrotum and so forms a covering for the testes and spermatic cords. From this it follows that its line of attachment to the fascia lata must pass along a line lateral to the superficial inguinal ring and spermatic cord (*fig. 212*, p. 207).

3. *The Superficial Perineal Pouch* is the fascial space between the superficial perineal fascia and the perineal membrane. Should the urethra rupture into this space, the attachments of superficial perineal fascia will determine the direction of flow of the extravasated urine—not to the anal triangle nor the thigh, but into the scrotum, around the penis, and upward into the abdominal wall. (*Footnote*, p. 206.)

4. *The Deep Perineal Pouch* is the space enclosed by the superior and inferior fasciae of the u.g. diaphragm. Among its contents are the membranous urethra and the Sphincter Urethrae.

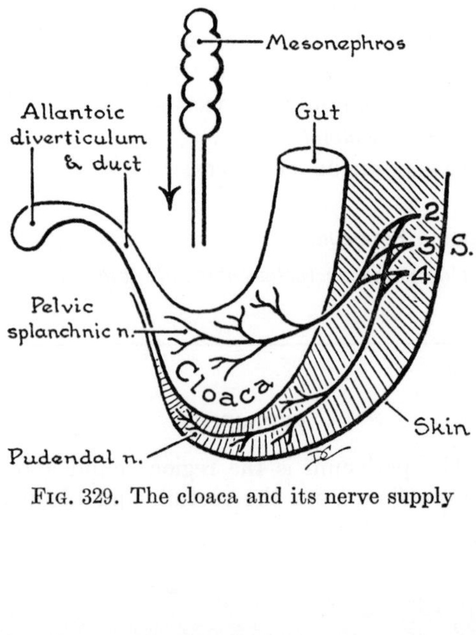

FIG. 329. The cloaca and its nerve supply

5. *The Perineal Body* is a small fibrous mass at the center of the perineum. Attached to each other here are the base of the perineal membrane and several muscles that converge from 5 directions: Sphincter Ani Externus, Transversus Perinei Superficialis (R. and L.), Bulbospongiosus, and in part the Levator Ani (*fig. 336*).

6. *The Anococcygeal Raphe* is a fibrous band between the anus and coccyx.

ANAL REGION (TRIANGLE)

Sphincter Ani Externus (Anus, L. = a ring). This is a sphincter of voluntary muscle, 1″ deep, placed around the anal canal. It has three parts—subcutaneous, superficial, and deep.

The Subcutaneous Part is slender and encircles the anal orifice. *The Superficial Part* is elliptical and extends from the tip of the coccyx and anococcygeal raphe to the perineal body. It moors the circular anus to the median plane, but offers it little support fore and aft.

The Deep Part encircles the anal canal like a collar; in front, however, some fibers decussate and join the opposite Superficial Transverse Perineal muscle. Above, it blends with the Levator Ani. It is supplied by many branches of the inferior rectal (hemorrhoidal) vessels and nerve. Its posterior end receives twigs from the perineal br. of S. 4; its anterior end, from the deep perineal nerve (*figs. 336 and 370*).

Ischiorectal Fossa. The ischiorectal fossae are the fascia-lined, wedge-shaped spaces, one on each side of the anal canal and rectum. Filled with fat, they allow the rectum to become distended and to empty. Each fossa is bounded laterally by the ischium, from which the Obturator Internus arises (*fig. 332*); medially, by the rectum and anal canal, to which the Levator Ani and External Sphincter are applied; posteriorly, by the sacrotuberous ligament and the overlying Gluteus Maximus; anteriorly, by the base of the urogenital diaphragm and its fasciae.

The fascia covering the Obturator Internus is fairly strong and it extends upwards be-

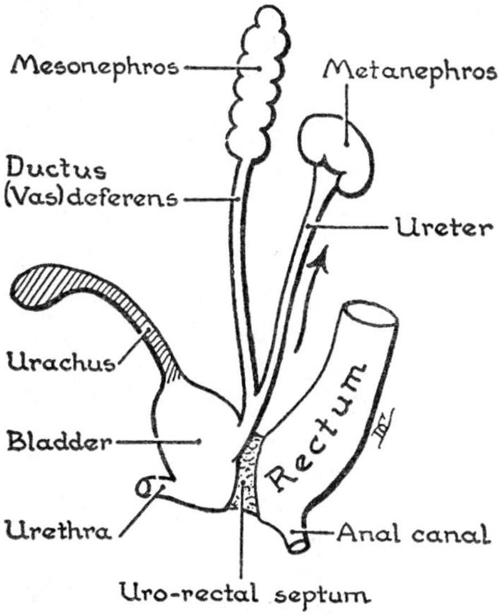

FIG. 330. The connections and subdivisions of the cloaca.

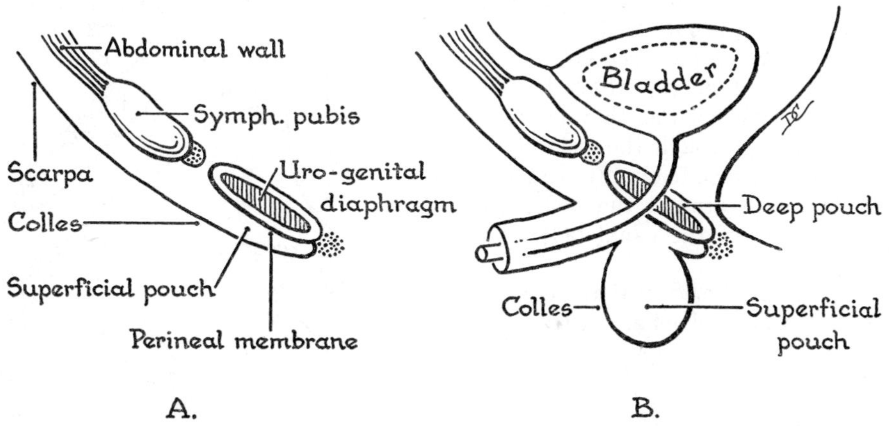

FIG. 331. To explain the urogenital diaphragm and the perineal pouches (schematic)

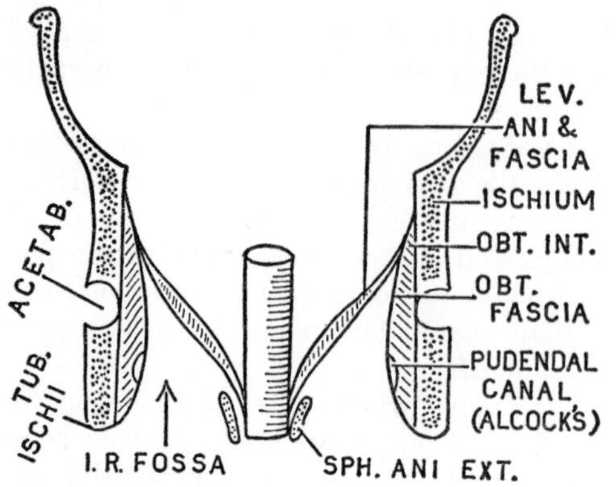

FIG. 332. The pelvis in coronal section to show the ischiorectal fossa (schematic).

yond the fossa, reaching posteriorly to the pelvic brim (*fig. 346*). The fascia covering the Levator Ani is weak. The apex or roof of this fascia-lined, wedge-shaped fossa is formed by the Levator Ani arising from the Obturator Internus fascia about 2½ inches above the ischial tuberosity.

» A finger tip may be passed forward into a short cul-de-sac above the base of the u.g. diaphragm. Here the superior fascia of the diaphragm and the fasciae of the medial and lateral walls and of the roof meet.

The fascial linings of the right and left fossae blend posteriorly, between anal canal and coccyx, to form a weak, median, areolar partition whose lower free border is the **anococcygeal raphe.**

Contents of the Fossa:

1. Fat.

2. Internal pudendal vessels and pudendal nerve (pudere, L. = to be ashamed; *cf.* impudent) run forward in an areolar sheath, the *pudendal canal,* which is adherent to the lateral surface of the Obturator Internus fascia, 1 inch above the tuberosity. Far back they give off the inferior rectal (hemorrhoidal) vessels and nerve, which become more and more superficial as they pass forward and medially through the ischiorectal fossa toward the surface to supply: External Sphincter Ani, skin around the anus, and mucous membrane of the canal below the anal valves (*fig. 371*).

Above the valves, the afferent and efferent nerves are the pelvic splanchnic nerves (*fig. 329*).

» 3. Two other cutaneous nerves, the *perforating cutaneous* branch of the 2nd and 3rd sacral and the *perineal branch* of the 4th sacral are shown in figure 328.

UROGENITAL REGION IN THE MALE

This triangular region comprises the superficial and the deep perineal pouch.

The **Superficial Perineal Pouch** (of Colles) is divided imperfectly into a right and a left side by an areolar septum, and, it is continued, deep to the fascia of Scarpa, into the ant. abdominal wall (*fig. 212*) and into the scrotum and penis.

The *two posterior scrotal branches of the perineal nerve* pierce the base of the perineal membrane, and the *perineal branch of the posterior cutaneous nerve of the thigh* pierces the attachment of the superficial perineal fascia to the pubic arch; thereafter these three sensory nerves can be followed forward on to the scrotum accompanied by the two *posterior scrotal arteries.* A small artery, called the *transverse perineal a.,* runs medially along the base of the pouch to meet its fellow.

THE CONTENTS OF THE SUPERFICIAL PERINEAL POUCH ARE:

1. Three superficial nerves.
2. Three superficial arteries.
3. Three superficial muscles (page 305) all of which are paired.
4. The root of the penis.

Penis (penis, L. = a tail). The penis is composed of three fibro-elastic cylinders, the right and left *corpora cavernosa penis* and the *corpus spongiosum penis* (*fig. 333*), which are filled with erectile tissue and are enveloped in fasciae and skin.

The corpora cavernosa fuse with each

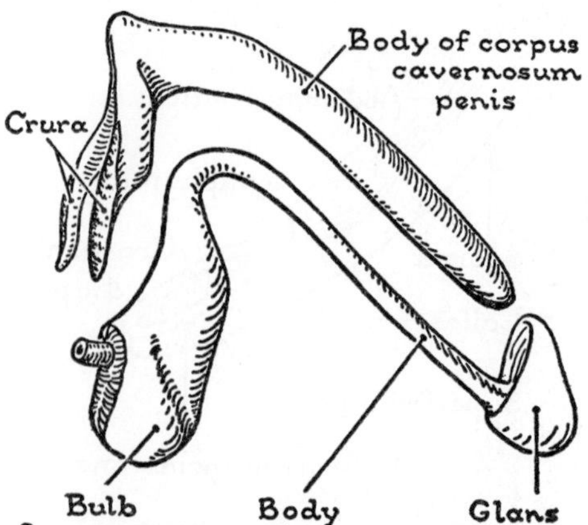

FIG. 333. The parts of the penis

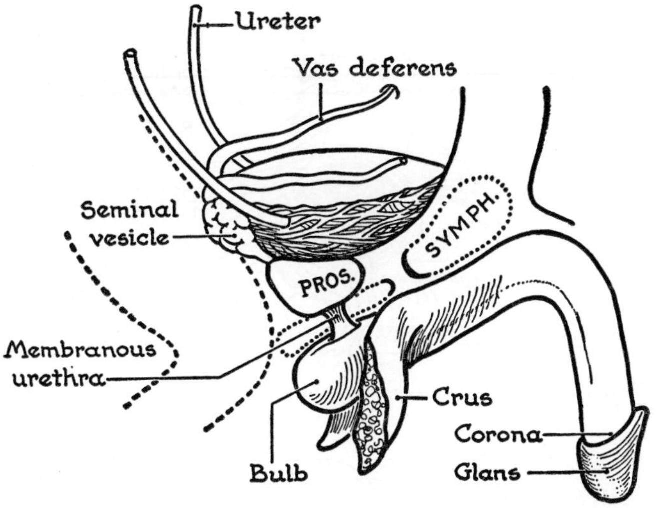

Fig. 334. The lower parts of the genital and urinary tracts and their relations

other in the median plane, except behind where, as two diverging *crura*, they separate to find attachment on each side to an inch of the pubic arch. They are the support of the corpus spongiosum, which lies below and between them, and which can easily be dissected free from them.

The corpus spongiosum is traversed by the urethra; it is swollen in front where, as the *glans penis*, it fits on to the blunt end of the united corpora cavernosa, and swollen behind where, as the *bulb of the penis*, it is fixed to the perineal membrane (inf. fascia of the u.g. diaphragm). This membrane serves to moor the bulb of the penis to the pubic arch, so, it is strong.

The crura and the bulb are the attached parts or *root of the penis* (*fig. 334*).

Skin and Fasciae of the Penis (*fig. 335*). The skin and fascia of the abdominal wall and scrotum are prolonged over the penis as a series of very loosely laminated envelopes which end as the *foreskin* or *prepuce*. The skin is devoid of hairs and the fascia of fat. Deep to these, a closed tube of denser and more tightly fitting fascia, *the deep fascia of the penis*, envelops the body of the penis from its root to the corona of the glans. This fascia is adherent on each side in the groove between the c. cavernosum and c. spongiosum.

The Suspensory Ligament of the Penis is a thick, triangular fibro-elastic band. Above, it is fixed to the lower part of the linea alba and upper part of the symphysis pubis; below, it splits to form a sling for the penis at the junction of its fixed and mobile parts (i.e., where the organ is bent), and here it blends with the fascia penis.

Vessels and Nerves of the Penis (*fig. 335*). There is a superficial and a deep dorsal vein of the penis. Each is single and occupies the median plane. The superficial dorsal vein is accompanied by lymph vessels, but it has no companion artery or nerve. The deep dorsal vein, on the other hand, has a companion dorsal artery and dorsal nerve on each side, and it also is accompanied by lymph vessels. They run along the dorsum penis deep to the deep fascia of the penis and end, or begin, in the glans. Encircling branches of the arteries conduct blood to the corpora cavernosa and corpus spongiosum, to be returned by encircling branches of the vein (*fig. 335*); encircling lymph vessels drain the spongy (penile) urethra; and encircling branches of the nerves are sensory to the spongy urethra (*fig. 49*).

The *deep dorsal vein* (unpaired) passes below the symphysis pubis to end in the prostatic plexus of veins.

The lymph vessels end in the deep inguinal nodes (p. 361).

The erectile tissue of the penis is supplied by three paired arteries—artery to the bulb, artery to the crus (deep artery, p. 306), and dorsal artery. The last named artery sends

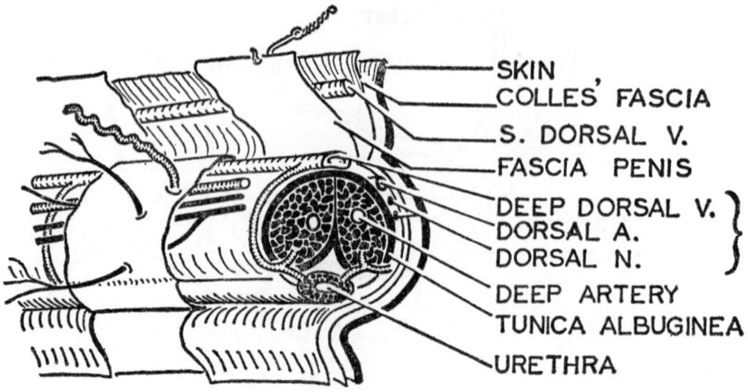

FIG. 335. The penis on cross-section, its coverings and its vessels

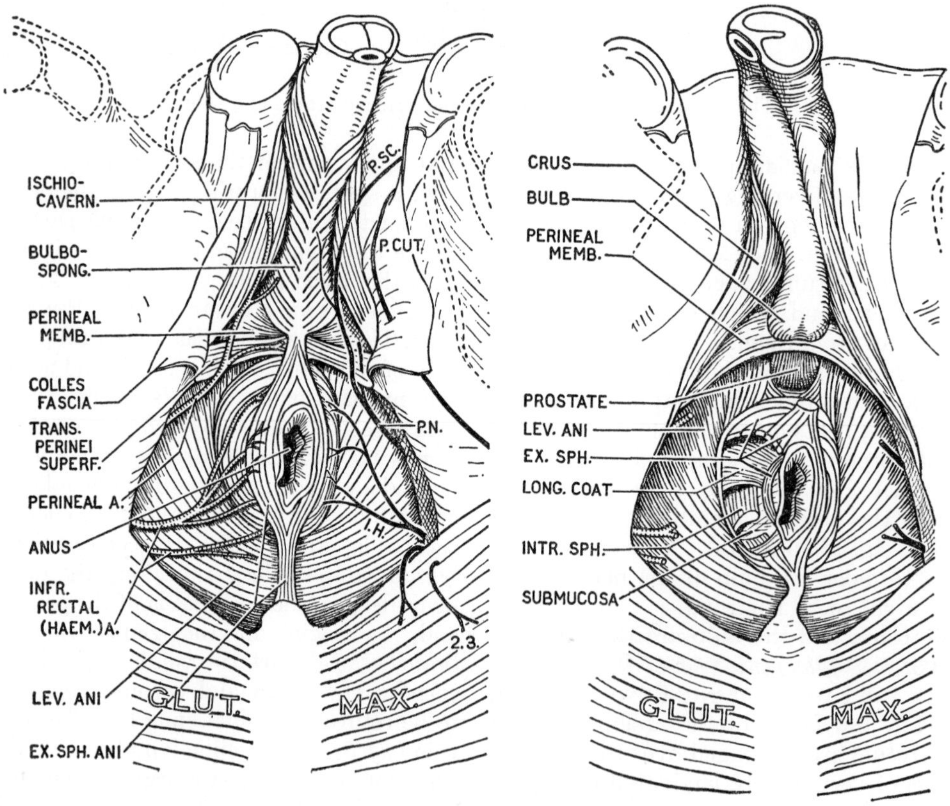

FIG. 336. *Left,* superficial dissection of the male perineum. (By Dr. H. C. Hair.) *Right,* exposure of the prostate. Dissection of the anal canal. (By Dr. V. P. Collins.) *I.H.* = inferior rectal (hemorrhoidal) n.; *P.N.* = perineal n.; *P.SC.* = posterior scrotal n.; *P.CUT* = perineal branch of posterior cutaneous n. of thigh.

encircling twigs to assist the former two arteries.

The vasomotor nerves are derived from the pelvic splanchnics (p. 306 and *fig. 49*).

The Coverings of the Penis (skin and fasciae) are supplied by the dorsal aa. of the penis and by the ext. pudendal branches of the femoral aa. They are drained by the *superficial dorsal vein,* which begins in the prepuce where it anastomoses with branches of the deep dorsal vein. The superficial dorsal vein ends by dividing into right and left branches which pass via the ext. pudendal veins to the great saphenous veins.

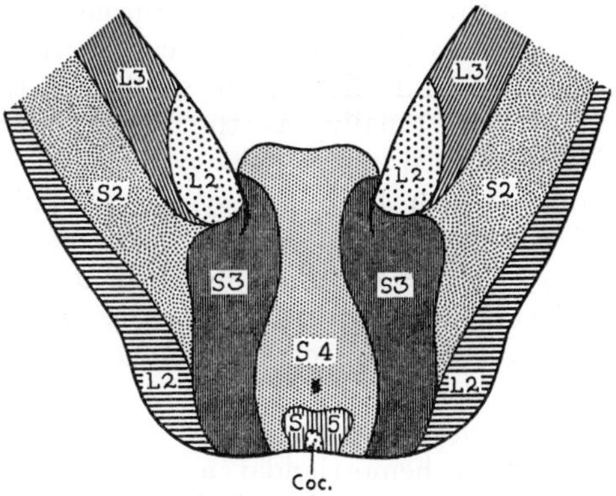

FIG. 336.1. The dermatomes of the perineum

The superficial lymph vessels anastomose in the prepuce with branches of the deep vessels and end in the superficial inguinal nodes.

The cutaneous nerves are branches of the dorsal nerves. The genital branch of the genitofemoral n. and the ilio-inguinal n. supply the parts near the pubis.

Superficial Perineal Muscles. On each side three muscles lie in the superficial perineal pouch. They are: the slender *Transversus Perinei Superficialis* which lies at the base of the pouch and extends from the ischial tuberosity to the perineal body, the *Ischiocavernosus*, which is applied to the crus, and the **Bulbospongiosus,** a bilateral structure, which arises from the perineal body and a median raphe below the bulb of the penis (*fig. 336*). The most posterior fibers of the Bulbospongiosus pass to the perineal membrane; the intermediate fibers of the two sides meet on the dorsum of the corpus spongiosum; and the most anterior fibers meet on the dorsum of the penis, where they blend with the fascia penis. The Bulbospongiosus is a sphincter that empties the bulb and the hinder part of the spongy urethra.

When the three muscles are gently separated from each other, a triangular area of perineal membrane is brought into view.

Deep Perineal Pouch (*fig. 331*). This pouch is the narrow space between the upper and lower fasciae of the urogenital diaphragm.

Contents: (1) the u.g. diaphragm or deep perineal muscles (viz., Transversus Perinei Profundus and Sphincter Urethrae), (2) the membranous urethra which, thin walled and ½″ long, perforates the diaphragm, (3) two small glands, the *bulbo-urethral glands* (of Cowper), each the size of a pea, lie deep to the diaphragm and alongside the urethra. Their long ducts travel in the wall of the urethra for an inch before opening into the spongy urethra (*figs. 339 and 347*), and (4) vessels and nerves to be described now.

Internal Pudendal Vessels and Pudendal Nerve. The artery, which is a branch of the internal iliac artery, and the nerve, which arises from sacral segments 2, 3, and 4, together leave the pelvis through the greater sciatic foramen to enter the gluteal region (*fig. 337*). This they leave immediately by crossing the ischial spine and passing through the lesser sciatic foramen to enter the pudendal canal. Thus do they arrive in the perineum. They have three territories to supply: (1) anal triangle, (2) urogenital triangle and scrotum (labium majus in female), and (3) penis (clitoris in the female). (*Dermatomes:* see *fig. 336.1.*)

The artery and nerve travel together, but, whereas the artery passes through without dividing, the nerve ends far back in the pudendal canal by dividing into three terminal branches. Consequently, the terminology is more complicated than the anatomy. Figures 337 and 338 are explanatory. Follow the nerve first.

The **Pudendal Nerve** supplies three regions by its three terminal divisions:

1. *The inferior rectal (hemorrhoidal) nerve* is a mixed nerve whose branches become more and more superficial as they are traced

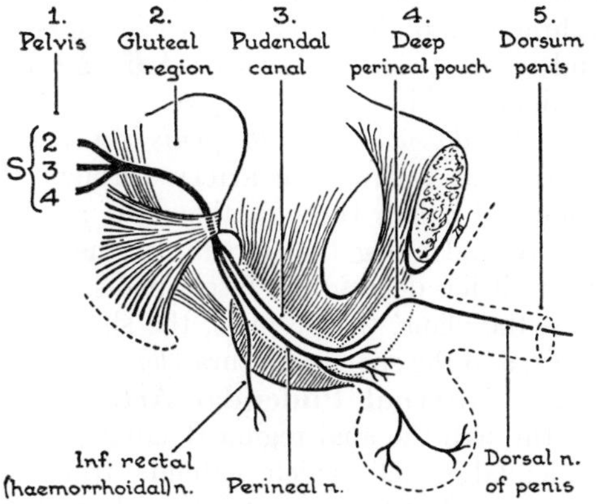

FIG. 337. The course of the pudendal nerve: Its three divisions and five regions traversed.

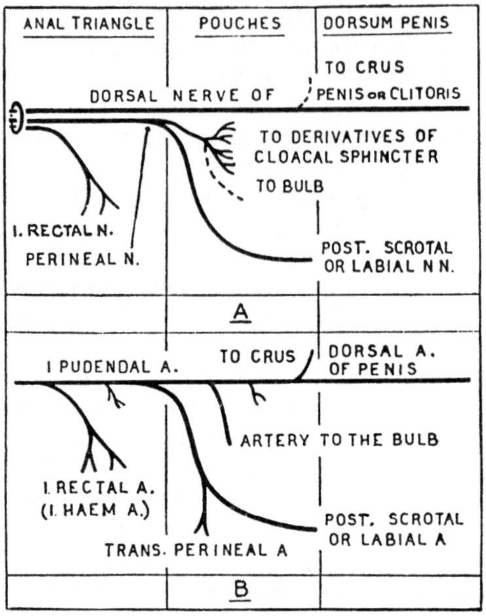

FIG. 338. *A*, the three *divisions* of the pudendal nerve: each for a region. *B*, The three *branches* of the pudendal artery. A necessary difference in terminology: an essential similarity in anatomy.

forward and medially, through the fat of the ischiorectal fossa, to supply the External Sphincter Ani, the skin about the anus, and the lining of the canal below the anal valves.

2. *The perineal nerve,* also a mixed nerve, runs below the artery through the pudendal canal to the base of the perineal membrane where its two cutaneous branches, the *posterior scrotal nerves,* enter the superficial perineal pouch, and continue forward to the scrotum, while its motor branch, the *deep perineal nerve,* enters the deep perineal pouch from which it innervates the diaphragm and the three superficial muscles, and sends twigs to Levator Ani and Ext. Sphincter Ani.

3. *The dorsal nerve of the penis* is a sensory nerve that follows the artery through the pudendal canal, through the deep perineal pouch, and along the dorsum of the penis, where it lies deep to the fascia penis. It supplies the glans, the prepuce, the skin of the penis, and the spongy urethra (*fig. 49*, p. 62).

The **Internal Pudendal Artery** travels through the anal region (triangle) in the pudendal canal, which extends from the lesser sciatic foramen to the deep perineal pouch. It then travels through the urogenital region in the deep perineal pouch, where it lies under shelter of the pubic arch. Finally, as the *dorsal artery of the penis,* it pierces the perineal membrane $\frac{1}{2}$ inch from the symphysis pubis and continues, deep to the fascia of the penis, as far as the glans in which it ends. On the dorsum of the penis, it lies, as arteries so commonly do, between its companion vein and nerve.

Its Branches are: (1) *The inferior rectal a.* (inf. hemorrhoidal a.) which supplies the anal triangle; (2) *The perineal a.* which at the base of the perineal membrane enters the superficial perineal pouch, and, after giving off the slender *transverse perineal a.* which runs to the center of the perineum, continues as the *posterior scrotal aa.* with the nerves of the same name to anastomose with the external pudendal branches of the femoral artery. (3) *The artery to the bulb,* which is a large vessel, runs in the deep pouch—$\frac{1}{3}$ inch from the base of the membrane—to the bulb. (4) *The artery to the crus* (deep artery of the penis) arises deep to the crus and at once plunges into it.

The **Vasomotor Nerves** to the cavernous tissue are derived from the pelvic splanchnic nerves and the hypogastric plexus. They pass through the prostatic plexus and below the symphysis pubis to reach the erectile tissue of the corpora cavernosa and corpus spongiosum either directly or indirectly via the pudendal nerve.

Erection. Stimulation of the pelvic splanchnic nerves produces erection of the penis—hence, the term "nervi erigentes" originally given to these nerves—by causing dilatation of the arteries and cavernous tissue. In the normal reflex act the afferent limb is the pudendal nerve (S. 2, 3, 4); the efferent is the pelvic splanchnic (S. 2, 3, 4) (see *fig. 49*). This is brought about by stimulation of the pudendal nerve endings in the glans penis. The fibers of the pelvic splanchnics pass through the prostatic nerve plexus and under the pubic arch to join the vessels of the penis.

Ejaculation. The impulse spreading, sympathetic nerves are stimulated to cause closure of the internal urethral orifice, to

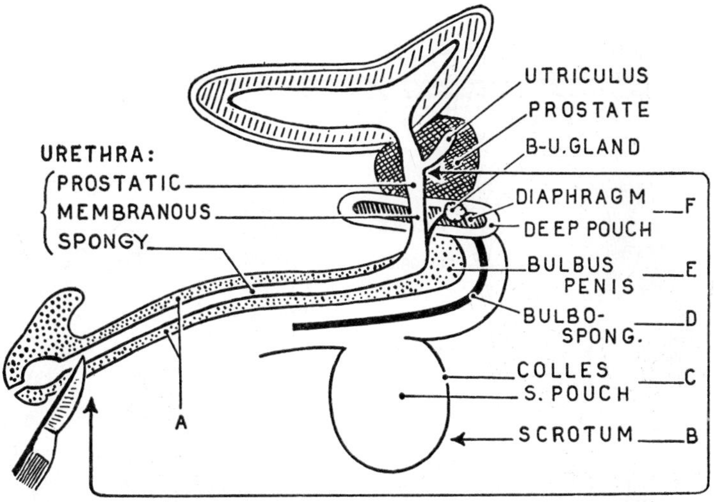

FIG. 339. Incision converting male perineum into female

set up peristaltic waves which empty the epididymis and propel its contents through the vas to the urethra, and to empty the seminal vesicles and prostate of their secretions. The cord segment is L. 1. The path is probably via the intermesenteric and hypogastric plexuses, because the usual operation for removal of the lumbar sympathetic does not impair ejaculation, but removal of the hypogastric plexus does so permanently (Learmonth). By causing the Bulbospongiosus to contract, the pudendal nerve is responsible for emptying the spongy urethra.

Exposure of the Prostate from the Perineum. Do not fail to get a glimpse of the prostate (*figs. 347* and *336*). To do so: (1) first, make the separation of the anal and u.g. triangles complete by detaching the Sphincter Ani Externus from the perineal body. (2) Next, pull the anal canal backward and define the anterior, free borders of the Levatores Ani. In doing so, work with the point of the knife very strictly in the median plane, because the free borders are but a third of an inch apart. (3) Then, keeping in mind the direction of the anal canal, insert the handle of the knife between the borders of the Levatores Ani, and ease the canal and rectum backward. Areolar tissue and involuntary muscle (Recto-urethralis), joining the rectum to the perineal body, require to be snipped through. (4) Lastly, proceed with the knife handle to push the structures developed from (and associated with) the anterior or urogenital part of the cloaca from the posterior or rectal part, and so expose the tough fascia covering the posterior surface of the prostate.

FEMALE PERINEUM

If you have familiarized yourself with the details of the male perineum, you will not have difficulty in appreciating the structure of the female perineum. The anal regions are the same in the two sexes; the urogenital regions differ.

An incision into the male urethra, entering it on the under surface just behind the glans penis, and carried back to the prostatic urethra, converts the male perineum into a female one or, perhaps better, restores to its fetal condition, which is similar in both sexes. The incision (*fig. 339*) divides everything encountered including the urethra, scrotum, Bulbospongiosus, bulb of the penis and u.g. diaphragm. However, the female penis, called the clitoris, is diminutive and is not traversed by the urethra. It comprises two *corpora cavernosa clitoridis* and a *glans clitoridis* which caps the conjoint corpora cavernosa (*fig. 340*).

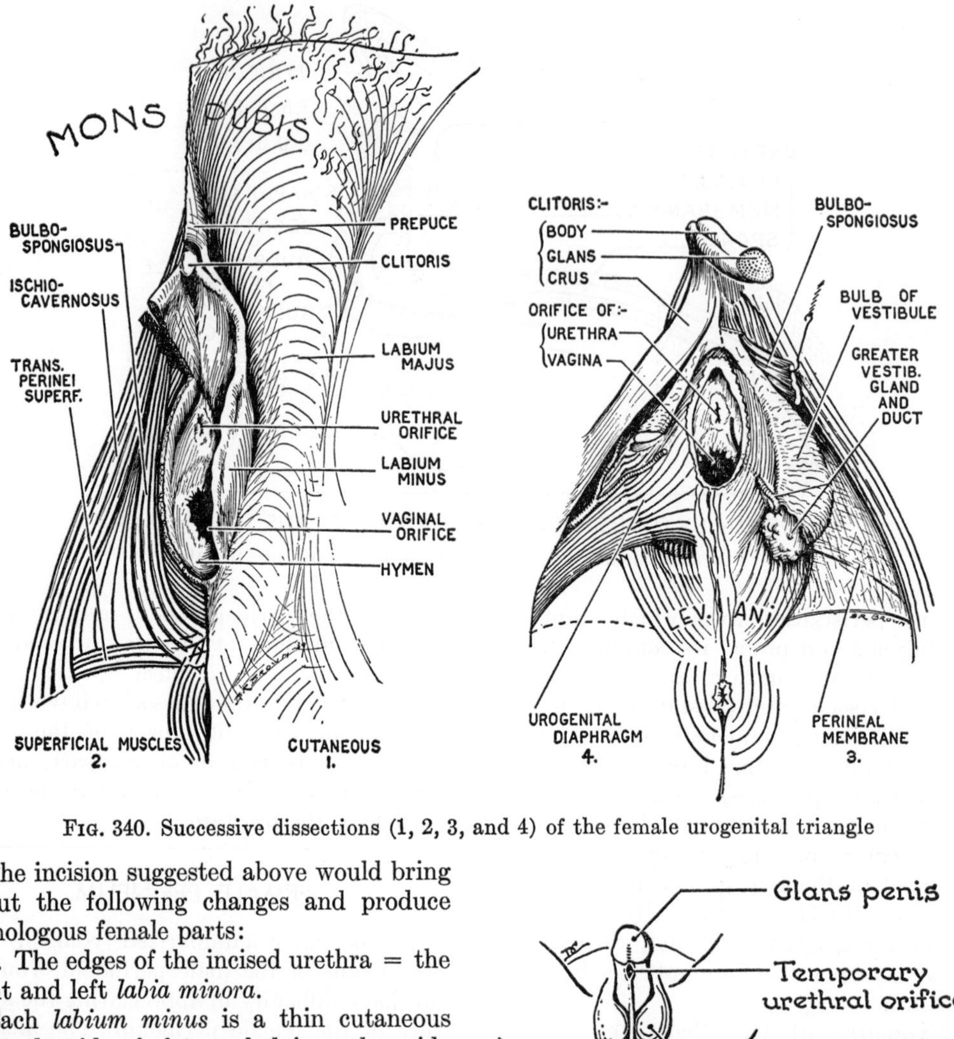

FIG. 340. Successive dissections (1, 2, 3, and 4) of the female urogenital triangle

The incision suggested above would bring about the following changes and produce homologous female parts:

1. The edges of the incised urethra = the right and left *labia minora*.

Each *labium minus* is a thin cutaneous fold, devoid of fat and lying alongside the orifice of the vagina. The posterior end is free. The anterior end divides into two lesser folds which unite with their fellows across the median plane, the upper folds forming a hood, the *prepuce of the clitoris*, over the glans, the lower joining to form a band, the *frenulum of the clitoris*, which is attached to the under surface of the glans.

2. The scrotum is split into—right and left *labia majora*.

Each *labium majus* is a broad, rounded, cutaneous ridge lying lateral to the labium minus and covering a long finger-like process of fat. This process extends backward from a median skin-covered mound of fat, the

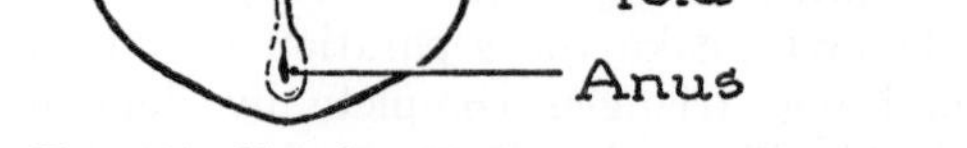

FIG. 341. Showing (1) the paired, right and left, labioscrotal (genital) folds about to unite below the penis to form the scrotum, and (2) the urethral orifice moved forward.

mons pubis situated in front of the pubis and continuous with the fascia of Camper. Entering the fat of the labium from behind and running forward are: the medial and lateral labial (*cf.* scrotal) nerves, arteries, and veins, and also the perineal branch of the posterior cutaneous nerve of the thigh. Entering it from the front are: branches of the ilio-inguinal nerve and external pudendal artery and vein, and a fibrous band, called the *round ligament of the uterus* (*fig. 382*).

Sebaceous glands open on to both surfaces of the labia minus and majus; hair covers the mons and the lateral surface of the labium majus.

3. The superficial perineal fascia and pouch into—r. and l. parts.

4. The Bulbospongiosus into—r. and l. parts (Sphincter Vaginae).

5. The bulb of the penis into—the r. and l. *bulbs of the vestibule.*

Each *bulb* is a loosely encapsuled mass of erectile tissue, shaped like a half pear. The convex surface is lateral and is covered with Bulbospongiosus; the flat or concave surface is medial and is applied to the perineal membrane which intervenes between it and the wall of the vagina; the enlarged end of the pear is posterior; the narrow stalk is anterior and, after joining its fellow, ends as the *glans clitoridis.*

6. The urogenital diaphragm, its inferior fascia (perineal membrane), and its superior fascia into—right and left parts. These blend with the vaginal wall.

7. The prostatic utricle comes to open on to the skin surface—the *vagina* (? uterus).

The *vestibule* of the vagina is the cleft between the labia minora. It represents the spongy urethra of the male. The *hymen* is a thin membranous fold of irregular outline that surrounds the vaginal orifice like the ruptured membrane of a drum. Opening into the vestibule are: the urethra, vagina, para-urethral glands, and greater and lesser vestibular glands. (The lesser glands are the many small mucous glands that open here.)

8. The bulbo-urethral glands come to open on to the skin surface—the *greater vestibular glands* (Bartholin's glands).

Each *gland* is larger than a pea (but smaller in the aged) and is situated at the hinder end of the bulb. Its duct, 2 cm. long, opens into the hinder part of the vestibule.

9. The remaining part of the urethra (i.e., the part above the utricle) is homologous with the entire female urethra. In the male this part is $\frac{3}{4}''$ long; in the female it is $1\frac{1}{4}$ inches. The female urethra lies immediately in front of the anterior wall of the vagina and is intimately adherent to it (*fig. 379*).

The *urethral orifice* opens just in front of the vaginal orifice and is 1″ behind the glans.

10. Though a prostate is not found in the female, the *para-urethral glands,* whose ducts open one on each side of the female urethra, are probably homologous with prostatic glands.

11. The ejaculatory ducts, which in the male open on to the lips of the prostatic utricle (*fig. 364*), generally disappear in the female, but, as the ducts of Gartner (*fig. 51*, p. 64), they may persist as blind tubes on the anterior wall of the vagina, and become cystic; rarely they open on to the skin surface, as in the sow.

12. In the male, the primitive urethral orifice opened in the perineum. Later, when the lips of the genital folds met and fused, a secondary orifice was formed behind the glans penis (*fig. 341*); subsequently, the urethra traversed the glans; so, a third and permanent orifice opens at the end of the glans. In the female, and as a rare anomaly in the male, the primary perineal orifice is the permanent one. The glans clitoridis is not canalized.

13. In the male, the gubernaculum testis passed to the scrotum, and the processus vaginalis peritonei and the testis followed it. In the female, the gubernaculum ovarii and the processus vaginalis (of Nuck) entered the labium majus but, owing to a side attachment that the gubernaculum makes with the uterus, the *ovary* enters the pelvis; only rarely does it descend into the labium (*fig. 382*).

CHAPTER 20

MALE PELVIS

Developmental Considerations

A mesodermal partition, the *urorectal septum* (*fig. 330*) growing down from above, divides the cloaca into: (1) an anterior portion—the future bladder and upper part of the urethra, and (2) a posterior portion—the future rectum and upper part of the anal canal. Within this septum certain reproductive organs develop, namely:

In the Male: deferent ducts, seminal vesicles, and prostate.

In the Female: uterine tubes, uterus, and vagina.

Male Pelvis Viewed from Above. From the preceding remarks it will be gathered that, on viewing a pelvis from above, one seeks the sigmoid colon and rectum dorsally, the urachus and bladder ventrally, and the genital organs in the plane between the two.

The following *peritoneal fossae* are seen: on each side of the partly filled rectum, the *pararectal fossae;* on each side of the partly filled bladder, the *paravesical fossae;* and, between the rectum and the bladder, the *rectovesical pouch.*

FOLLOW THE PERITONEUM IN THE MEDIAN PLANE (*fig. 342*) down the (1) anterior abdominal wall, (2) on to the back of the pubis, (3) across the superior surface of the empty bladder, (4) down its posterior surface for ½ inch, (5) over the upper ends of the seminal vesicles which are capped with peritoneum on each side of the median plane, (6) across the bottom of the rectovesical pouch, and on to the rectum. Where the rectum bounds the rectovesical pouch, it is covered with peritoneum in front only; a little higher where it bounds (7) the pararectal fossae, it is clothed with peritoneum in front and on the sides; above the level of the third piece of the sacrum (8) the gut acquires a mesentery and is known as the sigmoid colon.

DETACH THE PERITONEUM from the right half of the pelvic brim and note that four "visceral tubes" adhere to it even when it is detached and mobilized (*fig. 343*). They are: (1) the sigmoid colon and rectum dorsally; (2) the urachus and bladder ventrally; and (3) the ureter, and (4) ductus deferens laterally.

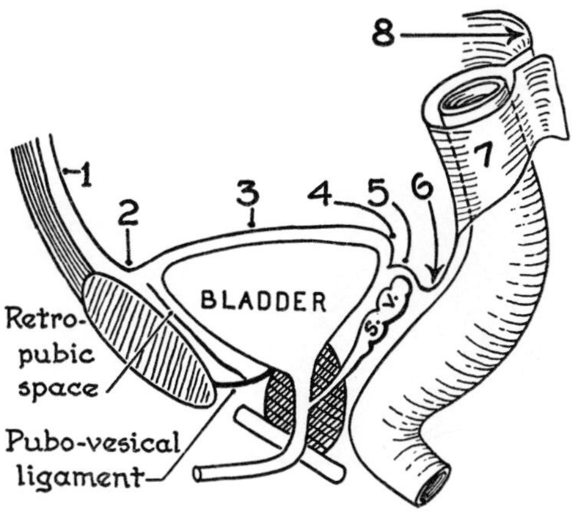

FIG. 342. The peritoneum of the male pelvis in paramedian section (see text and *fig. 380*).

»» Before cutting peritoneum, even though mobilized and detached, the surgeon makes sure that the adherent ureter is absolutely safe.

RAISE THE BLADDER and pull it back from the symphysis and thereby open up the retropubic space.

The **Retropubic Space** (*figs. 342* and *344*) is an extensive bursa-like cleft in the areolar tissue at the sides and front of the bladder which allows the bladder to fill and empty without hindrance. The space is bounded *medially* by the inferolateral surface of the bladder; *laterally* from above downward by bare pubic bone, Obturator Internus fascia, and fascia covering the Levator Ani; *below* by the reflexion of this fascia on to the bladder (*fig. 344*); *above* by the peritoneum passing from the upper surface of the bladder to the side wall of the pelvis.

The two sides of the space are continuous *in front*, between the symphysis pubis and the bladder. The space is limited *posteriorly* by a broad areolar sheet enclosing a leash of vessels that pass from the internal iliac artery and vein to the posterolateral border of the bladder (*fig. 375*). Two taut cord-like thickenings, one on each side of the median plane, attach the neck of the bladder to the lower end of the symphysis; these are the *puboprostatic* or *pubovesical ligaments* (*fig. 348*).

SUBPERITONEAL URETER AND DUCTUS (VAS) DEFERENS.

»» Before following these, glance again at figure 305 and recall that during the migration of the kidney

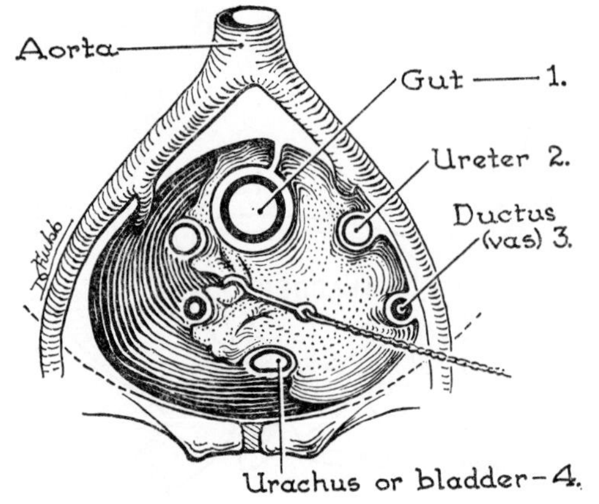

FIG. 343. Four visceral tubes adhere to the peritoneum. (The peritoneum has been detached from the side wall of the pelvis.)

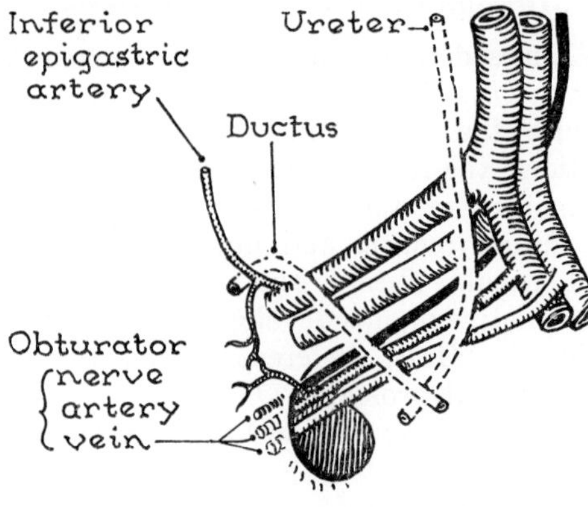

FIG. 345. The structures on the side wall of the male pelvis. Note the medial positions of the ureter and vas or ductus deferens.

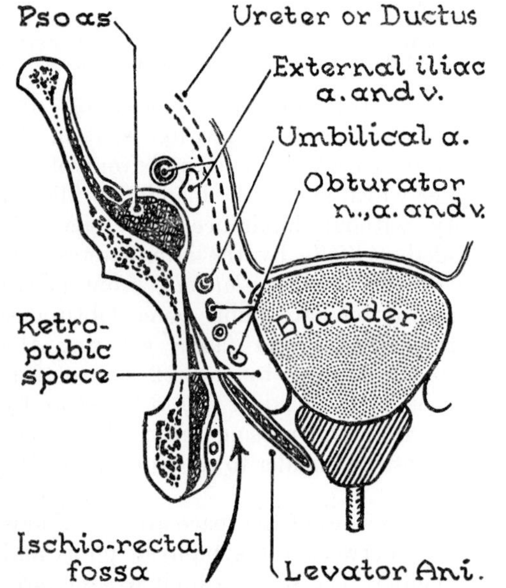

FIG. 344. The side wall of the male pelvis on coronal section (diagrammatic).

upward and of the testis downward, the testis crossed in front of the ureter and drew the testicular vessels and the ductus deferens after it. The testicular vessels cross in front of the ureter in the abdomen; the ductus (vas) deferens crosses in front of the ureter in the pelvis—close to where it enters the bladder.

The *ureter* crosses the external iliac artery, just in front of the bifurcation of the common iliac artery, and enters the lateral angle of the bladder where its last inch is enveloped in the leash of vessels just mentioned, and is crossed by the ductus deferens.

The *ductus deferens* runs from the deep inguinal ring, where it turns round the inferior epigastric vessels, to the lateral angle of the bladder where it crosses anterior to the ureter (*fig. 345*).

ORGANS THAT DEVELOPED IN THE PRIMITIVE URORECTAL SEPTUM (*fig. 347*). These are the seminal vesicles, which are situated lateral to the deferent ducts, which are here ampullated. These lie within a fascial fold, the rectovesical fascia (*fig. 348*).

Side Wall of the Pelvic Cavity

The side wall may be divided into two parts: the part above the obturator nerve and the part below it (*fig. 346*). *Above the nerve*, the wall is formed by bare pubic bone; *below* it, by the Obturator Internus and its fascia.

What is the line of the nerve? The obturator nerve arises from the ventral rami of L. 2, 3, and 4, and takes a straight course to the obturator foramen through which it passes into the thigh. In its course it crosses, but does not touch, the ala of the sacrum, pierces the psoas fascia at the medial border of the Psoas, crosses the pelvic brim lateral to the bifurcation of the common iliac vessels, and runs in contact with the pubic bone to the upper end of the obturator foramen.

The Obturator Internus, covered with its fascia (*fig. 346*), rises posteriorly to the pelvic brim, but falls anteriorly below the upper part of the obturator foramen leaving the pubic bone exposed and allowing the obturator nerve, artery, and vein to escape from the pelvic cavity via the foramen without piercing either muscle or fascia.

The obturator nerve springs from the lumbar plexus and, so, is above the obturator artery and vein which spring from the internal iliac vessels; and, according to RULE, the artery occupies the intermediate position; i.e., from above downward the order is: nerve—artery—vein.

The Levator Ani forms the greater part of the pelvic floor or diaphragm. It arises from the inner surface of the body of the pubis, from the inner surface of the ischial spine, and, between these two points, from the obturator fascia, which is commonly thickened to form a *tendinous arch* of origin (*fig. 346*).

From above downward, then, the side wall is formed by pelvic brim, bare pubic bone (anteriorly), Obturator Internus and its fascia.

The structures encountered on the side wall are successively: the external iliac artery, the external iliac vein, the obturator nerve, artery, and vein, all of which are somatic structures going to the lower limb. These are succeeded by the Levator Ani. [Being above the pelvic brim, the Psoas, its fascia, and the external iliac vessels, in a strict sense, lie within the abdominal cavity.] The ureter and the ductus deferens, being viscera, descend on the medial side of the structures enumerated (*figs. 345* and *347*).

Running forwards from the internal iliac artery to the umbilicus is the (obliterated) umbilical artery (p. 234). It tends to adhere to the side of the bladder and to supply it with superior vesical branches. Beyond these branches it is obliterated.

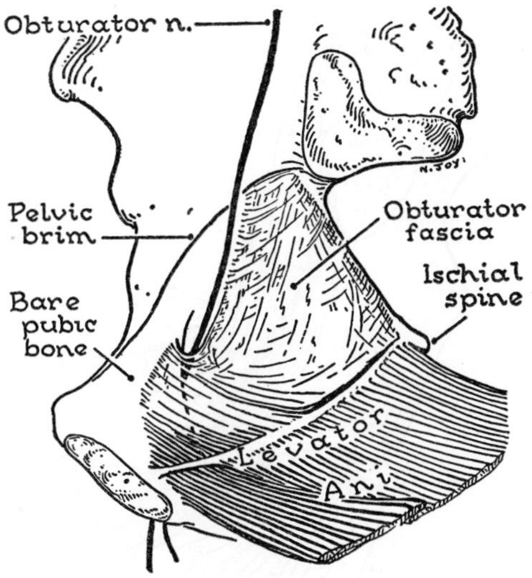

FIG. 346. The side wall of the lesser pelvis divided into upper and lower (anterior and posterior) parts by the obturator nerve.

Pelvic Fascia (*fig. 348*).

»» Just as all articles thrown into a basin of water become wet all over, so all the contents of the pelvis, whether they be muscles, viscera, or vessels, are covered all over with areolar tissue—in fact, with the areolar mesodermal tissue that in embryonic life filled the pelvic basin. This is perhaps not more true of the fascia of the pelvis than of the fascia of the abdomen or thorax; but the pelvic fascia attracts more attention.

The covering given by this areolar tissue to organs that expand and contract, notably the rectum and bladder, is necessarily loose; that given to organs that do not expand may be dense, as in the case of the prostatic fascia, or thin as in the case of the fascia covering the seminal vesicles and deferent ducts. Its texture depends upon the strains put upon it. Naturally, the fascia takes the shape of the surface it covers, forming a sheet where it covers a flat muscle or organ, forming a tube where it envelops a tubular structure, and blending with the periosteum where it touches exposed bone.

From the nature of its origin you will readily understand that though the different parts of the fascia are referred to as layers, they are not independent like sheets of paper, but are parts of a single whole, like the septa of a sponge.

SUBDIVISIONS OF THE PELVIC FASCIA. This fascia may be divided into *parietal*, *diaphragmatic*, and *visceral* layers: (1) The parietal layer covers the Obturator Internus at the side and the Piriformis at the back; (2) the diaphragmatic layer covers the upper surface of the pelvic diaphragm (or floor) formed by the Levator Ani and Coccygeus; and (3) the visceral layer covers the bladder, the rectum, and the genital organs in between the bladder and the rectum; and the particular coverings these viscera receive are called the *vesical*, *rectal*, and *rectovesical layers* of pelvic fascia.

You should establish the following:

1. In the pelvis minor, the pubis and ischium together with the obturator fascia form an osseofascial pocket for the Obturator Internus (*fig. 353*).

2. In the perineum the fascia has already been observed to give a complete lining to

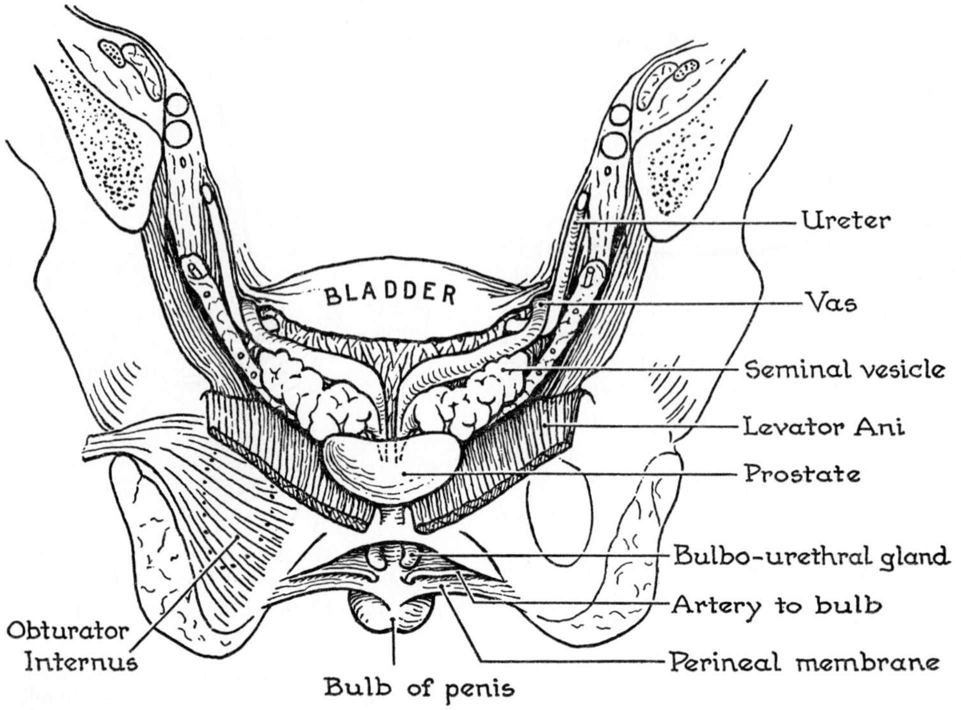

FIG. 347. A coronal section of the pelvis to show the genito-urinary organs from behind

the ischiorectal fossa, the lining being stronger laterally over the Obturator Internus than medially over the Levator Ani and Sphincter Ani Externus. It has also been seen to form the superior and inferior fasciae of the urogenital diaphragm.

3. The floor of the retropubic space is lined with a broad sheet of fascia which is continuous at the neck of the bladder with the vesical fascia. The portion of this sheet that passes forward to the symphysis pubis has developed in it two bands, the *puboprostatic ligaments*, which help to anchor the bladder and prostate and can easily be felt. The portion that spreads laterally covers the Levator Ani and blends with the obturator fascia and with the periosteum of the pubis.

4. The handle of the knife passed through the roof of the fossa enters the retropubic space. Note how thin the partition between them is (*fig. 344*). Appreciate that the Levator Ani, covered on both sides with fascia, is the roof of the fossa and the floor of the space.

5. The fascia invests the numerous veins and few arteries that are passing from the internal iliac vessels to the base of the bladder and internal genital organs (within the rectovesical fascia) (*fig. 375*). This limits the retropubic space posteriorly.

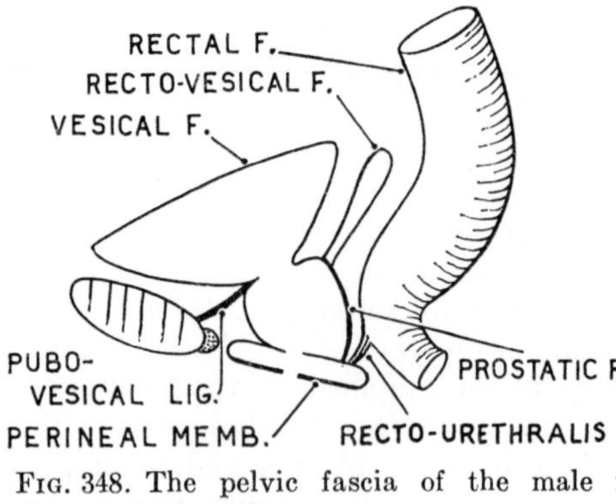

FIG. 348. The pelvic fascia of the male in median sagittal section.

6. Four layers of fascia separate the bladder from the rectum. They are the layer clothing the base of the bladder; the layer clothing the front of the rectum; and two other layers of which one clothes the deferent ducts and seminal vesicles in front, the other clothes them behind (*fig. 348*).

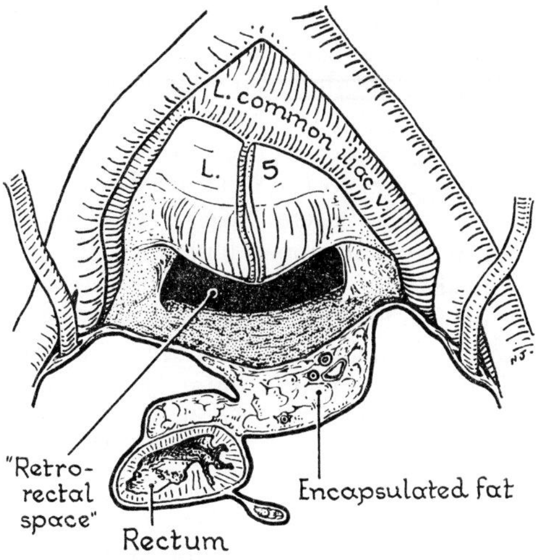

FIG. 348.1. The "retrorectal space"
Behind the rectum, incorporated in the rectal fascia, there is much fat. In this fat lie the superior rectal vessels (artery, vein, lymph vessels and nodes; see *fig. 397*).

7. The dense fascia clothing the back of the prostate was partially investigated from the perineum (p. 307). A finger, or the handle of a knife, passed downward between the rectum and the genital organs enters the perineum.

8. Pass two fingers downward behind the rectum and its fascia, which here encloses much fat and many lymph nodes (*fig. 397*), and ease them forward off the front of the sacrum and coccyx. The fingers occupy a potential space bounded on each side by an areolar fold containing the pelvic splanchnic nerves, which run from the 2nd, 3rd, and 4th sacral foramina to the side of the rectum (*fig. 348.1*).

INTERIOR OF BONY PELVIS

Pelvis is Latin for a basin. The pelvis is formed by the right and left hip bones, the sacrum, and the coccyx. The two hip bones articulate with each other in front at the symphysis pubis; behind they articulate with the first three sacral vertebrae at the sacro-iliac joints. The right and left hip bones constitute the pelvic girdle.

Each hip bone has three fundamental parts—ilium, ischium, and pubis. Of these, the ilium and ischium have homologous parts in the pectoral girdle (see below).

Sacrum and Coccyx

The **Os Sacrum** is composed of five fused vertebrae, and the **os coccygis** of 3–5, though before birth it has 7–11 cartilaginous caudal rudiments. Both sacrum and coccyx are triangular with base above and apex below (*fig. 349*).

The **base of the sacrum,** in reality the upper surface of the first sacral vertebra, is divided into three parts—a median and two lateral. The median part is the oval upper surface of the body of the first sacral vertebra. Its anterior border is an important landmark named the *promontory* of the sacrum. Behind its posterior border is situated the somewhat compressed triangular entrance to the *sacral canal.* This is guarded by extremely short pedicles, prominent superior articular processes, well developed laminae, and a much reduced spinous process. The right and left lateral parts, called the *alae,* are fan-shaped and represent fused costal and transverse elements (*fig. 23.1*).

Each ala is crossed by the constituents of the lumbosacral trunk, the iliolumbar artery, the obturator nerve, and the Psoas. Of these nerves, the 5th lumbar ventral ramus is so taut that it grooves the surface and anterior border of the ala; the branch of the 4th lumbar nerve is closely applied to the anterior border, whereas the obturator nerve is above, but not in contact with, the ala.

The **pelvic surface** of the sacrum is concave and is crossed by four rough ridges

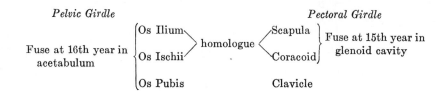

Pelvic Girdle				*Pectoral Girdle*	
Fuse at 16th year in acetabulum	Os Ilium	homologue	Scapula	Fuse at 15th year in glenoid cavity	
	Os Ischii		Coracoid		
	Os Pubis		Clavicle		

at the sites where fusion took place between the bodies of the five sacral vertebrae. Lateral to the four ridges, on each side, are the four *pelvic* or *anterior sacral foramina*. Their margins are smooth and rounded laterally, because the emerging ventral rami of the upper four sacral nerves pass laterally; but medially they are well defined and sharp.

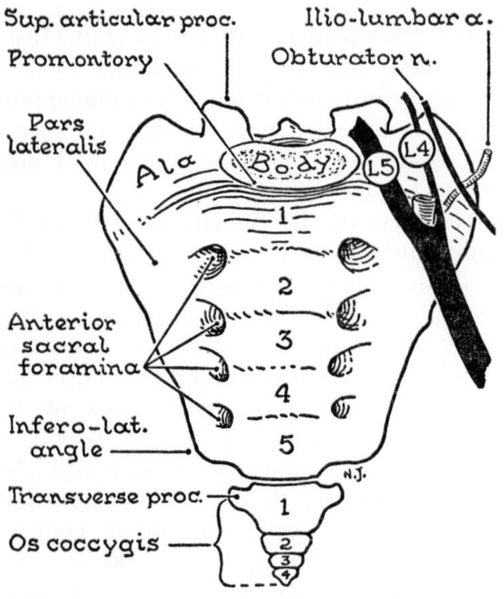

FIG. 349. The pelvic (anterior) aspect of the sacrum and coccyx.

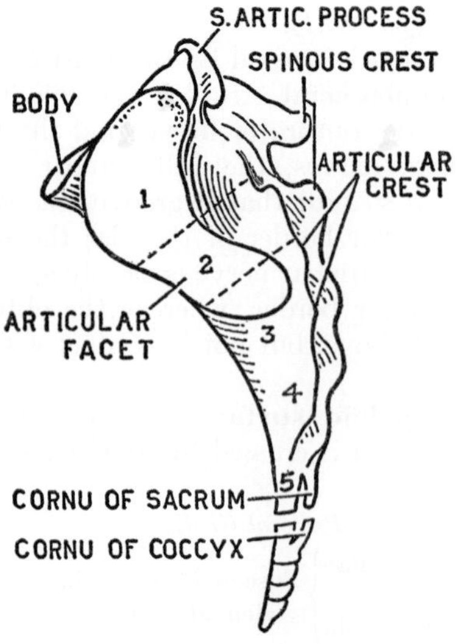

FIG. 350. The lateral aspect of sacrum and coccyx.

Though the sacrum as a whole tapers from above downward, the width of the bodies does not diminish appreciably, so the foramina of the two sides do not become appreciably closer to each other. The mass of bone lateral to the foramina is called the *pars lateralis* (lateral mass). It is deeply grooved by the upper four ventral rami.

The **sides** of the upper three pieces of the sacrum form a large *auricular* or *ear-shaped facet* which articulates with a corresponding auricular facet on the ilium (*fig. 350*); the sides of the lower two pieces, as well as the sides of the coccyx, are thin for the sacrotuberous and sacrospinous ligaments (*fig. 358*).

The **apex** of the sacrum is the lower articular surface of the 5th body, compressed anteroposteriorly to articulate with the body of the first piece of the coccyx.

(**Posterior Surface,** *see* p. 561.)

The **First Piece of the Coccyx** possesses a pair of *transverse processes* each of which is joined by a ligament to the lowest "transverse process" of the sacrum (inferolateral angle) thereby making a foramen through which the ventral ramus of the 5th sacral nerve enters the pelvis (*fig. 376*). The remaining pieces of the coccyx are nodular. The 1st piece commonly fuses with the sacrum, which then has six pieces; the joint between the 1st and 2nd pieces of the coccyx then commonly persists.

»» *Ossification.* The 5th, 4th, and 3rd pieces of the sacrum are always completely fused together by the 23rd year, the 3rd and 2nd by the 24th year, and the 2nd and 1st by the 25th year or even later (McKern and Stewart).

The **Pelvic Brim** is the boundary line between the greater or *major pelvis* above and the lesser or *minor pelvis* below, and at the same time it is the boundary line between the abdominal and pelvic cavities. Its component parts are: the promontory of the sacrum, the anterior border of the ala of the sacrum, the iliopectineal line (which extends from the ala to the pubic tubercle), the pubic crest, and the upper end of the symphysis pubis (*fig. 351*). The alar portion of the brim is weight-transmitting and therefore thick; the lumbosacral trunk and the

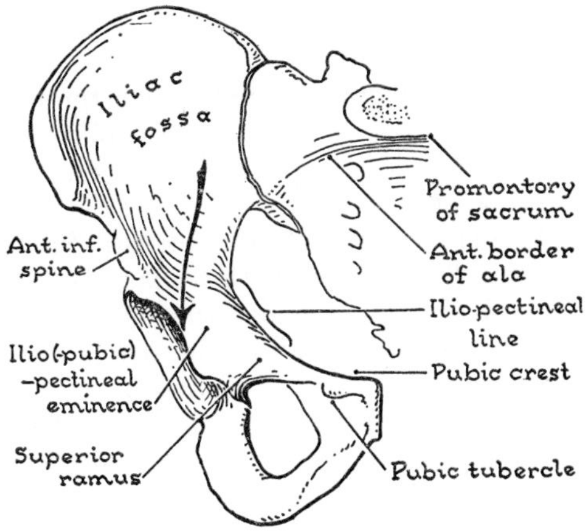

FIG. 351. The pelvis major (false pelvis) and the pelvic brim.

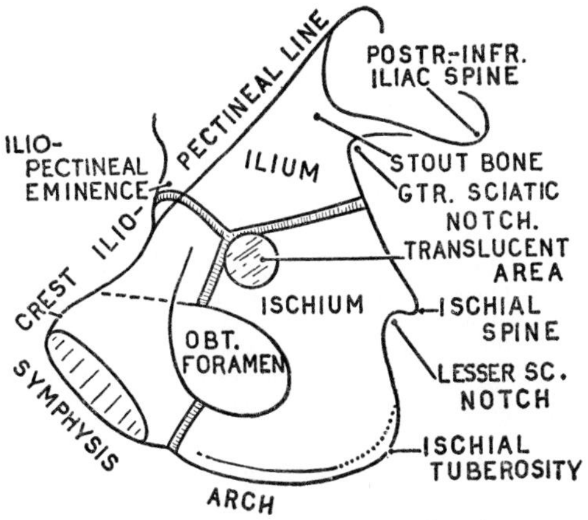

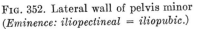

FIG. 352. Lateral wall of pelvis minor (*Eminence: iliopectineal = iliopubic.*)

iliolumbar artery curve over it, but no fascia is attached to it; so, it is rounded.

The posterior half of the iliopectineal line is formed by the ilium; the anterior half by the pubis; and a rough elevation, the *iliopubic eminence* (iliopectineal eminence), marks the site of their union. The iliac portion of the iliopectineal line has attached to it the fascia iliaca and the obturator fascia; so, it is sharp; and when a Psoas Minor is present a crest generally rises from this portion of the brim.

The pubic part of the iliopectineal line, called the **pecten pubis,** is sharp because it gives attachment in its whole length to the fascia covering the Pectineus, which is a muscle of the thigh, and in its medial ¾ inch to the lacunar ligament and conjoint tendon. A strong fibrocartilaginous band, of periosteum, the *pectineal ligament* (Cooper's lig.), through which a needle and thread can get a good grip, follows the line.

The triangular portion of the os pubis lying in front of the pecten pubis, and extending from the iliopubic eminence to the pubic tubercle, is the pectineal surface of the superior ramus of the pubis. Functionally, it belongs to the lower limb—not to the pelvis (*fig. 418*).

The **Pelvis Major** (False or Greater Pelvis) (*fig. 351*) is formed on each side by the ala of the sacrum, just described, and the iliac fossa. The *iliac fossa* is fan-shaped, concave, and, because the Iliacus which covers its entire surface is fleshy, it is smooth. The anterior two-thirds of the iliac crest forms the base of the fan and bounds the fossa above. The iliac tuberosity, the auricular surface, and the iliac part of the iliopectineal line bound it medially (*fig. 358*). The handle of the fan lies immediately above the acetabulum and is represented by a broad groove situated between the ant. inf. iliac spine and the iliopubic eminence. In this groove the Psoas tendon plays.

Pelvis Minor

The pelvis minor (*true or lesser pelvis*) is formed behind by the pelvic surfaces of the sacrum and coccyx, just described. In front and at the sides it is formed by the inner surface of the ischium and pubis, and by a small triangular part of the ilium that descends below the brim as far as a line joining the iliopubic eminence to the greater sciatic notch (*fig. 352*). Though small, this part of the ilium is an essential part of the pelvis, for it is weight-transmitting and therefore very thick; it extends backward below the auricular surface.

These parts of the pubis, ischium, and ilium together form a triangular, concave, smooth area. The base of this triangle is formed by the pubic crest and the iliopectineal line; the apex is the ischial tuberosity; one side is formed by the symphysis pubis, the inferior ramus of the pubis, and the ramus of the ischium, the rami being conjoint to form one half of the pubic arch;

and the other side is formed by the greater and lesser sciatic notches and the ischial spine which separates them.

The oval *obturator foramen* separates the pubis antero-superiorly from the ischium postero-inferiorly. The margin of the foramen forms a spiral which extends from the iliopubic eminence inside the pelvis to the pubic tubercle outside. The ends, therefore, do not meet, but bound the *obturator groove* on the under surface of the superior ramus of the pubis. Through this groove the obturator vessels and nerve escape from the pelvis. The ischium is thin and translucent immediately above the obturator foramen because here it forms the bottom of the nonarticular part of the acetabulum.

Foramina in the Walls of the Pelvis Minor. The posterior wall is perforated by the four *anterior or pelvic sacral foramina*. A probe entering one of these will emerge through the corresponding, much smaller posterior sacral foramen on to the dorsum of the sacrum. Two ligaments, the *sacro-tuberous* and *sacro-spinous*, so unite the posterior wall to the side wall as to leave two gaps, the *greater* and *lesser sciatic foramina* (*figs. 358* and *361*). The large, oval *obturator*

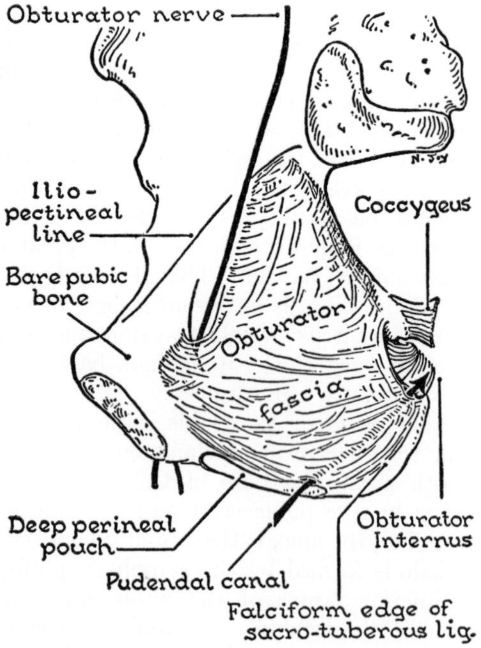

Fig. 353. The Obturator Internus Fascia

foramen, between the pubis and the ischium, is closed by the obturator membrane except above where a gap, through which the little finger can be passed, transmits the obturator nerve and vessels, and may be the site of a rare type of hernia.

Muscles of the Walls of the Pelvis Minor. *The Obturator Internus* arises by fleshy fibers from almost the entire inner surface of the side wall of the pelvis minor below the line of the obturator nerve (*fig. 353*). It leaves the pelvis through the lesser sciatic foramen to be inserted into the greater trochanter of the femur (p. 381).

The Piriformis arises by fleshy fibers from the three bars of bone that separate the four anterior sacral formina and from the pars lateralis. It leaves the pelvis through the greater sciatic foramen and is inserted into the greater trochanter (*fig. 420*).

»» *The obturator fascia* (*fig. 353*) with the side wall of the pelvis forms an osseo-fibrous pocket for the Obturator Internus. It is attached to the hip bone around the margin of its muscle; that is, to the border of the greater sciatic notch, to the iliac part of the iliopectineal line, along the line of the obturator nerve, to the pubic arch, and to the ischial tuberosity through the medium of the falciform edge of the sacrotuberous ligament; but it is not attached to the border of the lesser sciatic notch, this being the site of the *mouth of the pocket* through which the muscle escapes from the pelvis. Its lower part is tunneled by the pudendal canal.

The fascia covering the Piriformis is areolar and weak.

The Pelvic Diaphragm. The Levator Ani and Coccygeus of opposite sides stretch across the pelvis, like a hammock, separating the pelvic cavity from the perineum. This diaphragm is composed of voluntary muscle and is perforated by the urethra and the anal canal and, in the female, by the vagina also.

The pelvic diaphragm arises in front from the body of the pubis, behind from the spine of the ischium, and between these two points from an arched thickening of the obturator fascia, called the *tendinous arch* (*fig. 346*).

In tailed animals, the diaphragm consists of three separate muscles—the Pubococcygeus, the Iliococcygeus, and the Ischiococcygeus, which act upon the tail (*fig. 354*). In man, whose carriage is erect and whose tail is reduced to a coccyx, the muscles are modified for the support of the pelvic contents.

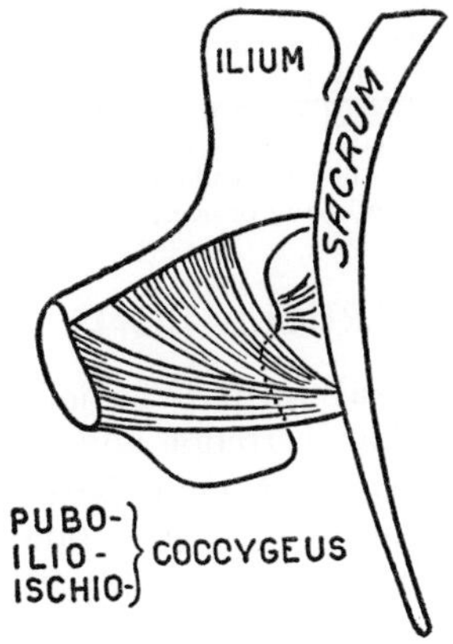

FIG. 354. The pelvic diaphragm of the monkey. (After Keith.)

FIG. 355. "The puborectal sling"

The Pelvic Diaphragm

1. Pubococcygeus } = Levator Ani
2. Iliococcygeus }
3. Ischiococcygeus = Coccygeus

The Ischiococcygeus or Coccygeus stretches like a fan from the ischial spine to the sides of the available segments of the sacrum (i.e., 4th and 5th) and to the coccyx. In the dog the Coccygeus wags the tail; in man it is largely transformed into the sacrospinous ligament. Some fleshy fibers, however, persist on the pelvic surface of the ligament, and they may form a complete fleshy sheet coextensive with the ligament.

The Iliococcygeus, formerly attached to the pelvic brim, has—as it were—atrophied above, become fibrous, and blended with the periosteum and with the obturator fascia above the level of the tendinous arch (*fig. 375*). It is inserted into the coccyx and into the anococcygeal raphe, which stretches from anus to coccyx.

The Pubococcygeus, which is the thickest and most important part of the diaphragm, runs downward and backward from the pubis and meets its fellow (a) in the perineal body in front of the anus and (b) in the anococcygeal raphe behind the anus; between the two (c) it is carried down by the rectum and anal canal, which perforate it and with which it blends. On the pelvic surface of the muscle many fibers pass backward from pubis to coccyx; others meet those of the opposite side in the angle between the rectum and anal canal and so form a U-shaped puborectal sling that maintains this angle (*fig. 355*). The different parts of the diaphragm, though overlapping somewhat, blend to form a single sheet.

The Levator Ani has a free anterior border which is separated from its fellow by ⅓ inch. Between the anterior borders the prostate can be exposed from the perineum (p. 307). The urethra and, in the female, the vagina pass between the anterior borders.

FUNCTIONS. The pelvic diaphragm supports the pelvic viscera. Figures 342, 347, and 379 demonstrate that the integrity of the pelvic floor depends especially on the Pubococcygeus, including the puborectal sling, since these hold forward the lower part of the rectum, which in turn helps to support the bladder, prostate and seminal vesicles in the male, and (which is more important) the bladder and vagina in the female.

The puborectal sling keeps the anorectal angle closed, but during defecation it relaxes and allows the anorectal junction to straighten, while other fibers draw the anal canal over the feces that are being expelled.

NERVE SUPPLY. Branches of S. (2), 3, and 4 supply the muscle on its pelvic surface; twigs of the perineal n. (S. 2, 3, and 4) supply it on its perineal surface.

Orientation of the Pelvis. In the "neutral" position of the pelvis the anterior superior iliac spines and the top of the symphysis are in a vertical plane. This is readily found by applying the pelvis to a wall. The ischial spine is then a little above the level of the top of the symphysis pubis,

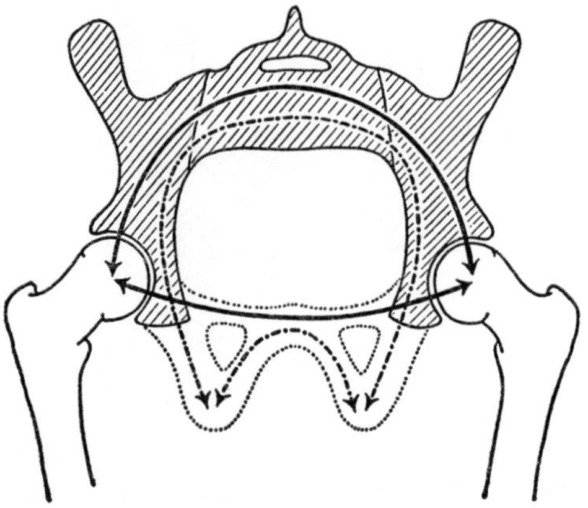

FIG. 356. The mechanism of the pelvis. *Solid lines* = the standing arch and its tie beam or counter arch which, like the clavicle, resists compressive forces. *Broken lines* = the sitting arch and its tie beam or counter arch which resists spreading forces. (After Braus.)

and the tip of the coccyx is a little below it. In the male the ant. sup. spines fail by about ½ inch to reach the vertical; so, the coccyx is behind the upper half of the symphysis.

In the female the ant. sup. spines overstep the vertical by about ½ inch; so, the coccyx is on a level with the top of the symphysis. In compensation for the forward tilting of the pelvis in the female, the lumbar curvature of the spine is increased and the erect posture thereby maintained. Hence, the lower part of the back, which is nearly flat in the male, is markedly concave in the female; the buttocks are more prominent than in the male, and so is the lower part of the abdomen.

Mechanism of the Pelvis (*fig. 356*). The weight of the body superimposed on the 5th lumbar vertebra is transferred to the base of the sacrum, thence to the upper three pieces of the sacrum, across the sacro-iliac joints to the ilia, and thence (1) when standing—to the acetabula and so to the femora, or (2) when sitting down—to the ischial tuberosities. Along these lines the bony parts are thickened. In the standing posture, the acetabula and the side walls of the pelvis tend to be forced together, but the pubic bones, acting as struts, prevent this from happening.

»» In cases of softening of the bones (osteomalacia) the side walls are actually driven in and the pelvis assumes a beak shape (*fig. 357*). In the sitting posture the ischial tuberosities tend to be forced apart—in rickets they actually are.

Many mammals possess a symphysis ischii as well as a symphysis pubis and so have a powerful strut. In birds the pubic bones are wide apart and, so, offer no obstruction to the laying of eggs.

ARTICULATIONS

Lumbosacral Joint. The joint between the 5th lumbar vertebra and the sacrum is an intervertebral joint possessing two peculiar ligaments on each side: (1) the iliolumbar ligament and (2) the lateral lumbosacral ligament.

The Iliolumbar Ligament is the greatly thickened lower part of the fascia covering the Quadratus Lumborum. It stretches from the tip of the 5th lumbar transverse process to the iliac crest.

The 4th lumbar vertebra lies at the level of the highest parts of the iliac crests; the 5th vertebra lies below this level and, so, it alone is in a position to be suspended from the crests. The large size, the upward tilt, and the conical shape of the 5th lumbar transverse processes are dependent on this fact.

The iliolumbar ligs. are important for they limit axial rotation of the 5th vertebra on the sacrum, and they assist the articular processes in preventing forward gliding of the 5th vertebra on the sacrum.

»» *The Lateral Lumbosacral Ligament* is a modified intertransverse ligament. It spreads, as a sheet, downward and laterally from the 5th lumbar transverse process to the ala of the sacrum. It has a sharp medial edge which abuts against the ventral ramus of the 5th lumbar nerve.

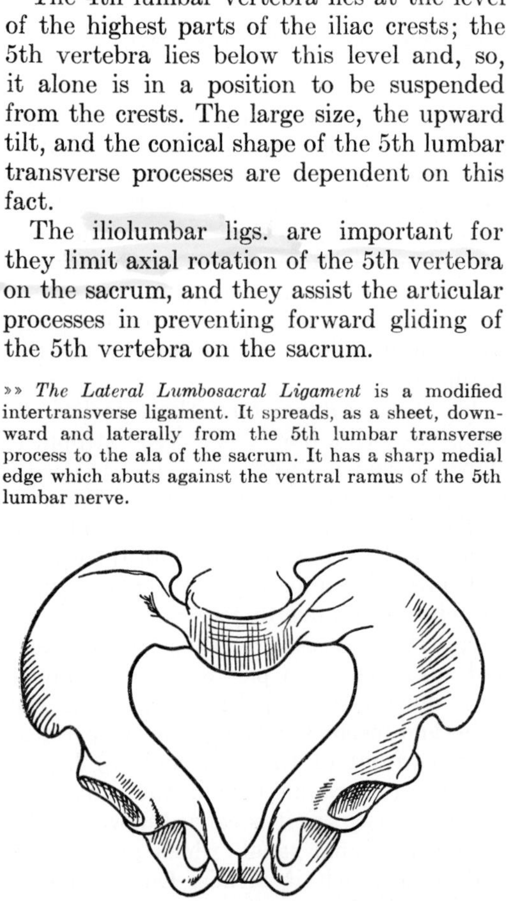

FIG. 357. Pelvis from case of osteomalacia. The femora have driven in the softened bones.

The Typical Ligaments of this joint:

The Intervertebral Disc is much thicker than other intervertebral discs, so more movement is permitted here than between other vertebral bodies. The bodies are narrower from front to back than from side to side; so, flexion and extension should be greater than side-to-side bending, provided the articular processes permit, and they do. The disc is so much deeper in front than behind that it contributes to the lumbar curve and, therefore, to the erect posture in man.

The Anterior and Posterior Longitudinal Ligaments of the Bodies descend to the first piece of the sacrum.

Capsular Ligaments, necessarily loose, unite the articular processes.

Ligamenta Flava unite the laminae.

Supra- and Interspinous Ligaments unite the spinous processes.

The disc, then, is here at its thickest, and the ligaments are at their strongest.

Joints of the Pelvis: (1) sacrococcygeal joint, (2) symphysis pubis, and (3) right and left sacro-iliac joints.

Sacrococcygeal Joint. This is an atypical intervertebral joint.

Attached to each side of the coccyx and lower two pieces of the sacrum (i.e., below the auricular surface) are: the Coccygeus, sacrospinous and sacrotuberous ligaments, and Gluteus Maximus. Movement backward of the coccyx takes place on defecation and on parturition.

» The bodies of the last sacral and 1st coccygeal vertebrae are united by an intervertebral disc, and the transverse processes and the cornua by ligamentous bands. And, a very tough membrane, which is a downward prolongation of the supraspinous and interspinous ligaments, closes the sacral canal posteriorly and extends to the posterior surface of the coccyx.

Symphysis Pubis. Here as between the bodies of two vertebrae, the opposed bony surfaces are coated with hyaline cartilage and are united by fibrocartilage. In the fibrocartilage a cleft generally appears. Dense anterior decussating fibers and a strong arcuate ligament (inf. pubic lig.) unite the pubic bones.

» *Age changes.* The surface and margins of the pubic symphysis undergo progressive metamorphoses, especially between the 20th and 40th years, which serve as a criterion of age. Todd has divided this into 10 phases.

Sacro-Iliac Joint

The Bony Surfaces of this synovial joint are:

(1) The *internal surface of the ilium* behind the iliac fossa. This part is bounded above by the posterior one-third of the iliac crest, below by the greater sciatic notch, and behind by the posterior superior and posterior inferior iliac spines and the slight notch between them (*fig. 358*).

It is subdivided into two parts: a lower, the *auricular surface;* and, an upper, the *tuberosity.* The auricular or ear-shaped part articulates with the sacrum, is covered with cartilage, and is traversed by a longitudinal sinuous ridge. The iliopectineal line begins at its most anterior part. The tuberosity is rough and tubercular for the numerous short fibers of the strong interosseous sacro-iliac ligament.

(2) *The sacrum* possesses the counterpart: thus, on the side of the pars lateralis there is an *auricular surface* with a sinuous furrow. This auricular surface extends on to the 3rd sacral segment but leaves the lower two segments free and attenuated for the sacrospinous and sacrotuberous ligaments. Posterosuperior to the auricular surface is the *sacral tuberosity* (*fig. 350*).

Structural Requirements. It is apparent that the weight transmitted to the sacrum by the superimposed part of the vertebral column will tend to cause its upper end to rotate forward and its lower end with the coccyx to rotate backward (*fig. 359*). Ligaments are so disposed as to resist this tendency. Further, the articular surfaces of the sacrum are farther apart in front than behind, so the sacrum behaves not as a keystone, but as the reverse of a keystone, and tends therefore to sink forward into the pelvis. As it does so, the posterior ligaments become taut and draw the ilia closer together with the result that the interlocking ridge and furrow engage more closely. Here is an automatic locking device (*fig. 360*).

Ligaments resisting forward rotation of upper end of sacrum:

1. *The Interosseous Sacro-iliac ligament*

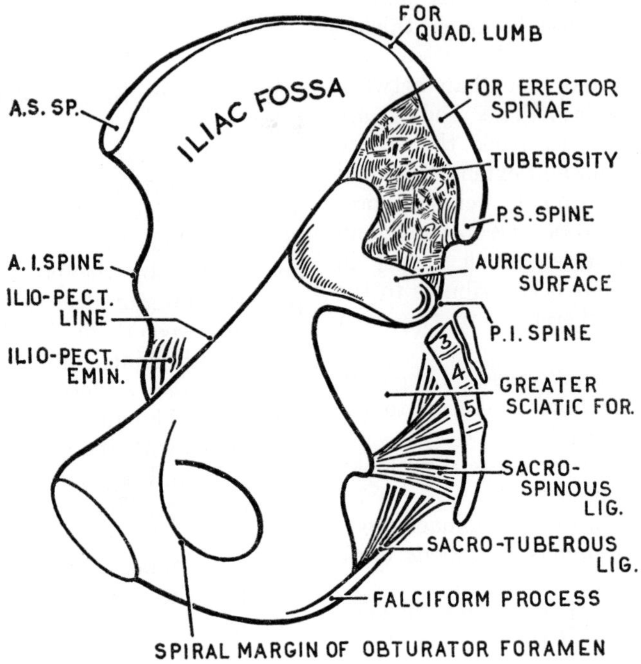

FIG. 358. Inner surface of hip bone

(*fig. 360*), which is a ligament of great strength, unites the iliac and sacral tuberosities. It lies posterosuperior to the joint.

2. *The Dorsal Sacro-iliac ligaments*, very strong bands, unite the transverse tubercles of the sacrum to the post. sup. iliac spine.

3. *The Iliolumbar ligament*, see lumbosacral joint (p. 320).

Ligaments resisting backward rotation of lower end of sacrum: the *sacrotuberous* and *sacrospinous ligaments* (*figs. 359* and *361*). The one passes from the tuberosity of the ischium, the other from the spine of the ischium, to the available parts of the side of the sacrum and coccyx, i.e., to the lateral border of the sacrum and coccyx below the articular facet.

The Sacrotuberous Lig. is a broad band that extends from an impression on the medial part of the tuber ischii to the free part of the sides of the sacrum and coccyx and to the adjacent part of the dorsal surfaces.

»» The lower end of the ligament curves forwards as a falciform process of which one edge creates a line (or ridge) on the ischium, while the other is continuous with the Obturator Internus fascia. The lateral part of the ligament arches from ischial tuberosity to posterior iliac spines (inf. and sup.); its only function is to afford origin to the Gluteus Maximus.

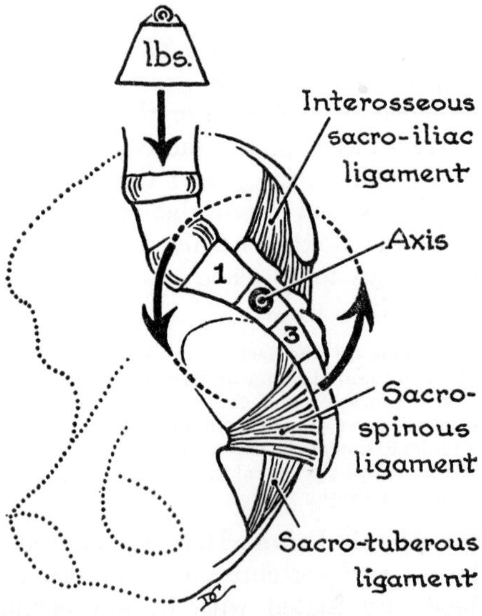

FIG. 359. Ligaments resisting rotation of the sacrum.

The Sacrospinous Ligament is a triangular sheet, co-extensive with the Coccygeus and regarded as its degenerated

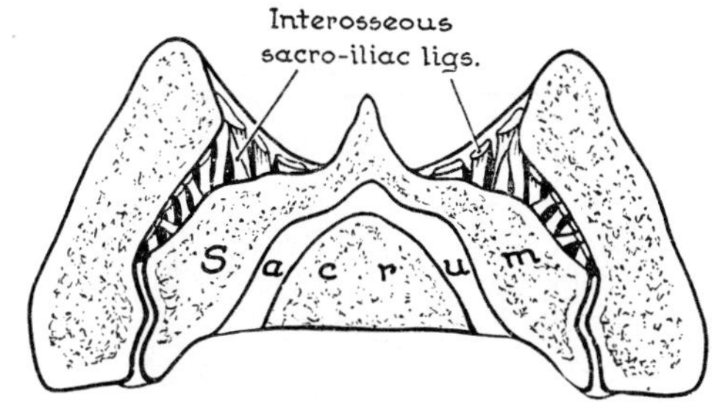

FIG. 360. The sacro-iliac joint on transverse section. Note the locking device.

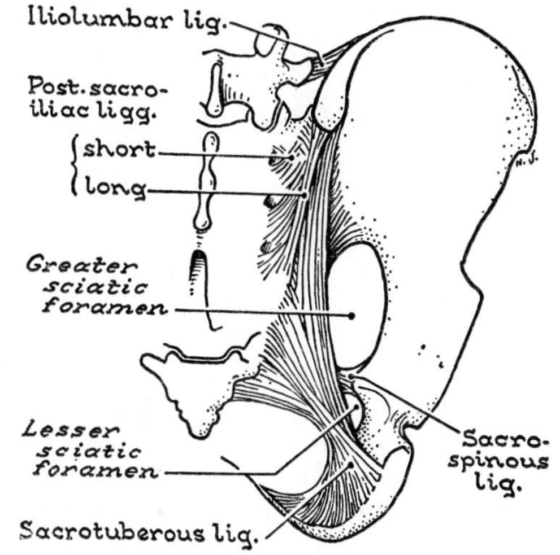

FIG. 361. The ligaments of the pelvis, posterior view.

posterior lamina; it extends from the ischial spine to the side and dorsum of the free parts of the sacrum and coccyx.

The sacrotuberous and the sacrospinous ligaments convert the greater and lesser sciatic notches into foramina. They are no doubt responsible for the curvature of sacrum, which is a characteristic of man, who alone walks erect.

The anterior part of the joint cavity is closed by a strong fibrous capsule called the *anterior sacro-iliac ligament.* After middle life, particularly in males, this ligament may ossify, forming a crust of bone that prevents movement of the joint (synostosis).

MOVEMENTS. In a fresh specimen it is easily demonstrated (1) that the sacrum can rotate backward and forward between the hip bones; and, after division of the disc and ligaments of the symphysis pubis, (2) that the pubic bones easily spread ½ inch, and (3) allow the hip bones to rock fairly freely on the sacrum.

During pregnancy the ligaments of the pelvis are relaxed and movements are more free.

ANTERIOR RELATIONS (*fig. 376*). The lumbosacral trunk, the superior gluteal a., and the 1st sacral nerve cross the pelvic surface of the capsule.

SURFACE ANATOMY. The ilium articulates with the 1st, 2nd, and 3rd sacral vertebrae, the center of the articulation being at the level of the 2nd. This is not readily identified, but the post. sup. iliac spine, which lies at the level of the 2nd sacral vertebra is readily palpated. The joint lies lateral to this (pp. 376–377 and *fig. 419*).

»» DEVELOPMENT AND VARIATIONS. The sacro-iliac joint and the symphysis pubis do not develop, like other joints, as clefts in a continuous rod of condensed mesenchyme but by the coming into apposition of the ilium and sacrum posteriorly and of the pubic bones of opposite sides anteriorly. The auricular surface of the sacrum is usually covered with hyaline cartilage, that of the ilium with fibrocartilage, and between them there is a joint cavity which is present before birth (Schunke).

Accessory articular facets, 1 to 2 cm. in diameter, are commonly found between the opposed tuberosities of the sacrum and ilium.

MALE UROGENITAL SYSTEM IN PELVIS

(continued)

Urinary Bladder. The empty and contracted urinary bladder, shaped not unlike the forepart of a ship, has four surfaces and four angles (*fig. 362*). To each of the *four angles* a duct is attached: the *urachus* to the anterior angle or apex, the *right and left ureters* to the posterolateral angles, and the *urethra* to the inferior angle or neck. The four surfaces are: the superior, the sides or inferolateral, and the base or inferoposterior.

The superior surface and ½ inch of the inferoposterior surface are the only parts covered with peritoneum. The superior surface is bounded by the rounded borders that connect the ureters to each other and to the urachus. It supports the sigmoid colon and ileum.

The urinary bladder like certain other organs, notably the lungs, the liver, the

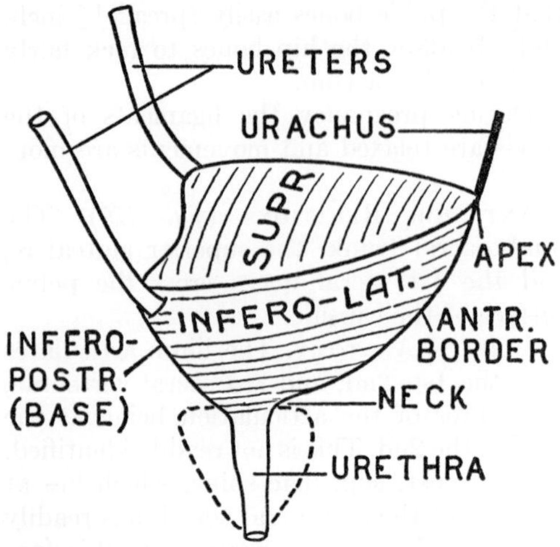

FIG. 362. The 4 surfaces, 4 angles, and 4 ducts of the urinary bladder.

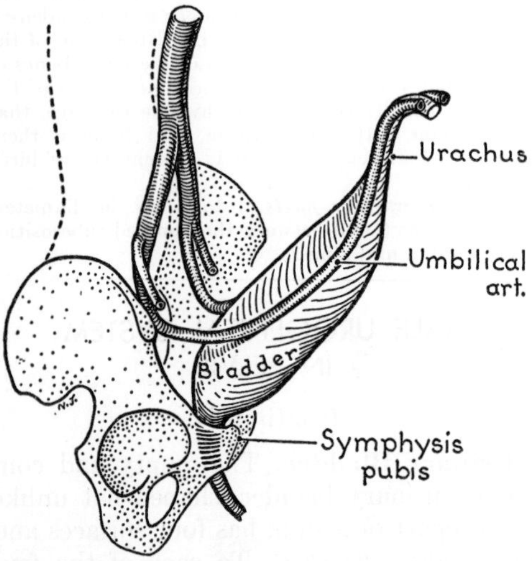

FIG. 362.1. The bladder is abdominal at birth

spleen, and the parotid salivary gland, owes its shape largely to the structures in contact with it. At birth the bladder is an abdominal organ (*fig. 362.1*) fusiform in shape, lying in the extraperitoneal tissue of the anterior abdominal wall; only by about the 6th year has the pelvis enlarged sufficiently to allow it to sink to its permanent pelvic position and tetrahedral shape.

Bed of Bladder. The bed or mould in which the bladder lies is formed on each side by bare pubic bone, the Obturator Internus, and the Levator Ani, and behind

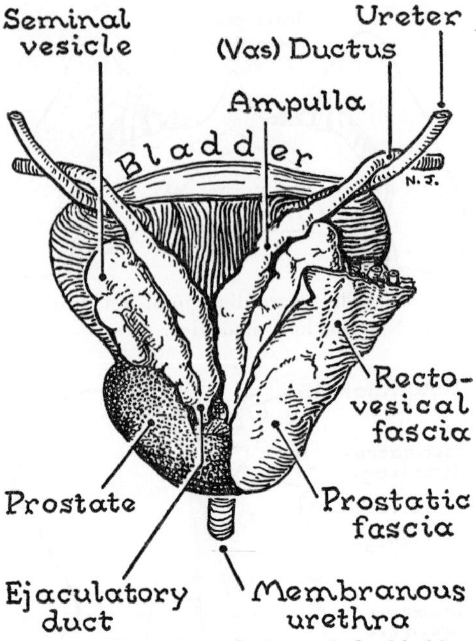

FIG. 363. Posterior relations of the bladder

by the rectum, hence the inferolateral and inferoposterior surfaces (*figs. 347* and *363*).

The entire organ is enveloped in areolar tissue, the *vesical fascia.* A dense plexus of veins, the *vesical plexus,* lies in this fascia on the side of the bladder, clings to the bladder, and separates it from the retropubic space.

The base or *inferoposterior surface* of the bladder is separated from the rectum by the seminal vesicles and ampullated ends of the deferent ducts, which are enclosed between the two layers of rectovesical fascia; above these the peritoneum of the rectovesical pouch separates the upper ½ inch of the bladder from the rectum (*figs. 342* and *348*).

It is not usually appreciated that the bladder rests upon the lower part of the rectum, which takes a course approaching the horizontal.

Pelvic Portion of the Ureter. Each ureter enters the pelvis at the bifurcation of the common iliac artery and descends immediately in front of the internal iliac artery. It lies subperitoneally, save where crossed by the deferent duct an inch or less from the bladder, and it crosses medial to the structures on the side wall of the pelvis; these are: external iliac a. and v., umbilical a., obtura-

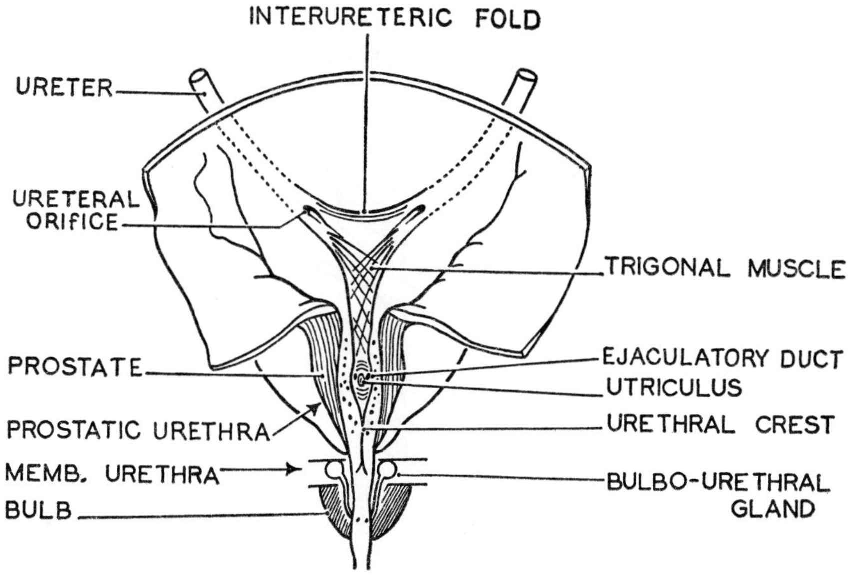

FIG. 364. The trigone of the bladder and the prostatic urethra

tor n., a., and v., and inferior vesical a. and v. Before passing through the bladder wall, it crosses the apex of the seminal vesicle and is there surrounded by a leash of vesical veins (*figs. 345* and *363*).

The Interior of the Bladder. The mucous membrane lies in folds, except over the trigone where it is smooth. *The Trigone* is an equilateral triangle on the interior of the base of the bladder (*fig. 364*). Its sides are an inch or so long; the two ureters and the urethra open at its angles. The internal urethral orifice lies at the lowest point of the bladder and, therefore, is situated advantageously for drainage. A pencil can be pushed into it.

The orifice of each ureter is guarded by a fold of mucous membrane and is collapsed. A ridge, the *interureteric fold*, connects the two ureters at the upper border of the trigone. An elevation, the *uvula*, overlying the middle lobe of the prostate, is sometimes to be seen at the apex of the trigone behind the internal urethral orifice.

The ureters are not continuous structurally with the bladder at the posterolateral angles, but penetrate its wall obliquely to open an inch apart at the base of the trigone. If a transverse incision is made through the mucous coat of the bladder at the upper border of the interureteric fold, and carried laterally through the bladder wall to the posterolateral angles, the ureters can be eased, with the aid of the handle of a knife, free from their areolar bed. Muscle fibers radiate from the ureters and blend with the muscle of the trigone.

The Trigonal Muscle is a submucous sheet distinct from the muscular wall proper. It is continuous with the muscular wall of the ureters above; its apex descends in the posterior wall of the urethra to the utricle. This trigonal area of the bladder and urethra is derived from the Wolffian or mesonephric ducts. It is supplied by the hypogastric plexus (L. 1, 2).

Though 500 cc. can be injected into the bladder without causing discomfort, urine is usually voided when little more than half this volume has accumulated; the exact volume depending largely on acquired habit.

As the bladder fills, the trigone enlarges but little, so the three orifices are only slightly displaced, but the rest of the bladder stretches. When the fundus reaches the level of the umbilicus, the peritoneum is stripped from the anterior abdominal wall for 1 to 2 inches above the symphysis pubis; and, it is reflected from the sides of the bladder on to the side walls of the pelvis at

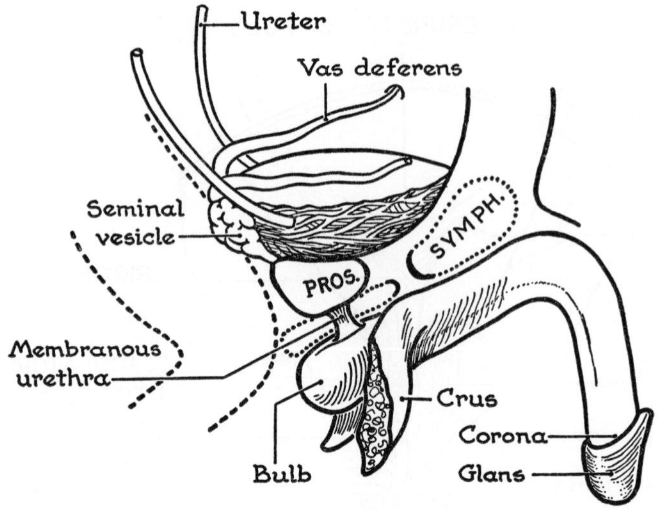

FIG. 365. The lower parts of the genital and urinary tracts and their relations

the level of the obliterated umbilical arteries; and the extent of the retropubic space is, of course, increased.

Vessels and Nerves of the Bladder.

Arteries: superior and inferior vesical.

Veins pass to the vesical plexus and thence to the internal iliac veins.

Lymph vessels (p. 355).

Nerves. Pelvic splanchnic nn. and hypogastric plexus (p. 61).

Male Urethra. The male urethra is a fibro-elastic tube, 8 inches long (*fig. 365*). It is divided by the superior and the inferior fascia of the urogenital diaphragm into three parts: *prostatic*, *membranous*, and *spongy*. The part above the superior fascia traverses the prostate; the part between the two fasciae has no covering; the part beyond the inferior fascia or perineal membrane traverses the corpus spongiosum penis.

THE PROSTATIC URETHRA (*fig. 364*) is the widest and most dilatable part of the urethra. It runs almost vertically and is an inch or more long. In shape it is fusiform; and on transverse section it is crescentic, owing to the presence of a prominent vertical ridge on the posterior wall, called the *urethral crest*. The gutter on each side of the crest is called the *prostatic sinus*. The urethral crest rises to a summit, the *colliculus*, and bifurcates below as it fades away. Opening on to the colliculus is a diverticulum, the *prostatic utricle*, up which a probe can be passed for ¼″ to ½″ into the substance of the prostate; and on to the lips of the utricle open the pinpoint orifices of the right and the left *ejaculatory duct*. On to the floor of each prostatic sinus several dozen *prostatic ducts* open.

THE MEMBRANOUS URETHRA passes through the urogenital diaphragm and its two fasciae an inch from the symphysis pubis. It is ½ inch long and has no proper clothing. Behind it on each side lies a bulbo-urethral gland. The enveloping fibers of the diaphragm, called the *Sphincter Urethrae*, form for it a sphincter of voluntary muscle supplied by the perineal branch of the pudendal nerve. Like the Sphincter Ani Externus, also supplied by the pudendal nerve, it is constantly on guard and relaxes only during micturition.

THE SPONGY OR PENILE URETHRA traverses the bulb, body, and glans of the corpus spongiosum penis. It enters the bulb on its upper surface and ends near the lower part of the apex of the glans at the external urethral orifice. Its lumen is dilated both in the bulb and in the glans. The dilatation in the glans is known as the navicular (terminal) fossa (*fig. 339*).

The external urethral orifice is commonly the narrowest part of the urethra. In this it resembles other ducts, such as the ureters ejaculatory ducts, common bile and pancreatic ducts, and the ducts of the parotid and submandibular salivary glands. A small renal calculus after leaving the kidney may stick at the vesical orifice of the ureter, or, having passed, it may yet stick at the external urethral orifice.

Although the membranous and spongy urethrae are lined with stratified columnar epithelium, the navicular fossa is lined with stratified squamous epithelium, as are other orifices opening on to the skin surface, such as the nostrils, mouth, mammary ducts, sebaceous ducts (but not the sweat ducts), anal canal, and vagina.

Palpation. A catheter passed into the bladder can be palpated in the *spongy urethra* from the under surface of the penis, in the *membranous urethra* from the perineum, and in the *prostatic urethra* per rectum.

Nerve supply (p. 353 and *fig. 395*).

Structure of the Urinary Tract

»» *The Tunica Propria* is thick and loose in the ureter and bladder, and it falls into folds when they are empty. It has no tunica muscularis mucosae—such is restricted to the alimentary passage beyond the pharynx.

Muscle. The urinary tract has both an inner longitudinal and an outer circular coat of muscle. The lower part of the ureter and the bladder have an additional outer longitudinal coat; the layers are interwoven in the bladder, the innermost being somewhat reticular. Fibers from the longitudinal and circular muscle coats loop from behind forward around the front and sides of the upper part of the prostatic urethra. These slings are known as the *Sphincter Vesicae.*

The circular and longitudinal fibers in the urethra are not numerous.

The intramural part of the ureter has longitudinal fibers, but no circular ones. Of these, some join their fellow in the interureteric fold, others radiate into the trigonal muscle (*fig. 364*).

Urethral Glands. Mucous cells, singly and in clusters lining recesses (lacunae urethrales), as well as in branching outpouchings (urethral glands) in the tunica propria, occur especially on the dorsum of the anterior two-thirds of the spongy urethra. They may extend to the neck of the bladder.

Common Direction. The mouths of all ducts and tubes opening into the urethra open forward, in the direction in which the urine flows. Hence, urine does not enter them during micturition, but fine instruments passed in the reverse direction may do so.

GENITAL SYSTEM OF THE MALE

The external parts—penis, scrotum, testes, epididymides, and parts of the deferent ducts—have been studied.

The internal parts—the terminal parts of the deferent ducts, seminal vesicles, ejaculatory ducts, and prostate—will be studied now.

Prostate (*fig. 365*). The prostate surrounds the urethra between the bladder and the u.g. diaphragm. It occupies the same bed as the bladder and it resembles the bladder in shape, its surfaces being superior, inferolateral, and inferoposterior. Of these, the superior faces the bladder; the inferolateral lie on the Levatores Ani; and the inferoposterior lies on the rectum. Its apex, from which the urethra emerges, abuts against the superior fascia of the diaphragm between the anterior borders of the Levatores Ani (*fig. 347*).

The prostate is encased in a strong envelope of pelvic fascia, which is continuous below with the superior fascia of the u.g. diaphragm, and which is anchored to the pubes by the puboprostatic (-vesical) ligaments. The *prostatic fascia* is distinct from the outermost part of the gland proper, which is called the *capsule of the prostate* (*figs. 348* and *363*).

On each side of the prostate the capsule is separated from the fascia by a venous plexus, called the *prostatic plexus of veins.* This plexus receives the deep dorsal vein of the penis in front, communicates with the vesical plexus above, and drains into the internal iliac veins behind.

The posterior part of the prostatic fascia forms a broad strong sheet, called by the surgeon the *fascia of Denonvilliers.* It is easily separated from the loose rectal fascia behind it.

The prostate can be palpated per rectum and exposed readily from the perineum (p. 307).

The urethra passes vertically through the forepart of the prostate; the prostatic utricle projects into the hinder part, and the ejaculatory ducts pierce its upper surface and open on to the lips of the utricle.

»» STRUCTURE. The prostate is a modified portion of the urethral wall. In composition it is one-half glandular, one-fourth involuntary muscle, and one-fourth fibrous tissue. The glands are arranged in three concentric groups (*fig. 366*). The innermost or *mucosal* are short and simple. They open all round the urethra above the level of the colliculus. "All hypertrophies of

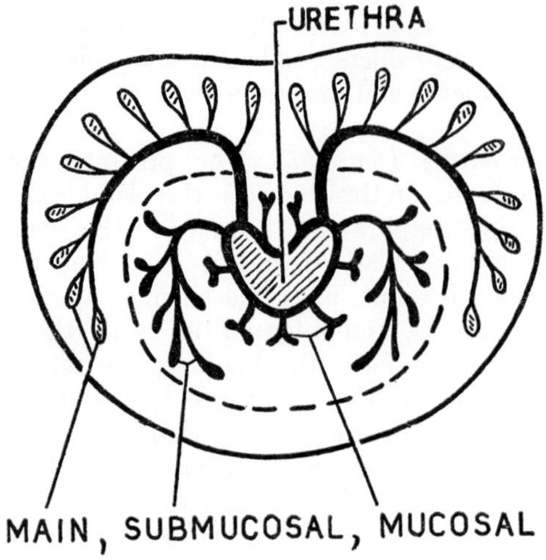

FIG. 366. Prostate in transverse section showing three concentric groups of tubules (schematic). (After Adrion.)

the prostate arise from these mucosal or suburethral glands" (Young). The intermediate or *submucosal* glands open into the prostatic sinus at the level of the colliculus. The outermost or *prostatic glands proper* are long and branching. They envelop the other two groups, except in front where those of opposite sides are joined by a non-glandular isthmus. Their ducts open into the prostatic sinus.

The **Ductus (Vas) Deferens,** like the femur, is about 18″ long. It has a course in the scrotum, in the inguinal canal, on the side wall of the pelvis, and between the bladder and rectum (*fig. 225*). The duct rounds the inf. epigastric vessels at the abdominal wall, and it rounds the ureter at the base of the bladder.

»» Before birth, it is subperitoneal from end to end; for in the scrotum and inguinal canal, where it is a constituent of the spermatic cord, the processus vaginalis peritonei accompanies it (*figs. 347* and *223*).

After birth, the ductus remains literally subperitoneal, in the abdomen and pelvis, as far as the base of the bladder. But, between the bladder and rectum, it ceases to be subperitoneal at about the 6th year, when the lowest part of the rectovesical pouch, which formerly descended to the apex of the prostate, is obliterated (*fig. 273*).

With these facts in your mind, note that the ductus, after turning round the lateral side of the inf. epigastric a., crosses the external iliac vessels, the obliterated umbilical a., the obturator nerve and vessels, and the ureter (*fig. 345*).

Where the ductus lies between the two layers of rectovesical fascia, medial to the

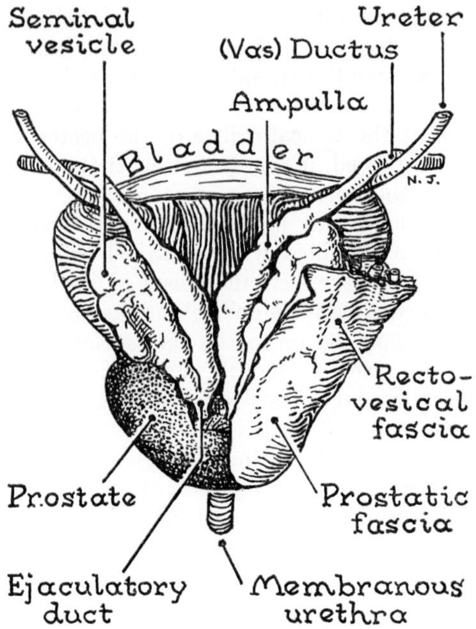

FIG. 367. The seminal vesicles and the deferent ducts (vasa deferentia).

seminal vesicle, it is ampullated, thin-walled, and easily torn (*fig. 367*). Here it is separated from its fellow by a triangular area bounded above by the peritoneum of the rectovesical pouch. This *triangular area behind the base of the bladder* is not to be confused with the trigone of the bladder.

Seminal Vesicles. Each vesicle is a tortuous, branching diverticulum developed from the ampullated end of the ductus deferens, and possessing much the same histological structure (*fig. 368*). It lies between the two delicate layers of the rectovesical fascia; i.e., in the primitive urorectal septum (*fig. 330*). *In front* is the bladder; *behind* is the cylindrical rectum on which it is moulded; *medial* to it is the ductus of which it is an outgrowth; *above* it is capped with peritoneum; and laterally it is separated from the Levator Ani by numerous vesical vessels. Below, it joins the ductus deferens to form the ejaculatory duct.

»» The vesicles, prostate, and bulbo-urethral glands each add a distinctive secretion to the semen. Storing spermatozoa, formerly thought to be a function of the vesicles, is now known to take place in the epididymis. Indeed, seminal vesicles are absent in dogs and other carnivora.

Ejaculatory Duct (paired). This duct is common to the ductus deferens and the seminal vesicle. It has the diameter of the lead of a pencil. It is easily torn away from the prostate, the upper half of which it pierces obliquely to open beside the prostatic utricle.

Vessels and Nerves. *The inferior vesical aa.*, with a little help from the middle *rectal aa.*, supply all the structures in between the bladder and the rectum, viz., prostate, seminal vesicles, ampullae of the deferent ducts, and the ends of the ureters. *The deferent a.* itself springs from an inferior vesical a.

Nerves. (*See* p. 353.)

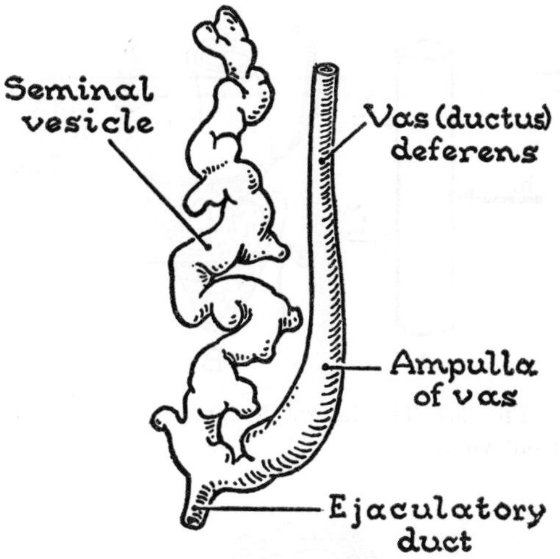

FIG. 368. The seminal vesicle unraveled

RECTUM AND ANAL CANAL

The (intestinum) rectum and anal canal are the terminal parts of the large intestine. The rectum begins where the colon ceases to have a mesentery, which is in front of the 3rd piece of the sacrum, and it is about 5 inches long. The rectum continues the curvature of the sacrum and coccyx downward and forward for 1½ inches beyond the coccyx, and there, at the apex of the prostate, makes a right angled bend and becomes the anal canal. The anal canal passes downward and backward for an inch or more to its orifice, the *anus*.

Rectum (*fig. 342*). The upper part of the rectum is covered with peritoneum in front and at the sides; the middle part is covered in front only; and the lower part, which is commonly dilated to form the *ampulla of the rectum*, lies below the level of the rectovesical pouch and, therefore, is devoid of peritoneal covering. The distance from the skin surface to the peritoneal cavity (i.e., to the rectovesical pouch), measured in front of the anal canal and rectum, is 3–4 inches (*fig. 342*).

The rectum in man is not straight as its name would imply; it has the anteroposterior curvature just described; it has also three lateral curvatures: thus, at the bottom of the rectovesical pouch, the right wall is indented with the result that a transverse fold or shelf projects into the lumen; and similar but less pronounced indentations from the left occur about an inch below and above this. The shelves within the gut are the *plicae transversales* (*fig. 369*). They consist of mucous membrane and circular muscle. Their form is maintained by the prolongations of the three teniae coli, which spread out to form a continuous outer longitudinal muscle coat, thick ventrally and dorsally but thin at the sides.

The plicae must be avoided by tubes and instruments introduced into the rectum.

Anal Canal (*figs. 370* and *371*). The anal canal extends from the anorectal junction, which lies above the level of the puborectal sling (*fig. 355*) and the sphincters, to the anus below. Its duty is to remain closed, except when the colon and rectum are expelling their contents. Accordingly, it is surrounded throughout by two sphincters, (1) an *External* (voluntary), described on page 301 and (2) an *Internal* (involuntary), which is merely the much thickened lower end of the circular muscle coat of the gut.

Between the two sphincters, the longitudinal muscle coat of the rectum, re-inforced by fibers of the Levator Ani and its fasciae, descends and splits into a number of *fibro-elastic septa*. Of these septa, one, the *anal intermuscular septum*, passes below the Internal Sphincter to reach the mucous membrane of the canal, whereas the others swing through the Subcutaneous External Sphincter to reach the skin (*fig. 370*).

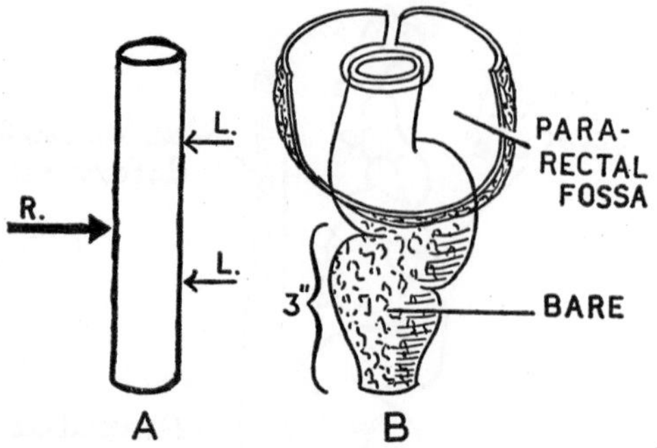

FIG. 369. The lateral flexures of the rectum, front view.

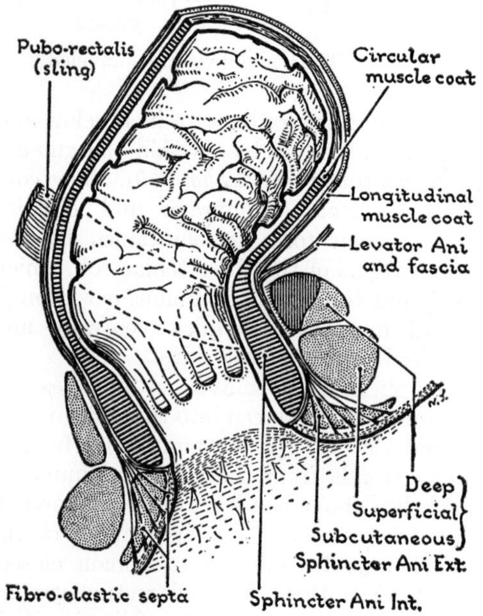

FIG. 370. The sphincters of the anus, and the puborectal sling.

The upper part of the anal canal possesses 5–10 permanent longitudinal folds of mucous membrane, the *anal columns* whose lower ends are united by semilunar folds, the *anal valves.*

Above the anal valves the canal is lined with columnar epithelium containing goblet cells. The ½ inch of canal below the valves is smooth, is lined with stratified squamous epithelium, and is known to the surgeon as the "pecten." The remainder is lined with skin.

»» *Anteroposterior versus side-to-side flattening.* When the rectum is empty, its anterior and posterior walls are in apposition; when the anal canal is empty, its lateral walls are in apposition. The same is true of the vagina and the vaginal orifice, and of the male spongy urethra and the external urethral orifice.

Arteries (*fig. 372*). The superior, middle, and inferior rectal (*hemorrhoidal*) aa. supply the rectum and anal canal, making five arteries in all—for the superior a. is unpaired.

The Superior Rectal Artery, the principal artery of the rectum, is the continuation of the inferior mesenteric a. It begins in front of the left common iliac a., and there lies medial to its own vein and to the ureter. It descends in the vertical part of the root of the sigmoid mesocolon to the beginning of the rectum where it divides into a right and a left branch.

»» The lowest sigmoid a. (*fig. 288*) commonly springs from the stem of the superior rectal a.; so also do several twigs that supply adjacent parts of the colon and rectum. As the right and left branches descend, they give off obliquely encircling branches which pass toward the front of the rectum (*cf.* the encircling branches of the dorsal vessels of the penis, *fig. 335*). Terminal branches, given off irregularly from these, pierce the muscle coat, ramify in the submucosa, and descend in the anal colums (*fig. 371*). They anastomose with each other and with the middle and inferior rectal arteries.

The Middle Rectal A. is either a small or a large branch of the internal iliac a. (*fig. 372*). It passes to the side of the rectum and makes variable anastomoses with the

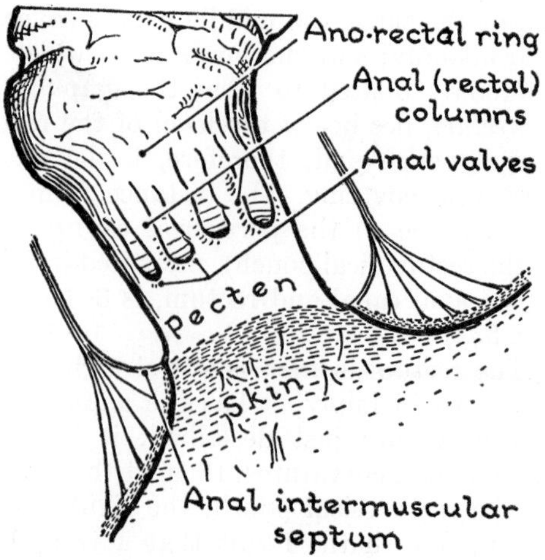

FIG. 371. The interior of the anal canal. (Partly after Wilde.)

superior and inferior rectal aa. and with the prostatic, vesical, (and vaginal) aa.

The Inferior Rectal A. is a branch of the internal pudendal a. It supplies the musculature of the anal canal and anus and much of its mucous membrane. It anastomoses by fine twigs with the superior and middle rectal aa.

Other Arteries (e.g., median sacral, inf. gluteal, int. pudendal) send twigs to the lower part of the rectum.

Veins. The superior, middle, and inferior rectal or hemorrhoidal veins accompany their arteries and drain corresponding parts of the rectum and anal canal. The superior vein becomes the inferior mesenteric vein and, therefore, belongs to the portal system. It is valveless. The middle and inferior veins are paired and belong to the caval system. They have valves.

The superior vein begins in the anal columns. It has extensive mucous and submucous plexuses, and it receives branches from the circumrectal tissues.

The middle rectal vein is a much more important vessel than the corresponding artery. It drains the rectum above the Internal Sphincter and communicates both submucously and in the rectal fascia with the inferior rectal vein, and it makes free anastomoses submucously with the superior rectal vein. Its branches communicate with the prostatic (vaginal and uterine) plexus. It is the chief link between the portal and caval systems, and it ends in the internal iliac vein.

The inferior vein begins in the Sphincter Ani Externus, the walls of the anal canal, and the subcutaneous veins at the anal margin. These subcutaneous veins are continuous above with the submucous veins of the anal canal and rectum.

Lymph Vessels. *See* p. 355.

Nerves. *See* p. 353.

»» **Relations.** The rectum extends from the 3rd piece of the sacrum to a point $1\frac{1}{2}$ inches beyond the coccyx (*fig. 373*). It is as broad as two or three fingers and much broader than the coccyx. So, *behind* the rectum are: three pieces of the sacrum, the coccyx, and sacrospinous lig.; Piriformis, Coccygeus, Levator Ani; the median sacral a. and v., the sympathetic trunks and ganglion impar, parts of the last three sacral and the coccygeal nerves, the lateral sacral vessels and in

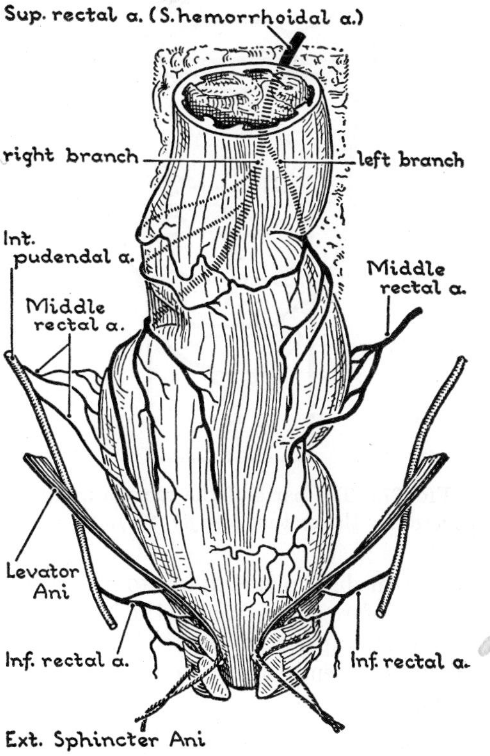

FIG. 372. The arterial supply of the rectum and anal canal, front view.

the rectal fascia, which is usually thick and fatty posteriorly, are branches of the superior rectal vessels and lymph nodes (*fig. 376*).

On each side are: the pararectal fossa containing sigmoid colon or ileum; the middle rectal vessels, the pelvic splanchnic nerves and the inferior hypogastric plexus, the Levator Ani, and the ischiorectal fossa.

In front are: the bladder separated by rectovesical pouch, seminal vesicles, and ampullae of the deferent ducts, and below these is the prostate (*fig. 365*). Strands of involuntary muscle, the *recto-urethral muscle*, connect the anorectal junction to the perineal body (*fig. 348*).

At the anorectal junction are: the puborectal sling, the base of the u.g. diaphragm, and the membranous urethra.

In front of the anal canal are the perineal body and the bulb of the urethra.

VESSELS AND NERVES OF PELVIS

The **Arteries of the Pelvis** are:

median sacral artery } unpaired
superior rectal artery }
internal iliac artery—paired.

The Median Sacral Artery is smaller than a lumbar artery. Being the continuation of the aorta, it clings to the vertebrae

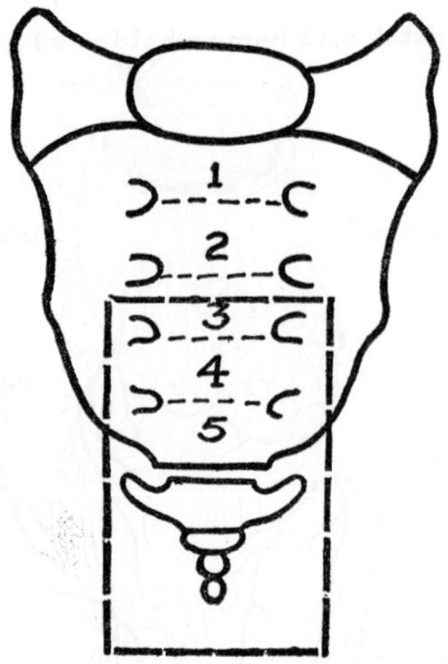

FIG. 373. The parts of the sacrum and coccyx covered by the rectum (see *fig. 376*).

in the median plane down to the coccyx, and therefore passes behind the left common iliac vein, superior hypogastric plexus, and rectum. It sends twigs to the neighboring structures.

»» As the continuation of the aorta, it should give off the 5th lumbar and the sacral arteries, but it does not—it is too small.

Its companion vein ends in the left common iliac vein.

The Superior Rectal (Hemorrhoidal) **Artery** is the continuation of the inferior mesenteric artery. It is described with the rectum on page 330.

The Internal Iliac (Hypogastric) **Artery** (*fig. 374*) takes origin from the common iliac artery one-third of the way, i.e., 2 inches, along the line joining the aortic bifurcation to the midinguinal point. About 1½″ long, it ends about the level of the pelvic brim by dividing into an anterior and a posterior division. It descends subperitoneally and crosses medial to the external iliac vein, the Psoas, and the obturator nerve. In front of it runs the ureter; behind it lies its vein.

Branches of internal iliac artery. These arise erratically. Usually the superior gluteal and the two somatic segmental branches come from the posterior division; the others from the anterior. They may be grouped thus:

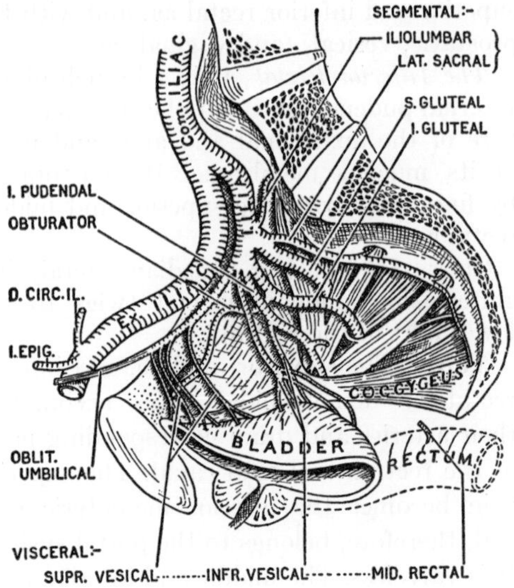

FIG. 374. Internal iliac artery and branches

1. Visceral branches:

Umbilical	*Superior vesical*
Inferior vesical	*Middle rectal*

(also, *Uterine* and *Vaginal* in the female)

2. Branches to the limb and perineum:

Superior gluteal	*Inferior gluteal*
Obturator	*Internal pudendal*

3. Somatic segmental branches:

Iliolumbar	*Lateral sacral*

1. The **Visceral Branches** supply the bladder, the internal genital organs behind the bladder, and they send small branches to the rectum. They are:

(a) *The umbilical artery* (*fig. 259*, p. 234). In prenatal life, the internal iliac artery of each side passed through the umbilical cord to supply the placenta. At birth the umbilical cord was severed and discarded with the placenta, whereupon the umbilical artery became obliterated as far back as the branches (superior vesical) to the fore part of the cloaca, now called the bladder.

The umbilical artery is, therefore, a visceral artery, and it clings to the peritoneum on the side wall of the pelvis, above the level of the bladder. The only structures crossing medial to it are the ureter and the deferent duct.

The superior vesical aa. are two or three branches that pass from the pervious part of the umbilical artery to the upper surface of the bladder.

(b) *The inferior vesical arteries* and (c) *the middle rectal artery* run in the leash of veins that form the posterior limit of the retropubic space.

»» Of the two inferior vesical aa., one (the *vesiculo-deferential a.*) is constant in arising from the umbilical a. at its origin (Braithwaite). The other has a variable origin. On each side, these arteries supply the side and base of the bladder, the prostate, seminal vesicle, ampulla of the deferent duct, and end of the ureter. One gives off the deferent a. *The middle rectal a.* varies in origin and in size (*fig. 372*).

2. The **Branches to the Limb and Perineum** leave the pelvis through the greater sciatic and obturator foramina. Thus: (a) *the superior gluteal artery*, which is much the largest branch of the internal iliac artery, makes a U-shaped turn round the angle of the greater sciatic notch into the gluteal region. Its vein and the superior gluteal nerve accompany it (*fig. 421*).

(b) *The inferior gluteal artery* and (c) *the internal pudendal artery* descend in front of the sacral plexus and pass between the borders of the Piriformis and Coccygeus into the gluteal region. There the int. pudendal artery, which is the smaller and more anterior, crosses the ischial spine and enters the perineum through the lesser sciatic foramen in company of its own nerve and the nerve of the Obturator Internus.

(d) *The obturator artery* runs forward on the side wall of the pelvis to the obturator foramen. It lies between its nerve and vein.

The obturator and inferior epigastric arteries both supply branches to the back of the pubis. These pubic branches anastomose, and the anastomotic channel is commonly (33 per cent) so large that the obturator artery derives its blood from the epigastric artery. This is known as an *accessory obturator artery*.

The obturator vein likewise is commonly "abnormal."

3. The **Somatic Segmental Branches** (i.e., to the body wall) are in series with the intercostal and lumbar arteries, but they arise from the posterior division of the internal iliac artery.

(a) *The iliolumbar artery*, being the artery of the 5th lumbar segment, ascends in front of the ala of the sacrum, and divides into iliac and lumbar branches. The iliac branches anastomose in the iliac fossa with the deep circumflex iliac and adjacent arteries. The lumbar branch sends a spinal branch through the 5th intervertebral foramen.

(b) *The lateral sacral artery* descends lateral to the pelvic sacral foramina and in front of the roots of the sacral plexus. It sends spinal branches into the sacral foramina.

Veins of the Pelvis (*fig. 375*). The pelvic viscera may be said to lie within a basket woven out of large thin-walled veins among which the arteries thread their way. The basket is divided into vesical, prostatic (or uterine and vaginal), and rectal venous plexuses, which drain largely into the internal iliac vein, but partly via the superior rectal (hemorrhoidal) vein into the inferior mesenteric vein and so to the portal vein.

The *middle rectal vein* is relatively large. It emerges from the lower part of the side of the rectum and passes to the internal iliac vein. It anastomoses with the superior and inferior rectal veins and also with the other plexuses of pelvic veins, thereby taking a prominent part in the portacaval anastomoses (p. 247).

Nerves of Pelvis

Sacral and Coccygeal Nerves. The lumbar, sacral, and coccygeal plexuses are derived from the ventral rami of spinal nerves Th. 12—Co. 1, as in table 13 (p. 334).

Note that rami L. 4 and S. 4 both contribute to two plexuses. Each does so by means of an upper and a lower branch.

The ventral rami of the sacral and coccygeal nerves, like all other ventral rami, receive gray sympathetic rami communicantes, which they conduct to the blood vessels, sweat and sebaceous glands, and arrectores pilorum in their territory. No white sympathetic rami communicantes arise caudal to L. 3, but parasympathetic fibers, called the *pelvic splanchnic nerves*, arise from the ventral rami of S. (2), 3 and 4 (*figs. 44.2* and *377*).

Sacral Plexus (*figs. 376* and *377*). Of the six **roots** of the sacral plexus, L. 4 crosses and grooves the fifth lumbar transverse process; L. 5 crosses and grooves the ala of the sacrum and joins with L. 4 near the

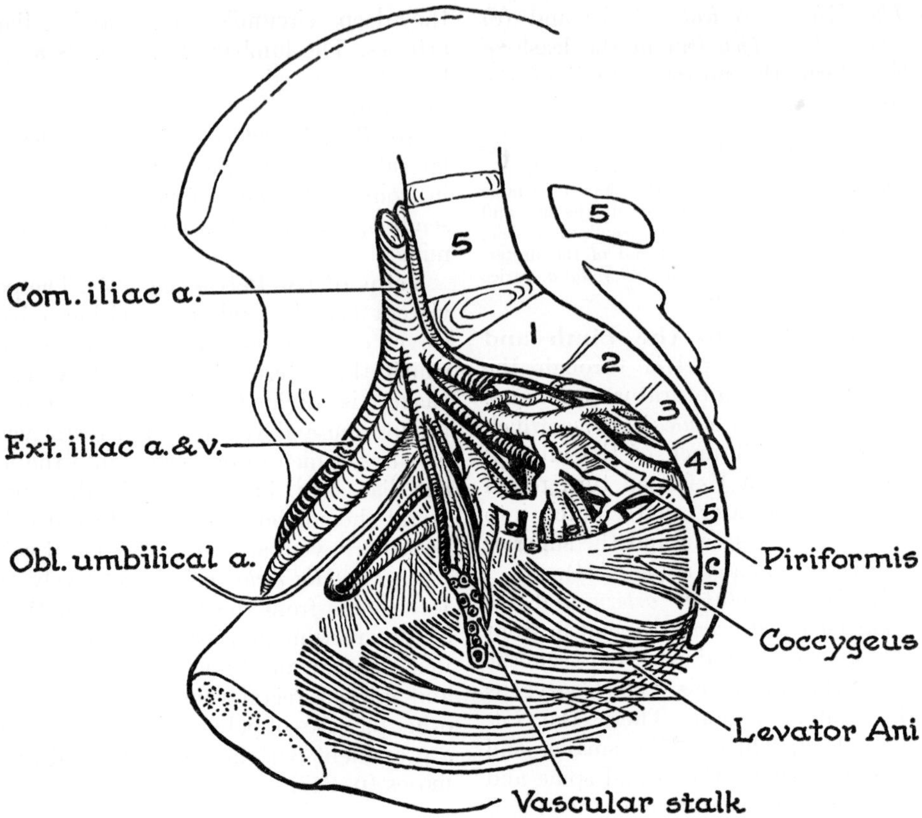

FIG. 375. The blood vessels of the pelvis. The vascular stalk to the pelvic viscera limits the retropubic space posteriorly.

pelvic brim to form the **lumbosacral trunk;** the upper 4 sacral ventral rami groove the pars lateralis of the sacrum. The lumbosacral trunk and S. 1 join as they pass in front of the sacro-iliac joint, and they unite with S. 2, 3, and 4 in front of the Piriformis to form the sacral plexus. The plexus has many collateral branches and it ends as two terminal branches, the *sciatic* and *pudendal nerves.* The sacral plexus is placed in front of the Piriformis and outside the pelvic fascia—as you would expect.

Arteries Piercing the Plexus. Four branches of the internal iliac artery pierce the plexus, thus: the *iliolumbar a.* passes between L. 4 and 5, the *superior gluteal a.* between L. 5 and S. 1, the *inferior gluteal a.* between S. 2 and 3, and the *internal pudendal a.* descends to the ischial spine between the sciatic and pudendal nerves. Commonly these four arteries are moved independently either cranialward or caudalward with regard to the roots of the plexus.

TABLE 13

Ventral rami of	Th.	L.	S.	C.
Lumbar plexus.	12,	1, 2, 3, 4		
Sacral plexus..	...	.... 4, 5,	1, 2, 3, 4	
Coccygeal plexus.......	...	....	.... 4, 5,	1

The Branches of the Sacral Plexus (table 14) may be grouped thus:

1. Branches from roots of plexus:
   (a) *Muscular* (to Piriformis, Levator Ani, and Coccygeus)
   (b) *The pelvic splanchnic nerves.*
2. Branches that pass through the greater sciatic foramen:
   (a) *Two terminal* (sciatic and pudendal)
   (b) *Five collateral.*

3. Branches that emulate the coccygeal plexus in piercing the structures attached to the side of the coccyx in order to become cutaneous:
   (a) *Perforating cutaneous of S. 2, 3*
   (b) *Perineal of S. 4.*

1. The Branches Arising from the Roots of the Sacral Plexus are, short twigs to Piriformis (S. 1, 2), long branches to Levator Ani and Coccygeus (S. 3, 4), and the pelvic splanchnic nerves (S. 2, 3, 4).

The pudendal nerve and the pelvic splanchnic nerves both spring from segments S. 2, 3, 4.

The *pudendal nerve* is a mixed spinal nerve (*fig. 329*). It supplies the muscles derived from the cloacal sphincter and the skin around the cloacal orifice. These muscles are voluntary and include the Sphincter Ani Externus and the Sphincter Urethrae.

The *pelvic splanchnic nerves* are "mixed" parasympathetic nerves. They supply the involuntary muscles derived from the cloaca that cause the involuntary sphincters guarding the rectum and bladder (Sphincter Ani Internus and Sphincter Vesicae) to relax while the organs contract, and they are sensory to them. They also cause dilatation of the arteries of the erectile tissue of the penis or clitoris and thereby produce erection, hence the alternative name *nervi erigentes.*

2. The Branches That Pass Through the Greater Sciatic Foramen enter the gluteal region and they should be studied with it. They are seven in number, two being terminal and five collateral. The exact segments of origin of the collateral branches

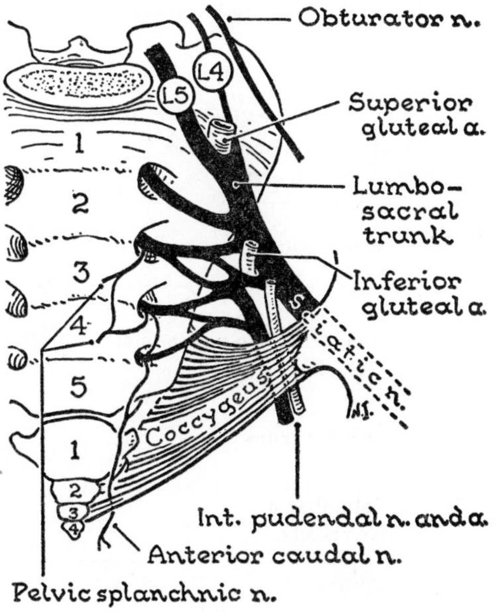

Fig. 376. The sacral plexus

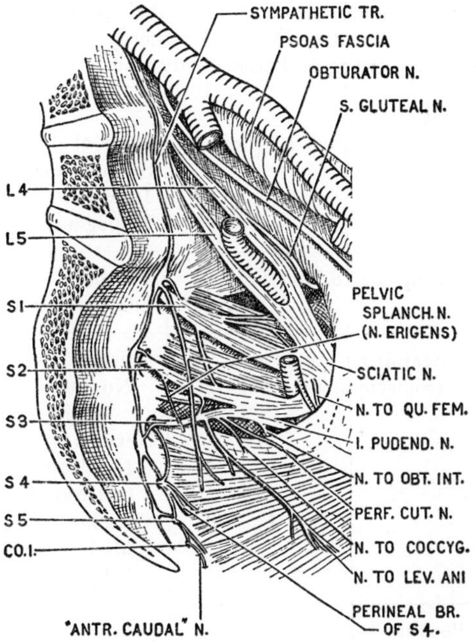

Fig. 377. The sacral and coccygeal plexuses

TABLE 14

Branches of the Sacral Plexus

Terminal	Collateral		
	From the back	From the front	From front and back
1. Sciatic 2. Pudendal	3. Superior Gluteal 4. Inferior Gluteal	5. N. to Quadratus Femoris 6. N. to Obturator Internus	7. Posterior cutaneous of the thigh

are unimportant, but they are given in order to make identification easier.

The sciatic nerve is the largest nerve in the body and it forms the greatest part of the sacral plexus. It bears some resemblance to the forearm, palm, and outstretched digits of a limb; the digits being its five roots (L. 4, 5, S. 1, 2 and 3), the palm being the flat main mass of the plexus in front of the Piriformis, and the forearm being the rounded sciatic nerve that leaves the pelvis between the Piriformis and the ischial border of the greater sciatic notch. The sciatic nerve will later be seen to be two nerves loosely held together: one is the *tibial nerve* (medial popliteal n.); the other is the *common peroneal nerve* (lateral popliteal n.)—peroneal is Greek for the Latin word fibular.

The pudendal nerve (S. 2, 3, 4) already seen in the perineum, escapes between the Piriformis and Coccygeus just medial to the sciatic nerve.

The superior gluteal nerve (L. 4, 5, 1) and the *inferior gluteal nerve* (L. 5, 1, 2) arise from the back of the plexus. The nerves to the *Quadratus Femoris* (L. 4, 5, 1) and *Obturator Internus* (L. 5, 1, 2) arise from the

TABLE 15

Structures Crossing the Pelvic Brim

It is a profitable exercise to make a list of the structures crossing the brim. The list you compile will probably have important omissions, unless your approach is systematic. Thus, you may name the structures encountered according to their position from front to back; or you may consider first the vessels, next the nerves, and then the viscera; or you may group them, as here, under the headings gastro-intestinal tract, urogenital tract, body wall, etc., which is the routine method adopted in this book.

Structures: Pertaining to G-I Tract	Coils of ileum. Sigmoid colon, mesocolon. Inferior mesenteric a., v., lymph vessels and nerves. Hypogastric plexus (to pelvic viscera generally).
Pertaining to U-G Tract	Ureter. Ductus deferens. Bladder when it fills.
Pertaining to body wall (somatic structures)	Muscles: No muscles cross the brim and obstruct the pelvic inlet. Therefore, fascia reaching the brim is attached to it. Nerves: Lumbosacral trunk. Obturator nerve. Sympathetic trunk. Vessels: Median sacral a. and v. Iliolumbar a. Internal iliac a., v., and lymph vessels.
Peculiar to the female	Ovarian a., v., lymph vessels and nerves. Round ligament of uterus. Uterus when it fills.
Variable with age	Cecum tends to glide into pelvis in the aged. Bladder is abdominal in children.
Abnormal and variable	Accessory obturator artery and vein. Appendix (commonly).
Of morphological interest	Urachus. Obliterated umbilical arteries.
Peculiar to race	?

front of the plexus; the former descends in front of the sciatic nerve, the latter on the medial side of the sciatic nerve. The *posterior cutaneous nerve of the thigh* (S. 1, 2, 3) arises from the back and front of the plexus.

The superior gluteal nerve and its companion artery and vein escape from the pelvis above the Piriformis at the angle of the greater sciatic foramen. All other structures passing through the foramen pass below the Piriformis. The inferior gluteal nerve and the posterior cutaneous nerve of the thigh escape below the Piriformis and behind the sciatic nerve.

3. THE TWO BRANCHES THAT EMULATE THE TERMINAL BRANCH OF THE COCCYGEAL PLEXUS are the *perforating cutaneous branch* of S. 2 and 3 and the *perineal branch* of S. 4. These descend in front of the Coccygeus and then pass through it.

»» Thereafter the former, which supplies the skin of the buttock, passes backward through the sacrotuberous ligament and round the lower border of the Gluteus Maximus; the latter passes forward in front of the sacrotuberous ligament, and is to be found on the Levator Ani between the tip of the coccyx and the anus, where it supplies the skin and gives twigs to the Sphincter Ani Externus.

The Coccygeal Plexus is formed by the ventral rami of S. 5 and C. 1 which emerge from the sacral hiatus on to the dorsum of the sacrum, because the lower ends of the sacrum and coccyx have, so to speak, been dissolved away (*fig. 669*).

»» Therefore, to enter the pelvis these two rami require to bore through the structures attached to the side of the sacrum and coccyx (i.e., Gluteus Maximus, sacrotuberous lig., sacrospinous lig., and Coccygeus). This they do independently, one above, the other below the transverse process of the coccyx. In the pelvis they unite, and a descending twig from S. 4 joins them. The slender trunk, the *anococcygeal nerve,* so-formed descends, pierces the same structures again and appears on the back. This nerve corresponds to the ventral *caudal nerve* of tailed mammals. A similarly formed nerve, derived from the dorsal rami of S. 4, 5, and C. 1, corresponds to the dorsal *caudal nerve* of tailed mammals.

In man the abbreviated caudal nerves, together with other contributions from S. 4 (via its perineal branch, and the inferior rectal nerve supply a circular area of skin around the coccyx—the area on which one sits down (*fig. 336.1*).

CHAPTER 21

FEMALE PELVIS

Female Pelvis in Median Section. Because of its obstetrical importance you should be able to draw this to scale. First sketch the skeletal parts, then insert the viscera, and lastly put on the peritoneal covering. It is a good plan to use dividers or a graduated ruler.

1. The symphysis pubis with the arcuate (inf.) pubic ligament is 1½ inches deep. Its posterior surface is flat and faces more upward than backward (*fig. 378*).

2. Erect a vertical line 3½ inches high on the symphysis. Draw two parallel horizontal lines, one at the level of the top of the symphysis, the other at the top of the 3½ inch line.

3. The sacral promontory lies on the upper horizontal line, three times the depth of the symphysis (4½ inches) from the upper end of the symphysis.

4. The tip of the coccyx lies on the lower horizontal line, three times the depth of the symphysis more or less (4½ inches) from the lower end of the symphysis.

5. The upper part of the sacrum is straight and parallel to the symphysis; its lower part and the coccyx are often much curved.

6. A line joining the upper end of the symphysis to the promontory of the sacrum indicates the plane of the pelvic brim, which bounds the pelvic inlet. The inlet makes an angle of 60° with the horizontal. A line bisecting the pelvic inlet at right angles passes through the umbilicus.

7. A line joining the lower end of the symphysis to the tip of the coccyx is the plane of the outlet of the pelvis. It makes an angle of 15° with the horizontal. A line bisecting the outlet at right angles passes through the promontory.

The soft parts are now to be inserted:

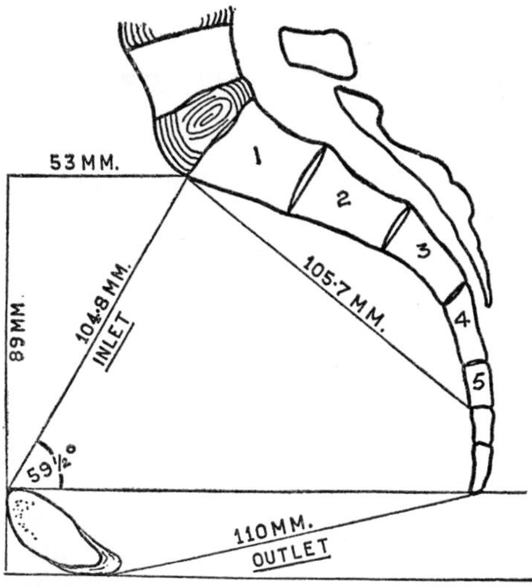

FIG. 378. Outlines of female pelvis in median section (drawn to scale).

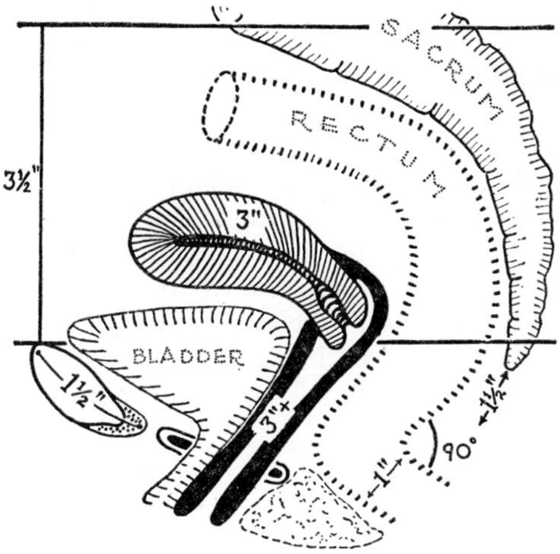

FIG. 379. The soft parts inserted in figure 378 (to scale).

8. Insert the urogenital diaphragm and its upper and lower fasciae.

9. The bladder and urethra, as in the male: The urethra pierces the urogenital diaphragm an inch or less from the symphysis. It is about 1½ inches long (*fig. 379*).

10. The rectum and anal canal, as in the male: The rectum curves downward and forward from the 3rd piece of the sacrum to a point 1½ inches beyond (not below) the coccyx. There it makes a right-angled bend and thereafter, as the anal canal, passes downward and backward for an inch or more.

The uterus and vagina developed in the urorectal septum (*fig. 330*, p. 301). Hence, they occupy in the female the positions taken by the seminal vesicles, ampullae of the deferent ducts, and prostate in the male.

11. The vagina is over 3 inches long. It lies nearly parallel to the pelvic brim. Its anterior wall is in structural continuity with the urethra in its lower part; it is in contact with the bladder in its middle part; and it is pierced by the cervix of the uterus in its upper part. Like the urethra, it pierces the urogenital diaphragm.

12. The posterior wall of the vagina is separated from the rectum by the rectal and the vaginal layer of fascia (rectovaginal septum), and from the anal canal by the triangular mass of fibromuscular tissue called the *perineal body* (the perineum of the gynecologist).

13. The uterus is 3 inches long. It lies nearly at right angles to the pelvic brim and to the vagina. Its upper 2 inches (or fundus and body) are 1 inch thick; its lower 1 inch (or cervix) is less than an inch thick. The external orifice of the uterus lies on (or below) the lower of the two parallel horizontal lines. The fundus does not reach to the pelvic inlet. The body and cervix meet at a slight angle, so the uterus is said to be anteflexed.

14. The anterior and posterior fornices (fornix L. = an arch) of the vagina are the shallow depression in front of the anterior lip of the cervix and the deeper depression behind the posterior lip. The depression runs like a gutter all round the cervix, so there are also a right and a left lateral fornix, but they are not seen in sagittal section.

15. The peritoneum passes from the symphysis on to the upper surface of the bladder, and from the third piece of sacrum on to rectum, as in the male. It falls an inch short of the anterior fornix of the vagina, but it clothes half an inch or more of the posterior fornix (*fig. 380*). Indeed, the peritoneum caps the posterior fornix of the vagina in the female much as it caps the seminal vesicles in the male (*fig. 342*), but much more intimately.

Female Pelvis Seen from Above (*fig.

381). The bladder and the paravesical fossae are seen in front; the rectum and the pararectal fossae are seen behind, as in the male. It is the genital organs that differ in the two sexes: (1) the uterus and vagina situated medianly replace the seminal vesicles, ampullae of the deferent ducts, and prostate of the male; (2) the ovaries and their ducts (the uterine tubes), which are pelvic, replace the testes, which are scrotal, and their ducts (the deferent ducts).

The homologue of the rectovesical pouch of peritoneum in the male is divided into an anterior and a posterior part by a transverse partition, formed by the uterus and the two folds of peritoneum, called the *broad ligaments of the uterus*, that pass from the lateral margins of the uterus to the side walls of the pelvis.

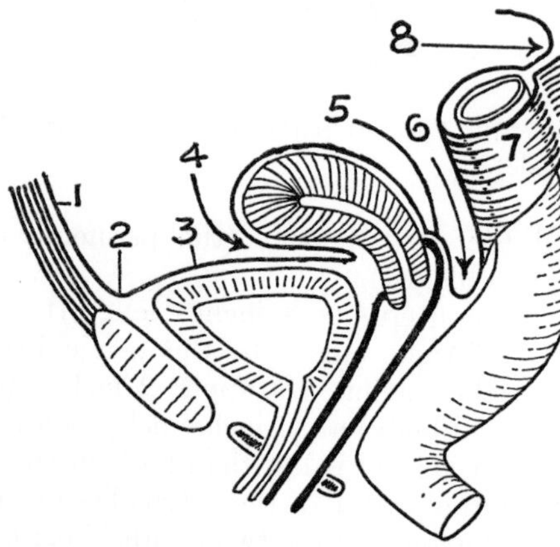

FIG. 380. The peritoneum of the female pelvis in median section (see text and *fig. 342*).

The anterior subdivision is the *vesico-uterine pouch;* the posterior is the *recto-uterine pouch.* The uterus rests on the empty bladder and the shallow vesico-uterine pouch is empty; the deeper recto-uterine pouch is occupied by sigmoid (pelvic) colon and ileum.

The ovary is attached to the back of the broad ligament of the uterus by a short "mesentery," the *mesovarium.* The uterine tube occupies the upper border of the broad ligament except at its lateral end. There the broad ligament is continued as a fold, the *suspensory ligament of the ovary*, across the external iliac vessels. A cord of fibromuscular tissue curves backward and upward from the junction of the body and cervix of the uterus, past the rectum, to the sacrum. It helps to suspend the uterus and is called the *uterosacral ligament.* The overlying crescentic fold of peritoneum is the *recto-uterine fold.*

A round fibromuscular cord, the *ligament of the ovary*, stands out in relief from the

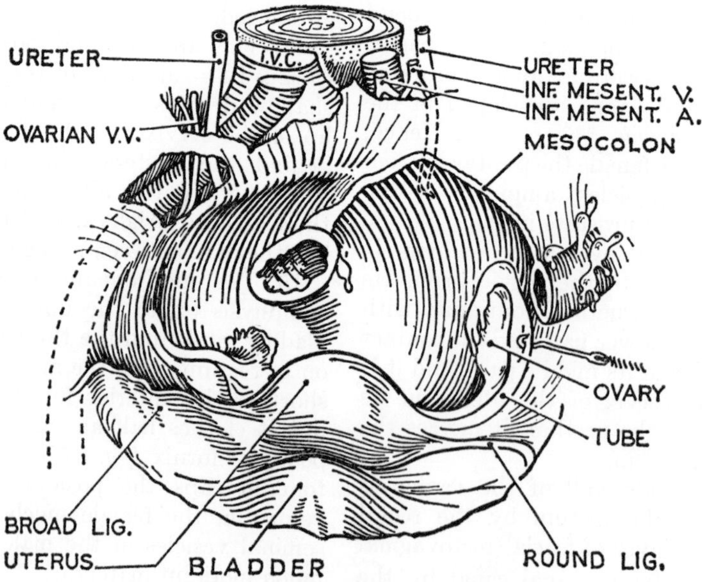

FIG. 381. Female pelvis (from above)

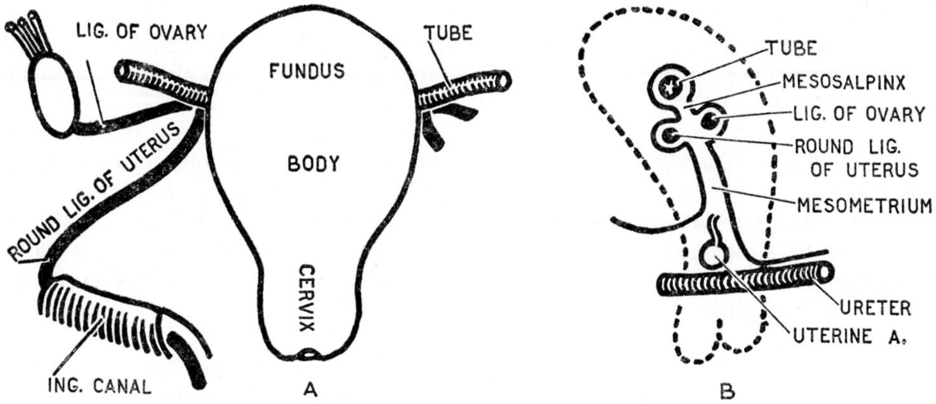

FIG. 382. *A*, derivatives of the gubernaculum ovarii—lig. of ovary and round lig. of uterus. *B*, sagittal section through broad lig. of uterus.

back of the broad ligament. It joins the lower pole of the ovary to the angle between the side of the uterus and the uterine tube. A similar cord, the *round ligament of the uterus* (lig. teres uteri), stands out from the front of the broad ligament. It passes from the angle between uterus and tube across the pelvic brim to the deep inguinal ring (*fig. 382*).

FEMALE INTERNAL GENITAL ORGANS

These comprise: ovaries, uterine tubes, uterus, and vagina.

Ovary (*fig. 384*). The ovary has the shape of a testis but is only half the size. It is covered with cubical epithelium—not peritoneum. The pits and scars on its surface mark the sites of the absorbed corpora lutea which result monthly from the shedding of ova. The mesovarium attaches its anterior border to the back of the broad ligament. The suspensory lig. of the ovary suspends the tubal (upper) pole of the ovary from the external iliac vessels and conducts the ovarian artery, vein, lymph vessels, and nerves to the ovary. The uterine (lower) pole of the ovary is attached to the lateral margin of the uterus by the ligament of the ovary.

The typical position of the ovary is on the side wall of the pelvis, behind the broad ligament, and in the angle between the external iliac vein and the ureter. It is hidden by the uterine tube which falls over it medially. But its position is variable.

Gubernaculum Ovarii. How comes the ovary to enter the pelvis? Just as in the male the gubernaculum testis passed through the inguinal canal into the scrotum followed by the processus vaginalis and the testis, so in the female the *gubernaculum ovarii* passed through the inguinal canal into the labium majus followed only by a short *processus vaginalis peritonei* (the canal of Nuck). But, the gubernaculum ovarii acquired a side attachment to the uterus. As a result, the ovary passed into the pelvis drawing its vessels and nerves after it.

The gubernaculum in the female becomes the ligament of the ovary and the round ligament of the uterus; and these two ligaments are all but continuous at their sites of attachment to the side of the uterus just below the uterine tube. The round ligament in the female practically repeats the course taken by the deferent duct in the male, i.e., it is subperitoneal; it crosses the side wall of the pelvis and the external iliac vessels; and it turns round the inferior epigastric artery, passes through the inguinal canal, and ends in the labium majus, which is the homologue of the scrotum.

Very rarely the ovary does follow the gubernaculum into the labium majus.

Derivatives of the Mullerian or Paramesonephric Duct. Before the sex of the embryo is apparent, two parallel, bilaterally symmetrical, mesodermal tubes grow caudally in the subperitoneal tissue of the posterior abdominal wall. In the urorectal septum all four tubes lie together and their terminal ends, which at this stage are blind, bulge into the caudal part of the ventral subdivision of the cloaca, called the *urogenital sinus.*

The four tubes are named: the right and left Wolffian or *mesonephric ducts* and the right and left Mullerian or *paramesonephric ducts.* The mesonephric ducts predominate in the male: they serve as sperm ducts and on each side become the duct of the epididymis, deferent duct, and ejaculatory duct.

The paramesonephric ducts predominate in the female: they serve as ducts for ova (*fig. 383*), their cranial parts becoming the uterine tubes; their intermediate parts fusing to form the uterus; and their caudal ends fusing to form the upper part of the vagina. As growth proceeds a solid plate of cells, the *vaginal plate,* extends downward between the urogenital sinus and the rectum. Eventually this plate becomes canalized and joined by a right and a left upwardly growing diverticulum of the sinus to form the lower part of the vagina.

The intermediate part of the paramesonephric duct has to pull away from the side wall of the pelvis in order to meet its fellow in the median plane to form the uterus. The peritoneal fold thus formed is called the **broad ligament of the uterus;** it is to be regarded as the "mesentery of the paramesonephric duct" (*fig. 383*).

Uterine Tube (of Fallopius) (*fig. 384*). The uterus is 2″ across at its widest part, which is where the tubes enter it. Each tube is about 4½″ long. The spread, therefore, of the uterus and its two tubes is 11 inches. This is twice the diameter of the pelvic inlet (5¼″). Evidently the tubes cannot lie in a straight line. Each tube occupies the free edge of the broad ligament, which is its "mesentery," and runs from the uterus upward, laterally, and backward to the side

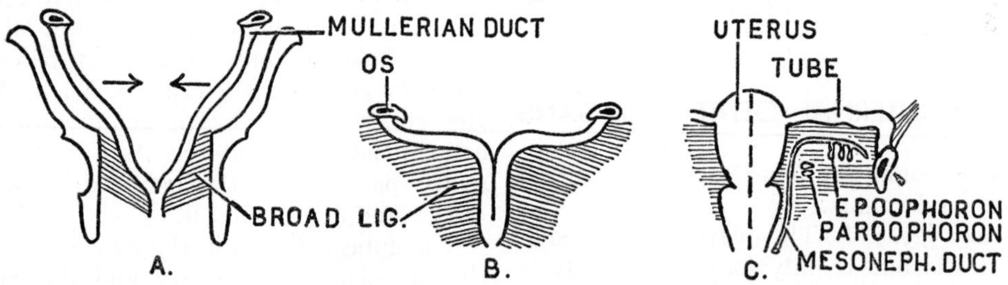

Fig. 383. Scheme of the development of the broad lig. of uterus as the "mesentery of the paramesonephric or Mullerian duct."

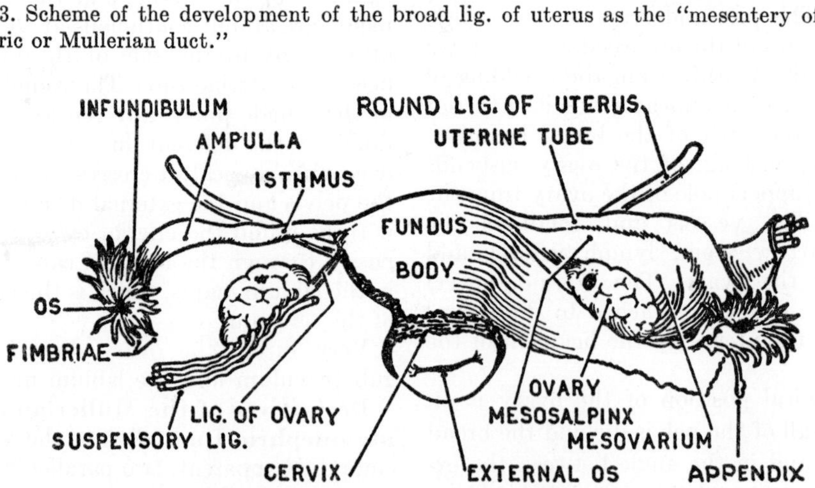

Fig. 384. The uterus and appendages (from behind)

wall of the pelvis and there curves backward over the ovary.

Each tube has the following parts: *infundibulum, abdominal orifice, ampulla, isthmus, uterine part,* and *uterine orifice.*

The *abdominal orifice,* 2–3 mm. in diameter, lies at the bottom of a funnel-shaped depression, the *infundibulum.* Fringes or fimbriae lined with ciliated epithelium, project from the infundibulum and encourage ova, when shed, into the tube. One fimbria is attached to the ovary.

The main part of the tube is long, irregular, and dilated, and is called the *ampulla.* The succeeding shorter part is straight and narrow and is called the *isthmus.* The *uterine part* passes through the uterine wall, which is ½ inch thick. Four longitudinal folds, bearing secondary folds, project into the lumen of the tube, which is lined with columnar ciliated epithelium.

The **Uterus** is thick walled and muscular. It is pear-shaped, 3 inches long, 2 inches at its widest part, and 1 inch or less at its thickest part. It is flattened in front where it rests on the bladder, and convex behind. The uterine tubes enter it at its widest part. The broad ligaments are attached to its margins; the ligament of the ovary and the round ligament of the uterus are attached just below the tube.

The uterus is divisible into three parts—*fundus, body,* and *cervix.* The fundus and body form the upper two inches; the cervix the lower one inch. The fundus is the part that rises above the tubes. The uterine artery runs tortuously up the side of the uterus between the layers of the broad ligament.

The *external os* of the uterus is round until the birth of the first child; thereafter, it becomes a transverse slit guarded by an anterior and a posterior lip. There is a slight angle at the junction of the body and cervix, so the uterus is said to be anteflexed. The long axis of the uterus seldom lies in the median plane, but is deflected to one side or other.

The potential *cavity of the body* of the uterus is triangular; the uterine orifices of the tubes, which are about 1 mm. in diameter, open at the upper lateral angles, the *internal os of the uterus* at the lower angle. The anterior and posterior walls are applied to each other. The *cervical canal* extends from the internal os to the external os of the uterus. It is spindle-shaped and 1 inch long.

» » STRUCTURE: The uterus has **three** coats—serous, muscular, and mucous. *In the fundus and body* the muscular coat (myometrium) is nearly ½″ thick and consists of interlacing bundles of smooth muscle, an arrangement which, after the birth of a child, brings about the natural arrest of hemorrhage by constricting the penetrating vessels. The serous (peritoneal) coat is adherent to the muscular coat except at the sides, where it passes on to the broad ligaments. The mucous coat (endometrium) is thick and is lined with columnar cells, many of which are ciliated, and it possesses numerous tubular glands which extend to, or even into, the muscle coat.

In the cervix the muscular bundles are largely circularly arranged, as at a sphincter. The mucous membrane is thrown into branching folds, is lined with columnar mucus secreting cells, and possesses both simple and branched tubular mucus-secreting glands.

Vagina (L. = a sheath or scabbard). The vagina is about 3 inches long and is approximately parallel with the pelvic brim. It extends from the vestibule of the vagina, which is guarded by the labia minora and where its orifice opens, through the urogenital diaphragm to the recto-uterine pouch. Its anterior and posterior walls are applied to each other.

Its anterior wall is structurally continuous with the urethra in its lower third; in contact with the bladder in its intermediate third; and is pierced by the cervix in its upper third. Around the cervix there is a circular gutter, described as the anterior, posterior, and lateral **fornices of the vagina.** Since the anterior aspect of the cervix is not covered with peritoneum, the anterior fornix is an inch from the vesico-uterine pouch of peritoneum; but the posterior fornix is clothed with peritoneum of the recto-uterine pouch.

Note that an instrument, forced upward through the posterior fornix, would enter the recto-uterine pouch, which is the lowest part of the peritoneal cavity and, therefore, well placed for drainage.

Each lateral fornix is crossed by the base of the broad ligament, the uterine artery, and the ureter. Because the uterus is seldom median in position, the ureter is less than ½″ from the cervix on one side (generally the left) and more than ½″ on the other (*figs. 385* and *386*).

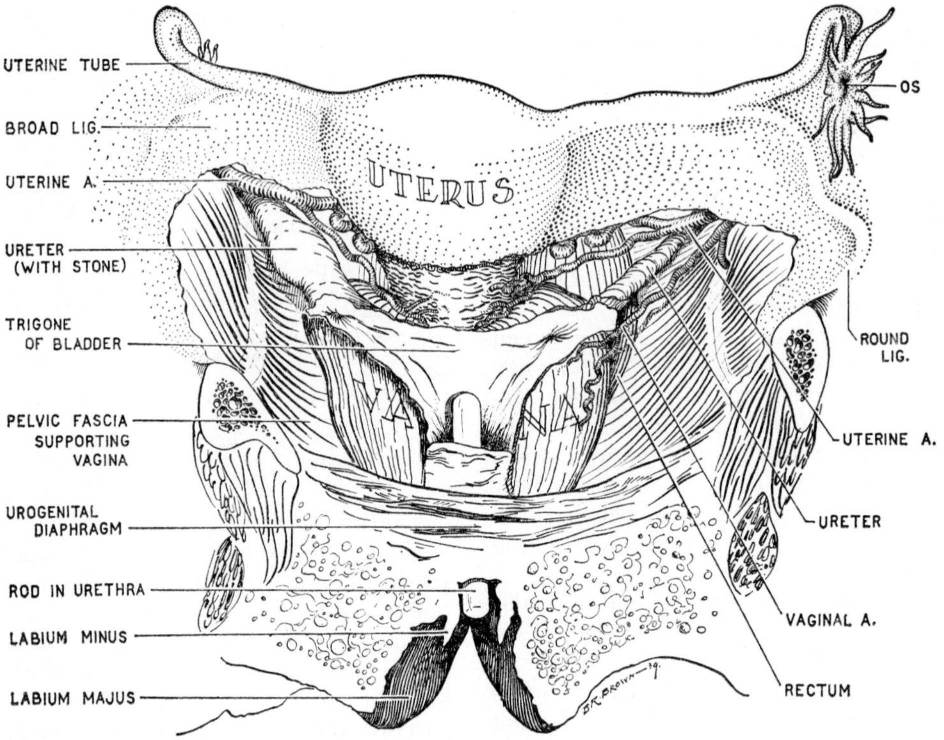

FIG. 385. The female internal genitalia. (Parts of the pubic bones and all of the bladder, the trigone excepted, have been removed.)
The uterus is here symmetrically placed; hence, the ureters are nearly equidistant from the cervix. (Note the stone in the right ureter. Dissection by Dr. B. L. Guyatt.)

RELATIONS. The posterior wall of the vagina is separated from the rectum by the vaginal and the rectal layer of pelvic fascia, and from the anal canal by the perineal body.

In the pelvic cavity, the side walls of the vagina rest on the Levatores Ani. On passing between the free anterior borders of the Levatores Ani, from which it receives fibers, the vagina enters the perineum and at once encounters, carries before it, and perforates, the u.g. diaphragm and its fasciae. These fasciae and the Levator Ani fascia and the superficial perineal fascia all fuse and blend with the laminated outer surface of the vaginal wall. Applied to this wall are the bulbs of the vestibule, the bulbo-urethral glands, and the Bulbospongiosus (*fig. 340*).

» » STRUCTURE: The vagina is lined with stratified squamous epithelium. This epithelium lines a *tunica propria* which presents numerous transverse folds (rugae). Outside the tunica propria there is a thin *muscular coat* of longitudinal fibers and some interlacing circular ones, and a thick fibro-areolar *adventitious coat*.

The stratified squamous epithelium is reflected from the vagina on to the cervix, clothing it as far as the external os. Though the vagina possesses no glands, its epithelial surface is moist from the secretion received from the cervical canal.

Remnants of the (Wolffian) Mesonephric Duct and Tubules (*fig. 383*) persist in the female as the *epoophoron*, *paroophoron*, and *duct of Gartner* (*of the epoophoron*). Because they commonly become cystic and cause trouble they are of clinical importance. Naturally, they are to be sought for at the sides of the (Mullerian) paramesonephric ducts, now converted into the uterine tubes, uterus, and vagina.

The epoophoron (= above the egg basket) lies between the layers of the broad ligament, above the ovary. It is a vestigial part of the mesonephric duct and tubules, and corresponds in the male to the duct of the epididymis and the efferent ductules of the testis (*fig. 229*, p. 215).

The paroophoron (= beside the egg basket)

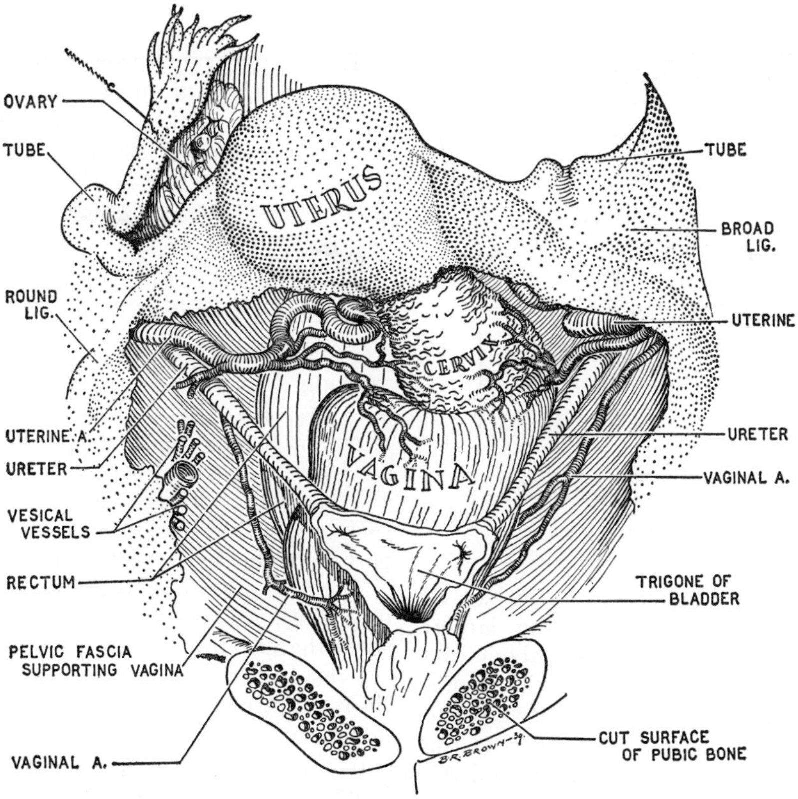

FIG. 386. The female internal genitalia. (Parts of the pubic bones and all of the bladder, the trigone excepted, have been removed.)
The uterus is asymmetrically placed; hence, one ureter is close to the cervix; the other is far removed from it.

lies between the layers of the broad ligament, medial to the ovary. It is formed from mesonephric tubules and corresponds in the male to the paradidymis. *The duct of Gartner* is the segment of the mesonephric duct that lies in front of the anterior wall of the vagina. It corresponds to the end of the ductus deferens.

The **Ureter,** after crossing the external iliac vessels close (½″) behind the ovarian vessels, descends subperitoneally on the side wall of the pelvis, as in the male, crossing in turn the Psoas, the pelvic brim, the obturator nerve, artery and vein, and the umbilical artery.

Relationships then become *Peculiar to the Female* (*figs. 385* and *386*). Thus: the ureter: (a) crosses the lateral fornix of the vagina, (b) below the broad ligament, and (c) below the uterine artery, and because of the obliquity of the uterine axis, (d) it lies closer to the cervix on one side (generally the left) than on the other. The ureters, now lying in front of the vagina, pierce the posterolateral angles of the bladder 2″ apart, and open on to the trigone of the bladder, 1″ apart.

Vessels Peculiar to Female Pelvis—ovarian, uterine, and vaginal.

The Ovarian Artery (*fig. 387*) arises from the aorta, like the testicular a., but differs from it in crossing the external iliac vessels, about ½″ in front of the ureter (*fig. 381*), to enter the suspensory lig. of the ovary. It supplies the ovary and part of the tube, and anastomoses freely with the uterine a. Commonly, it is so slender that its duties are largely assumed by the uterine artery.

The uterine and vaginal arteries spring from the anterior division of the internal iliac artery, and represent enlarged inferior vesical arteries of the male (*figs. 385–387*).

The Uterine Artery is a large vessel. It

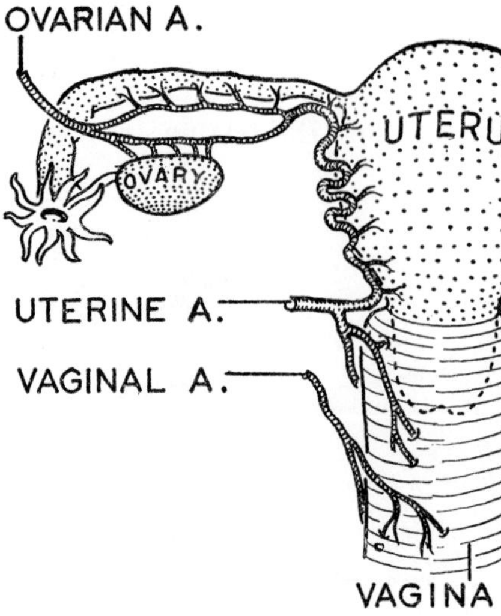

FIG. 387. The uterine vessels

descends in front of the ureter to the base of the broad ligament and, at the lateral fornix of the vagina, it crosses above the ureter. After sending branches to the vagina and cervix, it continues tortuously up the side of the uterus between the layers of the broad ligament, supplies the uterus and the tubes, anastomoses freely with the ovarian artery, and sends a branch to the round ligament.

The Vaginal Artery descends to the vagina (*fig. 387*) and supplies twigs to the bladder.

VEINS. *The Ovarian Vein* arises from the ovary as the *pampiniform plexus.* The plexus surrounds the ovarian artery, crosses the pelvic brim as a single vein, or as several veins that soon unite, and opens into the i. v. cava or left renal vein according to the side. The pampiniform plexus communicates freely with the uterine vein.

The uterine and vaginal *venous plexuses* join the vesical plexus and pass as several large branches to the internal iliac vein. These plexuses communicate with the rectal plexus.

Nerve Supply. The ovaries, like the testes, are supplied by (?) T. 10; the fibers travel with the ovarian vessels through the suspensory ligaments, and some of them supply the *uterine tubes.* The *uterus* is supplied by the hypogastric plexus and the pelvic splanchnic nerves which pass through the uterovaginal plexuses in the broad ligaments.

The afferent fibers from the fundus and body pass through the hypogastric plexus and enter the spinal cord via T. 11, 12; those from the cervix and vagina via the pelvic splanchnic nerves (S. 2, 3, 4); but the lowest part of the vagina is supplied by the pudendal nerve.

Support of the Female Pelvic Viscera. EXTERNALLY: As in the male, so in the female, the thick pubic parts of the Levatores Ani form a puborectal sling for the rectum, drawing it forward until it forms a sloping shelf (*fig. 355*). Upon this shelf the vagina rests, and on the vagina rests the bladder.

The pubic parts of the Levatores Ani are also inserted into the perineal body and thereby they act as a sling for the lower part of the posterior wall of the vagina.

The urogenital diaphragm and its fasciae blend with the lower third of the vagina and assist the Levatores Ani to support it.

INTERNALLY: *Fasciae:* The bladder and the rectum are clothed with vesical and rectal fasciae, as in the male (*fig. 348*). The uterus and the vagina likewise have their own fasciae, which are thick and tough around the cervix and vagina.

The apposed layers of rectal and vaginal fasciae are so loosely connected that a rectovaginal areolar space may be said to exist between them, whereas the apposed layers of the vesical and vaginal fasciae, being more closely blended, constitute a vesicovaginal fascial septum.

There are three paired suspensory structures:

1. *The Perivascular Stalk* is the first and most important of these. In effect, it includes (1) those branches of the internal iliac vessels that have been referred to previously as the leash of vessels (uterine, vaginal, vesical) that limit the retropubic space posteriorly (*fig. 375*), and (2) the fascia in which these vessels are imbedded. This fascia is conducted by its contained vessels to the side of the junction of the cervix and vagina and to the side of the bladder, and there it blends firmly with the fasciae of these organs, and with that of the rectum as well. This mass of fascia and vessels plus an accession of fibers

from the region of the ischial spine is commonly referred to as the *lateral cervical lig.* or the *cardinal lig.*

2. *The Uterosacral Ligament* lies in the recto-uterine fold of peritoneum and may be regarded as the posterior free curved margin of the lateral cervical ligament. It extends from the middle of the sacrum to the junction of the body and cervix of the uterus where it meets its fellow. It moors the cervix posterosuperiorly.

3. *The Round Ligament* of the uterus, by being attached along the side of the uterus as far caudally as the cervix, aids in mooring the uterus and vagina anterosuperiorly.

Anteflexion. The uterus is thrust forward into the anteflexed position by coils of ileum occupying the recto-uterine pouch of peritoneum, and the broad ligaments steady it there so that it rests upon the bladder. Hence, the uterovesical pouch is a potential space—normally unoccupied by gut.

Slips of involuntary muscle everywhere pervade the pelvic fascia and give it a supporting value not appreciated after death.

Differences between the Male and Female Pelvis

The female pelvis may be contrasted with the male pelvis under the following headings:

1. Features dependent on the fact that woman is the weaker vessel.
2. Features related to the peculiar function of the female pelvis.
3. Markings on the pubic arch for the crura clitoridis.
4. Other features.

Woman Is the Weaker Vessel. Women are less muscular than men; they are 5″ less in stature; and they weigh less. For these and other reasons their bones, including the bones of the pelvis, are lighter and the ridges and markings for tendons, aponeuroses, and fasciae are less pronounced.

JOINTS. The articular surfaces of all joints associated with the pelvis are relatively and absolutely smaller in the female. In order of significance these joints are: (1) the lumbosacral joint, (2) the hip joint, (3) the symphysis pubis, and (4) the sacro-iliac joint.

Thus, the oval articular facet on the base of the sacrum and the acetabulum are both strikingly small. (As a result of "rheumatic" conditions there may be a broad rim around the oval facet on the sacrum. This is not to be confused with the outline of the articular surface.) The symphysis pubis is short. The auricular facet of the sacrum crosses the 1st and 2nd sacral vertebrae and encroaches on the 3rd vertebra; in the male it extends nearly half way down the side of the 3rd vertebra (*fig. 350*).

Functions Peculiar to Female Pelvis. During parturition the pelvis minor becomes a passage for the child. The length of the passage and its diameters are modified in accordance with requirements, as follows:

1. THE CAVITY: The male true pelvis has been described very aptly as a long segment of a short cone; the female, as a short segment of a long cone (*figs. 388* and *388.1*), i.e., in the male it is deep and funnel-shaped; in the female it is shallow and tubular.

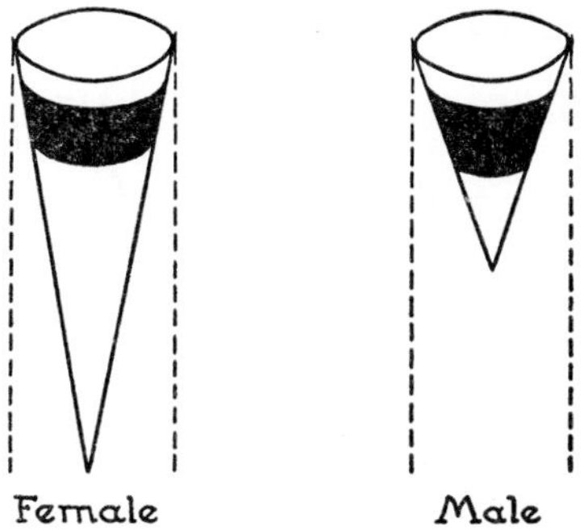

FIG. 388. The male and female true pelves (colored *black*) as segments of cones.

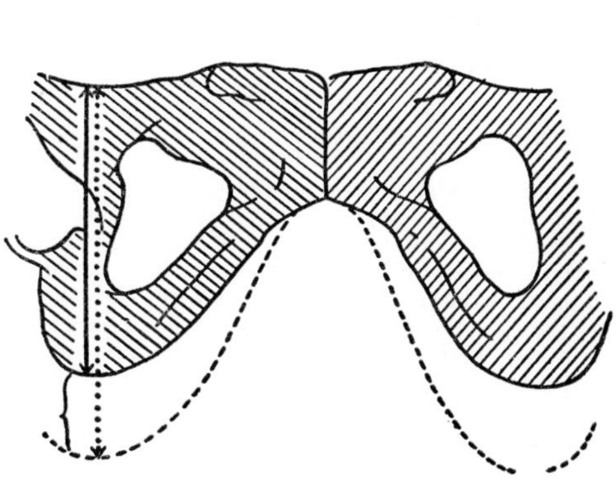

FIG. 388.1. The pelvic cavity is shallower in the female, and the subpubic angle is greater.

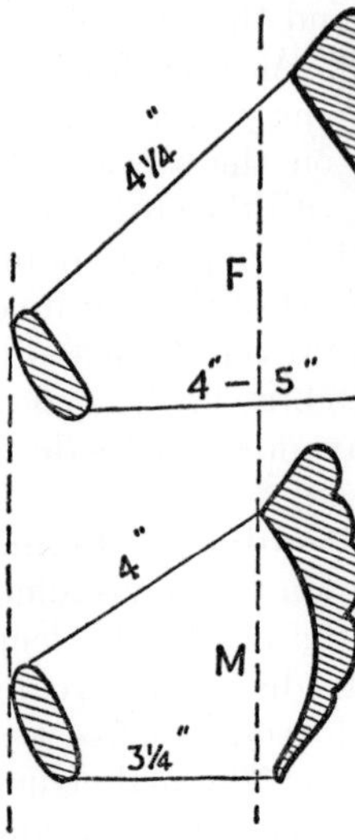

FIG. 388.2. Pelvic cavities on median section: male and female compared.

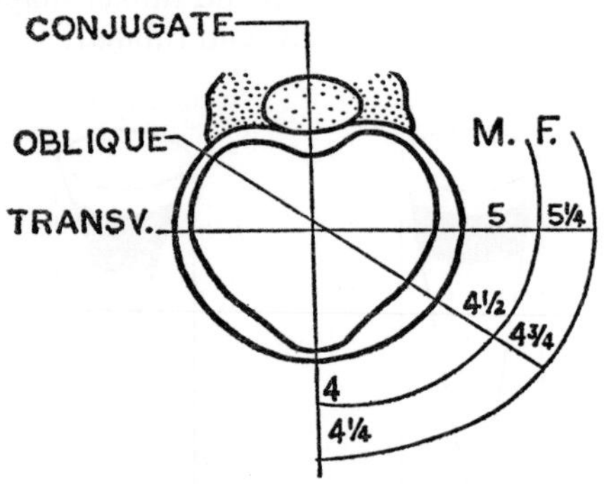

FIG. 389. Diameters of pelvic brim: male and female compared.

All **diameters** are absolutely greater in the female than in the male (*fig. 389*), each of the three diameters of the inlet being about ¼″ greater: and the anteroposterior and transverse diameters of the outlet being about 1″ greater.

»» *Diameters.* The three diameters of the pelvic brim or inlet are: the *anteroposterior diameter* measured from the sacral promontory to the top of the symphysis pubis; the *oblique diameter* measured from the sacro-iliac joint to the iliopectineal eminence of the opposite side (prior to the age of 16 this is the iliopubic synchondrosis), and, the *transverse diameter* measured at the widest part of the brim, which is behind the center. The diameters of the outlet are: the *anteroposterior diameter*, measured from the lower end of the symphysis to the tip of the coccyx. Its length depends largely upon the mobility of the sacrococcygeal joint; so, it is very variable. The *transverse diameter* is taken behind the ischial tuberosities.

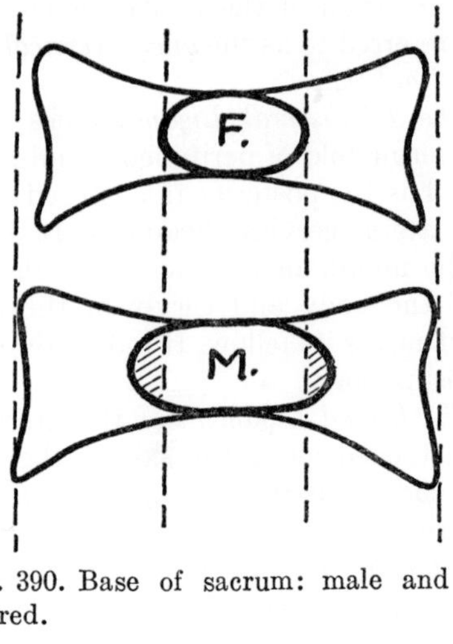

FIG. 390. Base of sacrum: male and female compared.

2. THE TRANSVERSE DIAMETER OR BREADTH is greater in the female than in the male. This reveals itself to inspection thus:

a. The body and crest of the pubic bone are wider in the female so, the pubic tubercles are farther apart.

b. The acetabulum is approximately its own diameter distant from the symphysis in the male, but in the female it is about an inch more than its own diameter distant from the symphysis. The fact that the female acetabulum is also relatively small accentuates this characteristic.

c. The base of the female sacrum is relatively wide, and, the oval facet on the base is relatively very small; so, for a twofold reason the alae are relatively long (*fig. 390*).

»» In the male the oval facet is nearly half (43.5 per cent) the maximum width of the base of the sacrum and is therefore much greater than either ala; in the female the oval facet is little more than a third (38.5 per cent) of the width of the base and is therefore approximately equal to the width of an ala.

d. The female pubic arch is almost a right angle; it equals the angle between the outstretched thumb and the index finger (*fig. 388.1*). In the male it is an acute angle, equal to the angle between the index and middle fingers when spread.

e. The female ischial tuberosities are everted.

3. THE ANTEROPOSTERIOR DIAMETER is

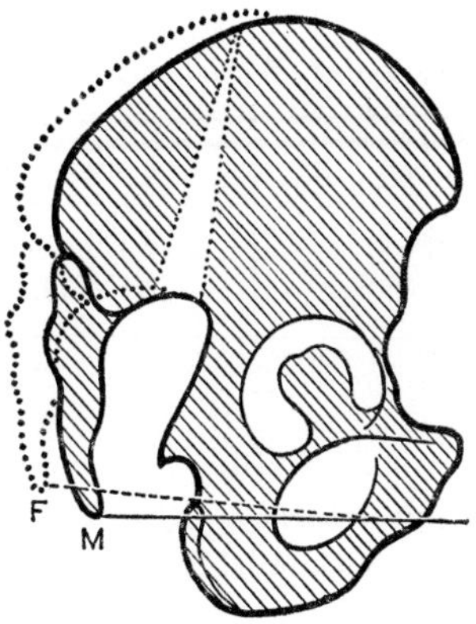

FIG. 391. Conversion of the male outlet into the female enlarges the angle of the greater sciatic notch.

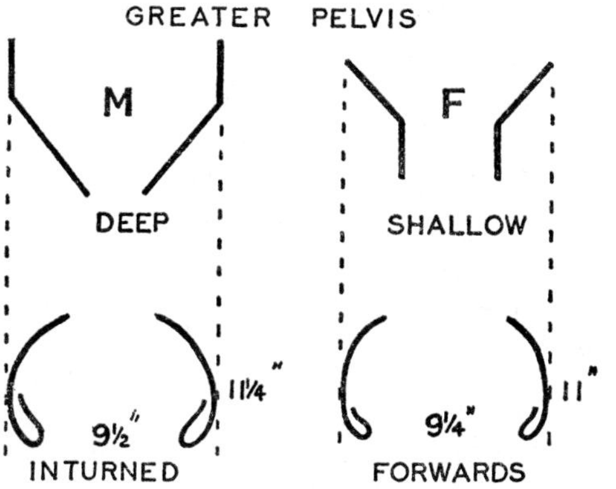

FIG. 392. Iliac crests: male and female compared.

greater in the female than in the male. This is revealed to inspection thus:

a. *At the inlet* the promontory is carried backward in the female. Consequently, the female inlet tends to be round; the male to be heart-shaped.

b. *At the outlet* the coccyx is carried backward in the female, (1) by raising the hinder part of the iliac crest, and thereby (2) increasing the angle of the greater sciatic notch, which in the male is an acute angle, to approximately a right angle in the female. The addition to the male pelvis of a wedge of bone, whose base is at the greater sciatic notch and apex at the iliac crest, would achieve these three effects (*fig. 391*), and consequently the sacrotuberous and sacrospinous ligaments would be lengthened.

Attachments of the Crura of the Clitoris. In the male the pubic arch has an expansive flat area for the attachment of the crus penis; so, it is thick and it appears to be everted. In the female the area for the crus clitoridis is narrow and the arch is thin.

Other Features. In the male the walls of the pelvis major are steep and the anterior superior iliac spines inturned. In the female the pelvis major is shallow and the anterior superior spines rather point forward (*fig. 392*).

»» The interspinous diameter (i.e., between anterior superior iliac spines) and the intercristal diameter (i.e., between the widest parts of the iliac crests) are each slightly less (10 mm.) in the female than in the male.

Skirting the anterior margin of the auricular facet on the ilium there may be a deep groove, the *pre-auricular sulcus* (Derry). A shallow groove may occur in the male.

Identification. In cases where it is difficult to arrive at a decision as to the sex of a given pelvis, greatest weight should be placed upon: (1) the area for the attachment of the crus penis or clitoridis; (2) the angle

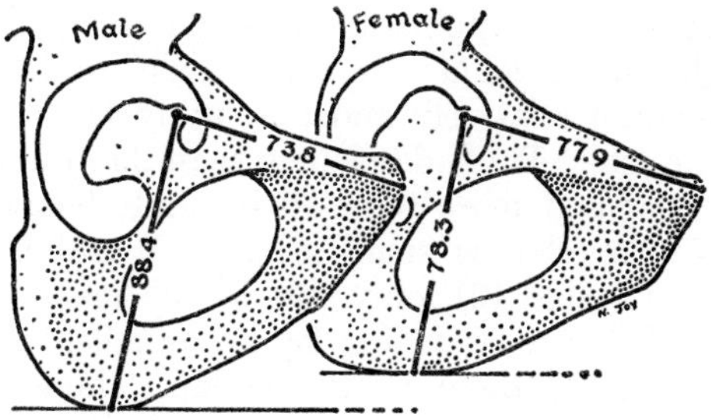

FIG. 393. The ischium-pubis index (see text)

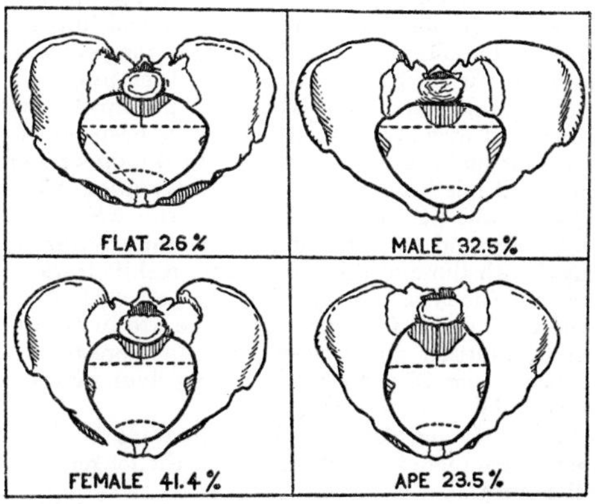

FIG. 394. The inlets of the four major types of female pelvis. (After Caldwell and Moloy.)

TABLE 16

Length of Pubis and Ischium and Ischium-Pubis Index (Washburn)*

White adults	Length of pubis (mean range)	Length of ischium (mean range)	Ischium-pubis index (mean range)
100 males	73.8 (65–83)	88.4 (75–98)	83.6 (73–94)
100 females	77.9 (69–95)	78.3 (69–93)	99.5 (91–115)

* Expressed in millimeters.

of the pubic arch; (3) the size of the acetabulum; (4) the size of the facet on the base of the sacrum relative to the alae; (5) the distance of the acetabulum from the symphysis pubis; and (6) the size of the greater sciatic notch.

If inspection leaves you undecided as to the sex, you should resort to measurement, Thus,

$$\frac{\text{length of pubis} \times 100}{\text{length of ischium}}$$

called the *Ischium-Pubis Index* (*fig. 393*), reveals the sex of an adult pelvis in more than 90 per cent of instances; that is because the pubic bone is relatively and absolutely longer in the female, and the ischium relatively and absolutely longer in the male. The index is less than 90 in adult males and more than 90 in adult females. The overlap is small, e.g., in Washburn's data (table 16), only five of the males exceeded the 90 index; in my smaller data (J.C.B.G.) there is no overlap. There are certain racial variations.

»» Types of Female Pelvis. Female pelves by no means all conform to the description given above; and since for the obstetrician it is of practical importance to know the dimensions and shapes of the pelves of his patients, various classifications have been proposed.

Thoms classified the pelves of 300 primiparous white women (delivered consecutively at a hospital clinic) into four major groups according to the dimensions of the pelvic inlet as determined by X-ray (see table 17).

When the pelves of 100 nurses, who were superior physically and more fortunate economically, are compared with those of the 300 women, a shift toward the dolichopellic type is seen. When the pelves of 107 girls, aged 5–15 years, from an orphanage are in turn compared, a further shift is seen. Indeed, before the age of 12 years over 75 per cent of these pelves were of the long or dolichopellic type.

The foregoing data, combined in table 17, indicate that where there is youth and vigor the longer types of pelvis prevail.

The size and shape of the pelvis are influenced by various factors (hormonal, environmental, hereditary, and mechanical), but it is not until puberty that the predominantly dolichopellic pelvis of childhood changes to one of the adult types. This remoulding takes about 18 months after which there is very little growth and almost no change in the shape of the inlet (Greulich and Thoms).

Caldwell and Moloy, with Todd's skeletal material as a basis, also have divided the white female pelvis into

TABLE 17

Percentage Incidence of Pelvic Types

(After Greulich and Thoms)

Type	300 clinic patients	100 nurses	107 girls age 5–15
Dolichopellic..........	16.3	37	57.9
Mesatipellic...........	44.0	46	33.6
Brachypellic..........	36.3	17	8.3
Platypellic............	3.3		

Dolichopellic (long): a-p. diameter > transverse diameter.

Mesatipellic (round): transverse > a-p. diameter by 0–1.0 cm.

Brachypellic (oval): transverse > a-p. diameter by 1.1–2.9 cm.

Platypellic (flat): transverse > a-p. diameter by 3 cm. or more.

TABLE 18

*Average Anteroposterior (Conjugate) and Transverse Diameters of the Pelvic Inlet in White Females, Classified According to the Four Pelvic Types of Caldwell and Moloy**

Pelvic type	No. of cases	Conjugate diameter	Transverse diameter
		cm.	
Gynecoid.............	26	10.86	13.76
Android...............	25	10.59	13.56
Anthropoid...........	19	11.75	12.94
Platypelloid..........	3	8.55	14.45
Mixed average for females..............	73	10.90	13.51
Average for males.....	43	10.10	13.00

* After T. W. Todd

four major groups: (1) anthropoid (ape), (2) android (male), (3) gynecoid (female), and (4) platypelloid (flat). Figure 394 illustrates the characteristics of the pelvic inlet in these four different groups and their percentage incidence. It shows the position of the greatest transverse diameter, and draws attention to the differences in the anterior and posterior segments of the inlet, to the size of the angle (retropubic angle) of the anterior segment, and to the lengths of the pubo-iliac and iliac portions.

Todd made measurements of part of this material when it was approximately fresh and unmacerated, so his mean measurements given in table 18 are of particular interest.

CHAPTER 22

PELVIC AUTONOMIC NERVES AND LYMPHATICS

PELVIC AUTONOMIC NERVES

Sympathetic Trunk; Superior Hypogastric Plexus; Inferior Hypogastric Plexus. Pelvic Splanchnic Nerves.

PELVIC LYMPHATICS

Pelvic Nodes; Structures Drained (area by area).

PELVIC AUTONOMIC NERVES

Sympathetic Trunk. *Within the Abdomen,* you will recall (p. 284), the sympathetic trunk descends on the bodies of the lumbar vertebrae at the anterior border of the Psoas, and, on crossing behind the common iliac vessels, enters the pelvis.

The lumbar part of each trunk has four ganglia. A *white ramus* communicans passes from each of the upper two or three lumbar nerves to the trunk; and one or more *gray rami* communicantes pass from the trunk to each of the five lumbar nerves. Branches *lumbar splanchnic nerves,* pass from the trunk (or ganglia) medially to the pre-aortic (intermesenteric) plexus, which is a downward extension of the celiac plexus (*fig. 319*).

Within the Pelvis, the trunks of the two sides, each having four ganglia, end in front of the coccyx in a medianly placed ganglion of no importance, the *ganglion impar*. The two trunks, therefore, converge as they descend on the bodies of the sacral vertebrae, and they lie medial to the pelvic sacral foramina (*figs. 324* and *377*). They receive no white rami (being caudal to L. 2 or 3), but they send gray rami laterally to each of the sacral nerves and to the coccygeal nerve and a few visceral twigs join the inferior hypogastric plexus (pelvic plexus).

Superior Hypogastric Plexus [Presacral Nerve]. This plexus lies below the bifurcation of the aorta and in front of the left common iliac vein and the 5th lumbar intervertebral disc (*fig. 319.1*). It is a downward prolongation of the pre-aortic (intermesenteric) plexus, reinforced by the lumbar splanchnic nerves.

On each side the 3rd lumbar splanchnic may join it after crossing anterior to the vessels, but usually the 3rd joins the intermesenteric plexus higher up. The 4th lumbar splanchnic nerve crosses the iliac vessels—almost always behind them—to join the superior hypogastric plexus in front of the sacrum (Mitchell).

The preganglionic cell stations are in the lowest thoracic and upper lumbar segments of the spinal cord. From one to four branches enter the pelvis and descend in front of the sacrum as *right and left hypogastric nerves.*

As each hypogastric nerve descends, it becomes plexiform and is joined by *twigs from the sacral sympathetic ganglia* and the pelvic splanchnic nerves of its own side to form the **inferior hypogastric plexus** [pelvic plexus].

Pelvic Splanchnic Nerves [Nervi Erigentes]. These threads are most easily found by passing two fingers far down in front of the body of the sacrum, easing the rectum forward, and feeling in the sheet of areolar fascia that runs forward on each side from sacrum to rectum (*fig. 348.1*).

These parasympathetic nerves spring from S. (2), 3, 4. They join the corresponding inf. hypogastric plexus which then becomes mixed sympathetic and parasympathetic. The plexus forms a dense network applied to the medial side of the vessels that limit the retropubic space posteriorly.

Mixed branches are distributed with these vessels to the various pelvic viscera, the pelvic splanchnic constituents being the more important. Branches continue forward to the side of the bladder and prostate; and beyond the prostate, branches pierce the urogenital diaphragm and enter the crus and bulb of the penis. Others pass below the symphysis pubis with the deep dorsal vein of the penis, join the dorsal nerve of the penis, and are distributed to the cavernous and spongy tissue of the penis.

The pelvic splanchnic nerves (both right and left) send ascending fibers across the left common iliac artery to join the sympathetic plexus on the inferior mesenteric artery and are distributed with it to the descending and sigmoid colons (Stopford).

Functions: It is generally believed that the sympathetic has no influence on the muscular walls of the bladder, urethra, or rectum—except as stated on page 61. The parasympathetic has exclusive control (Sheehan).

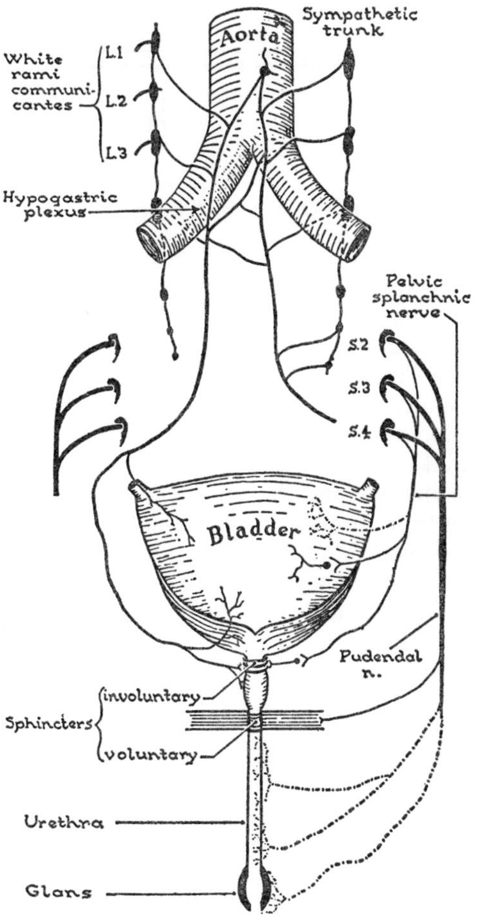

FIG. 395. Diagram of the nerve supply of the bladder and urethra.

The pelvic splanchnics by causing relaxation of the arteries to the erectile tissue, which normally are in contraction, produce erection of the penis (or clitoris), hence the term—*nervi erigentes* (*fig. 395*).

The hypogastrics, when stimulated, cause the epididymis, deferent duct, seminal vesicle, and prostate to contract and empty their contents; at the same time the region of the neck of the bladder is shut off (Learmonth). Hence, on ejaculation, the seminal fluid is hindered from entering the bladder.

The pelvic splanchnic nerves (S. 2, 3, and 4) also carry afferent fibers (e.g., pain, distention) from the bladder and prostatic urethra, rectum above the anal valves, cervix of the uterus and greater part of the vagina. But, the sympathetic is sensory to the body and fundus of the uterus (Mitchell).

PELVIC LYMPHATICS

Nearly two dozen efferent vessels leave the superficial and deep inguinal nodes (p. 361) pass behind the medial half of the inguinal ligament, and end in the external iliac nodes (*fig. 396*). These lymph vessels are arranged around the femoral artery and vein, some lying lateral to them, some in front of them, some behind them, and some medial to them. The medial vessels, numbering 9 or 10, pass through the femoral canal and may or may not be interrupted by a node (of Cloquet) that lies in the canal.

The Pelvic Nodes are in two groups: (1) those near the pelvic brim and (2) those within the pelvic cavity.

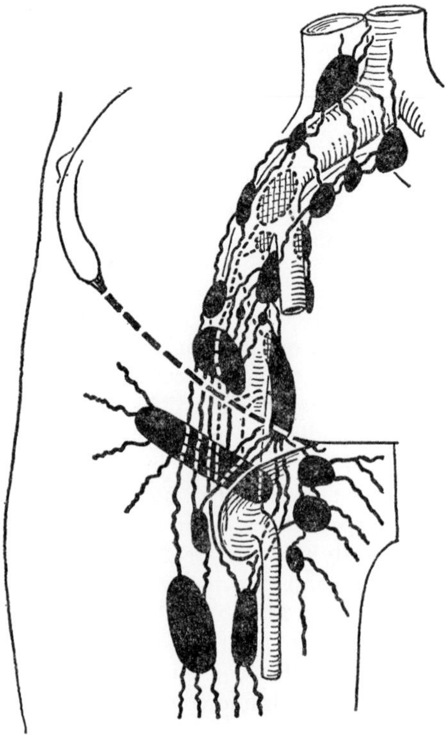

FIG. 396. Dissection of the inguinal lymphatics and those at the pelvic brim.

The nodes near the brim (12 or more) are (a) the *external and common iliac nodes,* which are arranged as several intercommunicating chains around the respective blood vessels, and (b) the nodes above the *sacral promontory*. The nodes within the cavity are (c) the *internal iliac, lateral sacral,* and *median sacral nodes* arranged on the respective blood vessels; and (d) others in the *vesical fascia,* in the *rectal fascia* mainly behind the rectum (pararectal nodes) and on the course of the superior rectal artery, *in the broad ligament* near the cervix uteri, and between the prostate and rectum.

Structures Drained. The following structures are drained by lymph vessels traveling to lymph nodes, thus:

THE SKIN OF THE PENIS AND THE PREPUCE → with the superficial dorsal vein in the subcutaneous tissues to the superficial inguinal nodes of both sides.

THE GLANS PENIS AND THE PENILE URETHRA → accompany the deep dorsal vein deep to the fascia penis to the deep inguinal nodes of both sides, thence to the external iliac nodes. Some vessels pass without interruption through the femoral and inguinal canals to the external iliac nodes. The lymph vessels of the glans and of the prepuce anastomose.

BULBAR URETHRA → follows the internal

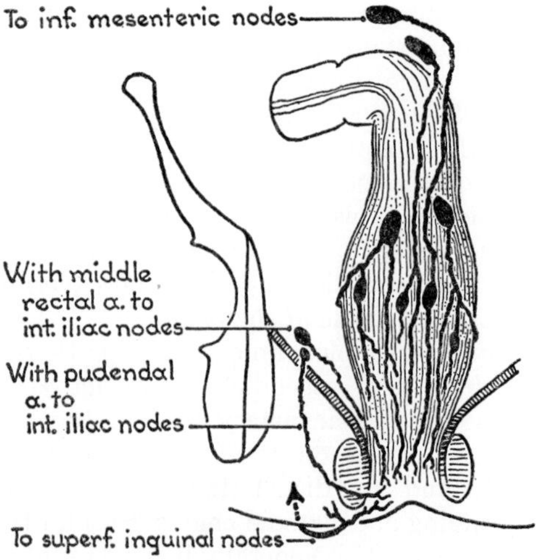

FIG. 397. The lymphatics of the rectum, from behind. (After Rouviere.)

pudendal artery to internal iliac nodes and the deep dorsal vein below the infrapubic ligament, thence to external iliac nodes.

MEMBRANOUS AND PROSTATIC URETHRAE (OR WHOLE FEMALE URETHRA) → internal iliac nodes.

BLADDER (superior and inferolateral surfaces) → follow the general course of the branches of the superior vesical artery, deferent duct, and ureter to external iliac nodes lying along the medial side of the external iliac vein, some being interrupted by anterior and lateral vesical nodes.

BASE OF THE BLADDER AND THE MALE INTERNAL GENITAL ORGANS (prostate, seminal vesicles, ampullae of the deferent ducts) → internal iliac nodes; also to the external iliac nodes; and on the Levator Ani to the sacral nodes.

ANUS AND LOWEST PART OF THE ANAL CANAL → by cutaneous vessels to the superficial inguinal nodes.

ANAL CANAL → internal iliac nodes by vessels piercing the Levator Ani (others crossing the ischiorectal fossa with branches of the pudendal vessels) and by others following the middle rectal vessels.

RECTUM, above the anal valves (*fig. 397*), → (1) pararectal nodes, which lie in the fatty tissue behind the rectum enclosed within the rectal fascia, thence to the superior rectal and inferior mesenteric nodes; (2) lateral and median sacral nodes; and, (3) with the middle rectal artery to internal iliac nodes.

OVARY, like the testis (*fig. 228*), → lateral aortic and pre-aortic nodes, between the levels of the common iliac vessels below, and the renal vessels above. Owing to the absence of a left inferior vena cava they are more accessible on the left side; here, however, the inferior mesenteric artery obtrudes itself. Occasionally a vessel passes to a node at the bifurcation of the common iliac artery.

UTERINE TUBE AND FUNDUS OF THE

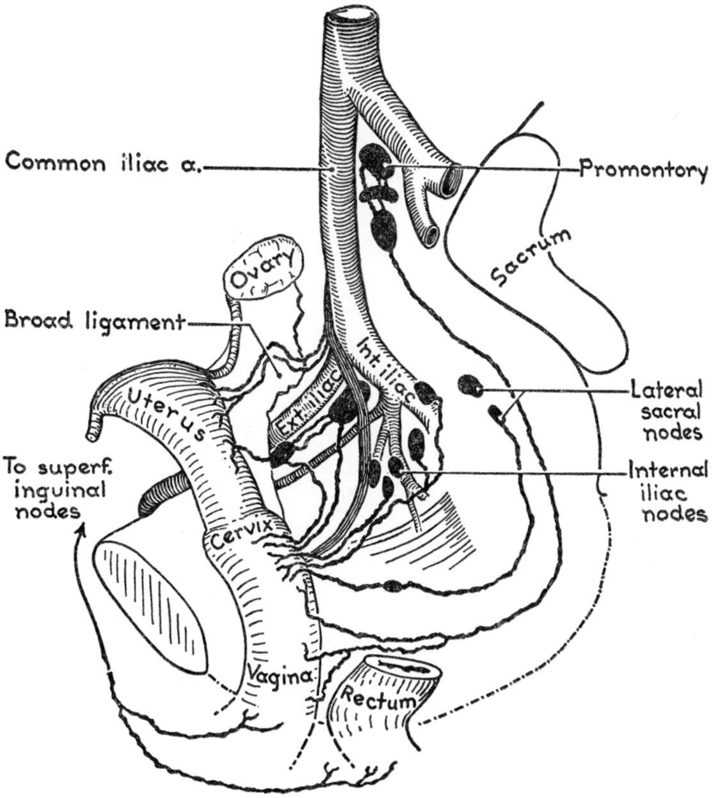

FIG. 397.1. The lymphatics of the uterus and vagina. (After Cuneo and Marcille.)

UTERUS → with those of the ovary, ending in the lower pre-aortic and lateral aortic nodes. They traverse the broad ligament and cross the pelvic brim.

BODY OF UTERUS (*fig. 397.1*) → via broad ligament to the external and common iliac nodes, and by a single vessel running in the round ligament to the superomedial group of superficial inguinal nodes.

CERVIX OF UTERUS AND UPPER END OF VAGINA → external iliac nodes; with uterine and vaginal arteries to internal iliac nodes; and, by vessels passing close to the rectum in the uterosacral fold, to lateral sacral nodes and nodes of the promontory.

LOWER END OF VAGINA and labium majus, like the scrotum → to superficial inguinal nodes.

SECTION V

Lower Limb

CHAPTER 23

FEMUR AND FRONT OF THIGH

FRONT OF THIGH

During intra-uterine life the tibia and big toe lie on the pre-axial border of the limb. To take up the Anatomical Position (*fig. 1*), they rotate to the medial side until the sole faces posteriorly—actually downward.

Bony Landmarks. The following bony parts should be located on the skeleton and palpated on the living model, which will likely be yourself or a fellow student: The *anterior superior iliac spine;* the *tubercle* at the widest part of the iliac crest, 2½ inches from the spine; the *tubercle, crest,* and *symphysis* of the pubis; the *pubic arch* and the *ischial tuberosity* on which you sit (*fig. 398*).

A line drawn horizontally from the pubic tubercle will pass through the head of the femur below the midinguinal point and through the upper end of the *greater trochanter*. The greater trochanter lies about 4 inches below the tubercle on the iliac crest. Grasp it between your fingers and thumb. It is covered with the aponeurosis of the Gluteus Maximus and Tensor Fasciae Latae, so it is not subcutaneous but subaponeurotic. It is palpated with difficulty when you stand on one leg, but with ease when you stand or lie down with legs well separated, for the aponeurosis is then relaxed.

The *body of the femur* is buried in muscles and obliquely placed, as is evident from the

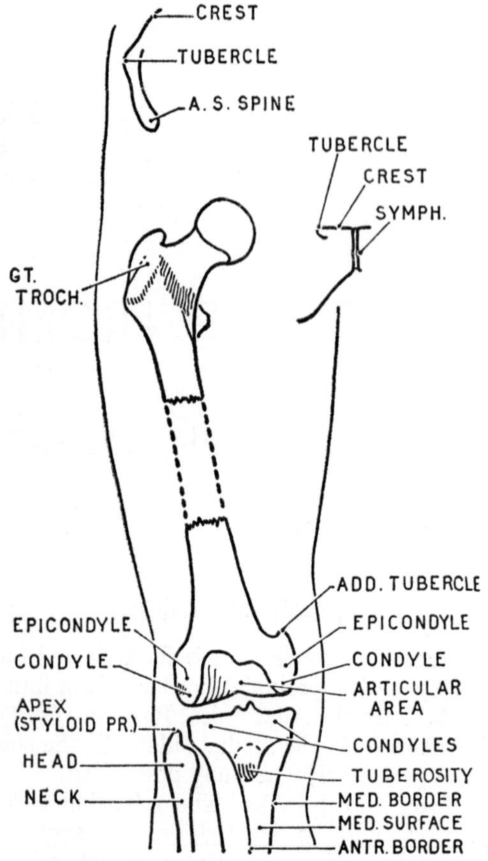

Fig. 398. Bony landmarks of the thigh

fact that the heads of the femora of opposite sides are separated by the width of the pelvis while the condyles of opposite sides touch, or almost touch, at the knees.

The *adductor tubercle*, through which the lower epiphyseal line runs, is felt on pressing downward and laterally at the upper part of the medial condyle. When the knee is flexed, the anterior parts of the *femoral condyles* can be felt and much of the articular surface. The *epicondyles*, lying at the centers of the posterior "discs" of the condyles (*fig. 405*), are readily located. The medial epicondyle is 1″ below the adductor tubercle.

Palpate the flat, subcutaneous *medial surface of the tibia* and the *anterior and medial borders* that limit it. Then follow the medial surface upward on to the *medial condyle of the tibia*, and follow the anterior border up to the *tuberosity* (tubercle) *of the tibia.*

The *patella* is easily moved from side to side when the limb is straight and the extensors of the knee are relaxed, as when you bend over a basin or when you rest your heel on a chair while sitting on another chair, and much of its posterior articular surface is then palpable. Place the fingers behind the lateral aspect of the knee and palpate the rounded *head of the fibula*, the *neck* supporting it, and the *apex of the head* in which it culminates.

SUPERFICIAL STRUCTURES

The Skin, both dermis or true skin and epidermis, is thick and tough on exposed surfaces and on surfaces subjected to pressure or friction, such as the dorsal aspect of the neck and trunk, the buttock, the lateral aspects of both limbs, the palm, and the bearing points of the sole of the foot. On the other hand, it is thin in regions that come within the field of vision and so can be protected by the hand or by curling up.

The Superficial Fascia of the lower limbs is continuous with that covering the body generally. On the front of the thigh it is continuous with the adipose layer of superficial fascia of the abdomen (Camper's fascia). The deep or membranous layer of the superficial fascia of the abdomen (Scarpa's fascia) is attached to the deep fascia of the thigh a finger's breadth below the inguinal ligament (*fig. 212*, and p. 200).

The amount of fat over bony points, such as the acromion, olecranon, knuckles, and patella, and under skin creases is generally reduced; over the ischial tuberosity and the heel the fat is imprisoned in much fibrous tissue. On the buttocks large quantities of fat may be deposited; in the Bushmen of South Africa, the quantity is enormous.

The Deep Fascia is especially strong in the lower limb. The portion enveloping the thigh is called the **fascia lata.** According to rule, it is attached to the anterior superior spine, inguinal ligament, body of the pubis, pubic arch, ischial tuberosity, sacrotuberous ligament, and as the gluteal fascia it is attached to the lower sacral spines and to the outer lip of the iliac crest.

It is extremely strong laterally because in between two thin layers of circularly disposed fibers there runs a broad band of coarse vertical fibers called the **iliotibial tract** (p. 377). This tract is the conjoint aponeurosis of the Tensor Fasciae Latae and the Gluteus Maximus.

The **Great (Long) Saphenous Vein** ascends throughout the length of the limb, in the subcutaneous fat.

It begins at the medial end of the dorsal venous arch of the foot, passing in front of the medial malleolus, crossing the lower third of the medial surface of the tibia, and following ½ inch behind its medial border as far as the knee. At the knee it is found on incising a hand's breadth (or slightly more) behind the medial border of the patella. From there it takes a straight, but oblique, course up the thigh to the femoral vein which it joins 1½″ inferolateral to the pubic tubercle.

It anastomoses freely with the short saphenous vein; it communicates along intermuscular septa with the deep veins; and it receives numerous tributaries including three *superficial inguinal veins.*

These veins accompany the three **superficial inguinal arteries,** which are branches of the femoral artery—(1) the (*superficial*) *external pudendal artery* which crosses in front of the spermatic cord to supply the scrotum; (2) the *superficial epigastric artery* which passes towards the navel; and (3) the *superficial circumflex iliac artery* which passes laterally below the inguinal ligament.

»» *Terminology. Saphenous, sesamoid, nuchal,* and *retinal* are among the few **terms of Arabic origin** that remain in our anatomical vocabulary (Singer).

Saphenous Opening or Hiatus (Fossa Ovalis) (*fig. 399*). The great saphenous vein has to pass through the fascia lata in order to reach the femoral vein; and evidently it is responsible for the large hole that exists, called the *saphenous opening,* for only in man is there such an opening in the fascia and only in man does the saphenous vein ascend far above the knee. Further, the vein would seem to have dragged down the lower margin of the opening to its present level, for it commonly hooks over it.

The saphenous opening is about 1½″ long. Above, it reaches to the pubic tubercle. It is free and sharp both above and below. Its lateral border is crescentic or falciform,

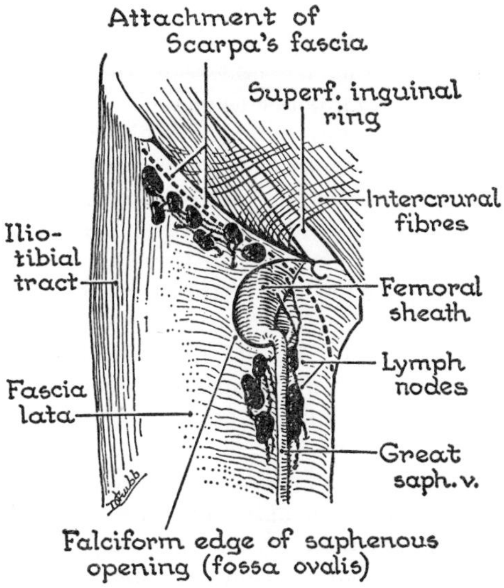

FIG. 399. Saphenous opening; great saphenous vein joining the femoral vein within the femoral sheath; lymph nodes; and the attachment of Scarpa's fascia.

and it blends with some areolar tissue (cribriform fascia) that covers the opening; hence, it is not sharply defined. Its medial border is continuous with the fascia covering the underlying Pectineus and as such it passes behind the femoral vessels.

Lymph Nodes. In the lower limb, the lymph nodes are situated at the knee and the groin; those at the knee (popliteal) being deep; those at the groin (inguinal) being superficial, except for two or three deep nodes.

The superficial inguinal nodes can be palpated against the fascia lata; the popliteal nodes are not palpable.

The **Inguinal Nodes** (*fig. 399*) are in two groups, a superficial and a deep. The *superficial nodes* are subdivided into (1) an upper horizontal group that lies parallel to the inguinal ligament below the attachment of the fascia of Scarpa to the fascia lata, and (2) a lower vertical group applied to both sides of the upper end of the great saphenous vein.

The lower superficial inguinal nodes, receive all the superficial lymph vessels of the lower limb save for the few that, following the small saphenous vein, end in the popliteal nodes. *The upper superficial inguinal nodes* drain the regions supplied by the three superficial inguinal blood vessels; namely, the subcutaneous tissues of the anterior abdominal wall below the navel, of the penis and scrotum (vulva in the female and lowest part of the vagina) and of the gluteal region, perineum, and lower part of the anal canal, but not of the testis (nor of the ovary).

The *deep nodes,* one to three in number, lie on the medial side of the femoral vein, in and below the femoral canal. They receive the deep lymph vessels of the limb. These follow the femoral vessels and include those draining the popliteal nodes. They also receive the lymph vessels of the glans penis (or clitoridis) and spongy urethra.

The inguinal lymph nodes drain into the external iliac nodes by 20 or so lymph vessels that ascend both within the femoral sheath and round about it. Since only about 10 of these traverse the femoral canal, a femoral hernia would not cause lymphatic obstruction in the limb (*fig. 396*).

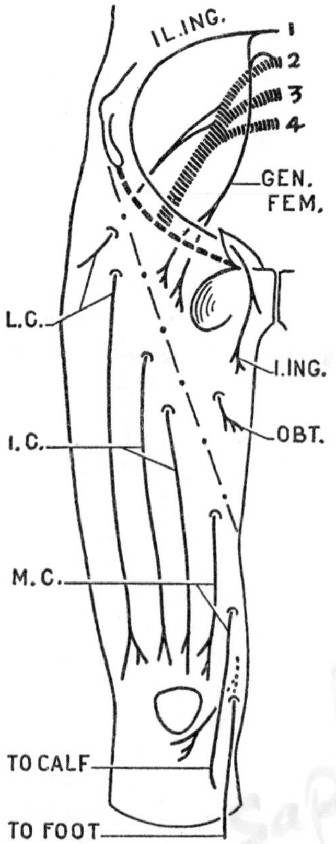

FIG. 400. Cutaneous nerves of the front of the thigh, above and below the line of the Sartorius.

Cutaneous Nerves (*fig. 400*). The cutaneous nerves of the front of the thigh are derived from the ventral rami of L. 1, 2, 3, 4. The *lateral, intermediate,* and *medial cutaneous nerves of the thigh* and the *saphenous nerve* are branches of the femoral nerve. They pierce the deep fascia along an oblique line that roughly marks the Sartorius.

The posterior branch of the lateral cutaneous nerve passes to the gluteal region; the posterior branch of the medial cutaneous nerve extends to the calf; and the saphenous nerve extends half way along the medial border of the foot. The other branches remain above the knee.

The *lateral cutaneous nerve* commonly arises independently from the lumbar plexus and enters the thigh close to the anterior superior spine. When it springs from the femoral nerve, it enters at some distance from the spine.

The *saphenous nerve* comes to the surface between the Sartorius and Gracilis, the width of the Sartorius behind the adductor tubercle. It gives off a *patellar branch,* which pierces the Sartorius and arches downward and laterally below the patella.

A branch of the *obturator nerve* becomes cutaneous at the middle of the thigh, medial to the Sartorius, and may extend to the calf.

The skin overlying the femoral triangle (p. 366) is supplied by (1) the *ilio-inguinal nerve,* which emerges through the superficial inguinal ring, and (2) the femoral branch of the *genitofemoral nerve,* which enters the thigh as several twigs lateral to the femoral artery.

Femoral Sheath (*fig. 401*). In the iliac fossa the Iliacus and Psoas are covered with fascia. The two muscles pass behind the inguinal ligament into the thigh; and, naturally, their fascial covering goes with them. The part covering the Iliacus blends loosely with the inguinal ligament and with the fascia lata; this too is natural. The part covering the Psoas is separated from the inguinal ligament and from the fascia lata by the femoral vessels which here escape from the abdominal cavity. The fascia turns dorsally, between Psoas and Pectineus, and

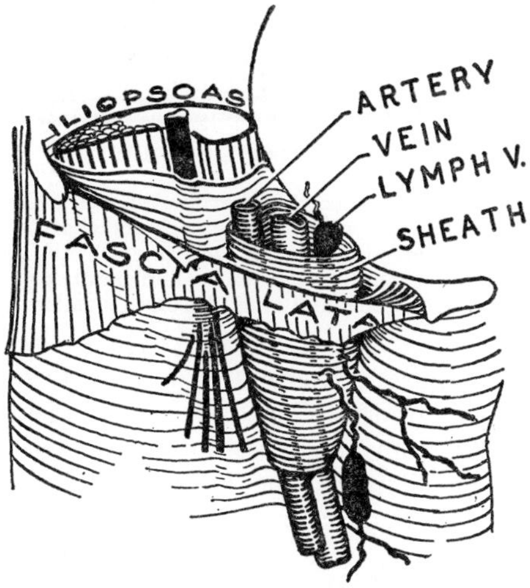

FIG. 401. The femoral sheath

adheres to the capsule of the hip joint (*fig. 412*). The femoral artery, vein, and some lymph vessels are wrapped up in a prolongation of the extraperitoneal areolar tissue that envelops the external iliac vessels in the abdomen. This wrapping is the femoral sheath.

The sheath is funnel-shaped; its lateral part lies behind the fascia lata, its medial part behind the saphenous opening. It has three compartments—a lateral one for the artery, a middle one for the vein, and a medial one partly occupied by lymph vessels. It is through the medial, partly occupied compartment that a femoral hernia may occur, and into it a distended femoral vein can bulge; this compartment is called the **femoral canal.**

The **Femoral Ring** is the mouth of the femoral canal. It is bounded *laterally* by the femoral vein; *posteriorly* by the superior ramus of the pubic bone covered with a coating of Pectineus and pectineus fascia; *medially* by the lacunar ligament and the conjoint tendon, both of which are attached to the pecten pubis (pectineal line); and *anteriorly* by the inguinal ligament and the spermatic cord.

To enlarge the ring in an emergency, (e.g., when reducing a femoral hernia), you dare not cut laterally into the vein; it would be useless to cut posteriorly on to the bone; you would require to cut either medially or anteriorly (*fig. 412*).

FEMUR

The femur is the longest bone in the body, being a quarter of the stature, or about 18 inches in an average man. It articulates above with the acetabulum, below with the tibia, and the patella plays on its lower end.

The **Proximal End** presents for examination, a head, neck, greater trochanter, and lesser trochanter (*figs. 402* and *403*).

The Head forms two-thirds of a sphere, and is directed medially, upward, and forward. It is much more secure in its socket than the head of the humerus, which forms only one-third of a sphere and is directed medially, upward, and backward.

The Neck is pyramidal and it is obliquely placed. Its apex carries the head; its base abuts against the greater trochanter. In reality, the neck is the medially curved upper end of the shaft, but the fact is masked by the presence of the greater trochanter (*fig. 404*). The anterior aspect of the neck is flat and would be flush with the anterior aspect of the shaft but for a broad, very rough,

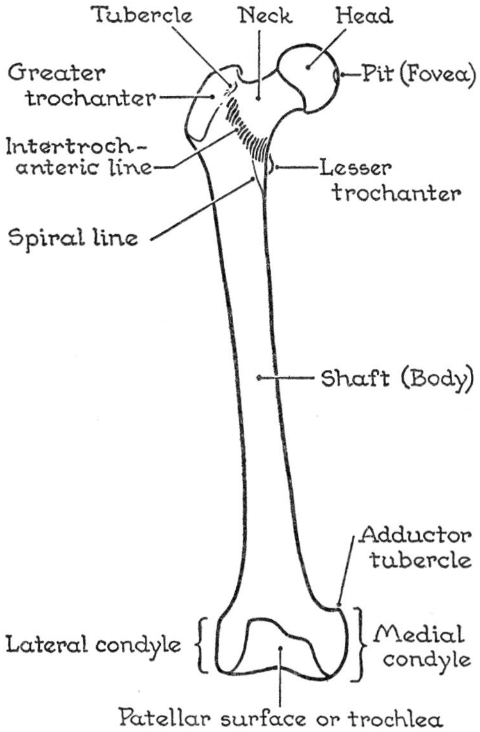

FIG. 402. The femur, front view

Externus runs horizontally across the back of the neck (*fig. 435*).

The **Shaft or Body** is slightly bowed forward. Its middle two quarters are approximately circular on cross-section; its upper and lower quarters are enlarged and are oblong on cross-section, the lower quarter being much the larger.

A broad rough line, the **linea aspera** stands out from the back of the middle two quarters of the shaft like a pilaster. The linea aspera bifurcates above and below into diverging lines that bound triangular areas.

The upper diverging lines are the *spiral line* and the *gluteal tuberosity*. The spiral line runs upward and medially and is continuous with the intertrochanteric line; the gluteal tuberosity ascends toward the side of the greater trochanter and there becomes continuous with the epiphyseal line that runs around the root of the greater trochanter. The lesser trochanter projects from the triangle bounded by these lines.

The lower diverging lines, the *medial* and *lateral supracondylar lines*, descend to the epicondyles and bound a flat triangular area, the *popliteal surface*, which is limited below by the condyles and a rough line, the *intercondylar line*, that separates the area from the intercondylar notch below. The lower inch of the medial supracondylar line curves abruptly medially to end in an upwardly projecting spine, the *adductor tubercle*.

The anterior and lateral aspects of the shaft give origin to the fleshy fibers of the Vastus Intermedius; the medial aspect is bare. The shaft, therefore, is smooth, and has no defined medial and lateral borders. The posterior border is the linea aspera. Many muscles and three intermuscular septa crowd on to it and on to its upward and downward prolongations; hence, their attachments are fibrous or aponeurotic, which accounts for the roughness of the border.

The **Distal End** of the femur is divided into two large knuckles, the *medial* and *lateral condyles*. The hinder parts of the condyles project backward like thick discs beyond the popliteal surface (*fig. 405*). Between the opposed surfaces of these discs is a U-shaped notch, the *intercondylar fossa*, the width and depth of the thumb. At the center or hub of the nonopposed surface of each disc there is a fullness, the *epicondyle*, to which the medial and lateral ligaments of the knee joint are attached (*fig. 507*). The femoral condyles are covered with cartilage below and behind for articulation with the tibia, and the cartilage of the two sides meets in front in a V-shaped pulley, the *patellar surface* or *trochlea* in which the patella plays. The lateral lip of this pulley projects further forward and further upward than the medial lip.

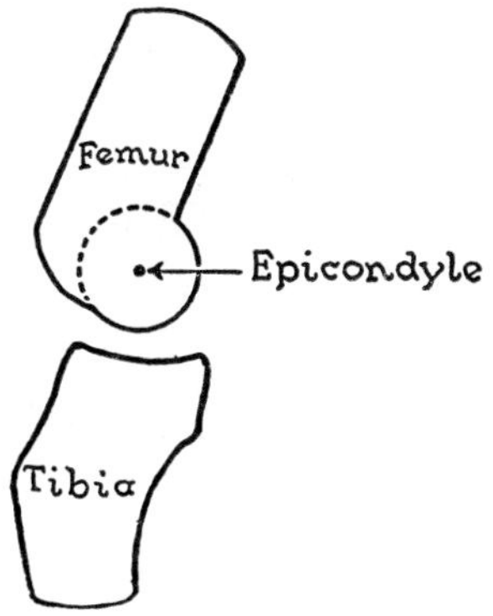

FIG. 405. A disc-shaped condyle and an epicondyle.

Orientation. The condyles of the femur rest on the tibia as on a horizontal platform. The head and neck are slightly in advance of the shaft; that is, they are directed forward, as well as medially and upward. The shaft does not lie vertically but is inclined forward above.

Epiphyses. The *head* fits like a cap on a blunt spike (*fig. 496*), as is the case with the upper end of the humerus. The *greater trochanter* joins the shaft along a line flush with the upper border of the neck, as described above. The *lesser trochanter* has a thick scale-like epiphysis.

The epiphyseal line of the *lower end* of the femur runs through the adductor tubercle and along the intercondylar line. The lower epiphysis possesses four shallow hollows into which four tubercles of the diaphysis fit. This is a primitive mammalian character, better developed in quadrupeds, which walk with bent knees and require greater security (*fig. 406*).

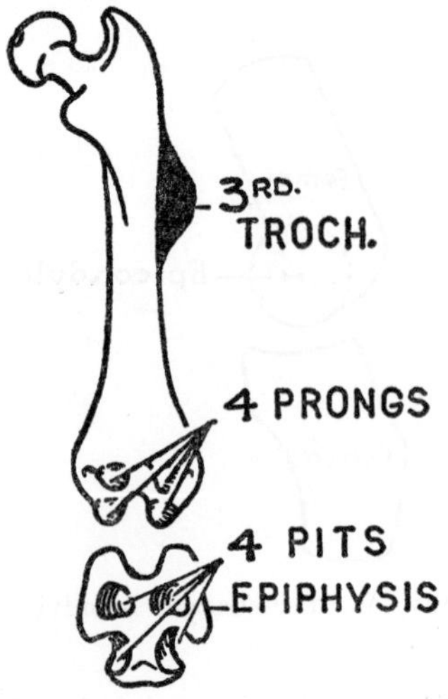

FIG. 406. Femur of muskrat showing two primitive mammalian characters.

At birth the lower epiphysis is an ossific nodule a quarter of an inch in diameter.

»» **Variations.** A *third trochanter*, also a primitive mammalian character, is constant in certain rodents and the horse, and may appear in any mammal including man as an enlarged gluteal tuberosity. *Platymeria*, or marked anteroposterior flattening of the upper part of the shaft of the femur, is common in primitive races.

FEMORAL TRIANGLE

The femoral triangle (of Scarpa) (*fig. 407*) is a triangular trough. Its base is formed by the inguinal ligament. Its lateral side is formed by the Sartorius, which arises from the anterior superior spine, and its medial side, by the Adductor Longus, whose flattened tendon, ¾″ wide, arises from the front of the body of the pubis.

The apex lies 4 inches (or less) below the inguinal ligament, where the Sartorius crosses the lateral border of the Adductor Longus.

THE CENTRAL AND DOMINANT STRUCTURE within this triangular frame is the *femoral artery*. It begins where the external iliac artery ends—at the *midinguinal point*. It leaves the triangle at its apex and enters the adductor canal (subsartorial canal). It follows, then, that only its upper 4 inches lie exposed within the undissected triangle; its remaining 6 inches travel through the adductor canal.

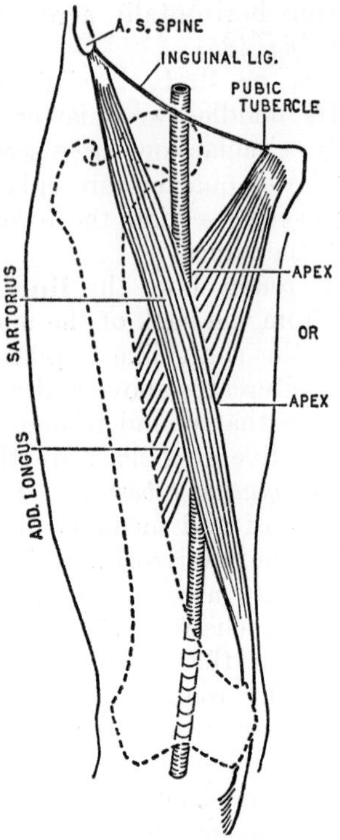

FIG. 407. The sides of the femoral triangle. The course of the femoral artery.

THE FLOOR OF THE TRIANGLE is muscular (see *fig. 408*). The Iliopsoas is inserted into the lesser trochanter; the *Pectineus* into the line that descends from the lesser trochanter to the linea aspera; the *Adductor Longus* into the linea aspera itself; and *Vastus Medialis* in part arises from the linea aspera (*figs. 435* and *437*).

Contents of the Triangle (*fig. 410*):

Femoral artery, vein, and nerve, certain of their branches, and the deep inguinal lymph nodes.

Profunda femoris artery and vein, and their circumflex branches (p. 393).

The **Femoral Artery** happens to run along a *boundary line* separating two motor nerve territories. The obturator nerve supplies the muscles of the medial territory; the femoral nerve those of the lateral territory. You may, therefore, run your knife down the entire course of the artery without fear of damaging any motor nerve, for no motor nerve crosses it—save the nerve to the Pectineus, which crosses posteriorly.

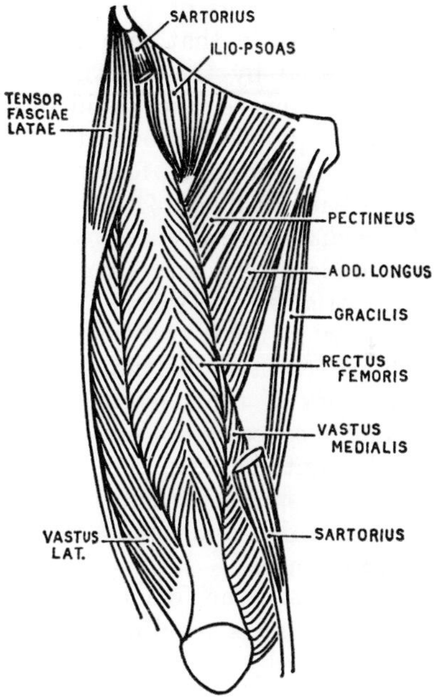

FIG. 408. The floor of the femoral triangle. The walls of the adductor canal.

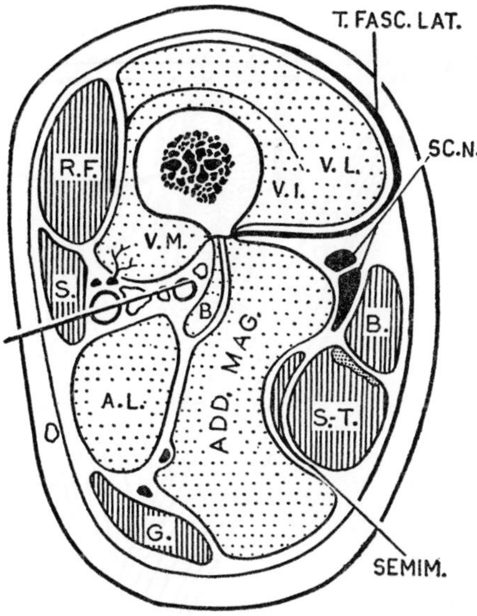

FIG. 409. Cross-section of thigh near apex of the femoral triangle showing (1) attachments of muscles to the linea aspera; (2) six muscles (*hatched*) that span the femur, and (3) that a bullet might penetrate the femoral and profunda femoris vessels.

The **Profunda Femoris Artery** may arise from the lateral aspect of the femoral artery at the level of the inguinal ligament, in which case two main arteries enter the limb; or it may arise 4 inches below the inguinal ligament, in which case only one artery traverses the femoral triangle; *usually* it takes origin between 1 and 2 inches below the ligament. It is only slightly smaller than the continuation of the femoral artery itself, and is therefore no mean vessel.

The **Femoral Vein** lies medial to the femoral artery in the femoral sheath, but lies behind the artery at the apex of the triangle; so do also the profunda artery and vein; all four vessels being almost inseparably united in a tough areolar sheath. A stab, therefore, or a bullet wound at the apex of the triangle would penetrate in succession the four great vessels of the limb. From before backward they are—femoral artery, femoral vein, profunda vein, and profunda artery (*fig. 409*).

The **Profunda Femoris Vein** ends in the femoral vein near the apex of the femoral triangle; i.e., about 2″ below the origin of the profunda artery. The large *lateral femoral circumflex venae comitantes* join the lateral side of the femoral vein at the level of the origin of the profunda artery; the *medial femoral circumflex vein* joins it at the same level; and the great *saphenous vein* is the last tributary to join the femoral vein.

Venous Valves. The i. v. cava and the common iliac vein have no valves. Indeed, in 24 per cent of 200 limbs no valve was found either in the external iliac or in the femoral vein above the level of the opening of the great saphenous, i.e., there was no valve between the saphenous vein and the heart. This may be important in relation to varicose veins.

In 76 per cent of 200 limbs one valve was found above the saphenous vein, usually in the femoral vein but sometimes in the external iliac, and sometimes a valve was found in each of these. There is usually (90 per cent) a valve just distal to the opening of the profunda vein and there may be two or three others (Basmajian).

The **Femoral Nerve** enters the thigh slightly lateral to the artery (*fig. 411*), deep to the fascia lata and also to the fascia iliaca.

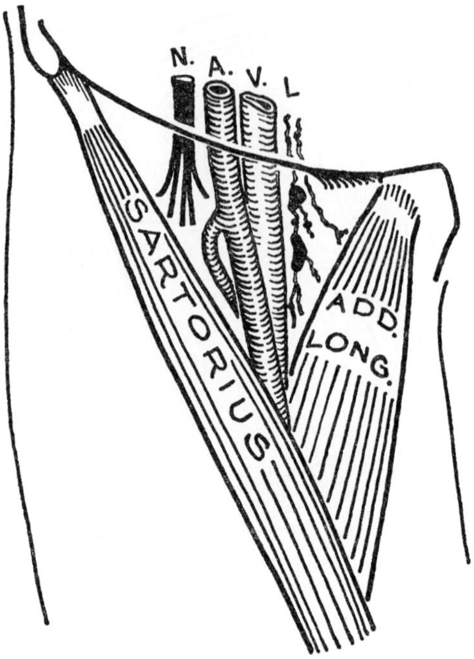

FIG. 410. The contents of the femoral triangle

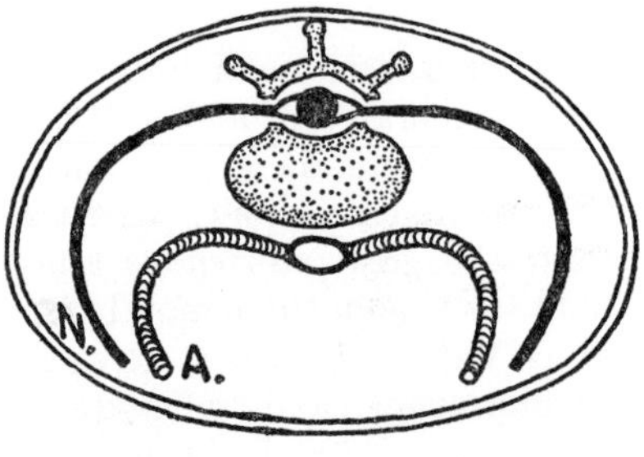

FIG. 411. The origins of the femoral nerve and artery account for their relative positions.

But in the thigh it has almost no existence, for within 1 inch of its crossing the inguinal ligament it breaks up like a "cauda equina" into numerous motor and sensory strands. Two of these follow the artery, closely applied to its lateral side, into the adductor canal; one, the *nerve to the Vastus Medialis* is motor; the other, the *saphenous nerve,* is sensory.

Only one motor strand, the *nerve to the Pectineus,* actually crosses the artery; and it crosses posteriorly within the femoral triangle.

At times, there is an extensive gap between the adjacent borders of Pectineus and Adductor Longus. In that case the Adductor Brevis, crossed by the anterior branch of the obturator nerve, appears in the floor of the femoral triangle. Through the lower end of this gap the profunda femoris artery and vein pass backward (*fig. 414*).

The *medial femoral circumflex* branch of the profunda artery passes backward, leaving the triangle between Pectineus and Iliopsoas, while the *lateral femoral circumflex* branch passes laterally through or behind the branches of the femoral nerve, disappears under cover of the muscles that arise from the anterior superior and anterior inferior iliac spines (namely, Sartorius and Rectus Femoris), and breaks up into three terminal branches.

Relationships. The femoral artery lies in front of the **Psoas tendon.** But the Psoas tendon is hardly wider than the artery; so, there is no room on it for either the femoral nerve or the femoral vein. They must lie in front of other structures; the nerve, in front of the Iliacus; and the vein and most lymph vessels, in front of the Pectineus (*fig. 412*). Hence, it may be said that the artery is separated from the hip joint by the strong, tough tendon of the Psoas; the nerve by the thickness of the

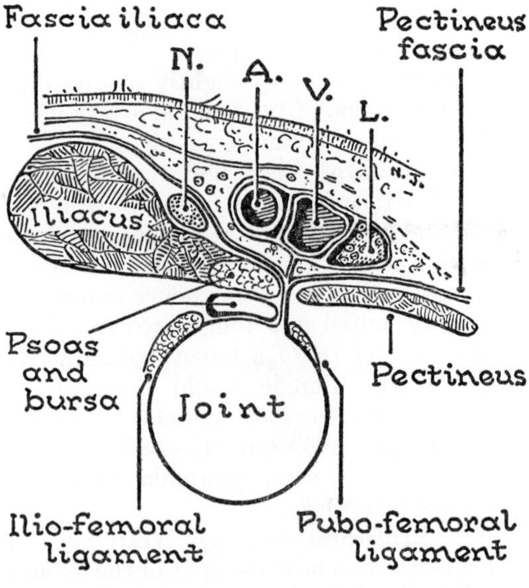

FIG. 412. The relationship of the femoral vessels and nerve to the hip joint.

fleshy Iliacus; the vein and the lymph vessels by the thinness of the fleshy Pectineus.

ADDUCTOR CANAL

The adductor canal of Hunter (the Subsartorial Canal) is the narrow outlet of the femoral triangle roofed in by the Sartorius and thereby converted into an intermuscular tunnel, triangular on cross-section and 6 inches long. It begins (less than) 4 inches below the inguinal ligament and ends 4 inches above the adductor tubercle (*fig. 413*). Only the femoral vessels and the saphenous nerve run right through it.

The Sartorius arises side by side with the inguinal ligament from the anterior superior iliac spine (and the notch below). It is inserted into the medial surface of the tibia below the level of the tuberosity (*fig. 442*).

It comes into contact with the medial condyle of the femur immediately behind the adductor tubercle and from there downward to its insertion it rubs against resistant structures (viz., medial condyle of femur, capsule of knee, medial condyle of tibia, medial ligament of knee, and tendons of Gracilis and Semitendinosus); therefore, its fleshy fibers give place to tendon. Between this tendon and the tendons of the Gracilis and Semitendinosus a *bursa* is interposed.

»» *Observations.* If you measure, you will find that the fleshy part of the muscle is 18 inches long; and, if you look, you will see that its fibers run longitudinally. It should, therefore, on contracting, shorten by about 6 inches, that is by about one-third of its fleshy length of 18 inches. If you measure on your own extended limb the distance between the points of origin and insertion of the Sartorius, and then while sitting down, approximate the insertion as close to the origin as possible, and measure again, you will find that the distance has been reduced by 6 inches. This explains why the Sartorius, which is the longest muscle in the body, requires so long a fleshy belly and why it needs a loose sheath in which to shorten and to lengthen.

When origin and insertion are approximated, the hip joint will be found to be flexed, abducted, and laterally rotated; the knee joint to be flexed and medially rotated. The limbs are brought into the position that the tailor (L. sartor = a tailor) traditionally assumes when at work.

Nerves. The Sartorius is supplied by the femoral nerve in its upper third.

It is commonly pierced by the intermediate and medial branches of the femoral cutaneous nerves and constantly by the patellar branch of the saphenous nerve.

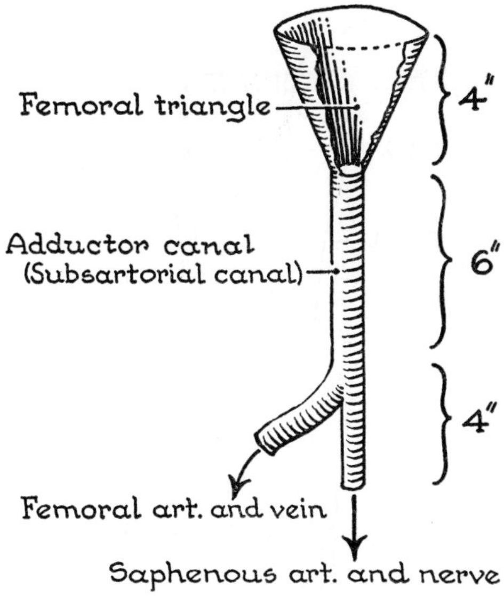

FIG. 413. The femoral "trough" and subsartorial "tunnel" and its two outlets.

Walls of the Adductor Canal. The adductor (subsartorial) canal is a V-shaped trough with medial and lateral sloping walls, closed over with Sartorius.

The muscles of the lateral sloping wall of this long trough are: Iliopsoas, Vastus Medialis, and Rectus Femoris. They are supplied by the femoral nerve.

The muscles of the medial sloping wall of the trough are five in number. They are **adductors** and, with the exception of the Pectineus, are supplied by the obturator nerve. Three of them (the Adductores Pectineus, Longus, and Gracilis) have a continuous curved origin from the pubic bone (*fig. 414*).

»» The *Pectineus* arises by fleshy fibers from the superior ramus of the pubis just in front of the pecten pubis and from the pectineal ligament. This origin extends from the iliopectineal eminence laterally to the pubic tubercle medially; the tendon of the *Longus* arises from the body of the pubis for ¾ of an inch medial to the tubercle, to be succeeded by the aponeurosis of the *Gracilis*, which being 2" wide extends down the margin of the pubic arch.

These three adductor muscles spread out fanwise as they descend to their aponeurotic insertions. As a result, the Brevis appears in

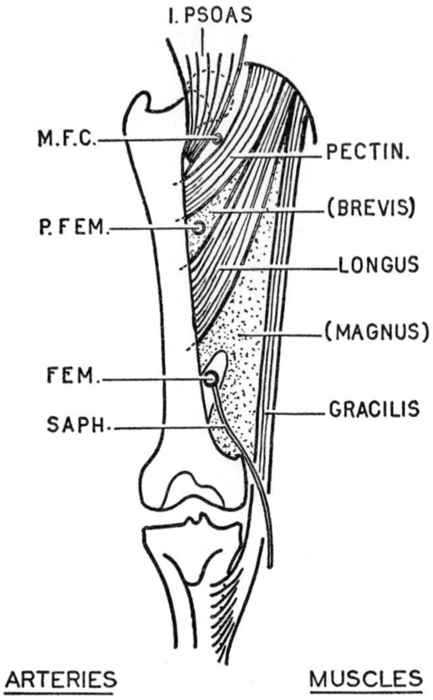

FIG. 414. The muscles posterior to the femoral and saphenous arteries. Three adductor muscles spread fanwise to their insertions. Arteries course between them.

the interval between Pectineus and Longus; the Magnus appears between Longus and Gracilis (*fig. 414*). The Gracilis is inserted into the medial surface of the tibia deep to the Sartorius, and it lies immediately behind the Sartorius as the two cross the medial femoral condyle. The Magnus descends as far as the adductor tubercle (*fig. 435*).

Contents of the Adductor Canal

The Femoral Artery and its branch, the Saphenous Artery. The course of these may be mapped out by a line joining the mid-inguinal point to the adductor tubercle. The upper two-thirds of this line maps out the course of the femoral artery, the lower third that of the saphenous artery. The femoral artery becomes the popliteal artery by passing through a gap or hiatus in the insertion of the Magnus 4 inches above the adductor tubercle. Here fleshy fibers of the Vastus Medialis prevent the artery from coming into direct contact with the femur. The saphenous artery becomes cutaneous at the medial side of the knee (*fig. 414*).

The Nerve to Vastus Medialis accompanies the femoral artery far into the canal, clinging to its muscle, the muscle of the lateral wall (*fig. 409*).

The Saphenous Nerve accompanies the femoral artery through the femoral triangle and adductor canal; then it accompanies the saphenous artery to the surface, and thereafter it accompanies the great saphenous vein through the leg, running behind it, and ending half way along the medial border of the foot.

»» The saphenous nerve, like the saphenous artery outcrops on to the surface between femoral nerve territory and obturator nerve territory, the representative muscles being the Sartorius and the Gracilis.

Note on Comparative Anatomy. In certain mammals the saphenous nerve, artery, and vein are companion structures that emerge from the canal and pass down the medial side of the leg to the foot. In man all three are present, but only the nerve persists in the old route. The artery is but a small branch that ends subcutaneously below the medial condyle. The vein is peculiar in man in not following the artery and nerve into the adductor canal to end in the distal part of the femoral vein, but in extending up the thigh and creating for itself a hole (saphenous opening) in the deep fascia through which it gets access to the proximal part of the femoral vein. True, it still sends a communicating branch via the old route to the lower end of the femoral vein.

Structures Entering the Adductor Canal from the Femoral Triangle:

1. The femoral artery and vein.
2. The profunda artery and vein.
3. The nerve to the Vastus Medialis.
4. The saphenous nerve.

The Structures Leaving the canal are:

1. The femoral artery and vein.
2. The saphenous nerve, artery, (and communicating vein).

The femoral vein lies medial to the femoral artery at the base of the femoral triangle, behind it at the apex of the triangle, and lateral to it where it passes through the opening in the Adductor Magnus into the popliteal fossa. Throughout, the two vessels are so firmly bound together in a common sleeve that the one cannot move without the other. The profunda artery and vein (or veins), almost as large as the femoral vessels themselves, soon disappear through the gap between Pectineus and Adductor Longus.

Internervous Line between the motor territories of the femoral and obturator nerves: an incision made from one end of the femoral artery to the other divides no motor nerve. The saphenous nerve will be cut and, more superficially, the medial cutaneous nerve of the thigh, but these are sensory nerves.

Regions of the Thigh

»» THEORETICALLY, the thigh may be regarded as divided into four regions, each separated from its neighbor by an intermuscular septum, and each containing a group of muscles and their nerve (*fig. 415*). The *anterior region*, supplied by the femoral nerve, would contain the flexors of the hip and also the extensors of the knee; the *posterior region*, supplied by the sciatic nerve, would contain the extensors of the hip and also the flexors of the knee; the *medial region*, supplied by the obturator nerve, would contain the adductors of the hip; and the *lateral region*, supplied by the superior gluteal nerve, would contain the abductors of the hip.

ACTUALLY, this scheme is departed from in the following main respects: Of the three abductors, all of which are supplied by the sup. gluteal nerve, two (Glutei Medius et Minimus) do not descend beyond the greater trochanter, while the third, the Tensor Fasciae Latae, spans the femur and gains attachment to the front of the lateral condyle of the tibia and to the side of the patella by means of the **iliotibial tract.**

It falls to the three remaining groups to surround the femur. This they do, but unequally. The anterior muscles envelop and monopolize the shaft of the femur, except along its posterior border which alone is free and available to the medial and posterior muscles and to all intermuscular septa. The attachments of the muscles to this restricted border are necessarily aponeurotic; hence, the roughness of the border and its name—the *linea aspera*.

In addition to the iliotibial tract, six muscles in all pass from the hip bone to the tibia or fibula; that is to say, they span the femur but they find no accommodation on it. Of these six, one belongs to the medial group, two to the anterior group, and three to the posterior group (*fig. 409—hatched muscles*).

Quadriceps Femoris

Of the *femoral nerve group* of muscles (Iliopsoas, Pectineus, Sartorius, and Quadriceps Femoris) the *Quadriceps Femoris* remains to be described. The four heads of this very powerful muscle are the Rectus Femoris and the 3 Vasti (Medialis, Lateralis, and Intermedius). Of these the Rectus arises from the ilium; the 3 Vasti arise from the shaft of the femur.

This enormous muscle is inserted into a small area of bone, namely, to the intermediate part of the tuberosity of the tibia and to the two diverging lines ascending from it; so, it follows that the insertion must be tendinous. Where the tendon plays across the front of the lower end of the femur a sesamoid bone, the *patella*, is developed. The portion of the tendon distal to the patella is called the *ligamentum patellae.*

The Iliopsoas acts on the hip joint, the Vasti on the knee joint, the Rectus on both hip and knee.

The **Rectus Femoris** (*fig. 408*) has a tendinous origin, which is practically coextensive with, and is immediately superficial to, the iliac attachment of the iliofemoral ligament of the hip joint, both being attached to the anterior inferior iliac spine and to the acetabular margin for an inch behind it. There is a slight interval between the spinous and acetabular origins of the Rectus which are known as the *straight* and *reflected heads* (*fig. 495*).

The tendinous insertion of the Rectus is to the upper border of the patella; some fibers, however, pass across the front of the patella and join the ligamentum patellae.

Structure. Though the Rectus Femoris and the Sartorius arise close together and are inserted close together, their courses, actions, and internal structures, are very different.

Sartorius was discussed on p. 369.

The Rectus Femoris assists in extending the knee joint by pulling on the patella. The patella can make an excursion of about 2 inches—this you can decide on your own limb—so, the fibers of the Rectus require to

FIG. 415. The regions of the thigh; theoretical and actual

be only 4–6 inches long. They arise from the front of the tendon of origin, diverge from each other in bipennate manner, turn round the borders of the muscle, and end behind in the tendon of insertion. By this arrangement the Rectus increases the number of its fibers and therefore its power. The Rectus also assists in flexing the hip joint; and next to the Iliopsoas is its most powerful flexor.

Internervous Line between the motor territories of the femoral and gluteal nerves: If an incision is made vertically downward from the anterior superior spine, the Sartorius may be pulled medially, the Tensor Fasciae Latae laterally, and the anterior inferior spine exposed; thereafter the Glutei Medius et Minimus may be pulled backward, the Rectus and Iliacus forward, and the hip joint exposed. The posterior branch of the lateral cutaneous nerve of the thigh and branches of the lateral circumflex vessels will be encountered, but no motor nerve crosses this line.

The **Three Vasti** clothe the shaft of the femur.

Origins. The Vastus Intermedius arises by fleshy fibers from the anterior and lateral aspects of the femur. No muscle arises from the medial aspect, but the Vastus Medialis overlies it. The Vasti Lateralis et Medialis arise largely by aponeuroses from the lateral and medial lips, respectively, of the linea aspera as well as from the upward and downward continuations of these lips: that is to say, above they diverge along the gluteal and spiral lines, pass below the greater and lesser trochanters, and meet in front on the intertrochanteric line. Below they diverge along the lateral and medial supracondylar lines, from which and from the intermuscular septa they arise.

Insertions. The Vasti Medialis et Lateralis are continuous at their insertions, and they occupy a plane between the Rectus Femoris and Vastus Intermedius, and all four are inserted into the base of the patella. The Medialis is attached to the upper two-thirds of the medial border of the patella and only slightly to the base (*fig. 501*), while the Lateralis is attached to the remainder of the base and only slightly to the lateral border. The fibers of the medial and lateral Vasti are obliquely set and numerous. They arise largely by aponeuroses and are inserted by aponeuroses.

The most distal fibers of origin of the Intermedius, called the *Articularis Genu*, are attached to the synovial capsule of the knee joint. Their purpose is to retract the capsule during extension of the knee, thereby preventing it from being nipped.

»» When the fleshy fibers of the Vastus Medialis are detached from the tendon of the Adductor Magnus and from the medial intermuscular septum, the articular branch of the *descending genicular artery* is seen descending on the septum to reach the joint.

Distribution of the Femoral Nerve (L. 2, 3, 4). Motor Distribution (*fig. 491* on p. 428). *The Psoas* is supplied by the roots of the femoral nerve. *The Iliacus* is supplied while in the iliac fossa. *The Pectineus* is supplied near its lateral border by a twig that passes behind the femoral sheath. *The Sartorius* and *Rectus Femoris* are both supplied by one or two branches which enter them from 3–6 inches from the anterior superior spine. *The Three Vasti* receive short, stout branches at their upper ends. The Vasti Medialis and Lateralis both receive one long branch also, which enters their respective anterior borders near their middles.

»» The long branch to the Medialis runs along the lateral border of the femoral artery far into the adductor canal. A slender twig runs on the femur along the medial border of the Intermedius and supplies the *Articularis Genu*. The long branch to the Lateralis follows the descending branch of the lateral femoral circumflex artery along the anterior border of the muscle and serves as a guide to it.

Cutaneous Distribution (*fig. 400* and p. 362).

Vascular Distribution. A few filaments of the external iliac nerve (sympathetic) extend beyond the inguinal lig. on to the femoral artery, but the femoral and profunda femoris arteries and their branches receive their main nerve supply from the femoral nerve and its branches (Mitchell).

Articular Distribution. The femoral nerve is distributed to the hip joint and to the knee joint, thus:

»» To the capsule of the *hip joint* via the nerve to Pectineus and either the nerve to Rectus Femoris or the nerve to Vastus Lateralis or directly from the femoral nerve itself.

To the capsule of the *knee joint* via the nerves to the three Vasti and the saphenous nerve (E. Gardner).

CHAPTER 24

HIP BONE AND GLUTEAL REGION

HIP BONE

The hip bone (os coxae) is a large irregular bone. The hip bones of opposite sides articulate with each other in front at the *symphysis pubis* and with the sacrum behind at the *sacro-iliac joints*. The two hip bones, the sacrum, and the coccyx make up the bony pelvis. When studying these bones, you should hold them in correct orientation (p. 319).

COMPONENT PARTS. The hip bone is composed of 3 elements—ilium, ischium, and pubis. These three meet at the cup-shaped cavity for the head of the femur, called the *acetabulum*, and are there united by a triradiate cartilage until the 16th year, when fusion takes place (*fig. 416*).

The *ilium* is a flat bone; the *ischium* and the *pubis* are irregular V-shaped bones. The ilium lies above the acetabulum; the ischium behind and below; the pubis in front and below. The site of fusion of ilium with pubis is conspicuous in front of the pelvic brim as the *iliopubic* (iliopectineal) *eminence* (*fig. 352*).

The pubis and ischium surround a large oval foramen, the *obturator foramen;* this lies below the acetabulum and is closed by a membrane, the *obturator membrane*, except in its upper part where the obturator vessels and nerve escape from the pelvis.

SURFACES. The hip bone, considered as a

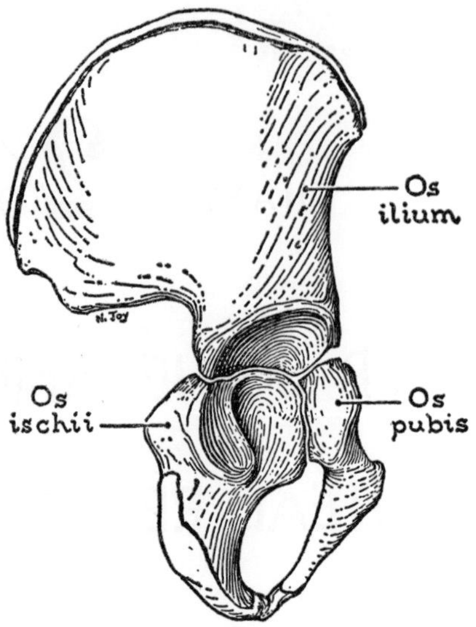

FIG. 416. A young hip bone

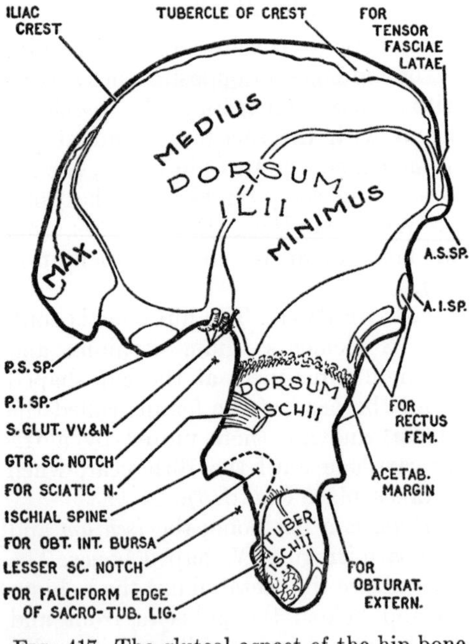

FIG. 417. The gluteal aspect of the hip bone

whole, has two surfaces—an inner and an outer:

1. The inner or pelvic surface is described on pages 315–318.

2. The outer surface is divisible into three areas—gluteal, adductor, and acetabular.

Gluteal Aspect (POSTEROLATERAL ASPECT) OF THE HIP BONE (*fig. 417*). This aspect is wide above and is there bounded by

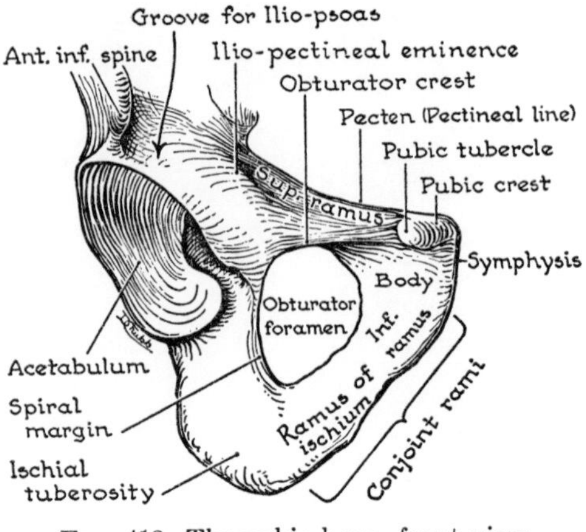

FIG. 418. The pubic bone, front view

the whole length of the iliac crest. Below, it is narrow and forms the lower part of the ischial tuberosity. It can be subdivided into three obviously different areas: (1) above is the fan-shaped *dorsum ilii*, (2) below is the rough, oval *ischial tuberosity*, and (3) between these is a large quadrate area, the *dorsum ischii*. The dorsum ischii is bounded laterally by the acetabular margin, and medially by the margin of the greater sciatic notch which ends below in the ischial spine.

Adductor Aspect (ANTERIOR ASPECT) OF THE HIP BONE (*fig. 418*). This comprises the anterior aspect of the part of the bone that surrounds the obturator foramen, exclusive of the acetabulum. It is limited above by the pelvic brim; medially by the symphysis pubis and medial border by the pubic arch; postero-inferiorly by the lateral border of the ischial tuberosity, and posterosuperiorly by the iliopubic eminence. It comprises the entire outer aspect of the pubic bone and ischial ramus and the lateral surface of the ischial tuberosity (i.e., the pillar of bone supporting the acetabulum). It affords origin to the adductor muscles.

Acetabulum, described with the hip joint on page 432.

ILIUM

The Ilium (os ilium) is fan-shaped, the handle of the fan being below, where the ilium joins the ischium and pubis.

The upper border, the *iliac crest*, is arched and is sinuous like the clavicle of its own side, being convex forward in its medial part, concave in its lateral. And, like the clavicle, it is subcutaneous, palpable throughout, crossed by cutaneous nerves, but not by muscles (there being no Platysma here); so, the deep fascia is attached to it. In front it ends in the rounded *anterior superior iliac spine*, behind in the sharp *posterior superior iliac spine*, and from its most lateral point (about 2½″ behind ant. sup. spine) a broad *tubercle* projects downward. The pull of the abdominal muscles creates a traction epiphysis along the whole length of the crest (*fig. 416*).

The *anterior border* extends from the ant. sup. spine to the iliopubic eminence and is deeply concave. The concavity is subdivided into two nearly equal lesser concavities by the *anterior inferior spine*, which, being the site of attachment and pull of the straight head of the Rectus Femoris, possesses an epiphysis.

The *posterior border* extends from the posterior superior spine toward the ischial spine. It is subdivided into two unequal concavities by the *posterior inferior spine* which lies at the posterior limit of the sacro-iliac joint. The upper concavity is slight; the lower one forms the upper part of the V-shaped *greater sciatic notch.*

Of the two surfaces of the ilium, (1) the *inner* is divided into an iliac fossa, a tuberosity, an auricular surface, and an area within the pelvis minor (true pelvis) (*figs. 352 and 358*); and (2) the outer is the *dorsum ilii.*

The **Dorsum Ilii,** or gluteal surface of the ilium, is concavo-convex (*fig. 417*), conforming with the iliac fossa, tuberosity, and auricular surface of the inner surface (*fig. 358*).

The dorsum ilii is crossed by three curved, tubercular lines (posterior, anterior, and inferior gluteal lines) which arch upward and forward from the greater sciatic notch. They subdivide the dorsum into four areas: the areas for the Gluteus Minimus and Gluteus Medius are extensive and equal; the restricted area remaining behind the Medius is for the Gluteus Maximus and slightly for the sacrotuberous ligament; the restricted area between the Minimus and the acetabular margin has a broad linear marking for the iliofemoral ligament and reflected head of the Rectus Femoris.

ISCHIUM

The Ischium (os ischii) has 3 parts—a *body* adjoining the ilium, a *tuberosity* projecting downwards from the body, and a *ramus* passing from the tuberosity upward and forward below the obturator foramen.

The **Body** is triangular on cross-section and has three surfaces separated by three borders. The borders are parts of the margins of the (1) obturator foramen, (2) acetabulum, and (3) greater sciatic notch. The surfaces are: (1) medial or pelvic (p. 317), (2) lateral or acetabular (p. 432), and (3) posterior or gluteal.

The Gluteal Surface of the Body or Dorsum Ischii lies between the acetabular margin and the greater sciatic notch. Above, it is continuous with the dorsum ilii; below, with the ischial tuberosity. Together with a small portion of the ilium just above it, it forms a quadrate, slightly convex surface. This the sciatic nerve crosses (*fig. 421*).

The **Tuberosity or Tuber Ischii** is the oval mass of bone from which the hamstrings arise; so it is rough and has an epiphysis (*fig. 429*). The upper part of its medial border has playing across it the tendon of the Obturator Internus; so, it is smooth, concave, covered with a *bursa*, and forms part of the lesser sciatic notch. The lower part of the medial border is a rough line or crest for the attachment of the sacrotuberous ligament. Its lateral border gives fleshy origin to the Quadratus Femoris. Between this and the acetabulum there is a deep groove occupied by fat and the Obturator Externus.

»» It is convenient and sufficient to extend the term "tuberosity" to the entire mass of bone between the tuberosity, as described above, and the obturator foramen—that is, to the pillar of bone below the acetabulum. The tuberosity, in this sense, is triangular on cross-section and has three surfaces—tuberosity proper (posterior), pelvic (medial), and adductor (lateral). Its chief functions are to support the body when sitting and to give origin to the hamstring muscles.

The Sciatic Notches, greater and lesser, extend from the posterior inferior iliac spine to the ischial tuberosity. They are separated from each other by a beak-shaped process, the *ischial spine.* This gives attachment to the sacrospinous ligament, and it is grooved below by the tendon of the Obturator Internus. The sacrotuberous and sacrospinous ligaments convert the sciatic notches into sciatic foramina (*fig. 361*).

The **Ramus of the Ischium** (*fig. 418*) is a flattened bar that unites with the inferior ramus of the pubis to form the *conjoint ramus* of the ischium and pubis. The conjoint rami of the two sides constitute the *pubic arch.*

PUBIS

The pubis (os pubis) (*fig. 418*) has 3 parts —a *body* lying medially, a *superior ramus* passing upwards and laterally from the body, and an *inferior ramus,* descending from the body and forming part of the pubic arch.

The **Body** is a squarish plate which articulates with its fellow at the symphysis. It has two surfaces: (1) a smooth *inner* or pelvic which supports the bladder and faces postero-superiorly, and (2) an *outer* which faces antero-inferiorly and is rough for tendinous attachments.

Its *medial border or symphyseal surface* is elliptical, covered with cartilage, and $1\frac{1}{2}''$ deep. Its *upper border* is the pubic crest; this is about 1″ long, smooth and thick; it ends laterally at the *pubic tubercle.* Its *lateral border* is the margin of the obturator foramen. Lateral to the pubic tubercle the body is continuous with the superior ramus; below the level of the symphysis it is continued as the inferior ramus.

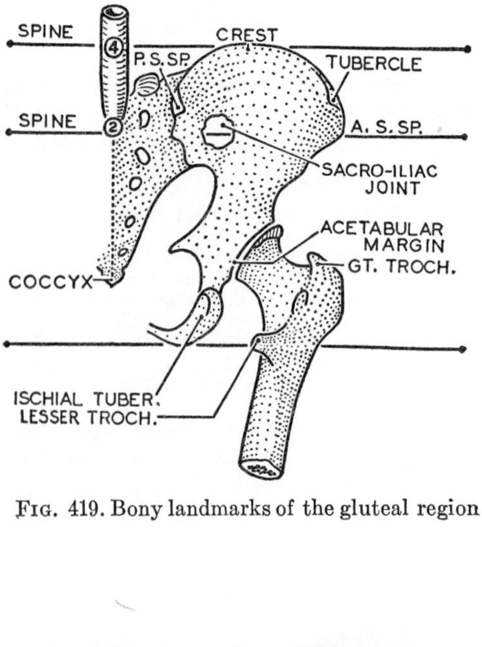

FIG. 419. Bony landmarks of the gluteal region

The **Superior Ramus** is a three-sided pyramid whose apex is continuous with the body at the pubic tubercle. The base forms a fifth of the articular part of the acetabulum and there fuses with the ilium and ischium, the site being marked above by the iliopubic (iliopectineal) eminence.

»» The three borders are formed by two lines that diverge from the pubic tubercle: (1) one, the *pecten pubis* (pectineal line), is the arc of the pelvic brim that extends from the pubic tubercle to the iliopubic eminence —the reasons for its sharpness are given on page 317; (2) the other line is the spiral *margin of the obturator foramen.* This margin begins at the pubic tubercle outside the pelvis and ends near the iliopubic eminence inside. The two ends of the spiral bound the inferior grooved surface of the ramus and account for two borders. The segment of the spiral that extends from the pubic tubercle to the acetabulum is a strengthening bar, called the *obturator crest.*

The three surfaces are—pelvic, pectineal, and inferior. The pelvic surface is separated from the pectineal surface by the pecten pubis; the pectineal surface is separated from the inferior surface by the obturator crest. The pectineal surface is triangular; it extends from pubic tubercle to iliopubic eminence; and it faces anterosuperiorly. The Pectineus arises from the whole length of the hinder part of this surface and overlies the anterior part. The inferior surface is the wide groove between the two ends of the spiral margin of the obturator foramen. In it run the obturator vessels and nerve.

The **Inferior Ramus of the Pubis** descends from the body for nearly an inch to join the ramus of the ischium, and fuse with it about the 8th year.

FUNCTION. See figure 356, page 320.

GLUTEAL REGION

Bony Landmarks (*fig 419*). The whole length of the *iliac crest,* including its anterior superior spine, tubercle, highest point, and posterior superior spine, is readily palpated because it is subcutaneous. The *tubercle* lies at the most lateral part of the crest, and, therefore, at the highest part visible from the front (*fig. 419*). The *anterior superior spine* is easily palpated. The *posterior superior spine* (or rather a flat elevation that lies a little above it and gives attachment to part of the sacrotuberous lig.) lies deep to a visible dimple. A line, or the edge of a folded towel, joining the highest points on the iliac crests crosses the *4th lumbar spine*, and is the guide to that spine.

A line joining the posterior superior spines crosses the *2nd sacral spine* and marks the bottom of the dural and arachnoid sacs with the contained cerebrospinal fluid. Produced laterally, this line obviously must cross about the *center of the sacro-iliac articulation*, because the auricular surface of the ilium articulates with the 1st, 2nd, and 3rd pieces of the sacrum and of these the 2nd is, of course, the middle (*fig. 350*).

The top of the *greater trochanter* lies a hand's breadth below the tubercle of the iliac crest (p. 359). A line drawn horizontally at the level of the ischial tuberosity crosses the *lesser trochanter* of the femur, and, as will appear later, indicates the interval between the borders of the Quadratus Femoris and Adductor Magnus.

As one does not sit on the lower end of one's vertebral column but on one's ischial tuberosities, it follows that the *coccyx* does not descend so far as the tuberosities. The tip of the coccyx is readily felt in the furrow between the buttocks about $1\frac{1}{2}''$ behind the anus.

Gluteus Maximus

This very coarse-grained muscle, with a thin fascial covering, is rhomboidal (*fig. 420*). It arises from the posterior superior spine and the tip of the coccyx, and from the available bony and ligamentous structures between these two points; namely, the portion of the dorsum ilii between the posterior gluteal line and the iliac crest, the back of the sacrotuberous ligament, and the back of the lower two pieces of the sacrum and the coccyx. [The upper three pieces of the sacrum are engaged in the sacro-iliac joint and, so, are not available.] When well developed the Gluteus Maximus spreads forward along the lateral lip of the iliac crest and, because there is no more unoccupied bone in the neighborhood, any further origin must be from adjacent fasciae; for example, the fascia covering the Gluteus Medius.

The lower border of the Gluteus Maximus extends from the tip of the coccyx across the tuber ischii and onwards to the shaft of the femur, which it reaches at the junction of its upper one-third and lower two-thirds. The tuberosity, though covered by the Maximus when you stand up, is uncovered when you sit down; i.e., you do not sit on your Gluteus Maximus; fleshy muscle fibers could not survive such abuse. There is a thick mass of stringy fibrous tissue between the tuberosity and the skin on which you rest when sitting, and in it a *bursa* may be embedded.

The upper border of this rhomboidal muscle runs from the post. sup. spine parallel to the lower border, passing about 1″ above the greater trochanter.

Insertion. One-quarter of the Gluteus Maximus—the deep portion of the lower half—is inserted into the gluteal tuberosity of the femur, whereas three-quarters end in a band-like aponeurosis which meets and joins a similar band-like aponeurosis of the Tensor Fasciae Latae, distal to the greater trochanter, to form the **iliotibial tract.** Now, the iliotibial tract descends between the circularly disposed layers of the fascia

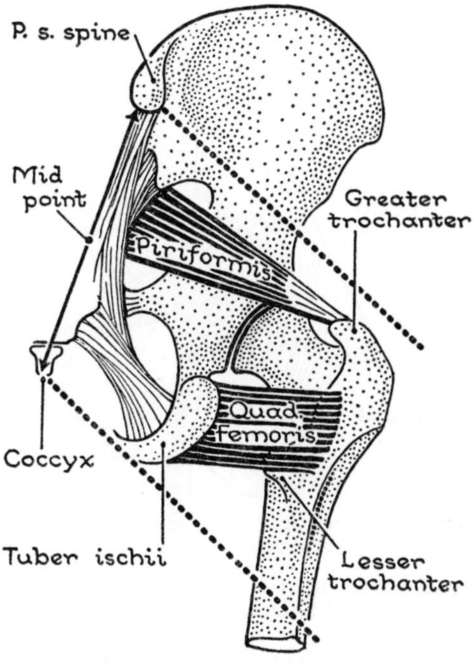

FIG. 420. To map Gluteus Maximus, Piriformis, and Quadratus Femoris. The lower border of the Piriformis is the key line of the gluteal region.

lata to be attached to the lateral condyle of the tibia well in front of the axis of the knee joint.

Owing to the fact that the tract is attached in front of the axis of the knee joint (*fig. 507*), it assists in maintaining the extended knee joint in the extended position.

» Of this you can easily satisfy yourself thus:—while sitting down with your limbs extended in front of you, raise your heel off the ground and by palpation note that the anterior border of the iliotibial tract, which runs longitudinally a finger's breadth behind the lateral border of the patella, becomes prominent and taut, only to become slack and indistinct again when your heel touches the ground once more.

Many fibers of the Maximus running in the iliotibial tract pass into the lateral intermuscular septum and thereby gain attachment to the linea aspera and to the lateral supracondylar line; hence, the lateral supracondylar line is so much better marked than the medial supracondylar line. Where the Gluteus Maximus plays across the hard, resistant surface of the greater trochanter, its fleshy fibers give place to an aponeurosis; and, intervening between that aponeurosis and the trochanter there must be a *bursa* (*fig. 427*). And between the aponeurosis and the fibrous origin of the Vastus Lateralis there is a *second bursa*.

» Vertical fibers of the fascia lata are continued upward, proximal to the greater trochanter, to be attached to the iliac crest between the ant. sup. spine and the tubercle; hence, the term, *iliotibial*. This upper part of the tract holds the aponeurosis of the Gluteus Maximus in position and it gives origin to the anterior part of the Gluteus Medius.

Nerve and Vessels (*fig. 421*). The inferior gluteal nerve and vessels enter the deep surface of the Maximus at its center. The superior gluteal artery also supplies it.

Functions. The Gluteus Maximus is the great extensor of the hip joint. As such, it is brought into action in rising from the sitting position, straightening from the bent to the erect position, walking upstairs, and running; but it is not required in gentle walking. It is also a lateral rotator.

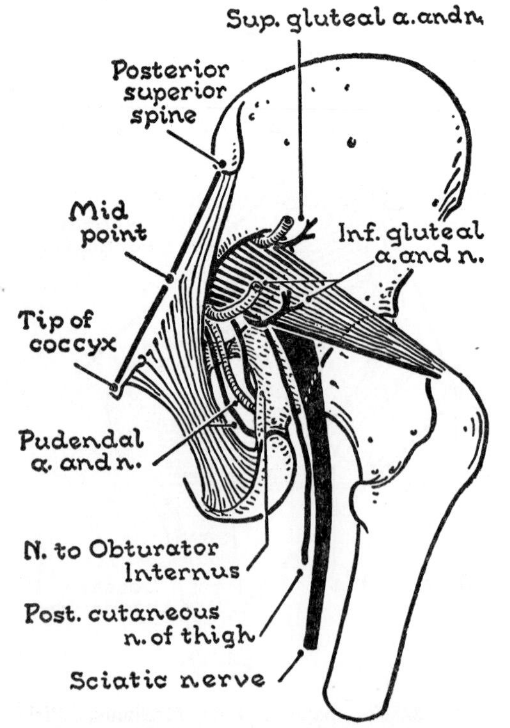

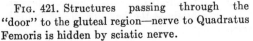

FIG. 421. Structures passing through the "door" to the gluteal region—nerve to Quadratus Femoris is hidden by sciatic nerve.

Structures Deep to Gluteus Maximus

The door through which all vessels and nerves pass, on leaving the pelvis to enter the gluteal region, is the **greater sciatic foramen.**

The **Piriformis** itself enters by this door and almost fills it. It occupies a *key position.*

Some vessels and nerves enter the gluteal region above the Piriformis; others enter below the Piriformis—but they all enter through the greater sciatic foramen. Some, having entered, at once disappear through the lesser sciatic foramen (*fig. 421*).

The Obturator Internus enters by the lesser foramen; it is the only structure that does so. Some small vessels taking part in a feeble anastomosis behind the neck of the femur (the cruciate anastomosis) reach the region between the local muscles (*fig. 438*).

At the Lower Border of Piriformis these nerves and vessels enter (*fig. 421*):

5 {
- Sciatic nerve, which hides nerve to Quadratus Femoris.
- Inferior gluteal nerve.
- Inferior gluteal vessels.
- Posterior cutaneous nerve of thigh.

3 {Nerve to Obturator Internus.
Internal pudendal vessels.
Pudendal nerve.

The lateral 5 of these are in contact with the dorsum ischii. The medial 3 cross the ischial spine (or the sacrospinous lig.), pass through the lesser sciatic foramen, whereupon the nerve to the Obturator Internus enters its muscle while the pudendal vessels and nerve run forward in the pudendal canal (*fig. 337*).

At the Upper Border of Piriformis these enter:

2 {Superior gluteal vessels.
Superior gluteal nerve.

Evidently, the Piriformis serves as the guide to the structures in this region. Fortunately, its lower border is easily and accurately indicated on the skin surface by a line joining a point midway between the posterior superior spine and the tip of the coccyx to the top of the greater trochanter. It is the **"key line" of the region.**

Given this line you can easily gauge the position of the upper border of the Piriformis.

»» Therefore, in this line either separate the fleshy fibers of the Gluteus Maximus until you meet areolar tissue or cut through its aponeurosis until you strike bone (*fig. 422*).

1. The simpler and surer way is to cut boldly right through its aponeurosis and subaponeurotic *bursa* on to the greater trochanter; then to slacken the muscle by imitating its action (i.e., by extending and laterally rotating the thigh) so that a finger can be inserted through the incision and moved about in this plane until it encounters the nerve and vessels to the Maximus (inf. gluteal) entering at its center. The finger will be deep to the Maximus and to the Maximus only, for it is the only muscle to cross the trochanter.

2. Alternatively, you may separate the fleshy fibers until the inevitable areolar tissue comes into view—inevitable, because the fleshy fibers of the Maximus are longer than, and take a different direction from, the fibers of the deep muscles. A layer of areolar tissue, perhaps laden with fat, must lie interposed between the Maximus and the deeper muscles in order to allow them independent movement.

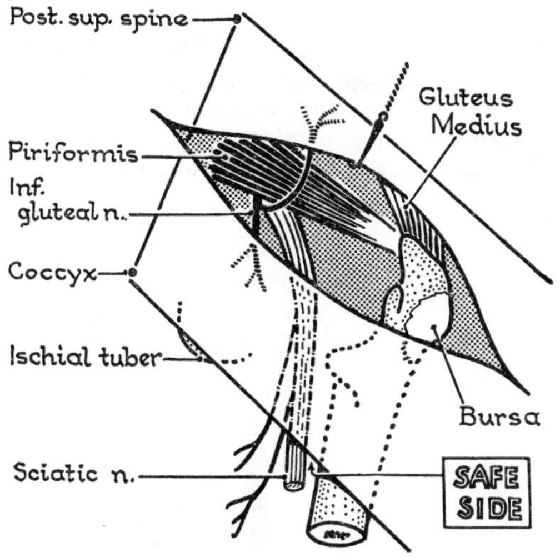

FIG. 422. Incision to be made through the Gluteus Maximus to expose the "key line" of the region.

The **Sciatic Nerve** appears from under cover of the lower border of the Piriformis and, curving inferolaterally, descends between the tuber ischii and the greater trochanter. Indeed, when the limb is in the anatomical position (i.e., toes pointing forward) the lateral border of the nerve lies midway between the medial aspect of the tuberosity and lateral aspect of the trochanter. Here the nerve is covered by the Gluteus Maximus, and not until it reaches the lower border of the Maximus does it become subfascial (*fig. 423.1*).

The sciatic nerve has two sides: a side of danger and a side of safety (*fig. 423*). This is due to the double fact (1) that it is the most lateral structure in the region and (2) that its branches spring from its medial side—because they supply the muscles (the hams) that arise from the tuber ischii. Therefore, work on its lateral side, disregarding some arterial twigs which here describe a *cruciate*

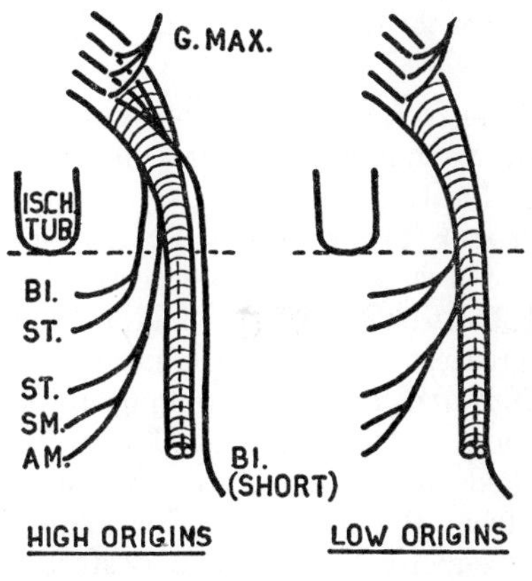

FIG. 423. Principle: Sides of safety and sides of danger.

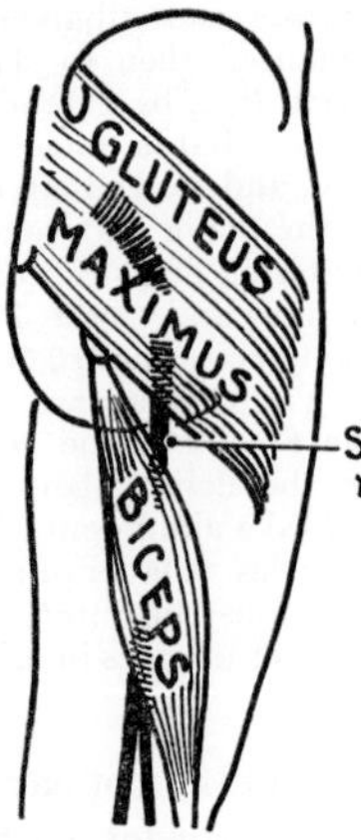

FIG. 423.1. Posterior relations of sciatic nerve

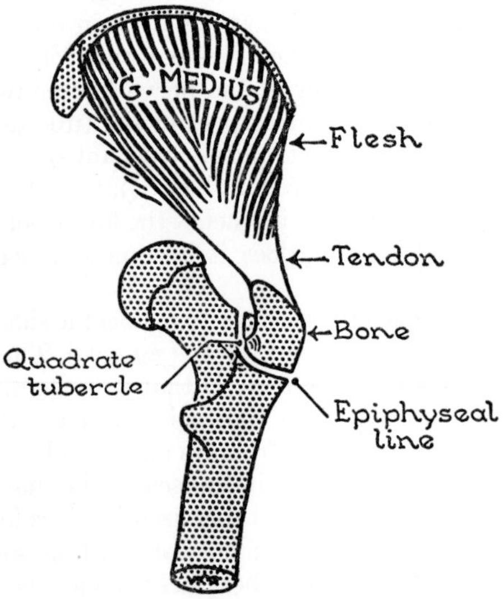

FIG. 424. The fleshy, tendinous, and bony portions of the Gluteus Medius.

anastomosis (i.e., twigs from sup. and inf. gluteal, med. and lat. femoral circumflex, and 1st perforating aa.) (*fig. 438*).

Greater Trochanter (*fig. 424*). The tendons of five muscles are inserted into this great traction epiphysis, and of these the two greatest are (1) the Gluteus Minimus, which is attached to its oblong anterior aspect, and (2) the Gluteus Medius, which is attached diagonally across its lateral aspect from the antero-inferior angle to the posterosuperior angle. The posterosuperior angle is free and may be regarded as the ossified part of the tendon of the Medius.

The Medius is mostly responsible for the shape of the trochanter, causing it to be curved upward, medially, and backward and to have a free, posterior border.

The tendon of the Piriformis is attached to the middle of the upper border; the tendon of the Obturator Internus and its Gemelli to the front of the upper border; and the tendon of the Obturator Externus to a pit on the medial surface.

The Intertrochanteric Crest (*fig. 403*) has the appearance of crystallized fibers. Its upper part is the posterior border of the greater trochanter, and is an extension of the Gluteus Medius. The lower part ascends from the lesser trochanter and is an extension of the Psoas tendon.

The two parts meet at a rounded eminence, the **quadrate tubercle,** to which the upper fibers of the Quadratus Femoris are attached. The quadrate tubercle is, however, not the creation of the Quadratus, whose insertion is largely fleshy, but corresponds to the epiphyseal line, which passes through it and follows the rough ridge that separates the greater trochanter from the shaft of the femur both laterally and in front. [The aponeurosis of the Vastus Lateralis is in part responsible for this ridge.]

The Superior Gluteal Nerve, accompanied by the superior gluteal vessels, passes through the greater sciatic foramen, above the Piriformis, in contact with the bony angle of the foramen, and it runs with the deep branches of these vessels between the Gluteus Medius and Gluteus Minimus.

The superior gluteal nerve supplies the 3 abductors and medial rotators of the hip

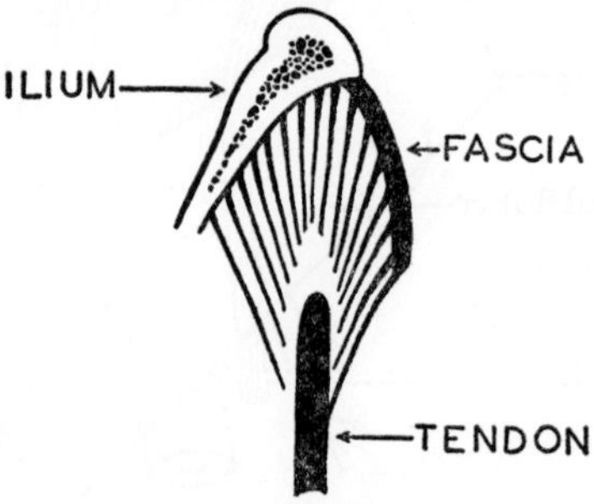

FIG. 424.1 The anterior part of the Gluteus Medius arises largely from the fascia covering it; hence, the thickness of this fascia.

joint, viz., the Gluteus Medius, Gluteus Minimus, and Tensor Fasciae Latae. These three muscles monopolize the entire dorsum ilii—save for two small areas: one at the post. sup. spine for the Gluteus Maximus; the other above the acetabular margin for the iliofemoral lig. and the reflected head of the Rectus Femoris (*fig. 417*).

Glutei Medius et Minimus. The Glutei Medius and Minimus are fan-shaped. They are but two parts of a single muscle; they are common in shape, in direction of fibers, in actions, and in nerve supply. Their attachments are contiguous and their anterior borders are commonly fused—or rather, undifferentiated. There is, therefore, no necessity for areolar tissue or fat between them, though a little is commonly present.

The anterior part of the Medius receives many fibers from the overlying fascia (*fig. 424.1*). Hence, the fascia covering the Medius is thick; whereas that covering the Maximus is thin.

The Tensor Fasciae Latae is about 6″ long and on transverse section is apt to be mistaken for the Sartorius, but it is thicker and is 1¼″ wide. It arises by a short aponeurosis from the ant. sup. iliac spine and from the adjacent part of the outer lip of the iliac crest. It is directed downward and slightly backward. The iliotibial tract is its aponeurosis of insertion (pp. 377–378).

The Quadratus Femoris (*figs. 420* and *427*). This oblong muscle may be regarded as an upward extension of the Adductor Magnus. The Quadratus arises from the lateral border of the tuber ischii. It is inserted into the quadrate tubercle of the femur and the line descending from that tubercle to the insertion of the Adductor Magnus at the level of the lesser trochanter.

»» The nerve to the Quadratus arises from the front of the sciatic nerve and descends on the ischium to the Quadratus. To display it, the sciatic nerve must be retracted and the Obturator Internus and the Gemelli divided. It supplies a twig to the hip joint and to the Gemellus Inferior.

The Obturator Internus and the Gemelli constitute a tricipital muscle that occupies the interval between the Quadratus and the Piriformis. The *Obturator Internus* arises from almost the entire pelvic surface of the hip bone below the level of the obturator nerve. It takes a right angled turn as it passes through the lesser sciatic foramen (*fig. 353*). From this you will infer that its anterior surface is here tendinous and that it is separated from the margin of the foramen by a *bursa*. Its tendon passes across the the posterior surface of the ischium and capsule of the hip joint to reach the most anterior facet on the upper border of the greater trochanter.

Of the *Gemelli*, the Superior arises from the upper margin of the lesser foramen (ischial spine); the Inferior from the lower margin of the lesser foramen (ischial tuberosity); and their fleshy fibers are inserted into the respective borders and the super-

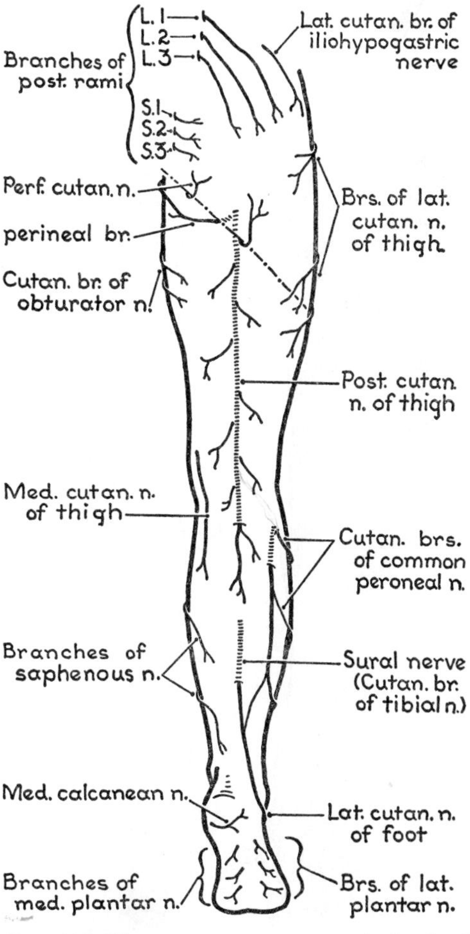

FIG. 425. The cutaneous nerves of the back of the lower limb.

ficial aspect of the tendon of the Obturator Internus.

The Two Gluteal Arteries, superior and inferior, are responsible for supplying the entire gluteal region, their largest branches being, of course, *muscular*. The superior artery sends a nutrient artery to the ilium via the foramen on the anterior gluteal line. The inferior artery sends a branch to the *sciatic nerve*, and *cutaneous branches* to accompany twigs of the posterior femoral cutaneous nerve down the thigh and around the lower border of the Maximus.

The Posterior Cutaneous Nerve of the Thigh is purely sensory (*fig. 425*). It lies first medial to the sciatic nerve and then behind it, clinging to Gluteus Maximus. Its *gluteal branch* turns round the lower border of the Maximus. Its *perineal branch* passes forward lateral to the tuber ischii to supply the scrotum or labium majus (*fig. 336*), while the main nerve continues down the middle of the thigh subfascially to end on the calf.

Dermatomes, see figure 425.1.

The Five Regions of the Back of the Limb. The back of the lower limb is divided for descriptive purposes into five regions (*fig. 426*):

1. The Gluteal Region.

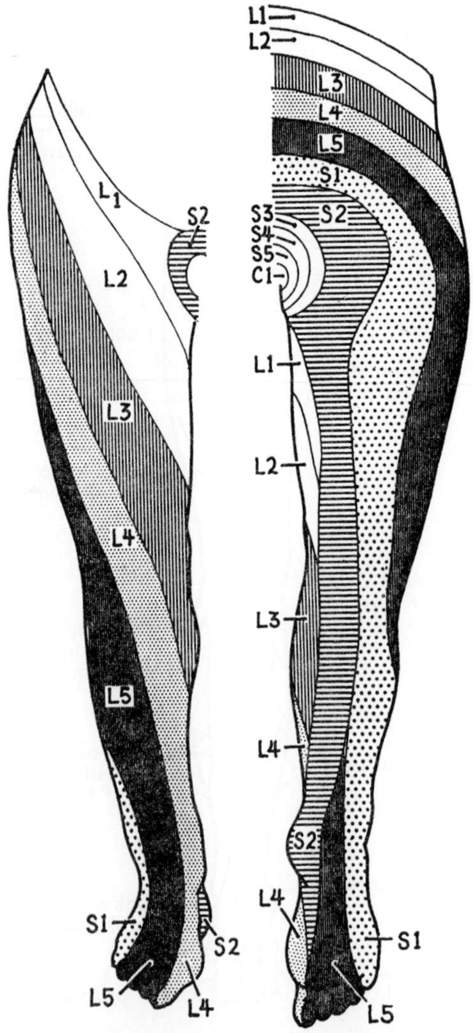

FIG. 425.1. Dermatomes of the lower limb

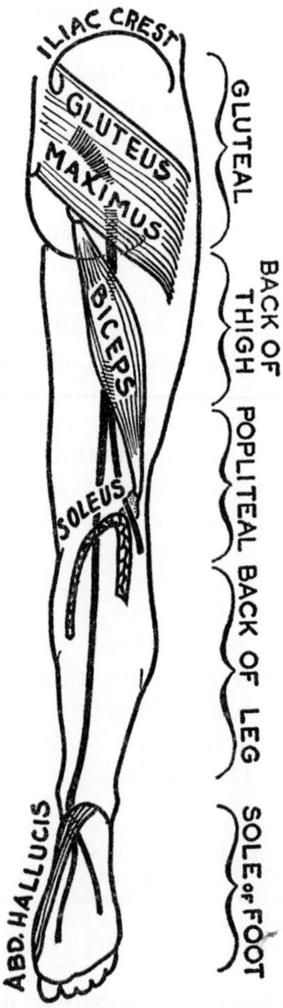

FIG. 426. The five regions of the back of the limb, the four muscles separating them, and the tibial division of the sciatic nerve running deep to the muscles.

2. The Back of the Thigh.
3. The Popliteal Fossa.
4. The Back of the Leg.
5. The Sole of the Foot.

The iliac crest limits the gluteal region above; the lower border of the Gluteus Maximus separates it from the back of the thigh; the lower border of the long head of the Biceps (beyond the point at which it crosses the Semimembranosus) separates the back of the thigh from the popliteal fossa; the upper border of the Soleus separates the popliteal fossa from the back of the leg; and the upper border of the Abductor Hallucis separates the back of the leg from the sole of the foot.

Now, passing deep to all four of these muscles—Gluteus Maximus, Biceps (long head), Soleus, Abductor Hallucis—is the tibial division of the sciatic nerve.

CHAPTER 25

BACK AND MEDIAL REGION OF THIGH

BACK OF THIGH AND POPLITEAL FOSSA

The Deep Fascia (fascia = a bandage) of these regions is composed of circularly arranged fibers, which, though not dense, are very strong, especially behind the knee where to the hamstrings they play the part of a restraining or retinacular ligament. It follows that a transverse incision made through the deep fascia will close of its own accord and that a longitudinal one will gape.

The **Floor of the Region** is flat (*fig. 427*). *The Floor of the Back of the Thigh* has two parts: (1) a part medial to the linea aspera formed by the Adductor Magnus, which is covered with the thin posterior intermuscular septum; and (2) a part lateral to the linea aspera formed by the Vastus Lateralis,

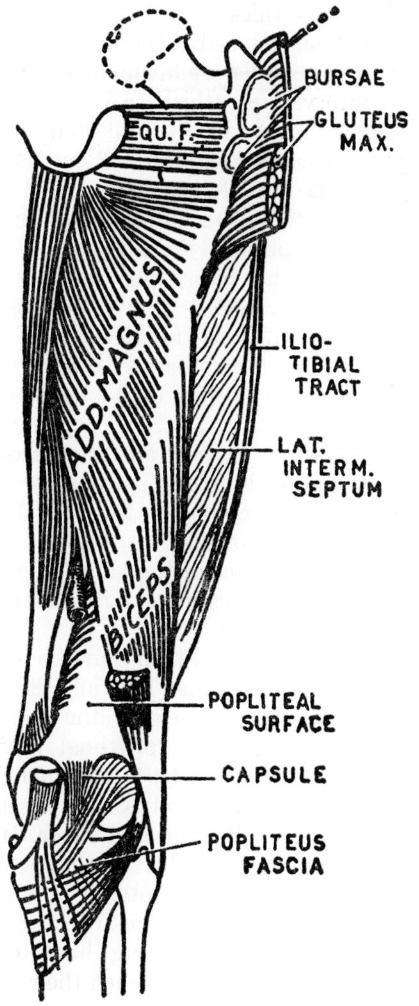

FIG. 427. The "floor" of the back of the thigh and popliteal fossa.

which is covered with the strong lateral intermuscular septum. The lateral septum is strong because it carries fibers from the iliotibial tract to the linea aspera (p. 378).

The Floor of the Popliteal Fossa (*fig. 427*) is formed from above downwards by: (1) the popliteal surface of the femur, overlaid with fat (*fig. 433*); (2) the posterior part of the capsule of the knee joint, and (3) the Popliteus fascia (fascia covering Popliteus), which is strong medially where it acts as an aponeurosis of insertion for the Semimembranosus.

Contents of the Back of the Thigh:

1. The hamstring muscles—
   Long head of Biceps Femoris
   Semitendinosus
   Semimembranosus
2. The short head of Biceps Femoris.
3. The sciatic nerve.
4. The posterior cutaneous nerve.
5. Certain vessels.

The Hamstring Muscles. A hamstring muscle may be defined as one that (1) arises from the tuber ischii (2) is inserted into one or other of the two bones of the leg, and (3) is supplied by the tibial (or medial) division of the sciatic nerve. The hamstring muscles, therefore, span the femur but gain no attachment to it.

They extend the hip joint and flex the knee joint, but they cannot do both fully at the same time, e.g., you cannot extend your knee fully while your hip is fully flexed. This is due to the relative shortness of the hamstrings.

On this basis of classification, the short head of the Biceps cannot be counted with the hamstrings. Nor can the part of Adductor Magnus that arises from the tuber ischii, is supplied by the tibial division of the nerve, and helps to extend the hip joint (*fig. 428*).

When the knee is flexed and the foot is

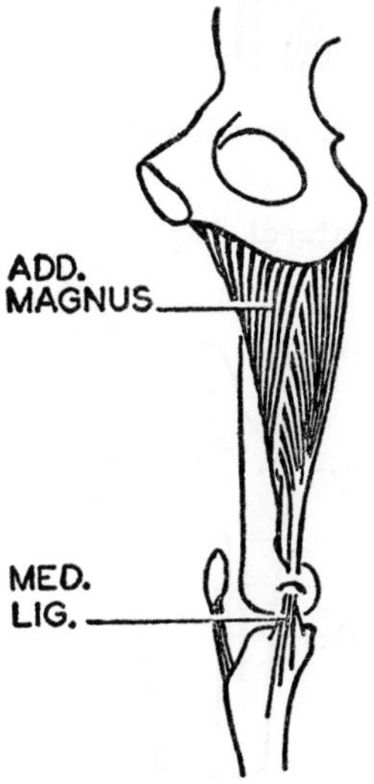

FIG. 428. The ischial part of the Adductor Magnus.

raised from the ground, the Biceps, being attached to the head of the fibula, rotates the leg laterally; the Semimembranosus and Semitendinosus, being attached to the medial side of the tibia, rotate the leg medially.

INSERTIONS. *The Biceps* is inserted by tendon into the head of the fibula just in front of its apex. It covers the attachment of the lateral ligament of the knee, a bursa intervening, and it partly blends with the deep fascia on the front of the leg (*fig. 428.1*). *The Semitendinosus* is inserted by aponeurosis into the medial surface of the tibia deep to the Sartorius and Gracilis (*fig. 428.2*). It is also extensively attached to the deep fascia of the leg. *The Semimembranosus* is inserted

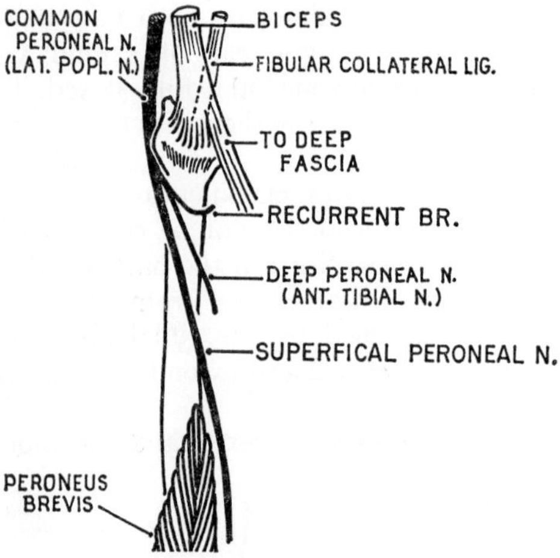

FIG. 428.1. Insertion of Biceps Femoris

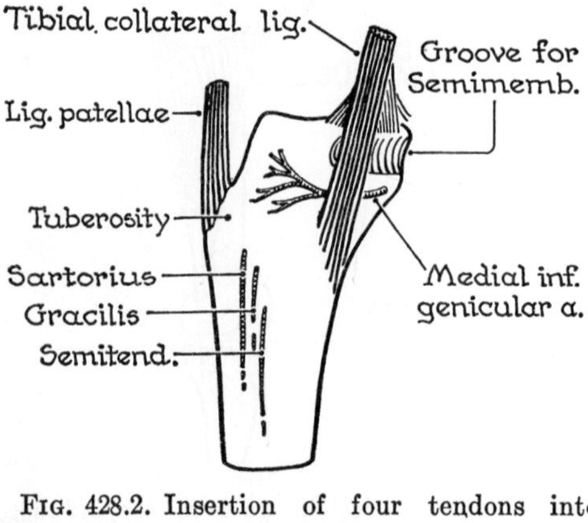

FIG. 428.2. Insertion of four tendons into tibia.

(1) by a very thick tendon into the horizontal groove on the medial condyle of the tibia, deep to the medial ligament of the knee, a bursa intervening; (this is a reflected insertion, comparable to the reflected head of origin of Rectus Femoris); (2) by the Popliteus fascia into the soleal line; and (3) by tendon into the posterior surface of the tibia above the Popliteus (*fig. 461*).

ORIGINS. The hamstring muscles arise from the **tuber ischii** (ischial tuberosity).

Tuber Ischii. This tuberosity is of much smaller surface area than a transverse section of the fleshy bellies of the ham muscles that spring from it, so it follows that their origins must be fibrous. On this account a traction epiphysis might reasonably be expected; and an epiphysis there is. (Cross-sections, see *fig. 437*.)

The precise origins of the hamstrings from the tuber ischii, though not important, are shown in figure 429.

Moulding. The Semimembranosus is membranous in its proximal half and fleshy in its distal half; conversely, the Semitendinosus is fleshy in its proximal half and tendinous in its distal half. The membrane of origin of the Semimembranosus resembles the blade of a hollow ground razor. Into it the rounded fleshy belly of the Semitendinosus fits and neither interferes with the action of the other. Of necessity, the Semimembranosus and the long head of the Biceps cross each other to reach their respective insertions.

Short Head of Biceps Femoris. The

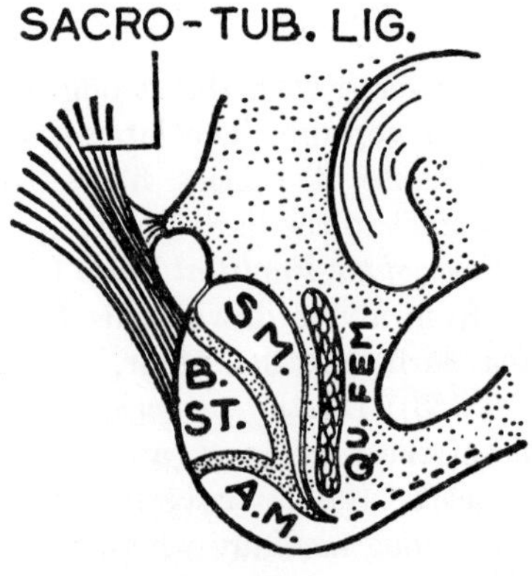

FIG. 429. The tuber ischii and the structures attached to it.

Liszt – Orpheus

short head arises by fleshy fibers from the linea aspera and from the upper part of the lateral supracondylar line and adjacent part of the lateral intermuscular septum (*fig. 427*). It belongs to the same muscular sheet as the Gluteus Maximus.

It is supplied by a branch of the lateral or peroneal division of the sciatic nerve. If you dissect this branch upward, you will find that it arises from the back of the sacral plexus in common with the nerve to the Maximus (*fig. 423*).

It is inserted with the long head.

Hybrid or Composite Muscles. *The Biceps* clearly is an amalgamation of two muscles. The long head, supplied by the tibial division of the sciatic nerve, belongs developmentally to the front of the limb; the short head, supplied by the peroneal division, belongs to the back.

The Adductor Magnus also is an amalgamation of two elements. The part arising from the pubic arch is supplied by the obturator nerve, whereas the part arising from the tuber ischii is supplied by the tibial division of the sciatic nerve.

The Pectineus, supplied by the femoral and obturator nerves, likewise, belongs to the composite class.

Nerves and Arteries

The Sciatic Nerve is readily accessible deep in the angle between the Gluteus Maximus and the long head of the Biceps, because it is there subfascial (*fig. 426*).

Posterior Relations. Above the angle, the Maximus covers the nerve; below the angle, the Biceps (long head) covers it.

Termination. Deep to the Biceps (long head), at a variable distance above the popliteal fossa, the sciatic nerve separates into its two terminal branches—*tibial and common peroneal nerves* (med. and lat. popliteal nerves). (Gk. perone = L. fibula = a pin or skewer.)

The two divisions are merely bound together by loose areolar tissue and may be separated from each other right up to the sacral plexus. In fact, the peroneal division sometimes pierces the Piriformis instead of passing below it with the tibial division (*fig. 430*).

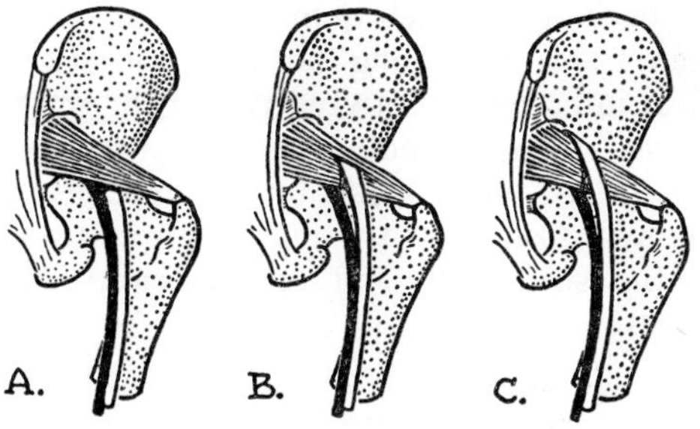

FIG. 430. The relationship of the sciatic nerve to the Piriformis: *A.*, in 87.5 per cent of 420 limbs both the tibial and the peroneal division of the sciatic nerve passed below the Piriformis; *B.*, in 12 per cent the peroneal division passed through the Piriformis; *C.*, in 0.5 per cent (i.e., in both limbs of one subject) it passed above.

»» The peroneal division and the femoral and gluteal nerves supply the morphological back of the limb. The tibial division and the obturator nerve supply the morphological front, as a consideration of their ultimate distributions to the sole and dorsum of the foot will suggest.

The sciatic nerve runs midway between the tuber ischii and the greater trochanter, and it is reasonable and correct to suppose that the branches it supplies to the hamstrings spring from its ischial or medial side (*fig. 423*).

AXIOM: The side from which a motor nerve leaves its parent stem is constant—it leaves from the side nearest the muscle it supplies—but the level at which it leaves is variable: it may arise high or it may arise low. Nerve trunks, therefore, have sides of danger and sides of safety or of relative safety; a side on which it is safe to dissect or operate and a side on which work must be done with caution.

The nerve to the short head of the Biceps springs from the lateral side of the sciatic nerve (peroneal division).

ANTERIOR RELATIONS. The immediate anterior relations of the sciatic nerve throughout its course are: the dorsum ischii (half an inch), Obturator Internus and Gemelli, Quadratus Femoris, and Adductor Magnus. It is separated from the hip joint by the Inferior Gemellus and upper part of the Quadratus Femoris.

Posterior Cutaneous Nerve of the Thigh (*fig. 425*). The posterior cutaneous nerve (S. 1, 2) travels down the middle of the back of the thigh immediately under the deep fascia (the long head of the Biceps alone intervening between it and the sciatic nerve) and gives cutaneous twigs to right and to left, but it is not until it reaches the popliteal fossa that the main stem outcrops on the surface to end on the calf. (Also p. 382.)

»» In cases where the sciatic nerve is divided by the Piriformis into peroneal and tibial divisions, the posterior cutaneous nerve derives a root from each. Hence, the nerve indicates the dividing line between the anterior and posterior cutaneous areas of the thigh (*fig. 425.1*).

Arteries to back of thigh (see page 394).

Popliteal Fossa

(*Back of the Knee*)

The anterior wall or floor of the fossa is described on page 385 (*fig. 427*).

The fossa is a potential one before dissection is undertaken. This is owing to the circular arrangement of the fibers in the deep fascia that bandage the structures together. The fossa is composed of an upper and a lower triangle, one being above the level of the knee joint and the other below it.

The sides of the upper triangle are: *medially*, the Semimembranosus overlaid by the Semitendinosus; *laterally*, the short head of the Biceps overlaid by and fused with the long head (*fig. 431*). These embrace

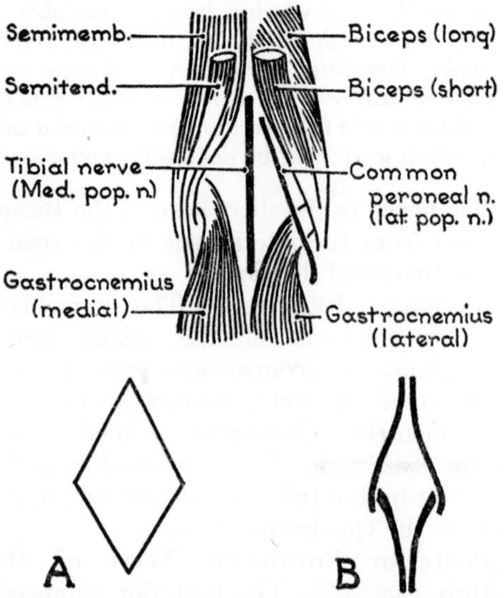

FIG. 431. Boundaries of the popliteal fossa.

the sides of the lower triangle, formed by the two heads of the Gastrocnemius, together with the unimportant and variable Plantaris which lies laterally.

Palpable Tendons. While sitting down—one knee being bent to a right angle or less and the fingers of each hand passed behind the respective sides of this knee—intermittently press the heel backward against the leg of the chair, noting that: (1) laterally, the *Biceps tendon*, which is here the most dorsal structure, becomes taut and is easily followed to the head of the fibula; do not mistake it for the prominent posterior border of the *iliotibial tract* which runs a full finger's breadth in front of it; (2) medially, the *Semintendinosus tendon* is felt to spring, like a bow string, backward from the lateral edge of the *Semimembranosus*.

The *Biceps tendon* becomes taut on lateral rotation of the leg (knee being flexed); it is the only lateral rotator. of Knee

Contents. The fossa contains four important structures:

1. tibial nerve (med. popliteal n.).
2. and 3. popliteal artery and vein.
4. common peroneal nerve (lat. popliteal n.).

The Tibial Nerve (L. 4, 5, S. 1, 2, 3), which is the larger of the two terminal branches of the sciatic nerve, descends to the ankle where it divides into the medial and lateral plantar nerves.

The section of the tibial nerve above the upper border of the Soleus is also known as the **medial popliteal nerve** and the section below it as the **posterior tibial nerve.**

The tibial nerve passes from the upper to the lower angle of the diamond-shaped popliteal fossa, bisecting it longitudinally.

BRANCHES.

1. *Motor:* to local muscles—Plantaris, medial and lateral heads of Gastrocnemius, Soleus, and Popliteus. Of these five muscles only one, the medial head of the Gastrocnemius, lies medial to and therefore receives its nerve from the medial side of the tibial nerve, whereas four lie lateral (*fig. 432*). See *Axiom* on page 387. Deep to it are the popliteal vessels (*fig. 432*).

2. *Articular* } See below under common peroneal nerve.
3. *Cutaneous* }

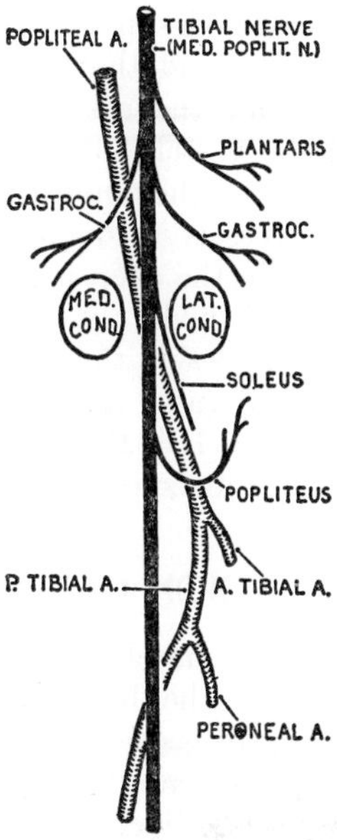

FIG. 432. The tibial nerve (med. popliteal n.)—its side of safety and side of danger and its relation to the bowed arterial stem.

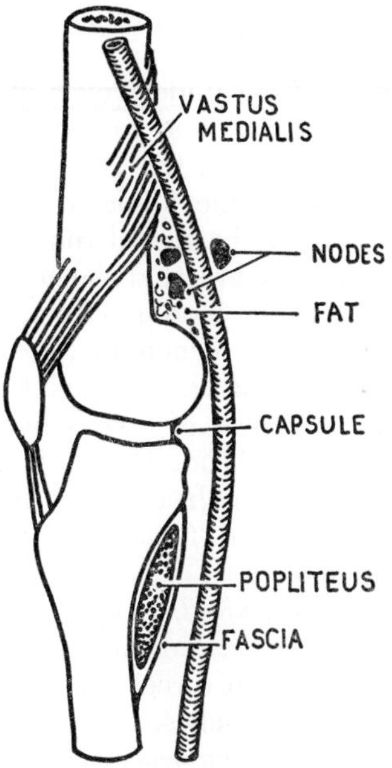

FIG. 433. Anterior relations of popliteal artery, diagrammatic, medial view.

Relationships. As the tibial nerve and the popliteal vessels are passing through the narrow ravine bounded on each side by a femoral condyle and a head of the Gastrocnemius, they are crowded one behind the other; the order from the surface to the floor of the fossa being retained—nerve, vein, artery. The customary order—nerve, artery, vein—does not hold here.

»» The relative positions of the popliteal artery, popliteal vein, and tibial nerve may be surmised from the following: (1) The femoral vessels pass down the front of the thigh to become the popliteal vessels at the hiatus in the Adductor Magnus. The sciatic nerve passes down the back of the thigh, and its medial branch, the tibial nerve, on meeting the popliteal vessels, continues on a posterior plane. (2) The femoral vein, which was seen to lie behind its artery at the apex of the femoral triangle, retains its posterior relationship in the popliteal fossa. (3) The vessels enter the popliteal fossa from the medial side and therefore, are at first medial to the nerve, which enters at the upper angle and bisects the space.

The vein and nerve cross the artery very gradually from lateral to medial side, and *figs. 432* and *461* give the reason why. It is that the nerve continues on a straight course, whereas the arterial stem curves laterally towards the neck of the fibula, being pulled there by the anterior tibial and peroneal arteries. Later, as the posterior tibial artery, the arterial stem resumes its course on the medial side of the tibial nerve.

The Popliteal Artery divides into its two terminal branches, the *anterior and posterior tibial arteries*, at the upper border of the Soleus or, which amounts to the same thing, at the lower border of the Popliteus. The arteries below the knee are accompanied by venae comitantes; so, the *popliteal vein* begins as an assembly of veins. The popliteal artery and vein are inseparably bound together in a fascial sheath, and are held in place by the prehensile genicular vessels (*fig. 438*). Between the hiatus and the Adductor Magnus, the artery is separated from the femur by a film of Vastus Medialis (*fig. 433*); between the hiatus and the intercondylar notch, it is separated from the bone by fat. Distally, it lies on the articular capsule and the Popliteus fascia (*figs. 433* and *427*).

BRANCHES: *Terminal:* ant. and post. tibial arteries.

Collateral: (1) Cutaneous, (2) muscular, and (3) articular (*fig. 438*, and p. 394).

The Common Peroneal Nerve (Lat. popliteal n.) (L. 4, 5, S. 1, 2), separates from the tibial nerve about the middle of the thigh and ends lateral to the neck of the fibula by dividing into two terminal branches —*deep peroneal* and *superficial peroneal* *nerves* (ant. tibial and musculocutaneous nn.).

It appears from under cover of the long head of the Biceps and follows the Biceps tendon. As, however, the Biceps is inserted into the head of the fibula and the nerve winds behind the head and round the neck of the fibula, it follows that the nerve recedes gradually from the tendon, crossing in turn: the Plantaris, Gastrocnemius (lateral head), and the back of the head of the fibula where a thin fleshy veneer of Soleus partly separates it from the head. Hence, it is readily palpated behind the head where it is felt to slip from under the fingertips drawn horizontally across it.

BRANCHES. *Terminal:* Deep and superficial peroneal nerves (*fig. 428.1* and p. 400).

Collateral: (1) no direct motor branches; (2) the sensory branches.

Articular and *cutaneous branches* spring from both popliteal nerves. The tibial nerve (med. popliteal n.) supplies three articular or genicular branches (superomedial, inferomedial, and middle). The common peroneal nerve (lat. popliteal n.) also supplies three (superolateral, inferolateral, and anterior tibial recurrent). They accompany the corresponding vessels.

The cutaneous branch of the tibial nerve, called the *sural nerve*, lies with the small saphenous vein in the furrow between the two bellies of the Gastrocnemius. It is joined by a cutaneous branch of the common peroneal nerve (called the *communicating peroneal nerve*) which travels distally on the lateral head of the Gastrocnemius.

The Small (Short) **Saphenous Vein** is the lateral continuation of the dorsal venous arch of the foot. It passes below and then behind the lateral malleolus and is accompanied in its course by the sural nerve. It pierces the popliteal fascia and, after dividing, ends in the popliteal and profunda femoris veins.

A large superficial branch connects it to the upper end of the great saphenous vein.

Lymph Nodes. The most distal nodes in the limb are small nodes beside the anterior and posterior tibial vessels. They intercept deep lymph vessels, drain into the popliteal nodes, and have little practical value.

The popliteal nodes, five or six in number, lie in the fat around the popliteal vessels. They receive all the distant deep lymph vessels and the vessels from the knee joint. The efferents from the popliteal nodes follow the femoral vessels through the adductor canal and end in the deep inguinal nodes.

One popliteal node, lying deep to the popliteal fascia, beside the small saphenous vein, drains the same superficial territory as the small vein. It is the most distal node in the limb draining superficial tissues.

MEDIAL REGION OF THE THIGH

Muscles. The muscles of the medial or adductor region of the thigh arise collectively from the anterior aspect of the hip bone between iliopubic eminence above and the tuber ischii below (including the superior ramus, body, and inferior ramus of the pubis; the ramus and tuber ischii, and the obturator membrane) (*fig. 434*).

From this compact area of origin they spread out fanwise to a linear insertion that extends from the trochanteric fossa of the femur above to the upper part of the medial surface of the tibia below (*fig. 435*). Their

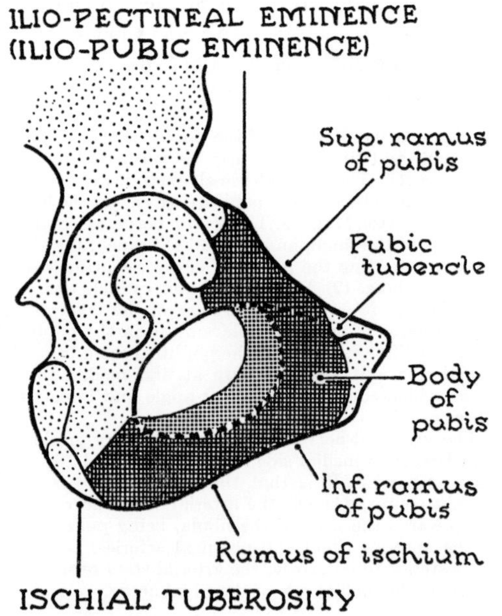

FIG. 434. The compact area of origin of the Adductors.

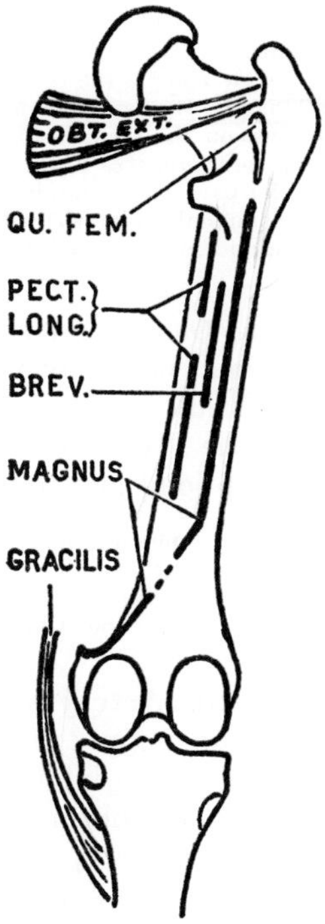

FIG. 435. The linear insertion of the Adductors extends from the trochanteric fossa above to the medial surface of the tibia below.

chief actions are those of adduction and lateral rotation of the hip joint. The obturator nerve innervates them. The profunda femoris and obturator arteries nourish them. They form a much larger mass than the Coracobrachialis, which is their homologue in the upper limb.

The large muscle mass consists of the following six individual muscles: Pectineus, Adductor Longus, Gracilis, Adductor Brevis, Adductor Magnus, and Obturator Externus.

»» **Origins** (*fig. 495*). The *Pectineus, Adductor Longus,* and *Gracilis* have a continuous curvilinear origin that extends from the iliopubic eminence to the ramus of the ischium. The origin of the Pectineus, which is fleshy, meets that of the Adductor Longus, which is tendinous at the pubic tubercle; the Gracilis has an aponeurotic origin. If the thigh be abducted, the tendon of the Longus becomes prominent and palpable and acts as a guide to the pubic tubercle. The *Adductor Brevis, Adductor Magnus,* and *Obturator Externus* arise by fleshy fibers in successively deeper, overlapping planes. (Some of the upper fibers of Adductor Magnus occasionally form a separate muscle, *Adductor Minimus.*)

Insertions. The restricted and therefore fibrous insertions of these six muscles are (*fig. 435*):

The *Pectineus:* to the line running from lesser trochanter toward the linea aspera.

The *Adductor Longus:* to almost the whole length of the linea aspera in line with the Pectineus. (Between the Pectineus and Longus the Brevis can be seen.)

The *Gracilis:* to the medial surface of the tibia below the level of the tuberosity and between the insertions of the Sartorius and Semitendinosus. The Gracilis is the only muscle of the adductor group to cross the knee joint. (Between the Longus and Gracilis the Magnus can be seen) (*fig. 414*).

The *Adductor Brevis:* to the lower part of the pectineal line and upper part of the linea aspera Its upper part is overlapped by the Pectineus; its lower part by the Adductor Longus.

The *Adductor Magnus:* to the linea aspera, extending upward on to its lateral continuation (the gluteal tuberosity), and downward on to its medial continuation (the medial supracondylar line). In fact, it extends from the level of the lesser trochanter above, where it is continuous with the Quadratus Femoris, to the adductor tubercle below. The portion of the Adductor Magnus that arises from the tuber ischii does so by tendon, belongs developmentally to the hamstring muscles, is supplied by the tibial nerve, and is inserted mainly by a palpable tendon into the adductor tubercle and into the supracondylar line just above it.

The *Obturator Externus:* to the trochanteric fossa. It passes below the head of the femur and grooves the back of the neck. It will be studied with the hip joint.

If you would be familiar with the shaft of the femur and the relations of the profunda artery and obturator nerve, you must spend some minutes defining the fibrous insertions of these muscles.

Three Hernial Sites. Observe (1) that the Pectineus and the superior ramus of the pubis would separate a femoral hernia from

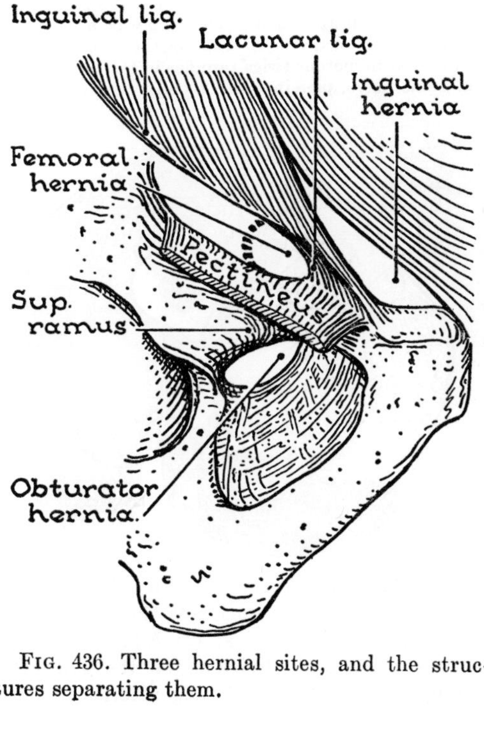

FIG. 436. Three hernial sites, and the structures separating them.

an obturator hernia; (2) that the inguinal ligament would separate a femoral hernia from an inguinal hernia (*fig. 436*).

Nerves and Vessels

The Obturator Nerve (*fig. 491* on p. 428), like the femoral nerve, is derived from L. 2, 3, and 4, and like it, has a motor, a cutaneous, an articular, and a vascular distribution.

On passing through the obturator foramen the nerve divides into an anterior and a posterior division which supply the six adductors (*fig. 437*).

» The anterior division passes over the upper border of the Obturator Externus and descends in front of the Adductor Brevis to supply (Pectineus sometimes), Longus, Brevis, and Gracilis. The posterior division pierces the upper border of the Obturator Externus, descends behind the Brevis, and supplies the Obturator Externus and the Magnus (in part).

The sole *Cutaneous Branch* is the continuation of the nerve to the Gracilis. It reaches the surface about the middle of the thigh, where it supplies a restricted area, but it may extend to the calf.

Articular Branches supply both the hip joint and the knee joint, thus:

» *The Branch to the Hip* springs from the main nerve within the obturator canal. (There may be a second br. from the anterior division.) This (or these) passes laterally and as numerous twigs ramifies in the pubofemoral lig. Some fibers, piercing with blood vessels, reach the synovial membrane and also run along the lig. of the head of the femur.

The Branch to the Knee is the continuation of the n. to Adductor Magnus. It pierces the Magnus above the hiatus, runs down on the medial side of the popliteal vessels, gives *vascular branches* to them and ramifies in the posteromedial part of the fibrous capsule. The anterior division commonly joins the articular br. of the saphenous nerve and so may reach the knee joint. (E. Gardner.)

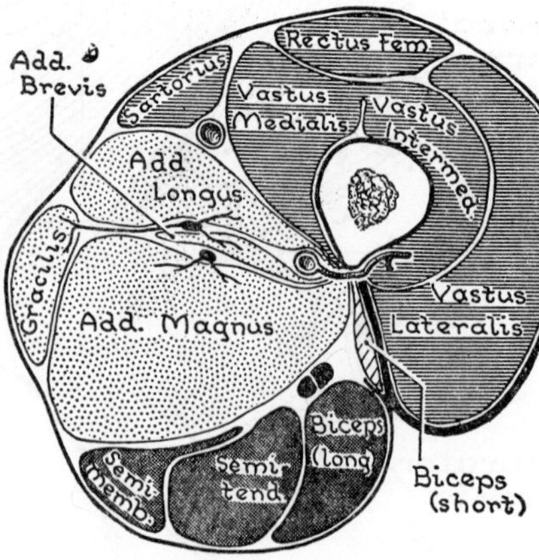

FIG. 437. Cross section of the thigh.
(1) Adductor Longus separates the femoral and profunda femoris arteries; (2) Adductor Brevis separates the two divisions of the obturator nerve; and (3) the perforating arteries hug the bone.

An *Accessory Obturator Nerve* sometimes follows the medial border of the Psoas over the superior ramus and rejoins the main nerve deep to the Pectineus. It may supply a twig to the hip joint and to the Pectineus.

» *Note:* (1) that the femoral and profunda femoris arteries are separated by the Adductor Longus, and (2) that the anterior and posterior divisions of the obturator nerve are separated by the Adductor Brevis (*figs. 437* and *438*).

The Obturator Artery assists the profunda artery to supply the adductors. Arising either from the internal iliac artery or as "an accessory obturator" from the inferior epigastric artery, it traverses the obturator canal, enters the thigh, and divides into anterior and posterior branches which skirt the circumference of the obturator foramen. The posterior branch and the medial femoral circumflex a. each send an *articular* twig through the acetabular foramen to the acetabular fossa. There they ramify in the synovial pad of fat, and one or other traverses the lig. of the head of the femur (lig. teres, *fig. 496*, and p. 435).

The Profunda Femoris Artery usually arises from the lateral side of the femoral artery about 1½ inches below the inguinal lig. At the apex of the femoral triangle it lies behind the femoral vessels with its own vein. It passes through the gap between the insertions of the Pectineus and Adductor Longus, and descends first between the Longus and Brevis, then between the Longus and Magnus, and ends as the 4th perforating artery. It is closer to the bone than the femoral artery, and it lies in turn on the Iliacus, Pectineus, Adductor Brevis, and Adductor Magnus (*figs. 437* and *438*).

Distribution. Its various branches supply most of the *muscles* of the thigh; *articular branches* to the hip and knee joints; and a *nutrient* branch (or two) to the femur; and they effect numerous *anastomoses*. Its named branches are:

1. Lateral femoral circumflex,

2. Medial femoral circumflex,
3. 1st, 2nd, 3rd and 4th perforating,
4. Muscular (unnamed branches).

The **Lateral Femoral Circumflex Artery** is a large artery that runs laterally between the branches of the femoral nerve, deep to the Sartorius and Rectus Femoris, and divides into three branches. The *ascending* and *transverse* branches anastomose in the gluteal region, and they send branches along the front of the neck of the femur to the head. The large *descending* branch follows the anterior border of the Vastus Lateralis and anastomoses at the knee.

The **Medial Femoral Circumflex Artery** is in series with the four perforating arteries and with the terminal part of the femoral artery as they wind dorsally, around the medial side of the femur, either passing between the borders of muscles or else interrupting the attachments of muscles to the bone (*fig. 438*).

Distribution. (1) The chief duty of the medial circumflex a. is to supply the neck and head of the femur. And, in the macerated bone the foramina that receive the "osseous" branches appear large and slit-like above and behind the neck, and smaller and circular around the articular margin of the head. (2) An *articular* branch passes through the acetabular foramen with a branch of the obturator a. (p. 392). Other branches are (3) *muscular*, and (4) *anastomotic*.

»» The medial circumflex a. passes first between Psoas and Pectineus then between Obturator Externus and Adductor Brevis, and abuts against the Quadratus

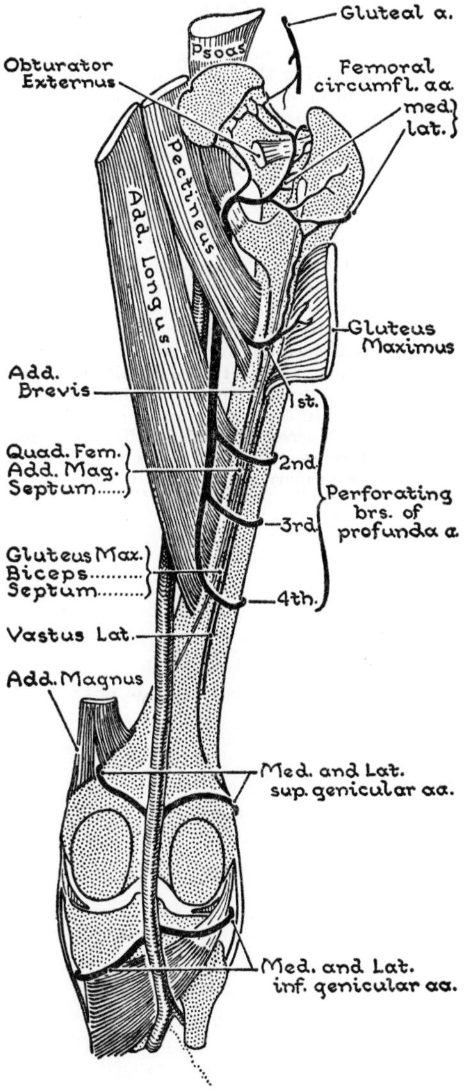

FIG. 438. The arteries of the thigh and knee, posterior view.

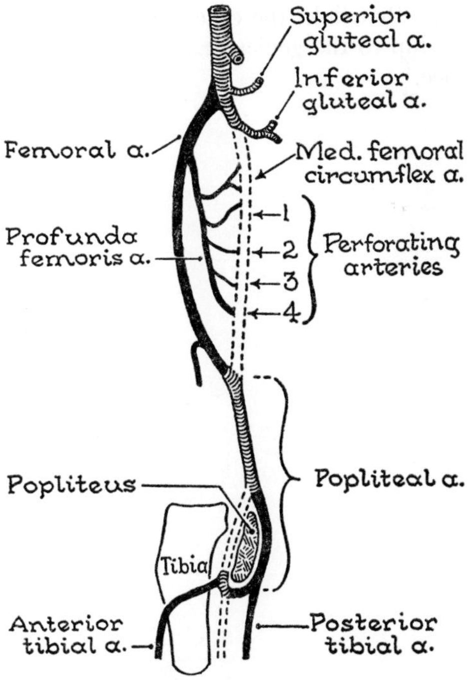

FIG. 439. Development of the main arterial trunk: (*hatched segments* are primary; *solid black* are secondary; *clear* disappear). (After Senior.)

Femoris. There it divides into (1) a transverse branch, which passes onward between the borders of the Quadratus and Adductor Magnus to anastomose with the transverse branch of the lateral femoral circumflex, and (2) an ascending branch, which passes upward deep to the Quadratus to anastomose with the inferior gluteal artery behind the neck of the femur.

The **Four Perforating Arteries** encircle the shaft of the femur, hugging it so closely that they must surely be torn, if the shaft is fractured. They interrupt the attachment of each muscle they encounter, as shown in *figs. 437–439.*

Distribution. The perforating arteries are essentially muscular in this most muscular of regions. Throughout their courses they send radiating branches to the adductors, hams, and other muscles whose paths they cross. The 2nd or 3rd perforating a. supplies the nutrient artery to the femur.

Anastomoses. The term *cruciate anastomosis* is applied to the union of the medial and lateral femoral circumflex arteries with the inferior gluteal artery above and the 1st perforating artery below. At the back of the limb the perforating arteries, by anastomosing with each other, form a feeble arterial chain that links the cruciate anastomosis at the hip to the genicular anastomosis at the knee.

The Branches of the Popliteal Artery are:

a few *cutaneous* branches;

muscular branches to the muscles of the ham and calf; and

five *genicular* (articular) branches. Of these, one, the middle genicular pierces the capsule of the knee joint and supplies the cruciate ligaments and other derivatives of the intercondylar septum (*fig. 513*); whereas the 4 others, like the perforating branches of the profunda a., grasp the skeletal framework, no muscle intervening (*fig. 438*).

»» **Primary Route of Arteries.** In the embryo the primary arterial trunk of the limb arises as a branch of the internal iliac a., and passes down the back of the limb, accompanying the sciatic nerve; at the knee it passes in front of the Popliteus; and in the leg it lies behind the interosseous membrane. A vessel, which becomes the external iliac and femoral arteries, grows down the front of the thigh and joins the primary trunk above the knee (*fig. 439*). The part of the primary trunk immediately distal to the union becomes the upper part of the popliteal artery; the proximal part is resorbed, save in the gluteal region where it persists as the inferior gluteal artery. Anastomotic branches—medial femoral circumflex and four perforating—persist.

The primary trunk sends a branch forward between the leg bones to become the anterior tibial artery, and a branch (or branches) downward behind the Popliteus to become the lower part of the popliteal artery and the posterior tibial artery. Thus, the Popliteus is encircled temporarily—until the portion of the primary trunk in front of it is superseded. Occasionally, the definitive popliteal artery passes in front of the Popliteus; that is, it pursues the primary route.

*Segmental Innervation of Muscles of Hip and Thigh**

<table>
<tr><th>L. 1</th><th>L. 2</th><th>L. 3</th><th>L. 4</th><th>L. 5</th><th>S. 1</th><th>S. 2</th></tr>
<tr><td colspan="4">Iliopsoas</td><td></td><td></td><td></td></tr>
<tr><td></td><td colspan="3">Gracilis
Sartorius
Pectineus
Adductor Longus
Adductor Brevis</td><td></td><td></td><td></td></tr>
<tr><td></td><td colspan="3">Adductor Minimus
Quadriceps Femoris</td><td></td><td></td><td></td></tr>
<tr><td></td><td colspan="5">Adductor Magnus</td><td></td></tr>
<tr><td></td><td></td><td colspan="3">Obturator Externus</td><td></td><td></td></tr>
<tr><td></td><td></td><td></td><td colspan="3">Tensor Fasciae Latae
Gluteus Medius
Gluteus Minimus</td><td></td></tr>
<tr><td></td><td></td><td></td><td colspan="4">Quadratus Femoris
Gemelli
Semitendinosus
Semimembranosus</td></tr>
<tr><td></td><td></td><td></td><td></td><td colspan="3">Piriformis
Obturator Internus
Biceps Femoris
Gluteus Maximus</td></tr>
</table>

* Modified after Bing; and Haymaker and Woodhall. (For Leg and Foot, page 427.)

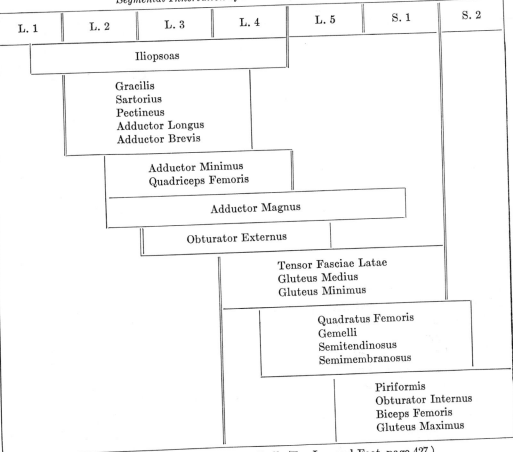

CHAPTER **26**

LEG AND DORSUM OF FOOT

The leg or crural region is the segment of the lower limb between the knee and the ankle. It is conveniently subdivided into four regions (*fig. 440*):

1. Anterior crural (ant. tibiofibular),
2. Posterior crural (post. tibiofibular),
3. Lateral crural (fibular or peroneal),
4. Medial crural (overlying the medial surface of the tibia).

The boundaries of these regions are well seen in a transverse section through the middle of the leg (*fig. 441*). The posterior region is much larger than the anterior because it contains the powerful muscles (Gastrocnemius and Soleus) that, by extending the ankle joint, raise the body in walking, whereas almost all that is expected of the muscles of the anterior region is that they cause the foot to clear the ground and not let the toes drag during the act of advancing the limb when walking.

Medial Crural Region and Body of Tibia (*fig. 442*). By palpation note that the

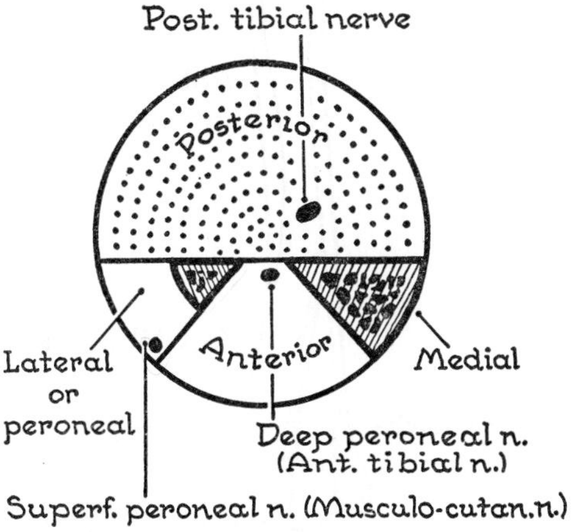

FIG. 440. Scheme of the four regions of the leg on transverse section, showing their relative sizes and their nerves. (After H. A. Cates.)

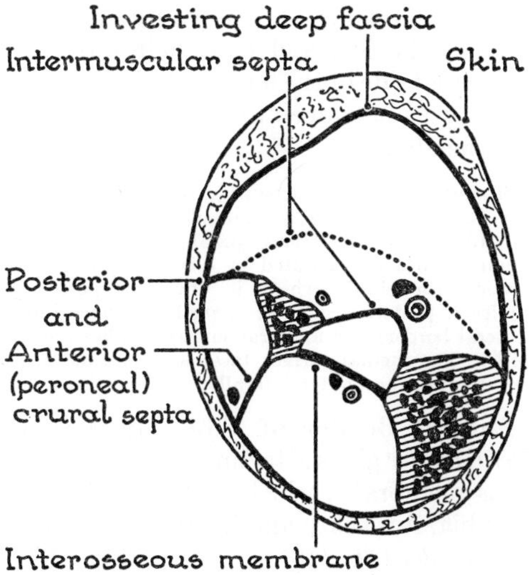

FIG. 441. The leg on cross section, showing the interosseous membrane and the various intermuscular fascial septa.

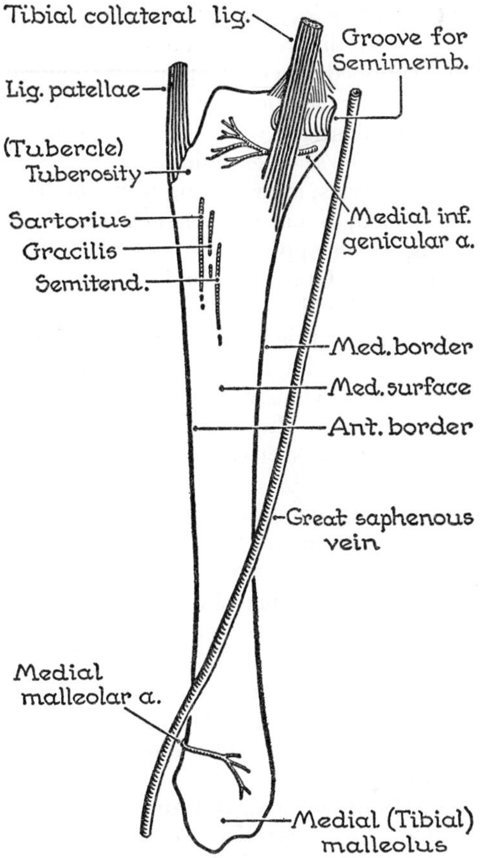

FIG. 442. The subcutaneous or medial aspect of the tibia.

medial surface of your own tibia is subcutaneous, smooth, and flat; that the skin covering it is free; that it passes imperceptibly on to the medial malleolus below and on to the medial condyle above; that it is bounded in front by the *subcutaneous anterior border* of the tibia, which may be traced from the anterior border of the medial malleolus to the tuberosity of the tibia; and that it is bounded behind by the *subcutaneous medial border* of the tibia, which may be traced from the posterior border of the medial malleolus to the horizontal groove on the medial condyle for the insertion of the Semimembranosus (*fig. 442*). The tibia is felt to be thinnest at the junction of its lower one-third with its upper two-thirds where it is most liable to fracture.

THE TENDINOUS EXPANSIONS of the Sartorius, Gracilis, and Semitendinosus find attachment to the medial surface of the tibia below the level of the tuberosity. Each represents a different region of the thigh; each is supplied by a different nerve (femoral, obturator, or sciatic); each passes across the medial ligament of the knee to reach its insertion, a *bursa* intervening.

The Sartorius, approaching from the front of the thigh, is naturally superficial to the Gracilis, which approaches from the medial side; and the Gracilis is in turn superficial to the Semitendinosus, which belongs to the back of the thigh. These 3 all obviously flex the knee joint and rotate the leg medially; and obviously they act to better advantage when the movement of flexion is well established than during its initial stages.

On pressing your heel against the leg of the chair you are sitting on, you can by palpation identify three tendons at the medial side of the knee. The rounded tendon of the Semitendinosus, which is the lowest and most lateral of these, and the massive tendon of the Semimembranosus are identified with ease; the Sartorius, which crosses the femur just behind the adductor tubercle, with difficulty.

The **tibial collateral ligament** (*medial lig. of the knee*) stretches in a fan-shaped manner from the medial epicondyle of the femur, situated an inch below the adductor tubercle, to the upper margin of the medial condyle of the tibia; but its more superficial fibers extend as a broad band beyond this to a rough marking in front of the medial border of the tibia. Like the cord of a bow, this band bridges both the groove on the medial condyle to which the Semimembranosus tendon is attached and the hollow below the condyle in which pass the *medial inferior genicular vessels and nerve* (*figs. 442* and *443*).

The *medial malleolar vessels* cross the medial surface of the tibia above the malleolus. The **great saphenous vein** and its companion, the *saphenous nerve*, cross the lowest third of the medial surface of the tibia obliquely and continue proximally, about half an inch behind the medial border, as far as the knee. At the knee they lie a hand's breadth behind the medial border of the patella (p. 361). The vein arises from the medial end of the dorsal venous arch of the

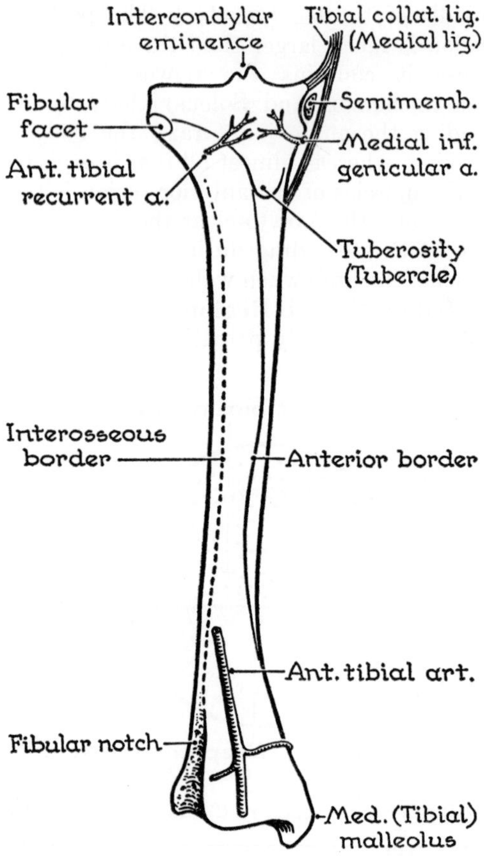

FIG. 443. Anterolateral aspect of the tibia

foot; the nerve appears between the Sartorius and Gracilis, accompanies the vein through the leg, and ends half way along the medial side of the foot; and, though many of its twigs pass deep to the vein, some pass superficially.

»» TERMINOLOGY OF SURFACES AND BORDER (*fig. 444*). The shaft of the tibia is triangular on cross-section, and, like other long bones (p. 5), it is described as having 3 surfaces separated by 3 borders. An anterior border, "the shin"—which it obviously possesses—implies a posterior surface; a medial surface implies a lateral border; and a lateral surface implies a medial border. The medial surface faces anteromedially, and the lateral surface, anterolaterally.

Lateral Border of Tibia. Because the *lateral border* gives attachment to the interosseous membrane, which unites the fibula to the tibia, it is sharp and is named the *interosseous border* (*fig. 443*).

This sharp lateral or interosseous border extends from near the small, flat, circular

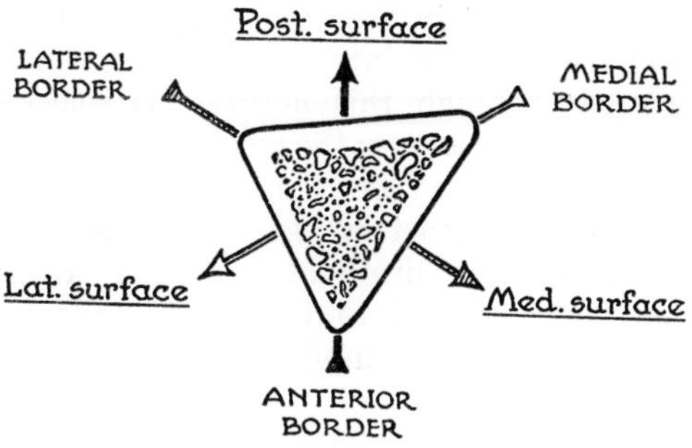

FIG. 444. Terminology: surfaces and borders are named by opposites.

facet on the lateral condyle, where the head of the fibula articulates, to the deep, rough, triangular notch for the reception of the lower end of the fibula. The fibula requires to be firmly united to the tibia at its lower end, otherwise the talus would prize the two bones apart, so the interosseous border splits to form the sides of the triangular *fibular notch*; and the interosseous membrane is thickened to form strong interosseous bands, so the notch is rough.

The **Lower End of the Tibia** is expanded and, so, offers a large bearing surface to the talus. And, the appearance of a 4th surface (the fibular notch) transforms the triangular cross-section into a quadrangular one.

The **Lateral Surface** is devoted to Tibialis Anterior. It is limited above by the epiphyseal line, which arching upward and laterally from the tuberosity to below the fibular facet, serves to separate this surface from the lateral condyle. The prominent overhanging ridge it creates, affords attachment to the fascia of the anterior crural region.

The Posterior Surface (see p. 406).

ANTERIOR CRURAL REGION AND DORSUM OF FOOT

These two regions make a single functional territory, so they will be considered together. The boundaries of the anterior crural region (*fig. 441*) are: lateral surface of tibia, interosseous membrane, anterior surface of fibula, anterior crural septum and investing deep fascia.

The Great Arterial Trunk of the front of the leg and dorsum of the foot, accompanied by venae comitantes, enters the anterior osseofascial compartment in contact with the medial side of the neck of the fibula, and ends near the web between the great and 2nd toes by dividing into dorsal digital branches for the adjacent sides of these toes. A fairly straight line joining these two points crosses the ankle joint midway between the two malleoli and defines the course of the great arterial trunk (*fig. 445*).

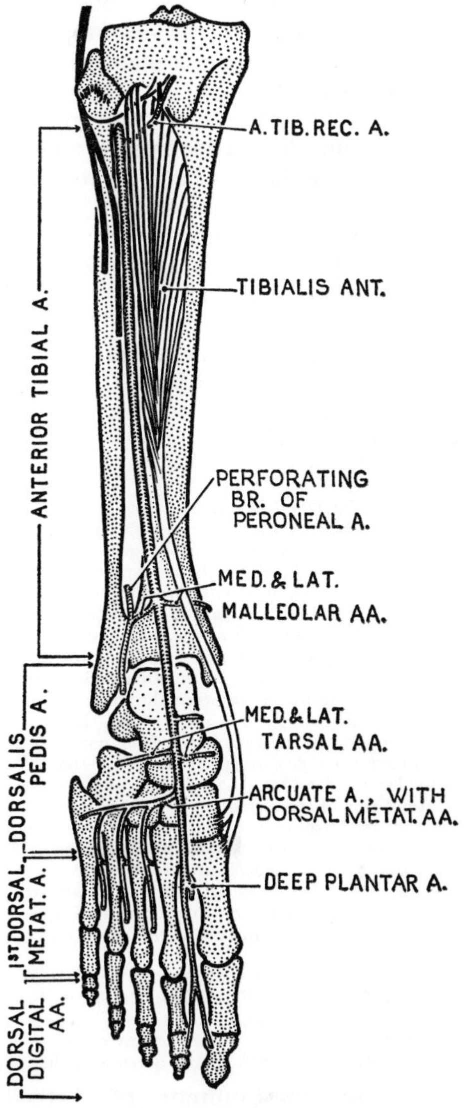

FIG. 445. The great arterial trunk and its named branches lie on the skeletal plane.

It lies literally on the "skeletal plane," crossing in turn the interosseous membrane, the lowest third of the lateral surface of the tibia, the ankle joint, the talus, the talonavicular joint, the navicular, the naviculocuneiform joint, the middle cuneiform, and the fascia covering the first dorsal interosseous muscle.

At the ankle joint it changes its name from *anterior tibial a.* to *dorsalis pedis a.*; at the proximal end of the first intermetatarsal space it sends a large *deep plantar branch* into the sole of the foot and changes its name to the *first dorsal metatarsal a.*; and at the distal end of the space it divides into two *dorsal digital* arteries.

If all five muscles in these two regions are stripped from their attachments and discarded, the arterial stem and all its named branches are left undisturbed.

THE UNDISTURBED BRANCHES are:

- anterior tibial recurrent artery.
- branch accompanying the superficial peroneal nerve.
- medial and lateral malleolar aa.
- medial and lateral tarsal aa.
- arcuate artery.
- dorsal metatarsal aa.
- dorsal digital aa.

»» The *Anterior Tibial Recurrent Artery* (*fig. 445*), with the anterior tibial recurrent nerve, runs upward to the lateral condyle to take part in the genicular anastomoses. To expose it, the Tibialis Anterior must be severed to the bone. A *slender branch* passes deep to the anterior crural septum to join the superficial peroneal nerve. The *lateral malleolar a.* joins the perforating branch of the peroneal a., which, like the anterior tibial a. at a higher level, enters this region through an osseofibrous foramen (between the lower end of the fibula and the interosseous membrane). It does not pierce or perforate the membrane. The common stem thus-formed runs downward in front of the inferior tibiofibular joint to take part in the anastomoses on the lateral side of the ankle.

The *lateral tarsal a.* and the *arcuate a.* run laterally on the dorsum of the foot deep to the Extensor Digitorum Brevis. The *dorsal metatarsal branches* to the 2nd, 3rd, and 4th spaces arise from the arcuate a.; each is joined by a perforating branch of the deep plantar arch; and each in turn divides into two *dorsal digital aa.*

The medial side of the 1st toe and the lateral side of the 5th toe receive digital branches from the 1st and 4th metatarsal arteries respectively. Hence, the arrangement of vessels on the dorsum of the foot is almost identical with that on the dorsum of the hand.

Note on Development of Arteries. During the early embryonic weeks, when the limbs are taking form, blood vessels, in the form of an anastomosing network of capillaries, sprout into them. One or more channels through this network is selected to be the main artery; the rest of the network either disappears or remains in part as branches of this artery (*fig. 446*). If some of the branches are firmly anchored, the artery may be compelled to take an angular or zigzag course as exemplified by the dorsalis pedis artery.

Variation. The anterior tibial a. may fail to grow more than a short way down the leg, in which case the dorsalis pedis artery springs from the perforating branch of the peroneal artery (*fig. 461*).

Common Peroneal Nerve (Lateral Popliteal N.). This subfascial nerve, after following the posterior border of the Biceps tendon and crossing the Plantaris, lateral head of the Gastrocnemius, and back of the head of the fibula, from which it is separated by a film of Soleus, comes finally into direct contact with the lateral side of the neck of the fibula where it divides into its two terminal branches (*fig. 451*):

1. Deep peroneal nerve.
2. Superficial peroneal nerve.

These two nerves taken origin on and, save for their terminal cutaneous branches, literally never leave the skeletal plane (*fig. 451*). Mark this! They curve round the neck and proximal end of the body of the fibula deep to all the structures they encounter,

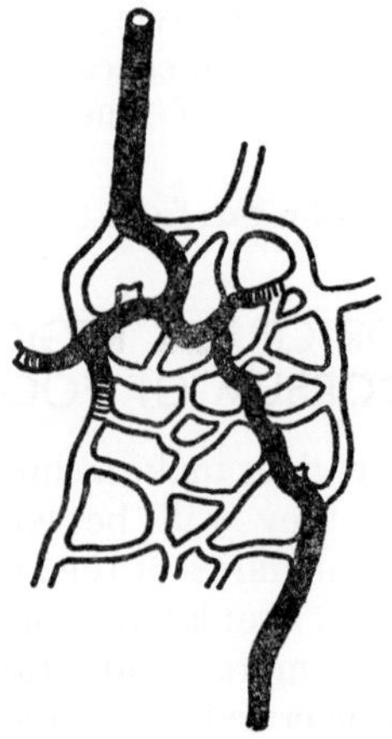

FIG. 446. Arteries are formed from channels through a network.

namely: the posterior crural septum, Peroneus Longus, anterior crural septum, and Ext. Digitorum Longus, and then part company.

»» The small branch, called the *anterior tibial recurrent nerve*, joins an artery of the same name and sends twigs to the knee joint and to Tibialis Anterior.

The **Deep Peroneal Nerve** (Anterior Tibial N.) approaches the anterior tibial artery from the lateral side and accompanies it through the leg; thereafter, it accompanies the dorsalis pedis and 1st dorsal metarsal aa. through the foot and, becoming cutaneous, divides into *two dorsal digital nerves*, which accompany the corresponding arteries along the adjacent sides of the 1st and 2nd toes.

It supplies the 4 muscles in the anterior crural region, and on the dorsum of the foot it sends a lateral branch to supply the Ext. Digitorum Brevis and the various joints.

The **Superficial Peroneal Nerve** (Musculocutaneous N.) runs obliquely downward and forward, in contact with the shaft of the fibula and covered by the Peroneus Longus (i.e., in an osseomuscular tunnel, 3″ long), till it meets the anterior border of the Peroneus Brevis which conducts it to the surface. This it reaches along the line of the anterior crural septum, a variable distance above the apex of the subcutaneous triangular area at the lower end of the fibula (*fig. 451*).

It supplies Peroneus Longus and Peroneus Brevis and sends digital branches to all the toes, save the adjacent sides of the 1st and 2nd (*deep peroneal n.*) and the lateral side of the 5th (*sural n.*) To these it sends communicating twigs (*fig. 447*).

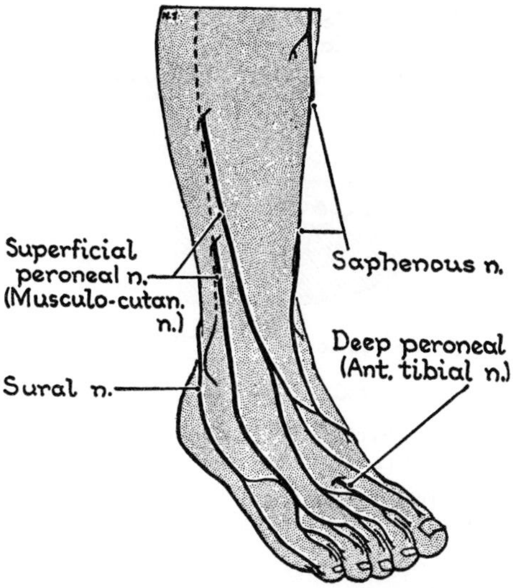

Fig. 447. The cutaneous nerves of the dorsum of the foot.

Muscles of Anterior Crural Region

As may be seen in the cross-sections (*figs. 448* and *449*), there are two fleshy muscles: *Tibialis Anterior* and *Extensor Digitorum Longus*, in the upper part of the region; and there are two more, *Extensor Hallucis Longus* and *Peroneus Tertius*, in the lower part. At the ankle these are represented by their four tendons.

The muscles arise from the walls of the compartment by fleshy fibers, so they leave no marks on the bones. The Tibialis Anterior takes origin from the tibia; the other three arise from the fibula. One muscle, the *Extensor Digitorum Brevis*, arises from, and confines itself to, the dorsum of the foot.

The **Tibialis Anterior** arises from the upper two-thirds of the lateral surface of the tibia and from the adjacent part of the interosseous membrane and investing deep fascia.

Incise the deep fascia longitudinally and note the muscle fibers arising from it. This explains why the upper part of the deep fascia is strong, its fibers largely longitudinal, and the upper part of the anterior border of the tibia sharp.

The stout tendon of the Tibialis Anterior turns medially to be inserted by two slips into the adjacent parts of the medial surface of the 1st metatarsal and 1st cuneiform, a *bursa*, which communicates with the underlying synovial cavity, intervening. The tendon fashions the lower part of the anterior border of the tibia, which, accordingly, turns medially; and, because the deep fascia is not attached here, the border is rounded.

The **Extensor Digitorum Longus** is a thin, unipennate muscle. It arises from the entire length of the narrow anterior surface of the fibula and from adjacent parts of the interosseous membrane, anterior crural septum, and deep fascia. It is inserted by

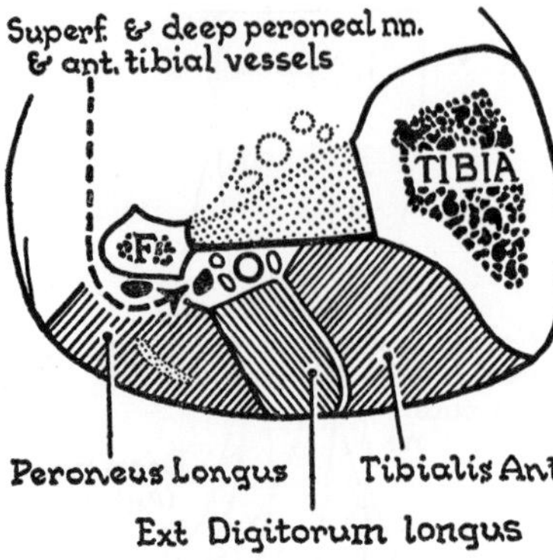

FIG. 448. Section through the upper third of the front of the leg. There are two muscles in the anterior region; one in the lateral. The vessels and nerves cling to the skeletal plane.

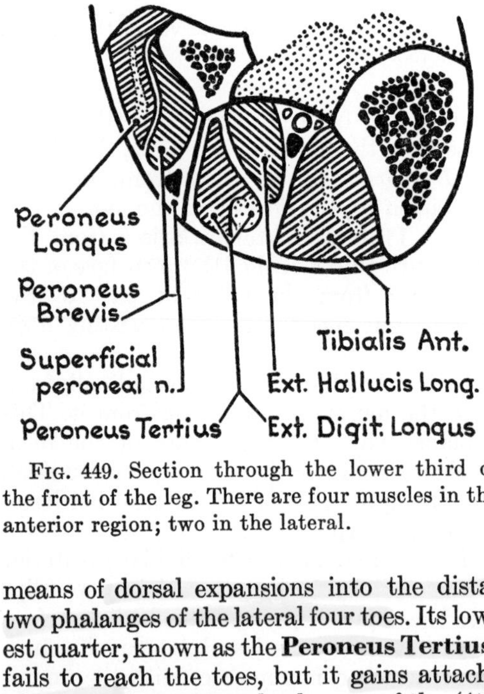

FIG. 449. Section through the lower third of the front of the leg. There are four muscles in the anterior region; two in the lateral.

means of dorsal expansions into the distal two phalanges of the lateral four toes. Its lowest quarter, known as the **Peroneus Tertius,** fails to reach the toes, but it gains attachment anywhere along the dorsum of the (4th or) 5th metatarsal. It is a special evertor of the foot, and is almost peculiar to man.

The **Extensor Hallucis Longus** arises from the middle two-quarters of the anterior surface of the fibula and from the interosseous membrane. It is inserted into the base of the distal phalanx of the hallux. It is the only muscle to cross the anterior tibial artery.

The **Extensor Digitorum Brevis** arises from the anterior part of the upper surface of the calcaneus and from the extensor retinaculum. Its four tendons pass to the medial four toes. The section serving the 1st toe is called the **Extensor Hallucis Brevis.** Its tendon is inserted into the base of its proximal phalanx; the three other tendons join the dorsal expansions of the Extensor Digitorum Longus to the 2nd, 3rd, and 4th toes.

The fleshy belly of the Ext. Dig. Brevis is responsible for the soft swelling seen in life on the dorsum of the foot two inches or so in front of the fibular malleolus. Deep to it lie the lateral tarsal and arcuate arteries and the lateral branch of the deep peroneal nerve. The Ext. Hallucis Brevis is the only muscle to cross the dorsalis pedis artery.

Deep Fascia. In the uppermost part of the front of the leg the deep fascia gives origin to muscles, so its fibers run longitudinally, are strong, and cause the corresponding part of the anterior border of the tibia to be sharp. In the middle part it gives origin to no muscle, so it is weaker. In the lowest part and in the ankle region it acts as retinacula (*fig. 55*, p. 70), preventing the tendons from bowstringing; so, the fibers are disposed circularly, like an anklet, and are strong. On the dorsum of the foot the fascia is thin.

The **Extensor Retinaculum** is in two parts—superior and inferior (*fig. 450*).

The *superior part* (transverse crural lig.) is a transverse band, one or two inches broad. Laterally, it is attached to the anterior border of the triangular subcutaneous area of the fibula; medially, it passes over the anterior border of the tibia, just above the malleolus, and blends with the periosteum.

»» This explains why the anterior border of the fibula is here sharp and that of the tibia rounded. In this is found one of the few exceptions to the generalization that where fascia encounters bare bone it unites with it.

The *inferior part* (crucial crural lig.) is placed in front of the ankle and has the appearance of a Y-shaped band. The stem of the Y is attached to the anterior part of the upper surface of the calcaneus; the upper limb blends with the periosteum on the medial malleolus; and the lower limb blends with the plantar fascia. The deeper fibers of the Y form loops or slings—especially for

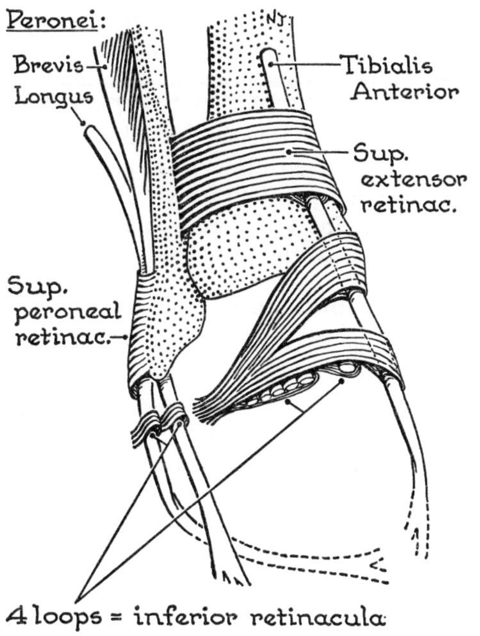

FIG. 450. Extensor and peroneal retinacula

Peroneus Tertius, Ext. Digitorum Longus, and Ext. Hallucis Longus—that prevent the tendons from bowstringing forward and also from bowstringing medially. (Note the angular course taken by the tendons when the foot is inverted.) The Tibialis Anterior tendon which, during dorsiflexion of the ankle joint, is the most prominent tendon in the region, is attached so far back on the side of the foot that it hardly requires restraining. Indeed, the retinaculum covering it is thin.

The **Inferior Peroneal Retinaculum** consists of two loops—the upper loop holds the Peroneus Brevis to the peroneal trochlea (tubercle); the lower loop bridges the Peroneus Longus tendon and extends from the trochlea postero-inferiorly to be attached to the lateral surface of the calcaneus. (Superior peroneal retinaculum, p. 411).

Synovial Sheaths that extend about an inch proximal and distal to the points of friction envelop the tendons.

LATERAL CRURAL REGION

(Fibular or Peroneal Region)

By **palpation** of your own limb determine the following points: The upper and lower ends of the fibula are subcutaneous; the body is buried in muscles. The fibula is not parallel to the tibia but is set obliquely to it. The *head of the fibula* is rounded and a blunt *apex* rises from its posterior part. The *common peroneal nerve* can be rolled behind the head.

The *malleolus* is triangular; its anterior and posterior borders are conspicuous and palpable; and its *blunt apex* descends from the posterior border. Its lateral surface is subcutaneous and is continuous with a subcutaneous area on the body, shaped like an isosceles triangle. The *apex of the subcutaneous triangle* is three or four inches above the malleolus, and it leads to the anterior crural septum which is attached to the anterior border of the fibula. The superficial peroneal nerve (musculocutaneous n.) becomes cutaneous along the line of the septum.

The cord-like *fibular collateral lig.* runs obliquely downwards and backwards to be attached to the head of the fibula, just in front of its apex. It can be felt when the knee is flexed, but not when it is extended, for the *Biceps* then covers it.

The cord-like *calcaneofibular lig.* is attached to the malleolus of the fibula, just in front of its apex. It also runs obliquely downwards and backwards. It cannot be palpated, for it is crossed by the long and short peroneal tendons.

Boundaries and Contents. (*See figs. 440, 441, 448, 449, and 451.*)

Muscles

Peronei Longus et Brevis fill the lateral crural compartment.

ORIGINS. They arise from the lateral aspect of the fibula and slightly from the anterior and posterior crural septa. The Peroneus Longus arises from the upper two-thirds of the compartment; the Peroneus Brevis from the lower two-thirds; and they overlap each other in the middle third. The two muscles are similar in structure, each being bipennate in its upper half and unipennate in its lower half (*fig. 451*).

INSERTIONS. The Peroneus Brevis is inserted into the dorsum of the base of the 5th metatarsal beyond its tip. The Peroneus Longus enters the sole behind the base of

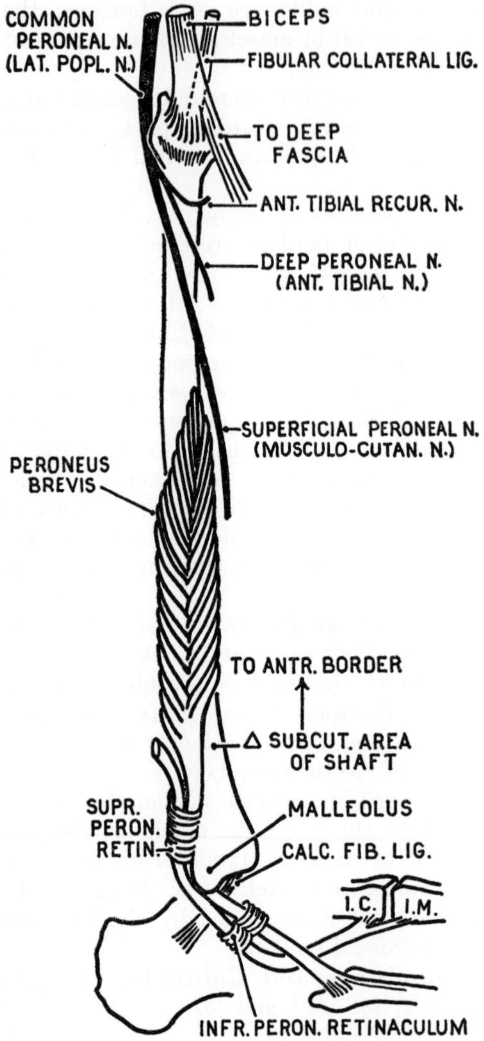

FIG. 451. Peroneal or lateral crural region

the 5th metatarsal, runs in the groove on the lateral and under surfaces of the cuboid, and is inserted into the same two bones as Tibialis Anterior (i.e., medial cuneiform and 1st metatarsal) but on their lateral aspects. So, Tibialis Anterior and Peroneus Longus make a stirrup for the foot.

The Peroneus Brevis is quite obviously anterior to the Longus in the leg and above it on the side of the foot. Obviously, the tendon of the Brevis fashions the posterior aspect of the fibular malleolus to play the part of a pulley.

The Brevis and Longus tendons both cross the calcaneofibular ligament. They are bound down by the superior and inferior peroneal retinacula. Behind the malleolus and below it, the two tendons lie within a single synovial sheath; at the peroneal trochlea, the sheath bifurcates and envelops each tendon separately for an inch or more. The sheath for the Peroneus Longus may be continuous with one in the sole.

Fibula and Its Joints

The three *Functions of the Fibula:*

1. To give origin to muscles.
2. To hold the talus in its socket.
3. To act as a pulley for the Peronei.

Of the nine muscles attached to the fibula, only the Biceps pulls upward; the others all pull downward (*fig. 452*). All

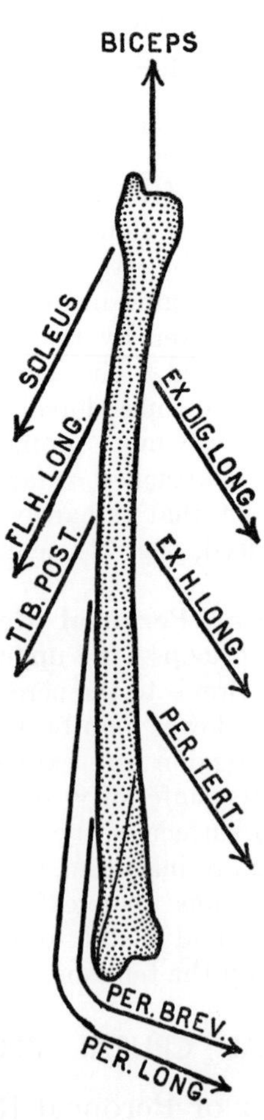

FIG. 452. The muscles attached to the fibula pull downward, except the Biceps.

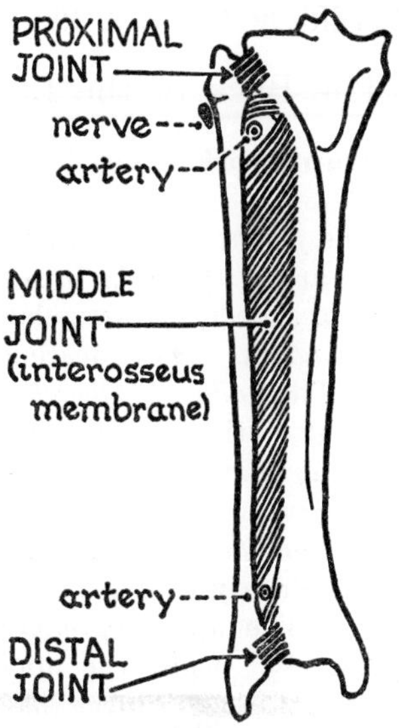

FIG. 453. The tibiofibular articulations. Note unity of direction of ligamentous fibers.

ligamentous connections between tibia and fibula are so directed as to resist this downward pull (see *fig. 453*).

»» *Note on Comparative Anatomy.* In amphibia the fibula is as large as the tibia. It articulates with the femur above and with the tarsus below and it is weight supporting. In reptiles it is smaller than the tibia and it bears less weight. In monotremes and marsupials it is still further reduced. In horses and ruminants the shaft of the fibula either disappears or is represented by a fibrous band that connects the upper and lower ends; and the ends are either incorporated with the tibia or in articulation with it. In carnivora and primates the complete fibula exists, but it does not bear weight. Only in man does the fibular malleolus descend below the level of the tibial malleolus.

Tibiofibular Joints. The fibula is moored to the tibia at its upper end, along its shaft, and at its lower end—at proximal, middle, and distal joints.

The Proximal Tibiofibular Joint has a synovial cavity and is of the plane or gliding variety. A small, flat, round facet on the head of the fibula articulates with a similar facet on the posterolateral part of the lateral condyle of the tibia. A capsule with very strong anterior fibers encloses the cavity. Behind the joint is the Popliteus tendon, separated by the Popliteus *bursa,* which may communicate with the joint (p. 444, *fig. 517*). In front it is practically subcutaneous.

The Middle and Distal Tibiofibular Joints are syndesmoses. The *interosseous membrane* (middle joint) extends down the respective sides of the tibia and fibula, producing a sharp line on each. Distally, each line expands into a large, rough, triangular area which is concave on the tibia (fibular notch, *fig. 443*) to receive the corresponding convex area on the fibula which may carry a narrow articular facet for the tibia (*fig. 454*).

It is obvious that union must here be strong in order to prevent lateral displacement of the talus, so the interosseous membrane expands to form an *interosseous ligament* which binds the opposed triangular areas together. In addition, a strong anterior band and a much stronger posterior one, called the *anterior* and *posterior distal tibiofibular ligaments* (ant. and post. ligs. of the lateral malleolus), stretch from the margins of the fibular notch of the tibia to the adjacent borders of the fibular malleolus.

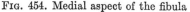

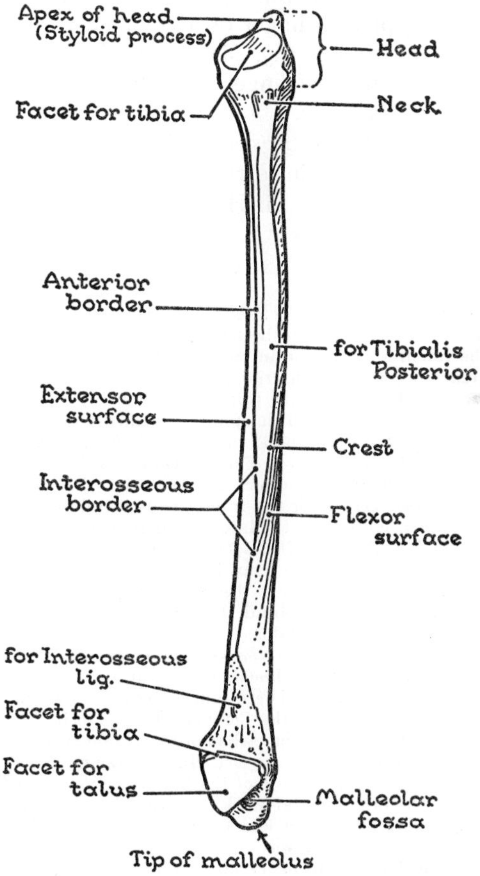

FIG. 454. Medial aspect of the fibula

»» The lowest and deepest fibers of the posterior lig. (transverse tibiofibular lig.) extend to the malleolar fossa and deepen the socket for the talus (p. 448).

Relations. The peroneal artery descends behind the distal joint; its perforating branch descends in front of it (*figs. 445 and 461*).

Body of the Fibula (*fig. 454*). The shape of the body depends largely on the muscles and septa attached to it. It is easiest to begin with the important peroneal surface.

The Peroneal Surface is found by placing a finger behind the malleolus, which is the pulley for the Peronei, and letting it run up the shaft to the head of the bone. This surface is broad and spiral, facing posteriorly below and laterally above. It is bounded by lines (the *anterior* and *posterior borders*) which give attachment to the anterior and posterior crural septa. To make doubly sure of the anterior border, which separates the peroneal from the extensor surface, place a finger on the subcutaneous, isosceles triangle (*fig. 451*) above the malleolus and run the finger straight up to the head of the bone.

The Flexor or Posterior Surface is broad and it gives origin to the Soleus in its upper third and to the Fl. Hallucis Longus in its lower two-thirds. It is spiral, like the peroneal surface next to it.

»» *The Surface for the Tibialis Posterior* is the enigma; it is fusiform and is to be found thus: put a finger on the rough area for the interosseous ligament—i.e., the area above the smooth, triangular facet on the malleolus for articulation with the talus—and follow it upwards. It becomes a line which splits, one-third to one-half of the way up the shaft, into an *anterior line* and a *prominent posterior crest.* These enclose a fusiform area for the Tibialis Posterior. The anterior line is the *interosseous border* for the interosseous membrane; the prominent crest is for the intermuscular septum behind the Tibialis Posterior (*fig. 441*). It is common to mistake the crest for the interosseous border.

There is a deep hollow, the *malleolar fossa,* between the grooved pulley behind the malleolus and the triangular facet for the talus.

The Extensor or Anterior Surface faces consistently forward and is almost linear, because it gives origin to the unipennate Ext. Digitorum Longus in its upper three quarters and to the Peroneus Tertius in its lower quarter. It broadens somewhat in its middle two quarters to afford origin to the Ext. Hallucis Longus.

Ossification. The shaft of the fibula begins to ossify about the 8th prenatal week, like the shafts of other long bones. The upper end begins to ossify about the 5th year; fusion is always complete by the 22nd. The lower end begins to ossify about the 2nd year; fusion is always complete by the 20th.

POSTERIOR CRURAL REGION

(The Back of the Leg)

Bony Framework, viewed from behind (*fig. 455*).

Above, the *femoral condyles* project backward; they are a thumb's breadth apart; their posterior aspects are articular and oval. The *supracondylar lines* descend to the *epicondyles.* The *adductor tubercle* rises from the lower end of the medial supracondylar line, and is the guide to the *lower epiphyseal line of the femur.*

The *tibial condyles* overhang the shaft of the tibia posteriorly and at the sides, but not in front. The *upper epiphyseal line of the tibia* runs ½″ below the upper surface (*fig. 455*). The horizontal *semimembranosus groove* occupies the hinder part of the epiphysis on the medial side, whereas the round *fibular facet* occupies the hinder part of the epiphysis on the lateral side. The rounded *head of the fibula,* supported by its neck, ends in an *apex* which fails to rise to the level of the knee joint.

The smooth, flat, posterior surface of the body of the tibia, narrowest at the junction of its upper two-thirds and lower one-third is crossed by an oblique, rough line, the *soleal line,* from which a *vertical line* descends in the middle ²⁄₄ of this surface. The *nutrient foramen,* which is the largest in the body. The *tibial malleolus,* which plays the part of a pulley for two tendons is ¾″ shorter than the fibular malleolus.

The following parts of the talus and calcaneus are in view: The hinder part of the *upper articular surface* of the talus ending at a *deep groove* between the *medial* and *lateral tubercles.* The groove lodges the Fl. Hallucis Longus tendon and, therefore, runs downwards and medially. It is continuous above with a faint groove on the lower end of the tibia and below with a decided groove on the under surface of the sustentaculum tali. The *posterior third of the calcaneus* projects backwards beyond the talus, forming the prominence of the heel. Its most posterior part, the *tuber calcanei,* is narrow above and broad below where it ends in a large *medial process* and a small *lateral*

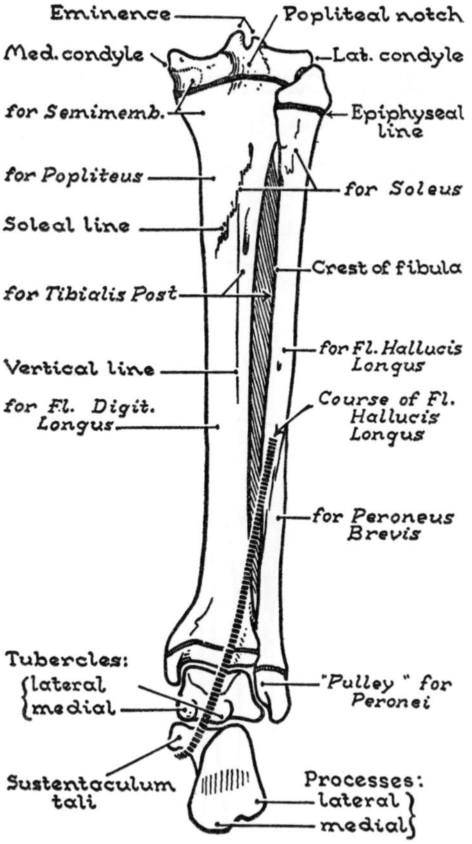

FIG. 455. Posterior aspect of the bones of the leg and foot.

process. Only the medial process rests on the ground.

Muscles of the posterior crural region (*fig. 456*). The muscles are disposed in two groups, a superficial and a deep:

Superficial group:

1. Gastrocnemius,
2. Plantaris,
3. Soleus.

The Gastrocnemius has two bellies, which bound the lower half of the popliteal fossa. The Soleus arises at the lower limit of the fossa. The Plantaris lies between them. All three are inserted into the heel, which they raise in walking. They are supplied by the tibial nerve (med. popliteal n.) near their upper borders.

Deep group:

1. Popliteus, a rotator of the knee
2. Flexor Hallucis Longus and
3. Flexor Digitorum Longus to the end phalanges of the toes.
4. Tibialis Posterior to every small tarsal and most metatarsals.

THE **Gastrocnemius** has two flattened heads of origin which are largely tendinous. The lateral head arises from the epicondyle of the femur (just above the impressions for the Popliteus and fibular collateral lig.); the medial head arises from the popliteal surface of the femur, above the medial condyle. The two resulting fleshy bellies are united by a fibrous line at the bottom of a furrow which lodges the small saphenous vein and the sural nerve (p. 412).

The bellies end at the middle of the leg in a broad aponeurosis that blends with the aponeurosis of the Soleus to form the *tendo calcaneus* (tendon of Achilles). The two bellies of the Gastrocneumius account for the fullness of the calf. The Gastrocnemius and Soleus are referred to as the Triceps Surae (Sura, L. = the calf).

A constant *bursa* between the tendon of the Semimembranosus and the medial head of the Gastrocnemius may communicate with a *bursa* between the latter and the capsule of the knee joint.

»» This in turn may communicate with the knee joint (in 42.4 per cent of 528 dissecting room limbs). So, fluid in the joint, resulting say from a sprain, can in this circumstance pass from the knee joint via the Gastrocnemius bursa into the Semimembranosus bursa and cause a swelling at the back of the knee. A

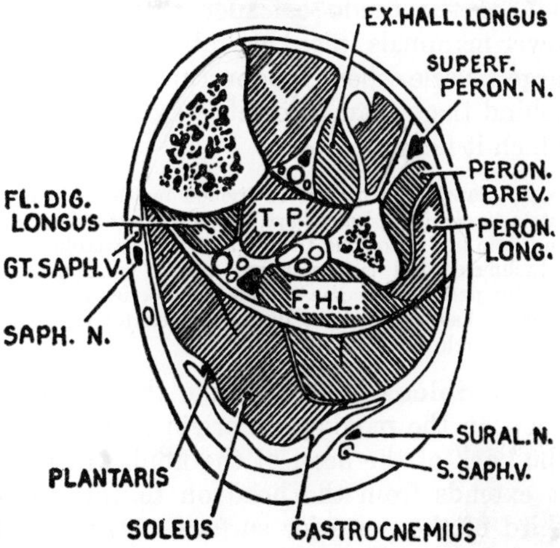

FIG. 456. Transverse section through middle of leg.

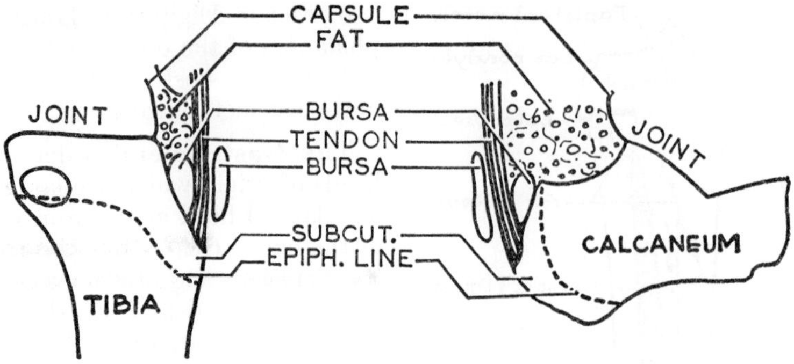

FIG. 457. The tendo calcaneus and ligamentum patellae compared

sesamoid bone is commonly found in the lateral head of the Gastrocnemius, and less commonly in the medial head.

The **tendo calcaneus** [Achillis] and the ligamentum patellae are comparable (*fig. 457*). They are approximately equal in length. Each is inserted into the intermediate three-fifths of an epiphysis, the lower one-fifth of which is subcutaneous, while the upper one-fifth has a subtendinous bursa. There is a large pad of fat between the bursa and the capsule of the nearest joint. Superficial to the lig. patellae is the superficial infrapatellar bursa; superficial to the tendo calcaneus there may be a bursa.

The **Plantaris** is placed between the Gastrocnemius and the Soleus. It has a fleshy part, the size of an Interosseus muscle, and a tendon about a foot long. It arises near the lateral head of the Gastrocnemius and it is inserted along the medial side of the tendo calcaneus (Achillis). In lower mammals (monkey, rabbit, dog) it is a large muscle whose tendon runs in a groove behind the calcaneus on its way to the toes, which it flexes.

» In plantigrade man it is divided by the calcaneus into a *sural* and a *plantar* part. The sural part is vestigial and, like its homologue the Palmaris, is variable in its attachment and is sometimes absent (p. 29). The plantar part has become the plantar aponeurosis, and, as such, has assumed the duties of a tie for the longitudinal arches of the foot.

The **Soleus** is shaped like the sole of a boot. In the monkey its origin is limited to the back of the head of the fibula. In man, it extends from the head on to the upper third of the posterior surface of the fibula, spreads across the posterior tibial vessels and tibial nerve, and acquires attachment

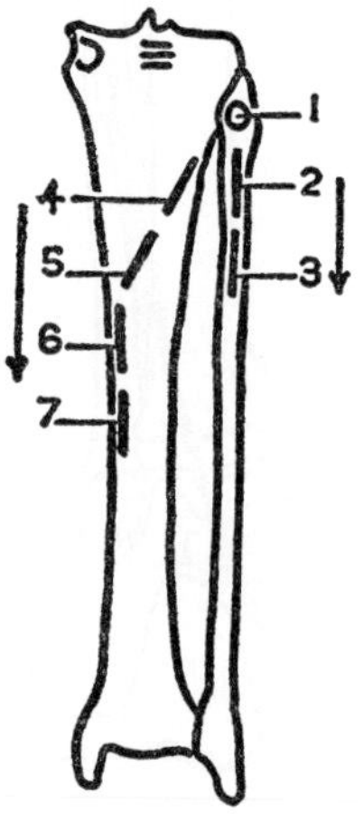

FIG. 458. The increasing origin of the Soleus is horseshoe-shaped.

to the soleal line (oblique line) of the tibia and to the medial border of the tibia for a variable distance below the soleal line (*fig. 458*). So, its *origin is horseshoe-shaped*.

Short fleshy fibers pass from tendinous septa in the muscle to an aponeurosis covering its posterior surface. On this aponeurosis the Gastrocnemius plays before joining it to form the tendo calcaneus, just as the Rectus Femoris plays on the Vasti. The Soleus is more powerful than the Gastrocnemius, and it contributes more to the thickness of the tendon. Its fleshy fibers are inserted into the deep aspect of the tendon to within an inch of the calcaneus.

THE DEEP MUSCLES. *Above the horseshoe-shaped origin* of the Soleus, the **Popliteus** is inserted into the posterior surface of the tibia by fleshy fibers (*figs. 460 and 461*). The Popliteus arises by tendon just below the lateral epicondyle of the femur, runs backward between the fibular collateral lig. and the lateral meniscus, and occupies the groove behind the proximal tibiofibular joint before passing to its insertion.

›› A variable bundle of fleshy fibers from its upper border gains a fibrous attachment to the hinder part of the lateral meniscus, thereby forming an *articular muscle* (R. J. Last).

The Soleal Line of the tibia is rough medially and indistinct laterally. It owes its presence mainly to the Soleus, whose origin is fibrous, and partly to the medial fibers of the *fascia covering the Popliteus* which are strong and vertical where they form part of the insertion of the Semimembranosus (*fig. 461*).

Below the horseshoe-shaped origin of the Soleus there are three bipennate muscles (*fig. 459*). These three feathers are of unequal length: the middle one (Tibialis Posterior) is the longest; the medial one (Fl. Digitorum Longus) is intermediate in length; while the lateral one (Fl. Hallucis Longus) is the shortest. The tendons of these three muscles are, then, the quills of the feathers, and in passing downward and medially to enter the sole of the foot they groove the lower end of the tibia.

FIG. 459. Three bipennate muscles resembling three feathers.

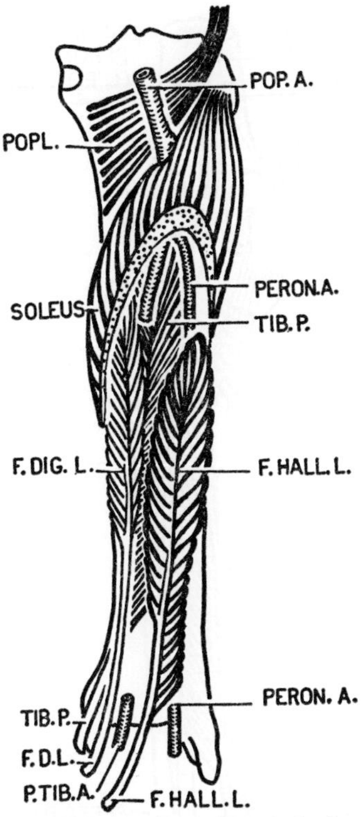

FIG. 460. The deep muscles of the back of the leg—above the horseshoe-shaped origin of the Soleus and below it.

The Tendons behind the Ankle (*fig. 462*) are the tendo calcaneus and 5 others. Of these, two, the Peronei Brevis et Longus, groove the back of the fibular malleolus; two, the Tibialis Posterior and Fl. Digitorum Longus, groove the back of the tibial malleolus; and one, the Fl. Hallucis Longus, grooves the lower end of the tibia midway between the malleoli (*fig. 460*).

The **Tibialis Posterior** arises from the upper two-thirds of the interosseous membrane and from the bone on each side of the membrane (i.e., the fibula anterior to the crest and the tibia lateral to the vertical line). Its tendon inclines medially to reach its pulley, which is the medial malleolus, and in so doing it leaves the lower part of this surface of the tibia uncovered. From its origin in the leg to its insertion in the foot the Tibialis Posterior clings faithfully to the skeletal plane.

Insertion (see *fig. 484* and p. 425).

The *fascia covering Tibialis Posterior* is

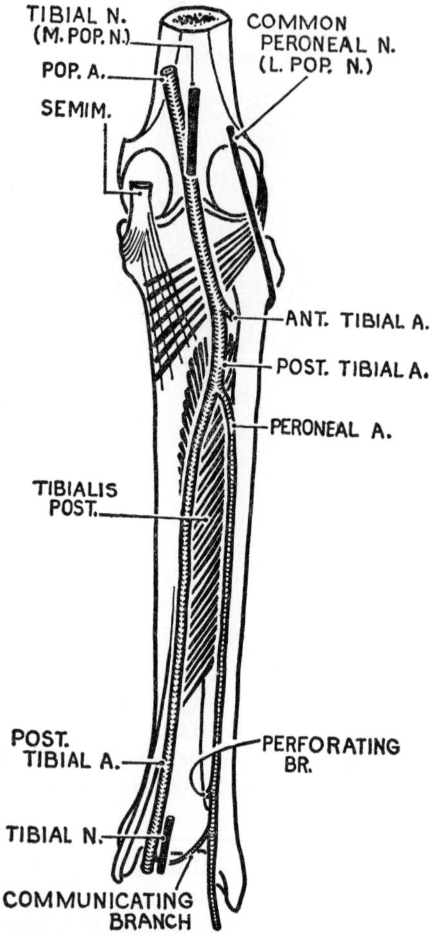

FIG. 461. The arteries and nerves of the back of the leg.

largely an aponeurosis of origin for Fl. Digitorum Longus, so its fibers run inferomedially from the crest on the fibula to the vertical line on the tibia.

The **Flexor Digitorum Longus** arises from the posterior surface of the tibia below the soleal line and medial to the vertical line, and from the fascia covering the Tibialis Posterior. Its tendon crosses the Tibialis Posterior tendon superficially behind the medial malleolus.

The **Flexor Hallucis Longus** is inserted into the terminal phalanx of the great toe—the toe off which one rises when walking and running—consequently, like the Soleus, it acquires an extensive origin. Not content with the limited surface the fibula has to offer, the origin of the Flexor Hallucis Longus encroaches upon every adjacent territory.

Thus—it gains attachment laterally to the posterior crural septum; medially to the fascia covering the Tibialis Posterior, to reach which it spreads across the peroneal artery, which consequently runs through a tunnel; below the level at which the Tibialis Posterior becomes tendinous, its fleshy fibers seize the opportunity to gain attachment to the interosseous membrane and to the tibia as far down as is functionally possible.

When the Soleus fails to occupy its allotted part of the upper third of the fibula, the Flexor Hallucis Longus commonly creeps up on to it. Indeed, there seems to be a struggle between these two muscles for possession of this disputed territory. The muscle is so bulky it overlaps and largely conceals the fleshy part of the Tibialis Posterior.

(*Continued on pages* 423 and 429).

Arteries and Nerves

There are two large arteries and one nerve in this region (*fig. 461*), namely:

Posterior tibial artery
Peroneal artery
Tibial nerve (post. tibial n.)

Tibial Nerve. The proximal segment of the tibial nerve is also known as the *medial popliteal n.* and the distal segment as the *posterior tibial n.* The change in name takes place where Popliteus ends and Soleus begins.

It will be recalled that the sciatic and tibial nerves take a straight course through the limb (*fig. 426*), from buttock to ankle, and there the tibial nerve ends, deep to the flexor retinaculum, by dividing into the *medial* and the *lateral plantar nerve.*

The tibial nerve is applied to the lateral side of the posterior tibial artery (*fig. 432*), on the fascia covering tibialis posterior, until that muscle inclines medially; it then continues its course on the skeletal plane.

Distribution of (posterior) tibial nerve. Branches: (1) *muscular* to the three deep bipennate *muscles* and the deep part of the Soleus (which also is bipennate); (2) *cutaneous*, called the medial calcanean nerves, to the medial and plantar aspects of the heel after piercing the flexor retinaculum (*fig.

489); (3) *articular*, to the ankle joint; (4) *vascular*, branches to the local vessels; and *terminal*, the medial and lateral plantar nerves.

The **Posterior Tibial Artery** is the larger of the two terminal branches of the popliteal artery. It begins at the upper border of the Soleus, and ends deep to the flexor retinaculum by dividing into the *medial* and the *lateral plantar artery*. Venae comitantes and the tibial nerve accompany it. The Fl. Digitorum Longus lies medially (*fig. 456*); the Fl. Hallucis Longus lies laterally; the fascia covering the Tibialis Posterior, the shaft and lower end of the tibia, and the capsule of the ankle joint lie anteriorly. The Soleus is superficial to it above; near the ankle two layers of fascia cover it (*fig. 462*).

When this fascia is relaxed by inverting the foot, the pulsations of the artery can be felt the breadth of two tendons (Tibialis Posterior and Fl. Digitorum Longus) from the border of the medial malleolus.

The **Peroneal Artery** arises from the posterior tibial artery before the latter is crossed by the tibial nerve (*fig. 432*). It descends first behind the fascia covering the Tibialis Posterior and lies deep to the Fl. Hallucis Longus, which has spread across it; it then continues downward behind the fibula, distal tibiofibular joint, and ankle joint, and ends on the lateral surface of the calcaneus as the *lateral calcanean artery*.

Branches. Both the posterior tibial artery and its peroneal branch have *muscular*, *cutaneous*, *nutrient*, *communicating*, and *calcanean* branches.

The communicating br. unites the peroneal and posterior tibial arteries behind the lower end of the tibia. The peroneal artery ends as the lateral calcanean artery (see above). The posterior tibial artery and its lateral plantar branch give off *medial calcanean branches* which perforate the flexor retinaculum and supply the medial and inferior aspects of the heel. The peroneal artery gives off a *perforating branch* which "pierces" the interosseous membrane, runs down in front of the distal tibiofibular joint, and anastomoses on the lateral side of the ankle.

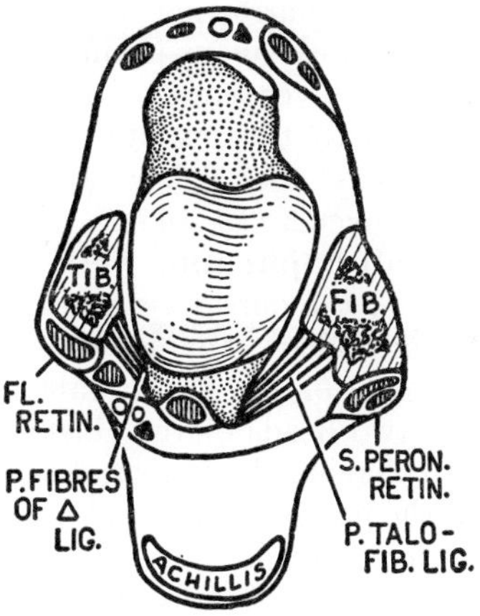

FIG. 462. Horizontal section through ankle joint showing (1) wedge-shaped socket, (2) direction of ligaments, (3) five posterior tendons, and (4) the investing and intermuscular deep fascia.

Variation of clinical importance. In cases where the anterior tibial artery fails to descend to the ankle (3.5 per cent of 536 limbs), the dorsalis pedis artery springs from the perforating peroneal artery.

Deep Fascia. The deep fascia at the back of the leg is in several sheets: (1) the investing layer, (2) the intermuscular layer between the Soleus and the three deep bipennate muscles, also (3) the layer covering Tibialis Posterior (pp. 409–410), and (4) the layer covering Popliteus (*fig. 461* and p. 409).

The Investing Deep Fascia is attached to the medial border of the tibia and posterior border of the tibial malleolus medially; and to the posterior crural septum and, through it, to the fibula laterally. No muscle arises from it; and it is not thick, except at the ankle where it forms strong medial and lateral bands, the *flexor retinaculum* and *superior peroneal retinaculum*. These stretch postero-inferiorly from the tibial and fibular malleoli, respectively, to the corresponding sides of the calcaneus.

The Intermuscular Layer of Fascia between the Soleus and the three deep bipennate muscles is limited above and at the sides by the horseshoe-shaped origin of the Soleus; below, it forms an anklet which holds in place the five deep tendons at the back of the ankle, so it is strong and is composed of transversely placed fibers. It is owing to the narrowing of the Soleus to form the tendo calcaneus [Achillis] that this intermuscular layer comes to the surface and blends with the investing deep fascia and reinforces the flexor and superior peroneal retinacula (*fig. 462*).

The Small Saphenous Vein drains the lateral end of the dorsal venous arch of the foot. It runs below the lateral malleolus, along the side of the tendo calcaneus, between the two heads of the Gastrocnemius, and, after piercing the popliteal fascia, ends partly in the popliteal vein and partly in the profunda femoris vein.

The cutaneous veins of the leg form an open anastomotic network between the great and small saphenous veins, and they communicate along the intermuscular septa with the deep veins. Above the ankle the valves in the communicating veins are so directed that the blood flows from the superficial veins into the deep veins, and from the small saphenous vein into the great saphenous vein.

Cutaneous Nerves (*fig. 425*): terminal twigs of the (1) posterior cutaneous nerve of the thigh, (2) medial cutaneous nerve of the thigh, and (3) obturator nerve (sometimes), all three of which end in the proximal part of the calf; (4) twigs of the saphenous nerve throughout the medial side of the leg; (5) the cutaneous branch of the medial popliteal (tibial) nerve, called the *sural nerve*, which descends in the furrow between the two heads of the Gastrocnemius and is joined at a variable level by (6) a cutaneous branch of the lateral popliteal (peroneal) nerve, called the *communicating peroneal n.*

The sural nerve continues with the *small* saphenous vein along the lateral border of the tendo Achillis, below the lateral malleolus, and along the lateral border of the foot to end as the digital nerve to the lateral side of the little toe. It communicates with the superficial peroneal nerve and commonly takes over part of its territory. The patterns formed by these nerves are numerous.

CHAPTER 27

BONES AND SOLE OF FOOT

BONES OF ARTICULATED FOOT

»» The study of the bones of the foot is too often undertaken as a difficult task. This should not be so, for if the student will give thought to the remarks describing the accompanying diagrams, verify the statements by referring to an articulated foot, and make use of his own foot to study the surface relations, he will find himself familiar in a practical way with the important details of the foot; and, when he comes to read in the textbook descriptions of the individual bones, he will find that he is able to anticipate much of what is written. He can, of course, test his own knowledge by reproducing the diagrams.

Examine the dorsum of an articulated foot and make the following observations:

1. *Outline.* The medial border of the foot is almost straight; the most projecting toe is the big toe, or quite commonly the 2nd (*fig. 463*).

2. The line joining the midpoints of the medial and lateral borders of the foot is oblique. In front of it lie the long bones—metatarsal bones and phalanges; behind it lie the tarsal bones, which are short or cubical bones.

The middle and distal phalanges are in reality nodular and rudimentary; those of the little toe are commonly fused together even in the feet of primitive peoples who wear no constricting footgear. The hallux has but two phalanges both of which are stout.

Metatarsals. Of the five metatarsals, the

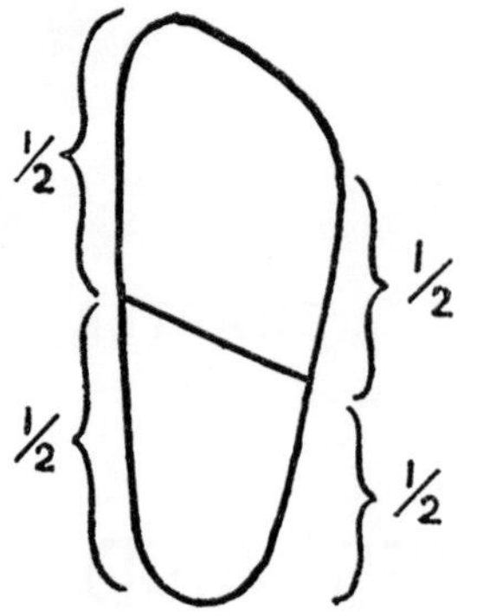

FIG. 463. The outline of the foot

FIG. 464. The dorsum of the foot

1st is the stoutest and strongest; the 2nd projects fore and aft the metatarsals on each side of it; the 5th has a pointed, projecting base (*fig. 464*).

»» *Metatarsals* are told from metacarpals by their length and side to side flattening. The 1st is rounded medially and dorsally, in conformation with the transverse arching of the foot; its lateral surface is flat; its base is kidney-shaped, the hilus being lateral. The student commonly refers it to the wrong side of the body.

3. *The Transverse Tarsal Joint.* The movements permitted at the ankle joint are flexion and extension; it is a hinge joint. When, therefore, you turn your foot in to obtain a view of the sole, that is when you invert your foot, some joint other than the ankle must be involved.

It is evident that to permit of this rotatory motion a joint or joints in which convex surfaces are in articulation with concave surfaces are requisite. This condition is found where the head of the talus, which is globular, fits into the posterior surface of the navicular, which is cup-shaped; and where the anterior surface of the calcaneus, which is cut away inferomedially, articulates with the posterior surface of the cuboid, which, being the counterpart, has a backwardly projecting process called the *calcanean angle* or *process.*

At these two joints, the *talonavicular* and *calcaneocuboid*, collectively known as the transverse tarsal joint, part of the movement of inversion and eversion takes place; it augments the more important movements at the talocalcanean joints.

4. *The Three "Units" of the Foot.* The

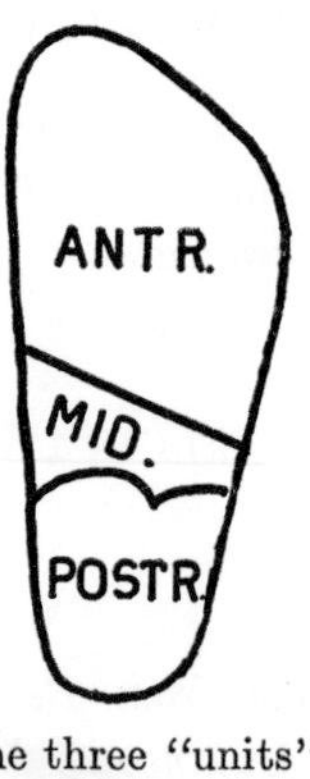

FIG. 465. The three "units" of the foot

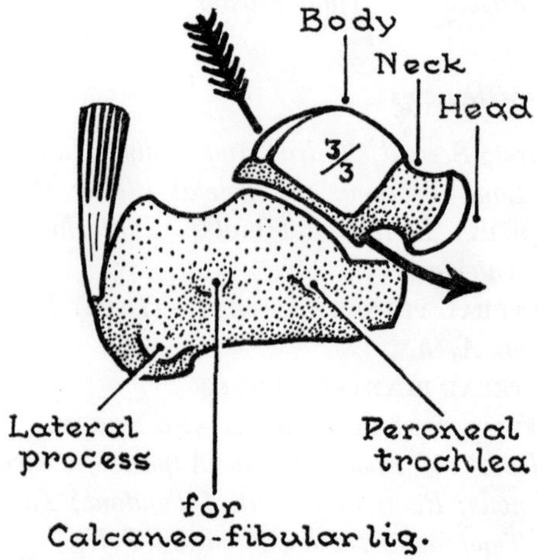

FIG. 466. Lateral aspects of talus and calcaneus. (The *arrow* traverses the tarsal tunnel.)

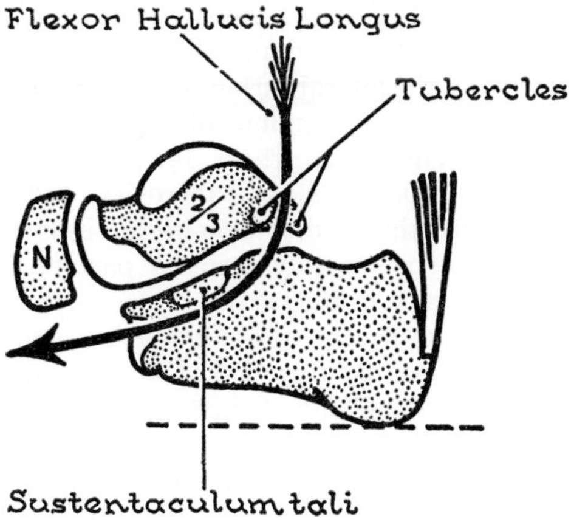

FIG. 467. The medial aspects of the talus and calcaneus.

obliquely placed tarsometatarsal articulation and the concavoconvex transverse tarsal joint of inversion and eversion serve to divide the foot into three units: anterior, middle, and posterior (*fig. 465*).

The Posterior Unit comprises the two large tarsal bones: talus and calcaneus (*figs. 464, 466* and *467*).

The **Talus** rests on the anterior two-thirds of the calcaneus and projects slightly in front of it. It has a body, neck, and head. The upper surface of the body supports the tibia, is entirely articular, and is saddle-shaped. The sides of the body are grasped by the malleoli, and the facets that result correspond in length and shape with those of the malleoli. The posterior surface of the body is restricted to two tubercles, a *medial* and a *lateral*, separated by a groove for Fl. Hallucis Longus tendon and, therefore, running downward and medially. The head is rounded in front to articulate with the navicular bone. Below, it partly rests on the calcaneus.

The **Calcaneus** is large and oblong. It is divided into three thirds. The anterior two-thirds supports the talus; the posterior one-third forms the prominence of the heel and rests on the ground. The anterior surface is wholly in articulation with the cuboid. The posterior third of the upper surface is saddle-shaped, horizontal, and free; the intermediate third is oblong, convex, articular, and oblique; the anterior third forms a nonarticular horizontal platform laterally, and has a small facet medially for the head of the talus. This facet is commonly continuous with a facet on a medially projecting shelf, the *sustentaculum tali.*

Pass a probe through the tunnel between talus and calcaneus. Enter it behind the sustentaculum and observe that it passes downwards and laterally and opens on to the anterior third of the upper surface of the calcaneus (*fig. 468*). The lateral surface is almost flat and vertical (*fig. 466*). It has a tubercle, the *peroneal trochlea*, placed ½ inch below the fibular malleolus and a fulness ½ inch behind this for the calcaneofibular ligament.

The medial surface is hollowed out between the sustentaculum and the posterior surface—deep enough to receive the thumb. The posterior surface [tuber calcanei] is nonarticular, and is wider below than above. It is continuous, on the plantar surface, with

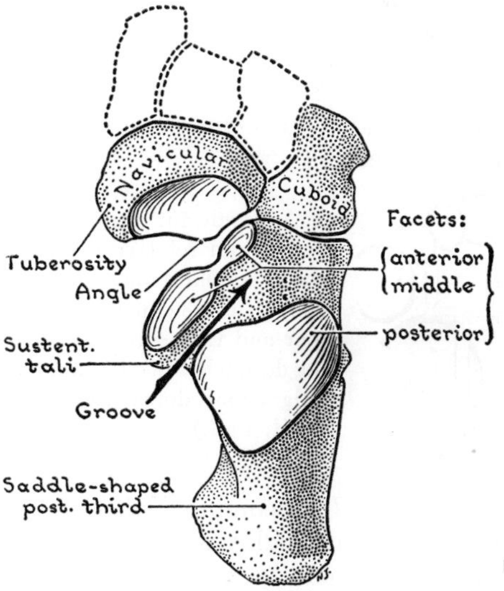

FIG. 468. The upper surface of the calcaneus

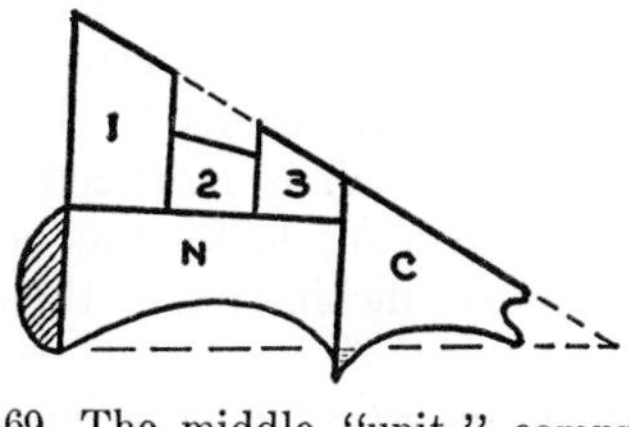

FIG. 469. The middle "unit," comprising the five small tarsal bones, is a modified wedge.

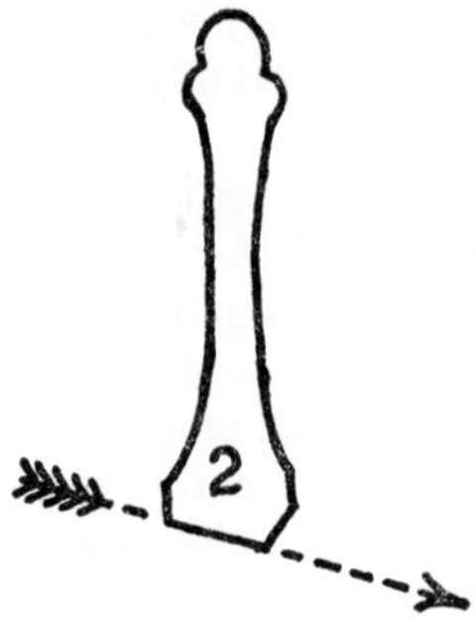

FIG. 470. The base tells the side

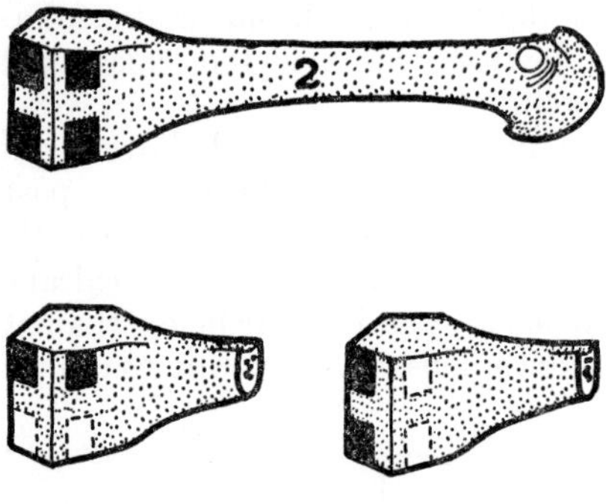

FIG. 471. Variations in metatarsal facets

a large medial process (tubercle) and a small lateral process.

As an aid for beginners to the names and relative positions of the 7 tarsal bones—calcaneus, cuboid, and 3 cuneiforms, navicular and talus—the accompanying design has been found useful. (Right foot, dorsal aspect, after G. H. Paff.)

The Middle Unit comprises the five small tarsal bones and roughly resembles a triangle or a wedge whose apex is lateral and base medial (*figs. 468* and *469*). The triangle is not geometrically perfect; the anterior side does not present a straight side to the five metatarsals, but is indented between the 1st and 3rd cuneiforms to receive the base of the 2nd metatarsal which is morticed between them. This morticing locks the bone and prevents side to side shifting of the anterior unit.

The posterior side, when viewed from behind, is seen to be doubly concave, so it allows of inversion and eversion of the middle unit on the posterior unit. The blunt apex, formed by the lateral surface of the cuboid, is grooved for the tendon of the Peroneus Longus. The base, where formed by the navicular, presents a tuberosity; where formed by the medial cuneiform, it is not distinctive but merely forms a part of the arched dorsum of the foot.

5. If you accept the following generalization and apply it, you will have no difficulty in converting figure 469 into the *shaded part* of figure 464. *Two continuous articular facets never, or hardly ever, lie in precisely the same plane; even when two facets on one bone are continuous with one another, they always, or almost always, meet at an angle, forming inclined planes.*

»» On putting this to the test you find that the anterior surface of the navicular presents to the cuneiforms not one plane but three; and that the medial surface of the cuboid presents to the navicular and lateral cuneiform not one plane but two. Again, the base of the 2nd metatarsal fits not into a square recess but into an obtuse angled one; and the bases of the 3rd, 4th, and 5th metatarsals occupy not one plane but three different planes for the lateral cuneiform projects beyond the cuboid, and the facets on the cuboid for the 4th and 5th metatarsals are inclined to one another. Hence, the oblique anterior surface of the wedge interlocks with the bases of the metatarsals.

The *posterolateral angles of the bases* of the 2nd, 3rd, 4th, and 5th metatarsals point to the sides to which they belong (*fig. 470*); not so the base of the 1st metatarsal. Its posterior surface is concave from side to side, suggesting that it once possessed a lateral hinge movement and that, like the great toe of the ape, it was at one time used for prehensile purposes.

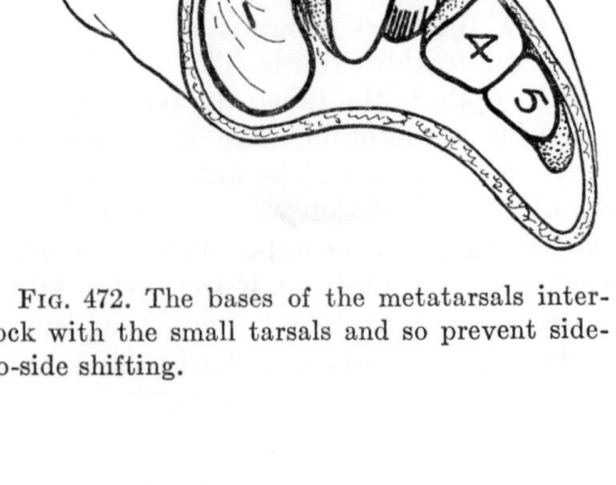

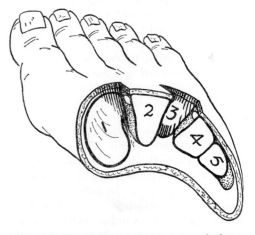

FIG. 472. The bases of the metatarsals interlock with the small tarsals and so prevent side-to-side shifting.

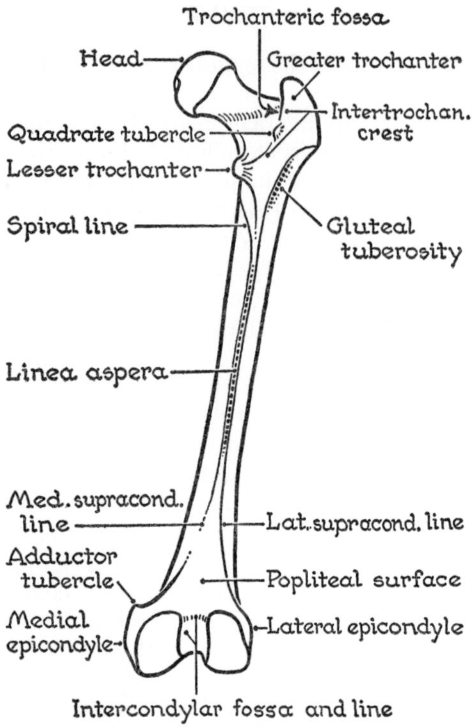

FIG. 403. The femur, posterior view

FIG. 404. The neck is the incurved shaft to which the trochanters are added.

oblique line that runs from the upper end of the greater trochanter downwards and medially to a point a finger's breadth in front of the lesser trochanter. This roughness, the *intertrochanteric line,* is due to the attachment of the massive iliofemoral ligament and slightly to the aponeurosis of the Vastus Medialis.

The posterior aspect of the neck is convex from above downward. It is separated from the shaft by a very prominent and rounded ridge, the *intertrochanteric crest,* that unites the two trochanters. The neck is buttressed below by a rounded strengthening bar that ascends from the lesser trochanter.

»» In the child the pelvis is narrow before the bladder descends into the pelvis; so, the neck and shaft of the femur are nearly in line with each other. As the pelvis widens the neck becomes more horizontal and the angle between neck and shaft becomes smaller (125° male).

The Lesser Trochanter is the traction epiphysis of the Iliopsoas. It is conical; it projects from the posterior surface of the bone; and it points medially. From it, three lines radiate: one runs upward and medially below the neck and buttresses it; the second (*the pectineal line*) runs downward and gives attachment to the aponeurosis of the Pectineus; the third runs upward and laterally and forms the lower half of the intertrochanteric crest.

The Greater Trochanter is the traction epiphysis of the Gluteus Medius and the Gluteus Minimus, (also of Piriformis, Obturator Internus and Gemelli, and Obturator Externus). The pull of the Gluteus Medius draws it upward, medially, and backward; so, its lateral surface is convex; its upper and posterior borders are free; and its highest point is its posterosuperior angle. Its anterior and lateral aspects would be flush with the corresponding aspects of the shaft but for the presence of a rough line that marks the site of fusion of the trochanter and shaft (*fig. 424*). A chisel driven along the upper border of the neck would remove the greater trochanter at this rough line of fusion. The aponeurosis of the Vastus Lateralis is in part responsible for the rough line in front and laterally.

A tubercle, called the *quadrate tubercle,* marks the site where this epiphyseal line crosses the intertrochanteric crest. The part of the crest above the tubercle is the posterior free border of the greater trochanter; the part below is the upwardly radiating line from the lesser trochanter.

On the medial side of the greater trochanter there is a circular depression, the *trochanteric fossa,* in which the Obturator Externus is inserted. From the fossa a shallow groove for the tendon of the Obturator

The *contiguous sides of the bases* of the lateral four metatarsals have articular facets (*fig. 471*). But there are no such facets between the bases of the 1st and 2nd metatarsals, thus indicating further that the great toe was once a free member like the thumb.

The 2nd metatarsal is morticed between the medial and lateral cuneiforms; hence, the anteroposterior facets on the 2nd metatarsal and 2nd cuneiform that face the 3rd metatarsal and 3rd cuneiform do not occupy a single plane, but three. The facets on the medial side of the base of the 4th metatarsal for the 3rd cuneiform and 3rd metatarsal are nearly, but not quite, flush with each other. To the generalization enunciated above there is, then, no exception in the foot.

This interlocking of the various bones results in an increase in the stability of the foot; it prevents side-shifting of the bones, and to that extent it is beneficial (*fig. 472*).

6. *Arches.* The foot is described as having two longitudinal arches. It should be remembered that the human foot is designed not for standing, but for walking. It is not a static structure, a piece of masonry, but an active structure. Regard it, then, as a spring rather than as an arch.

The three medial digits, their metatarsals, and cuneiforms, the navicular and talus, which are collectively known as the *medial longitudinal arch* (spring) of the foot, can be detached from the two lateral digits, their metatarsals, the cuboid and the calcaneus, collectively known as the *lateral longitudinal arch* (spring). Perhaps it is better to regard the calcaneus as common to both springs (*figs. 473* and *538*).

The foot is arched not only longitudinally but also transversely, the dorsum being

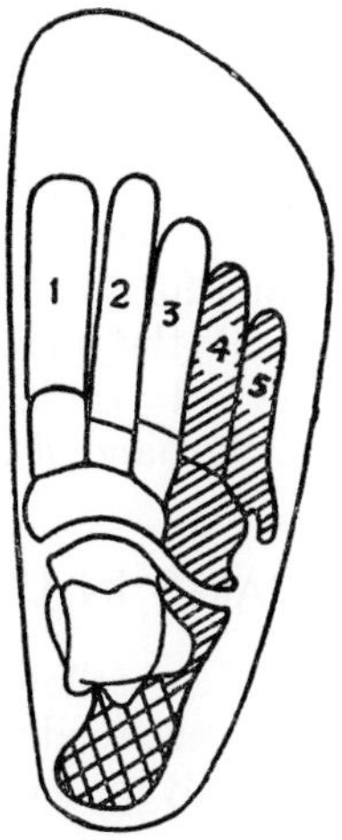

FIG. 473. The medial and lateral longitudinal arches. The calcaneus is common to both.

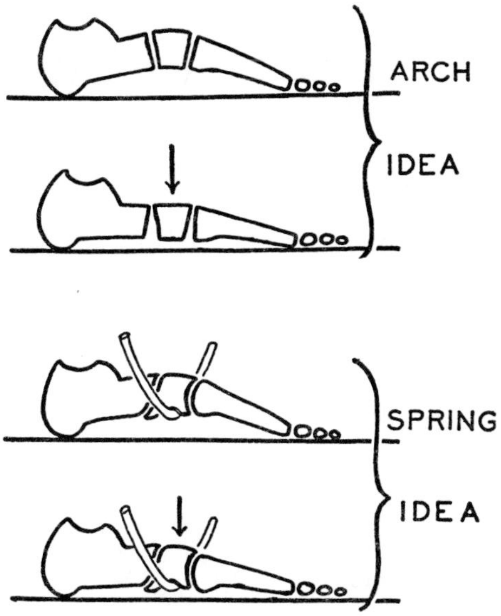

FIG. 474. The foot has certain features of a spring.

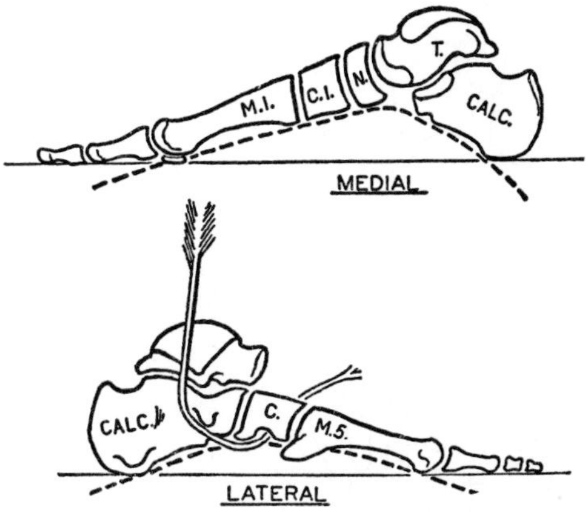

FIG. 475. The medial and lateral longitudinal arches.

convex both anteroposteriorly and from side to side; the plantar aspect is concave in both directions. Each *transverse arch* forms only half an arch. Have this in mind when you orient a tarsal or a metatarsal bone (*figs. 472* and *536*).

7. *Viewed from the lateral side* the foot appears as a low, flat arch of which the posterior pillar is the medial process of the calcaneus; the anterior pillar, the heads of the 4th and 5th metatarsals (*fig. 474*). Though the cuboid occupies the position of a

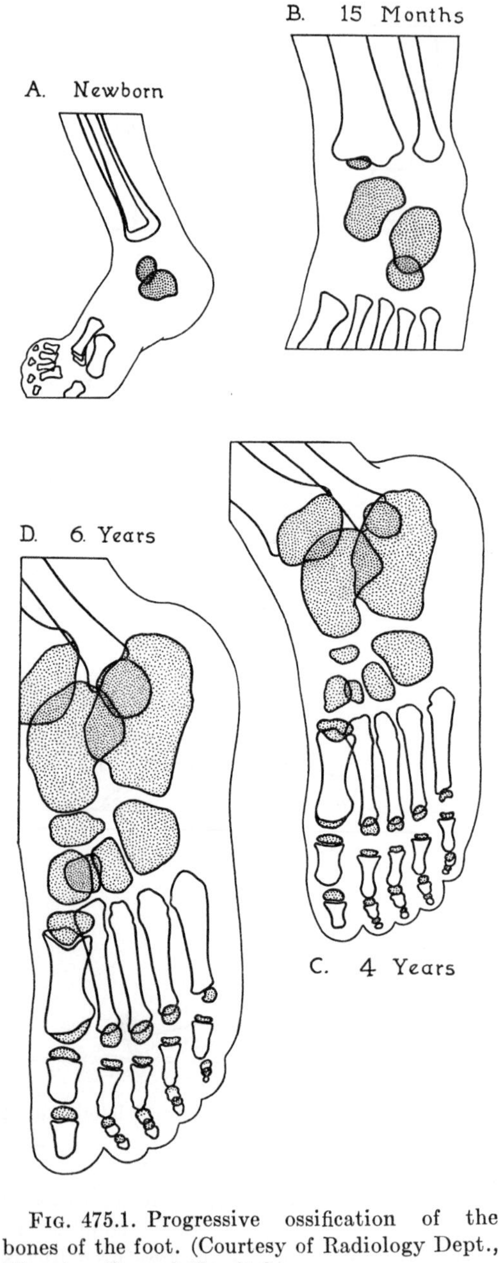

FIG. 475.1. Progressive ossification of the bones of the foot. (Courtesy of Radiology Dept., Kingston General Hospital.)

keystone, it receives the support of the *Peroneus Longus*, which passes below it. When you stand, the spring tends to flatten under your weight, the cubometatarsal joints being hinge joints, as are the corresponding joints in the hand. (The supporting mechanisms are described on page 456.)

8. *Viewed from the medial side* the foot appears highly arched. The medial process of the calcaneus forms the posterior pillar; the heads of the 1st, 2nd, and 3rd metatarsals and the sesamoid bones under the head of the 1st form the anterior pillar (*fig. 475*). The summit of this arch lies at the junction of its posterior one-third and anterior two-thirds.

The round head of the talus is placed at the summit, between the sustentaculum tali and the tuberosity of the navicular, and here receives no bony support. But the spring ligament (plantar calcaneonavicular), which extends between these two bony processes, lies below the head and supports it (*fig. 533*). The spring ligament is in turn supported by the tendon of the *Tibialis Posterior*, whose main attachment is to the tuberosity of the navicular.

Ossification of the Bones of the Foot. X-ray photographs (*fig. 475.1*) show that at the time of birth the calcaneus and talus are well ossified and the cuboid is starting to ossify. The sequence is calcaneus, talus, cuboid, 3rd, 1st, 2nd cuneiform, navicular, epiphysis of calcaneus (table 9 on p. 195).

The calcaneus is the only short bone (either tarsal or carpal) that regularly has an epiphysis. This epiphysis gives attachment to the tendo calcaneus and the plantar aponeurosis; hence, it includes the posterior surface and the processes of the calcaneus (*fig. 457*). It appears about the 11th year and fuses about the 17th year.

The metatarsals and phalanges have each a primary center for the body, which appears about the 3rd prenatal month, and secondary centers for the heads of the 2nd–5th metatarsals and for the bases of the 1st metatarsal and all the phalanges. These appear about the 3rd year and fuse about the 18th year (*cf.* the hand, *fig. 140*).

IDENTIFIABLE PARTS IN LIVING FOOT

Familiarity with the following important bony parts, joint levels, tendons, and vessels of the foot can easily be acquired from a study of your own foot:

1. The blunt end of the medial malleolus.

2. The sustentaculum tali lying a full inch below the malleolus.

3. The tuberosity of the navicular lying 1½″ in front of the sustentaculum.

4. The head of the talus, occupying the space between these two. All four are easily palpated, and may indeed be rendered visible through the skin. In palpating the tip of the malleolus, the sustentaculum, and the tuberosity, *approach them from below.*

5. The position of the joint between the base of the first metatarsal and its cuneiform may be gauged to be the breadth of a cuneiform, 1″ anterior to the tuberosity of the navicular.

6. The sesamoid bones, which play on the under surface of the head of the 1st metatarsal, may be felt under the ball of the big toe (*figs. 476, 481,* and *483*).

7. Just distal to them is the 1st metatarsophalangeal joint. Verify this by flexing the toes when the rounded head of the metatarsal, which is thereby uncovered, may be felt.

8. The lateral malleolus is visible; its pointed end is ¾″ lower than the medial malleolus and on a posterior plane.

9. The subcutaneous surface of the lateral malleolus extends like an isosceles triangle for 3 or 4 inches up the shaft of the fibula; and from its apex the submerged anterior border of the bone, which gives attachment to the anterior crural (peroneal) septum, continues up the fibula to its head (*fig. 451*).

10. The projecting base of the 5th metatarsal is easily felt about half way along the lateral border of the foot.

11. The calcaneocuboid joint lies two-thirds of the way between the tip of the lateral malleolus and the projecting base of the 5th metatarsal.

12. Verify this by inverting the foot and palpating the superolateral portion of the anterior surface of the calcaneus which is thereby uncovered. This is easily done.

13. With the foot still inverted, palpate the upper part of the front of the head of the talus. It lies just superomedial to the front of the calcaneus and marks the site of the talonavicular joint. It is evident that at these two joints, collectively called the transverse tarsal joint, movements of inversion and eversion take place.

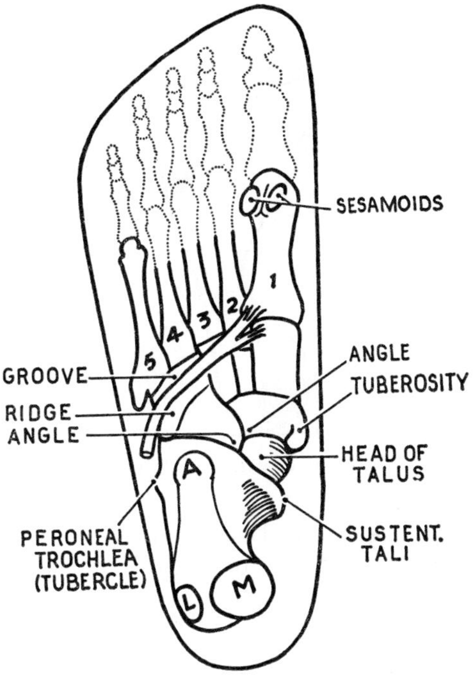

FIG. 476. The chief features of the plantar aspect of the articulated foot.

14. Of necessity the muscles of inversion and eversion, the *2 Tibiales* and the *3 Peronei,* must be inserted anterior to the transverse tarsal joint. With the foot inverted and ankle plantarflexed, the tendon of the Tibialis Posterior may be felt as it passes midway between the medial malleolus and the sustentaculum tali on its way to the tuberosity of the navicular. Here it lies superficial to the deltoid ligament. With the foot inverted and the ankle dorsiflexed, the tendon of the Tibialis Anterior may be observed an inch anterior to the medial malleolus, as it passes toward its insertion into the lower part of the medial surface of the 1st metatarsal and adjacent part of the 1st cuneiform (*fig. 484*).

15. Now, with the foot everted, trace the tendons of the Peronei Longus et Brevis as they turn forward below the lateral malleolus; the Brevis to pass to the upper surface of the base of the 5th metatarsal, the Longus to pass into the sole of the foot in the groove on the cuboid, and therefore just behind the base of the 5th metatarsal (*fig. 451*).

16. The tendons of the Ex. Hallucis

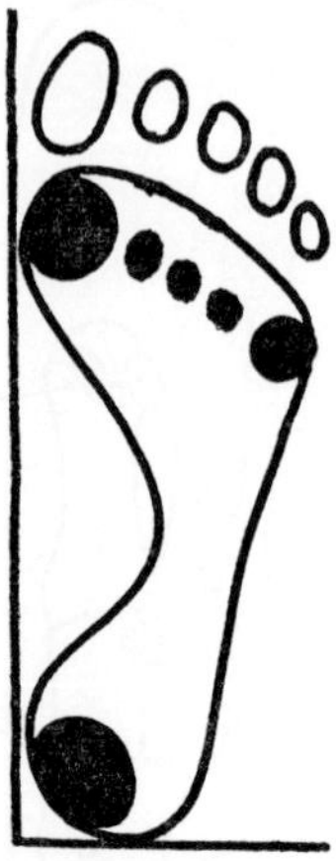

FIG. 477. The bearing points of the foot

Longus and Ex. Digitorum Longus can generally be made to stand out on the dorsum of the foot.

17. The soft cushion-like mass in front of the lateral malleolus, caused by the relaxed Ex. Digitorum Brevis, is apt to be mistaken for a swelling, the result of a sprain.

18. The pulsation of the anterior tibial artery may be felt midway between the two malleoli where two tendons (Tibialis Anterior and Ex. Hallucis Longus) lie medial to it, and two tendons (Ex. Digitorum Longus and Peroneus Tertius) lie lateral (*figs. 445* and *462*).

19. On the dorsum of the foot the pulsation of the dorsalis pedis artery may, perhaps, be made out on the line leading to the first intermetatarsal space. The posterior tibial artery may be felt to pulsate the breadth of two tendons (Tibialis Posterior and Flexor Digitorum Longus) behind the medial malleolus. For success in this, the foot should be slightly inverted (passively) in order to relax the fascia, and you should palpate firmly forward and laterally (*fig. 489*).

THE SOLE OF THE FOOT

In the following pages on the foot, the student will recognize many structures (bones, muscles, vessels, nerves and fasciae) as homologues of those already met in the hand.

Articulated Foot from Below

The 3 units (anterior, middle, posterior), so conspicuous in the foot viewed from above, are in evidence when viewed from below (*fig. 476*). The features of particular note fall into three groups:

1. *The Bearing Points of the Foot* are the *medial process of the calcaneus* posteriorly, and the *heads of the five metatarsal bones* anteriorly—the *two sesamoid bones* that play one on each side of the V-shaped ridge below the head of the 1st metatarsal raise that head off the ground (*fig. 477*).

These bearing points are, of course, the ends of the longitudinal arches of the foot, the posterior point being common to both. (See also pp. 417–418.)

2. *The Five Processes of the Calcaneus*—three on the plantar surface and one on each side: In addition to the *medial process*, which is large and weight-bearing, a small *lateral process* and a small (anterior) *tubercle* project from the under surface of the calcaneus. A pulley projects from each side of the calcaneus—the *sustentaculum tali* medially, the *peroneal trochlea* laterally.

The *Flexor Hallucis Longus* grooves the under surface of the sustentaculum and subsequently passes between the two sesamoid bones. The *Peroneus Longus* grooves the side of the calcaneus below the peroneal trochlea and is bound to it by the inferior peroneal retinaculum. Thereafter, it passes obliquely across the sole to the adjacent parts of the 1st metatarsal and 1st cuneiform. It makes a *groove* under the cuboid and therefore a *ridge* also.

3. *The Transverse Tarsal Joint.* The part of the inferior surface of the cuboid behind the ridge is large and triangular. It ends behind in the *calcanean angle*, which lies below the calcaneus, which is cut away to receive it. The under surface of the navicular also has an *angle* which is almost on a level with its *tuberosity*. The head of the talus is without bony support between the sustentaculum tali behind and the tuberosity and angle of the navicular in front.

Function of the Toes. In man their function is to press into the ground and there to form a friction surface during the act of walking.

They afford a purchase for the forward thrust of the body at each step. If there were no toes, when the heel left the ground one would rise on the uneven heads of the metatarsals.

Superficial Structures. The epidermis and dermis are both much thicker on the palms and soles than elsewhere. It is so at birth. With intermittent pressure and friction the thickness increases. The subcutaneous fat is contained within small fibrous compartments that serve as cushions.

Cutaneous Nerves: The medial plantar nerve supplies the 3½ digits on the hallux side of the foot, just as the median nerve supplies the 3½ digits on the pollex side of the hand, leaving the lateral plantar nerve, which corresponds to the ulnar nerve in the hand, to supply 1½ digits (*fig. 479*). The skin under the heel is supplied by the medial calcanean branches of the posterior tibial nerve which pierce the flexor retinaculum with their companion arteries (*fig. 489*).

»» **A Complete Display of the Sole** can be made by reflecting or excising the *four central structures:*

1. The plantar aponeurosis.
2. *The Flexor Digitorum Brevis.*
3. *The Flexor Digitorum Longus.*
4. *The Adductor Hallucis Obliquus.*

and by so doing you leave the marginal structures intact thereby preserving the outline of the foot.

The Plantar Fascia (*fig. 478*). In lower mammals the **plantar aponeurosis,** or central portion of the plantar fascia, is continuous with the Plantaris behind the calcaneus; in man it has become detached from the sural portion of the Plantaris and modified to act as a strong tie for the longitudinal arches of the foot (p. 457). Posteriorly, it is attached to the front of the medial process of the calcaneus; anteriorly, it splits into five bands, one for each digit (*fig. 478*), to be attached as in the hand (p. 151). The *medial* and *lateral portions* of the plantar fascia cover the abductors of the great and little toes and are thin, except for one strong *cord* (sometimes fleshy) that passes from the medial process of the calcaneus to the tip of the projecting base of the 5th metatarsal, and is presumably responsible for its shape and direction.

Observe that dorsiflexion of the toes, as in walking, renders the plantar aponeurosis taut.

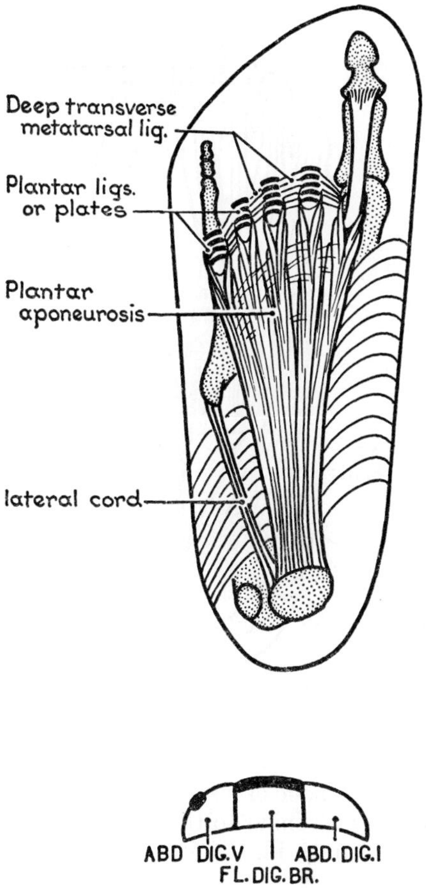

FIG. 478. The plantar fascia

Plantar Muscles

These are arranged in four layers.

First or Superficial Layer:

These arise from the calcaneus (*fig. 479*).

1. Flexor Digitorum Brevis (inserted into middle phalanges).
2. Abductor Hallucis and
3. Abductor Digiti Quinti (inserted into proximal phalanges).

Each of these lies deep to the plantar fascia encased in a fascial compartment of its own (*fig. 478*). *The Flexor Digitorum Brevis* lies deep to the plantar aponeurosis, and to display it this must be reflected. It arises mainly from the aponeurosis and slightly from the medial process of the cal-

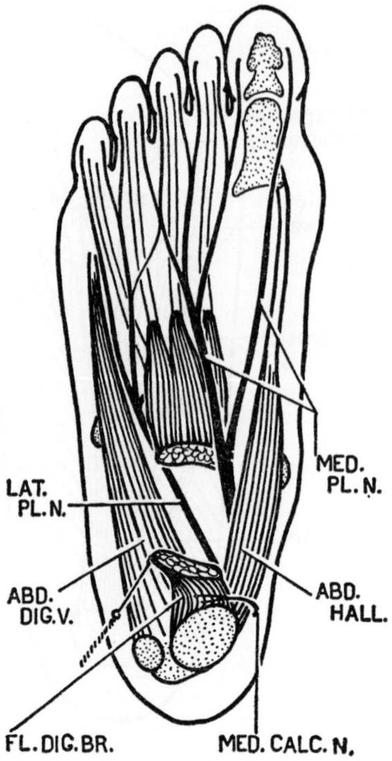

FIG. 479. The first layer of muscles

caneus. Its mode of insertion into the middle phalanges is similar to that of its homologue in the hand, Fl. Digitorum Superficialis (*fig. 150*).

The abductors of the 1st and 5th digits have a continuous fleshy origin; the *Abductor Digiti V* arising from the front of the lateral and medial processes; the *Abductor Hallucis* from the medial side of the medial process as well as from the lower border of the flexor retinaculum. Each abductor derives a slight origin from the fascia covering it and from the septum between it and the Fl. Digitorum Brevis.

The insertions are into the bases of the proximal phalanges. Though these two muscles are abductors morphologically, they are not employed as such in man, who finds no occasion to abduct his toes, but as elastic ties for their respective arches (*fig. 480*).

The direction of the pull of the fibers of the Abd. Digiti V and the fact that it is inserted more into the under than into the lateral side of the proximal phalanx causes it to behave as a flexor.

Second Layer of Muscles (*fig. 481*).

1. Flexor Digitorum Longus.
2. Quadratus Plantae or
 Flexor Accessorius.
3. Lumbricals.
4. Flexor Hallucis Longus.

The Fl. Digitorum Longus and Fl. Hallucis Longus are obviously the homologues of the deep digital flexors of the hand, viz., Fl. Digitorum Profundus and Fl. Pollicis Longus.

»» **To display the 2nd layer,** it is necessary to remove one muscle, Fl. Digitorum Brevis. And it is wise to retain the two abductors, thereby preserving the outline of the foot. When this is done, the muscles of this layer are seen lying within a triangular frame the

FIG. 480. The short plantar muscles act as elastic springs or ties for the arches of the foot.

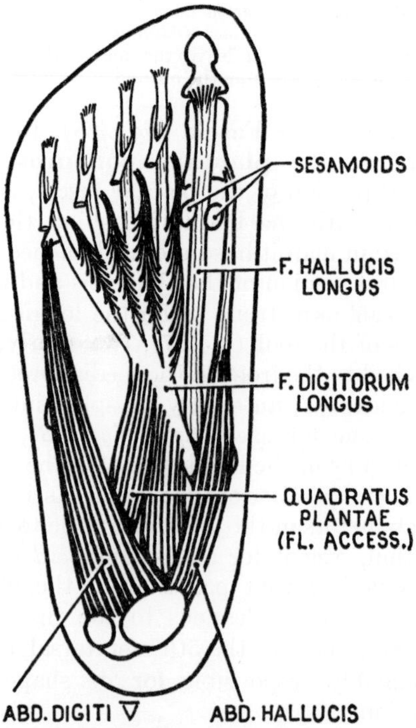

FIG. 481. The second layer of muscles displayed by removal of the Flexor Digitorum Brevis.

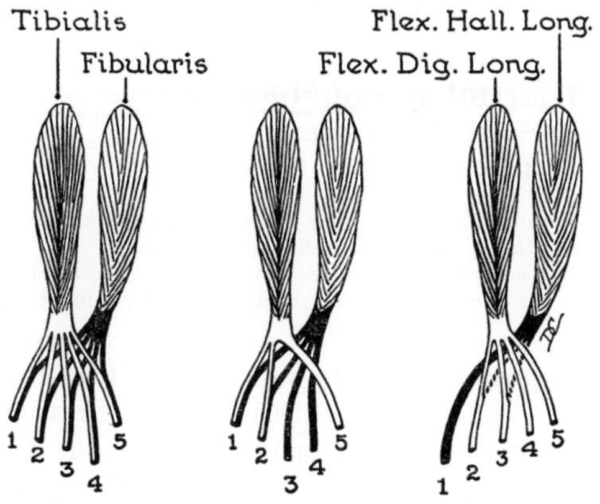

FIG. 482. Scheme explaining the crossing of the long digital flexors. (After Straus.)

sides of which are formed by the abductors, the base by the roots of the five digits (*fig. 481*).

The tendon of the *Fl. Digitorum Longus* is the central structure within this frame. It has already been seen crossing superficial to the tendon of the Tibialis Posterior at the back of the medial malleolus; it is now seen appearing from under cover of the Abductor Hallucis and crossing superficial to the tendon of the Fl. Hallucis Longus, abreast of the tuberosity of the navicular bone. It is, then, twice superficial.

Insertion. As for Fl. Digitorum Profundus, see figure 150.

The Quadratus Plantae [Fl. Accessorius] arises from the medial side of the calcaneus (*fig. 488*), and it is inserted into the tendon of the Fl. Digitorum Longus (*fig. 481*).

The four Lumbricals arise from the tendons of the Fl. Digitorum Longus and are inserted into the dorsal digital expansions.

The Flexor Hallucis Longus tendon, beyond the point at which it is crossed by the Fl. Digitorum Longus, runs along the lower surface of the Fl. Hallucis Brevis, passes onward between the sesamoid bones developed in the tendons of insertion of this short flexor, and finally is inserted into the distal phalanx of the hallux. The Fl. Hallucis Longus, however, also sends fibrous slips to those tendons of the Fl. Digitorum Longus that pass to the 2nd (and 3rd) digits.

»» EXPLANATORY NOTE. Primitively both the Fl. Hallucis and the Fl. Digitorum send slips to each of the five digits (*fig. 482*), but as the primate scale is ascended the muscle arising from the fibula concentrates its attention, apparently for mechanical reasons, on the medial side of the foot, whereas the muscle arising from the tibia concentrates on the lateral side. This is the explanation of the strange crossing and variable connections of the long digital flexors.

Third Layer of Muscles (*fig. 483*).

1. Flexor Hallucis Brevis.
2. Flexor Digiti Quinti and
3. Adductor Hallucis Transversus
   (form three sides of a square open posteriorly).
4. Adductor Hallucis Obliquus
   (largely fills the square).

The muscles of the third and fourth layers practically confine themselves to the anterior half of the foot. They could be studied in a specimen disarticulated at the tarsometatarsal joint.

»» In order to obtain access to the 3rd layer, the Fl. Digitorum Longus and the Quadratus Plantae should be divided far back and thrown with the Lumbricals well forward.

The base of each metatarsal may be thought of as giving origin to a muscle, the

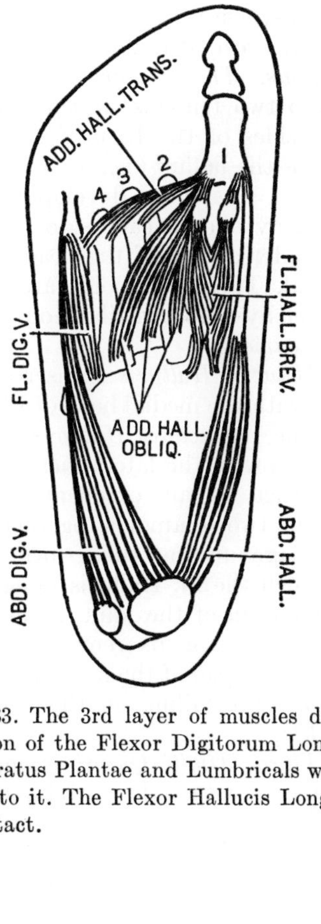

FIG. 483. The 3rd layer of muscles displayed by excision of the Flexor Digitorum Longus and the Quadratus Plantae and Lumbricals which are attached to it. The Flexor Hallucis Longus may be left intact.

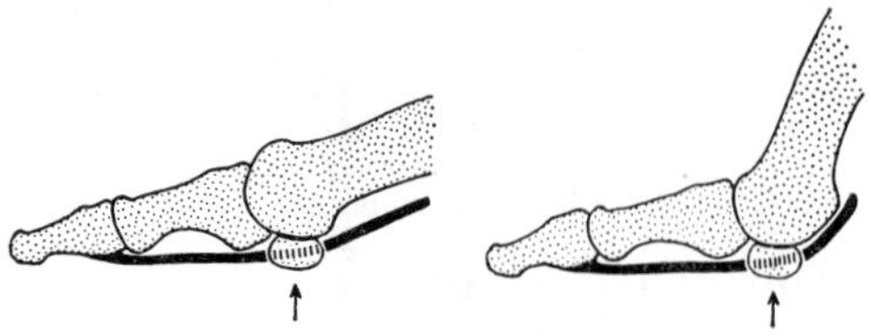

FIG. 483.1. The sesamoids are always the bearing points for the head of the 1st metatarsal, allowing free play for the long flexor tendon.

1st metatarsal to the *Flexor Hallucis Brevis*, the 2nd, 3rd, and 4th to the *Adductor Hallucis Obliquus*, and the 5th to the *Flexor Digiti Quinti.*

»» Truly, a few of the fleshy fibers of the last two muscles creep back on to the long plantar ligament which is attached to the bases of 2nd, 3rd, 4th, 5th metatarsals, and in point of accuracy the Flexor Hallucis Brevis does not arise from the base of its own metatarsal, but by means of two fibrous slips prolonged backward to the tendon of the Tibialis Posterior and either the 3rd cuneiform or cuboid.

The remaining muscle of this layer, the *Adductor Hallucis Transversus*, is a diminutive structure that springs from the tissues (deep transverse metatarsal ligs.) about the heads of the 5th, 4th, and 3rd metatarsals.

Insertions. The Flexor Hallucis Brevis splits into two tendons, which are inserted into the sides of the base of the proximal phalanx of the hallux (*fig. 483*).

The two sesamoids developed in these tendons play one on each side of the ridge on the under aspect of the head of the 1st metatarsal. These sesamoids are united to each other by a fibrocartilaginous plate, the *plantar ligament.*

The Abductor Hallucis is inserted in conjunction with the medial head of Fl. Hallucis Brevis; the *Adductores Hallucis Obliquus et Transversus* with the lateral head.

Here then is an excellent mechanical device: the two sesamoids together with the fibrocartilage uniting them form a pulley under which the Fl. Hallucis Longus glides. With extension of the joint, as in rising on tiptoes, the sesamoids remain the bearing points for the head of the metatarsal without undue pressure falling on the long tendon (*fig. 483.1*).

The Flexor Digiti Quinti is inserted in conjunction with the Abductor Digiti Quinti into the plantar aspect and lateral side of the proximal phalanx of the little toe.

Fourth Layer of Muscles:

1. Seven Interossei.
2. Two tendons on the skeletal plane.

»» To obtain access to the 4th layer, one large muscle, Add. Hallucis Obliquus, must be removed.

For complete exposure, Add. Hallucis Transversus and the deep transverse metatarsal ligs. must be severed.

Interossei, 4 Dorsal and 3 Plantar. These seven muscles are similar to their homologues in the hand, except that the axis runs through the 2nd metatarsal, not the 3rd. The dorsal muscles abduct and the plantar adduct.

»» *Explanatory:* Each of the five toes is fundamentally capable of being abducted and adducted, and 10 muscles are required to perform the 10 movements. The great toe has its own abductor and adductor and the little toe has its own abductor, accounting for 3 of the 10 required muscles. Seven Interossei perform the remaining seven movements.

From the dorsum of the foot, an Interosseus is seen to arise in bipennate manner from the adjacent sides of two metatarsal bones, and to fill each of the four intermetatarsal spaces. These are the four Dorsal Interossei. By exclusion there are three Plantar Interossei. They are unipennate and they arise from the plantar border of the metatarsal of the toe on which they act—3rd, 4th, and 5th.

Each is inserted partly into the side of a proximal phalanx and partly into a dorsal expansion.

Actions and *Functions.* In walking, the Interossei flex the metatarsophalangeal joints and thereby draw the heads of the metatarsals together (i.e., they keep the foot from spreading), and they extend the interphalangeal joints and thereby keep the toes from curling up.

Two Long Tendons on Skeletal Plane. The Tibialis Posterior and the Peroneus Longus belong to the ligamentous or deepest layer of the posterior half of the foot. They enter the sole below the summits of their respective arches, i.e., beneath the head of the talus and beneath the cuboid. One being an invertor of the foot, the other an evertor, they must find attachment in front of the transverse tarsal articulation.

1. The **Peroneus Longus** enters the sole deep to the Abductor Digiti V, passes obliquely across the sole in the groove on the cuboid (which the anterior fibers of the long plantar ligament convert into a tunnel) to its insertion into the lateral side

of the base of the first metatarsal and adjacent part of the first cuneiform (*fig. 476*).

Within the tunnel, the tendon is wrapped in a synovial sheath that is commonly continuous with the sheath on the side of the foot.

The *Tibialis Anterior* is inserted into the same two bones as the Peroneus Longus, but on their medial side (*fig. 484*); so, together these two muscles form a stirrup beneath the middle of the sole of the foot.

2. The **Tibialis Posterior** (*fig. 484*) sends two-thirds of its tendon to be inserted into the tuberosity of the navicular and some fibers, passing beyond this, reach the under surface of the first cuneiform. The remaining one-third divides into a number of finger-like bands that pass below the spring ligament and diverge to reach the cuboid, cuneiforms, and 2nd, 3rd, 4th metatarsal bases. The anterior parts of the bands are often dissociated into a series of short plantar ligaments. Indeed, the tendon may be said to spread like an open hand to grasp all the small tarsal bones and most of the metatarsals—i.e., the bones anterior to the transverse tarsal joint—and to draw them medially, backward, and upward. Its pull criss-crosses that of the Peroneus Longus, so between them they create the transverse arch and support the longitudinal arches.

Plantar Vessels and Nerves

The Lateral Plantar Artery (*fig. 487*) is much larger than the medial plantar

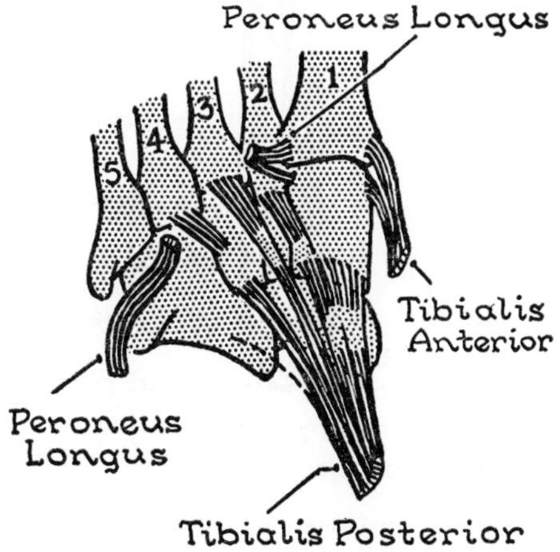

FIG. 484. The grasp of the Tibialis Posterior extends to the small tarsals and to the metatarsals.

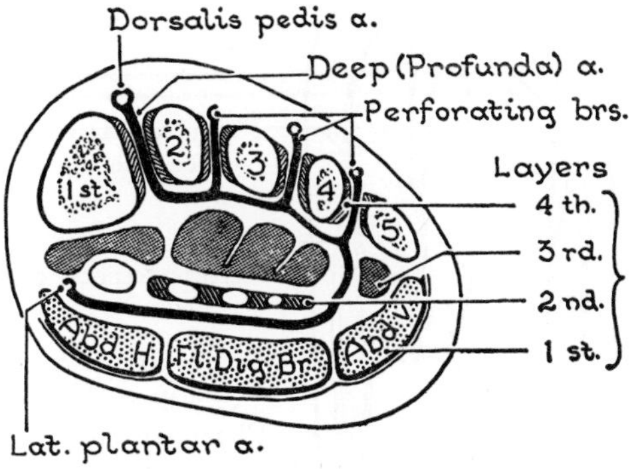

FIG. 485. Scheme to show the lateral plantar artery coursing first between the 1st and 2nd layers of muscles, then between the 3rd and 4th layers.

FIG. 486. Scheme of arteries in the anterior part of the foot (compare with *fig. 155*).

artery. It is, therefore, the continuation of the posterior tibial artery, in fact if not in name. It appears from under cover of the Abductor Hallucis and, with its companion nerve, runs forward and laterally between the 1st and 2nd layers of muscles (represented by Fl. Digitorum Brevis and Quadratus Plantae). Then, dipping deeper, it runs medially between the 3rd and 4th layers (represented by Add. Hallucis Obliquus and the Interossei, *fig. 485*), to anastomose with the deep branch of the dorsalis pedis artery, thereby forming the (deep) **plantar arch** exactly as the deep branch of the ulnar artery and the radial artery form the deep palmar arch.

The arteries of the anterior half of the foot are arranged like the arteries of the hand (*fig. 486*). There are several anastomotic channels through which the bloodstream has the option of flowing. In no case, however, are more than a few channels well developed.

BRANCHES. The deep branch of the dorsalis pedis a. is but an enlarged (1st) perforating a. (*fig. 485*). From the deep plantar arch spring: (1) the three other *perforating aa.*,

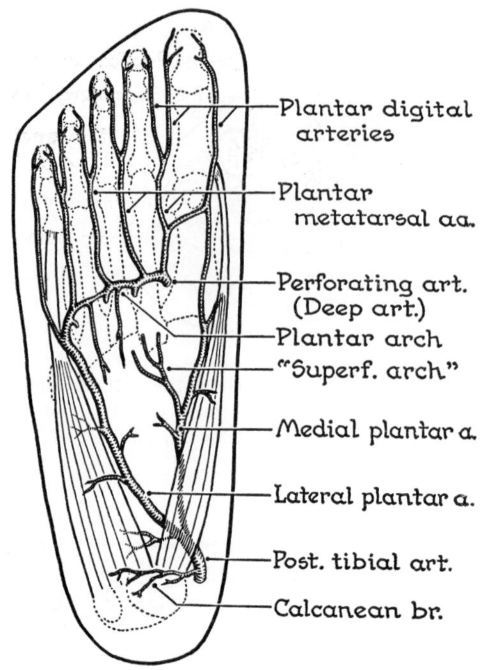

FIG. 487. The plantar arteries

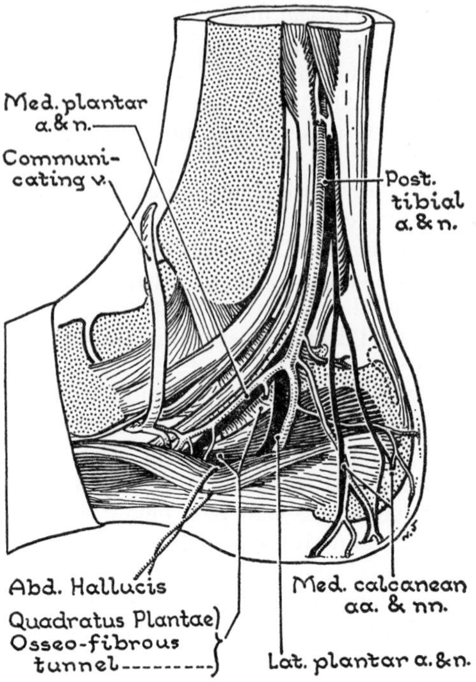

FIG. 489. "At the door of the foot"—structures passing deep to the Abductor Hallucis.

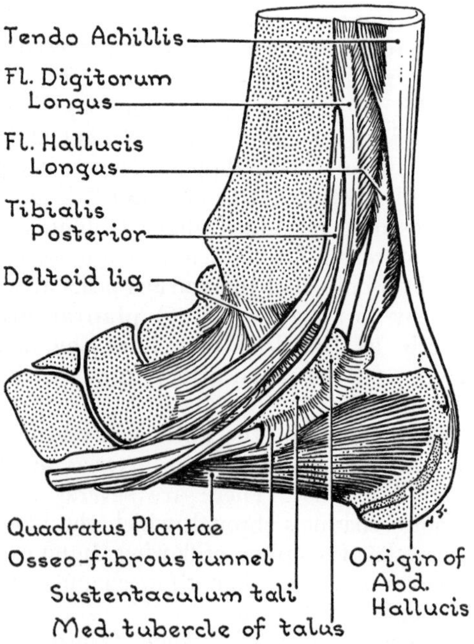

FIG. 488. The tendons of the 3 deep muscles, at the ankle.

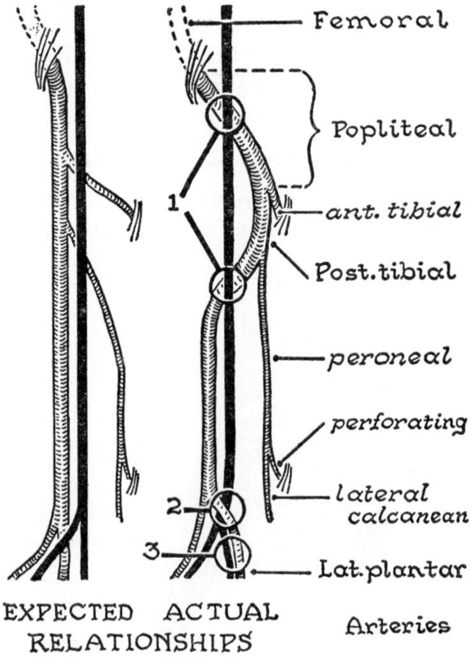

FIG. 490. Unexpected relationships of arteries to nerves.

which join the dorsal metatarsal aa.; (2) four *plantar metatarsal aa.*, which bifurcate into *plantar digital aa.*; and (3) a branch to the medial side of the big toe and one to the lateral side of the little toe.

The **Lateral Plantar Nerve** follows its artery closely and sends: (1) cutaneous branches to the lateral 1½ digits, and (2) motor branches to all the muscles of the sole not supplied by the medial plantar nerve. This includes all seven Interossei and the Adductor Hallucis (*cf.* ulnar nerve).

The **Medial Plantar Artery and Nerve** runs forward in the furrow between the Abductor Hallucis and the Flexor Digitorum Brevis. The nerve, like the median nerve of the hand, sends:

1. Cutaneous branches to 3½ digits which fan out subjacent to the plantar fascia.
2. Motor branches to the four muscles between which the nerve runs, namely:
   a. Abductor Hallucis
   b. Flexor Digitorum Brevis
   c. Flexor Hallucis Brevis
   d. Lumbricalis I.

Delicate common plantar digital arteries spring from an ill-developed superficial plantar arch (*fig. 487*).

"The Door of the Foot". (1) Since the lateral and medial plantar vessels and nerves and three tendons enter the sole on the medial side by passing deep to the Abductor Hallucis, this entrance may be thought of as the door of the sole of the foot. (2) The Peroneus Longus enters on the lateral side deep to the Abductor Digiti V, through the back door, so to speak. (3) The perforating vessels pass through the intermetatarsal spaces, as it were, through windows. The Abductor Hallucis, then, guards the door (*fig. 489*).

Medial Aspect of the Calcaneus. Not until the Abductor Hallucis is reflected and the plantar vessels and nerves are displaced can access to the Flexor Hallucis Longus be obtained where it lies in the groove between the two tubercles of the talus and winds under the sustentaculum tali. Even then the tendon is not seen till the fibrous part of the osseofibrous tunnel in which it is running is slit up.

The Quadratus Plantae arises from most of the medial surface of the calcaneus behind the tunnel (*fig. 488*) and forms there a soft muscular pad for the vessels and nerves.

»» A small fibrous lateral head arises from the under surface of the calcaneus just in front of the lateral process.

Rearrangement of Tendons. In this neighborhood the tendons, vessels, and nerves adjust their positions before finally dispersing. Here is a sorting house.

On crossing its portals, the various structures pass almost directly to their destinations. It will be remem-

*Segmental Innervation of Muscles of Leg and Foot**

Muscles	L. 4	L. 5	S. 1	S. 2
Tibialis Anterior	x	x		
Popliteus, Plantaris	x	x	x	
Peroneus Tertius	x	x	x	
Extensor Digitorum Longus	x	x	x	x
Abductor Hallucis, Flex. Digitorum Brevis, Flex. Hallucis Brevis, Ext. Hallucis Brevis		x	x	
Flexor Digitorum Longus, Peroneus Longus, Peroneus Brevis		x	x	x
Tibialis Posterior, Flexor Hallucis Longus		x	x	x
Extensor Hallucis Longus, Soleus		x	x	x
Gastrocnemius, Ext. Digitorum Br., Accessorius (Quad. Pl.), Add. Hallucis, Abd. Digiti V, Fl. Digiti V Brevis, Interossei			x	x
Lumbricals of the Foot	x	x	x	x

* Modified after Bing; and Haymaker and Woodhall. (For Hip and Thigh, p. 395.)

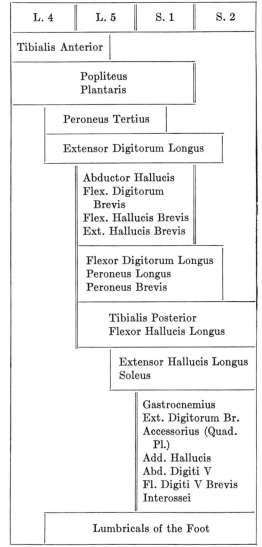

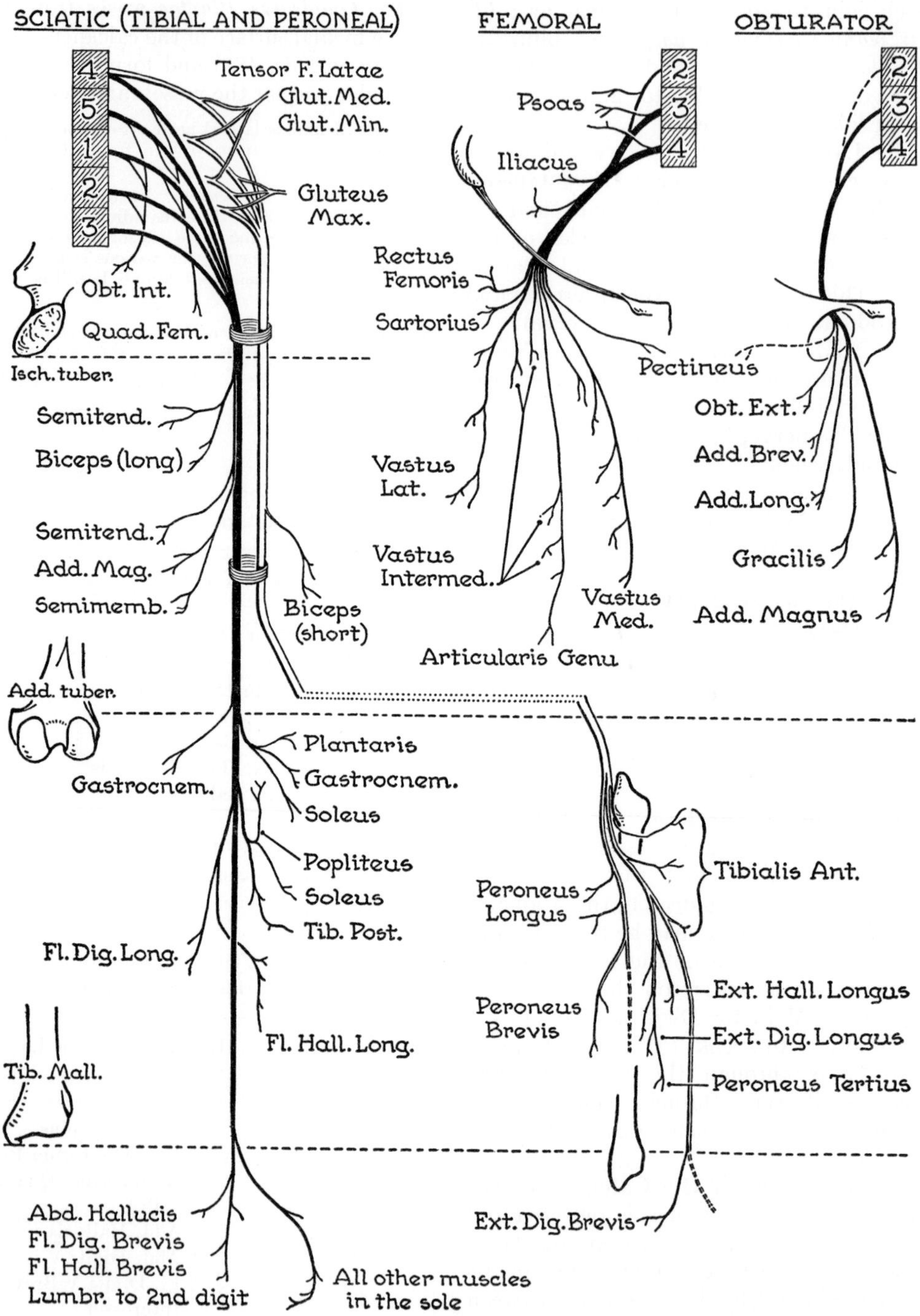

FIG. 491. The motor distribution of the nerves of the lower limb. (You may find it profitable to compare the levels of origin of the branches in the limb you are dissecting with these average levels.)

A List of the Muscles of the Lower Limb

(This list may be found useful in review work.)

Iliopsoas
- Iliacus
- Psoas Major

Sartorius
Quadriceps Femoris
- Rectus Femoris
- Vastus Lateralis
- Vastus Intermedius
- Vastus Medialis

Articularis Genu

Pectineus
Gracilis
Adductor Longus
Adductor Brevis
Adductor Magnus
Obturator Externus

Gluteus Maximus
Gluteus Medius
Gluteus Minimus
Tensor Fasciae Latae

Piriformis
Obturator Internus
Gemellus Superior
Gemellus Inferior
Quadratus Femoris

Biceps Femoris
- long head
- short head

Semitendinosus
Semimembranosus

Tibialis Anterior
Extensor Digitorum Longus
Peroneus Tertius
Extensor Hallucis Longus
Extensor Hallucis Brevis
Extensor Digitorum Brevis

Peroneus Brevis
Peroneus Longus

Gastrocnemius
- lateral head
- medial head

Soleus
Plantaris
Popliteus

Tibialis Posterior
Flexor Digitorum Longus
Flexor Hallucis Longus

Abductor Hallucis
Flexor Hallucis Brevis
Adductor Hallucis
- oblique head
- transverse head

Abductor Digiti Minimi (V)
(Abductor Ossis Metatarsi Quinti)
Flexor Digiti Minimi Brevis

Flexor Digitorum Brevis
Quadratus Plantae (Accessorius)
Lumbricales
Interossei
- Dorsales
- Plantares

bered that, contrary to expectation, the Fl. Digitorum Longus arises from the tibia, and the Fl. Hallucis Longus from the fibula. The relative positions of the two tendons must, of course, be reversed before their insertions are reached. This is achieved by the Fl. Digitorum Longus crossing the Fl. Hallucis Longus abreast of the tuberosity of the navicular; and it crosses superficially.

The Tibialis Posterior arises from both tibia and fibula, and, in its endeavor to reach the tuberosity of the navicular (its main site of insertion), it also must cross the Fl. Digitorum Longus. This crossing is effected behind the medial malleolus where the Fl. Digitorum Longus is again superficial. Twice therefore is the Fl. Digitorum Longus superficial, first to the Tibialis Posterior, then to the Fl. Hallucis Longus.

Three Tendons and the Sustentaculum Tali. From its origin to its insertion the *Tibialis Posterior* is never parted from the skeletal plane. After winding round its pulley (the medial malleolus), it must cross the deltoid ligament to reach the tuberosity of the navicular; one-third of its tendon passes below the spring ligament, which separates it from the head of the talus, and so it reaches the sole.

The *Flexor Digitorum Longus* rubs on the medial side of the sustentaculum.

The *Flexor Hallucis Longus* is the only muscle whose tendon actually passes below the sustentaculum. Its tendon grooves three bones: the lower end of the tibia, the back of the talus between the medial and lateral tubercles, and the sustentaculum tali.

Fibrous bands convert the grooves into an osseofibrous tunnel. Finally, it passes between the two sesamoid bones. As the tendon is traveling through the tunnel, the plantar vessels and nerves seize the opportunity to cross it, and so to gain its lateral side where they come to lie on the soft Quadratus Plantae (*fig. 489*).

Comment on Vessels and Nerves. It is helpful to recollect the general rule that *an artery accompanies its companion nerve on the side from which it approaches it.* In the lower limb, arteries mostly approach their companion nerves from the medial side and accompany them on the medial side, e.g., the femoral artery and nerve, the inferior gluteal artery and sciatic nerve, the anterior tibial artery and nerve, and the medial plantar artery and nerve. The rule is broken at three and sometimes four sites in the lower limb, namely, (1) at the back of the knee, (2) at the ankle, and (3) in the sole of the foot, as illustrated in figure 490.

Review of Nerve Supplies. See the tables on pages 395 and 427 and figure 491.

CHAPTER 28

JOINTS OF LOWER LIMB

Dynamics of Foot

STANDING—*Weight Distribution; Arch Support; Height of Arch; Muscles.*

PENTADACTYL HAND AND FOOT.

OSSIFICATION OF BONES OF FOOT.

Supernumerary Ossicles.

THE HIP JOINT

The hip joint is a ball and socket joint. The head of the femur is the ball; the acetabulum, deepened by (1) the transverse acetabular ligament and (2) the acetabular labrum, forms the socket.

The Ball and the Socket. The *head of the femur* forms two-thirds of a sphere, flattened above where the acetabulum rests most heavily upon it. It points medially, upward, and forward, so its anterior part is not engaged in the socket when the body is in the anatomical position.

The *acetabulum* (acetum, L. = vinegar), or vinegar cup, lies at the site of union of ilium, ischium, and pubis. The lowest part of the cup is deficient and is known as the *acetabular notch.* The remainder of the peripheral part of the cup is horseshoe-shaped; it articulates with the femur and is therefore covered with cartilage. The bottom of the cup, the *acetabular fossa,* is nonarticular, thin, and often translucent.

The acetabular notch is converted into a foramen by a strong ligament, the *transverse acetabular ligament* (*fig. 492*). The acetabulum is deepened by a complete ring of pliable fibrocartilage, the *acetabular labrum,* which is attached to its brim and to the transverse ligament. The labrum grasps the head of the femur beyond its equator.

Epiphyses. The epiphysis of the head of the femur fits like a cap on a spike, and the epiphyseal line encircles the articular margin. It lies entirely within the synovial capsule (*fig. 496*). *Ossification* of the head, which starts during the 1st year, is always complete by the 20th year (McKern and Stewart).

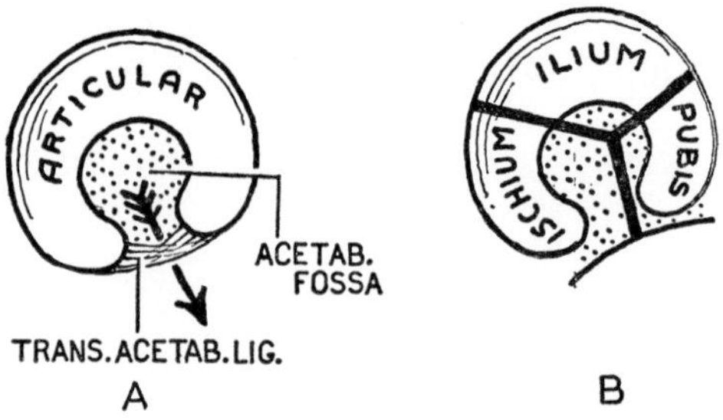

FIG. 492. *A,* the acetabulum shown in correct orientation and the transverse acetabular ligament. The *arrow* passes through the acetabular foramen. *B,* triradiate "epiphyseal" cartilage uniting the pubic, iliac, and ischial parts of the acetabulum.

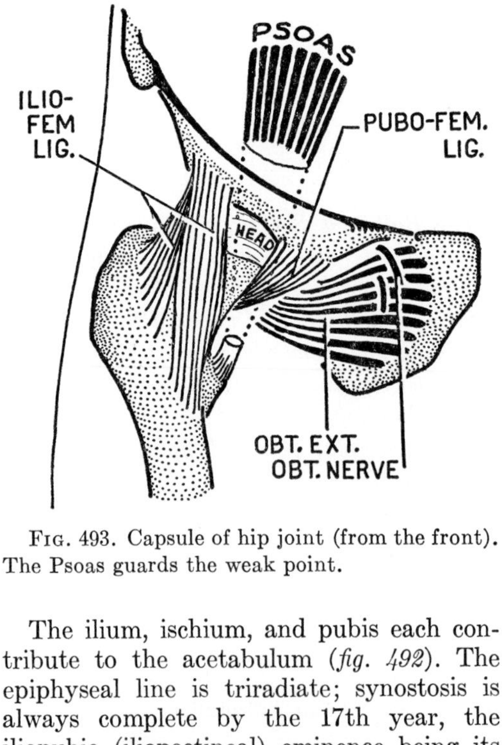

FIG. 493. Capsule of hip joint (from the front). The Psoas guards the weak point.

The ilium, ischium, and pubis each contribute to the acetabulum (*fig. 492*). The epiphyseal line is triradiate; synostosis is always complete by the 17th year, the iliopubic (iliopectineal) eminence being its most conspicuous part (*fig. 352*).

Fibrous Capsule and Ligaments. The fibrous capsule is a very strong, thick sleeve. Proximally, it is attached around the brim of the acetabulum and to some extent to the labrum and transverse ligament. Distally, it is attached to the femur along the whole length of the intertrochanteric line and to a line on the under surface of the neck beside the lesser trochanter, but

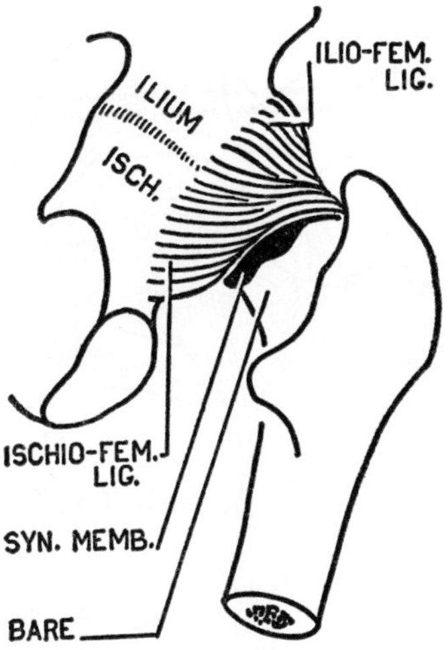

FIG. 494. Capsule of hip joint (from behind)

it is not attached to the femur either posteriorly or above. The fibers run an oblique or spiral course.

If it is assumed that the fibers were originally parallel and took a horizontal course, then the oblique or spiral course they take definitively can be attributed to the assumption of the erect posture, which involves extension of the joint. Since the ilium, pubis, and ischium each take part in the acetabulum, capsular fibers proceed from each of these to the femur, as iliofemoral, pubofemoral, and ischiofemoral ligaments.

The Iliofemoral Ligament (*fig. 493*) is a broad, strong band, shaped like an inverted Y. Above, it is attached to the ant. inf. iliac spine and to the acetabular margin for an inch behind the spine, so it lies deep to the two heads of origin of the Rectus Femoris and is co-extensive with them. Below, it creates the broad, rough intertrochanteric line of the femur (*fig. 402*).

The Pubofemoral and *Ischiofemoral Ligaments* are attached to the pubic and ischial parts, respectively, of the acetabular margin and they pass across the back of the neck of the femur to the tubercle at the upper end of the intertrochanteric line (*fig. 494*). Some pubofemoral fibers pass to and create a line below the neck of the femur. *The orbicular zone* is a collection of deep fibers that run circularly and cause an hourglass constriction within the capsule (*fig. 496*).

Sequences. When you stand erect, your line of gravity (p. 15) passes behind the centers of your hip joints. Consequently, your trunk tends to fall backward, or rather to rotate backward, the points on which it pivots being the heads of the femora. It is to resist this backward rotation that the anterior part of the capsule is thickened in man and anthropoids to form the iliofemoral ligament.

In a ball-and-socket joint, which permits free movement in all directions, it is self-evident that the ball must have a larger articular area than the socket. When you stand erect with toes out-turned, the excess of articular cartilage on the ball-like head of the femur is directed forward. Its lateral part is protected by the iliofemoral ligament; its medial part by the pubofemoral ligament; but the intermediate part, which most requires support, has no covering ligament; indeed, this part of the capsule is commonly perforated. You are not, however, to accuse Nature of constructing a mechanically insecure joint, because playing across this critical area is the **tendon of the Psoas**—active and alert.

The generalization that tendons rubbing on hard structures acquire a bursa is true for Psoas here. The *Psoas bursa* commonly communicates with the joint between the

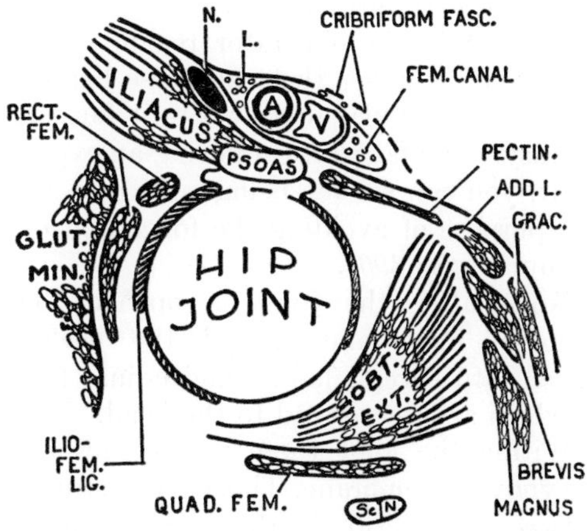

FIG. 495. Sequences: The hip joint and its relations; coronal section, semidiagrammatic.

iliofemoral and pubofemoral ligaments (*fig. 495*).

Relationships. Monopolizing the front of the Psoas tendon is the femoral artery. The femoral nerve, which is lateral, is in front of the Iliacus; the vein and lymph vessels, which are medial, are in front of the Pectineus. Indeed, the nerve is separated from the joint by the thickness of the fleshy Iliacus, the artery by the toughness of the Psoas tendon, the vein by the thinness of the fleshy Pectineus.

Synovial Membrane lines all parts of the interior of the joint, except where there is cartilage. It is so with all synovial joints. The membrane lines the neck of the femur completely in front, and as far as the Obturator Externus tendon behind, and it stretches across the acetabular fossa.

Note before the joint is opened: the Psoas bursa communicates with the hip joint rarely in the young, but commonly in the adult (20 per cent of 478 limbs, aged 20–92 years).

The synovial membrane protrudes posteriorly between the free lower border of the fibrous capsule and the neck of the femur—just as at the elbow it protrudes between the anular ligament and the neck of the radius—and acts as a bursa for the Obturator Externus tendon (*fig. 494*). So, an incision or puncture made above the tendon will certainly enter the joint; one made below will almost certainly miss it, for here the neck is bare or extra-articular.

The fat in the obturator region sends a prolongation under the transverse ligament into the acetabular fossa where it forms an extrasynovial fat pad. On flexing an exposed joint, you can see fat being sucked in with the purpose of avoiding the formation of a vacuum (*fig. 496*).

Note after the joint is opened: The synovial membrane around the neck is raised into several loose longitudinal folds, in which arteries ascend to the head.

Within the joint there is a hollow cone of synovial membrane. This cone is situated between the head of the femur and the acetabular fossa, so it is flattened and triangular like a flattened megaphone. The margins are free; the apex is attached to the pit or fovea near the center of the articular surface of the head; the femoral side of its base is reflected on to the transverse ligament; the acetabular side of its base is continuous with the sheet of synovial membrane that covers the fat pad in the acetabular fossa—this sheet is attached to the articular margins of the fossa.

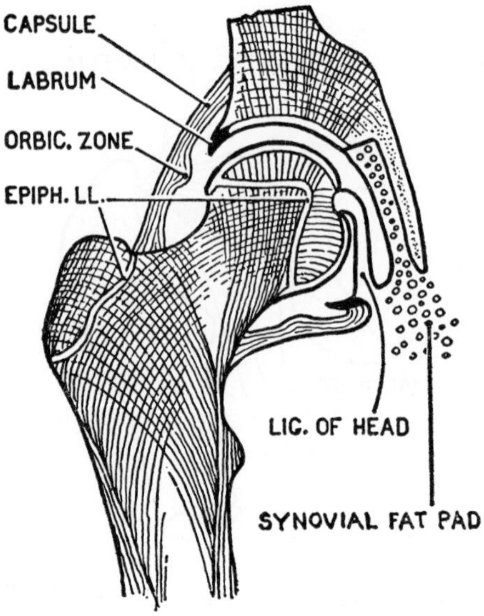

FIG. 496. The hip joint in coronal section. Note the lines of strain and stress.

The synovial cone transmits blood vessels to the head of the femur, and it surrounds a fibrous band, called the **ligament of the head,** which connects the head to the transverse ligament and to the lips of the acetabular notch. The acetabular notch is situated inferiorly, so it follows that the ligament ascends and that it becomes taut on adduction, as when the knees are crossed.

It is evident that a probe, pushed through the acetabular foramen, would pass extrasynovially either into the acetabular fossa, or through the synovial cone to the head of the femur (*fig. 496*). Branches of the medial femoral circumflex and obturator arteries follow both courses.

»» *Comparative Anatomy.* The ligament of the head is present in amphibians and reptiles with limbs, in birds, and in most mammals. It is absent however in some, e.g., the elephant, rhinoceros, seal, sloth, and the orang.

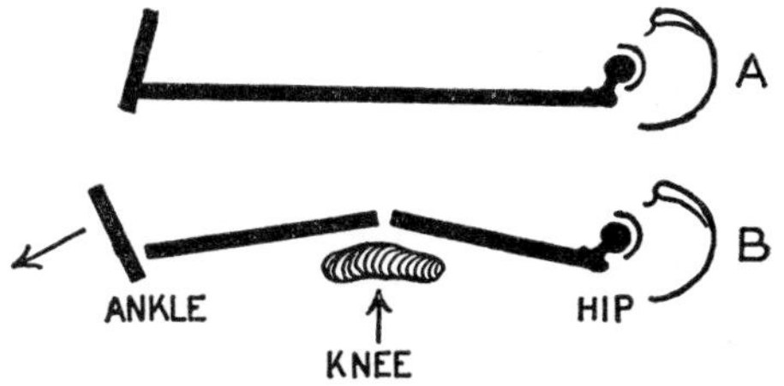

FIG. 497. The lower limb. *A*, rigid; *B*, flail, due to pillow flexing the knee.

Observations:

1. When you stand erect or bend forward over a basin, your ankle and knee joints are locked, and your foot, leg, and thigh bones become temporarily a rigid unit (*fig. 497*). A side force then applied to the foot is greatly amplified at the upper end of the femur—as at the end of a long screw driver—and may possibly result in fracture of the neck of the femur.

2. A pillow placed under your knee, when you lie down, automatically results in flexion of the hip, knee, and ankle.

3. The posture conducive to **dislocation of the hip joint** is one in which the joint is fully flexed and medially rotated, as on bending forward with toes turned in. Flexion brings the shallow part of the acetabulum to rest on the femur; medial rotation brings the head of the femur to the back. A weight (such as a sack of potatoes) then falling on the back will dislocate the head of the femur on to the dorsum ilii. The ligament of the head is torn in the process.

Relations. *Anteriorly*—Psoas tendon and femoral artery, Iliacus and femoral nerve, Pectineus and femoral vein (*fig. 495*). *Laterally*—Rectus Femoris in front of iliofemoral ligament, and Gluteus Minimus. *Inferiorly*—The Obturator Externus crosses below the head and runs behind the neck. *Posteriorly*—Piriformis, Obturator Internus and Gemelli, upper border of Quadratus Femoris, and the sciatic nerve. The relationship of the sciatic nerve is appreciated only when the obliquity of the acetabular margin is kept in mind (*figs. 419–421*).

Blood Supply. Medial femoral circumflex, lateral femoral circumflex, obturator, and gluteal arteries.

The head of the femur receives three sets of arteries: (1) The never failing and main set of three of four arteries that ascends in the synovial retinacula on the posterosuperior and postero-inferior parts of the neck, perforate the neck just distal to the head, and bend at 45° toward the center of the head where they anastomose freely with (2) terminal branches of the nutrient artery of the shaft, and in 80 per cent of instances with (3) the artery of the lig. of the head (lig. teres). This last artery has established a precarious anastomosis in the epiphysis of the head by the 10th year, further improvement occurring during adolescence (Trueta). This anastomosis persists even in those of advanced age, but in 20 per cent it is never established (Wolcott).

Nerve Supply. *Femoral nerve* (via n. to Rectus Femoris) p. 372. *Obturator nerve* (via one or two branches that pass laterally) p. 392. *Sciatic nerve* (via n. to Quadratus Femoris) to the back of the capsule, and sometimes twigs from the *Superior gluteal nerve* (E. Gardner).

Movements. The movements permitted are circumduction and rotation. *Flexion* is arrested by the hams, when the knee is extended, and by the thigh coming into contact with the abdominal wall, when the knee is bent and the hams thereby relaxed. *Extension* "winds up" the spirally running fibers of the capsule and thereby forces the head deeper into the socket, and is self-arresting. When the joint is slightly hyperextended, the articular surfaces are completely congruous (T. Walmsley). *Medial rotation* also winds up the fibers; *lateral rotation* unwinds them and is more free.

Table 19 shows that *abduction* and *medial rotation* are practically controlled by the three muscles supplied by the superior gluteal nerve (Gl. Med., Gl. Min., and T. F. Latae); and that the muscles controlling adduction largely control lateral rotation.

To understand the *Actions* of the abductors and medial rotators, the pelvis and femur must be held in correct orientation. Thus, (1) the anterior superior spines and the upper end of the symphysis lie on the same coronal plane, and (2) the head of the femur is directed forward as well as medially

TABLE 19

Muscles Acting on the Hip Joint

Circumductors			
Flexors	**Extensors**	**Abductors**	**Adductors**
Iliopsoas	Gluteus Maximus	Gluteus Medius	Adductor Magnus
Tensor Fasciae Latae	The three hams	Gluteus Minimus	Adductor Brevis
Sartorius	Adductor Magnus	(Tensor Fasciae Latae)	Adductor Longus
Pectineus	(Ham part)		
		Piriformis	Pectineus
Rectus Femoris		Sartorius	
Adductor Longus			Gluteus Maximus
Adductor Brevis			
Adductor Magnus			Short Muscles
(Obt. part)			Obturator Internus
			Gemelli
			Obturator Externus
			Quadratus Femoris
		Rotators	
		Medial	**Lateral**
		Gluteus Medius	Gluteus Maximus
		Gluteus Minimus	Short Muscles
		(Tensor Fasciae Latae)	Piriformis
			Obturator Internus
			Gemelli
		Adductor Magnus	Obturator Externus
		(Ham part)	Quadratus Femoris
		With foot on ground:	
		Pectineus	Pectineus
		Upper adductor mass	Upper adductor mass
		Iliopsoas?	Iliopsoas?

and upwards, i.e., the greater trochanter lies behind the plane of the head. The *function of the abductors* is to prevent the pelvis from becoming adducted, that is, to prevent the body from falling to the unsupported side when one foot is off the ground, as in walking (*fig. 498*). The *function of the medial rotators* is to rotate the unsupported, or opposite, side of the pelvis forward and thereby to increase the stride.

The *Gluteus Maximus* is necessary to rising from the sitting position, to climbing stairs, and to running and jumping, but it is hardly required in walking on the flat, which is essentially movement for flexors, and there the hams suffice as extensors.

»» When the foot is on the ground, rotation of the femur, relative to the hip bone and the tibia, takes place around an axis passing through its head and intercondylar notch. This being so, any rotatory power the Iliopsoas, Pectineus, and Adductor Longus may possess is one of medial rotation, because they are inserted lateral to the axis (*fig. 499*). But, when the foot is off the ground, they are lateral rotators of the femur. It is a mistake, obviously, to suppose that the axis passes through the greater trochanter and along the shaft of the bone.

THE KNEE JOINT

General Observations. It is apparent that the chief movements occurring at the knee joint are *flexion* and *extension* and that the joint is of the hinge variety. Some degree of *axial rotation* is also permitted while the knee is in the position of flexion and semiflexion. Later you will see that a slight degree of medial rotation of the femur

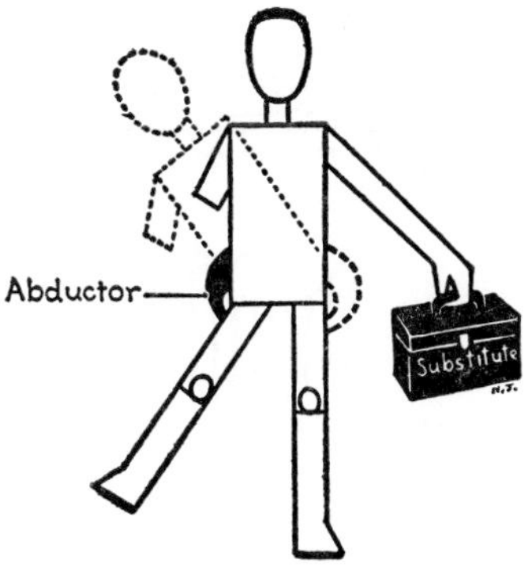

FIG. 498. Weight, substituting for paralyzed Abductors, demonstrates the chief function of Gluteus Medius and Gluteus Minimus.

is necessary to the completion of the act of extension.

When standing up and leaning forward, as when washing your face, you can, using your hands, *move your patella from side to side* because the Quadriceps Femoris is then relaxed. Hence, an unexpected blow on the back of the knee may cause you to fall. The Quadriceps is not required to be in action when you stand erect, because the *line of gravity* passes in front of the axis of the knee joint (*fig. 23*). A considerable economy in muscular effort is effected thereby.

Bursae. When the knee is extended, *the skin in front of the patella* is loose and can be picked up between the fingers and thumb (*cf.* the skin behind the olecranon). When, however, the knee is flexed, the slackness is taken up and there is no longer any redundant skin. A bursa, the *prepatellar bursa,* interposed between the skin and bone, permits this free movement of the skin. The precise depth of the *prepatellar bursa* varies; it may be either in the subcutaneous areolar tissue, or deep to the fascia lata, or actually in the substance of those fibers of the Quadriceps tendon that pass across the front of the patella. Commonly, two bursae are present, one in front of the other, with the intervening partition largely broken down.

In front of the lig. patellae, there is another bursa, the *superficial infrapatellar bursa.*

Divisions of the Joint. The bones taking

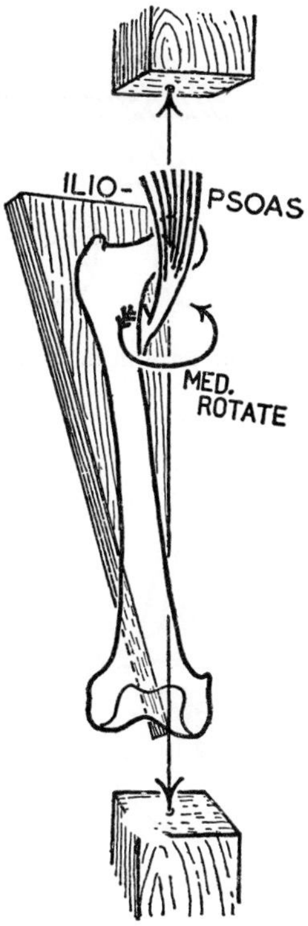

FIG. 499. Explaining why the Upper Adductors (and perhaps the Psoas) are medial rotators of the hip joint—when the leg is fixed.

part in the knee joint are: femur, tibia, and patella; the fibula is only indirectly associated. Primitively, there were *three joint cavities* now merged into one. One is situated between the medial condyles of the femur and tibia; one between the lateral condyles of the femur and tibia; and one between the patella and the femur. They may be referred to as the *medial and lateral condylar articulations* and the *patellar articulation.* The condylar articulations are partly subdivided by medial and lateral menisci (semilunar cartilages) into upper and lower parts.

The Patella and the Patellar Articulation

The tibiae are parallel to each other. Not so the femora; they are set obliquely, being separated above by the width of the pelvis. There is, accordingly, an open angle at the lateral side of the knee, toward which the patella tends to become dislocated, when the Quadriceps contracts. Dislocations are,

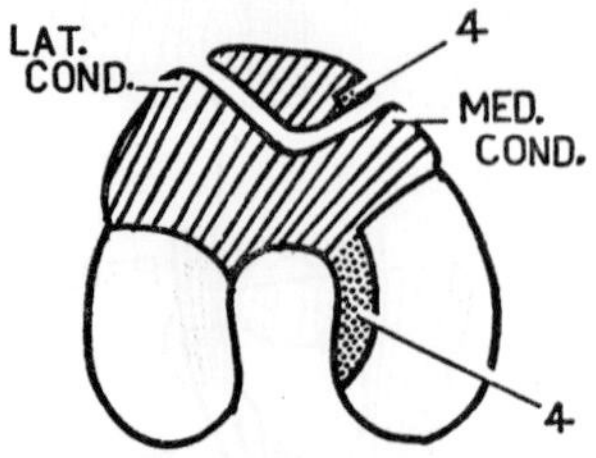

FIG. 500. The patella in its trochlea

FIG. 502. The three paired facets on the posterior surface of the patella articulate with the femur as shown in figure 503. The medial vertical facet (*4*) articulates along the margin of the intercondylar notch during full flexion (see fig. 500).

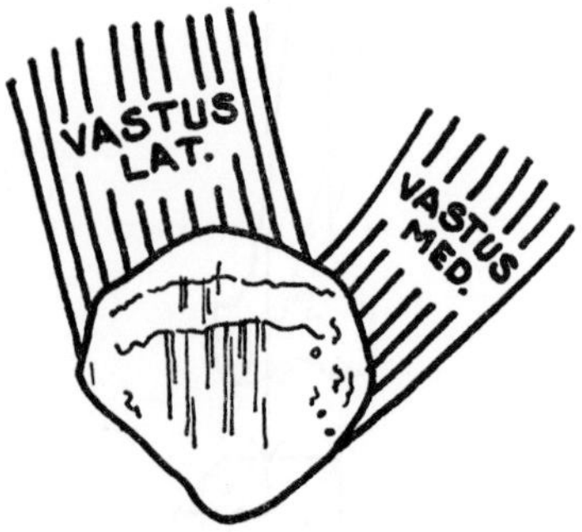

FIG. 501. The patellar attachments of the Vasti Medialis and Lateralis.

however, not common, largely because of two factors:

1. The forward projection of the lateral condyle of the femur.

2. The low attachment of the Vastus Medialis to the patella.

The 1st is a bony mechanism: The front of the lower articular end of the femur is a trochlea in which the patella glides (*fig. 500*). The lateral bank of this trochlea is deep—much deeper than the medial. From this it follows that the posterior aspect of the patella is, as the counterpart of this trochlea, divided into two areas, of which the posterolateral is larger than the posteromedial.

»» *To Identify the Side.* Hence, a patella falls to the side to which it belongs when it is placed on a table with its articular surface down and its apex pointing away from the observer—a right bone will fall to the right; a left bone to the left. It falls, of course, to its larger and more heavily weighted side.

The 2nd is a muscular mechanism: The Vastus Medialis and Vastus Lateralis are continuous with each other at their patellar attachments (*fig. 501*), and they occupy the plane between the Rectus Femoris and Vastus Intermedius. The Medialis is attached to the upper two-thirds of the medial border of the patella and only slightly to the upper border; the Lateralis is attached to almost the whole length of the upper border and only slightly to the lateral border. Hence, the lower fibers of the Medialis draw the patella medially, and therefore, actively prevent lateral displacement of the patella; the lateral condyle of the femur does so passively.

A transverse incision opening into the knee joint above the patella incises, successively—skin, fat, fascia lata, Rectus tendon, tendons of Vasti Lateralis et Medialis, tendon of Vastus Intermedius, and the synovial capsule of the joint—making a bewildering array of laminae when seen for the first time.

THE POSTERIOR SURFACE of the patella (*fig. 502*) has paired lower, intermediate, and upper articular facets, and also a fourth, or medial vertical, facet. The lowest quarter of this surface is nonarticular. The facets articulate in turn during extension, slight flexion, flexion, and full flexion (*fig. 503*).

The human patella would be less liable to fracture if it possessed a single concave facet the whole of which was continuously in articulation with the femur, as it is in lower mammals (*fig. 504*).

PALPATION. A considerable amount of the articular surface of the knee joint can be palpated. When the Quadriceps is relaxed (heel on chair position), push the patella first medially and then laterally and learn how much of its articular (posterior)

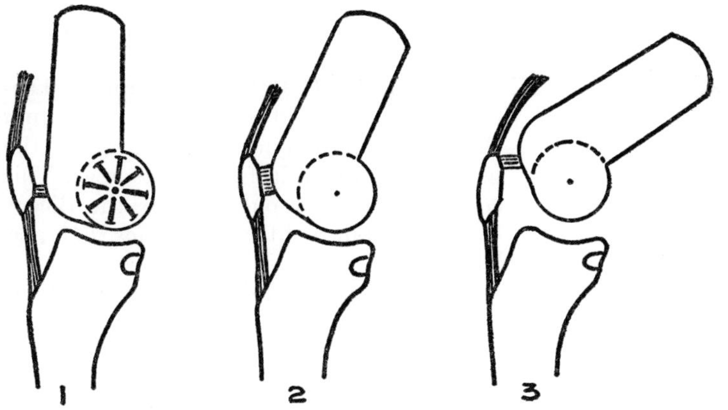

FIG. 503. The knee joint during (*1*) extension, (*2*) slight flexion, (*3*) flexion. At the hub of the wheel, or center of the disc, lies the epicondyle.

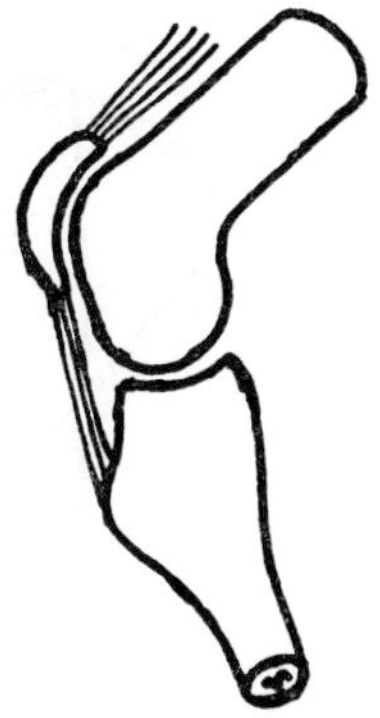

FIG. 504. Knee joint of a sheep showing the single concave facet on the patella.

surface is palpable. When the knee is bent, you can easily feel the anterior parts of the margin of the upper aspect of the tibia, and you can trace the margin of the patellar surface of the femur. As the knee moves gradually from the extended to the fully flexed position, you can feel the patella glide laterally on to the under aspect of the lateral condyle of the femur and leave the trochlea and the entire under aspect of the medial condyle exposed, except for a strip bounding the medial border of the intercondylar notch (see facet 4 in *figs. 500* and *502*).

» **Functions of the Patella.** Experimental work has shown that when the knee joint is flexed, the patella is a mechanical hindrance to extension. Indeed, the removal or excision of the patella results in increased efficiency—but in the later degrees of extension (say 150°–180°) the patella improves the efficiency by holding the patellar tendon away from the axis and thereby increasing the extending momentum of the Quadriceps pull (H. Haxton) (*fig. 505*).

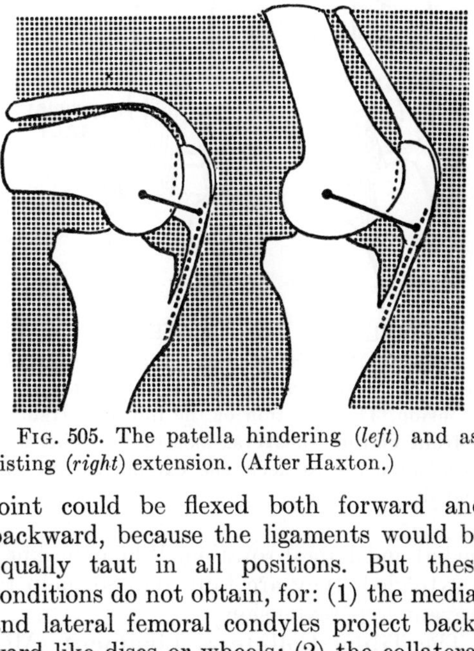

FIG. 505. The patella hindering (*left*) and assisting (*right*) extension. (After Haxton.)

Tibiofemoral or "Condylar" Articulations

On the upper surface of each tibial condyle there is an oval articular area for the corresponding femoral condyle. The articular areas are separated from each other by a narrow nonarticular area, which widens in front and behind into an *anterior* and a *posterior intercondylar area* (*fig. 509*).

COLLATERAL LIGAMENTS. Were the femoral condyles round and their collateral ligaments arranged as in figure 506, the joint could be flexed both forward and backward, because the ligaments would be equally taut in all positions. But these conditions do not obtain, for: (1) the medial and lateral femoral condyles project backward like discs or wheels; (2) the collateral ligaments are attached above the the epicondyles which project like hubs from the centers of the superadded wheels; and (3) below they are attached far back—the tibial collateral lig. (medial lig.) to the medial surface of the tibia adjacent to its medial border; the fibular collateral lig. (lateral lig.) to the head of the fibula just in front of its apex (*figs. 507* and *508*). As a result, when the knee is flexed, the collateral ligaments are slack and permit of

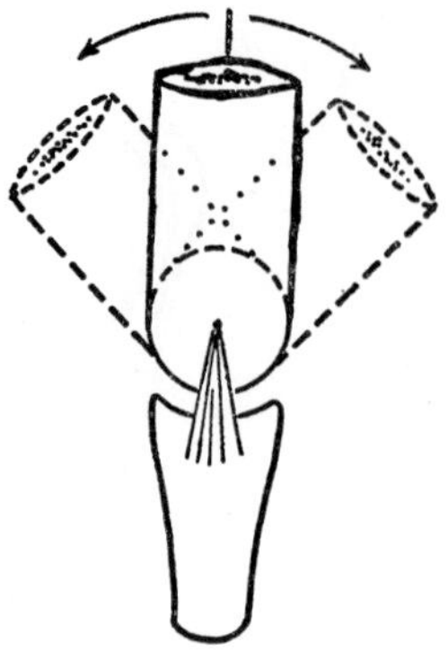

Fig. 506. The hypothetical tibiofemoral joint, as a perfect hinge, which it is not.

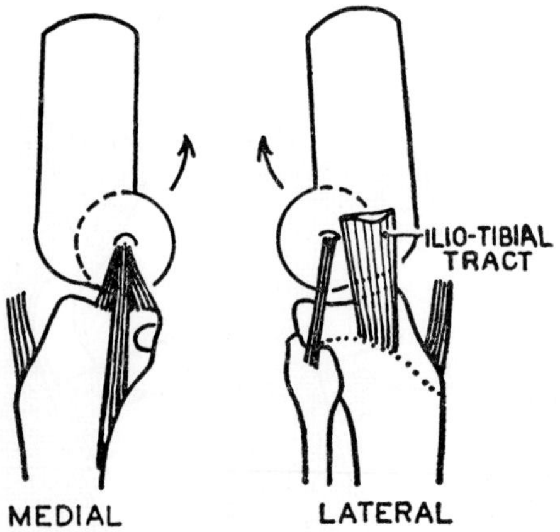

Fig. 507. Because of their eccentric attachments the collateral ligaments are taut during extension. The insertion of the iliotibial tract is in front of the transverse axis of the joint and therefore helps to keep the extended joint extended.

medial and lateral rotation. When the knee is extended, they are taut and, so, help to prevent hyperextension.

The **Tibial Collateral Ligament** (Medial Lig.) has a superficial and a deep part. The superficial part is a long band that bridges the groove on the tibial condyle where the Semimembranosus is inserted, and the hollow below the condyle (*fig. 511*). This band is crossed by three tendons—Sartorius, Gracilis, and Semitendinosus (*fig. 442* and p. 398).

The deep part is deltoid and is attached to the margin of the tibial condyle.

One or more *bursae* lie deep to the long band and help it to slide backward and forward on the deep part of the ligament and on the tibial condyle.

The **Fibular Collateral Ligament** (Lateral Lig.) is a round cord that extends from the lateral epicondyle to the margin of the head of the fibula in front of its apex. This cord is crossed by one tendon—the Biceps tendon—a bursa intervening (*figs. 517* and *451*).

Directed downward and backward, it restricts lateral rotation of the leg when the foot is off the ground, and medial rotation of the femur when the foot is on the ground.

The Head of the Fibula is situated far back. To palpate it, place your fingers behind your bent knee and carry them forward around its lateral side.

Menisci, Cruciate Ligaments, Condyles, and Movements

Sequences. The upper ends of the tibia and fibula may arbitrarily be fitted into *an oblong frame* in which the head of the fibula occupies the posterolateral angle

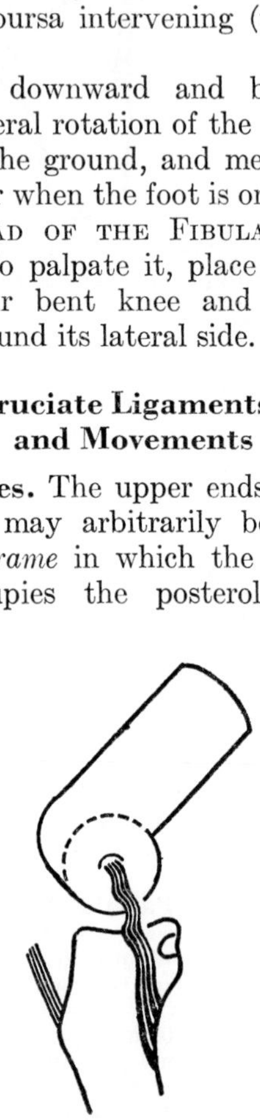

Fig. 508. The collateral ligaments are slack during the flexion and permit rotation.

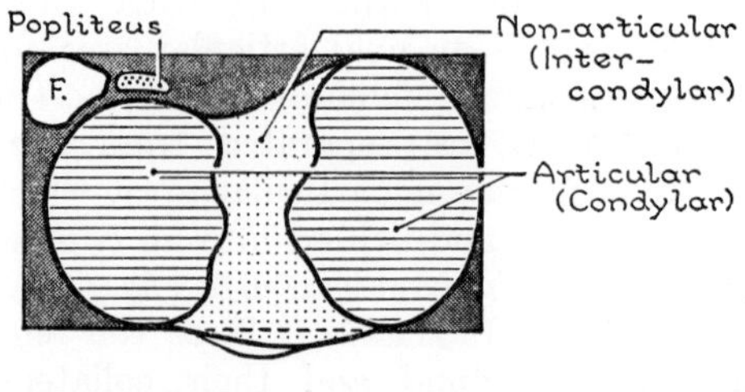

Fig. 509. The upper ends of the tibia and fibula in an oblong frame.

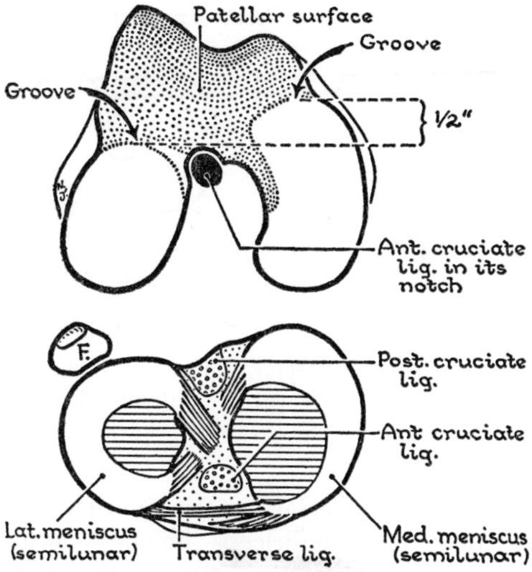

FIG. 510. The articular surfaces of the knee joint, analyzed.

(*fig. 509*). From a consideration of this fact the following sequences might reasonably be surmised:

1. The lateral condyle of the tibia is shorter from before backward than the medial condyle by approximately the thickness of the head of the fibula.

2. Therefore, of the two **menisci (semilunar fibrocartilages)** that rest on and fit the tibial condyles and are bound to their margins by *coronary ligaments*, the lateral is shorter than the medial. The shorter lateral meniscus is shaped like a small "o," the longer medial meniscus like a capital "C." The ligamentous ends of the "o" are attached to the nonarticular part of the upper surface of the tibia close together; the ligamentous ends of the "C" are attached far apart, embracing those of the "o" (*fig. 510*).

3. Therefore, the portion of the lateral condyle of the femur that articulates with the lateral condyle of the tibia (and its meniscus) is shorter anteroposteriorly than the corresponding part of the medial condyle of the femur. (Note, the condyles of the femur have patellar and tibiomeniscal areas. Just now reference is to the tibiomeniscal areas.)

4. Therefore, as the joint passes from full flexion to full extension, the medial condyle of the femur has farther to travel than the lateral condyle.

5. During extension, the two femoral condyles revolve on the tibia and its menisci as do the two rear wheels of a vehicle on a road, when a drag is applied to the axle. Here, the posterior cruciate lig., acting as a drag, greatly restricts the forward roll of the condyles and causes them to spin. In effect, the movement is a *hinge movement* (as at the humero-ulnar joint) with the addition of some true *forward roll.*

When the shorter lateral femoral condyle has run its course, the longer medial condyle has still a certain distance (½ inch) to revolve (*fig. 510*).

6. During extension the revolving lateral femoral condyle is arrested by two mechanical obstacles. Both leave their mark on it. One, the anterior margin of the lateral meniscus, creates and fits into the *curved groove on* the femur running from the anterior part of the intercondylar notch to the lateral margin of the condyle; the other, the taut anterior cruciate ligament, creates and fits into the *subsidiary notch* at the anterolateral part of the intercondylar notch (*fig. 510*).

7. The Quadriceps Femoris, however, continues to contract with the result that, while the medial femoral condyle is completing its course (½ inch), the femur is rotating medially on its long axis, the pivot around which it rotates being the anterior cruciate ligament.

8. At the same time the lateral femoral condyle and the lateral meniscus, whose sharp anterior margin is locked in the

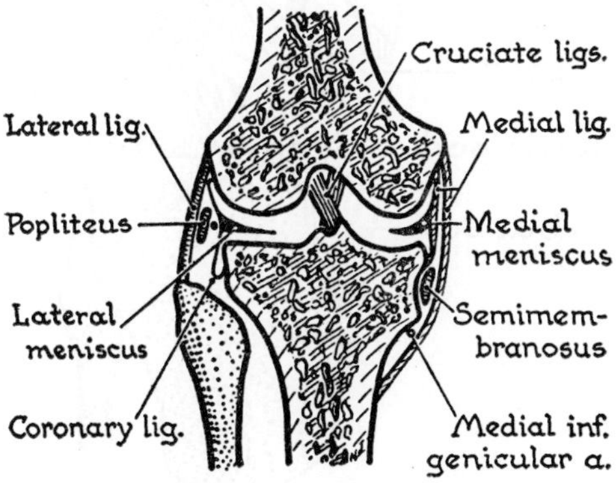

FIG. 511. The knee joint, in coronal section

groove on the lateral femoral condyle, slide forward together on the tibia, moving as one structure.

It is a matter of interest and significance that the posterior end of the lateral meniscus is attached to the femur by an oblique band that passes either in front of or behind the posterior cruciate lig.

»» In many mammals this oblique band, greatly enlarged, is almost the sole posterior attachment of the lateral meniscus, indicating thereby that its allegiance is to the femur rather than to the tibia.

A few fleshy fibers of the Popliteus are attached to the posterior end of the lateral meniscus. These may serve as a retractor muscle (R. J. Last).

9. The upper surface of the lateral tibial condyle is, therefore, flat to allow this forward gliding; and the lateral meniscus is broad and expansive in order to act as a carriage or toboggan for the lateral femoral condyle (*fig. 511*).

10. The upper aspect of the medial tibial condyle is concave to allow flexion, extension, and rotation. And its meniscus, having but restricted sliding action, is narrow; indeed, it tapers anteriorly.

11. The medial femoral condyle is, then, completing the process of extension at the same time as the femur is undergoing axial rotation. No special rotator muscles are provided; the Quadriceps Femoris, acting against the obstruction offered by the anterior cruciate lig., is alone responsible. When these movements are completed, the anterior border of the medial meniscus fits into a *curved groove* on the medial femoral condyle (*fig. 510*).

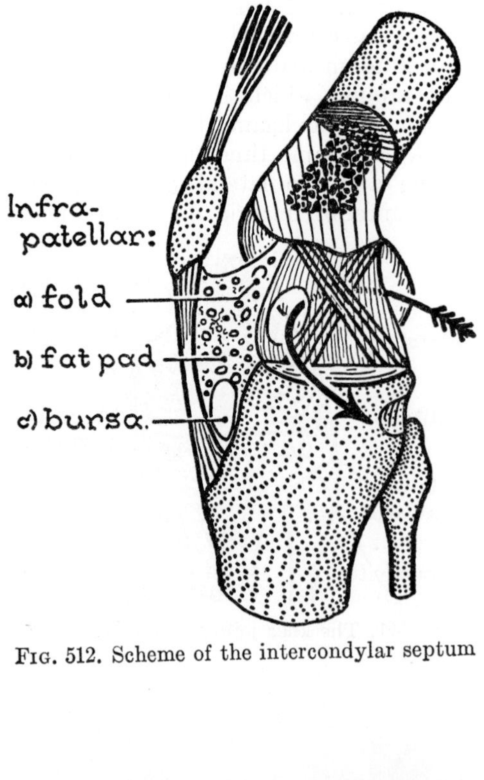

Fig. 512. Scheme of the intercondylar septum

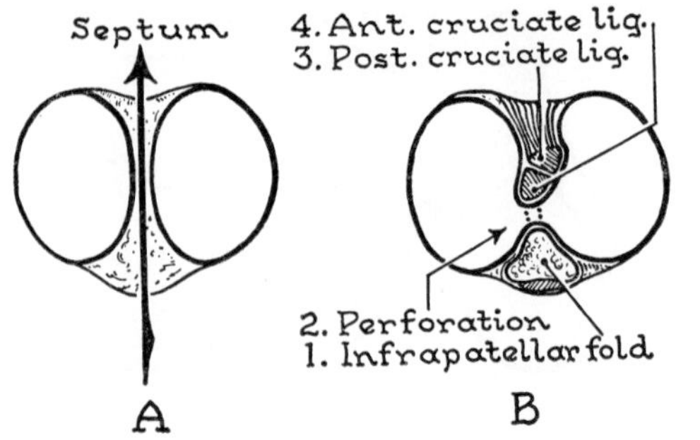

Fig. 513. Intercondylar septum as seen from above on the tibia. *A*, early; *B*, later. Four derivatives are seen.

12. The fibular collateral lig. passes to the lateral margin of the head of the fibula. Therefore, it lies wide of the lateral tibial condyle and lateral meniscus. In fact, the space between them is wide enough to afford a passage for the Popliteus tendon (*fig. 511*).

13. But with the tibial collateral lig. it is different; its deeper deltoid part is attached to the margin of the medial condyle of the tibia, and therefore does come into contact with the medial meniscus and blends with it.

»» The anterior cruciate lig. has been seen to occupy, on full extension, a small subsidiary notch at the anterolateral part of the intercondylar notch of the femur. The presence of this notch in the dried femur affords evidence that the particular knee joint was capable of being fully extended, and therefore that its owner walked erect.

Prehistoric Man. The femora of certain prehistoric men, such as Java Man (Pithecanthropus Erectus) and Rhodesian Man, present such well marked notches for the anterior cruciate ligament that they unquestionably are entitled to the term "Erectus"; but the term would be ill applied to Neanderthal Man whose femora have no suggestion of a notch. For this and other reasons, it is believed that his was a crouching gait.

The Intercondylar Septum (*figs. 512* and *513*). In prenatal life a vertical septum or partition separates the medial and lateral condylar joints from each other. The lower border of this septum is attached to the intercondylar area on the upper aspect of the tibia. The posterior half of its upper border is attached to the intercondylar notch of the femur; the anterior half is free and extends from the intercondylar notch of the femur to the patella just below its articular surface. So, it is possible—theoretically at least—to pass a needle from the front of the joint to the back without entering the synovial cavity, the needle remaining within the intercondylar septum.

A *perforation* usually appears in the septum and extends backward to the anterior cruciate lig. (*fig. 513*). It divides the septum into an anterior part, the *infrapatellar synovial fold*, and a posterior part in which the *anterior* and *posterior cruciate ligaments* develop.

The **Infrapatellar Synovial Fold** resembles the ligament of the head of the femur in being a hollow cone of synovial membrane which is flattened and triangular in shape. It has an anterior and a posterior surface. Its apex remains attached to the most anterior point of the intercondylar notch of the femur (*fig. 512*); its open base extends from just below the articular cartilage of the patella to the anterior intercondylar area of the tibia; its two sides are free, and from each a small wing, the alar fold, projects.

The *infrapatellar pad of fat* (i.e., the fat behind the lig. patellae) is continued upward into the infrapatellar fold and, in stout subjects, into the alar folds also.

The **Cruciate Ligaments** develop in the hinder part of the septum and cross each other obliquely, like the limbs of a St. Andrew's cross. Thus, the limb attached to the tibia antero-inferiorly is attached to the femur postero-superiorly, and contrariwise. It is from their tibial attachments that they take their names.

The anterior cruciate lig., already observed to groove the anterolateral part of the intercondylar notch, is attached above to the lateral femoral condyle; by exclusion the posterior cruciate lig. is attached above to the medial femoral condyle. Figure 514 makes clear their functions.

A glance at the upper surface of the tibia

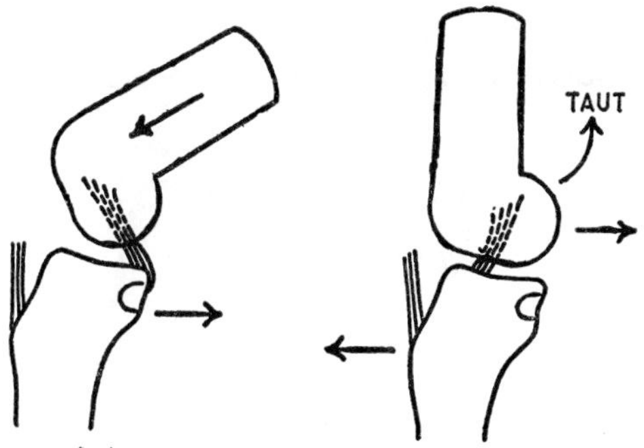

POSTR."X" LIG. ANTR."X" LIG

FIG. 514. The posterior cruciate ligament prevents forward displacement of the femur or backward displacement of the tibia. The anterior "X" ligament prevents backward displacement of the femur and hyperextension.

suffices to answer the question, "How are side to side movements of the femur prevented?" It is seen that the articular surface of each tibial condyle rises gently toward the nonarticular area and ends in a tubercle. The medial and lateral tubercles together constitute the *intercondylar eminence* (*fig. 443*). Side-to-side movement of the femur would cause one or other condyle to mount an incline. This the cruciate and collateral ligaments, obviously, would resist.

Synovial Cavity and Communicating Bursae

The intricacies of this joint fade into simplicity once you appreciate the following:

1. Developmentally, the joint possesses *three synovial cavities:* a patellar and two condylar. The partition separating the patellar from the condylar cavities disappears, leaving only the vestigial alar folds. The partition separating the condylar cavities from each other (the intercondylar septum) is reduced to the infrapatellar fold and the cruciate ligs.

2. Each condylar cavity is divided into an *upper* and a *lower part* by an inwardly projecting meniscus. The two parts communicate around the free concave border of each meniscus. Loose coronary ligaments attach the convex margins of the menisci to the upper end of the tibia below (¼ inch) the articular margin (*fig. 515*). The

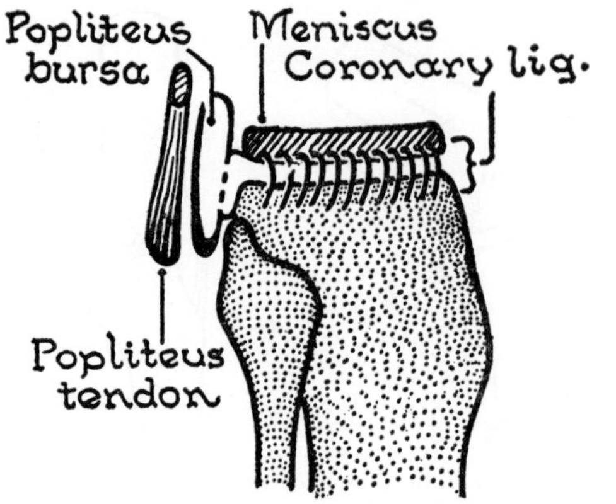

Fig. 515. Showing the popliteus bursa communicating with the joint cavity, and the coronary ligament attaching the convex border of the meniscus to the tibia.

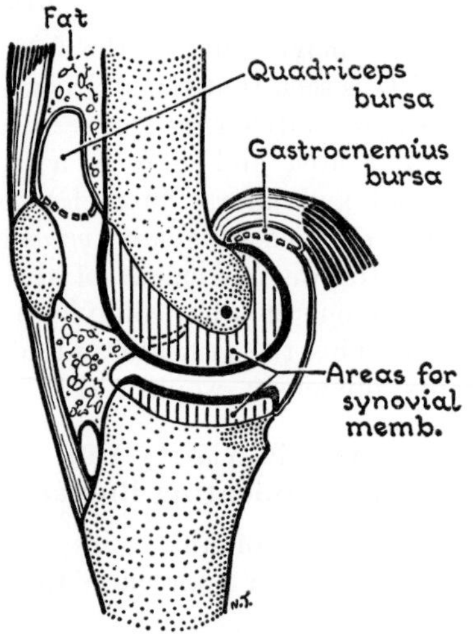

Fig. 516. Showing the Quadriceps and Gastrocnemius bursae communicating with the synovial cavity.

lateral coronary ligament is deficient where the Popliteus tendon rubs.

3. **Three bursae** communicate with the knee joint, *one joining each of the three primitive cavities* (*figs. 515–517*). These bursae lie deep to the tendons of Quadriceps Femoris, Popliteus, and Gastrocnemius.

a. The bursa deep to the *Quadriceps Femoris* tendon, known as the *suprapatellar bursa,* almost always opens into the patellar cavity. Between this bursa and the femur a layer of fat is spread (*figs. 516* and *517*), so this is not a frictional bursa. During flexion of the knee the bursa is peeled off the femur; during extension the articularis genu muscle retracts it.

b. The *Popliteus bursa* opens into the lateral condylar cavity (*figs. 515* and *517*). It is situated between the Popliteus tendon and all the hard structures (lateral meniscus, tibial condyle, superior tibiofibular joint) upon which the tendon plays, so it is elongated. Sometimes the partition between this bursa and the tibiofibular joint gives way, bringing it and the knee joint into communication.

c. The *Gastrocneumius bursa* (deep to the medial head) very commonly (43 per cent of 528 limbs, C. G. Smith) communicates with the medial condylar cavity. This bursa may communicate with a bursa deep to the Semimembranosus and, so, may bring the semimembranosus bursa and the knee joint into communication.

Extent of the Synovial Cavity (*fig. 517*). An incision may be carried upward on the tibia to within ¼ inch of its articular margin without opening the synovial cavity, except behind, where the Popliteus bursa lies. How

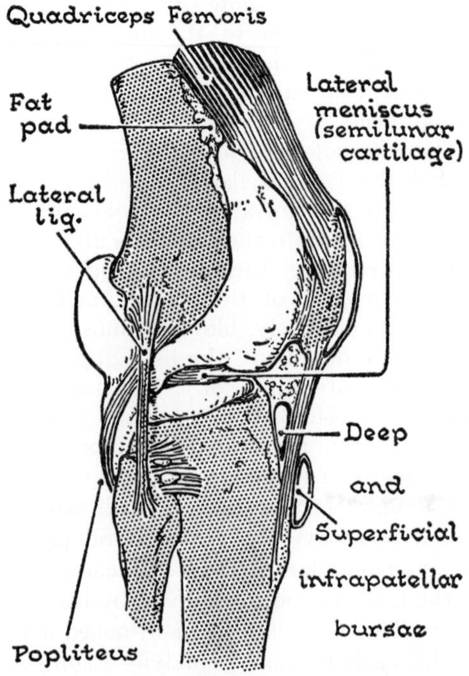

Fig. 517. Knee joint filled with latex to show the extent of the synovial cavity, lateral view.

far may an incision be carried downward on the femur? In front, to the top of the suprapatellar bursa, that is two fingers' breadth above the patella; at the back, to the origins of the heads of the Gastrocnemius; at the sides the level must fall below the epicondyles, for they give attachment to the collateral ligaments, which are, of course, outside the synovial membrane. Hence, a curved line joining the three points marks the upper limit of the membrane.

The posterior cruciate lig. may be exposed from behind and the infrapatellar fold from the front without opening into the synovial cavity, for they represent the post. and ant. margins of the intercondylar septum (*fig. 513*).

The Fibrous Capsule. Like other synovial joints, the knee possesses a fibrous capsule as well as a synovial one. The lig. patellae and the medial ligament are part of the fibrous capsule. The fibrous capsule is reinforced in front and at the sides by expansions from the Vasti, Sartorius, Semimembranosus, Biceps, and iliotibial tract. Behind, it is composed of fibers that run parallel with the Popliteus, i.e., obliquely downward and medially from femur to tibia; and one band, known as the *oblique popliteal ligament*, is attached to the Semimembranosus tendon. The fibular collateral lig. and the Popliteus tendon lie between the synovial and fibrous capsules.

Relations. All muscles crossing the joint are relations of the joint. The **iliotibial tract** is to be noted especially, on account of its great protective value to the exposed lateral side of the knee. An inch or more wide and placed between the lig. patellae and the Biceps tendon, it alone separates the skin from the synovial membrane. The common peroneal nerve follows the posterior border of the Biceps. The tibial nerve is behind the popliteal vein, which in turn is behind the popliteal artery (*fig. 438*).

»» **Blood Supply.** Of the five articular branches of the popliteal a., the middle genicular a. passes forward and supplies the structures in the intercondylar septum. The two medial and two lateral genicular aa.

TABLE 20

Muscles Acting upon the Knee Joint (All the Muscles That Cross It)

Nerve Supply	Muscles	Accessory Actions	Main Actions
Sup. Gluteal Inf. Gluteal	Iliotibial tract T. Fasciae Latae Gluteus Max. (pt.)	Retain knee in the extended position	Extensors
Femoral	Quadriceps Femoris Rectus Femoris V. Intermedius V. Lateralis V. Medialis	Responsible for the final "screw home" movement	
	Sartorius	Rotate leg medially	Flexors
Obturator	Add. Gracilis		
Tibial division of sciatic	S. Tendinosus S. Membranosus Popliteus		
	Gastrocnemius Plantaris		
	Biceps (Long)	Rotate leg laterally	
Peroneal division of sciatic	Biceps (Short)		

course deep to all muscles and ligaments they encounter, and embrace either the femur or the tibia. The lat. inf. genicular a. is an exception in as much as it passes (1) behind the Popliteus tendon (*fig. 438*), and then (2) runs along the margin of the lateral meniscus.

These arteries anastomose with each other, with the lateral circumflex (descending branch), the descending genicular, and the ant. tibial recurrent artery.

Nerve Supply. This is derived from the *femoral n.*, via branches to the Vasti, and the saphenous nerve; the *obturator n.* via the branch to the Adductor Magnus; and the tibial and common peroneal branches of the *sciatic n.* via the six genicular branches that accompany the corresponding arteries (Details on pp. 372, 392, & 390).

Bursae about the Knee, in summary. Of these, there are 11 or more:

—3 communicate with the joint—Quadriceps (suprapatellar), Popliteus, and Medial Gastrocnemius.

—3 related to the patella and lig. patellae —prepatellar, superficial infrapatellar, and deep infrapatellar (*fig. 517*).

—2 Semimembranosus bursae—the one between Semimembranosus and Gastrocnemius tendons may communicate with the Gastrocnemius b. and so may communicate indirectly with the knee joint; the other lies between Semimembranosus tendon and the tibial condyle.

—2 superficial to the collateral ligaments —the one between the fibular collateral lig. and the overlying Biceps tendon; the other between the tibial collateral lig. and the three overlying tendons (Sartorius, Gracilis, and Semitendinosus). The latter is commonly continuous with a bursa between Sartorius superficially and Gracilis and Semitendinosus deeply.

—1 bursa between the superficial and deep parts of the tibial collateral lig.

Epiphyses. The more actively growing ends of the femur and tibia are at the knee (p. 8). The directions of the nutrient canals —away from the knee—tell you so.

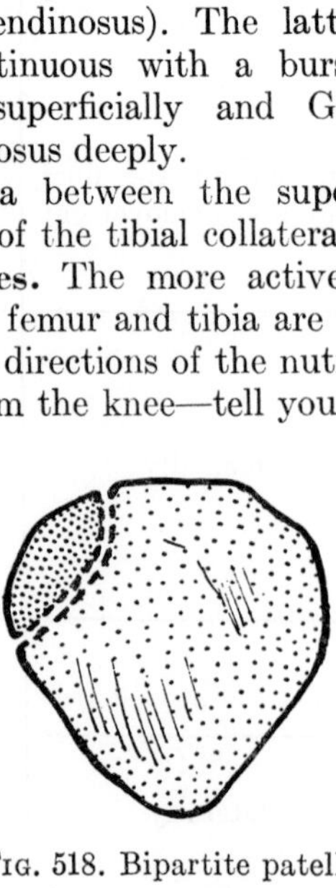

FIG. 518. Bipartite patella

The lower epiphysis of the femur begins to ossify about the 9th intra-uterine month and fuses with the diaphysis about the 19th year. The epiphyseal line runs through the adductor tubercle, along the intercondylar line, and shaves the upper ends of the cartilage of the condyles. Four blunt prongs from the diaphysis fit into four shallow cups in the epiphysis (*fig. 406*).

The upper epiphysis of the tibia includes the groove for the Semimembranosus on the medial condyle, the facet for the fibula on the lateral condyle, and the tibial tuberosity. Ossification begins before birth or soon after birth; fusion occurs about the 19th year.

The patella begins to ossify about the 3rd year, probably from several centers. The superolateral angle may remain unossified (emarginate patella) or may ossify independently (*fig. 518*).

Tibiofibular Joints. (p. 405).

THE ANKLE JOINT

[Talocrural Joint]

Ten Basic Observations

1. In walking, the Triceps Surae (i.e., two heads of the Gastrocnemius and the Soleus) raises the heel from the ground—it causes *plantarflexion* of the ankle joint. During the act of advancing the limb, the four anterior crural muscles cause the foot to clear the ground—they cause *dorsiflexion.* The value of the ankle joint resides in this hinge action, in this to and fro movement in walking.

2. The weight of the body is transmitted to the talus through the tibia. The malleoli grasp the sides of the talus (*fig. 519*).

3. The sharp tip of the fibular malleolus is felt ¾″ below the level of the blunt end of the tibial malleolus. The top of the sustentaculum tali of the calcaneus is felt ¾″ below the tibial malleolus and, therefore, on a level with the tip of the fibular malleolus. This is because the fibular malleolus extends the whole depth of the lateral side of the body of the talus, whereas the tibial malleolus covers only a third of the medial side.

Hence, the lateral side of the body of the talus is three-thirds articular, and the medial side is one-third articular and, as we shall see, two-thirds ligamentous (*figs. 520* and *521*).

4. The sides of the malleoli and of the shafts of the bones above them are subcutaneous—there are no muscles at the sides of the ankle. They are grouped in front and

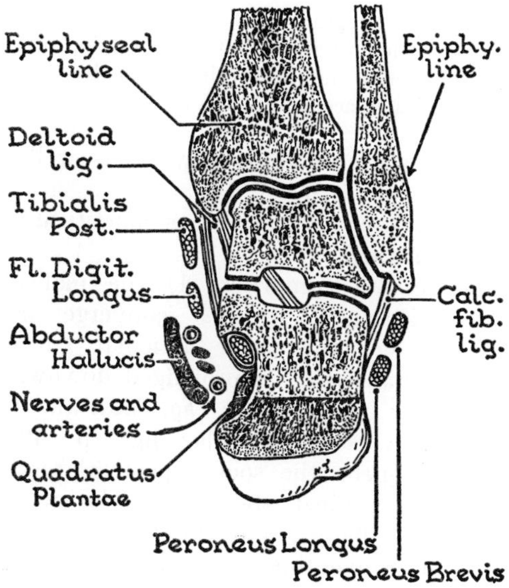

FIG. 519. Coronal section through the ankle region.

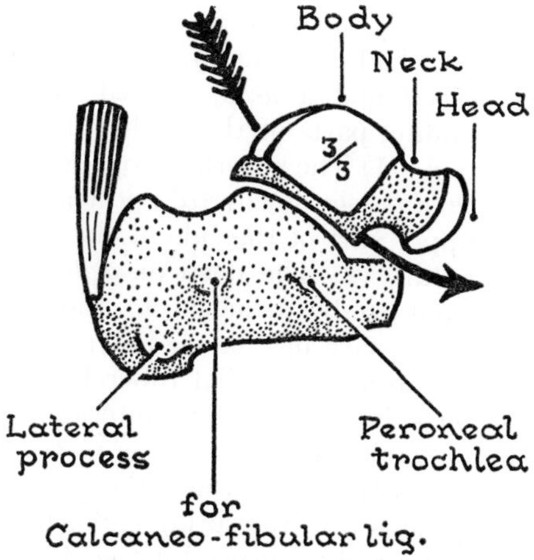

FIG. 520. Lateral aspect of calcaneus and talus. The lateral surface of the body of the talus is three-thirds articular. The *arrow* traverses the tarsal tunnel (tarsal sinus).

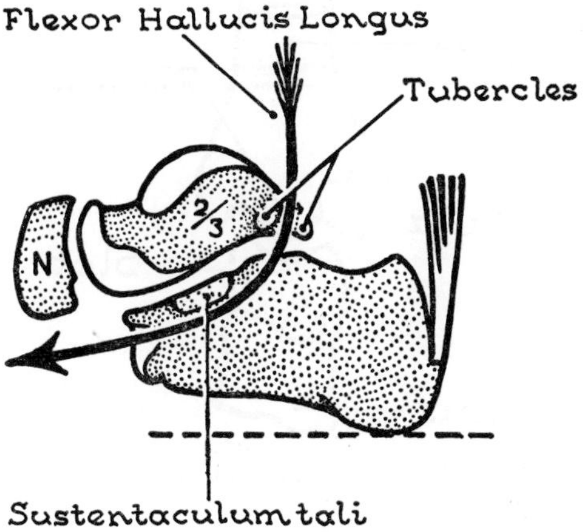

FIG. 521. Medial aspect of calcaneus and talus. The medial surface of the body of the talus is one-third articular; two-thirds rough for ligament.

behind as they obviously should be at an ideal hinge joint.

5. Because of the hinge movements, the upper surface of the body of the talus is necessarily articular and convex from before backward, and the under aspect of the lower end of the tibia is necessarily articular and concave.

»» *Comparative Anatomy.* In lower mammals, such as the sheep, movements at the ankle joint are restricted to flexion and extension partly by an anteroposterior flange that projects from the tibia into a slot in the talus (*fig. 522*). In man, this feature, though much reduced, is notable (*fig. 519*).

6. With the exception of the tendo calcaneus, all muscles or rather all tendons crossing the ankle joint—4 in front, 5 behind—pass forward to be inserted into the foot anterior to the transverse tarsal joint (*fig. 523*). On contracting they tend to produce forward dislocation of the leg bones at the ankle joint.

7. When we rise on our toes, the force of gravity also tends to displace the leg bones forward.

8. The strength of a joint depends upon four factors: (1) bones, (2) ligaments, (3) muscles, and (4) gravity.

The muscles and gravity here tend toward forward displacement of the leg bones, so it falls to the bony parts and the ligaments to resist this.

9. This demands that the socket shall be

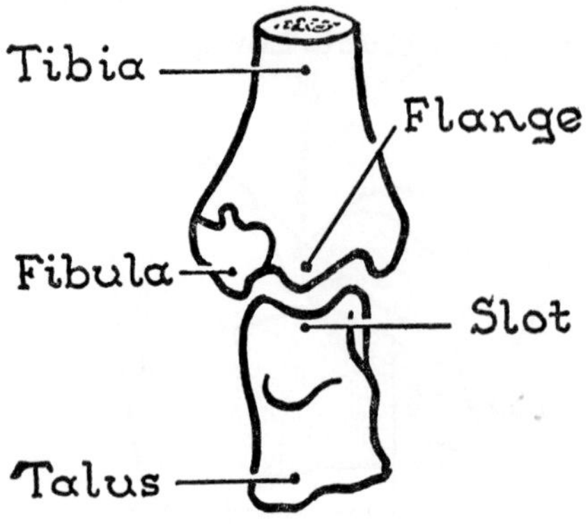

Fig. 522. The ankle joint of the sheep

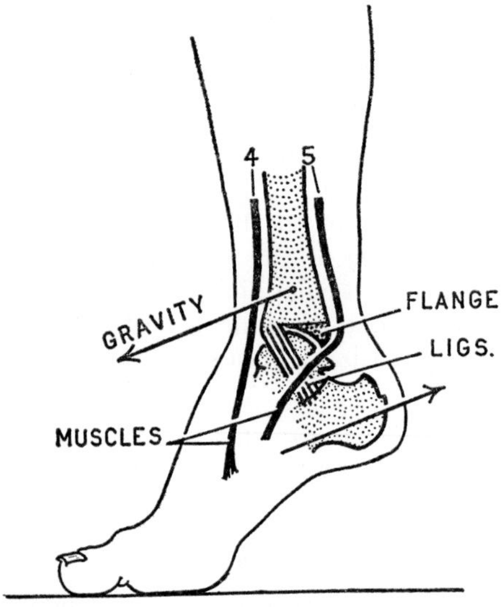

Fig. 523. At the ankle joint the ligaments and bones resist the forces of the muscles and of gravity.

so fashioned that it cannot slide forward on the talus,

10. and that the ligaments shall pass downward and backward.

Bony Parts of the Ankle Joint. These include (1) parts of the talus and (2) its socket.

The Talus. The upper surface of the body of the talus is saddle-shaped and articular, and it is continuous with an extensive facet for the fibular malleolus and with a restricted facet for the tibial malleolus.

Note that the body is wedge-shaped (*fig. 524*), the broad end being in front, and that

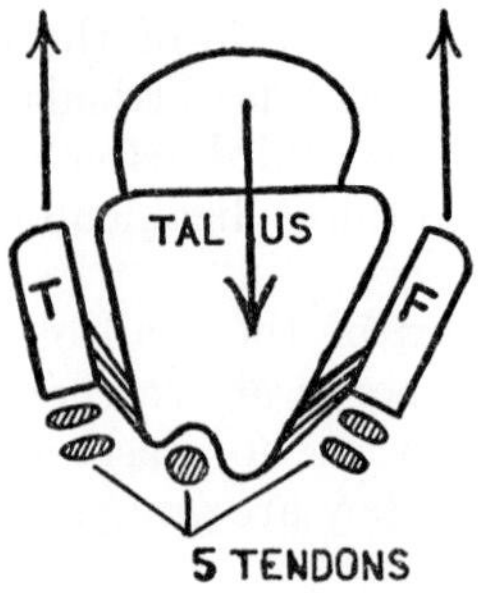

Fig. 524. Diagram of the ankle joint in horizontal section to show that the direction of the ligaments and the converging malleoli prevent backward displacement of the talus.

the fibular facet faces upward as well as laterally (*fig. 519*).

These three articular areas constitute the **trochlea tali.**

The Socket comprises (1) the malleoli, whose articular surfaces converge posteriorly, (2) the lower articular surface of the tibia, which is prolonged downward posteriorly into a flange (*fig. 523*), and (3) the transverse tibiofibular lig. (p. 406), which deepens the socket posterolaterally and rubs against the talus. The wedge shape, the flange, and the ligament each assist in preventing forward displacement of the two leg bones.

Ligaments. The anterior and posterior parts of the capsule are loose to allow of hinge movements. The **medial** or **deltoid ligament** (*fig. 525*) arises from the blunt end of the tibial malleolus and has two parts, a *superficial* and a *deep*, shaped like the corresponding parts of the medial ligament of the knee: (1) The superficial or "*calcaneotibial*" *band* passes downward and backward to the upper part of the side of the sustentaculum tali. (2) The deep or *deltoid part* spreads out to be attached to the whole nonarticular part of the medial aspect of the talus—from the medial tubercle behind to the neck in front. A few anterior fibers reach the navicular bone. Fibers placed between the sustentaculum and the navicular are continuous with the spring ligament and they may be said to suspend it (*fig. 525*).

The **lateral ligament** (*fig. 526*) has three parts: (1) The *calcaneofibular ligament* is a cord that passes downward and backward

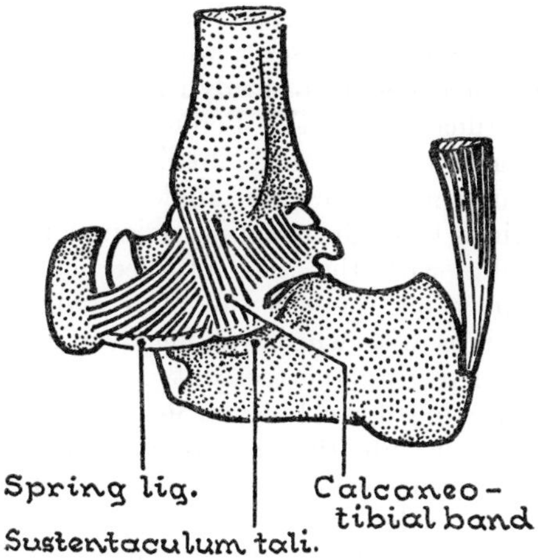

FIG. 525. The medial or deltoid ligament of the ankle joint.

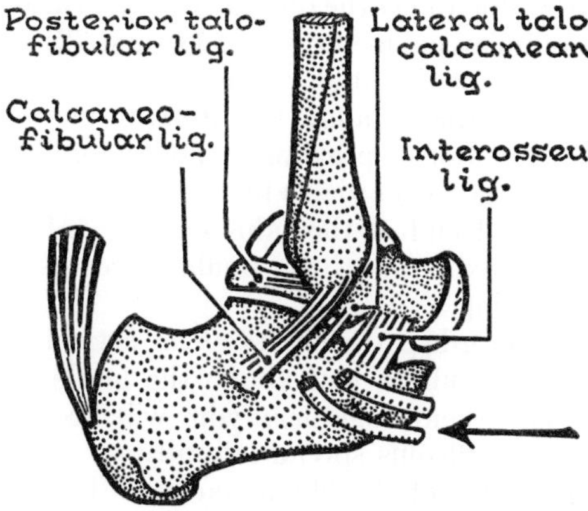

FIG. 526. Lateral view of the ligaments about the ankle, so directed as to prevent backward displacement of the bones of the foot.

from in front of the tip of the fibular malleolus to a fulness on the side of the calcaneus. In shape and direction it resembles the lateral ligament of the knee. (2) The *posterior talofibular ligament* (*fig. 528*) passes medially and backward from the malleolar fossa of the fibula (*fig. 454*) to the lateral tubercle and adjacent part of the talus. (3) The *anterior talofibular ligament* is a band that passes from the anterior border of the malleolus to the neck of the talus immediately in front of the fibular facet.

IN SUMMARY. Four ligaments pass backward, thereby resisting forward displacement of the leg bones, or, which is equivalent, backward displacement of the foot. The "calcaneotibial" and calcaneofibular ligs. pass from the respective malleoli downward and backward to the calcaneus, and in so-doing span the talus. The posterior fibers of the deltoid lig. and the posterior talofibular lig. are very strong. They pass from the malleoli to the respective tubercles of the talus and to the adjacent parts of the talus (*fig. 528*).

The anterior talofibular lig. is the weakest ligament of the joint. It and the anterior part of the deltoid lig. pass downward and forward from the respective malleoli.

The Synovial Membrane extends well forward on to the neck of the talus. A puncture here, when the toes are pointed, may enter the joint cavity (*fig. 527*). As in other joints, synovial folds extend between the articular surfaces, and a pad of fat is present.

Relations. In front, the anterior tibial vessels and deep peroneal nerve lie midway between the malleoli with 2 tendons on each side of them. Behind, the Fl. Hallucis Longus tendon lies midway between the malleoli and there are 2 tendons behind each malleolus; the posterior tibial vessels and tibial nerve lie between Fl. Digitorum Longus and Fl. Hallucis Longus (*fig. 528*).

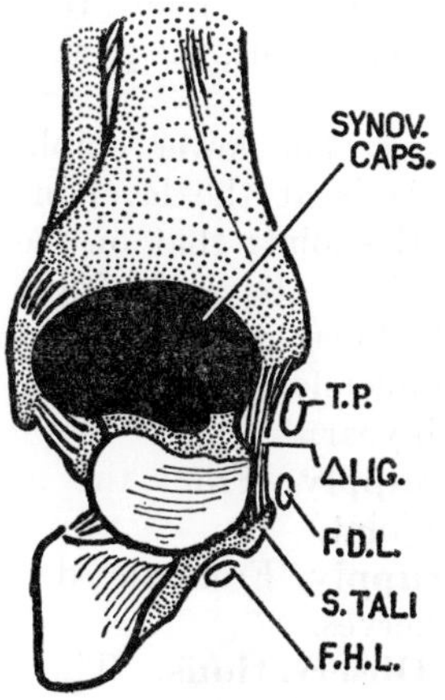

FIG. 527. The synovial cavity of the ankle joint, distended. The posterior surface of the transverse tarsal joint, i.e., anterior surfaces of the talus and calcaneus, are shown. Note the positions of the long tendons in relation to the sustentaculum tali.

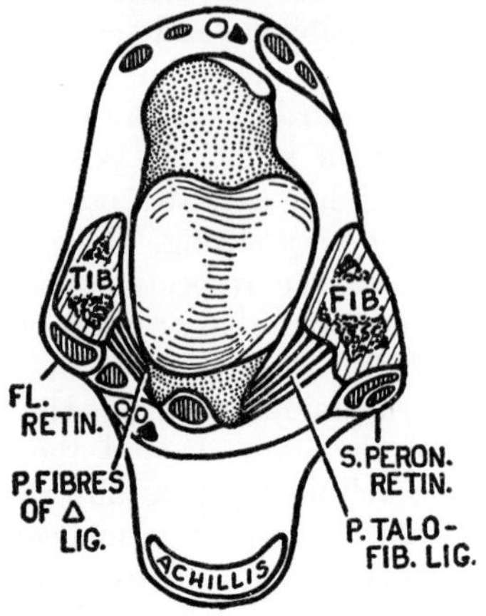

FIG. 528. Horizontal section through ankle joint showing (1) wedge-shaped socket, (2) direction of ligaments, (3) five posterior tendons, and (4) the investing and intermuscular deep fascia.

The deltoid ligament is crossed by Tibialis Posterior and Fl. Digitorum Longus, whereas the calcaneofibular ligament is crossed by Peronei Longus and Brevis.

Movements. *Dorsiflexion* (*Flexion*)—Tibialis Anterior, Peroneus Tertius, and the long extensors of the toes. *Plantarflexion* (*Extension*)—Gastrocnemius and Soleus.

The 5 tendons passing behind the ankle are too close to the axis of the joint to act to advantage on the joint. In fact, if the tendo calcaneus is cut, the power to plantarflex is lost.

Epiphyses. The lower epiphyseal plate of the fibula is at the level of the upper surface of the joint; that of the tibia is a third of an inch above the joint (*fig. 519*). The distal fibular and tibial epiphyses are always completely fused to their diaphyses by the 20th year.

Blood Supply. From the anastomoses around the joint.

Nerve Supply. From the deep peroneal and tibial nerves.

Other Observations. The most unstable position the joint can assume is plantar flexion, as when you rise on your toes, because the narrow end of the wedge-like body of the talus is then only loosely engaged by the malleoli, and slight degrees of inversion and eversion are permitted.

The ankle joint depends upon the 2 tibial and 3 peroneal muscles, which act like the ropes of a rudder, to steady it. It is, perhaps, unfortunate that the Peroneus Tertius is not as strong as the Tibialis Anterior. It might then save the ankle from being sprained through forced inversion when you stumble with the toes inturned, as when stepping off the sidewalk. To avoid this risk, it is wise when walking over difficult ground to turn the toes out.

On going down hill you instinctively dig your heels into the ground, (1) because in this position of dorsiflexion the broad edge of the wedge is closely grasped by the malleoli, and (2) because the heel is at the short end of a lever; the toes being at the long end.

The suppleness of the ankle socket (*fig. 529*) is due to (1) the obliquity of the various tibiofibular ligaments (*fig. 453*) and (2) the obliquity of the fibular facet.

The ligaments allow the fibula to move in two directions—proximally and laterally—hence, the socket yields by broadening when the broad end of the talus engages. Movement proximally of the fibula increases the broadening.

If you grasp the shafts of an articulated tibia and fibula just above the ankle and squeeze them together, you will see the fibular malleolus spread laterally.

The apex of the fibular facet of the talus resembles the cutting edge of a chisel. Should one fall from a height on to ones heels this chisel-like edge may drive its way into the calcaneus (*fig. 520*).

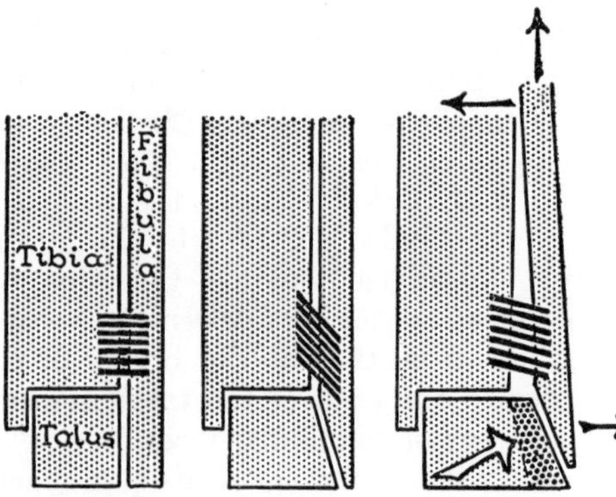

FIG. 529. Transverse fibers would make a rigid ankle socket; oblique fibers make a supple socket.

JOINTS OF THE FOOT

Joints of Inversion and Eversion:

1. Talocalcanean Joint:
   Post. talocalcanean or Subtalar joint.
   Ant. talocalcanean joint.
2. Talonavicular Joint.
3. Calcaneocuboid Joint, which is auxiliary to the talonavicular joint, according it extra freedom.

Definitions Of Movements. Rotation about the long, or anteroposterior, axis of the foot is called *supination* and *pronation.*

»» If you will sit with the palms of your hands on your knees, your 1st digits (thumbs and big toes) lie medially and the dorsa of your hands and feet face upwards. Then, raising the 1st digits and turning the dorsa laterally is supination, and the reverse is pronation.

Rotation about a vertical axis through the leg, when the foot is on the ground and the leg is the moving part, is called *medial and lateral rotation of the leg;* when the foot is off the ground and is the moving part, it is called *adduction and abduction of the foot.*

The movement of turning the sole of the foot to face the opposite sole is a combination of supination and adduction, and it is called **inversion.** Conversely, **eversion** is a combination of pronation and abduction, and it results in the sole facing slightly laterally. But the movements are complex and the terms are often used loosely, e.g., inversion as synonymous with supination, and eversion with pronation.

Inversion is usually associated with plantarflexion of the ankle joint and eversion with dorsiflexion.

Inversion and eversion are movements: (*1*) *Of the entire foot* (except the talus) *about the talus*; here the articular surfaces involved are all the facets below and in front of the talus and (as seen in figure 531) all 3 facets above the calcaneus and the concave facet behind the navicular; and (*2*) *Of the forepart of the foot on the hindpart,* where the small tarsal bones articulate with the 2 large ones.

Talocalcanean Joint

It is between the talus and its bony socket or bed, formed by (1) the calcaneus below and (2) the navicular in front, that much of the movement of inversion and eversion occurs (*figs. 530 and 531*).

»» **Bony Parts, Reviewed.** The entire body and part of the head of the talus rest upon the anterior two-thirds of the calcaneus and project slightly in front of it (*fig. 530*). The *Upper Surface of the Calcaneus* is divided into three areas: (1) The posterior third is saddle-shaped and above it lies a pad of fat. (2) The anterior third occupies a lower level than the posterior third and forms a horizontal platform (*fig. 531*). It presents medially a small facet (anterior talar facet) which is usually continuous posteromedially with a

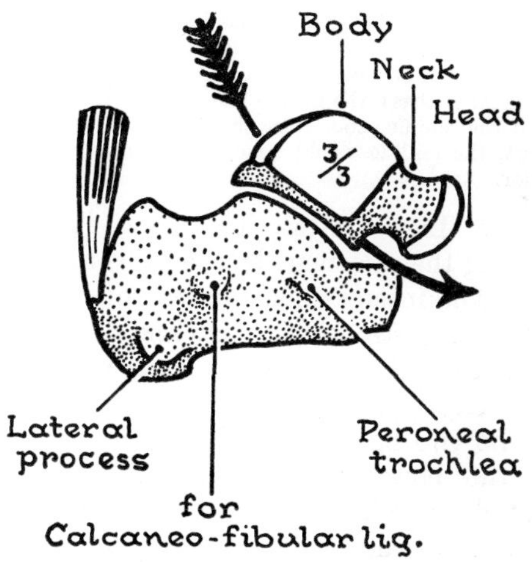

FIG. 530. The lateral aspect of the talus and calcaneus. *Arrow* traverses the tarsal sinus.

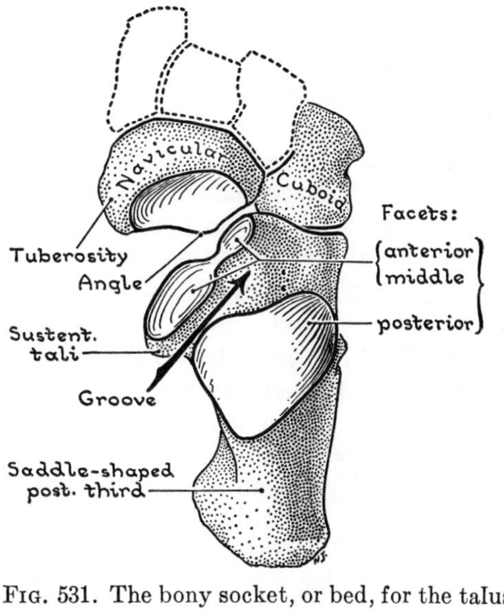

FIG. 531. The bony socket, or bed, for the talus formed by the calcaneus inferiorly and the navicular anteriorly.

larger facet (middle talar facet) on the sustentaculum tali. (4) The intermediate third (posterior talar facet) occupies the large inclined plane between the anterior and posterior thirds. In contrast with the combined anterior and middle talar facets which are concave, the posterior talar facet is convex. A deep groove separates the posterior facet from the middle facet.

When the talus and calcaneus are in articulation, the groove is converted into a tunnel, the *tarsal sinus.* A probe entering the sinus behind the sustentaculum tali will travel downward, laterally, and forward to open on to the lateral part of the anterior third of the upper surface of the calcaneus. This sinus lodges some fat through which run several fibrous bands, the *interosseous talocalcanean ligament,* which unite the two bones.

The platform on to which the sinus opens affords attachment to the stem of the inf. extensor retinaculum, the Ext. Digitorum Brevis, and the bifurcate lig.

The talus and calcaneus have, then, three areas of contact: of these, the anterior is commonly continuous with the middle, and, were there no interosseous ligament, the middle would be continuous with the posterior.

The **Ligaments.** The two ligaments uniting the calcaneus to the talus are:

1. The interosseous talocalcanean, which is not very strong (*figs. 519* and *526*).

2. The lateral talocalcanean, which is a mere slip (*fig. 526*).

The two ligaments uniting the calcaneus to the bones of the leg—and therefore spanning the talus—are:

3. The calcaneofibular portion of the lateral ligament of the ankle (*fig. 526*).

4. The calcaneotibial portion of the medial or deltoid ligament of the ankle (*fig. 525*).

All four ligaments take one and the same direction—downward and backward. They, therefore, prevent backward displacement of the foot.

The **five tendons** (Peronei Longus et Brevis, Fl. Hallucis Longus, Tibialis Posterior, and Fl. Digitorum Longus) that play so important a part as stabilizers of the ankle joint play a similar role here at the talocalcanean joints.

Subdivisions of talocalcanean joint. This joint is divided into a posterior and an anterior part by an interosseous ligament. The posterior talocalcanean joint has a synovial cavity of its own, and is known as the **Subtalar Joint,** but the anterior talocalcanean joint shares a synovial cavity with the talonavicular joint—hence their collective name, the **Talo-calcaneo-navicular Joint** (*fig. 532*).

The Socket of the talocalcaneonavicular joint (*fig. 532*) is formed: in front by the posterior surface of the navicular; below, by the middle and anterior talar facets; and, between the under surface of the navicular and the sustentaculum tali by the *plantar calcaneonavicular ligament,* commonly called "the spring ligament" (*fig. 533*).

The **Spring Ligament** is continuous medially with the deltoid ligament, which

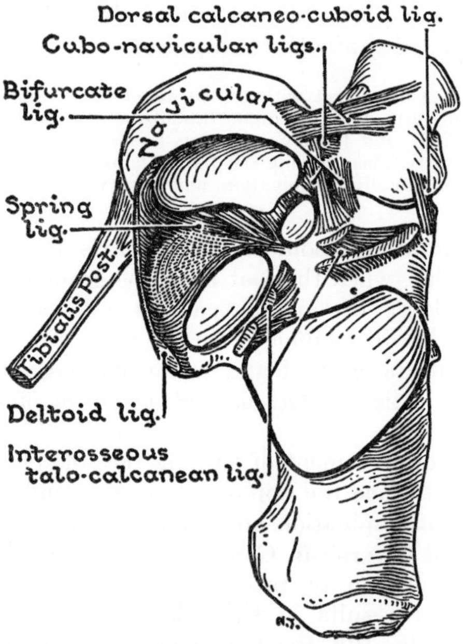

Fig. 532. The talus has been removed in order to show its bed and the ligaments of the joints of inversion and eversion.

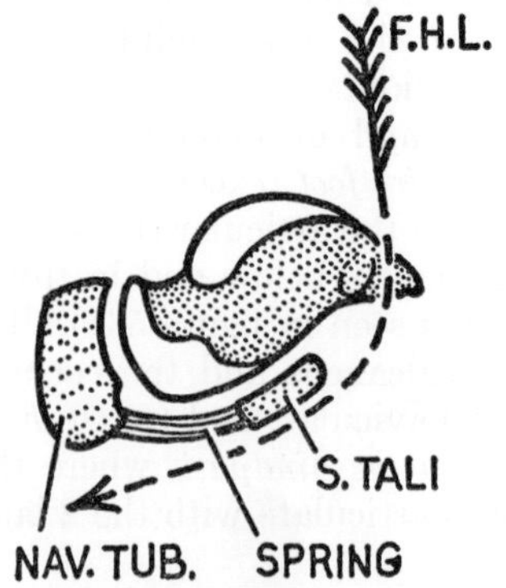

Fig. 533. The spring ligament. The *arrow* indicates the position of the Fl. Hallucis Longus tendon.

appears to suspend it from the tibial malleolus. It is sandwiched between the Tibialis Posterior, which supports it below, and the head of the talus which lies above it, and which in turn it supports. Where it is compressed between the tendon and the bone, it is fibrocartilaginous; but its attachments remain pliable and ligamentous.

It extends from the calcaneus in front of the middle and anterior talar facets to the navicular tuberosity and the whole length of the plantar surface of the navicular (*figs. 532* and *535*).

The **Bifurcate Ligament** is attached posteriorly to the front of the upper surface of the calcaneus. The medial fibers (calcaneonavicular band) of this V-shaped ligament pass forward to the lateral surface of the navicular bone; whereas the lateral fibers (calcaneocuboid band) pass to the medial surface of the cuboid bone. Thus the two bands form collateral ligaments for the respective joints.

The capsule of the joint is formed thus: spring lig. below; deltoid lig. medially; interosseous lig. posteriorly; bifurcate lig. laterally; and dorsal talonavicular lig. above.

The portion of the head of the talus that rests upon the "spring ligament" is at the summit of the medial arch of the foot (*fig. 475*). If the Tibialis Posterior becomes weak or paralyzed, the "spring ligament", having an undue strain to bear, stretches. Then the head of the talus, like the apex of a wedge, descends forcing the anterior portion of the foot downward and also laterally into abduction, a condition known as flat foot.

The Transverse Tarsal Joint has two component parts:

1. Talonavicular Joint,
2. Calcaneocuboid Joint.

The talonavicular joint has been described above with the talocalcaneonavicular joint. It must also be considered with the calcaneocuboid joint. If you drive a nail upward through the calcaneus and talus into the tibia, thereby immobilizing the talocalcanean and ankle joints, you will find that the movements of inversion and eversion, though restricted, are not abolished.

Observations:

1. On palpating the dorsum of the inverted foot, the front of the head of the talus and the anterior aspect of the calcaneus are found to be partly uncovered. Evidently inversion and eversion take place at the transverse tarsal joint.

2. Invert slightly against resistance and note by inspection and palpation that the Tibiales Anterior et Posterior are in action —their tendons being taut. They are the invertors of the foot.

3. Evert and by palpation (not always easy) note that the three Peronei are in play. They are the evertors of the foot.

The two muscles of inversion and three of eversion are inserted in front of the transverse tarsal joint.

4. The hollowed-out navicular bone forms a socket for the front of the head of the talus; so, the articulation is ball-and-socket in conformation but not in movements because encumbrances, in the form of adjacent bones and ligaments, restrict its movements to gliding.

5. Dorsal, interosseous, and plantar ligaments unite the cuboid to the navicular and cuneiforms, so when the two tibial muscles cause inversion, the cuboid cannot choose but follow.

6. From this it may be concluded that of the apposed surfaces of calcaneus and cuboid, one must be convex from side to side, the other concave.

The **Calcaneocuboid Joint** is an accessory joint of inversion and eversion. Medially, it is bounded by the *calcaneocuboid band* of the bifurcate ligament; dorsolaterally, by a weak band, the *dorsal calcaneocuboid ligament.* Cut through these in order to see that the anterior surface of the calcaneus is rounded off medially (i.e., convex); that the posterior surface of the cuboid is concave from side to side, thus allowing inversion; and that a process (the calcanean angle) projects from the inferomedial part of the cuboid backward below the calcaneus. The upward thrust given by the Peroneus Longus to the cuboid is transmitted by this angle to the calcaneus. The joint is closed below by two ligaments, the *long and short plantar ligaments.*

The **long plantar ligament** (*fig. 534*) extends from the plantar surface of the

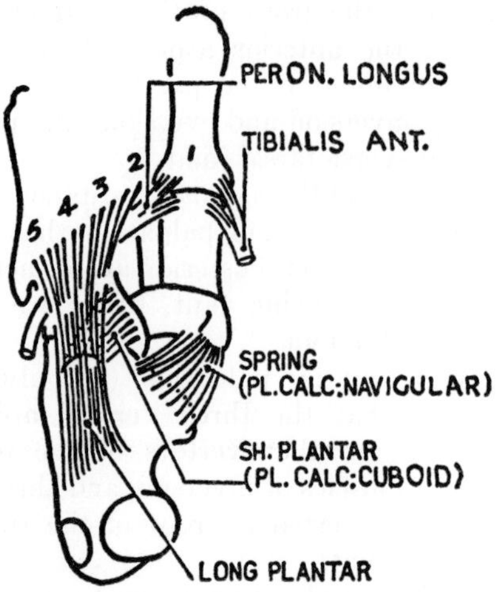

FIG. 534. Three plantar ligaments, and the two tendons that form a stirrup.

calcaneus in front of its medial and lateral processes to the ridge on the cuboid, while its more superficial fibers, passing beyond this, gain attachment to the bases of (2), 3, 4,(5) metatarsals. These superficial fibers convert the groove on the cuboid into a tunnel for the Peroneus Longus tendon.

The **short plantar ligament** [plantar calcaneocuboid lig.] is fan-shaped, and is not completely exposed till the band-like long plantar ligament is reflected. It stretches from the anterior tubercle of the calcaneus (and the area in front of it) to the large area behind the ridge on the cuboid. It belongs solely to the calcaneocuboid joint.

Note. The fibers of two ligaments:

plantar calcaneo— navicular (spring) / cuboid (short plantar)

form an almost continuous sheet of thick parallel fibers that run anteromedially from calcaneus to cuboid and navicular (*fig. 535*). They are, in fact though not in name, the deep components of the *plantar lig. of the transverse tarsal joint*, the long plantar lig. being the superficial component.

Arches of the Foot

The lateral longitudinal arch is formed by the calcaneus, cuboid, and metatarsals IV and V. It is a small arc of a large circle; the arch is low (*fig. 535.1*).

In the act of walking it commonly bears

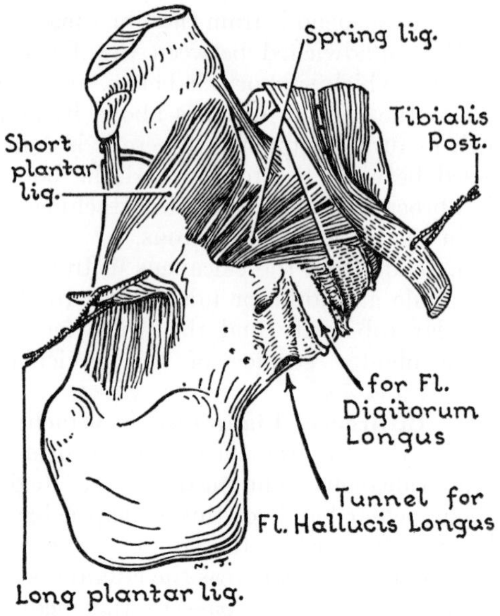

FIG. 535. The calcaneonavicular and calcaneocuboid ligaments (i.e., spring lig. and short plantar lig.), from below.

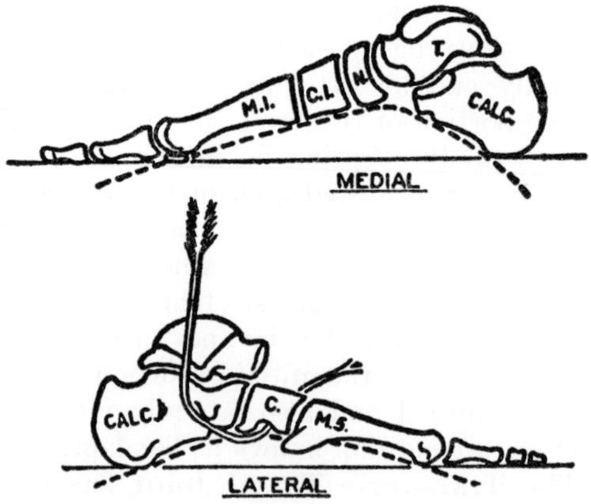

FIG. 535.1. The longitudinal arches

the weight of the body before the medial arch comes into play. It can yield or flatten at the hinge surfaces between the cuboid and metatarsals IV and V. The Peroneus Longus passes under the cuboid at the summit of the arch, and acts as a sling for it, and the upward thrust it gives to the cuboid is transmitted to the calcaneus by the calcanean angle of the cuboid.

The medial longitudinal arch is formed by the calcaneus, talus, navicular, three cuneiforms, and three medial metatarsals, and the sesamoid bones. It is a high arch. At its summit, placed at the junction of its posterior one-third with its anterior two-thirds, lies the head of the talus with the sustentaculum tali behind it and the navicular in front. The Tibialis Posterior is largely (two-thirds) inserted into the tuberosity of the navicular bone, but the part (one-third) that passes below the spring ligament acts as a sling for the arch. At the hinge surfaces between the talus and the navicular and also between the navicular and the three cuneiforms, the spring or arch can flatten and recoil.

»» Examination of the dried bones does not reveal this; they must be examined fresh, with the cartilage on.

The transverse arch of the foot. The medial longitudinal arch being higher than the lateral, it follows that when the medial borders of the two feet are in contact with each other a transverse arch is formed, each foot contributing half an arch. Since the heads of all the metatarsals make contact with the ground, it is evident that they do not contribute to this arch, but the bases and the small tarsal bones do. The crossed insertions of Tibialis Posterior and Peroneus Longus largely create the transverse arch and help to support the longitudinal arches (p. 424).

Joints Distal to the Transverse Tarsal Joint

These include: small intertarsal, tarsometatarsal, intermetatarsal, metatarsophalangeal, and interphalangeal joints.

The *Metatarsophalangeal and Interphalangeal Joints* are fashioned and supplied with ligaments like the corresponding joints of the hand.

The *deep transverse metatarsal ligs.* (ligs. of metatarsal heads) extend to the hallux; in the hand the corresponding ligaments leave the pollex free (*fig. 149*).

The *Small Intertarsal Joints* (i.e., between cuboid, navicular, and cuneiforms), the *Tarsometatarsal Joints*, and the joints between the *Bases of the Metatarsals* may be considered together under the headings: (1) *side-to-side joints* and (2) *end-to-end joints.*

The **Side-to-Side Joints,** or those concerned in the transverse arch, have strong *plantar ligaments* which act as transverse ties (*fig. 536*). These ties are not limited to the plantar aspect but, as *interosseous ligaments,* extend dorsalward between the individual bones, being absent only between the bases of metatarsals I and II. The *articular facets* are generally situated near the dorsal part of the surface, where ligaments would have least value. The *dorsal ligaments* are weak.

The **End-to-End Joints,** or those concerned in the longitudinal arches. Observe that the apposed anterior and posterior surfaces of all the bones of the foot are completely covered with cartilage, and that the joints, accordingly, do not possess interosseus ligaments (*fig. 472*). They have, however, *strong plantar ligaments, weak dorsal ligaments,* and in some instances, *collateral ligaments* (*fig. 537*). The side-to-side facets are commonly continuous with the end-to-end facets.

»» **Arrangement of Ligaments.** The ligaments of the foot are so disposed as to resist certain forces. Accordingly, (1) the dorsal, interosseous, and plantar ligaments between any two bones have a common direction. Further, from figure 538 it may be noted that (2) the ligamentous bands uniting the bones of the lateral arch to each other and to the bones of the medial arch, all—or practically all—take a common direction; this is the *direction of resistance* (a) to the backward pull of the muscles inserted into the lateral arch, and (b) to backward thrusts applied to the 4th and 5th toes (as in walking and kicking); and similarly that (3) the ligamentous bands of the medial arch

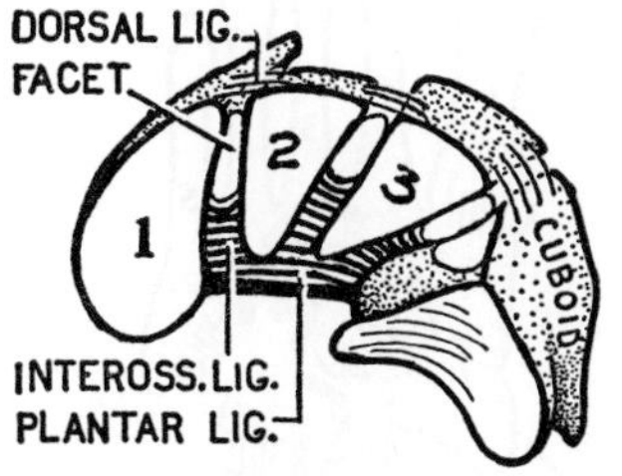

FIG. 536. The ligaments or ties of the "side-to-side" joints. Note that the cuboid supports the cuneiforms and the navicular.

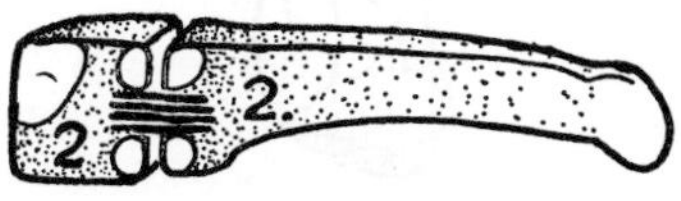

FIG. 537. The collateral ligament of an "end-to-end" joint.

are so directed that the backward thrust given to the 1st metatarsal (as in rising on the ball of the big toe in walking) is dispersed laterally to the 2nd and 3rd metatarsals which, therefore, share in conducting the thrust via the cuneiforms and navicular to the talus and so to the tibia.

DYNAMICS OF FOOT

Standing. WEIGHT DISTRIBUTION. The body weight of a person weighing say 120 pounds and "standing relaxed in a naturally held position" is distributed through the feet as follows: 60 pounds is distributed through each foot; of this, 30 pounds is through the hindpart (calcaneus) and 30 pounds through the forepart, as might be expected since the line of gravity passes slightly in front of the ankle joint. Now, the forepart of the foot has six points of contact with the ground, namely, the two sesamoids under the head of the 1st metatarsal and the heads of the lateral four metatarsals, each supporting approximately 5 pounds; the 1st metatarsal through its sesamoids supports a double load (D. J. Morton).

If the ligaments at the base of a metatarsal or at the proximal end of a cuneiform became lax, that metatarsal, being mobile, will largely cease to be a weight-distributing bone (*figs. 538.1* to *538.3*).

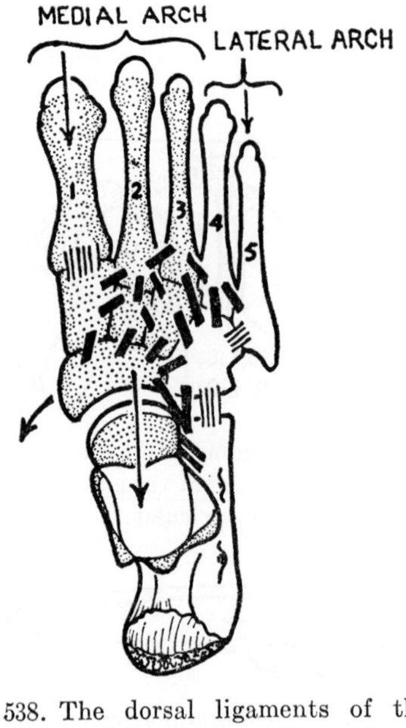

FIG. 538. The dorsal ligaments of the foot are not scattered in a haphazard way (*see text*).

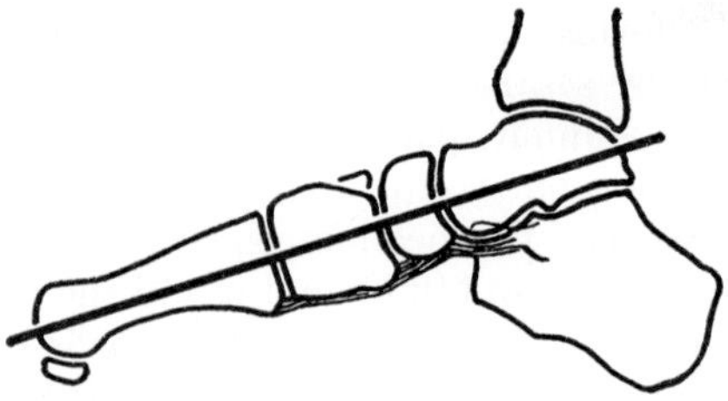

FIG. 538.1. Tracing of radiogram of a normal foot, standing. (After Ewen A. Jack.)

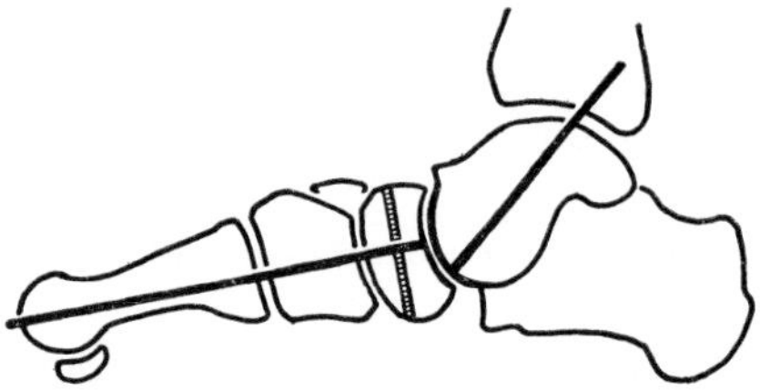

FIG. 538.2. One form of flatfoot, talonavicular joint, standing. (After Ewen A. Jack.)

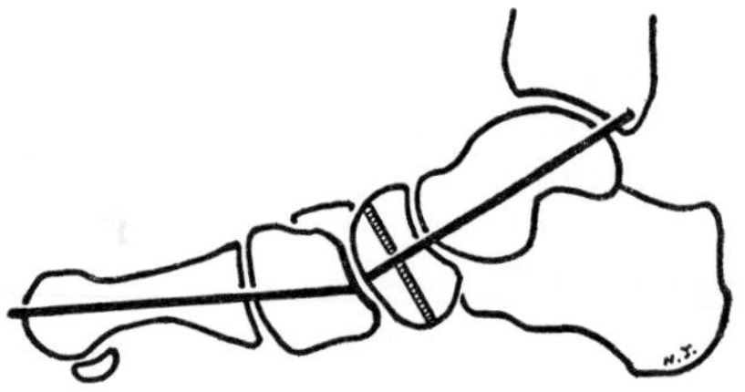

FIG. 538.3. Another form of flatfoot, naviculo-cuneiform joint, standing. (After Ewen A. Jack.)

Arch Support. It has long been the teaching that muscles are all important for the support of the arches of the foot. It would appear that this view must be abandoned. R. L. Jones calculated that the plantar ligaments and aponeurosis bear the greatest stress. The chief function of the invertor and evertor muscles is to preserve a relative constancy in the ratio of the weight distribution among the heads of the metatarsals.

Peroneus Longus is more than four times as efficient in producing a shift of pressure from the lateral metatarsal heads to the first metatarsal head as the Tibialis Posterior or Fl. Digitorum Longus are in producing a shift from the first metatarsal head to the lateral heads.

A medial inclination of the tibia (as in knock-knee) shifts the weight toward the 1st metatarsal while a lateral inclination (as in bow legs) shifts it toward the lateral metatarsals.

Any failure of the arch is related to the duration of the stress to which it is subjected rather than to the severity of the stress; e.g., athletes and those who walk much subject their arches to great stress intermittently; whereas those who stand immobile subject their arches to relatively continuous stress, and it is these latter who develop trouble with their arches.

It has been demonstrated electromyographically that Tibialis Anterior, Peroneus Longus, and the intrinsic muscles of the foot play no important role in the normal static support of the long arches of the foot. They are commonly completely inactive. Even with the addition of abnormally great weights to the static arches, the muscles are relatively inactive (Basmajian and Stecko). During locomotion it is different, the intrinsic muscles of the foot being then very active when one rises on the toes even to the slightest degree (Basmajian and Bentzon).

Other points have been clarified also (*fig. 538.4*). Passive dorsiflexion of the big toe (as in rising on the ball of the foot), even without direct aid from muscles, through the "windlass action" of the plantar aponeurosis approximates the heads of the metatarsals to the heel, thereby shortening the foot and heightening the arch (J. H. Hicks).

If, while standing on one foot (knee flexed, if you wish), you overbalance laterally, in order to compensate, the arch rises and the leg rotates laterally; and vice-versa when overbalancing medially. Indeed, when the foot is fixed, these two movements (supination of the foot and lateral rotation of the leg) are invariably associated. If, however, the foot is free and the leg stationary, rising of the arch (supination) is associated with adduction of the foot (inversion).

Explanation. Of two joints (1) the subtalar

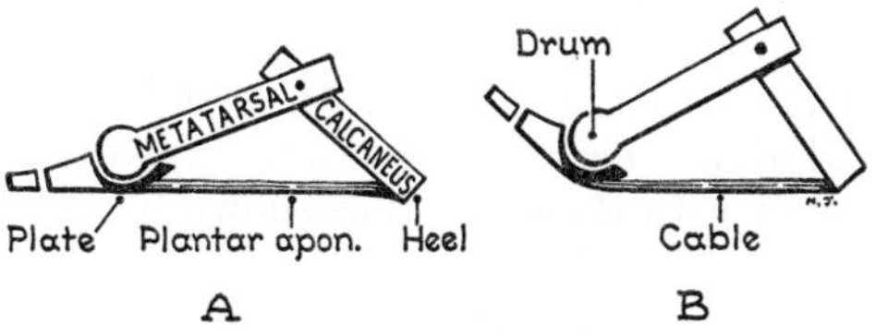

Fig. 538.4. Traction on the plantar aponeurosis causes heightening of the arch. (After J. H. Hicks.)

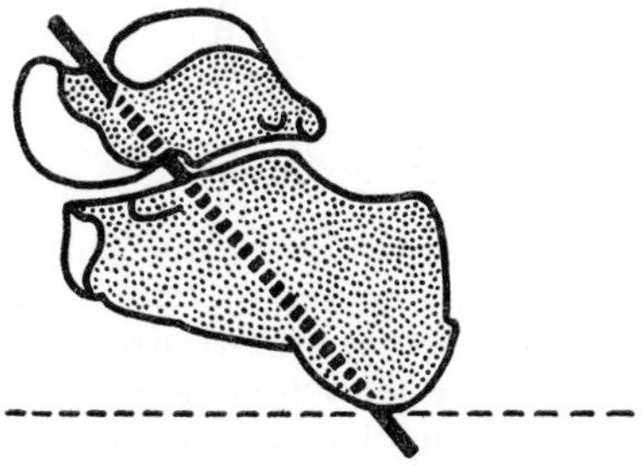

Fig. 538.5. The axis of the oblique hinge. (After J. H. Hicks.)

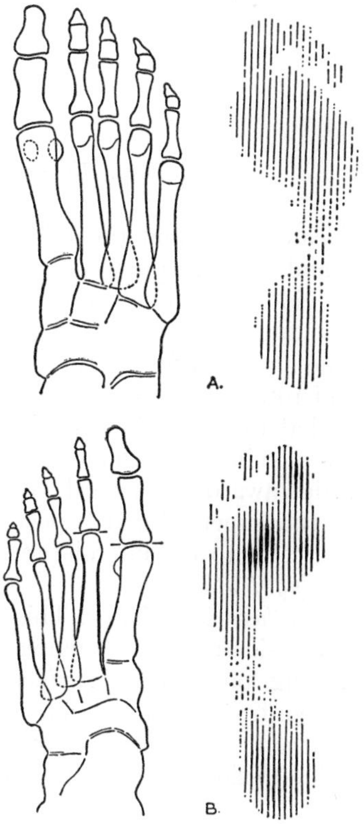

Fig. 539. *A*, tracing of a radiogram and an accompanying print of a normal right foot made by walking on a corrugated mat.

B, tracing, and a print of a left foot with a short 1st metatarsal bone. (After Morton.)

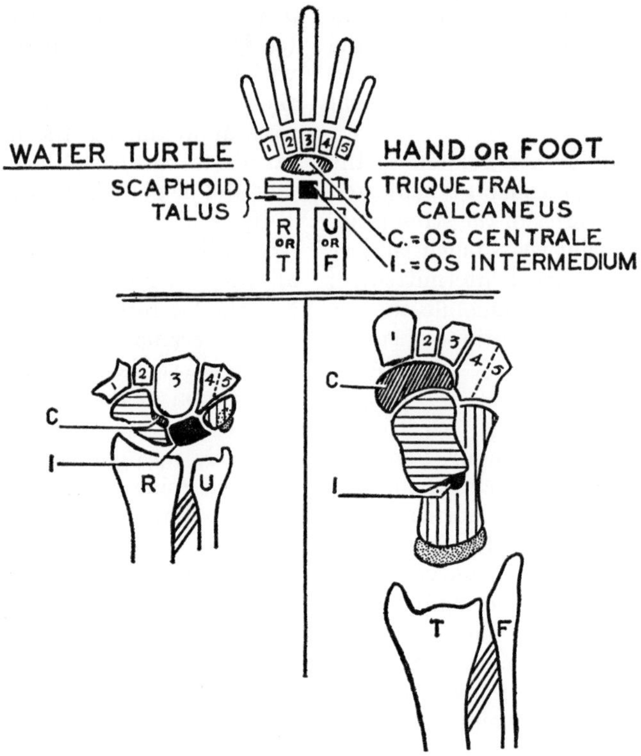

FIG. 540. Homologies in the bones of the hand and foot

(post. talocalcanean) and the talocalcaneonavicular and (2) the transverse tarsal, the former provides for hinge action between the leg + talus and the foot; the latter between the hind and fore parts of the foot. The axes of rotation of these two joints are so similar that they may be thought of as a single "oblique hinge" of which the axis runs obliquely downward, backward, and laterally from the superomedial aspect of the head of the talus to the inferolateral aspect of the heel (*fig. 538.5*).

Function of these Two Joints. This oblique hinge allows side-to-side swinging of the body, walking on sloping surfaces, and, above all, control of side-to-side balance. Indeed, without this hinge you cannot maintain side-to-side balance while standing on one leg.

Each of the five rays of the foot (metatarsals 5 and 4 and metatarsals 3, 2, and 1 and their cuneiforms) has an independent flexion-extension component. The medial and lateral rays commonly act reciprocally, flexion of the 1st ray being associated with extension of the 5th ray and vice-versa, which results in a twist of the anterior part of the foot.

Distribution of Weight. In walking, the head of each metatarsal has a weight-bearing contact with the ground; as shown by figure

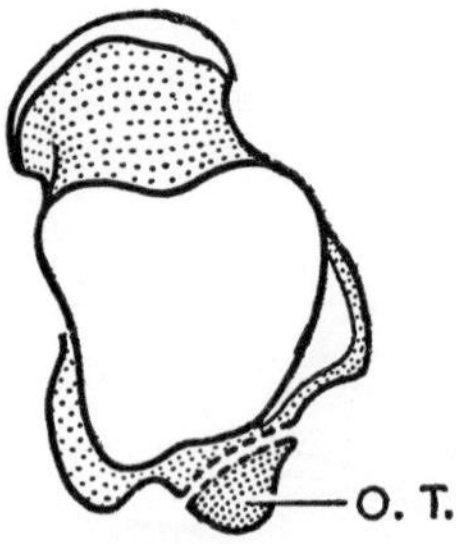

FIG. 541. Os trigonum. In 558 paired lower limbs (i.e., 279 adult cadavers) 43 or 7.7 per cent had ossa trigona. Of these, 22 occurred bilaterally (in 11 subjects); whereas 21 occurred unilaterally (in 21 subjects), 10 being in the right foot and 11 in the left. In other words, it occurred twice as commonly unilaterally as bilaterally (C. Storton.)

539*A* which is the print of a normal foot made by walking on "a rubber mat with compressible corrugations. The mat was covered with an inked fabric, a layer of paper, and finally a strip of cloth to hold the others in position". The distribution of the pressure in the feet is registered by the width of the corrugations printed on the paper. Contrast this with figure 539*B*, which is the print of a foot whose 1st metatarsal was short—a common atavism—with the result that the 2nd metatarsal had to carry more than its normal share of the load. This accounts for the increased thickness of the 2nd metatarsal in the radiogram, and for the width of the corrugations under the head of the 2nd metatarsal in the print (D. J. Morton).

The Height of the Arch of the Foot. When you stand erect with both feet on the ground, your knee and ankle joints are locked, so that the femur, leg bones and talus of each limb become temporarily rigid rods (*fig. 497*). If while so standing, you rotate your hip joints laterally you can palpate your trochanters moving backward and your Glutei Maximi becoming hard, and you can see your patellae come to face laterally and your arches to rise. If you rotate your hip joints medially, your arches will fall.

Hence, the Gluteus Maximus and the other lateral rotators of the hip joint cause the arch to rise; the Glutei Medius and Minimus and the other medial rotators cause it to fall. So, the height of the arch varies with your posture.

Muscles. The Gastrocnemius and Soleus, by plantar-flexing the ankle joint, raise the heel from the ground. The two Tibiales and the three Peronei steady the ankle joint and control the joints of inversion and eversion, much as ropes steady the rudder of a boat.

The Pentadactyl Hand and Foot. The limbs of amphibia are evolved from fins to be used as paddles in the water and as legs on the land. Having the same function, all four limbs are built to the same design. Hence, we may speak of homologous parts of the upper and lower limbs.

The bones of the hand and foot of man, when compared with those of the water turtle, are seen to retain the primitive generalized plan. The turtle has three proximal carpal and tarsal bones, the middle being the *os intermedium*, five distal carpal and tarsal bones, and several central bones, *ossa centralia*, on which the distal carpals and tarsals pivot (*fig. 540*).

In man the preaxial bones (radius and tibia) become weight-bearing bones; the postaxial bones (ulna and fibula) cease to articulate with the triquetrum or calcaneus. The os intermedium becomes the lunate or lateral tubercle of the talus; the 4th and 5th distal bones fuse to form the hamatum or cuboid. One os centrale persists as an entity in most primates; in man it fuses with the dorsum of the scaphoid of the hand and becomes the navicular of the foot.

Supernumerary Ossicles. The commonest ossicles are: (1) The *os trigonum* or separate lateral tubercle of the talus (*fig. 541*). Phylogenetically it is an ununited os intermedium (*fig. 540*). (2) The *tibiale externum* or separate navicular tuberosity. (3) A *bipartite medial cuneiform*, in upper and lower halves. (4) A fibrocartilaginous nodule in the Peroneus Longus tendon lateral to the cuboid is common and commonly it is ossified. (5) A sesamoid bone in the Tibialis Posterior tendon—not to be confused with a separate navicular tuberosity. (6) The tuberosity of metatarsal V, existing as a separate bone (Os Vesalianum), is rare.

SECTION VI

Thorax

CHAPTER 29

WALLS OF THORAX

BONY THORAX AND ITS LIGAMENTS

The thorax is the region between the abdomen and the neck. It contains the heart and lungs; it is traversed by structures that pass from the neck to the abdomen; by expanding and contracting like bellows, it aerates the blood circulating in the lungs.

The thoracic cavity is the largest of the three great bony cavities—cranial, thoracic, and pelvic. Each of these, in addition to offering protection to the viscus or viscera it contains, has diverse functions to perform, so each differs notably from the others.

The bony thorax comprises: 12 vertebrae, 12 pairs of costae (ribs and costal cartilages), and 1 sternum.

The Upper Aperture of the Thorax is formed by the body of the 1st thoracic vertebra, the 1st ribs, 1st costal cartilages, and the thick upper part of the manubrium sterni—very thick where it is a buffer between the two clavicles. It is like a kidney in shape and size, its diameters varying between 2 by 4 inches and 2½ by 5 inches (*fig. 547*).

The Lower Aperture of the Thorax is formed by the lower six costal cartilages and the 12th rib on each side, the xiphoid process in front, and the body of the 12th thoracic vertebra behind. It is cut away like a morning coat. The 10th rib is the lowest rib seen from the front. The 11th rib is much longer than the 12th rib and reaches to within two or three fingers' breadth of the iliac crest.

The Cavity of the Thorax also is kidney-shaped on transverse section (*fig. 542*). This is because the ribs are carried backward beyond the vertebral bodies almost as far as the tips of the spinous processes, where they bend to form angles. The transverse processes, which in this region act as buttresses for the ribs, are tilted backward to allow this. In consequence, the anteroposterior diameter of the thoracic cavity is least in the median sagittal plane and greatest in a lateral sagittal plane passing through the angles of the ribs.

When one considers that the dome of the diaphragm rises to the level of the 5th or 6th rib, it becomes apparent that the bony thorax affords protection not only to the heart and lungs, but also to the upper abdominal viscera—notably the liver, stomach, and spleen.

»» **Comparative Anatomy**. In the quadruped mammal, the thorax is suspended between the forelimbs by the Serrati Anteriores and Pectorales, so it is compressed from side to side. Its cavity is heart-shaped on transverse section, the greatest sagittal diameter being in the median plane (*fig. 542*). The ribs have no angles.

In the *Child at Birth* the chest is nearly circular on transverse section, and the ribs horizontal.

Man's Upright Posture is associated with anteroposterior flattening of the thorax, backward curving of the ribs, broadening of the sternum, and dorsally placed scapulae (*fig. 23*). Hence, a man can lie comfortably on his back, but a dog cannot.

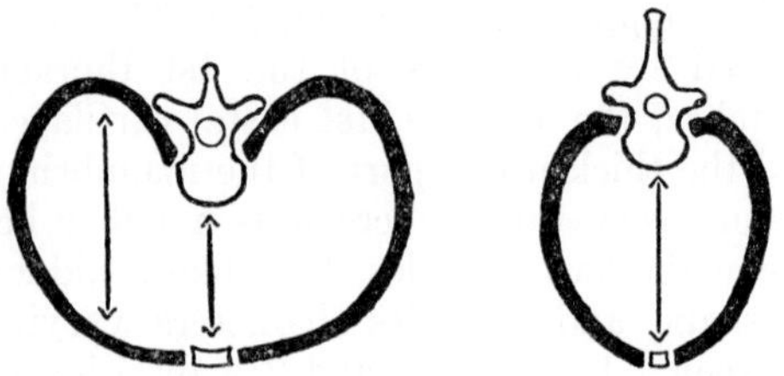

FIG. 542. Transverse section of thorax

Thoracic Vertebrae

The features of a thoracic, or rib-bearing vertebra, are these (*figs. 543* and *544*):

The **Body** has far back on each side an upper and a lower demifacet. The upper demifacet is for the head of its own rib (i.e., the rib that corresponds numerically with it), the lower and smaller facet being for the head of the rib next below.

The upper costal facet on the 1st vertebra is a complete facet for the 1st rib. The lower demifacet on the 9th vertebra is absent when the 10th vertebra has a complete facet for the 10th rib. The costal facets on the 11th and 12th vertebrae for the 11th and 12th ribs are large, complete, and on the pedicles (*fig. 543*).

The bodies in the middle of the thoracic series are heart-shaped. Each body is deeper behind than in front and so contributes to making the thoracic portion of the vertebral column concave forward (*fig. 544*). The upper and lower surfaces are flat, and the surface areas increase progressively from the first to the last, as might be expected. The left sides of the bodies of vertebrae 5, 6, and 7 are commonly flattened by the aorta.

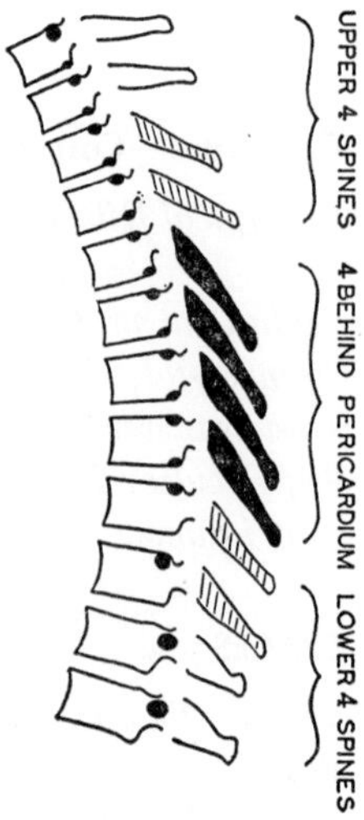

FIG. 543. Thoracic vertebrae, showing costal facets (for heads of ribs) and the inclination of the spinous processes.

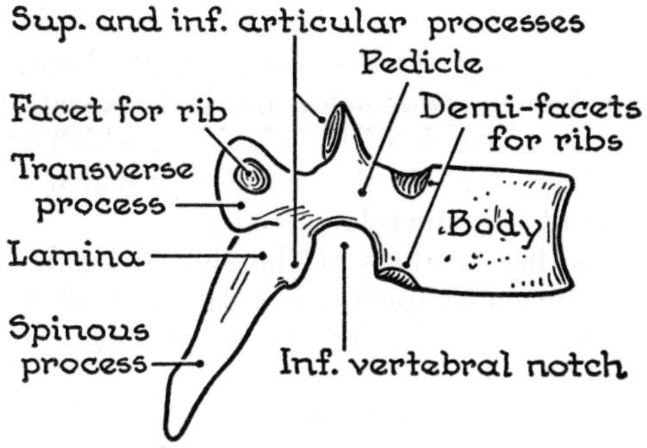

FIG. 544. A typical thoracic vertebra, side view.

The **Transverse Processes** act as buttresses or fulcra for the ribs, and accordingly are strong and stout. They are directed posterolaterally in conformity with the backward sweep of the ribs. On their tips are facets for the tubercles of the ribs. For functional reasons given on page 470, the facets are concave and in front of the tips of the 1st–7th transverse processes; flat and above the tips of the 8th, 9th, and 10th transverse processes; and absent from the 11th and 12th.

The transverse processes become progressively shorter from the 1st to the 12th. The 12th is nothing more than three tubercles corresponding to the mamillary, accessory, and "transverse" processes of a lumbar vertebra.

Of the **Spinous Processes** (**Spines**) of the 12 thoracic vertebrae, four lie above the level of the pericardium, four behind it, and four below it (*fig. 543*). The spines of those behind it (5th, 6th, 7th, and 8th) are almost vertical, and their tips lie at the level of the body of the vertebra immediately below. Those of the first two and last two (1st, 2nd, and 11th, 12th) are almost horizontal. Those of the 3rd, 4th, 9th, and 10th are somewhat oblique.

The **Articular Processes** are set almost vertically on the arc of a circle whose center is situated near the front of the vertebral body (*fig. 545*). This decides that such movements as take place between adjacent thoracic vertebrae shall be mainly rotary. The facets on the superior articular processes face posterolaterally; those on the inferior articular processes, anteromedially (*fig. 544*).

Though the number of thoracic vertebrae equals that of the cervical and lumbar combined, the thickness of the thoracic intervertebral discs is relatively less than in either of the other regions, so the range of movement is less (*fig. 20*).

The **Vertebral Foramen.** Because the thoracic portion of the spinal cord has no enlargement, it is circular on cross section, so the *vertebral foramen* is small and circular; you can hardly pass a finger through it (*fig. 546*). The cervical enlargement of the cord extends down to the 2nd Th. vertebra, and the lumbar enlargement begins at the 10th Th. vertebra. Accordingly, the vertebral canal in the upper and lower two (or

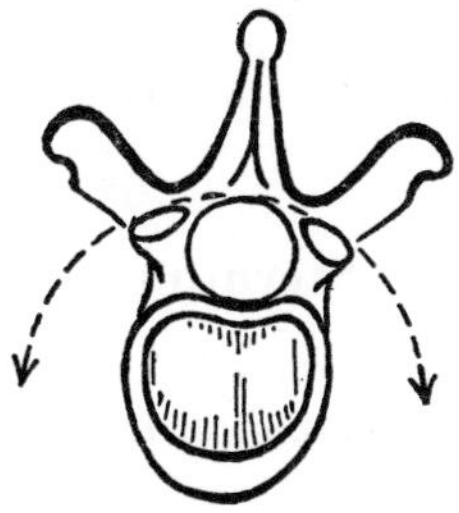

FIG. 545. The thoracic articular processes are set on an arc, so they permit rotation. The transverse processes support ribs, so they have facets and are stout.

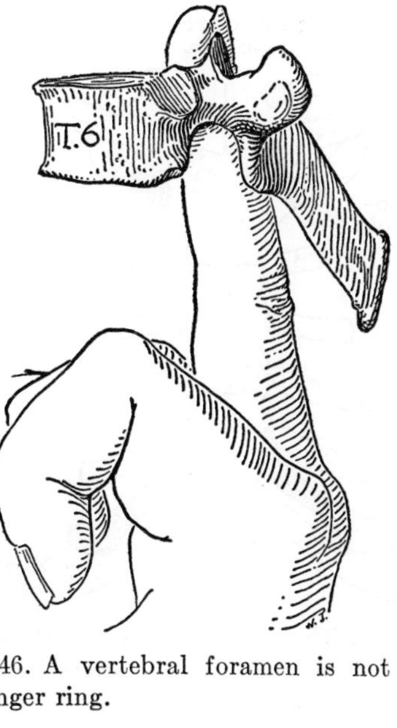

FIG. 546. A vertebral foramen is not larger than a finger ring.

three) thoracic vertebrae is somewhat triangular, as in the cervical and lumbar regions.

The inferior **Vertebral Notches** are large; the superior ones are absent (*fig. 544*).

As the thoracic vertebrae are followed from the middle of the series up and down, they are found gradually to assume the characteristics of cervical and lumbar vertebrae.

»» Thus, *the upper half of the first thoracic vertebra* conforms to the cervical in the following respects: (1) The body has upturned sides—it is not flat. (2) The superior articular processes face posterosuperiorly—not posterolaterally. (3) A superior vertebral notch is present—not absent. (4) The vertebral foramen is triangular—not circular.

The lower half of the last thoracic vertebra conforms to the lumbar in the following respects: (1) The body is reniform. (2) The inferior articular processes face laterally. (3) The vertebral foramen is triangular. (4) Each transverse process consists of three tubercles, and has no costal facet.

Sternum

The sternum (*fig. 547*), or breast bone, likened to a broad sword, is composed of three parts:

1. Manubrium sterni or handle.
2. Corpus sterni or body.
3. Xiphoid process or point.

Manubrium Sterni. Two features at its upper end are noticeable in the living: (1) the very thick concave upper border, called the *jugular notch,* much deepened by the sternal ends of the clavicles, which are too large for (2) the notches provided for them at the superolateral angles.

The flat tendons of the sternal heads of the Sternomastoids cross in front of the sternoclavicular joints to be attached just caudal to them.

On the side of the manubrium, immediately below the clavicular notch, the 1st costal cartilage unites the 1st rib to the manubrium in the same manner as an epiphyseal cartilage unites an epiphysis to a diaphysis. This is a synchondrosis (p. 17). The 1st ribs, their cartilages, and the manubrium form a single kidney-shaped unit (*fig. 547*), and between the five elements of this unit there is no movable joint.

The manubrium is 2 inches long—as long as two vertebrae. Its upper border lies at the level of the lower border of Th. vertebra 2, and is 2 inches from it (*fig. 548*). Its lower border articulates with the body at an angle, the *sternal angle.* Traced laterally the transverse ridge that indicates the angle conducts the palpating fingers to the 2nd costal cartilage, the starting point from which all ribs should be counted (*fig. 547*).

The **Body of the Sternum** is composed

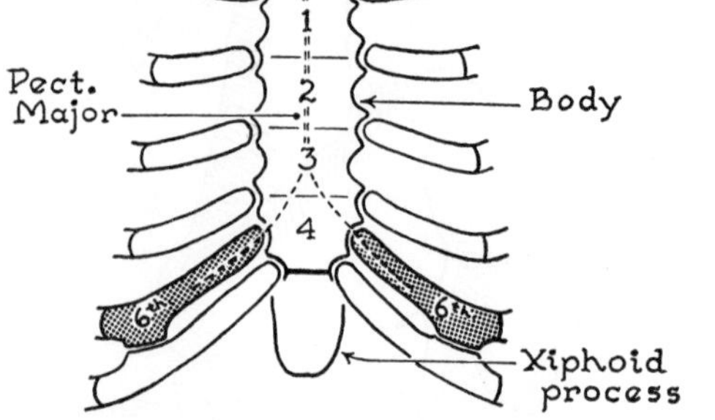

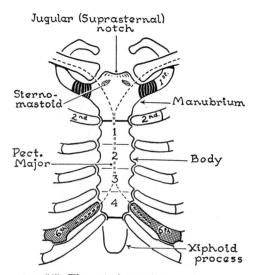

FIG. 547. The anterior surface of the sternum. The *broken lines* indicate the origins of the Pectorales Majores.

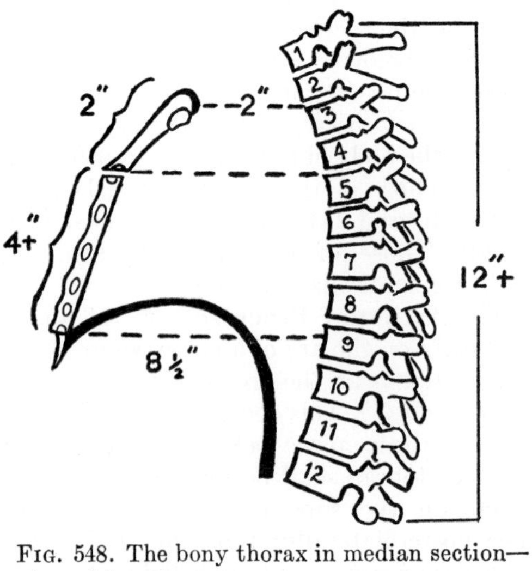

FIG. 548. The bony thorax in median section—levels and lengths.

of four pieces or *sternebrae,* which together are slightly more than twice the length of the manubrium. In the adult, lines marking the sites of fusion of the sternebrae may be seen crossing the anterior surface of the body between angular depressions on the sides for the 3rd, 4th, and 5th rib cartilages.

The 2nd rib cartilage articulates in the angular interval between body and manubrium; the 7th cartilage articulates with the lower angle of the body and the front of the xiphoid. What of the 6th cartilage? There is a special facet for it on the side of the 4th sternebra; hence, the lower cartilages are crowded.

»» *Comparative Anatomy.* In man the right and left Pectorales Majores merely meet in the median plane, but in birds a keel or crest projects from the sternum in order to afford the powerful wing muscles an increased surface of origin. This crest is akin to that which appears on the skull of the gorilla (*fig. 647*) and of some dogs to afford origin to their massive temporal muscles. No such crest is encountered on the sterna of cursorial birds, such as the ostrich, which cannot fly.

The **Xiphoid Process** extends downwards for a variable distance into the posterior wall of the sheath of the Rectus Abdominis. It is only half as thick as the body of the sternum, and its posterior surface is flush with the posterior surface of the body. The ends of the 7th costal cartilage lie in front of the process, creating demifacets.

The tip of the xiphoid is not suitable as a landmark because it is variable in length and efforts to palpate it cause discomfort; so the sharp easily palpated edge of the lower end of the body of the sternum, at the *xiphisternal synchondrosis* or joint, is preferred.

Vertebral Levels of the jugular notch, sternal angle, and xiphisternal joint are 2nd, 4th, 8th+ (*fig. 548*).

Muscles attached to posterior aspect:
of manubrium—Sternothyroid,
Sternohyoid.
of body—Transversus Thoracis.
of xiphoid process—Diaphragm.

Posterior Relations: Pleurae and lungs, heart and great vessels, thymus.

Ossification: The manubrium ossifies from one or more centers about the 6th intra-uterine month. The sternebrae and xiphoid develop from right and left mesenchymal bars, which chondrify and fuse in the median plane. The four sternebrae, then, ossify from single or bilateral centers. Ossification starts, from above downward about the 6th, 7th, 8th, and 9th intra-uterine month or later; fusion takes place from below upward about the 15th, 20th and 25th years. The xiphoid process starts to ossify in youth. The xiphisternal synchondrosis commonly becomes a synostosis in middle age.

FIG. 549. A perforated sternum, the result of faulty ossification.

»» **Common Anomalies.** (1) The lower two or three sternebrae commonly ossify separately from right and left centers. If these fail to fuse, a perforation, suggestive of a bullet wound, will appear in an X-ray photograph (*fig. 549*). (2) The sternomanubrial joint may be lacking, its place being taken by a joint between the 1st and 2nd sternebrae, as in the gibbon. The sternal angle is then situated about halfway down the sternum.

The Manubriosternal Joint plays an important part in the mechanism of respiration, because it allows hinge-like movements of the body of the sternum forward and backward. It is a replica of the symphysis pubis, and it is similar in structure to the joints between the bodies of the vertebrae. All of these joints lie in the median plane. They are Symphyses (p. 18).

Synostosis of the manubrium and body of the sternum is found in no less than 10 per cent of adults, and is equally common in all 10-year age groups after the age of 30 years (Ashley; Mildred Trotter).

Ribs and Their Cartilages—Costae

Classification. A rib and its cartilage constitute a costa. In all, there are 12 pairs of costae. Every rib articulates posteriorly with the vertebral column. The cartilages of the upper 7 pairs of ribs articulate directly with the sternum; hence, they are known as *true* or *vertebrosternal ribs*. The remaining 5 pairs are *false ribs:* of these, the cartilages of three pairs (8th, 9th, 10th) articulate with the cartilages immediately above them and, so, form a subgroup of *vertebrochondral ribs*. Their connection with the sternum is indirect. The cartilaginous ends of the last two pairs (11th, 12th) are free; hence, they form a subgroup of *floating* or *vertebral ribs*.

The sternal ends of the costae are cartilaginous owing to the fact that ossification, which starts near the angles and spreads both forward and backward, fails to reach the sternal ends.

Ribs are not triangular on cross-section and therefore rigid like the long bones of the limbs, but are flattened, have a very thin outer compact layer, and are highly resilient.

A Typical Rib (*fig. 550*) consists of the following parts:

1. *Body:* Internal and external surfaces; superior and inferior borders; an angle and a costal groove. The posterior ¼ of the body is cylindrical; the anterior ¾ is compressed.
2. *Vertebral End:* head, neck, and tubercle.
3. *Sternal End:* pit for costal cartilage.

Examination of the Costae *in situ*. *With the articulated skeleton before you, confirm the following facts,* because they have an important bearing on the mechanism of respiration.

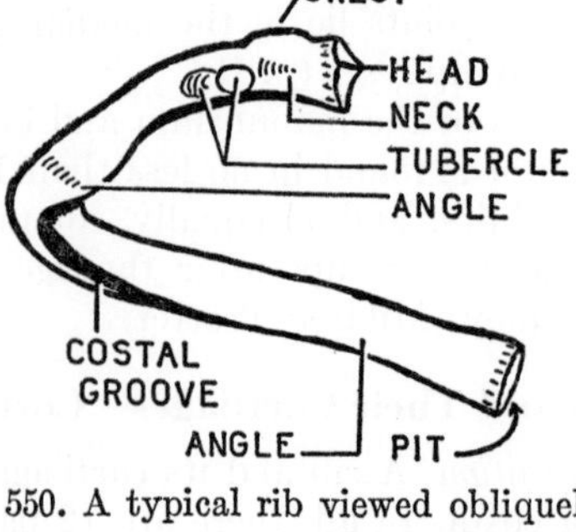

FIG. 550. A typical rib viewed obliquely from behind.

1. When the costae (i.e., the ribs and cartilages) of the somewhat barrel-shaped thorax are examined *in situ*, the rib is seen always to take a downward slope; the cartilage generally an upward slope (*fig. 551*). Each costa is arched.

The cartilages of the first (1st) and of the last two (11th and 12th) arches, however, continue the downward inclination of their ribs; that of the 2nd is generally horizontal; the remaining cartilages (3rd–10th) are inclined upward (*fig. 547*).

2. The sternal end of the 1st arch lies 1½ inches lower than its vertebral end (*fig. 566*).

3. The sternal end of each arch lies at a lower level than the vertebral end.

4. The middle of each arch (except the 1st) lies at a lower level than a straight line joining its two ends (*fig. 551*).

5. The intercostal spaces are widest where rib and cartilage join.

6. Both ribs and cartilages increase in length progressively from 1st to 7th; the 7th rib being the longest of the ribs; the 7th cartilage the longest of the cartilages.

7. The transverse diameter of the thorax increases progressively from 1st to 8th rib, the 8th rib having the greatest lateral projection.

8. The ribs increase in obliquity progressively from 1st to 9th; the 9th rib being the most obliquely placed.

9. The cartilage of the 10th rib lies at the lowest point on the thoracic wall visible or palpable from the front, though actually the tip of the 11th cartilage is lower.

10. The anterior ends of the 11th and 12th ribs, not being subjected to terminal pressure, are tapering, as are the ends of the

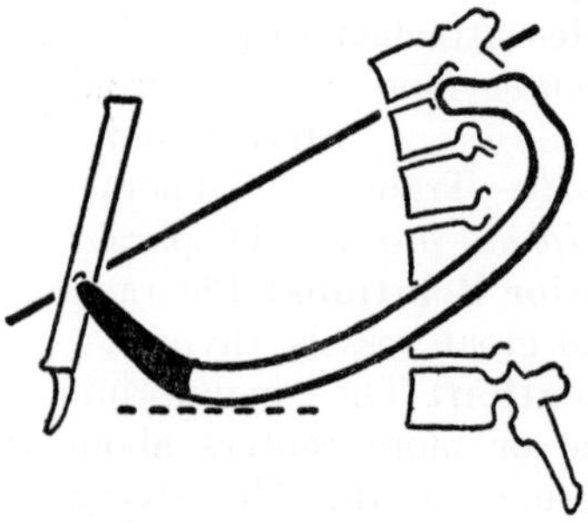

FIG. 551. A costal arch (side view)

distal phalanges of the fingers and toes and the tip of the coccyx.

Joints

Articulations of Costae. Typically the head of a rib articulates with the sides of the bodies of two vertebrae; the tubercle of a rib articulates with the tip of a transverse process; and the costal cartilage articulates either with the sides of two sternebrae or with the adjacent cartilage. Hence, the following:

1. Costovertebral articulation:
   a. Joint of the head of a rib.
   b. Joint of the tubercle of a rib.
2. Sternocostal articulation and interchondral articulation.

Joint of the Head of a Rib. The head of each typical rib (2nd to 10th) articulates with the demifacet of two adjacent vertebrae and with the intervertebral disc between these vertebrae (*fig. 552*). Accordingly, these heads are wedge-shaped. The lower or caudal surface of the wedge is in articulation with its own vertebra; whereas the upper or cranial surface articulates with the vertebra next above. The apex of this wedge, the *crest of the head,* is attached to the intervertebral disc by a transversely placed *intra-articular ligament.* The joints of these heads have each, therefore, *two synovial cavities,* closed by a *capsule* which is strongest in front where its fibers *radiate* from the anterior margin of the head, horizontally to the intervertebral disc, upward to the vertebra above, downward to its own vertebra.

The heads of ribs 1, (10), 11, and 12, being confined to single vertebrae, are rounded and their joints have no intra-articular ligaments.

Sternocostal Articulations. A true, or vertebrosternal, rib and its cartilage have been likened to a bucket-handle and, like a bucket-handle, the extreme ends articulate in similar fashion (see *fig. 552*).

Thus, in the highly developed joint, especially the 2nd and 3rd, the sternal end of the costal cartilage is wedge-shaped (or rounded); its socket, which is V-shaped, is formed by the demifacets of two adjacent sternebrae; the joint cavity is divided into

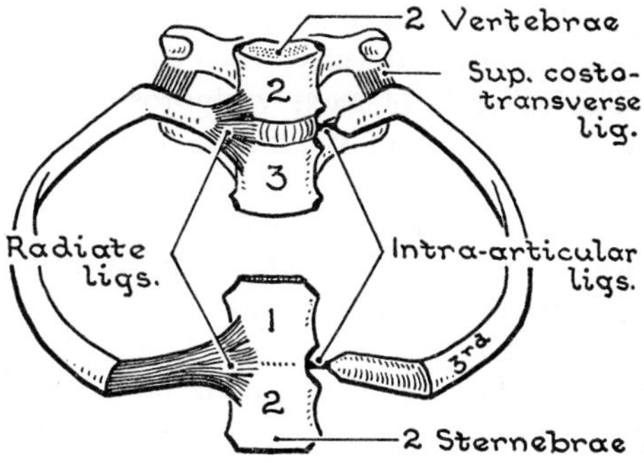

FIG. 552. The articulations at the dorsal and ventral ends of a costal arch, compared.

two by an intra-articular ligament, and it is closed ventrally by a ligament that radiates from the perichondrium to the sternum.

However, figure 547 shows that (1) the 1st costal cartilage unites the 1st rib to the manubrium by a synchondrosis; (2) the 2nd cartilage articulates between the side of the manubrium and the 1st sternebra; (3) the 6th cartilage articulates with the side of the 4th sternebra; and (4) the 7th cartilage articulates between the 4th sternebra and the front of the xiphoid process.

By resorption of its intra-articular ligament, a double cavity becomes single; by extension of its ligament a cavity may be obliterated, which is the rule in the lower joints. (See Gray and Gardiner.)

Interchondral Articulations. By means of upward and downward projections, separated by synovial cavities, the cartilages articulate with each other—the 5th and 6th very often; the 6th and 7th, and 7th and 8th as a rule; and the 8th and 9th sometimes. Otherwise, the lower joints are either fibrous or synchondroses. Between the 9th and 10th cartilages the connection is fibrous; there is no joint cavity (Bristoe).

Joint of the Tubercle of a Rib. *The tubercle of a rib* articulates with the facet at the tip of the transverse process of its own vertebra (i.e., the vertebra with which it corresponds numerically) to form a synovial joint, called a **costotransverse joint.** As the thoracic transverse processes become progressively shorter from 1st to 12th, so the tubercles of the ribs become progressively closer to the heads. The 11th and

12th ribs have no tubercles; so, their necks are not defined laterally. (See *fig. 553.*)

The tubercle of each vertebrosternal rib lies at the back of its rib, is olive-shaped, and articulates with a concave facet on the front of the tip of a transverse process. This allows it to rotate (*fig. 554*). The tubercle of each vertebrochondral rib lies near the lower border of its rib, is flat, obliquely set, and articulates with a similar facet on the upper border of the tip of a transverse process. This allows it to slide.

Ligaments. Figure 555 shows that the strong ligamentous fibers that bind a rib to a transverse process are divided into a medial and a lateral group by the cavity of the joint. The medial group binds the back of the neck of a rib to the front of a transverse process; it is the (*medial*) *costotransverse ligament* (lig. of the neck). The lateral group binds the tubercle of a rib to the tip of a process; it is the *lateral costotransverse ligament* (lig. of the tubercle).

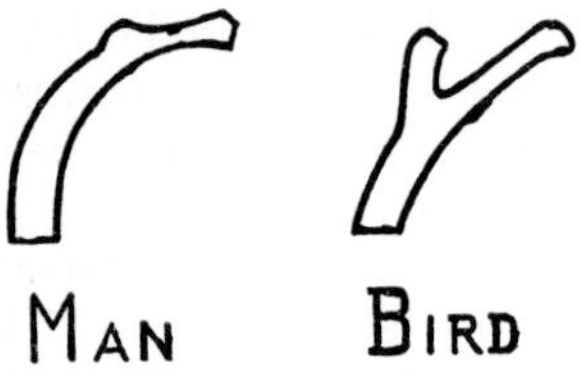

Fig. 553. The tubercle of a rib is a reduced second head.

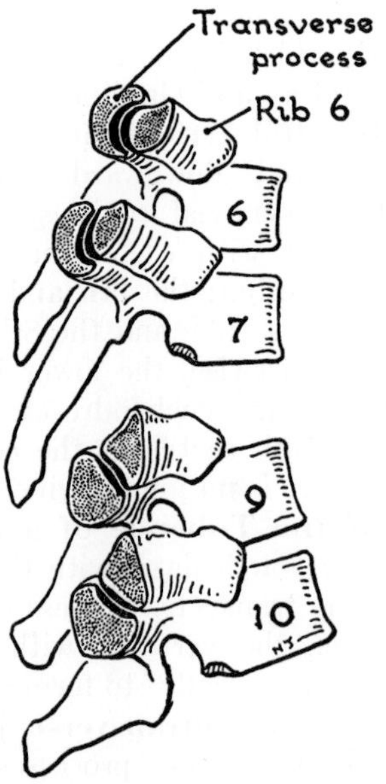

Fig. 554. To demonstrate that the upper ribs rotate on the transverse processes, and that the lower ribs glide.

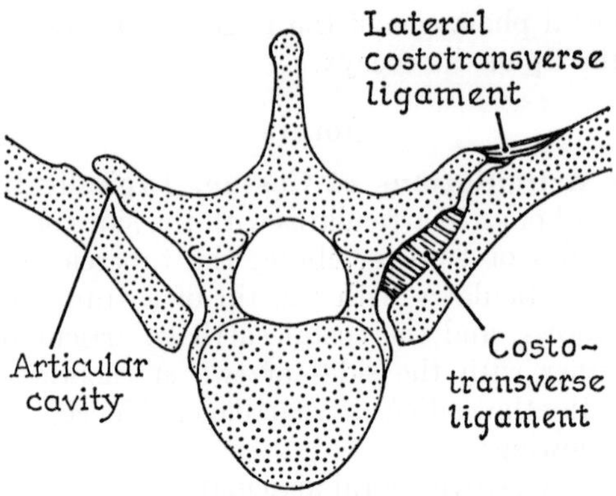

Fig. 555. Costotransverse articulation

A tubercle has, then, a smooth medial articular portion and a rough lateral ligamentous portion.

A band, the *superior costotransverse lig.*, descends from the lower border of a transverse process to the upper border of the neck of the rib next below; and it may produce there a sharp crest, *the crest of the neck*.

Angles of the Ribs. An oblique line, produced by the tendinous insertion of the Iliocostalis (the lateral column of the deep muscles of the back), crosses the most backwardly projecting part of the outer surface of the ribs (*fig. 671*). Anterior to this the ribs are twisted downward, forward, and medially.

»» Since the deep muscles of the back diminish in bulk as they ascend, it follows that the angles become progressively nearer the tubercles from below upward till the 1st rib is reached, and there angle and tubercle coincide. Although ribs 1 and 2, and 11 and 12 have rough impressions for the Iliocostalis, they are scarcely twisted at all and therefore have no true angle.

Anterior Angles: Anteriorly, at the sites of attachment of the External Oblique of the Abdomen to the lower eight ribs (about a hand's breadth from the costal margin) the ribs are bent slightly backward, flattening the thorax. The angles and slight roughnesses so produced are best marked on the middle four ribs (5, 6, 7, and 8) where the digitations of the External Oblique and Serratus Anterior interlock.

Peculiar Ribs. The **1st Rib** is a very superlative rib, being the highest, shortest, strongest, flattest, and most curved of all the ribs. To a small triangular area on its outer surface, *the scalene tubercle*, the Scalenus Anterior is attached. It separates the groove for the subclavian vein in front from the groove for the subclavian artery and lowest trunk of the brachial plexus behind. Between the latter groove and the tubercle of the rib the Scalenus Medius, Levator Costae, and the first digitation of the Serratus Anterior are attached. The fascia, the *suprapleural membrane* (Sibson's fascia), clothing the deep surface of the Scalenes is attached to the sharp upper border of this rib.

To the outer surface of the *1st costal cartilage* are attached: the intra-articular disc of the sternoclavicular joint, the costoclavicular lig., and the origin of Subclavius.

»» *The 2nd Rib* has spreading across its outer surface a large rough impression for Serratus Anterior.

The 10th Rib is a transitional rib, resembling either the 9th or the 11th, thus: its head may have two demifacets or one facet; its tubercle may be articular or not; its cartilage may be united to the 9th cartilage by fibrous tissue or else be floating.

The 11th and 12th Ribs have large heads, no tubercles, and pointed ends.

Identification of side. Students commonly relate ribs to the wrong side of the body. Note that: (1) The head and neck of the 1st rib are *turned downward*—not upward like those of the other ribs. (2) The anterior or pleural aspect of the necks of all (save the highest) ribs look upwards as well as forward. If the 12th rib is so held, the side to which it belongs will be obvious.

Ossification begins near the angle (about the 9th prenatal week) and spreads in both directions but fails to reach the sternal end; hence, the costal cartilages. Scale-like epiphyses, which cap the head and tubercle, are in all cases fused by the 24th year.

Variations:

1. Either the 7th cervical or the 1st lumbar vertebra may carry a rib; in either case there are 13 ribs (*fig. 556*).
2. The sternal end of the 3rd or 4th rib and its cartilage is sometimes bifid (*fig. 557*).

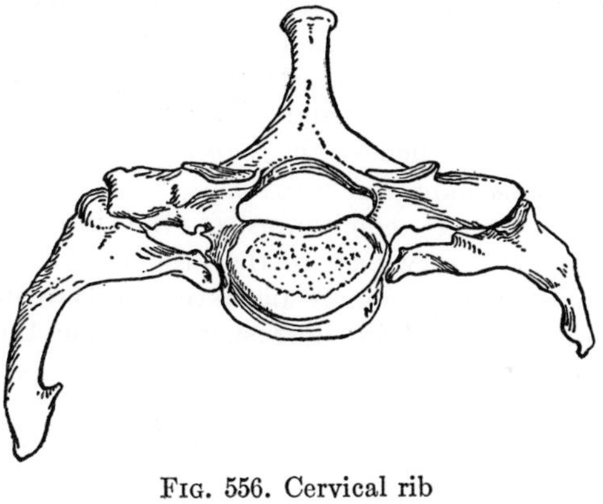

FIG. 556. Cervical rib

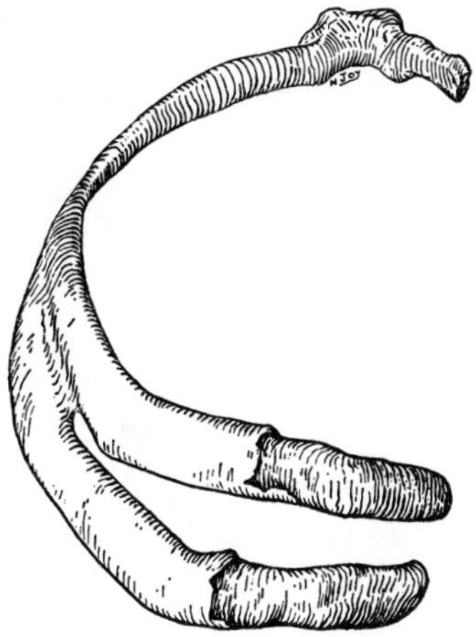

FIG. 557. A bifid rib

3. The 12th ribs are commonly very short in the female.
4. Not uncommonly the 8th cartilage reaches the sternum. So, it is not wise to count the ribs from the infrasternal angle.

INTERCOSTAL SPACES

Muscles Covering the Thorax. Except at the *triangle of auscultation*, bounded by Trapezius, Latissimus Dorsi, and Rhomboideus Major (*fig. 77*), the costae and intercostal spaces are completely covered with muscles.

These muscles are: Pectorales Major et Minor, Rectus Abdominis, Obliquus Externus Abdominis, Serratus Anterior, Latissimus Dorsi, Trapezius, Rhomboidei Major et Minor, Levator Scapulae, Serratus Posterior and Erector Spinae. All but four of these are inserted into the bones of the limb.

Muscles of the Thoracic Wall. These are disposed in three layers, like the flat muscles of the abdominal wall, and they have the same derivation. In both regions the nerves and vessels course between the middle and inner layers of muscles (*fig. 558*).

Abdominal	*Thoracic*
1. Obliquus Externus	Intercostales Externi
2. Obliquus Internus	Intercostales Interni
Nerves and Vessels	
3. Transversus	Intercostales Intimi or Innermost; Subcostalis; Transversus

The fibers of the **Intercostales Externi** run downward and forward between the

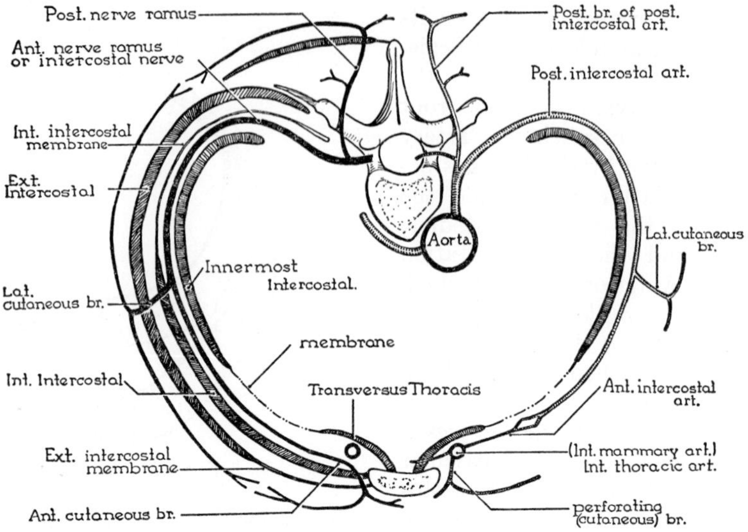

FIG. 558. The contents of an intercostal space (horizontal section). (*Nerve rami: posterior and anterior = dorsal and ventral.*)

adjacent borders of two costae. Their intercartilaginous parts, called the *external intercostal membranes*, are fibrous; their interosseous parts are fleshy and extend backward to the tubercles of the ribs.

»» The Obliquus Abdominis Externus and the Levatores Costarum overlap and blend with the Intercostales Externi in front or behind, as the case may be.

Each **Levator Costae** arises from the tip of a transverse process and extends fanwise to the rib below; so, of the 12 pairs of Levatores Costarum the first springs from vertebra C. 7; the last from Th. 11.

The fibers of the **Intercostales Interni** and **Intercostales Intimi** run obliquely downward and backward, crossing those of the Intercostales Externi at right angles (*fig. 559*). An internal muscle extends from the sternal end of a space to behind the midlateral line where it overlaps an innermost muscle, which extends from in front of the midlateral line to the angles of the ribs.

The difference between the two muscles is that one is attached to the outer lip of a costal groove; and the other to the inner. The internal muscles belong to the same layer as the Obliquus Abdominis Internus; the innermost, to the same layer as the Transversus Abdominis.

So, both in the thoracic wall and in the abdominal wall the intercostal nerves are to be found between the 2nd and 3rd layers of muscles (*fig. 558*).

»» The posterior part of an Internal Intercostal, called an *internal intercostal membrane*, merges with a superior costotransverse ligament.

Subcostalis is the name given to fibers of the Intercostales Intimi that bridge more than one intercostal space.

The **Transversus Thoracis** is the upward continuation of the Transversus Abdominis. It arises from the back of the xiphoid and lower two or three sternebrae and fans out to be inserted into the 3rd to 6th costochondral junctions. It fails to cross the upper two interchondral spaces.

The Internal Thoracic Artery (Internal Mammary A.) (*fig. 558*) is a branch of the subclavian artery. It descends a finger's breadth from the sternum, behind the Internal Intercostals and upper six costal cartilages, and divides into two terminal branches, the *superior epigastric* and *musculophrenic arteries*.

The venae comitantes of the internal thoracic artery pass to the brachiocephalic (innominate) vein. A **parasternal lymph node** is found in most spaces, beside the vessels.

»» The internal thoracic a. is most readily exposed in the 1st or 2nd space, because these are the widest spaces, but here it rests directly on the pleura, which

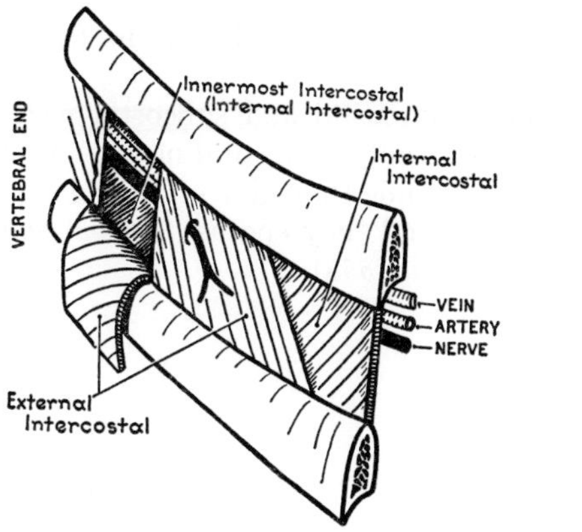

FIG. 559. The contents of an intercostal space (vertical section).

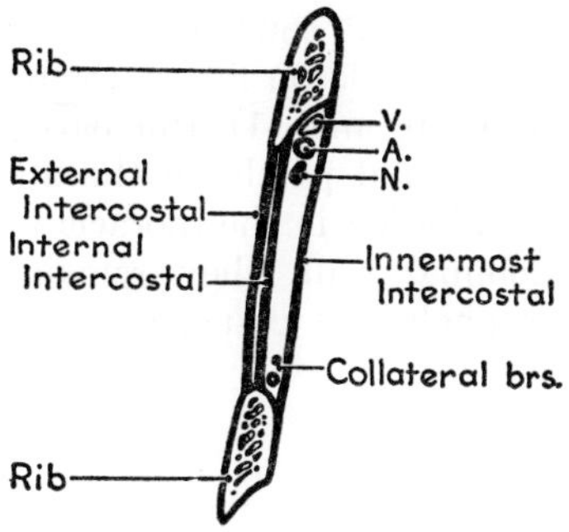

FIG. 559.1. The Intercostal Muscles, on coronal section.

is in danger of being punctured. On this account it is safer to expose it in a lower space where the Transversus is interposed between it and the pleura.

Being the sole artery in the neighborhood, the internal thoracic art. supplies the entire neighborhood.

Branches.

1. *Perforating* (or cutaneous) *branches* perforate the Internal Intercostal, external intercostal membrane, and Pectoralis Major in the upper six spaces and supply the cutaneous structures, including the breast.

2. *Anterior intercostal branches*, an upper branch and small lower one, run laterally in the upper six intercostal spaces (*fig. 559.1*).

3. The *musculophrenic art.* sends corresponding branches to the 7th, 8th, and 9th spaces. It also sends branches to the abdominal muscles and the diaphragm, as its name suggests.

The 10th and 11th spaces are too short to require anterior branches.

4. The *pericardiacophrenic art.* follows the phrenic nerve.

5. *Mediastinal branches* pass to the thymus, and twigs pass to the bronchi, lymph nodes, fat, and pericardium.

6. The *superior epigastric art.* descends behind the 7th costal cartilage and upper part of the Rectus Abdominis to anastomose with the inferior epigastric branch of the external iliac art. thereby bringing the great vessels of the upper and lower limbs into communication (*fig. 216*).

Variant. An occasional branch, the *lateral costal artery*, arises above the 1st rib, and descends subpleurally near the midlateral line, linking the upper five or six intercostal arteries.

A Posterior Intercostal Artery and Vein, under the shelter of a costal groove, accompany each intercostal nerve, the artery occupying the middle position (*fig. 559*).

A posterior intercostal artery, being much larger than an anterior intercostal artery, supplies much more than half its intercostal space (*fig. 558*), and from it springs a *lateral cutaneous branch* as well as a *dorsal* (posterior) *branch.*

Of the 11 posterior intercostal arteries, the upper 9 anastomose with anterior intercostal arteries derived from the internal thoracic and musculophrenic arteries; whereas the lower two continue beyond the open ends of their spaces into the abdominal wall.

The upper two posterior intercostal arteries arise from the supreme intercostal artery; the lower nine from the aorta (p. 531, and *fig. 642*).

The Intercostal Nerves. Of the ventral rami of the 12 pairs of thoracic nerves, 11 are intercostal and 1 is subcostal. The 1st and 12th differ notably from the others: the 1st because of the very large contribution it sends across the 1st rib to the brachial plexus; the 12th because, being subcostal, it has to run its course in the abdominal wall. The upper five (2, 3, 4, 5, and 6) run typical intercostal courses in the thoracic wall; whereas the lower five of the remaining 10 (7, 8, 9, 10, and 11) run partly in the thoracic wall and partly in the abdominal wall. But, whether in the thoracic wall or in the abdominal wall, they remain in the same morphological plane, as indicated in the table on page 471 and in figures 558 and 216.

The intercostal and subcostal nerves are typical, serially segmental nerves. About the midlateral line they give off *lateral cutaneous branches*, and they end as *anterior cutaneous branches* (*fig. 558*).

CHAPTER 30

PLEURAE

Subdivisions of Thoracic Cavity; Pleurae: parietal; visceral; and root of lung.

LINES OF PLEURAL REFLEXION—*Surface Anatomy; Variations; Relationship of Costal Reflexion to Costal Margin; Three Pleural Recesses.*

Mediastinum

Subdivisions: Superior, Anterior, Posterior, and Middle; Mediastinal Pleura.

RIGHT ASPECT OF MEDIASTINUM—*Structures Seen; Meso-esophagus.*

Root of Lung and Pulmonary Ligament; Bronchi; Nerves and Vessels.

LEFT ASPECT OF MEDIASTINUM—*Structures Seen.*

Ligamentum Arteriosum; Great Vessels; Nerves and Viscera.

Cupola of Pleura.

SYMPATHETIC TRUNK—*Course; Relationships; Connections; Distribution to Viscera; Splanchnic Nerves.*

Subdivisions of the Thoracic Cavity. The thoracic cavity is divided into:

1. Right and left pleural cavities.
2. Mediastinum, or region between the two pleural cavities.

The contents of the mediastinum are briefly: (1) the heart within its pericardium, (2) the vessels proceeding to and from the heart, (3) the trachea, and (4) the structures in transit from neck to abdomen, e.g., esophagus, the vagus nerves, phrenic nerves, and thoracic duct.

The pleural, pericardial, and peritoneal cavities are closed potential cavities within thin walled sacs of serous membrane (*fig. 560*). In prenatal life these cavities are continuous and together make up the embryonic celom. The lung invaginates the pleural cavity (*fig. 561*).

The Pleurae. Each pleura has three parts —parietal, visceral, and connecting.

1. *The Parietal Layer.* As wall paper assumes the shape of the room it lines, so does the parietal layer of pleura. Since each room or pleural cavity is shaped like a cone bisected sagittally, it possesses two walls (costal and mediastinal), a base, and an apex (*figs. 560* and *561*). The parietal layer may therefore be subdivided into: (1) The *costal pleura,* which lines the costae (i.e., ribs and their cartilages). (2) The *mediastinal pleura,* which is applied to the side of the mediastinum. (3) The *diaphragmatic pleura,* which covers most of its own half of the diaphragm. (4) The *cupola* (cervical pleura) which rises into the neck.

2. *The Visceral Layer* or the *Pulmonary Pleura* invests the lung precisely as the peritoneum invests the liver or the spleen.

3. The connecting portion, like an *isthmus,* connects the visceral or pulmonary pleura

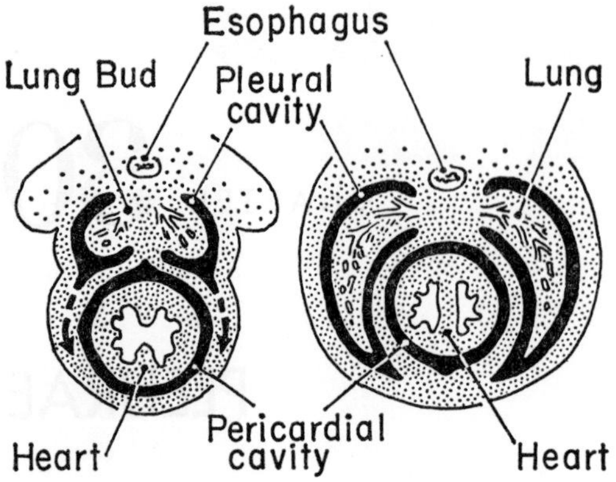

FIG. 560. The lung buds expand in their pleural cavities to embrace the heart in its pericardial sac. (After Patten.)

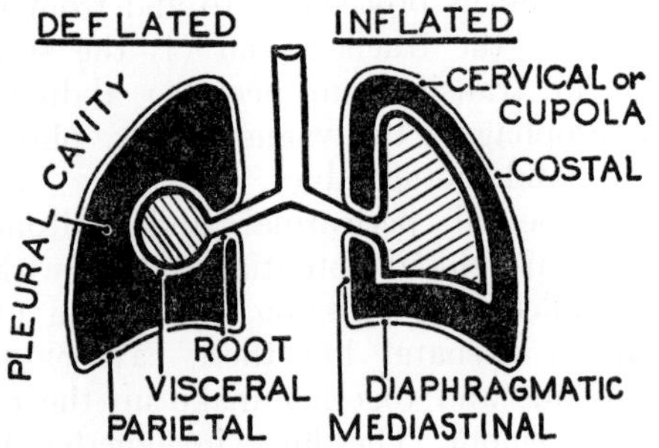

FIG. 561. The pleura: The lung represented as a balloon with a stalk.

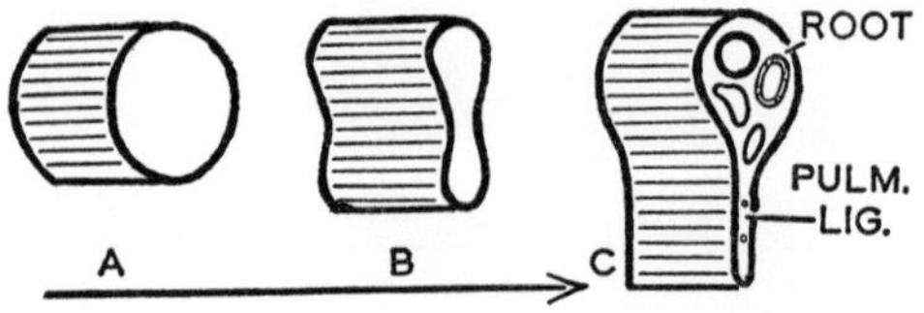

FIG. 562. Diagram of pleura at root of lung

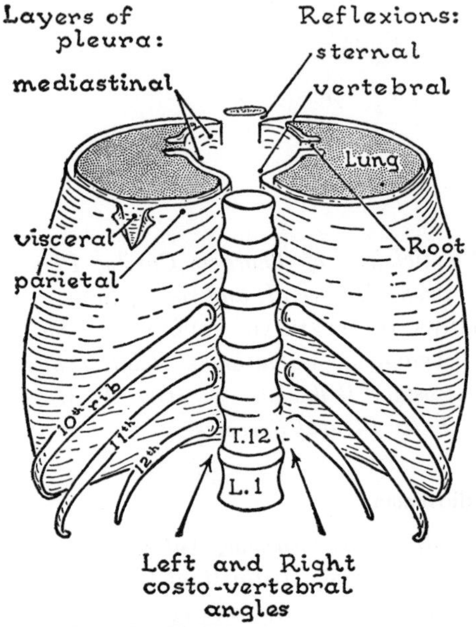

FIG. 563. Pleural reflexions, from behind

to the mediastinal layer of parietal pleura. Actually, it is a tube or sleeve of pleura in whose upper half lie all the structures that pass to and from the lung, and hence called the root of the lung; whereas its lower half, being empty (except for a few lymph vessels), is collapsed and is known as the *pulmonary ligament* (lig. pulmonale) (*fig. 562*).

Lines of Pleural Reflexion (*fig. 563*). The costal pleura is continuous with (1) the mediastinal pleura in front of the vertebral column—the *vertebral reflexion.* (2) It is also continuous with the mediastinal pleura behind the sternum—the *sternal reflexion.* (3) And, it is continuous with the diaphragmatic pleura near the chest margin—the *costal reflexion.*

Because the *vertebral reflexion* extends throughout the entire thoracic region, from 1st to 12th thoracic vertebra, it follows that a needle, passed forward through the posterior part of any intercostal space, must of necessity enter the pleural cavity.

Surface Anatomy. The sternal and costal reflexions are of high clinical importance. To plot them on the surface of the body you employ the even numbers—2, 4, 6, 8, 10, and 12 (*figs. 563* and *564*). Thus: the right and left *sternal reflexions* pass behind the respective sternoclavicular joints, meet each other in the median plane at (or above) the sternal angle, which lies at the level of the 2nd costal cartilages. Thereafter, the right reflexion continues downward in the midline to the back of the xiphoid process; the left parts from the right at the level of the 4th cartilage, where it is deflected as far as (short of or beyond) the margin of the sternum, along which it is continued downward to the 6th cartilage.

Thereafter, as the left costal reflexion, it

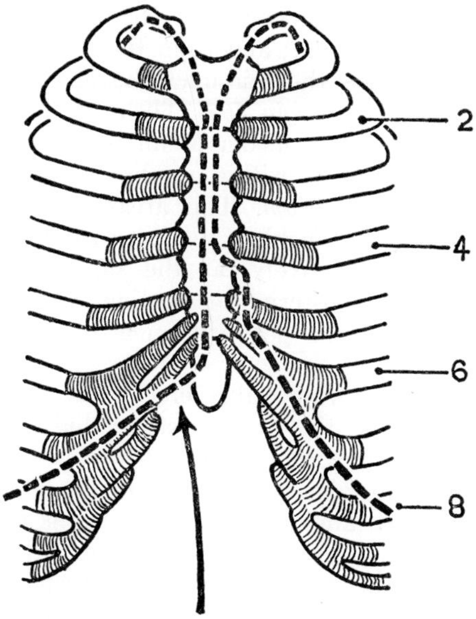

FIG. 564. Sternocostal reflexion of pleura

passes obliquely across the 8th, 10th, and 12th ribs, crossing the 8th in the midclavicular line, the 10th in the midlateral line, and the 12th at its neck.

The right costal reflexion likewise cuts the 8th, 10th, and 12th ribs in the midclavicular line, the midlateral line, and at the neck of the 12th rib. It differs, however, from the left costal reflexion in descending to a lower level anteriorly; for whereas the left reflexion follows the line of the 6th cartilage, the right reflexion passes from the back of the xiphoid across the xiphicostal angle to the 7th costal cartilage.

»» *Variations.* In 95 adult cadavera, the line of left pleural reflexion in the precardial area varied from person to person especially in the 5th and 6th interspaces where there is a horizontal range of 5 cm. Indeed, 85 per cent of reflexions lay medial to the line depicted in figure 564. Enlarged hearts seem not to effect the line (Woodburne).

Relationship of Costal Reflexion to Costal Margin. From the facts mentioned it is evident that the pleurae descend below the costal margin in three regions:

1. Right xiphicostal angle.
2. Right costovertebral angle.
3. Left costovertebral angle.

In cases where the 12th rib is very short the line of reflexion comes, of course, to lie below the costal margin after crossing the 11th rib, and is therefore in surgical danger.

The costal reflexion reaches its lowest limit in the midlateral line, i.e., half way around the body. At this point it is situated about two fingers' breadth above the costal margin. The distance between the reflexion and the margin diminishes, so to speak, to zero or rather to subzero, as the reflexion is traced (1) backward and upward to the right and left costovertebral angles (*fig. 563*), and (2) forward and upward to the right xiphicostal angle (*fig. 564*).

Below the level of the costal reflexion (*fig. 565*), the diaphragm lies in direct contact with the costae and intercostal muscles. At the sides and back of the chest the lower border of the lung does not descend to the level of the costal reflexion of the pleura; and, in consequence, the diaphragmatic and costal layers of parietal pleurae come into apposition with each other. The potential space unoccupied by lung is known as the *costodiaphragmatic recess.* This recess becomes alternately smaller and larger as the lung advances into it and recedes from it during inspiration and expiration (*fig. 565*).

From these observations it follows that an instrument passed through the anterior parts of the (7), 8, 9, 10, and 11 intercostal spaces would miss the pleural cavity but would penetrate intercostal muscles, diaphragm, and enter the peritoneal cavity. At a slightly higher level it would penetrate intercostal muscles, costodiaphragmatic re-

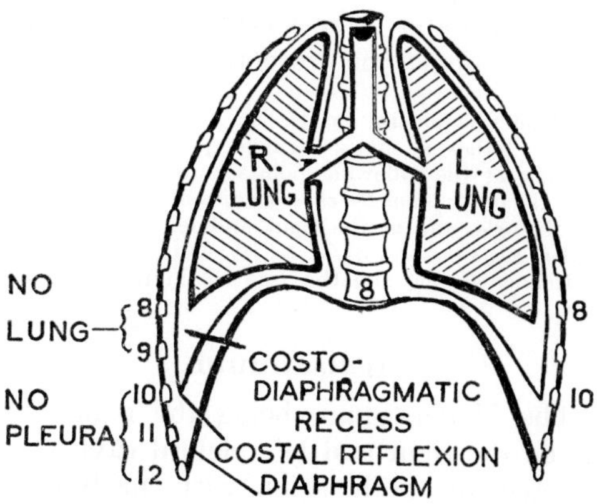

FIG. 565. Coronal section of thorax (semi-schematic).

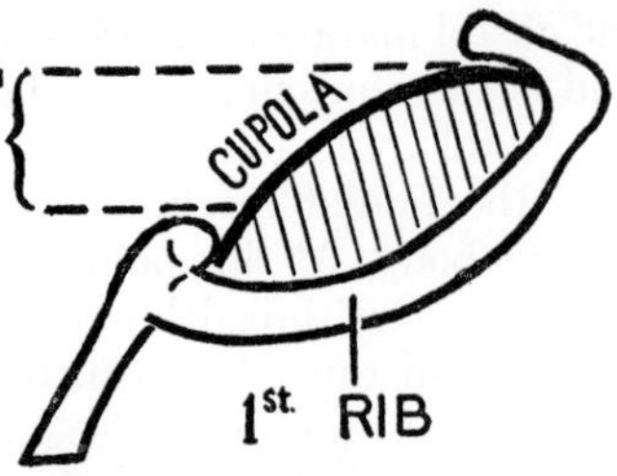

FIG. 566. The cupola of the pleura

cess, diaphragm, and enter the peritoneal cavity. Still higher it would penetrate the lung also.

The only other region of the pleural cavity not occupied by lung lies at the anterior ends of the 4th and 5th left interspaces. Here, owing to a deficiency in the anterior border of the left lung, where it overlies the heart, and hence called the *cardiac notch of the lung*, the costal and mediastinal layers of the left pleura come into direct contact with each other and form the *costomediastinal recess*. So, there are **3 pleural recesses:**

1. Right costodiaphragmatic recess.
2. Left costodiaphragmatic recess.
3. Left costomediastinal recess.

Cupola. Does the cupola of the pleura rise above the level of the 1st rib? The answer "Yes" and the answer "No" are alike correct (*fig. 566*). The cupola rises to, but not above, the neck of the 1st rib, which therefore protects it from injury from behind. But, since there is a drop of 1½ inches between the vertebral and sternal ends of the 1st rib, it follows that the pleura rises 1½ inches above the sternal end. Here the clavicle offers some protection.

»» When the pleural cavities have been opened, observe whether a sharp, straight probe passed horizontally at the following points enters or misses the pleural cavity: *below the chest margin* at the right xiphicostal angle, and at the right and left costovertebral angles; *above the neck of the 1st rib;* at the *8th rib* in the midclavicular line and the *10th rib* in the midlateral line.

Mediastinum

The Mediastinum, being the region between the right and left pleural cavities, is covered on both sides with mediastinal pleura (*fig. 563*). The right and left layer of mediastinal pleura extend from the sternum in front, to the bodies of the 12 thoracic vertebrae behind; and from the diaphragm below, to the thoracic inlet above.

SUBDIVISIONS (*fig. 567*). The central structure within the mediastinum is the heart. It is contained within a fibrous sac, the *fibrous pericardium*. The areas above, in front of, and behind the pericardium are known, respectively, as the superior, anterior, and posterior mediastina, while the area *within* the pericardium is the middle mediastinum.

In man, who walks erect, but not in quadrupeds, the fibrous pericardial sac is fused below with the central tendon of the diaphragm; above, it reaches to the level of the sternal angle. In fact, it happens to be co-extensive in the median plane with the body of the sternum, perhaps overstepping it slightly at the upper and lower ends, so one may say—in front of the pericardium are the 4 sternebrae that comprise the body, or middle piece, of the sternum; behind it are the middle 4 thoracic vertebrae (*fig. 567*).

The Superior Mediastinum is the subdivision of the mediastinum above the level of the fibrous pericardium. This is equivalent to saying the region above the plane joining the sternal angle to the intervertebral disc between the 4th and 5th thoracic vertebrae.

On or about the almost horizontal plane

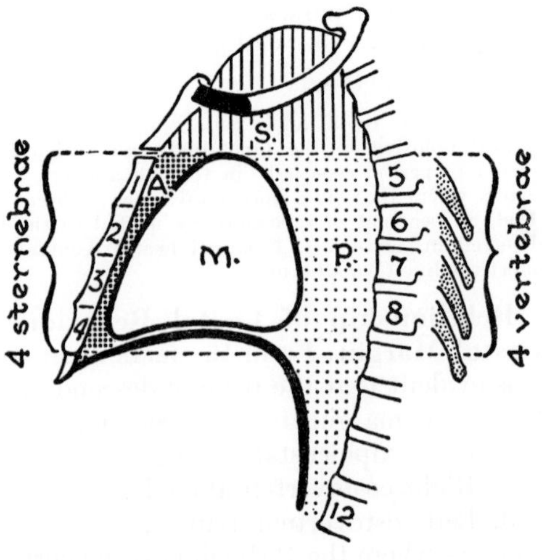

FIG. 567. Subdivisions of the mediastinum

that separates the superior mediastinum above from the anterior, middle and posterior mediastina below, many structures will in due course be seen to end, or to begin, or to arch, or to bend. Hence, it is a critical plane.

The Anterior Mediastinum is the small area in front of the pericardium where the sternal reflexion of the left pleura fails to meet the right pleura in the median plane (*fig. 564*). It may extend to the sternal ends of the (4th), 5th, and 6th left intercostal spaces. It contains only a little fat and some lymph nodes.

The Posterior Mediastinum lies behind the pericardium and also extends downwards below the level of the pericardium. In fact, the lower 8 thoracic vertebrae bound it behind; the pericardium and diaphragm bound it in front.

The Middle Mediastinum, of which the fibrous pericardium is the envelope, contains not only the heart but also the roots of the eight great vessels passing to and from the heart. Lateral to the pericardium on each side run the phrenic nerves and their companion vessels, the pericardiacophrenic vessels.

Mediastinal Pleurae

»» The mediastinal pleurae cannot be studied satisfactorily until the lungs have been removed. To **remove a lung** sever its root and the pulmonary ligament, which descends from the root. Before doing so, observe that just as a finger can be passed over the rounded upper border of the root of the lung, so it can be passed under the sharp lower border of the pulmonary ligament. The phrenic nerve and its companion vessels, covered with mediastinal pleura, run half an inch in front of the root and, so, need not be touched.

The structures covered with the right and left sheets of mediastinal pleura are readily displayed as there is but little fat within the thorax to conceal them. For reasons that will become apparent, they should be considered under the groupings given below, and not in a haphazard manner.

The thoracic contents were originally disposed symmetrically on the two sides of the body, but this initial symmetry was early lost, largely in consequence of the disappearance of certain veins from the left side and of certain arteries from the right, as explained on page 520. The right side is the simpler; so, it will be examined first.

Right Aspect of Mediastinum. On the right side investigate the structures in the following order:

1. Pericardial sac.
2. Two sites devoid of contents.

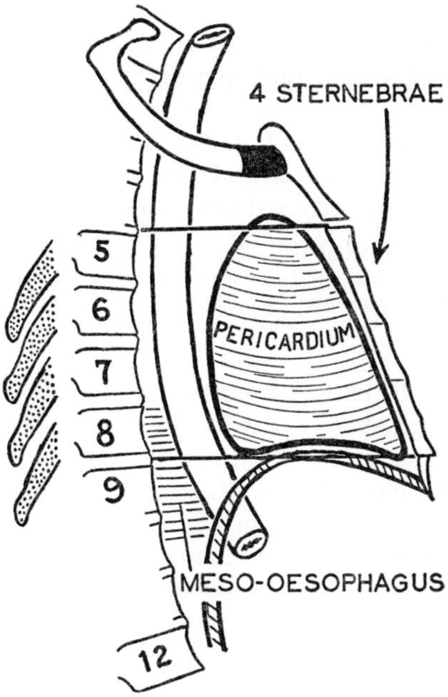

FIG. 568. The pericardial sac has 4 sternebrae in front of it and 4 vertebrae behind.

3. Great veins
   - Inferior vena cava
   - Superior vena cava
     - Right brachiocephalic (innominate) vein
     - Right jugular vein
     - Right subclavian vein

   } Right phrenic nerve
4. Esophagus, Trachea, and Right Vagus Nerve.
5. Root of lung and pulmonary ligament: Bronchus, Pulmonary artery, Pulmonary veins, and Vessels and Nerves.
6. Arch of the azygos vein.

The Pericardial Sac encloses the middle mediastinal contents[7] and is co-extensive in the median plane with the body of the sternum. It is separated from the right half of the body of the sternum by the thickness (or rather thinness) of the anterior border of the right lung and pleura. The sac is separated from the middle four thoracic vertebrae by the thickness of the aorta and the collapsed esophagus (*fig. 568*).

Two Sites Devoid of Contents. In two places the mediastinum has no contents;

[7] Exclusive of the phrenic nerves and their accompanying vessels.

so, the right and left layers of mediastinal pleura come into apposition: (1) between the sternum and pericardium from the level of the second to the fourth costal cartilages, and (2) between the lower part of the esophagus and the aorta. Here the two layers form a dorsal **meso-esophagus.**

»» Place a hand in each pleural cavity and feel the thin partitions at these two sites. Inspect them also—they are translucent. If either were to break down the result would be a single common pleural cavity (*fig. 578*).

Great Veins. A wicker stick passed upward through the i. v. cava will enter and traverse the right atrium (unless filled with hardened blood clot), the s. v. cava and the right brachiocephalic vein and, if continued into the neck, will enter the internal jugular vein. Palpate this stick, noting that the venae cavae enter the pericardium and open into the right atrium on a plane anterior to the root of the lung and pulmonary ligament. These veins may be likened to two rivers that flow due north and south to empty into a lake, the *right atrium* (*fig. 569*).

On each side of the body the internal jugular and subclavian veins unite behind the sternal end of the clavicle to form the corresponding brachiocephalic (innominate) vein. The left brachiocephalic vein crosses behind the upper half of the manubrium and

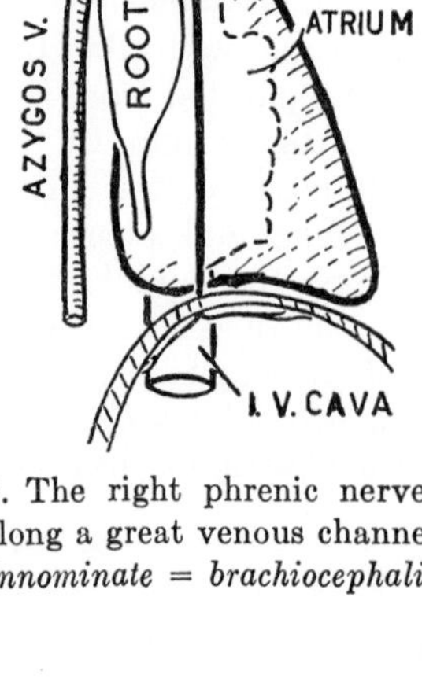

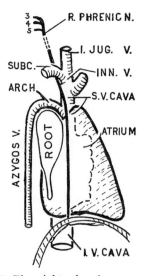

FIG. 569. The right phrenic nerve runs subpleurally along a great venous channel. (*Innominate = brachiocephalic.*)

joins the right brachiocephalic vein at the right margin of the sternum to form the s. v. cava. The s. v. cava descends from the 1st to the 3rd right costal cartilage and there opens into the right atrium. Its upper half is outside the pericardial sac; its lower half is inside. The i. v. cava, which likewise is partly outside and partly inside the pericardial sac, pierces the diaphragm and enters the heart at the levels of the xiphisternal joint and 6th costosternal joint, respectively.

The Right Phrenic Nerve enters the thorax behind the junction of the subclavian and the internal jugular vein (*fig. 576*), and descends subpleurally *along the line of the wicker stick* that traverses the great venous channel mentioned in the preceding paragraphs; that is, it lies in contact with the right side of the right brachiocephalic vein, superior vena cava, pericardium, and inferior vena cava—the pericardium separating it from the lower part of the s. v. cava, right atrium, and upper part of the i. v. cava. It then pierces the diaphragm and spreads out on its abdominal surface.

The phrenic nerve is joined high up, and accompanied through the thorax, by the *pericardiacophrenic artery*—a branch of the internal thoracic artery.

Esophagus, Trachea, and Right Vagus Nerve. The *esophagus* lies in front of the vertebral column except below, where the aorta gains the median plane and interposes itself. The *trachea* lies immediately in front of the esophagus throughout the superior mediastinum, and on reaching the plane between the superior and posterior mediastina it bifurcates into a right and a left bronchus.

Throughout its entire thoracic course the esophagus is clothed on its right side with mediastinal pleura, save only where the azygos arch crosses it above the root of the lung. A wicker stick passed through the esophagus aids greatly in its identification.

»» A fish has neither lungs, bronchi, nor trachea; so, its stomach occupies a much more cephalic position than in a mammal. Its esophagus is merely a sphincter separating its stomodeum from its stomach: it has no length. The nerve supply to this sphincter and stomach is the vagus, the vagrant or wandering nerve.

In man (i.e., mammals) lungs bronchi, and a

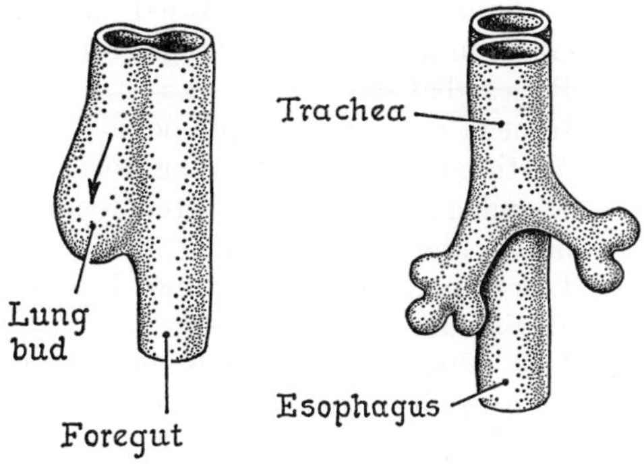

FIG. 570. The air passage buds downward from, and remains an intimate relation of, the front of the food passage. (Modified after Langman.)

trachea make their appearance as an outgrowth from the upper part of the food passage and, therefore, the vagus nerves, being the nerves of the food passage, are called upon to supply them (*fig. 570*).

The vagus nerve, on developmental grounds, ought to be found in direct contact with either the trachea or the esophagus. In point of fact, the right vagus, after entering the thorax between the subclavian artery and brachiocephalic vein, passes obliquely downward and backward first on the side of the brachiocephalic trunk (*fig. 571*), then on the side of the trachea to the back of the root of the lung where it takes part in the posterior pulmonary plexus. From this plexus the main trunk then passes to the esophagus and adheres to it thereafter.

ROOT OF LUNG AND PULMONARY LIGAMENT. The three chief structures in the root of a lung are:

1. *The pulmonary artery* which brings blood, charged with carbon dioxide from the heart to the lungs.

2. *The pulmonary veins* (two on each side, an upper and a lower) which return oxygenated blood to the heart.

3. *The bronchus* or air passage, which can be identified by the cartilage in its wall.

Since no rearrangement of structures takes place in the root of the lung, it follows that the bronchus, which has common derivation with the esophagus, lies posterior to the vessels, which are passing to and from the heart. Of the vessels, the two pulmonary veins of each side pierce the pericardium to end in the left atrium and are, therefore, below the corresponding right

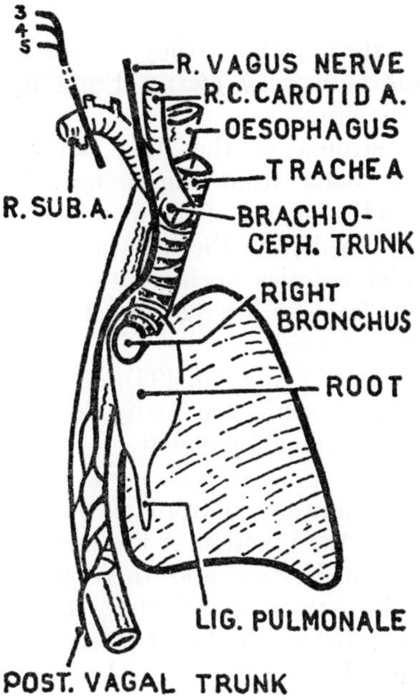

FIG. 571. The right vagus nerve is applied to the trachea and esophagus.

or left pulmonary artery, which lies along the upper border of the atria (*fig. 599*).

The order is the same on both sides; namely, bronchus behind, artery above, veins below (*fig. 573*). On the right side, however, the bronchus to the upper lobe of the lung is higher even than the artery—hence, it was formerly called the *eparterial bronchus*.

These structures occupy the upper part of the sleeve of pleura that connects the pulmonary pleura to the mediastinal pleura. Because the lower part of the sleeve is traversed only by a few lymph vessels, it is collapsed; its anterior and posterior walls are applied to each other and form the *pulmonary ligament* (lig. pulmonale).

Also in the root of the lung are:

4. Nerve plexuses.
5. Bronchial vessels.
6. Lymph nodes.

Branches of the vagus form a plexus behind the root of each lung, and joining it are branches from the sympathetic ganglia, mainly Th. 2, 3, and 4 having corresponding cord connections. From this *posterior pulmonary plexus* branches proceed into the lung. Some fibers from the vagus pass to the front of the root where, with others from the cardiac plexus, they constitute the *anterior pulmonary plexus.* From it, fibers enter the lung.

The stroma of the lung derives pure arterial blood from the *bronchial artery,* much as the stroma of the liver derives pure arterial blood from the hepatic artery. The bronchial arteries spring either from the aorta or from an intercostal artery and run with the bronchi.

Bronchial Veins (p. 495). In the root of the lung there are many *lymph nodes,* black from inhaled pigment.

The Arch of the Azygos Vein. The azygos vein runs upward in front of the vertebral column to the junction of the posterior and superior mediastina and there arches forwards above the root of the lung to end in the s. v. cava before the latter pierces the pericardium. The arch crosses lateral to the esophagus, trachea, and right vagus.

» In due time it will be seen that the brachiocephalic trunk (or innominate artery), the right end of the left brachiocephalic (or innominate) vein, the beginning of the aortic arch, and the fatty remains of the thymus are also in contact with the right mediastinal pleura.

Left Aspect of Mediastinum. The structures covered with left mediastinal pleura should now be identified, and investigated under the following groupings:

1. Pericardial sac.
2. Root of left lung and pulmonary lig.
3. Aortic arch and descending aorta.
4. Esophagus, trachea, left recurrent nerve, and thoracic duct.
5. Left common carotid and left subclavian arteries.
6. Left phrenic and vagus nerves and left superior intercostal vein.
7. Esophagus.

The Pericardial Sac, the *Root of the Left Lung,* and the *Pulmonary Ligament* are disposed as on the right side. It will, however, be noted that (1) two-thirds of the pericardium lie on the left of the median plane; that (2) owing to deficiencies in the anterior border of the left lung and pleura the pericardium comes into contact with the left half of the body of the sternum below the level of the 4th costal cartilage; and that (3) the left pulmonary artery is the highest structure in the root of the left lung (*fig. 573*).

The Aortic Arch (*fig. 572*) is the portion of the aorta lying in the superior mediastinum. It begins where the ascending aorta leaves the pericardium, which is at the level of the sternal angle. It arches backward and to the left above the root of the left lung, rising half way up the manubrium

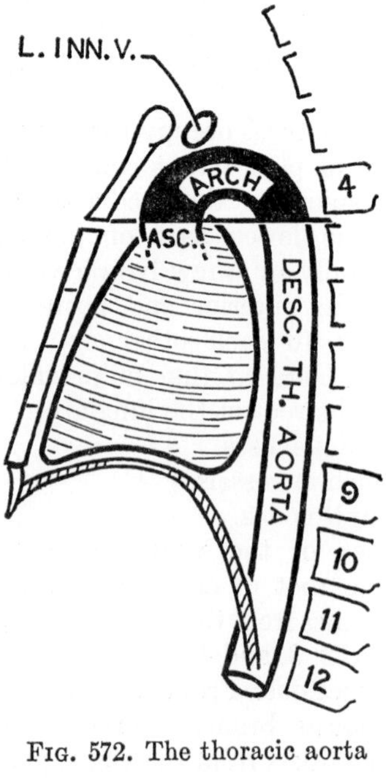

FIG. 572. The thoracic aorta

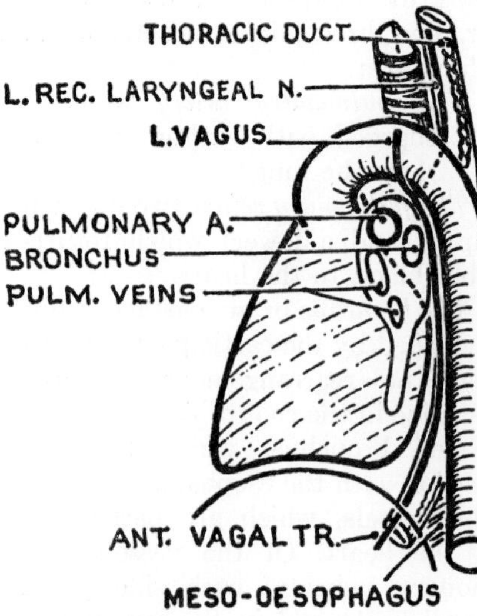

FIG. 573. Trachea and esophagus, left side

sterni and reaching the vertebral column at the lower border of the 4th thoracic vertebra.

Continued as the *descending aorta*, it traverses the posterior mediastinum in contact with the bodies of the lower eight vertebrae, first on their left sides, but gradually gaining the median plane, it intervenes between the esophagus and the vertebrae. Finally, at the disc between the last thoracic and the first lumbar vertebra, it passes behind the median arcuate ligament of the diaphragm to become the abdominal aorta.

(*Anomalies of the Arch, fig. 627.*)

The Trachea and Esophagus in the Superior Mediastinum (*figs. 573* and *574*). Here the esophagus projects to the left beyond the edge of the trachea. In the angle between them runs the *left recurrent laryngeal nerve.* On the side of the esophagus, the thin-walled *thoracic duct* ascends embedded in a film of fat.

These 4 structures lie side by side, like a bundle of sticks. They may be regarded as a "unit." The aortic arch crosses each of the 4 structures in this unit.

The arch and its two left branches obscure the trachea completely from view and the esophagus partially.

(*The Thoracic Duct* is described on page 531.)

The Left Common Carotid and Left Subclavian Arteries (*fig. 575*) arise from the convexity of the aortic arch, where it crosses the trachea, and pass obliquely upward and backward in semispiral fashion round the "*unit of 4*," crossing in turn the trachea, recurrent nerve, esophagus, and thoracic duct.

The Left Phrenic Nerve (*fig. 576*) enters

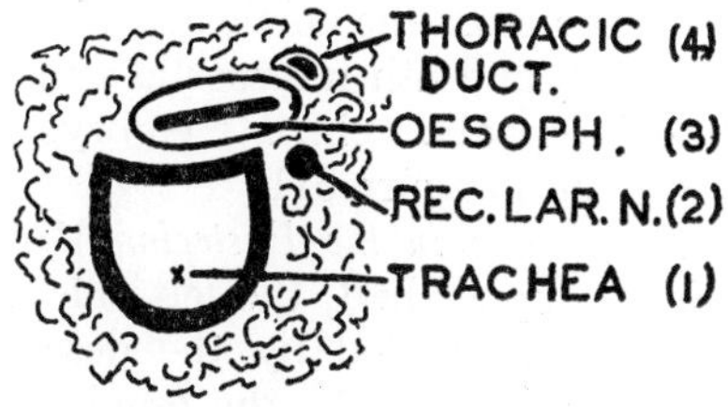

FIG. 574. Four parallel structures—a "unit of 4" (transverse section).

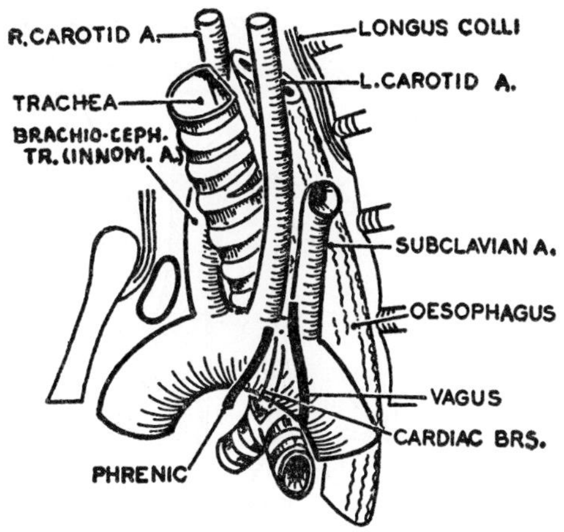

FIG. 575. Arteries ascend the "unit" in semispiral fashion.

the thorax between the subclavian artery and vein (at the beginning of the brachiocephalic or innominate vein), and runs a subpleural course, being covered throughout with mediastinal pleura.

After crossing the subclavian a., it at once crosses either anterior or posterior to the internal thoracic artery (int. mammary a.) and from it acquires a companion, the *pericardiacophrenic a.*, which accompanies it through the thorax. In its course it runs about ½″ in front of the root of the lung. It ends by supplying the diaphragm (*fig. 326*).

Now, in the foregoing respects the left nerve is identical with the right. In the following respects it differs: The left nerve descends lateral to the common carotid artery, which conducts it to the aortic arch; this it crosses anterior to the vagus nerve. Thereafter, it is applied to the left side of the pericardium.

(*Origin* in the neck, page 622.)

(*Distribution*, page 496.)

The Left Vagus Nerve, after traversing the neck within the carotid sheath on the lateral side of the common carotid a. (*fig. 576*), continues through the superior mediastinum on the lateral side of the same artery, and, therefore, between it and the subclavian artery. These two arteries conduct it to the aortic arch which it crosses to gain the back of the root of the lung. Thereafter, it

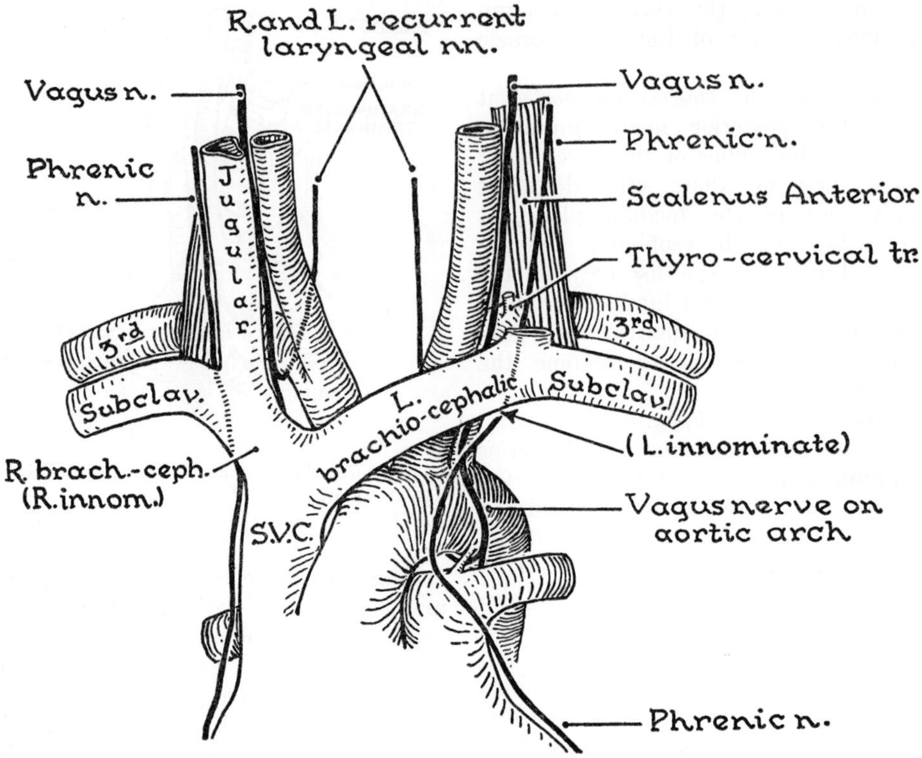

Fig. 576. The courses of the phrenic and vagus nerves

passes to the esophagus and behaves like the right vagus.

The Left Recurrent Laryngeal Nerve springs from the vagus where the latter crosses the left side of the aortic arch. It then passes below the arch and up on its right side to gain the angle between the trachea and the esophagus where it will be studied later (*fig. 631*).

Embryologically speaking, the left recurrent laryngeal nerve recurs around the lig. arteriosum rather than around the aortic arch. **The ligamentum arteriosum** is the obliterated posterior half of the primitive VI left aortic arch (*fig. 625*).

» In prenatal life the lig. arteriosum was a patent vessel, the *ductus arteriosus* (*fig. 40*). Its duty was to exclude (or partially to exclude) the functionless lungs from the circulation by "short-circuiting" the impure blood from the (left) pulmonary artery to the (left) aortic arch. Since the aorta carried the purest blood, the brain, head, neck, and upper limbs were assured of the purest blood, because the ductus discharged into the aorta beyond the origin of the left subclavian artery.

The aortic end of the lig. arteriosum is, therefore, to be sought just beyond the origin of the left subclavian artery, but on the concave side of the arch.

Two slender cardiac nerves arising in the neck, one from the vagus, the other from the sympathetic trunk, cross the aortic arch between the left phrenic nerve in front and the left vagus behind (*fig. 575*), and join the (*superficial*) *cardiac plexus*, which lies on the immediate right of the lig. arteriosum.

The Left Superior Intercostal Vein (*fig. 641*), being in a sense equivalent to the arch of the azygos vein, passes lateral to the vagus nerve and medial to the phrenic nerve as they cross the aortic arch. It drains the 2nd, 3rd, and 4th intercostal veins into the brachiocephalic vein. Its embryological value is given in figure 611.

The Esophagus in the Posterior Mediastinum. In the upper half, the left side of the esophagus is concealed by the descending aorta. In the lower half, the esophagus, in the meso-esophagus, crosses the aorta very obliquely to gain the left side of the thorax and is clothed with left mediastinal pleura

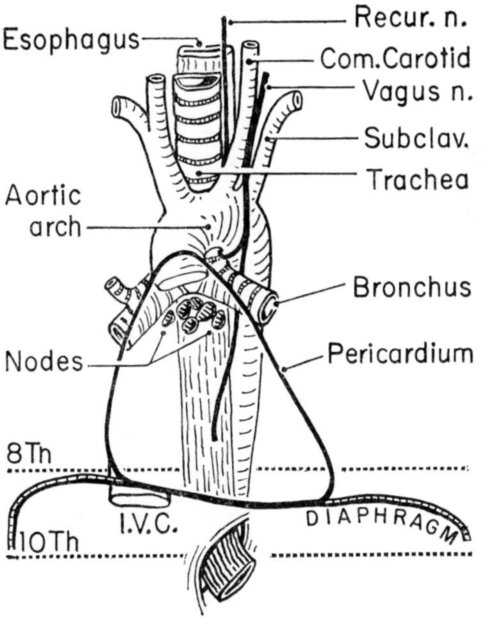

FIG. 577. The anterior relations of the esophagus, thoracic part.

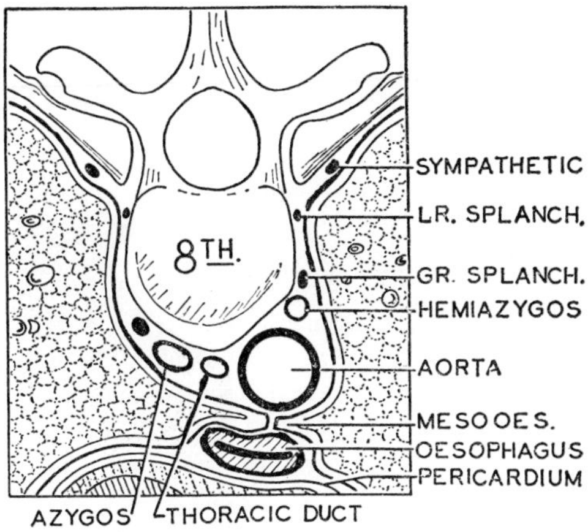

FIG. 578. Transverse section through posterior mediastinum, showing meso-esophagus and general relations.

down to the level of the 10th thoracic vertebra where it pierces the diaphragm (*fig. 577*).

The esophagus is ventral to the descending aorta for embryological reasons given in figure 627. Since this is fundamental, you should not fail to appreciate it.

Relationships to Arteries and Pleura. Several great arteries intervene between the esophagus and the left mediastinal pleura, *viz.*: left common carotid art., left subclavian art., aortic arch, and descending aorta.

The left mediastinal pleura is in contact with the esophagus at two sites only, (1) in the angle between the aortic arch and the left subclavian art., though even here the thoracic duct intervenes; and (2) in the lowest part of its thoracic course. Here it is attached to the front of the aorta by a *meso-esophagus* (*fig. 578*), as described on p. 480.

This meso-esophagus commonly extends far cranially, thereby allowing the esophagus to advance several centimeters from the vertebral column. The lungs then approach each other behind the esophagus, particularly on inspiration and with the subject erect. A lateral X-ray picture reveals this *retro-esophageal space* or *"window."*

The Cupola of the Pleura (Cervical Pleura) (*fig. 579*) rises to the neck of the 1st rib, which is $1\frac{1}{2}''$ above the level of the sternal end of the 1st costal cartilage. It forms both the roof of the pleural cavity and the floor of the root of the neck (*fig. 723*). It is protected externally by Scalene muscles, which are in series with Intercostal muscles. The Scalenes are lined internally with fascia, the *suprapleural membrane* (Sibson's fascia).

The following structures may be seen on stripping off the cupola (*fig. 579*): The subclavian artery, arching laterally and disappearing between the Scalenus Anterior and Scalenus Medius. Of its four branches, three are seen; namely, the *internal thoracic artery* passing downward and forward, the *supreme intercostal branch* of the costocervical trunk passing downward and backward, and the *vertebral artery* ascending.

The union of the *subclavian* and *internal jugular veins* to form the brachiocephalic vein takes place on the cupola at the medial border of the Scalenus Anterior. From this point the *right brachiocephalic vein* descends vertically somewhat in front of the *brachiocephalic trunk* (artery).

Crossing the neck of the 1st rib subpleurally are the *supreme intercostal artery*, with the *sympathetic trunk* medially and the branch of the ventral ramus of the *first thoracic nerve* to the brachial plexus laterally.

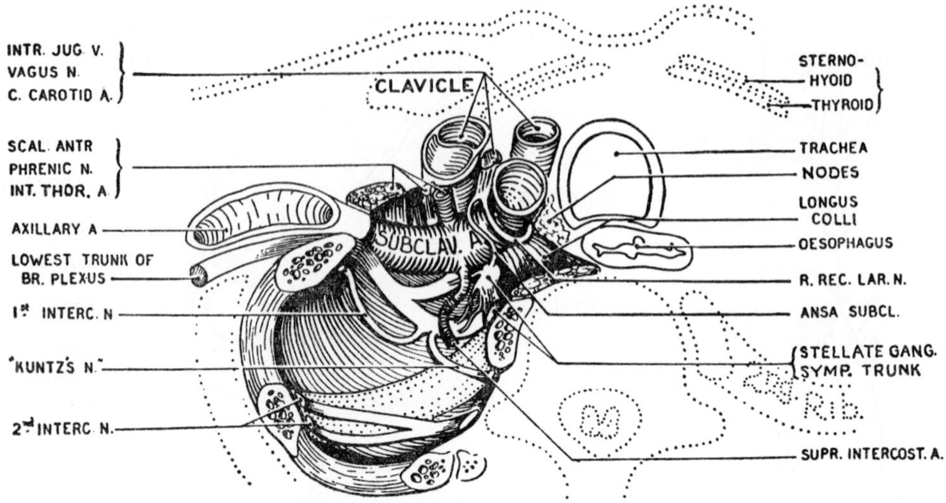

FIG. 579. The cupola of the pleura has been removed in order to display its immediate relations. (Viewed from below.)

The supreme intercostal artery supplies the first two intercostal spaces from behind. The first thoracic sympathetic ganglion is large and lies behind the vertebral artery. A small twig, the *ansa subclavia*, in descending from the middle cervical ganglion to the inferior ganglion, makes a loop in front of and below the subclavian artery.

The Phrenic and Vagus Nerves enter the thorax between the brachiocephalic vein and the subclavian artery, the phrenic nerves being lateral to the vagus nerves, and they descend subpleurally, as described on pages 480, 481, and 483.

The *right vagus* gives off the *right recurrent laryngeal nerve* which winds tightly below and behind the subclavian artery to ascend in the neck.

The **Sympathetic Trunk** (thoracic portion) (*figs. 578* and *580*) is covered throughout with costal pleura, nothing intervening, and it lies a little wide of the mediastinum. Traced caudally, the trunks of the two sides become progressively closer together as they converge on the coccyx.

At the superior aperture of the thorax, the trunk lies on the neck of the 1st rib. In the thorax, it crosses the heads of the 2nd to 9th ribs, the 10th costovertebral joint, and the bodies of the 11th and 12th vertebrae. It continues into the abdomen along the anterior border of the Psoas, and

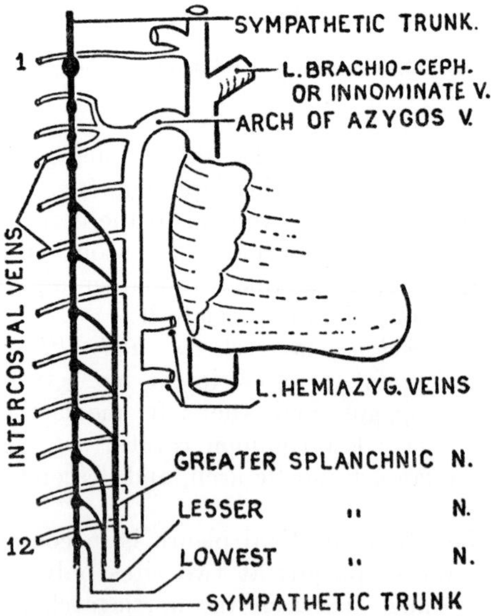

FIG. 580. The sympathetic trunk and splanchnic nerves.

therefore passes behind the medial arcuate lig.—though it may pierce the crus of the diaphragm. The intercostal arteries and veins cross the trunk posteriorly; so does the large branch from Th. 1 to the lowest trunk of the brachial plexus.

Typically, a ganglion is to be found in front of each rib. Since *ganglia* are segmental structures, there is developmentally 1 for each of the 31 spinal nerves.

The inferior cervical and the 1st thoracic ganglion are usually amalgamated to form the *cervicothoracic or stellate ganglion*, which lies behind the origin of the vertebral artery.

»» Owing to their tendency to amalgamate, there are with fair constancy only 3 (or 4) cervical, 11 thoracic, 4 lumbar, 4 sacral pairs, and 1 coccygeal (unpaired).

CONNECTIONS. From the ventral rami of a limited number of spinal nerves (all the thoracic and the upper two or three lumbar) a white ramus communicans, carrying preganglionic fibers, passes anteromedially to join a sympathetic ganglion; whereas the ventral ramus of every spinal nerve, without exception, receives from a sympathetic ganglion one or more gray rami communicantes, carrying postganglionic fibers.

DISTRIBUTION TO VISCERA. From the upper five thoracic ganglia, postganglionic fibers pass to the cardiac plexus, posterior pulmonary plexus, and upper thoracic parts of the esophagus and aorta. Fibers either from the lower thoracic ganglia or from the splanchnic nerves contribute to the supply of the lower thoracic portions of the esophagus and aorta.

The **Splanchnic Nerves** (*fig. 580*) are preganglionic fibers coming from white rami communicantes and making "nonstop journeys" through sympathetic ganglia. They end in the celiac and renal ganglia, whence they are relayed as non-medullated postganglionic fibers (*fig. 44.1*).

There are three (paired) splanchnic nerves—greater, lesser, and lowest. Their sources vary widely; they are rarely bilaterally symmetrical; and the lowest may be absent (A. F. Reed). Thus:

1. The *greater splanchnic nerve*, larger than the sympathetic trunk itself, springs from the (4th), (5th), (6th), (7th), **8th, 9th, and 10th** ganglia, runs caudally just lateral to the azygos (or hemiazygos) vein, pierces the crus of the diaphragm, and ends in the celiac ganglion.

2. The *lesser splanchnic nerve* springs from the (9th), **10th, 11th,** and (12th) ganglia, runs caudally—lateral to the greater nerve—pierces the crus, and ends in the lower part of the celiac ganglion (specifically, the aorticorenal ganglion).

3. The *lowest splanchnic nerve*, when present, springs from either the **11th** or **12th** ganglion or from both ganglia, takes a similar course, and ends in the renal plexus.

»» *Note.* (1) Whether a nerve be white or gray depends on whether or not its individual nerve fibers have or have not medullary sheaths. Preganglionic fibers usually have medullary sheaths and so appear white; whereas postganglionic fibers, fibers that have their cell stations in ganglia, usually have no medullary sheath and so appear gray. (2) Gray rami communicantes and the branches to the thoracic viscera (heart, lungs, aorta, and esophagus) are nonmedullated fibers that have been relayed in sympathetic ganglia. (3) As might be expected, rami communicantes run posterolaterally from the ganglia to the ventral nerve rami; whereas, visceral branches run anteromedially from the ganglia to the viscera or to the aorta to be distributed with its branches.

CHAPTER 31

LUNGS

Shape and Parts; Borders and Surface Anatomy; Cardiac Notch.
Lobes and Fissures; Variations.
Bronchial Tree; Bronchopulmonary Segments; Removal of Mucus and Foreign Matter.
Structure of Bronchi and Lungs; Lung Units.
Vessels and Nerves: Pulmonary Artery and Veins; Bronchial Arteries and Veins; Lymphatics; Nerves.
Movements; Surface Anatomy of Living.

Mechanism of Respiration

Inspiration and Expiration; During Quiet Inspiration; On Deeper Inspiration; Expiration; Nerve Supply; Posture.

Lungs (Pulmones)

»» The shape of the lungs, like that of the liver and spleen, depends largely upon the surrounding structures, and the impressions these make are best observed in formalin-hardened specimens. A full description of the form and relations of the lungs is in large measure redundant, since it is a description of the counterpart of the parietal pleura already given.

The weight of the lungs varies with their content of blood. With the vessels empty, the right lung weighs $8\frac{1}{2}$ ounces (240 gms.); the left, being smaller, an ounce less. Filled with blood, they weigh 22 and 20 ounces, respectively (Gradwohl).

The lungs (*pulmones*) are conical (*fig. 581*). Each lung has an apex and base, costal and medial surfaces, anterior and inferior borders, and a hilus.

The Apex rises to the neck of the 1st rib.

The Base or diaphragmatic surface is concave. Because the right dome of the diaphragm rises higher and is more convex than the left dome, the right lung is shorter and its base is more deeply excavated than the left. The right base overlies the liver; the left base overlies the liver, stomach, and spleen.

The Costal Surface may bulge slightly into the obliquely set intercostal spaces.

The Medial Surface has two parts: (1) vertebral and (2) mediastinal. *The vertebral part* (formerly called the posterior border) is full and rounded; it passes imperceptibly into the costal surface; and it occupies the gutter at the side of the vertebral column.

»» *The mediastinal part* (*fig. 583*) bears the impress of the structures covered with the mediastinal pleura. The most noticeable feature of this surface is the *hilus* of the lung and the line of the attachment of the pulmonary lig. which descends from the hilus (*fig. 582*). In front of these, an excavation, the *cardiac impression*, is deeper on the left side than on the right, because two-thirds of the heart lie on the left of the median plane.

Two vertical grooves for the caval veins join the right cardiac impression: (1) the *groove for the s. v. cava* descends in front of the root of the lung; (2) the much deeper *groove for the i. v. cava* ascends in front of the pulmonary ligament. The phrenic nerve and its vessels create no perceptible groove.

Arching over the root of the lung, and therefore in the superior mediastinum, is the *arch of the azygos vein* on the right side; the *arch of the aorta* on the left. The grooves produced by these two vessels can be followed downward, behind the hilus and ligament of the respective lung, through the entire length of the posterior mediastinal surface. Only when the azygos vein is engorged, is its groove well marked.

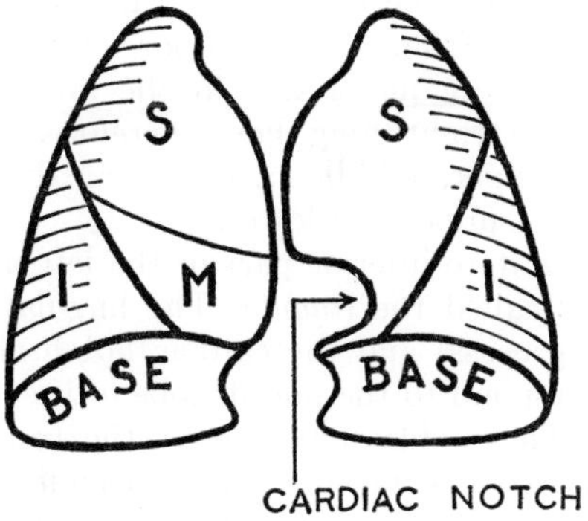

FIG. 581. The lungs, anterior aspect

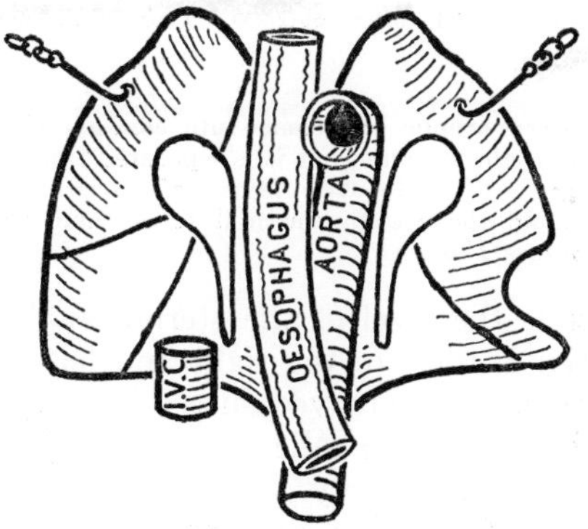

FIG. 582. The mediastinal surfaces of the lungs. This picture reveals the posterior, lateral, and anterior relations of the pericardium.

The right margin of the *esophagus* produces a groove between the hilus and ligament of the right lung in front and the groove for the azygos vein behind; the lower end of the left margin of the esophagus makes an imprint on the left lung between the lower end of the left pulmonary lig. and the *groove for the descending aorta* (*fig. 583*).

The right lung, above the level of the arch of the azygos vein, presents three grooves (or areas) for—the esophagus, trachea, and s. v. cava (and its upward continuation called the right brachiocephalic or innominate vein). Behind the latter is the brachiocephalic trunk or innominate artery. The right vagus makes no mark.

The left lung, above the level of the aortic arch, presents areas or grooves for—the left subclavian and left common carotid arteries which largely conceal the trachea and esophagus; and in front of the common carotid is the left brachiocephalic or innominate vein. The left vagus and the thoracic duct make no mark.

Borders of Lungs: Surface Anatomy. As stated already (p. 478), the lungs fill the *pleural cavities* except at three sites: right and left costodiaphragmatic and left costomediastinal recesses. The lower limits of the costodiaphragmatic recesses are related to ribs 8, 10, and 12; the lower borders of the lungs are related to ribs 6, 8, and 10, so they are two ribs higher.

The **cardiac notch,** or "bite" that the heart takes out of the anterior border of the left lung, is greater than the bite it takes out of the left pleura—hence the left costomediastinal recess. During inspiration the lungs invade, but by no means fill, the pleural recesses.

The Anterior Borders of the lungs are insinuated between the body of the sternum and the pericardium, so they are thin and sharp. On the left side the cardiac notch

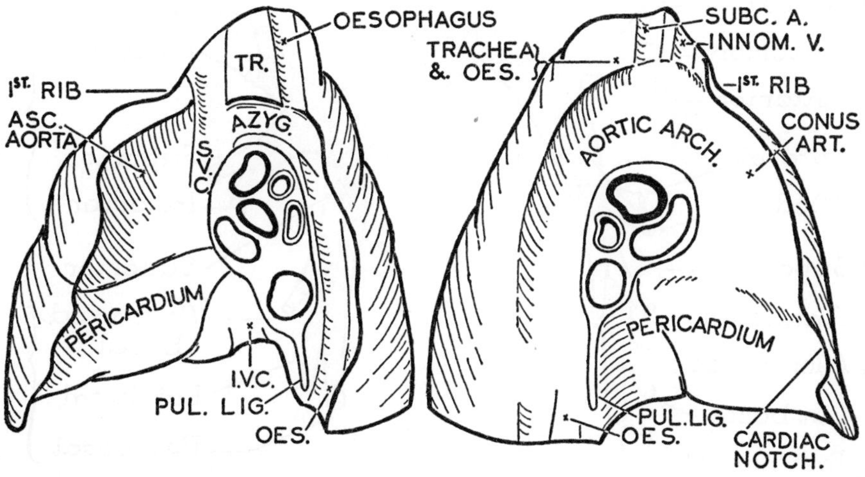

FIG. 583. Impressions commonly made on the mediastinal surfaces of the lungs. Of course, some intimate relations (e.g., phrenic n.) make no impressions.

extends from the 4th to the 6th costal cartilage.

»» The pericardium here comes into contact with the left side of the sternum, but it is separated from costal cartilages 4–6 by the two layers of parietal pleura that bound the costomediastinal recess and by the Transversus Thoracis.

Above the level of the sternal angle the anterior borders of the right and left lungs diverge and are grooved successively by the 1st rib, brachiocephalic (innominate) vein, and subclavian artery.

The Inferior Border projects into the costodiaphragmatic recess, so it also is sharp.

Lobes and Fissures. In each lung a complete fissure, the *oblique fissure,* cuts through the costal, diaphragmatic, and mediastinal surfaces as far as the root. In the cadaver, it crosses the posterior border 2½ inches below the apex, and the inferior border 2 inches or more from the median plane (but, see p. 497). When the arm is raised above the head, the medial border of the scapula practically overlies this oblique fissure.

On the right side a second equally complete fissure, the horizontal fissure, lying at the level of the 4th costal cartilage runs backward from the anterior border to meet the oblique fissure in the midlateral line. The right lung has, therefore, three lobes—upper, middle, and lower; the left has two—upper and lower.

The antero-inferior part of the left upper lobe is called the *lingula.* The lingula (lingular process) and the cardiac notch above it correspond to the middle lobe of the right lung. The middle lobe lies at the front of the chest, its tail-like apex reaching the midlateral line. You can cover it with your own hand placed on your chest.

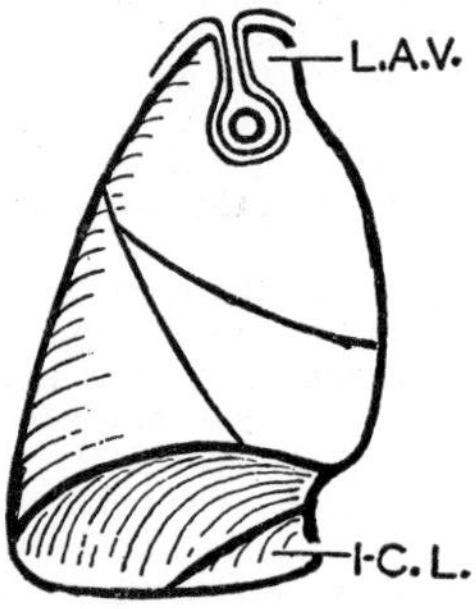

FIG. 584. Accessory lobes of the right lung: lobe of the azygos vein; infracardiac lobe.

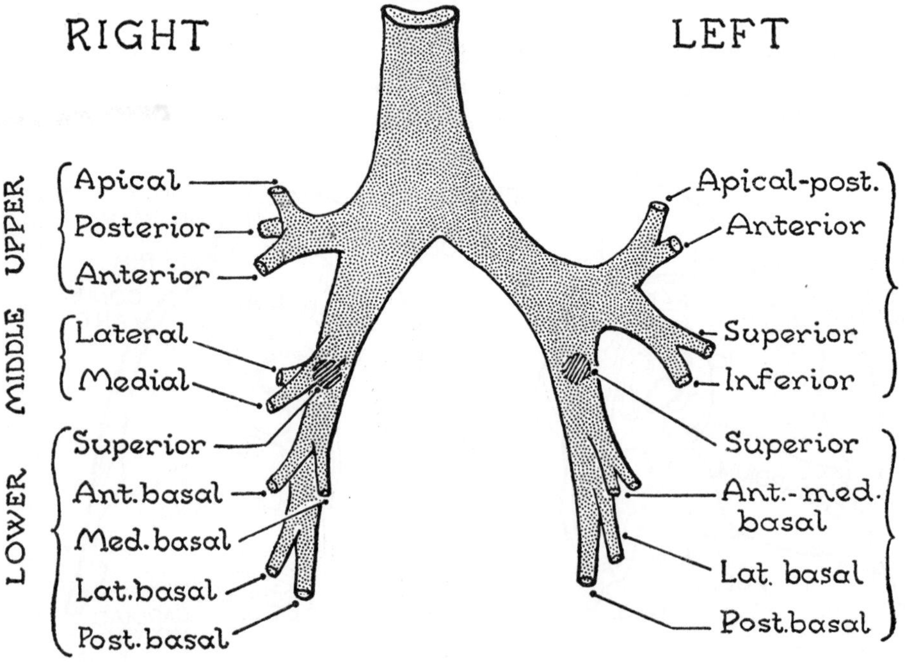

FIG. 585. The 10 right and 8 left segmental bronchi. (After Jackson and Huber.)

Variations in trachea, lobes, and fissures. A right **tracheal bronchus** (present in the sheep and pig) occurs occasionally in man. It is usually a right apical bronchus displaced onto the trachea (Boyden).

A **lobe of the azygos vein** results when the apex of a developing right lung encounters the arch of the azygos vein and is cleft by it (*fig. 584*). The vein is suspended in a pleural "mesentery," and it may cause a shadow by X-ray.

Fissures. The horizontal fissure (r. lung) is very commonly either completely or partially absent. The upper part of the oblique fissure (r. or l.) is commonly absent, and lower part sometimes is absent.

Additional fissures have been described between most bronchopulmonary segments and between many subsegments (Foster-Carter). Notably, they commonly define the superior segment (r. or l. lower lobe), the lingula (l. upper lobe), and a slight fissure commonly defines the right cardiac, or medial basal, segment.

The Bronchial Tree (*figs. 585* and *587*). The trachea bifurcates on the plane between the superior and posterior mediastina (4–5 disc) into a right and a left *primary* (main) *bronchus* for the supply of the respective lungs. Each primary bronchus descends to the hilus of its own lung where it lies behind the pulmonary vessels and on a level with the 5th and 6th vertebral bodies. On the right side it gives off three *secondary* (lobar) *bronchi*, and on the left side, two, for the corresponding lobes of the lungs. The secondary or lobar bronchi divide into *tertiary* (segmental) *bronchi*. Each segmental bronchus, together with the portion of the lobe it supplies, is called a **bronchopulmonary segment** (*fig. 586*).

» In some instances the segmental bronchi are quaternary, conspicuously those of the left upper lobe (*fig. 585*).

As seen from figure 585, there are usually 10 segmental bronchi on the right side, and 8 on the left. These are constant within certain limits, determined by minor variations in the branching of the bronchi.

As the bronchi continue to branch and rebranch, the bronchopulmonary segments subdivide into smaller and smaller subsegments, until the ultimate, called a *lung unit*, or *primary lobule*, is reached (p. 492).

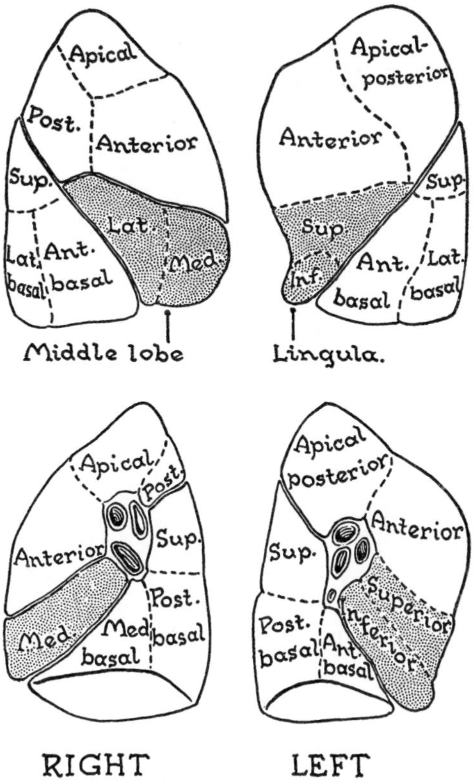

FIG. 586. The 10 right and 8 left bronchopulmonary segments. (After Jackson and Huber.)

The bronchi are distributed very nearly symmetrically in the two lungs. But, there are *Three Points of Contrast:*

(1) the direct equivalent of the right upper and middle lobar bronchi are partially fused on the left to form the left upper lobe bronchus (*fig. 585*). (2) The apical and posterior segmental bronchi of the right side divide late on the left side—they spring from a common stem, and (3) the anterior basal and medial basal also divide later.

» **Removal of Mucus and foreign Material.** In man, who has assumed an upright posture, the natural method of emptying the tracheobronchial tree of accumulated secretion and particulate matter is by ciliary action and by coughing. But, by assuming various recumbent postures, the assistance of gravity may be obtained. This was appreciated by H. P. Nelson who investigated the bronchi with this fact in mind and described the particular posture best suited to draining into the trachea the contents which, under pathological conditions, have accumulated in a given bronchus. Others have related the bronchopul-

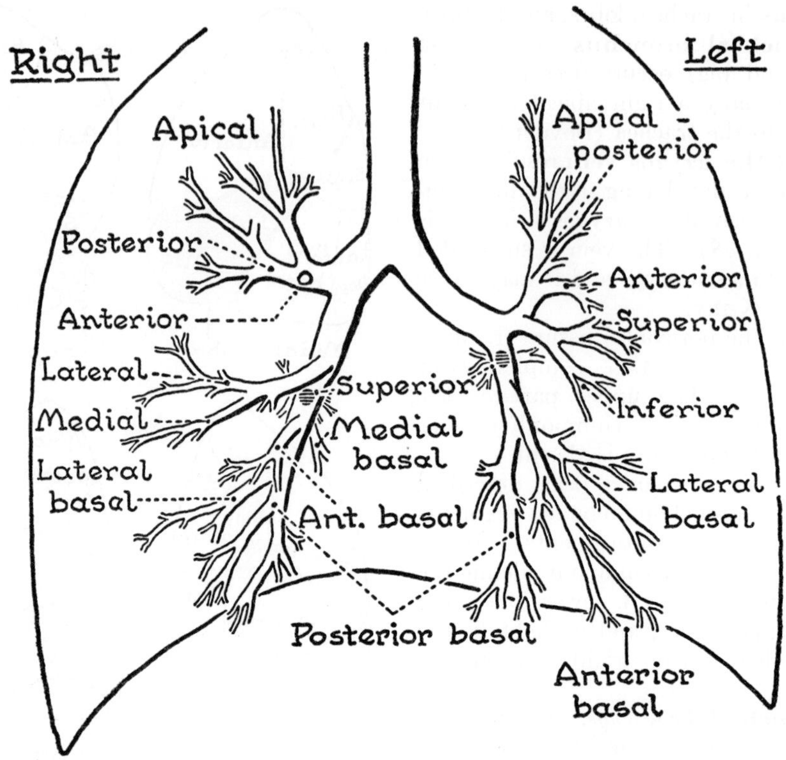

FIG. 587. The distribution of the bronchi, front view. (After Nelson, modified.)

monary segments to the surface of the lung and to the surface of the body, thereby indicating where they are accessible to surgical treatment (e.g., removal or drainage). The bronchoscopist's approach (e.g., removing an aspirated foreign body) is via the larynx and trachea.

It can be observed that the right upper lobe bronchus (eparterial bronchus) arises 1 inch from the tracheal bifurcation. After the course of 1 cm. it divides into its three segmental bronchi.

The right middle lobe bronchus arises about 2 cm. below the upper lobe bronchus.

The left upper lobe bronchus arises 2 inches from the tracheal bifurcation. After the course of less than 1 cm., it bifurcates and then both of the forked branches bifurcate again into four segmental bronchi. Owing to its low origin, the apical posterior bronchus and its branches make a steep ascent.

The superior (apical) lower lobe bronchi of both sides arise almost opposite the mouths of the right middle and left upper lobe bronchi, respectively.

The posterior basal bronchus is the largest of the lower lobe segmental bronchi; it may be regarded as the continuation of the stem of the bronchial tree (*figs. 587—589*, and table 21).

Structure. The C-shaped bars of hyaline cartilage found in the trachea and extrapulmonary bronchi give place in the intrapulmonary bronchi to plates of cartilage which are scattered irregularly around a circular lumen. The *bronchi* branch and rebranch until their diameter is reduced to 1 mm. or less, whereupon, the cartilage and the mucous glands ceasing, the bronchi enter the lung tissue as bronchioles. The noncartilaginous terminal bronchioles divide several times until the cilia cease and alveolar outpouching appear on their walls, whereupon they are aptly called *respiratory* bronchioles, as they are the beginning of the respiratory part of the lung. Each respiratory bronchiole opens into a number of *alveolar ducts* [*ductules*]. From the ducts arise the alveolar sacs and alveoli (*air cells*) (*fig. 590*).

Lung Units. On the surface of the lung dark lines are seen to enclose *polygonal fields*, 10–20 mm. in diameter. They are the bases of pyramidal portions of lung, supplied by bronchioles, 1 mm. or less in diameter, and enclosed by areolar septa rendered black by inhaled pigment contained in lymphatics. These portions of lung are anatomical or secondary lobules (*fig. 591*).

With or without a lens, finer lines are seen to subdivide the bases into smaller areas

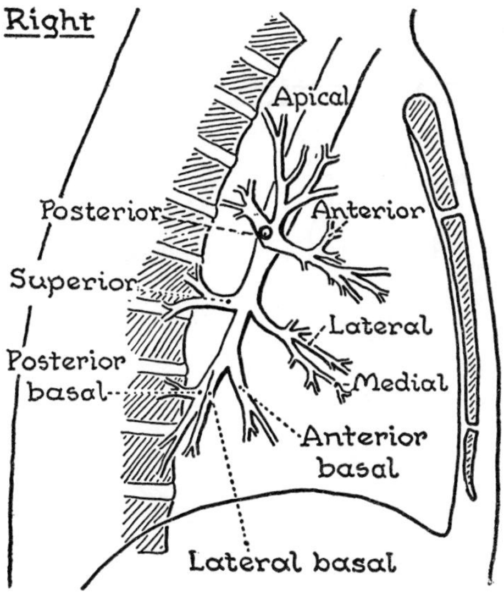

FIG. 588. The distribution of the right bronchus, side view.

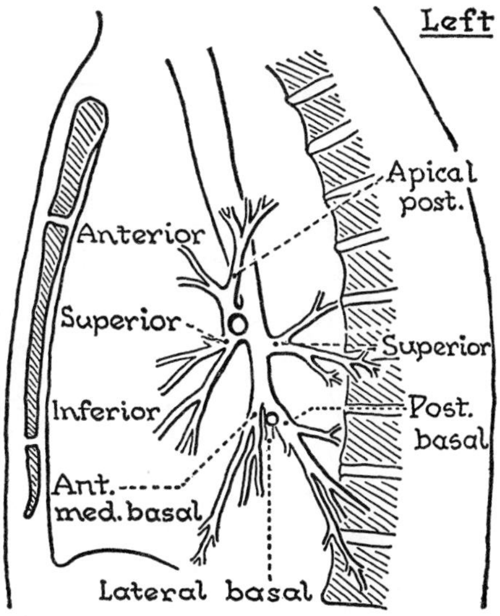

FIG. 589. The distribution of the left bronchus side view. (After Nelson, modified.)

TABLE 21

Names of the Bronchopulmonary Segments*

Right lung: Lobes	Right lung: Segments		Left lung: Lobes		Left lung: Segments	
Upper	Apical	1	Upper	Upper Division	Apicoposterior	1 and 2
	Posterior	2			Anterior	3
	Anterior	3		Lower Division [Lingula]	Superior Lingular	4
Middle	Lateral	4			Inferior Lingular	5
	Medial	5	Lower		Superior [Apical]	6
Lower	Superior [Apical]	6			Anteromedial Basal	8 (and 7)
	Medial Basal [Cardiac]	7			Lateral Basal	9
	Anterior Basal	8			Posterior Basal	10
	Lateral Basal	9				
	Posterior Basal	10				

* *Nomenclature.* By the pioneers various names, each appropriate in its own way, have been applied to the various bronchopulmonary segments. To resolve the many conflicting synonyms employed, Jackson and Huber suggest the nomenclature here given, because of its simplicity and ease. Each segment is named according to its position in a lobe. The term anterior is preferred to pectoral, and lateral to axillary; all segments that contribute to the basal or diaphragmatic surface of the lower lobe are described as basal; hence, medial basal is preferred to cardiac. The numerals given in table 21 are those suggested by the Thoracic Society, September 1950.

representing *primary lobules* or *lung units,* each served by a respiratory bronchiole. The units show to good advantage when the bronchial tree has been filled with a white or a pale yellow injection mass.

Blood Vessels of the Lungs

Pulmonary Artery (*fig. 592*). The arterial tree, in general, follows the bronchial pattern, so we may speak of segmental and subsegmental arteries. Since the arteries are

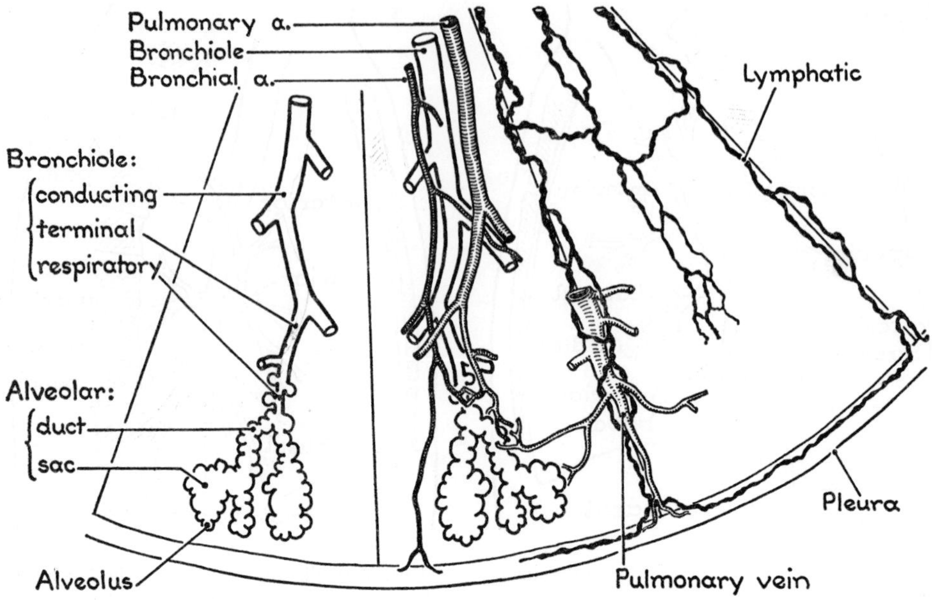

FIG. 590. Structure of a lobule of the lung

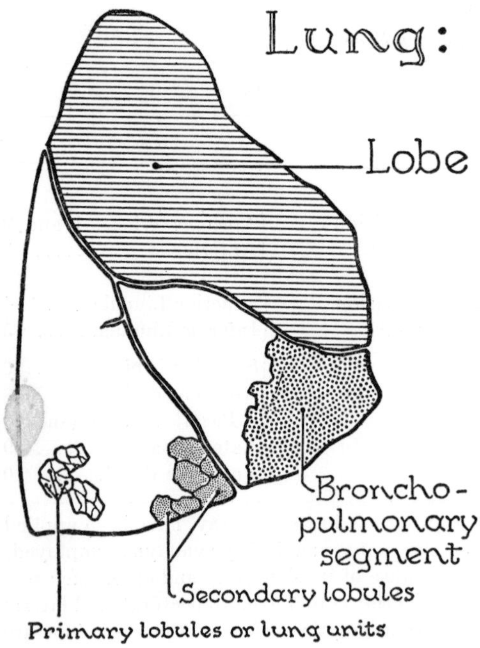

FIG. 591. The subdivisions of the lung

applied closely to the bronchi and are filled under pressure, they are flexion-resistant supports (v. Hayek). You have already noted that:

1. *The right pulmonary artery* passes dorsally between the right upper and middle lobe bronchi, separating them widely—so widely that the origin of the upper lobe bronchus is, so to speak, pushed to within 1 inch of the trachea. Only the azygos vein arches over it.

2. *The left pulmonary artery* and also the aortic arch pass dorsally over the left upper lobe bronchus which is, so to speak, pushed the width of these two vessels, about 2 inches, from the trachea, and as a result it shares a common stalk with the lingular bronchus, which is the equivalent of the right middle lobe bronchus.

Note (1) that, after giving off branches to the upper lobe, each pulmonary artery descends on the posterolateral side of the "stem" bronchus, and (2) that the segmental and subsegmental arteries radiate from the hilus *medial* to ascending bronchi, *cranial* to transverse bronchi, and *lateral* to descending bronchi.

Segmental arteries vary in origin, and may, indeed, be absent, in which case the subsegmental arteries arise independently from the "stem" arteries or elsewhere (see Boyden).

Pulmonary Veins. On each side two pulmonary veins, an upper and a lower, enter the left atrium of the heart; on the left side they come from the respective upper and lower lobes of the lung; on the right side the upper vein drains the upper and middle lobes.

Within the lung, the veins lie in areolar intrasegmental and intersegmental septa; they alternate with the arteries, each vein receiving a share of the blood delivered by two arteries (including arteries from contiguous segments) and each artery contributes blood to two veins.

The **Bronchial Arteries** are to the lungs what the hepatic artery is to the liver. Derived on the left side from the aorta, on the right either from an intercostal artery or from the left bronchial artery, each bronchial artery clings closely to the wall of the bronchus. It supplies the bronchi, the walls of the pulmonary vessels, and the lymph nodes, and, after passing with radicles of the pulmonary vein through interlobular septa, it supplies the pulmonary pleura.

Now, the blood delivered to the lungs by the bronchial arteries is returned by radicles of the pulmonary veins, except that to the first two or three divisions of the bronchi which is returned by the *bronchial veins* to the azygos system of veins (*fig. 590*).

The bronchial arteries deliver arterial blood under high pressure; whereas the pulmonary artery delivers venous blood under low pressure. Hence, anastomoses between these two arteries might be expected not to occur. But they do occur—there being anastomoses between their capillaries at the respiratory bronchioles. Further, the pulmonary a. may anastomose with, and assist, the bronchial a. to supply the intrapulmonary bronchi and the mediastinal layer of pulmonary pleura: in the newborn and in disease these anastomoses may achieve a diameter of about 0.5 mm. Again, arteriovenous shunts between the pulmonary artery and vein occur both in the lobules of the lung and in the pulmonary pleura (Tobin and Zariquiey).

»» As a rare *anomaly* the bronchial artery replaces the pulmonary artery

Comparative Anatomy. In the rabbit it is the pulmonary artery—not the bronchial—that supplies the lymphoid tissue and sends branches to the pleura.

Lymphatics (*fig. 590*). Lymph channels, accompanying small blood vessels, occur adjacent to the alveolar walls, but not in the interalveolar partitions. Lymph drainage is mainly centripetal along the branches of the pulmonary artery and bronchi to the hilar region. Lymph channels in the pleura and at the periphery of the lobules likewise drain centripetally to the hilar region, but they do so along the branches of the pulmonary vein.

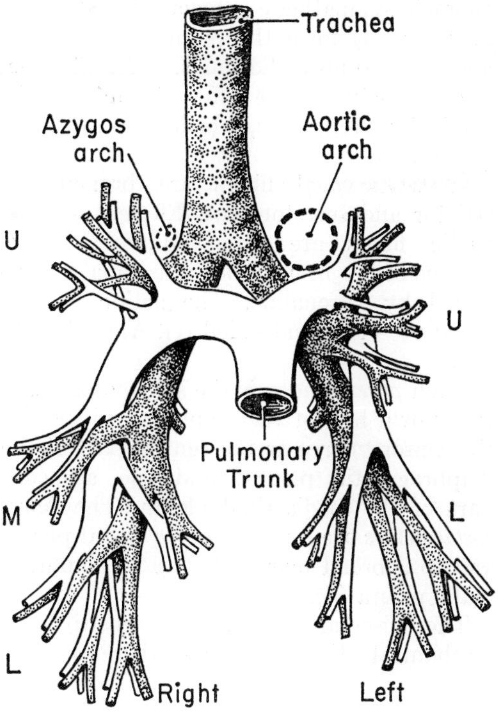

FIG. 592. To show the relationship of pulmonary arteries to bronchi, front view. U, M, L = branches to upper, middle, and lower lobes. (After Hayek, translated by V. E. Krahl.)

If certain lymph nodes or vessels in the lung are occluded, the lymph vessels in the pleura can act as accessory outlets by conducting lymph around a lobule or a segment to the next or a subsequent septum and so to the hilar region (C. E. Tobin).

The lymph vessels anastomose within the lung and they drain into the bronchopulmonary nodes in the hilus. These in turn drain into the tracheobronchial nodes. A few vessels from the lower lobe drain by way of the pulmonary lig. to the posterior mediastinal nodes.

Nerves. Branches of the vagus and of the

thoracic sympathetic ganglia 1 to 5 (mainly 2, 3, and 4) form the pulmonary plexuses and these supply the lungs. Afferent vagal fibers constitute the afferent limb of the respiratory reflex arc, which arrests further inspiration.

Efferent vagal fibers are bronchoconstrictor and secretomotor. Efferent sympathetic fibers are bronchodilator; hence, spasms of the bronchi, as in asthma, are relieved by adrenaline. The action on the blood vessels is undecided (G. A. G. Mitchell).

Each *phrenic nerve* is the sole motor nerve to its own half of the diaphragm; it is also the sensory nerve to the central part of the diaphragmatic pleura, and the adjacent part of the mediastinal pleura. The *intercostal nerves* are sensory to the costal pleura and to a broad marginal strip of diaphragmatic pleura (*fig. 326*).

The visceral pleura is insensitive to mechanical stimulation and therein it resembles the visceral peritoneum, apparently most of the mediastinal pleura, and both the visceral and the parietal pericardium.

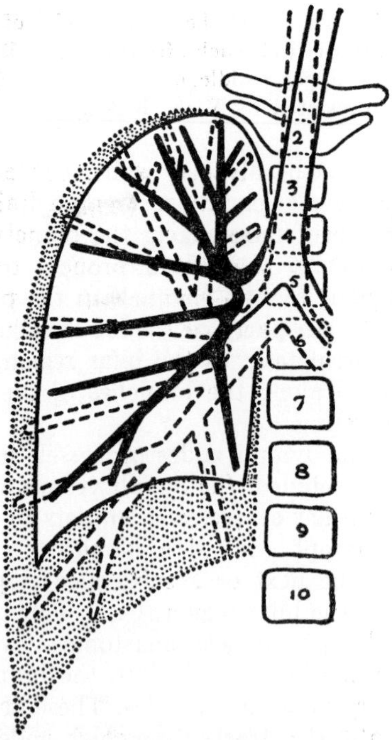

FIG. 593. Excursion of bronchial tree in forced inhalation (*dotted lines*) and forced exhalation (*solid black*) from X-ray pictures. (After C. C. Macklin.)

Movements. The alterations in form of the bronchial tree are shown in figure 593. Observe that during inspiration (1) the bronchi become longer and wider but undergo little, if any, angle change; and (2) the root of the lung moves downward and forward.

This root movement is of particular importance to the apex of the lung and to the part lying posterosuperior to the root which cannot expand either upward or backward, since the upper and posterior parts of the bony thorax are practically fixed. They can, however, expand in the opposite direction (downward and forward) provided the root moves in this direction. If for any reason the root is fixed, the apical region can hardly expand.

Elastic fibers form a longitudinal network within the tunica propria throughout the entire tracheobronchial tree and this network is probably by far the most efficient part of the recoil mechanism of the entire lung (Macklin).

Surface Anatomy in the Living. The data given in the text on the positions and levels of viscera and other structures with reference to the vertebrae, costae, and sternum are from observations made on the cadaver. Under dissecting room conditions the cadaver is supine; the elastic lungs have collapsed; the thorax is in the extreme phase of expiration, and the diaphragm, being relaxed, is forced cranially and dorsally by the abdominal viscera. Now, X-ray examinations of the living adult subject, particularly when in the erect posture, modify the cadaveric picture and show a general lowering of the viscera due to gravitational pull. Thus:

The Tracheal Bifurcation, both in the cadaver and in the supine living subject, lies at T. 4–5; but when erect it is commonly at T. 6 or even lower. Moreover, it descends during inspiration (*fig. 593*). During the 1st year of life it lies at T. 3 or 4; from the 2nd to 6th year at T. 4 or 5; and from the 7th to 12th year at T. 5 or 6.

The Domes of the Diaphragm fall nearly 1″ when the erect posture is assumed; similarly the *Aortic Arch* may sink below the superior mediastinum; and the *Heart* likewise descends (pp. 503–504).

The Oblique Fissure of the Lung, during life, is much lower than in the cadaver. Its posterior (upper) end lies deep to the 5th rib or 5th interspace; it follows the line of the 6th rib to its costochondral junction, which is 2″ from the sternal margin. On the left side it is a little higher and more vertical than on the right (Brock).

The Inferior Border of the Lung, which on p. 489 is said to cross ribs 6, 8, and 10, lies at a lower level, reaching its lowest when the patient is prone.

The Costal Reflexion of the Pleura is quite variable posteriorly. Instead of crossing the 12th rib near its neck, it may cross as low as its tip, i.e., it descends to the level of vertebra L. 2 (Lachman).

MECHANISM OF RESPIRATION

The two phases of respiration, *inspiration* and *expiration,* are brought about by the alternate increase and decrease in the three dimensions of the thoracic cavity. As the dimensions increase, air is drawn through the trachea and bronchi into the lungs, and blood is sucked into the thoracic veins, and thereby the formation of a vacuum is avoided. At the same time the capillaries in the lung dilate and, so, facilitate the pulmonary circulation; and any fluid in the neighborhood is encouraged into the thorax, e.g., lymph, the contents of an abscess.

At birth the ribs are horizontal and are, therefore, in the position of full inspiration; movement either upward or downward would be an expiratory act. At this age respiration is performed by the upward and downward piston-like action of the diaphragm and is said to be *abdominal in type.* By the end of the 2nd year the ribs are oblique, and by the 7th year respiration is largely performed by the ribs and is said to be *thoracic in type.*

During Quiet Inspiration the kidney-shaped unit (manubrium and right and left 1st costal arches) remains at rest.

The Intercostals cause the 2nd–7th costal arches, each of which hangs like the handle of an inverted bucket, to rotate at the costovertebral and costosternal joints; in consequence, their middle parts rise and their lower borders are everted. Hence, the transverse diameter of the chest increases, and the infrasternal angle widens.

The Intercostals at the same time cause the sternal ends of the arches to rise; in consequence, the body of the sternum is thrust forward and the anteroposterior diameter of the chest increases.

The position of the facets on the transverse processes prevents the vertebrosternal arches from being forced backward. The shape of the facets allows the rotary movement described (*fig. 554*).

The Diaphragm and the False Arches. The anterior and lateral portions of the diaphragm are attached to the costal margin, so they necessarily rise when the margin rises. The posteromedial portion is attached to the upper lumbar vertebral bodies, arcuate ligaments, and 12th ribs, and it is steadied by the Quadratus Lumborum. Owing to the intra-abdominal pressure, the right and left domes of the diaphragm are rounded when relaxed, and they rise above the level of the central tendon. When on inspiration the diaphragm contracts, its fibers shorten and straighten, and thereby enlarge the costodiaphragmatic recesses and cause the domes to descend. Consequently, the upper abdominal viscera, especially the pliable liver, stomach, spleen, and kidneys descend before the contracting diaphragm, and the muscles of the abdominal wall yield sufficiently to afford these viscera accommodation. Thus is the vertical diameter increased.

The three pairs of vertebrochondral ribs (8, 9, and 10) do not imitate the movements of the vertebrosternal ribs. Owing to the shape and position of the costotransverse facets they cannot rotate, but they can and do glide backward and upward (*fig. 554*). By this movement, which resembles a pair of curved spreading calipers opening, the transverse diameter of the lower part of the thorax and upper part of the abdomen increases. When the inspiration is deep, the anteroposterior diameter of the abdomen diminishes in the median plane but increases on each side. This results in a further widening of the infrasternal angle. For this, the diaphragm, acting against the resistance offered by the abdominal muscles, is responsible. It forces the upper abdominal contents laterally, and this causes the lower ribs to spread. (In an animal from which the abdominal viscera have been removed, the lower ribs are drawn inward.) Acting against the same resistance the diaphragm also raises the lower ribs; and the interchondral knobs transmit the upward thrust to the cartilages of the true ribs.

During inspiration the intercostal spaces widen, and during expiration they diminish. The tone and elasticity of the Intercostals prevents sucking in of the spaces; a fibrous membrane would not suffice here.

On Deeper Inspiration the movements described are amplified. The Scalene muscles raise the first and second costal arches and the sternal heads of the Sternomastoids raise the manubrium (Jones, Beargie, and Pauly). Perhaps the Levatores Costarum and the Serratus Posterior Superior assist. The Serratus Posterior Inferior and Quadratus Lumborum steady the lower ribs.

On still deeper or forced inspiration associated with shortness of breath (whether from exertion or disease) and when sneezing and coughing, the Pectoralis Minor (perhaps also the Pectoralis Major, and Serratus Anterior) assists in elevating the ribs. For the Pectoralis Minor to act, the scapula must first be fixed. In the quadruped, standing on all fours, fixation is already achieved. In man, in whom the forelimbs are free, the scapulae must be fixed either (1) by finding a purchase for the upper limbs, for example by grasping the arms of the chair in which one is sitting, or (2) by the muscular action of the Trapezius, Levator Scapulae, and Rhomboidei. The Erector Spinae and deep muscles of the back, by straightening the thoracic curvature, help still further to cause the ribs to open out.

The nostrils and glottis dilate rhythmically to allow of easier entrance of air.

Expiration is brought about by the elastic recoil of the lungs, Transversus Abdominis, and costal cartilages. The rotation that the ribs undergo at the costovertebral joints during inspiration involves twisting of the costal cartilages and widening of the costochondral angles. It is from this twisting and widening that the cartilages recoil. Deep or forced expiration brings into play the Oblique and Transverse Abdominal muscles, and perhaps the Iliocostalis and Latissimus Dorsi.

»» *Notes:* (1) The thoracic and abdominal types of respiration are usually not sharply demarcated but merge into each other, one or the other type predominating. By practice and exercise the type can be modified. (2) In quiet respiration the domes of the diaphragm move about half-an-inch. The region of the caval foramen remains stationary. (3) A certain intra-abdominal pressure is necessary for the upstroke of the piston-like action of the diaphragm. This is supplied by the muscles of the anterior abdominal wall (particularly the Transversus Abdominis). (4) In expressing the contents of the hollow abdominal viscera (i.e., during micturition, defecation, vomiting, and parturition) a deep inspiration is taken and is held by closing the glottis, while the abdominal muscles and the diaphragm act in concert.

Nerve Supply. The respiratory center is located diffusely in the reticular formation of the medulla oblongata. If the center is destroyed or if the spinal cord between the center and the origin of the phrenic nerves, which supply the diaphragm, is severed, respiration ceases. The normal stimulus to the center is the excess CO_2 in the circulating blood. Efferent impulses descend from the center to the motor nuclei of the phrenic (C. 3, 4, 5) and intercostal nerves (Th. 1–11) in the spinal cord and along these nerves to the diaphragm and intercostal muscles, causing them to contract. When the lung is distended, afferent impulses ascending in the vagus nerve inhibit further inspiration and provoke expiration.

The bronchial muscles (circular) are made to contract by the vagus nerves and to relax by the sympathetic.

Posture. Gravity may work with the diaphragm or against it, thus: the diaphragm rises highest and its excursion is greatest when the subject lies flat on his back with the foot of the bed raised; it is less high and the excursion is less when horizontal; still less when erect (the abdominal muscles are then antagonistic), still less when sitting down, because then the abdominal muscles are relaxed; and finally in persons whose abdominal muscles have lost their tone (e.g., cases of poliomyelitis, large umbilical herniae, visceroptosis), the diaphragm ceases to act and respiration becomes thoracic. When the subject lies (horizontally) on one side, the dome of the diaphragm of that side is higher and makes a greater excursion than the dome of the upper side.

Unless the head and neck are extended and fixed, the muscles that raise the pectoral girdle cannot act to advantage; in consequence, the Pectoralis Minor and other accessory muscles of inspiration that attach the girdle to the trunk cannot act. The weight of the upper limbs has then to be borne by the thorax.

Unless the thoracic region of the spine is extended, the costal arches cannot spread fully. So, with head and chin dropped, shoulders rounded, and back bent—a position that through faulty placing of pillows a patient can easily assume—the lungs are least well aerated.

CHAPTER **32**

HEART AND PERICARDIUM

Pericardium

Pericardium (Gk. Peri = around; Kardia = the heart) consists of an outer *fibrous sac*, lined with an inner *serous sac.* The heart and the roots of the great vessels lie inside the fibrous sac and invaginate the serous sac from behind (*fig. 594*). Hence, the serous pericardium has both a visceral and a parietal layer; whereas the fibrous pericardium has a parietal layer only. The visceral layer is known as *epicardium.*

The Fibrous Pericardium might be called the envelope of the middle mediastinum. Within it are the heart and also the roots of the eight great vessels that proceed to or from the four chambers of the heart. In man, the fibrous pericardium blends with the central tendon of the diaphragm; in other mammals, the infracardiac lobe of the right lung intervenes (*fig. 584*). The ascending aorta carries the pericardium upward beyond the heart to the level of the sternal angle,

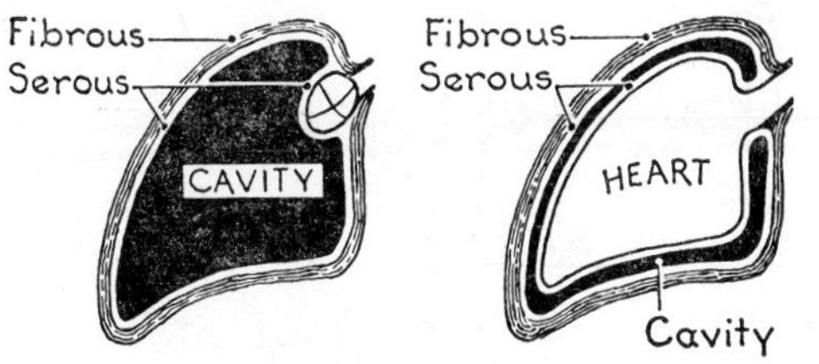

FIG. 594. To explain the layers of the pericardium

where it has a rounded summit. Its vertical diameter in the median plane is coextensive, therefore, with the body of the sternum, i.e., from sternomanubrial joint to xiphisternal joint. Its left border curves downward and laterally to the apex of the heart, passing just medial to the lig. arteriosum and, therefore, to the recurrent laryngeal nerve, which are outside the sac. The right border curves downward, crossing the s. v. cava obliquely below the entrance of the azygos vein, so part of the s. v. cava is without and part within the fibrous pericardium (*fig. 594.1*).

The Serous Pericardium (see p. 504).

»» INSTRUCTIONS. Obtain *five wicker sticks* 6–8 inches long. Pass (1) vertically upward through the i. v. cava, right atrium, s. v. cava, right brachiocephalic (innominate) vein and perhaps into the right internal jugular vein (*fig. 594.1*), (2) horizontally through the left pulmonary artery, and right pulmonary artery (3) horizontally through the left upper pulmonary vein, left atrium, and right upper pulmonary vein, and (4) horizontally through the left lower pulmonary vein, left atrium, and right lower pulmonary vein, and (5) up the esophagus.

If left in position and palpated from time to time, these sticks will assist greatly in obtaining a clear idea of the orientation and relationships of parts.

Contents of Pericardial Sac

HEART (L. Cor = the heart). This muscular pump is somewhat larger than a closed fist. It has four chambers, the *right* and *left atria* and the *right* and *left ventricles.* The atria are separated from the ventricles by a constriction that completely encircles the heart and is appropriately called the *coronary* (*atrioventricular*) *sulcus.* The ventricles are separated from each other by the *anterior* and *posterior interventricular* (*longitudinal*) *sulci.* The notched anterosuperior part of each atrium resembles a dog's ear and is called the *auricle* (L. auris = an ear.)

The heart has 3 surfaces: *sternocostal* (anterior), *diaphragmatic* (inferior), and *base* (posterior); it also has an *apex* (i.e., the lowest and leftmost point).

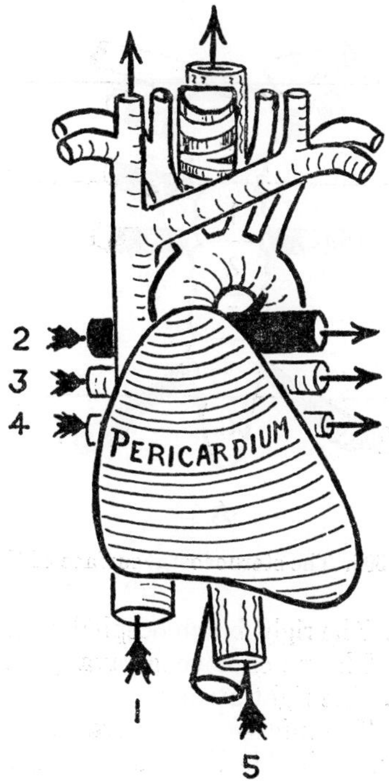

FIG. 594.1. The fibrous pericardium and the channels through which five wicker sticks have been passed.

Sternocostal Surface of Heart and Great Vessels. It is obviously of high importance to be able to plot the heart and great vessels on the skin of the living person.

»» INSTRUCTIONS. You should practice drawing them on paper; and, in order that the finished sketch shall be more or less to scale, first draw the *sternum:* The body, consisting of four sternebrae, is to be more than twice the length of the manubrium. Project horizontal lines at the levels of the upper and lower borders of the manubrium, and at the level of the xiphisternal joint. The region above the upper line is the neck; between the upper and intermediate lines, the superior mediastinum; between the intermediate and lower lines, the middle mediastinum; below the lower line, the abdomen. Insert the clavicles and the 1st, 3rd, and 6th cartilages (*fig. 595A*).

1. A vertical line drawn from the neck to the abdomen, less than a finger's breadth from the right margin of the sternum (*fig. 595B*), represents from above downward the *right borders* of:

a. The right internal jugular vein.

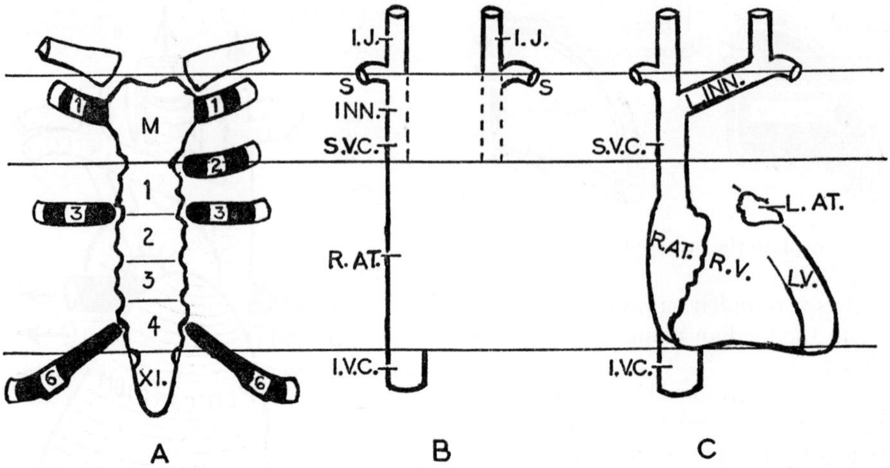

FIG. 595. The sternocostal surface of the heart and the great veins constructed on projection lines

b. The right brachiocephalic vein.
c. The superior vena cava (s. v. c.).
d. The right atrium.
e. The inferior vena cava (i. v. c.).

2. On each side the *internal jugular* and the *subclavian vein* unite behind the sternal end of the clavicle to form the brachiocephalic or innominate vein.

3. The *left brachiocephalic vein* passes obliquely behind the upper half of the manubrium and joins the right brachiocephalic vein to form the superior vena cava (*fig. 595C*).

4. The *superior vena cava* ends in the right atrium at the 3rd costal cartilage.

5. The *inferior vena cava* pierces the diaphragm at the level of the xiphisternal joint, and after a course of ½ inch enters the right atrium, at the level of the 6th costal cartilage.

6. A slight bulge or convexity in the line between the 3rd and 6th cartilages represents the right atrium, and also the *right border* of the heart.

7. An appropriately crenated, oblique line will define the *left margin of the right atrium* and at the same time the right part of the coronary (atrioventricular) sulcus.

8. The *inferior margin* of the heart extends from the i. v. cava, across the xiphisternal joint, and then slightly downward, to the apex of the heart, which is situated in the 5th left intercostal space or behind the 6th rib, 3½ inches from the median plane. One-third of the heart, therefore, lies to the right of the median plane; two-thirds to the left.

9. The *left margin* is rounded, and passes from the apex to the 2nd left interspace a finger's breadth from the sternal border.

10. The tip of the *left auricle* peeps round this margin in the 2nd interspace.

11. A line parallel to the left margin, and about one-third of the distance from it to the right margin, separates the right and left ventricles and represents the *anterior interventricular sulcus.* Portions of all four chambers are now outlined on this sternocostal surface. The portion of left ventricle appearing on this surface can almost be covered by a finger.

12. The *ascending aorta* (*fig. 596*) is the segment of the aorta lying within the pericardium, and therefore below the level of the sternal angle, i.e., behind the 1st sternebra. As the continuation of the left ventricle, it passes upward and *to the right* and overlaps the s. v. cava.

The *arch of the aorta* passes backward and to the left behind the lower half of the manubrium, and therefore below the level of the left brachiocephalic vein, to reach the lower border of the 4th thoracic vertebra on its left side. There, crossing the plane between the superior and posterior mediastina, it becomes the *descending aorta* (*fig. 596A*).

13. The *pulmonary trunk* (*fig. 596*), as the continuation of the right ventricle, passes

upward and *to the left* between the right and left auricles, which embrace it. It lies in front of and conceals the root of the aorta. As it pierces the parietal pericardium below the aortic arch, it divides, like the letter T, into *right* and *left pulmonary arteries;* they pass to the roots of the lungs (*fig. 596B*).

Earlier we saw that the descending aorta passes behind the root of the left lung and that the s. v. cava passes in front of the upper part of the root of the right lung, so the courses of the right and left pulmonary arteries are evident—the *left* passes anterior to the descending aorta; the *right* posterior to the ascending aorta and s. v. cava (*fig. 594.1*).

»» Observe that the stick passed through the right and left pulmonary arteries inclines downwards from the left 2nd to the right 3rd cartilage; for later it will be seen that these arteries define the upper limit of the heart.

14. The *ligamentum arteriosum,* being the fibrous remains of the ductus arteriosus or posterior segment of the left primitive 6th aortic arch (*fig. 625*), passes from the *left* pulmonary artery to the "aortic arch" beyond the origin of the subclavian artery. Indeed, it continues the direction of the stem of the pulmonary trunk (*fig. 40*). It lies outside the pericardium.

Surface Anatomy of the Heart. Figure 597*A* depicts the surface anatomy of the heart of an average adult cadaver lying on its back. During life, however,

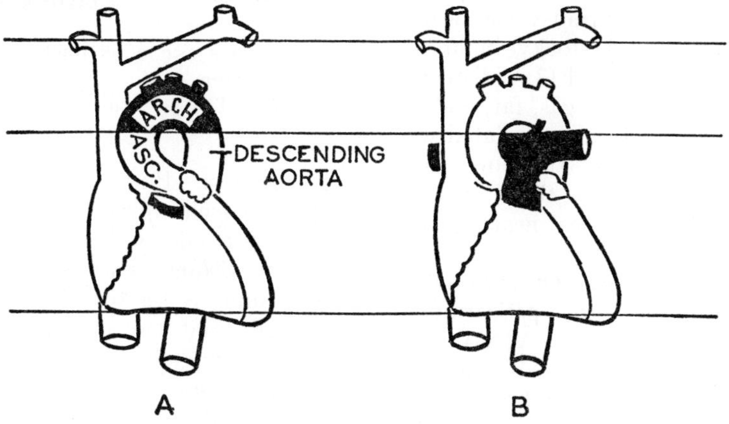

FIG. 596. *A*, the aorta. *B*, the pulmonary trunk and arteries

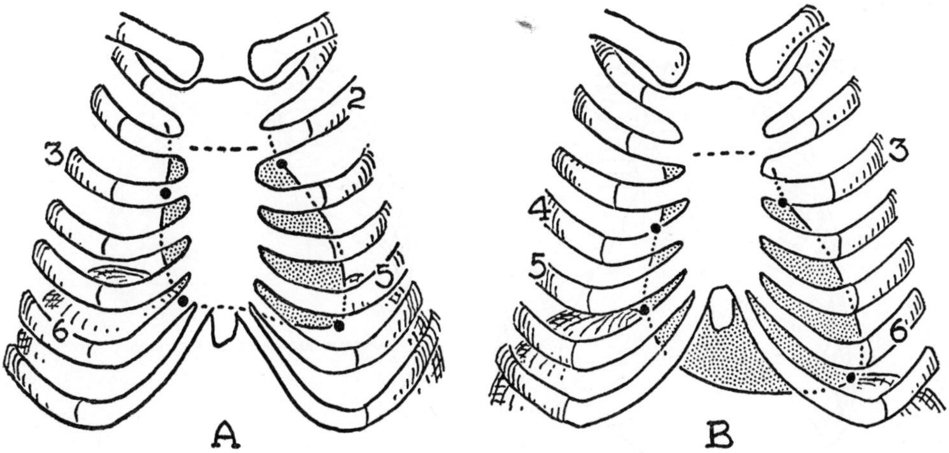

In the supine cadaver

In the erect living subject

Fig. 597. The surface anatomy of the heart. (From Lachman, after Mainland and Gordon.)

and standing erect, X-rays give the lower position seen in figure 597*B*. The inferior border of the heart crosses the median plane 5.5 cm. below the xiphisternal joint. From this it would appear that the diaphragm passes from the xiphoid first dorsally and caudalward—not dorsally and cranialward. While recumbent, the cadaveric position is almost achieved, except for the inferior border which is now 3.5 cm. below the xiphisternal joint (Mainland and Gordon.)

The pericardium is attached to the diaphragm, so the heart must move with the diaphragm. Accordingly, deep inspiration and expiration have most effect on the position and shape of the heart (*fig. 598*). On inspiration it is a "vertical heart"; on expiration it is a "transverse heart."

Further, (1) a broad stocky build, (2) the recumbent position, and (3) a distended abdomen (e.g., pregnancy, gas, fat, and the large liver of childhood) are associated with a high diaphragm and, therefore, with transverse hearts; whereas those who are tall and slender have vertical hearts (Lachman).

Serous Pericardium. Observe these three points about the serous pericardium:

1. The S. V. Cava and I. V. Cava are clothed in serous pericardium in the same fashion as the ascending and descending colons are clothed in peritoneum—in front and at the sides, but they are bare posteriorly (*fig. 599*).

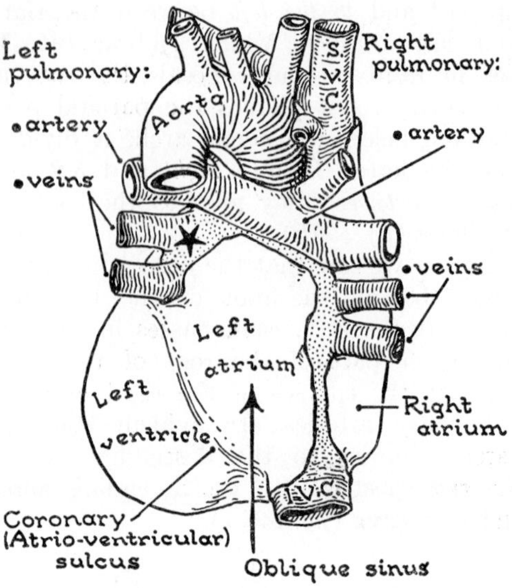

★ Indicates site of contact of left bronchus with left atrium.

Fig. 599. The posterior aspect of the heart

2. Oblique Pericardial Sinus. Two fingers, passed upward behind the heart, on the left side of the i.v. cava, enter a recess, the *oblique pericardial sinus* (*fig. 600*).

The sinus is limited *at the sides* by the two right and two left pulmonary veins (which having pierced the fibrous pericardium, soon enter the left atrium) as well as by the i. v. cava on the right. *In front* is the left atrium (*fig. 599*). Immediately *behind* is the esophagus.

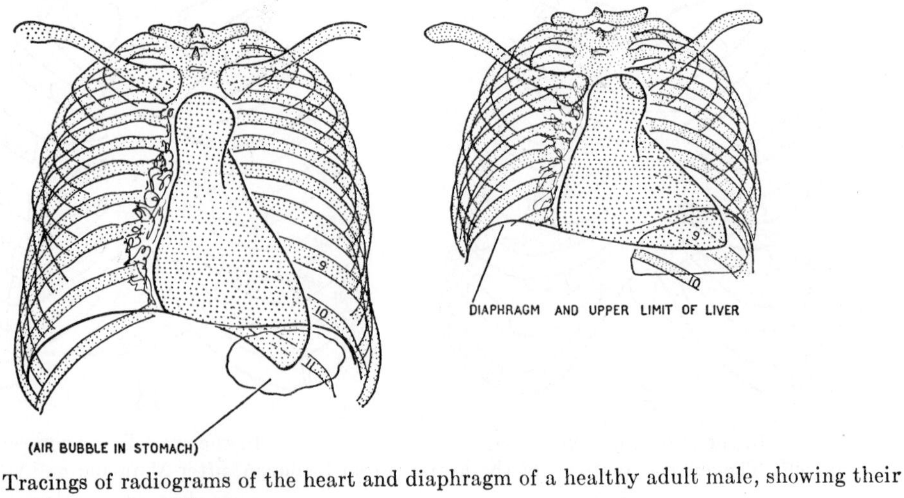

Fig. 598. Tracings of radiograms of the heart and diaphragm of a healthy adult male, showing their ever changing shapes and positions.

»» If you cut across the i.v. cava as low as possible within the pericardial sac, raise the heart, and then cut vertically through the parietal pericardium behind the oblique sinus, you will expose the esophagus and the descending aorta, situated between the two lungs (*fig. 582*). Then you will recognise that the thickness of the pericardium and wall of the esophagus is all that separates the left atrium from the food you swallow.

3. TRANSVERSE PERICARDIAL SINUS. The stems of the pulmonary trunk and ascending aorta, lying within a single sleeve of serous pericardium, can be grasped and encircled by your index finger and thumb. They form the *anterior boundary* of a potential space, the transverse pericardial sinus. The *posterior and side boundaries* of this concave space are the upper portions of the atria, their auricles, and the end of the s.v. cava.

»» *To explore the sinus.* The left index should be insinuated, from the right side, between s.v. cava and aorta and encouraged to the left until it emerges between left auricle and pulmonary trunk. If the two great arteries be now cut across and displaced, the limits of the sinus will be seen.

The Upper Border of the Atria, which is also the upper border of the heart, should be exposed (*fig. 599*). This is done by rendering prominent the stick traversing the right and left upper pulmonary veins, and then incising the serous pericardium along it. Its course is slightly oblique.

The Diaphragmatic (Inferior) Surface of the Heart, formed by the ventricles, is separated from the liver and stomach by the diaphragm. The posterior interventricular sulcus divides this surface into a right one-third and a left two-thirds.

The Base (Posterior Surface) of the heart is formed by the atria and variably by the left ventricle (*fig. 599*). It is quadrangular. Like the diaphragmatic surface, it is divided into a right one-third and a left two-thirds, the dividing line running vertically from the i. v. cava to the two right pulmonary veins. The right and left pulmonary arteries run along its upper border; the coronary venous sinus, lying in the coronary sulcus, runs along, or just above, its lower border. The pericardium separates this surface from the esophagus, the descending aorta, and on each side of these, the right and left lungs (*fig. 582*).

Sulci (*fig. 602*). The **coronary sulcus** (atrioventricular sulcus) completely encircles the heart between the atria and the ventricles.

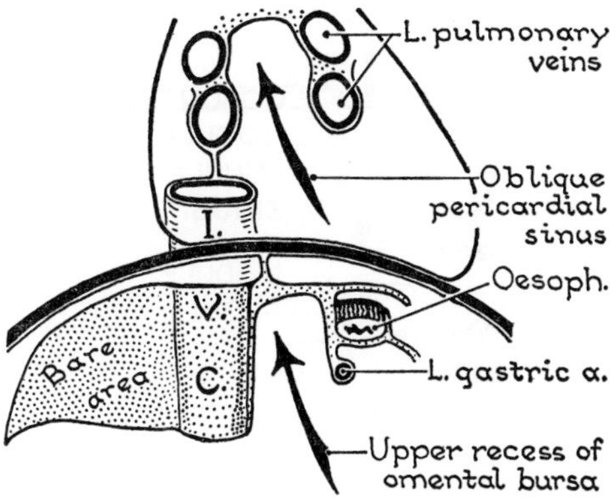

FIG. 600. The oblique pericardial sinus and the upper recess of the omental bursa, compared.

Follow it from in front of the i. v. cava, round the inferior margin, upward across the sternocostal surface between the right atrium and the right ventricle, through the transverse pericardial sinus, and between the left auricle and left ventricle, to the left margin of the heart. The remainder of its course may be indicated by means of a (*dotted*) *line* joining the point where it crosses the left margin to where it crosses the inferior margin (*fig. 602*). This is seen when the apex is raised up.

The **anterior interventricular sulcus** extends from the coronary sulcus at the left of the root of the pulmonary trunk, downwards across the sternocostal surface, around the inferior border ¾″ to the right of the apex. There it becomes continuous with the **posterior interventricular sulcus,** which continues backward on the diaphragmatic surface to meet the coronary sulcus again at a point called "the *crux*." The main cardiac vessels, including the coronary sinus, occupy the sulci and are often embedded in fat.

Ascending Aorta and Pulmonary Trunk. These lie within the fibrous pericardium behind the 1st sternebra, the pulmonary trunk extending beyond its left margin to the 2nd intercostal space. Having a common derivation from the truncus arteriosus, they lie within a common sleeve of serous pericardium. The upper parts of the atria, their auricles, and the entering s. v. cava embrace the two great arteries from behind but fail to meet in

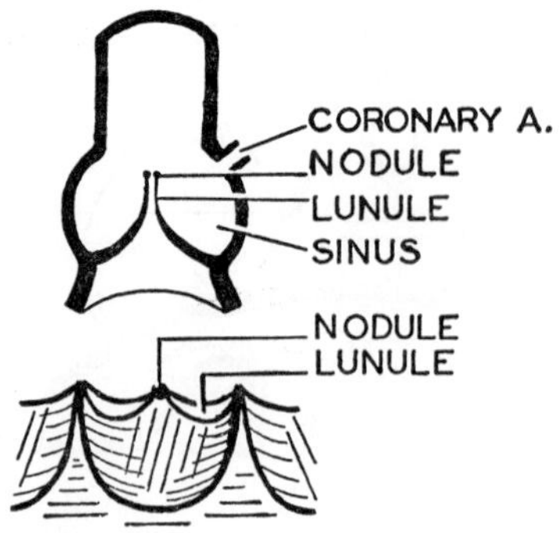

FIG. 601. The aortic valve: on sagittal section, opened up.

front of them. There the pleurae and lungs cover them.

The **pulmonary trunk,** 2″ long, begins in front of the aorta and passes semispirally (upward, backward, and to the left) around it until it reaches the concavity of the aortic arch where it bifurcates into the right and the left pulmonary artery. The stems of the right and left coronary arteries pass forwards, one on each side of the root of the pulmonary trunk (*fig. 602*).

The *right* and *left pulmonary arteries* lie along the upper borders of the atria and of the upper pulmonary veins (*fig. 599*) like the cross-stroke of the letter T, set slightly obliquely. Behind the right and left arteries lie the bronchi and the inferior tracheobronchial lymph nodes. These nodes exclude the esophagus from contact with the arteries (*fig. 633*).

The **ascending aorta** begins behind the pulmonary trunk and passes obliquely upward, forward, and to the right to reach the right margin of the sternum. Being within the pericardial sac, it must lie below the level of the sternal angle. Its posterior relations are the upper parts of the atria and the left margin of the s. v. cava, the right pulmonary artery (and slightly the right bronchus).

On cross-section the outline of the ascending aorta is seen to be not circular but elliptical, for where the current of blood expelled from the left ventricle beats against its right wall, it is dilated, and is known as the **bulb of the aorta.**

Aortic Valve and Valve of the Pulmonary Trunk (Pulmonary Valve). The aortic valve lies ¼″ lower than the valve of the pulmonary trunk, is posteromedial to it, and faces a different direction (*fig. 602*). The aortic valve faces upward, forward, and to the right; the valve of the pulmonary trunk faces upward, backward, and to the left. Both valves prevent back flow of blood into the ventricles, and both have three semilunar cusps, the aortic cusps naturally being stronger than the pulmonary cusps.

Each *cusp* has a fibrous basis covered on both surfaces with endothelium. At the middle of the free edge of each cusp there is a *fibrous nodule*, and on each side of the nodule there is a thin, crescentic area, the *lunule* (*fig. 601*). When the valve closes, the nodules meet in the center of the lumen and the ventricular surfaces of the lunules of contiguous cusps are applied to each other. The lunules may be fenestrated.

At the root of both of the arteries there are three dilatations, the *sinuses;* one is placed external to each cusp. But for these sinuses, the cusps would stick to the wall of the artery when the valve is open. The pressure of blood in the sinuses after ventricular systole (contraction) closes the valve.

The aortic orifice and the first quarter of an inch of the aorta are fibrous and not dilatable, so the valve remains competent. The disposition of the cusps is explained on page 510 (*figs. 610* and *619*).

Blood Supply of the Heart:

1. Coronary arteries,
2. Cardiac veins,
3. Collateral circulation—
   a. cardiac,
   b. extracardiac.

The Right and Left Coronary Arteries supply the heart. They spring from the (primitive) right and left aortic sinuses (*fig. 610*) usually just below the level of the free edges of the cusps. The three cusps of the aortic valve are the right cusp, the left cusp, and the posterior or noncoronary cusp.

The two coronary arteries swing forward, one on each side of the root of the

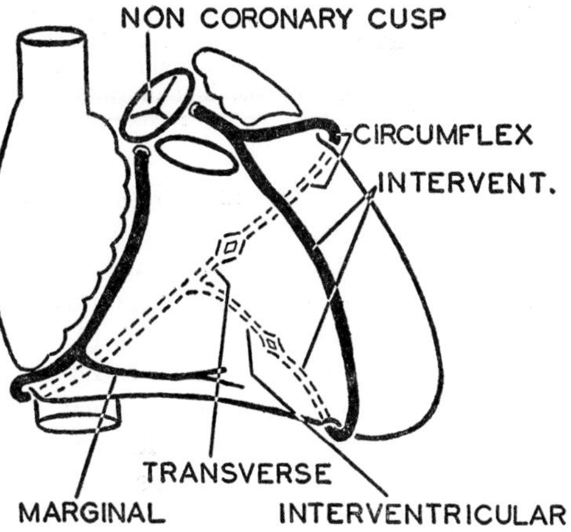

FIG. 602. The coronary arteries

pulmonary trunk, sheltered by the corresponding auricle. They occupy the coronary (atrioventricular) and interventricular sulci (*fig. 602*). So, if you can picture the sternocostal surface of the heart, the courses of the arteries will present no difficulty.

The **left coronary artery** divides into: (1) an *anterior interventricular branch* which descends in the anterior interventricular sulcus to the inferior margin of the heart, where it turns round into the posterior interventricular sulcus, and (2) a *circumflex branch* which runs in the coronary sulcus round the left margin of the heart and gives off a *left marginal branch,* which runs down the left margin of the left ventricle.

The **right coronary artery** descends in the right part of the coronary sulcus, turns round the inferior margin of the heart in it, and divides into: (1) a *posterior interventricular branch* which descends in the posterior interventricular sulcus to meet the interventricular branch of the left coronary artery, usually in the lower ⅓ of that sulcus, and (2) a *transverse branch,* which, continuing in the coronary sulcus, meets the circumflex branch of the left coronary artery. It sends (3) a large *right marginal branch* along the inferior margin of the right ventricle.

The *left coronary artery* supplies—the anterior part of the interventricular septum and the adjacent part of the right ventricle, as well as the anterior surface, rounded left margin and a small part of the inferior surface of the left ventricle (*fig. 603*).

The *right coronary artery* supplies—the remainder of the right ventricle, the posterior part of the interventricular septum, and the extensive remaining part of the left ventricle.

Variations. (1) The posterior interventricular artery springs from the left coronary art. via its circumflex branch in about 10 per cent of hearts. (2) Accessory coronary arteries are not uncommon, but most of them are very fine. (3) For a single coronary art. to supply the entire heart is rare.

The Cardiac Veins mostly accompany the arteries in the sulci and tend to lie superficial to them (*fig. 604*). Five of the seven cardiac veins mentioned below end in the coronary sinus.

The **Coronary Sinus** is derived from the left horn of the sinus venarum; it is about 1½″ long, lies in the coronary sulcus at the lower end of the oblique pericardial sinus, and opens into the right atrium at the left of the orifice of the i. v. cava. At its left end it receives the companion of the left coronary artery, called the *great cardiac vein.* This vein follows first the course of the interventricular branch of the left coronary artery and then the circumflex branch. The companion of the right marginal artery, called the *small cardiac vein,* enters the right end of the coronary sinus. The companion of the posterior interventricular artery, called the *middle cardiac vein,* ends in the coronary sinus; so do the *posterior ventricular veins* from the diaphragmatic surface of the left ventricle. The *oblique vein* is a twig that lies behind the left atrium and ends in the coronary sinus.

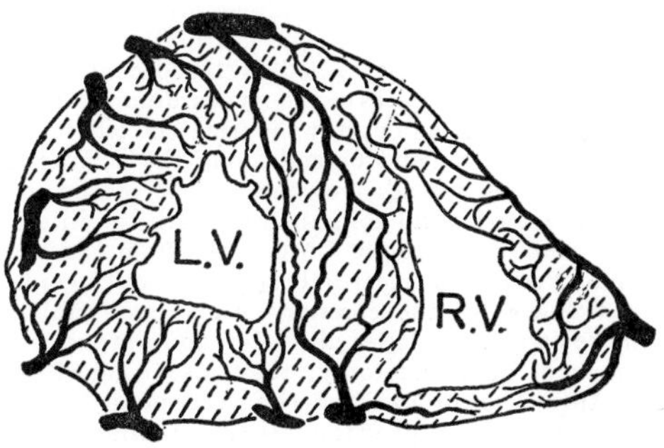

FIG. 603. Transverse section of ventricles showing branches of coronary arteries plunging into the heart substance. (After Gross and Kugel.)

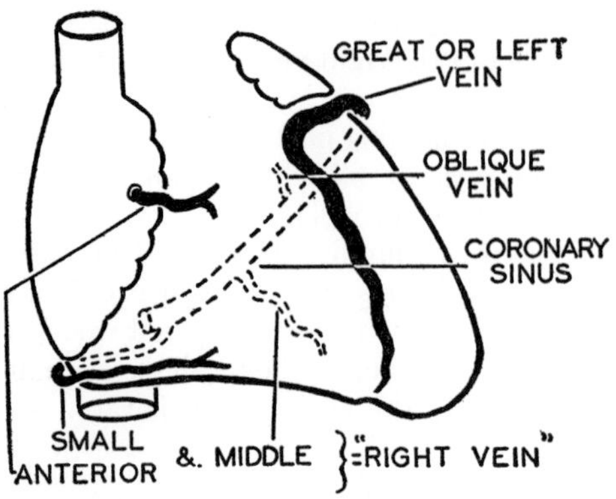

FIG. 604. The cardiac veins

»» Developmentally, the oblique vein is the terminal part of the primitive left common cardinal vein.

One or two large *anterior cardiac veins* pass from the front of the right ventricle, across the coronary sulcus, and open directly into the right atrium.

The mouths of the great and small cardiac veins commonly have single cusped valves, but these are rarely competent. Tiny veins, *venae cordis minimae* (*Thebesian veins*) begin in the heart wall and open directly into the chambers of the heart.

»» **Comparative Anatomy. The Myocardial Circulation** can best be understood by reference to the facts of *Comparative Anatomy* and of embryology. Thus, the primitive vertebrate heart (the lamprey) is a nonvascular heart—there are no coronary vessels, and the myocardium is spongy or trabecular. It is nourished entirely by the blood within its chambers passing through intertrabecular spaces which extend right out to the epicardium. The same is true of the ventricle of the heart of the amphibian, except that its bulbus cordis has a cortex of compact muscle with a vascular supply. In the heart of the reptile the proportion of compact cortical muscle is greater; the coronary vessels are more important; venae minimae are present.

The developing mammalian heart (the rabbit) is spongy, and early is nourished by blood contained in the intertrabecular spaces of the myocardium. Coronary veins appear later as outgrowths from the left horn of the sinus venarum and extend along the sulci. From them, branches spread over the surface of the myocardium, enter it, and communicate with the intertrabecular sinusoidal spaces. Outgrowths from the endocardium give rise to epicardial capillaries which connect with branches of the coronary veins (and probably with the coronary arteries also later) to form the venae minimae of adult anatomy; they also connect with each other. The coronary arteries then sprout from the future aorta, spread over the heart, and unite with the capillary network already formed by the veins and intertrabecular spaces in the developing myocardium. With further development the intertrabecular spaces of the ventricles are for the most part reduced to capillaries and, being incorporated with the arteries and veins, persist as an integral part of the adult coronary circulation. The accompanying scheme (*fig. 605*), which indicates how the human (mammalian) myocardium is irrigated, now becomes intelligible (R. T. Grant and L. E. Viko).

Numerous investigators, using media of different viscosities and at different pressures, have injected the coronary arteries, cardiac veins, and venae minimae and seem to have established the facts that (1) when physiological saline solution or India ink is perfused through a coronary artery most (about 90%) escapes into the lumen of the heart via the venae minimae and very little passes through the capillaries to the coronary sinus. (2) Similarly, when a vein is perfused most escapes by venae minimae and a little passes through the capillaries to the arteries. (3) A fluid too viscous to pass through the capillary bed will, when injected into an artery (or vein), escape into the lumen of the heart vià the venae minimae. (4) A fluid too viscous to flow out through the arteries may yet, when injected into a coronary vein, enter the heart via the venae minimae. Evidently, then, the pathway from cardiac vein via venae minimae to the lumen of the heart is wider than from coronary artery via venae minimae to the lumen, and this in turn is wider than the passage through the capillary bed. (5) It is found that when particles (e.g., carborundum), too large to traverse either the capillaries or venae minimae of the heart or the capillaries of the lung, are injected during life into the external jugular vein of the dog, they accumulate

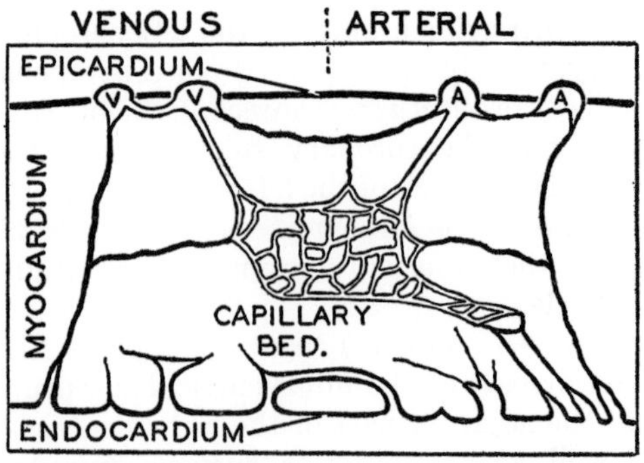

FIG. 605. Scheme of the myocardial circulation. (After Batson.)

in large numbers in the coronary sinus and in the veins on the surface of the heart. To get there they must have taken a retrograde course in the veins (Batson).

Collateral Circulation. (1) *Cardiac.* Branches of the coronary arteries seldom anastomose on the epicardiac surface of the heart. In the myocardium there are rich anastomoses, but the vessels taking part are small.

»» Intercoronary arterial anastomoses were found in less than 10 per cent of apparently normal hearts, in 40 per cent of anemic hearts, and in 100 per cent of hearts with old coronary occlusion (Zoll, Wessler, and Schlesinger). Evidently the anastomoses can enlarge.

(2) *Extracardiac anastomoses.* If both coronary arteries are obstructed, there is an extracardiac collateral circulation to be called upon, but it may not effectively answer the call. Thus, injections of India ink into healthy coronary arteries in part follow the vasa vasorum and vessels in the tunica adventitia of the aorta as far as the diaphragm, and of the pulmonary arteries as far as the lungs. Other anastomosing twigs pass through the pericardium with the four pulmonary and two caval veins to anastomose with branches of the internal thoracic, bronchial, and phrenic arteries.

Since the coronary arteries and cardiac veins have no adequate valves, it is not impossible that blood may take a retrograde course in the veins, irrigate the myocardium, and enter each of the four chambers via the venae cordis minimae.

Development of the Heart. The following notes may assist in the appreciation of the inter-relationships of the various parts of the heart and explain certain anomalies.

Elongation of the Tubular Heart. The primitive tubular heart received blood at its caudal end and discharged it from its cephalic end. This tubular heart had *five sacculations*—sinus venarum, primitive atrium, primitive ventricle, bulbus cordis, and truncus arteriosus (*fig. 606*). The constriction between the primitive atrium and ventricle becomes the *coronary or atrioventricular sulcus.*

Just as the intestine has a (dorsal) mesentery, so the tubular heart had a *dorsal mesocardium.* Now, when the developing intestine

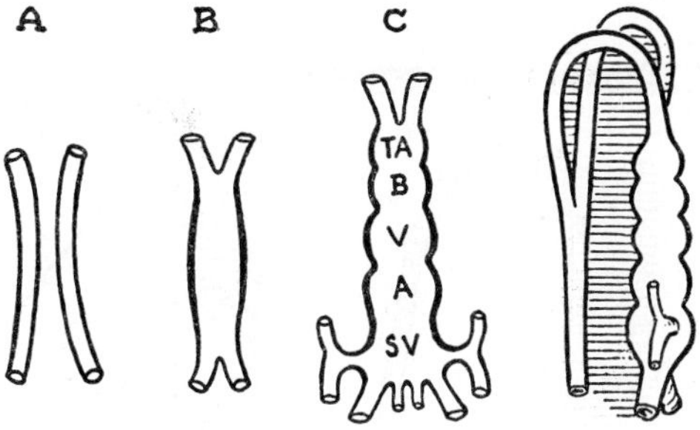

Fig. 606. Scheme of the development of the tubular heart.

became much too long for the peritoneal cavity, it became convoluted. When the cardiac tube became too long for the pericardial cavity, it formed an S-shaped loop (*fig. 607*). Its two caudal segments (sinus venarum and atrium) and the entering veins came to lie dorsal to the three cephalic segments of which the last (truncus arteriosus) divided to form the ascending aorta and the pulmonary trunk. Hence, the atria and the entering veins of adult anatomy lie posterior to the ventricles and the emerging arteries (*fig. 608*). The atria, cramped as it were for space and prevented from enlarging forward, expand laterally on both sides of the truncus (aorta and pulmonary trunk), embracing it.

Perforation of Dorsal Mesocardium. In consequence of a perforation in the mesocardium, the *transverse pericardial sinus* appears and the truncus arteriosus finds itself enveloped in a tube or sleeve of visceral pericardium. Hence, when a septum divides the truncus into two, both resulting vessels (aorta and pulmonary trunk) lie within a single pericardial sleeve in front of the transverse sinus.

Oblique Pericardial Sinus (p. 504).

Spiral Septum in Truncus Arteriosus. The fact that a spiral septum develops within the truncus explains the twisted courses of the pulmonary trunk and ascending aorta around each other (*fig. 609*). The course of the spiral septum was such that its cardiac end bisected the right and left lateral cusps of the primitive four-cusped valve of the truncus arteriosus; hence, the relative positions of the definitive

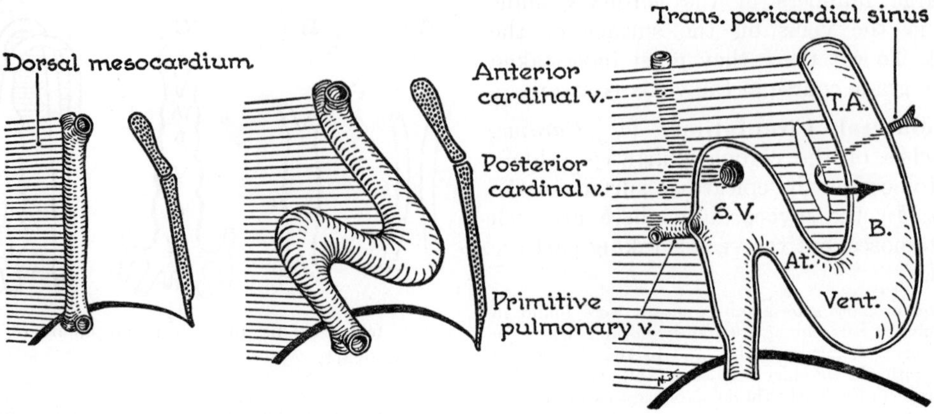

FIG. 607. The elongated tubular heart becomes "S-shaped"

cusps of the aortic valve and valve of the pulmonary trunk (*fig. 610*).

The upper end of the septum left the aorta connected to the upper 5 paired primitive aortic arches, and the pulmonary trunk connected to the 6th or lowest pair (see *fig. 625*). That is why the pulmonary trunk ends by bifurcating below the level of the definitive aortic arch.

AXIAL ROTATION OF THE HEART. The heart undergoes a slight rotation to the left on its long axis (opposite in direction to the rotation of the stomach). In consequence of this, (1) the right atrium is conspicuous at the right margin of the heart and anteriorly; the left atrium is conspicuous posteriorly; (2) the right ventricle is largely in front and slightly inferior; the left ventricle is largely inferior and slightly in front; and, as will be seen later, (3) the interatrial and interventricular septa come to face forward and to the right (and backward and to the left); so do both cusps of the mitral valve and the septal cusp of the tricuspid valve, for these three cusps are approximately parallel to the septum; and lastly (4) the cusps of the valves of the two great arteries, which were originally disposed anteriorly, posteriorly, to right, and to left (*fig. 610*), share in the rotation.

Terminology of the Valvulae or Cusps. Confusing terms are often applied to the cusps of the aortic valve. It is simplest to relate the cusps to the coronary arteries. Figure 610 makes clear that there is a

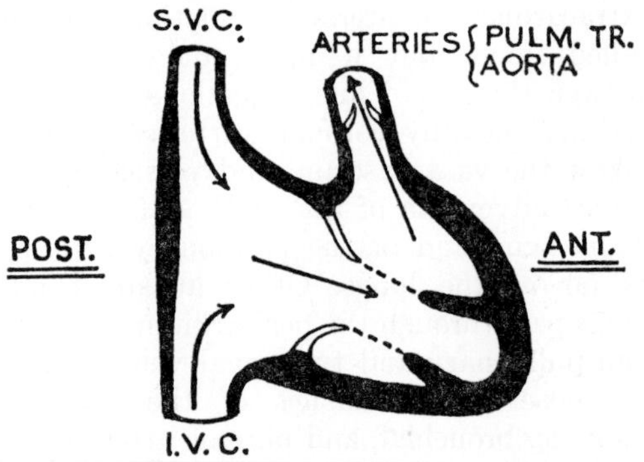

FIG. 608. Diagram of heart in sagittal section to show that the atria and entering veins are posterior to the ventricles and emerging arteries.

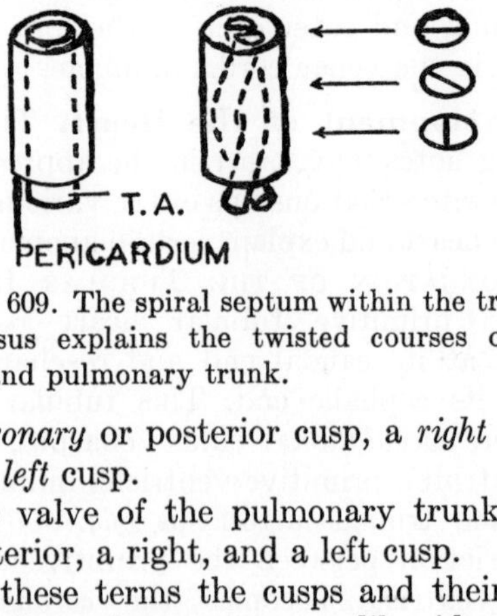

FIG. 609. The spiral septum within the truncus arteriosus explains the twisted courses of the aorta and pulmonary trunk.

noncoronary or posterior cusp, a *right* cusp, and a *left* cusp.

The valve of the pulmonary trunk, has an anterior, a right, and a left cusp.

By these terms the cusps and their corresponding sinuses are readily identified irrespective of whether the heart is in the body or removed from it.

PRIMITIVE VEINS (*fig. 611*). The cardiac

end of the right anterior cardinal vein plus the entire common cardinal vein become the sup. vena cava, and the thoracic part of the posterior cardinal vein (largely supracardinal) becomes the azygos vein.

This early arrangement is symmetrical until cross-communicating veins (left brachiocephalic and hemiazygos veins) develop and shunt the blood from the left side of the upper half of the body to the right, whereupon breaks appear in the left posterior cardinal system of veins and the left common cardinal vein disappears.

Similarly, in the lower half of the body cross-shunts (left common iliac, left lumbar, and left renal veins) allow most of the remainder of the left posterior cardinal system of veins to disappear.

The left horn of the sinus venarum ceases to develop *pari passu* with the right horn, and becomes known as the *coronary sinus*. So, although the coronary sinus plays the part of a vein, it was not as a vein that it developed, but as a part of the heart.

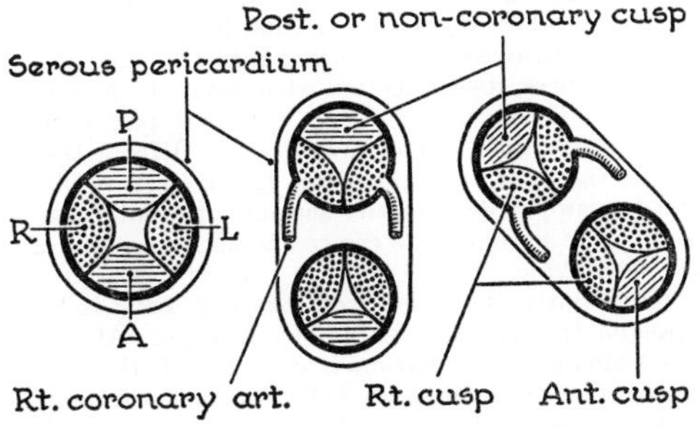

FIG. 610. The four-cusped valve of the truncus splits to form two valves, each with three cusps. Axial rotation occurs, but it need not affect the nomenclature.

When the left s.v. cava persists, it ends—as expected—in the coronary sinus; and in its course it bears the same relation to the root of the left lung as the (right) s. v. cava bears to the right root, i.e., it crosses in front.

Chambers of the Heart

Right Atrium. EXTERIOR. The right atrium extends from the orifice of the s. v. cava behind the 3rd right costal cartilage to the orifice of the i. v. cava behind the 6th right costal cartilage. It forms the whole of the rounded right border of the heart; it also forms parts of the sternocostal surface and base (*fig. 595*). It is demarcated from the right ventricle by the coronary sulcus. The parietal pericardium intervenes between it and the right phrenic nerve. It developed from the right half of the sinus venarum and right half of the primitive atrium which merged to form a single chamber. The line of mergence is indicated on the surface by a slight groove, the *sulcus terminalis*, which extends from the front of the s. v. cava to the front of the i. v. cava.

INTERIOR (*figs. 612* and *613*). On opening the rather cubical atrium, a ridge, the *crista terminalis*, is seen to correspond in position

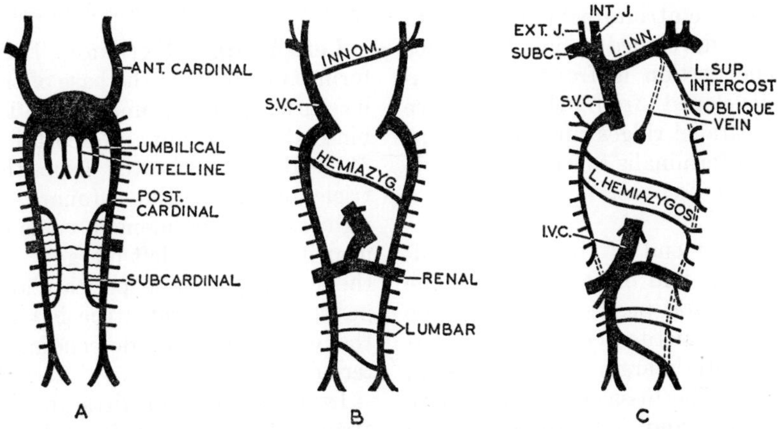

FIG. 611. Veins. *A*, six veins join the sinus venarum. *B*, cross-communications appear. *C*, only two of the six veins survive. They become caval veins. (After Arey.)

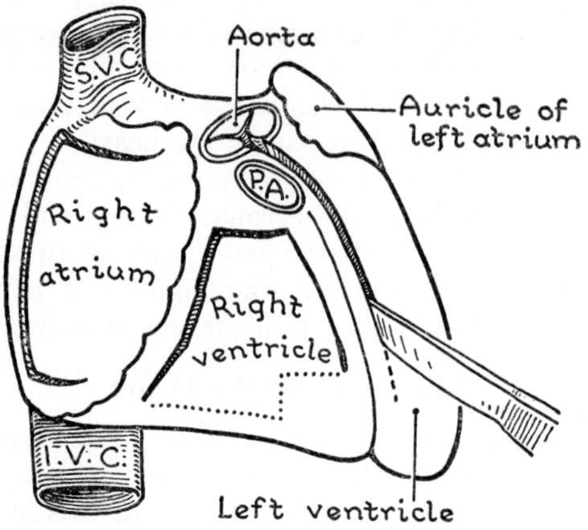

FIG. 612. Incisions for opening into the chambers of the heart.

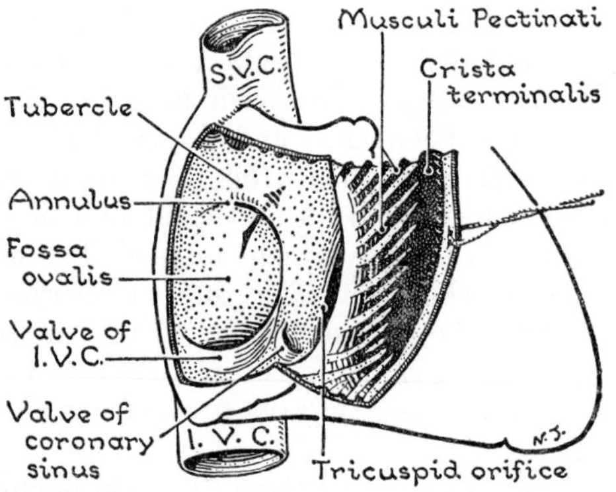

FIG. 613. The interior of the right atrium

to the sulcus terminalis on the exterior. The portion of the atrium behind the crista is smooth; it developed from the sinus venarum. The portion in front is trabeculated; it developed from the primitive atrium. The parallel ridges running forward from the crista terminalis toward the auricle are the *musculi pectinati* (L. pecten = a comb).

From the lower end of the crista terminalis a prominent fold of endocardium, the *valve of the i. v. cava,* passes in front of the orifice of the i. v. cava to become continuous with the crescentic margin of a depression, the *fossa ovalis.* The fossa ovalis is the size of a thumb nail and is situated on the interatrial septum, which forms the medial wall of the right atrium. The right atrioventricular or *tricuspid orifice,* takes the place of an anterior wall (*fig. 608*). The *orifice of the coronary sinus* opens between the orifice of the i. v. cava and the tricuspid orifice. It is guarded by a fold, detached from the valve of the i. v. cava. This fold, often perforated like a piece of lace, is the *valve of the coronary sinus.* If the handle of the knife or tip of the forceps be passed up the i. v. cava from its cut abdominal end, it will be arrested by the crescentic upper margin of the fossa ovalis. But in about 25 per cent of cases it will pass onward through a valve-like slit in the septum, the *foramen ovale,* into the left atrium. This is the course much of the blood took until birth.

»» **The History of the Foramen Ovale** is this: an anteroposterior partition, the *septum primum,* grew downward from the roof of the primitive common atrial chamber dividing it into right and left atria (*fig. 614*). But, before its lower end fused with the anterior and posterior endocardial cushions that divided the common primitive atrioventricular orifice into the tricuspid and mitral orifices, its connection with the roof was severed, giving it a free upper edge. A second partition, the *septum secundum,* then grew downward from the roof of the right atrium till its free lower edge overlapped the free upper edge of the septum primum. This free lower edge becomes the crescentic upper margin of the foramen ovale.

Until birth the blood from the i. v. cava is largely directed through this valve-like foramen. After birth the pulmonary circulation is established, the pressure in the left atrium rises, and the flap valve is closed.

Variations. In about 75 per cent of individuals the opposed surfaces fuse. In 25 per cent of individuals the edges of the primary and secondary septa overlap but fail to fuse, so the foramen is patent anatomically, though closed physiologically (*fig. 41*). Rarely the edges of the septa fail to meet; the result is a foramen patent both anatomically and physiologically. In consequence, the pulmonary circulation is disturbed.

Left Atrium. EXTERIOR. The left atrium forms two-thirds of the base of the heart and its auricle peeps round the left border behind the 2nd left intercostal space (*fig. 599*). It is demarcated from the left ventricle below by the coronary sulcus. The right and left pulmonary veins open into it near its right and left margins, and between them is the oblique pericardial sinus. The pericardium separates the left atrium from the esophagus and descending aorta posteriorly.

INTERIOR. There is little to see inside this atrium. The auricle is trabeculated; the rest of the cubical cavity is smooth. The mouths of the four pulmonary veins open

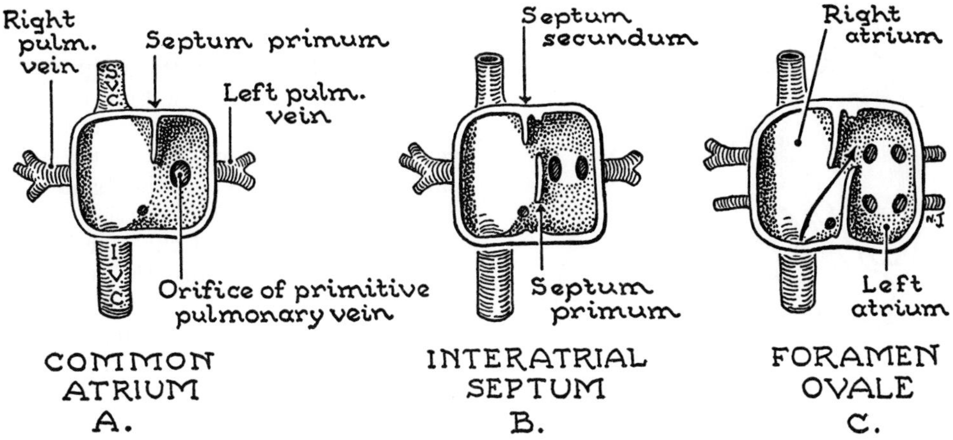

FIG. 614. Development of the left atrium. Incorporation of the stem of the primitive "common pulmonary vein." The history of the foramen ovale.

on the posterior wall; the left atrioventricular or *mitral orifice* replaces the anterior wall. The interatrial septum is set obliquely; hence, two-thirds of the left atrium and only one-third of the right atrium lie posteriorly (*fig. 615*). The foramen ovale, when patent, can be seen.

» **History.** The trabeculated part of the left atrium is derived from the left half of the primitive atrium. The smooth part is formed thus: the primitive pulmonary vein, draining both lungs, passed forward through the dorsal mesocardium and joined the left atrium (*fig. 614*). Its stem and primary branches then became incorporated in the definitive left atrial wall and formed its smooth part. From this it will be understood that the number of pulmonary veins opening into the atrium may be either decreased or increased. Hence, the left atrium, like the right atrium, has a double origin. The left half of the sinus venarum becomes the coronary sinus, and does not contribute to the formation of the left atrium.

The pericardial cavity extends upward into the widening dorsal mesocardium, which now transmits the two right and two left pulmonary veins, and separates them. The recess thus formed is the *oblique pericardial sinus* (*fig. 599*). Clearly, it corresponds on the exterior of the left atrium to the smooth part of the interior (*fig. 614C*).

Ventricles. The ventricles, right and left, lie in front of the atria (*fig. 608*). They form the apex of the heart, the entire inferior margin and diaphragmatic surface (*fig. 599*), most of the left margin and sternocostal surface, and a trivial part of the base below the coronary sulcus.

WALLS. On cross-section it is seen that the thickness of the walls of the two ventricles is proportional to the amount of

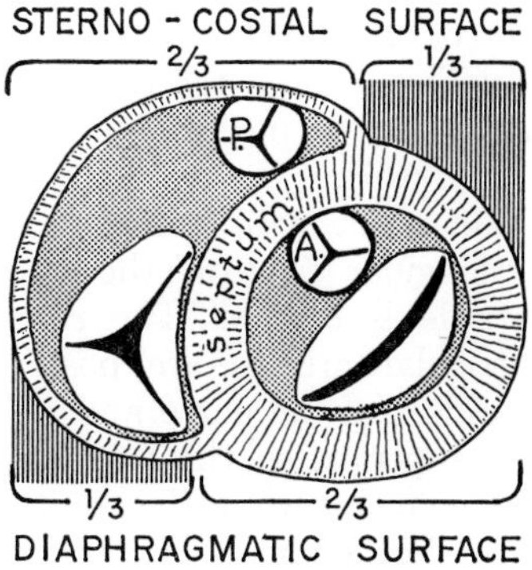

FIG. 615. The ventricles on cross-section, front view.

work each has to do. Before birth, both chambers pumped blood into the aorta—the left ventricle directly, the right ventricle via the ductus arteriosus—and their walls were equal in thickness. After birth, the left ventricle is the pump of the systemic system; the right ventricle of the pulmonary system, and the ratio of their thickness is as 3:1. This explains why the interventricular septum bulges into the right ventricle, and why the cavity of the left ventricle is circular on section and that of the right ventricle crescentic. You might expect that the interventricular septum would occupy the median plane and that the two ventricles would present equally to the front; but the rotation of the heart to the left causes one-third of the left ventricle and two-thirds

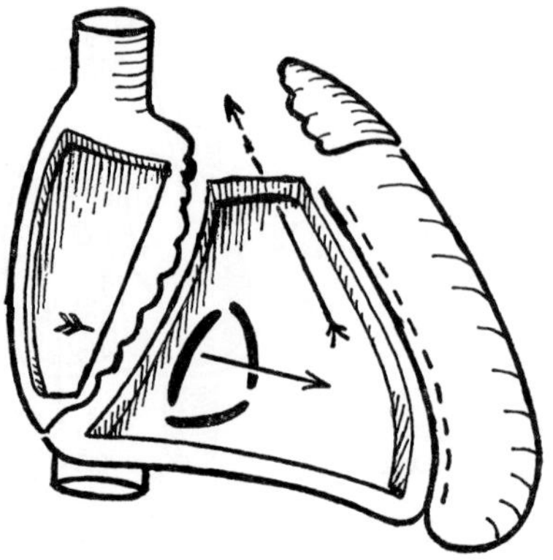

FIG. 616. Interior of the right ventricle showing relative positions of orifices.

of the right ventricle to face anteriorly, and two-thirds of the left ventricle and one-third of the right ventricle to face inferiorly. This is indicated by the positions of the anterior and posterior interventricular sulci (*fig. 615*).

INTERIORS. The *cavity* of the right ventricle is triangular (*fig. 616*); the cavity of the left ventricle is conical. The *entrances* or atrioventricular orifices are posterior; the *exits* or orifices of the aorta and pulmonary trunk are superior, so the blood pursues a V-shaped course within the ventricles. In each ventricle the exit is on the septal side of the entrance.

Except near the exits, the ventricular walls are lined with muscular bundles, *trabeculae carneae* (L. carnea = flesh; *cf.* carnal). Some of these bundles are merely elevated *ridges*, others are attached at both ends like *bridges*, and others form finger-like projections, the *papillary muscles.* One bridge in the right ventricle, the *septomarginal band* (moderator band), passes from the septum to the base of the right *anterior papillary muscle.* In each ventricle an anterior and a posterior papillary muscle rise from the corresponding walls. Those on the left side are larger than those on the right. In the right ventricle small papillary muscles rise from the septum also. From the apices of the papillary muscles fibrous cords, *chordae tendineae*, pass to the cusps of the atrioventricular valves.

The Septomarginal Band (Moderator Band) (present in 56.8 per cent of 500 human hearts) was thought to moderate or prevent over-dilatation of the right ventricle during diastole. It is now known to transport a fascicle of the right crus of the atrioventricular bundle (p. 517) to the anterior papillary muscle. When the band is (apparently) absent, the anterior papillary muscle usually arises at the junction of the septal and anterior walls. Hence, the band has no occasion to free itself from the septal wall in order to reach the papillary muscle so placed (Truex and Warsham).

The portion of the right ventricular cavity preceding the pulmonary trunk is smooth and is called the *conus arteriosus* or *infundibulum.* The corresponding portion of the left ventricle is smooth, largely fibrous and nondistensible, and called the *aortic vestibule.* It cannot contract and empty; neither can it dilate.

The Interventricular Septum is fleshy except at its uppermost part where an area, the size of a thumbnail, is membranous. The two parts have different origins. The *fleshy part* is an upgrowth from the apex; the *membranous part* is a downgrowth from the interatrial septum and right side of the root of the aorta (*fig. 620*). Failure of the fleshy and membranous parts to fuse results in an interventricular septal defect with subsequent leakage into the right ventricle from the high pressured left ventricle.

The *pars membranacea* of the septum is best seen on the right side after removing the septal cusp of the tricuspid valve. It can be felt between the finger and thumb placed one in each ventricle (*fig. 624*) and recognized to be the thinnest part of the interventricular septum. The thinnest part of the

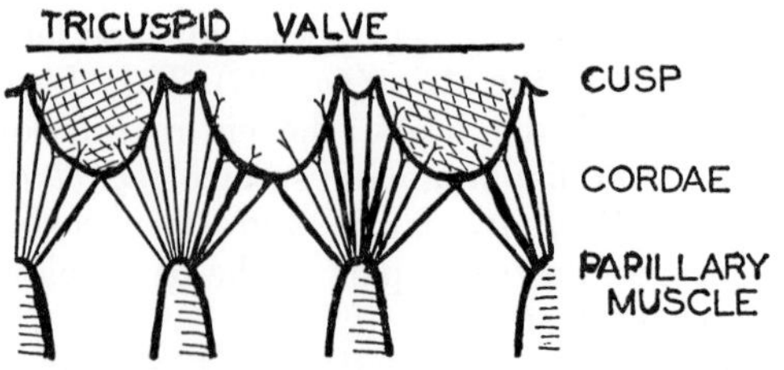

FIG. 617. The right atrioventricular valve spread out.

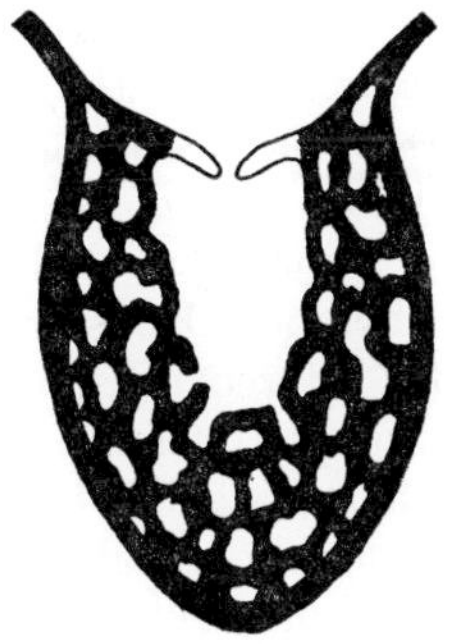

FIG. 618. The primitive muscular spongework of the ventricles.

muscular wall of the left ventricle is at the apex.

The Atrioventricular Valves. The right atrioventricular valve is tricuspid, and the left, *bicuspid.* The bicuspid valve was likened to a bishop's miter by Vesalius, hence the left valve is referred to as the *mitral valve.* The chordae tendineae are attached to the edges and ventricular surfaces of the cusps, and they leave the atrial surfaces free. In this way they do not offer obstruction to the incoming blood. The chordae of each papillary muscle control the contiguous margins of two cusps (*fig. 617*). Hence, there are two papillary muscles on the left side and three, or groups of three, on the right. The bases of the cusps unite to form a short cuff which is attached to the fibrous atrioventricular orifice. The margins of the cusps are dentate where the chordae are attached. The edges and surfaces of the cusps must meet when the valve is closed, otherwise the valve will leak. Therefore, the two cusps of the mitral valve are parallel to each other; they are also parallel to the septum, and also to the septal cusp of the tricuspid valve. *All four structures* face forward and to the right, and backward and to the left (*figs. 615* and *619*).

The cusps of the mitral valve are called *anterior* and *posterior*. The anterior cusp is interposed between the atrioventricular and the aortic orifice. Accordingly, the current of blood flows over both surfaces of this cusp, so the chordae are largely confined to its margin. The clinician prefers to think of this anterior cusp of the mitral valve as *the aortic cusp.*

The cusps of the tricuspid valve are named *anterior*, *posterior*, and *septal.*

Structure. The papillary muscles, chordae tendineae, and cusps of the atrioventricular valves are developed from the (primitive) muscular spongework of the heart (*fig. 618*); and in fetal life the cusps are both fleshy and vascular. Before birth the muscle fibers and the vessels undergo regression. In adult life muscle fibers are found in the bases of all five cusps; they include smooth nonstriated fibers.

Blood vessels do not occur in the cusps of healthy human heart valves, except for 1 to 3 mm. at their bases. Inflamed valves, however, do become vascularized.

»» When valves, which are apparently healthy, are found to be vascularized, it is probable that they have recovered from an inflammatory infection (e.g., rheu-

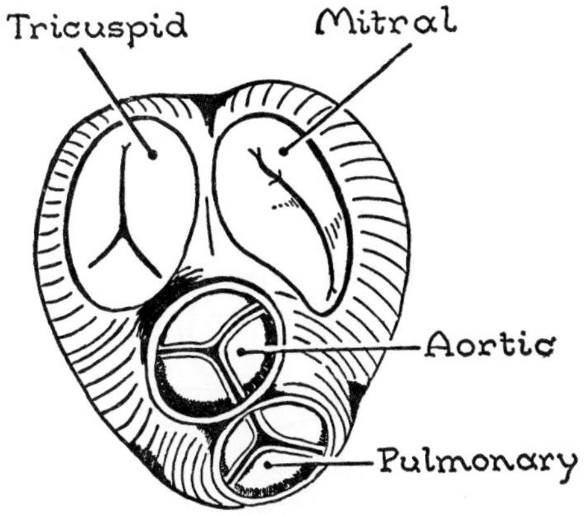

FIG. 619. The four orifices guarded by valves, showing the cusps, also the superficial muscle ayer of the ventricle. (After Spalteholz.)

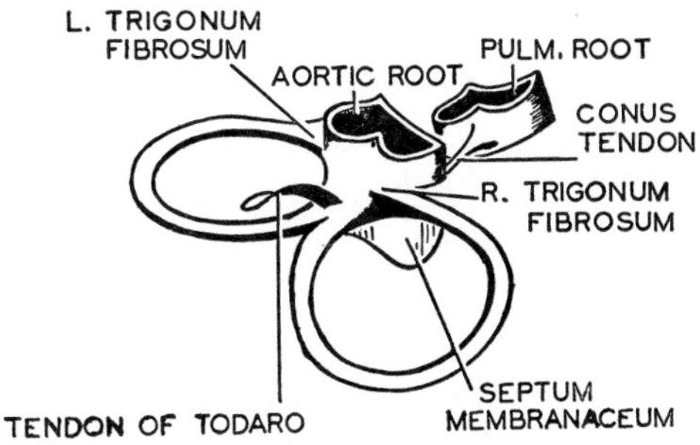

FIG. 620. The skeleton of the heart. (From Walmsley, after Ungar).

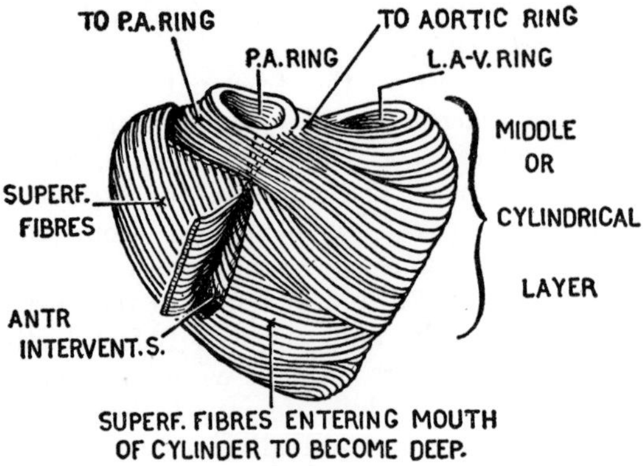

FIG. 621

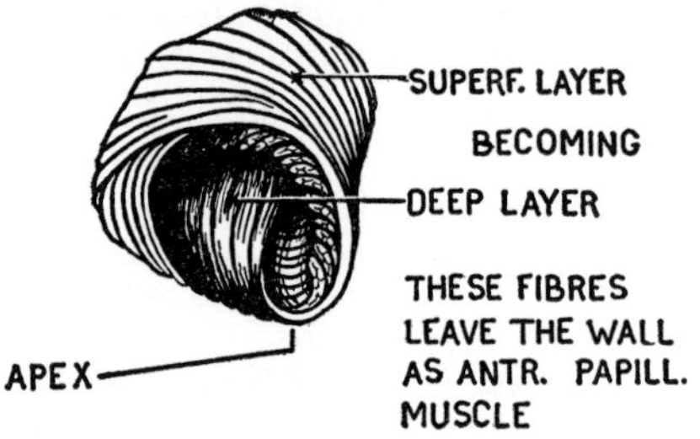

FIG. 622

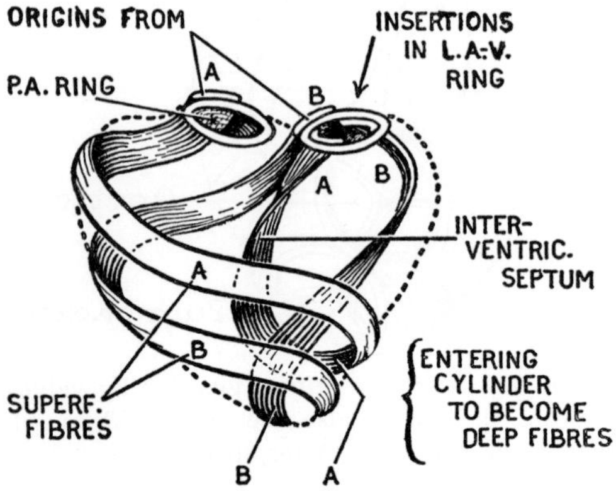

FIG. 623. Dissections of the ventricles of the heart of the sheep. (By B. Leibel.)

matic fever) and that the vessels have not completely receded (Gross; Harper).

Comparative Anatomy. The valves of certain domestic animals (horse, dog, cat, ox, sheep, goat, and pig) normally contain vessels; they are vascularized. The valves of the rabbit, like those of man, are not vascularized.

Surface Anatomy of the Four Cardiac Orifices guarded by functioning valves —pulmonary, aortic, mitral, and tricuspid: These lie behind the sternum on an oblique line joining the 3rd left sternocostal joint to the 6th right: thus, the *orifice of the pulmonary trunk* is deep to the left 3rd sternocostal joint; the *aortic orifice*, being slightly lower, more medial, and more posterior, is behind the sternum at the level of the 3rd intercostal space; the *mitral orifice*, is still lower and more medial at the level of the 4th costal cartilage; and the *tricuspid orifice* is on the right of the median plane at the level of the 4th and 5th spaces.

Structures of Walls of Heart

Skeleton of the Heart (so-called) (*fig. 620*). The ventricles are not emptied as the urinary bladder and other hollow organs are emptied, but the blood is wrung from the cavities like water from a wet cloth. A fibrous ring surrounds each of the four orifices guarded by a valve (*fig. 619*). The aortic ring is the strongest and is like a cuff. Without the rings the orifices would stretch and the valves be rendered incompetent. The rings are joined to each other, as shown in figure 620, and to the pars membranacea septi. In some animals, e.g., the sheep, there is a bone, *os cordis*, in the right triangular fibrous area (trigonum fibrosum).

Musculature of the Heart. The cardiac muscle, *myocardium*, is clothed externally with serous pericardium, *epicardium*, and is lined internally with *endocardium*, and under the epicardium there may be much fat, especially in the sulci. (Definitions on p. 32.)

Atrial Musculature. The atrial walls are translucent. The superficial muscle fibers run transversely; the deep fibers arch over the atrium from front to back and are attached to the skeleton by both ends; other fibers encircle the mouths of the great veins.

Ventricular Musculature (*figs. 621 to 623*). The ventricular *musculature* is composed of three layers—(1) superficial, (2) middle, and (3) deep.

All the fibers of the ventricles arise from the skeleton of the heart, and eventually they return to be inserted into the skeleton.

The arrangement of the muscular fibers should be read to be appreciated, not to be remembered in detail.

»» *The Superficial Layer.* If you twist your coat sleeve to the left, the spiral creases thereby produced will indicate the direction in which all superficial heart fibers run, whether at the front, sides, or back of the heart.

The Middle Layer. The *middle layer of the left ventricle* is a cylinder that surrounds the cavity of the left ventricle. It is the thickest and most basic layer of the whole heart. This cylindrical left middle layer is distinguished by possessing a free lower border. The fibers forming this lower border turn or roll upon themselves like the fibers of the lower border of the Pectoralis Major.

The fibers of the middle layer arise from around the left atrioventricular ring and run from left to right across the front of the heart to be inserted around the pulmonary ring, conus tendon, and septal side of the aortic ring.

The *middle layer of the right ventricle.* Its fibers arise from the left a-v. ring, run round the back of the left ventricle to the posterior interventricular sulcus where (1) some run vertically downward in the interventricular septum, while (2) others run round the ventricle to meet and interdigitate with the septal fibers at the anterior interventricular sulcus, and from there they continue over the anterior surface of the left ventricle.

The Deep Layer. The deep layer is a direct continuation of the superficial layer which, after running obliquely downward like a twisted sleeve on the superficial surface of the middle layers, turns around the lower border of the cylinder (or penetrates to the deep surface of the right ventricle's middle layer) and then ascends to gain attachment to the skeleton either directly, or indirectly through the papillary muscles, chordae tendineae and cusps of the valves.

As the superficial fibers are turning or twisting around the lower border of the cylinder, they skirt it for a third of a circle before proceeding upward as the fibers of the deep layer. As the mouth of the cylinder becomes more and more filled by these entering fibers, the orifice becomes progressively narrower and the third of a circle, which the most superficial fibers describe, becomes diminishingly smaller until ultimately the apex is represented by a fibrous pinpoint.

Note:

1. The ascending fibers of the deep layer take a direction at right angles to the descending fibers of the superficial layer. If, therefore, a block of muscle is removed from any part of the ventricular wall and examined, the fibers of the inner and outer surfaces are seen to run at right angles to each other.

2. Both ends of all ventricular fibers are attached to the cardiac skeleton, thereby insuring that the aorta and pulmonary artery shall not be shot from the heart, like a cork from a bottle during ventricular systole.

3. Contraction of the superficial and deep layers serves to shorten the ventricles. Contraction of the middle layer results in narrowing the lumina of the ventricles.

4. Further, owing to its attachment to the pulmonary ring, etc., the middle cylindrical layer on contracting tends to pull the left ventricle forward and to the right, so in systole the heart rotates anteriorly and to the right and strikes the chest wall. (This description is based on work done by B. Liebel).

Impulse Conducting System (*fig. 624*). This comprises—sinu-atrial node, atrioventricular node, and atrioventricular bundle.

1. The *sinu-atrial node* initiates the heart beat. Composed of peculiar, longitudinally striated cells, it is 2 cm. long by 2 mm. wide, and is situated along the upper end of the sulcus terminalis. It is supplied by the right or left coronary artery (anastomoses are free) and by the right vagus nerve.

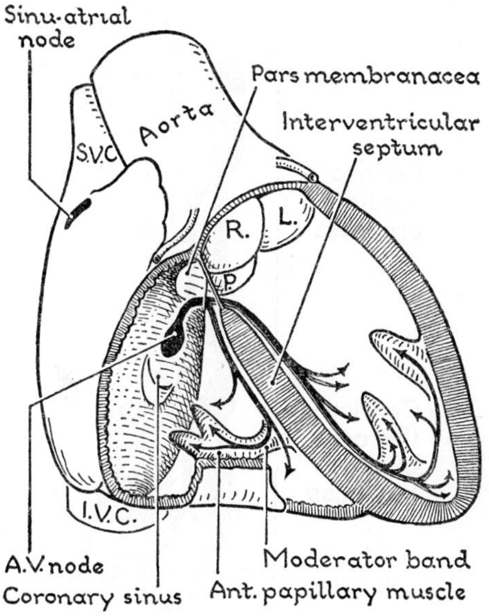

FIG. 624. The conducting system of the heart

2. The *atrioventricular node* has the same structure and is situated in the interatrial septum beside the mouth of the coronary sinus. It also is usually supplied by the right coronary artery (and anastomoses are free and ample) but by the *left* vagus nerve (James and Burch).

3. The *atrioventricular bundle* (of His) is a pale bundle of peculiar muscle fibers about 2 mm. thick, enveloped in a loose sheath. This slender bundle is the sole muscular connection between the musculature of the atria and the musculature of the ventricles. It extends from the a-v. node, through the fibrous skeleton, to the interventricular septum. It skirts the hinder part of the membranous septum and, at the upper part of the muscular septum, it divides into a right and a left crus. These descend in their sheaths, subendocardially, to the bases of the papillary muscles, that of the right side passing through the septomarginal or moderator band. In the properly prepared heart the whole system is easily injected with India ink and water.

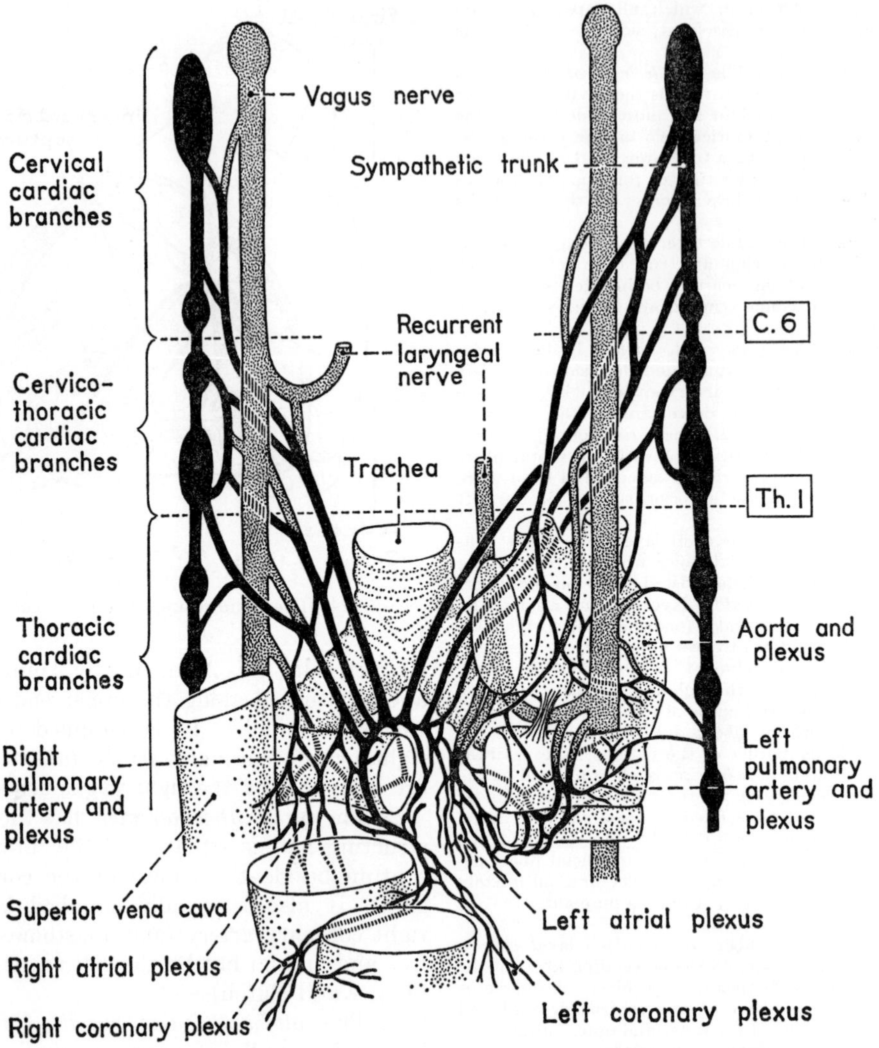

FIG. 624.1. Cardiac nerves and plexuses. (After Mizeres, modified.)

Purkinje fibers, in connection with the fibers of the a-v. bundle, ramify both subendocardially and throughout the myocardium of the ventricles (Davis and Francis).

Nerve Supply to the Heart. *Sympathetic,* via one to three *cervical cardiac branches* arising at variable levels from the cervical part of the sympathetic trunk; two or three *cervicothoracic branches* arising from the region of the cervicothoracic (stellate) ganglion; and two to four *thoracic branches* from the upper four thoracic levels of the sympathetic trunk (*fig. 624.1*). (2) *Vagus,* via a single *cervical cardiac branch* in its cervical course; one or two *cervicothoracic cardiac branches* from the main nerve at the inlet to the thorax (or its right recurrent laryngeal branch); and two to four *thoracic cardiac branches* from the thoracic part of the vagus nerve (and its left recurrent branch). Mizeres, upon whose studies the above description is based, has shown that most of the cardiac nerves tend to fuse with each other early in their descent to the cardiac plexus (described on page 526).

Distribution. Branches of the *cardiac plexus* find a ready path in front of and behind the right pulmonary artery to the back of the atria, which they supply, the right nerves controlling the s-a. node; the left nerves, the a-v. node. Other branches descend in front of the pulmonary trunk to join the *right coronary plexus*. They also pass forward, mainly on the sides of the pulmonary trunk, and as *coronary plexuses* are distributed with the coronary arteries to the ventricles. The cardiac plexuses can communicate with or may include the *anterior pulmonary plexuses* by branches that run laterally along the pulmonary arteries.

The vagal fibers are cardio-inhibitory; the sympathetic fibers are cardio-accelerator, vasodilator, and sensory.

CHAPTER 33

SUPERIOR AND POSTERIOR MEDIASTINA

Prelude to Study of Region

Development of Great Arteries. In the embryo, the thoracic contents are bilaterally symmetrical; later this symmetry is lost, largely in consequence of the disappearance of certain veins from the left side of the body and of certain arteries from the right side. Clearly, if you would appreciate the relations of the superior and posterior mediastina in the adult, you should have some knowledge of the symmetrical arrangement in the embryo. Without this knowledge the anatomy of the region is unintelligible. The facts are simple and interesting; they explain many relationships and most of the common anomalies.

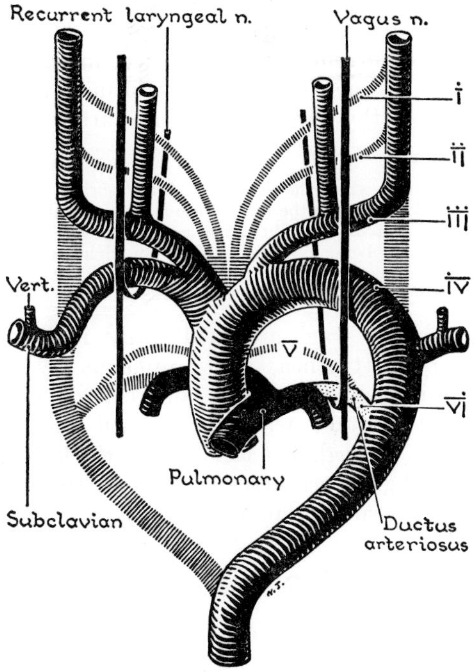

FIG. 625. The six paired primitive aortic arches

Veins. The disappearance of the left s. v. cava was rendered possible by the establishment of certain cross communications between the right and left veins, described on pages 510–511 (*fig. 611*).

Fate of the Aortic Arches (*figs. 625* and *626*). Transitionally, in the early embryo, six primitive aortic arches, which are comparable with, though not identical with, the gill vessels of the fish, pass through the six pharyngeal arches on each side of the neck.

1. They connect the right and left primitive ventral aortae with the corresponding right and left primitive dorsal aortae, which fuse to form the descending aorta (*fig. 625*).

2. The vagus nerves descend on the side of the pharynx and esophagus (and of the trachea after it has taken form), the six primitive aortic arches alone intervening.

3. The recurrent laryngeal nerve on each side recurs below the VI primitive arch to supply the larynx (*fig. 626*).

4. It is on the IV, V, and VI pairs of primitive aortic arches that your interest is centered at the moment. Of these arches, the IV pair belongs to the systemic circulation, the V pair is transient and need not be mentioned again, and the VI pair may be called, and should in any case by thought of as, the *right and left pulmonary arches*, for, after the spiral splitting of the truncus arteriosus into the ascending aorta and pulmonary trunk, this pair remains connected to the pulmonary trunk. From each VI or pulmonary arch branches sprout into the corresponding lung. Thereafter, the ventral portion of each VI arch becomes the stem of the corresponding right and left pulmonary artery of adult anatomy.

5. Now, in man a certain economy is early exercised in the paired primitive aortic arch system, two channels not being retained where one would suffice. Thus: (1) the portion of the right primitive dorsal aorta caudal to the III right arch disappears and (2) the dorsal end of the VI right arch, which is thereby rendered useless, disappears also. The left arteries, having now to do double duty, enlarge. The dorsal part of the VI left arch is the ductus arteriosus (*figs. 625* and *636*).

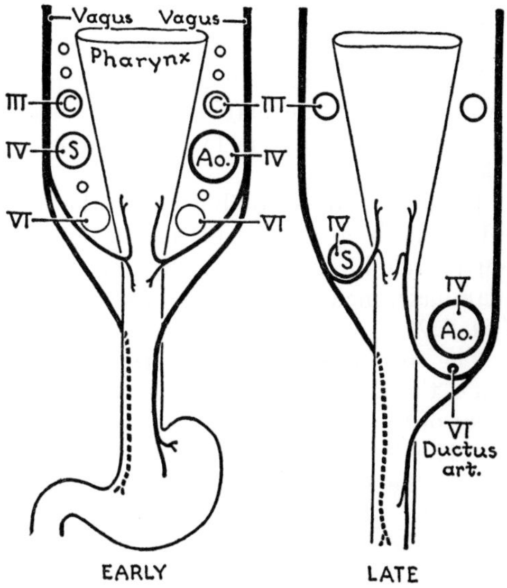

FIG. 626. Coronal section of figure 625 showing: that only the arches separate the vagus nerves from the digestive tract (*early*). A later stage of explaining the asymmetrical courses of the recurrent laryngeal nerves (*late*).

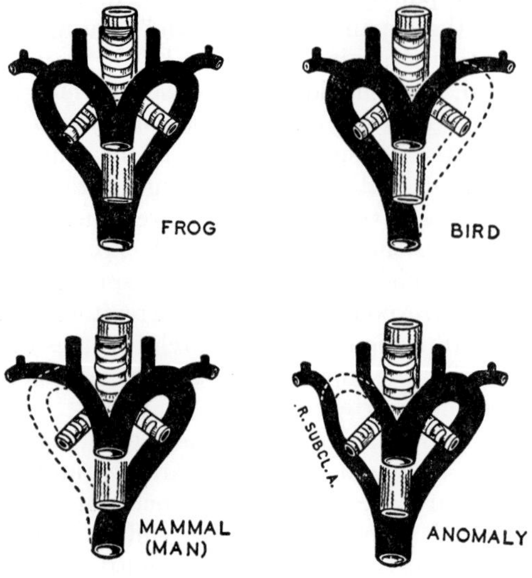

FIG. 627. Variations of the aortic arch

6. The *definitive aortic arch* is derived from the entire IV left primitive aortic arch and the adjacent parts of the primitive ventral and dorsal aortae.

7. The brachiocephalic trunk or *innominate artery* is derived from the right primitive ventral aorta. It is equivalent on the right side to part of the definitive aortic arch.

The right subclavian artery has greater "value" than the left subclavian artery because it includes the IV right aortic arch (*fig. 625*).

Reptiles and Amphibia (e.g., the frog) retain both a right and a left definitive aortic arch; birds retain a right arch; whereas mammals, including man, retain a left arch (*fig. 627*).

The **Asymmetrical Results** consequent upon the disappearance of the caudal segment of the right primitive dorsal aorta are: (1) The left aortic arch enlarges and displaces the esophagus slightly and trachea markedly to the right. (2) The esophagus lies to the right of the aortic arch and beginning of the descending aorta. (3) When the heart descends and the neck elongates, the recurrent laryngeal nerves are dragged down by the lowest persisting aortic arches (*fig. 625*). Hence, the left recurrent laryngeal nerve recurs around the lig. arteriosum (VI arch) which is overshadowed by the enlarged definitive left aortic arch; but the right recurrent laryngeal nerve, in the absence of a right lig. arteriosum, recurs around the right subclavian artery (IV arch).

»» In cases where the right IV arch is absorbed and the arterial channel to the upper limb is maintained by the caudal part of the right dorsal aorta (*fig. 627*, anomaly), there being nothing to drag the right recurrent laryngeal nerve down, it does not recur but passes directly to the larynx.

(4) The vagi are held away from the pharynx, trachea, and esophagus by the primitive aortic arches and cannot make direct contact with them until the last arch is crossed. The last arch on the left side is the lig. arteriosum (VI) and on the right side, the subclavian artery (IV) (*fig. 626*).

SUPERIOR MEDIASTINUM

Boundaries. The superior mediastinum is the portion of the mediastinum above the level of the pericardium or, which is the same thing, above the imaginary plane passing from the sternomanubrial joint to the disc between thoracic vertebrae 4 and 5 (*fig. 567*).

Behind, it is bounded by the bodies of the upper four thoracic vertebrae, intervertebral discs, and anterior longitudinal lig.

In front is the manubrium, attached to which are two paired, strap-like muscles—

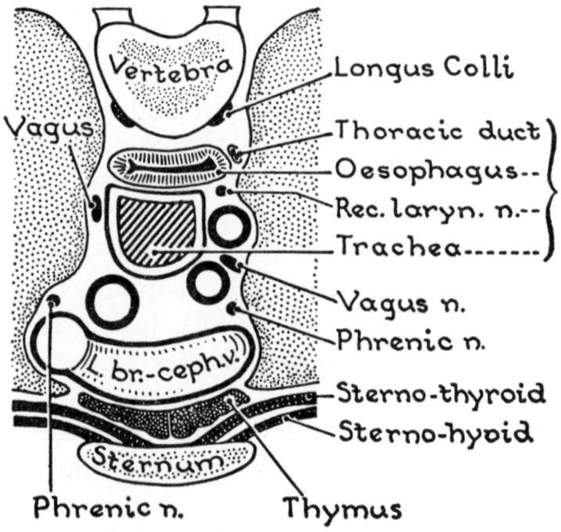

FIG. 628. Cross section of the superior mediastinum showing the arrangement of the contents.

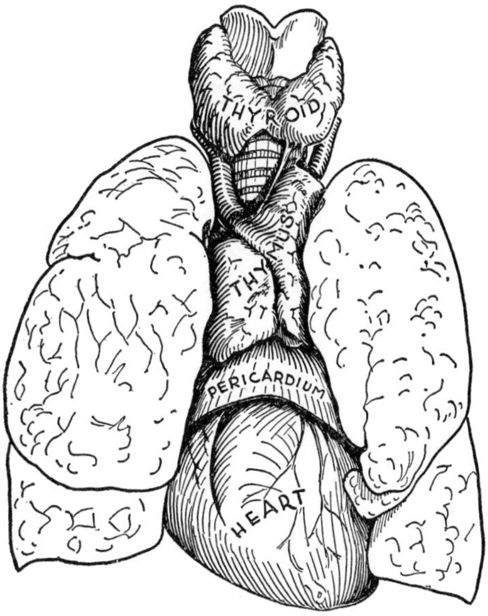

FIG. 629. The thymus gland of a child

Sternohyoid and Sternothyroid (*fig. 628*), which muscles form fleshy cushions behind the sternoclavicular joints.

On each side is mediastinal pleura.

Contents. The contents of this region are now to be examined from the front. They are:

1. Retrosternal structures:
   a. Thymus.
   b. Great veins.
2. Prevertebral structures: (Unit of four parallel structures)
   a. Trachea
   b. Esophagus
   c. Left recurrent nerve
   d. Thoracic duct
3. Intermediate structures:
   a. Aortic arch and its three great branches.
   b. Vagus nerves.
   c. Phrenic nerves.

Their general disposition is well revealed in a tranverse section (*fig. 628*).

Retrosternal Structures

The Thymus in the adult is an elongated, encapsulated, fatty, and lymphoid mass, lying in the loose tissue behind the manubrium sterni (*fig. 628*). On each side of it are the diverging anterior borders of the lungs and pleurae. Behind it are the left brachiocephalic vein and the aortic arch.

It is supplied mainly by the internal thoracic vessels. Little is understood of its function, of its lymph supply, or of the twigs supplied to it by the sympathetic, vagus, and phrenic nerves.

The thymus consists of two asymmetrical lobes, which are easily separated from each other by blunt dissection. The fact that it has a bilateral origin—having developed from the third right and left pharyngeal pouches—explains the two lobes. At birth, its upper end (or ends) reaches nearly to the thyroid gland (*fig. 629*), while its lower end covers the upper part of the pericardium.

It is relatively largest and most extensive at birth; absolutely it is largest at puberty, after which it diminishes rapidly.

Great Veins (*fig. 630*). The **Left Brachiocephalic Vein** is a cross-channel that deflects the blood from the left side of the head, neck, and upper limb toward the right or venous side of the heart.

Formed by the confluence of the left internal jugular and subclavian veins behind the sternal end of the clavicle, it passes behind the upper half of the manubrium to unite with the right brachiocephalic vein half way down the right margin of the manubrium to form the s.v. cava (*fig. 628*).

In front, it is relieved from contact with the sternoclavicular joint and manubrium by the thymus and the Sternothyroid and Sternohyoid muscles.

Below lies the aortic arch.

Behind are the three great arterial branches of the arch.

At its origin it grooves the left lung and pleura. At its termination it touches the right pleura. In youth and when engorged, its upper border rises above the jugular notch into the neck where it is in surgical danger.

The **Right Brachiocephalic Vein** is formed similarly behind the sternal end of the right clavicle. It descends vertically. After being joined by the left brachiocephalic vein, it continues vertically, as the **Superior Vena Cava,** to the 3rd right costal cartilage where it joins the right atrium.

This vertical venous channel projects beyond the right margin of the sternum.

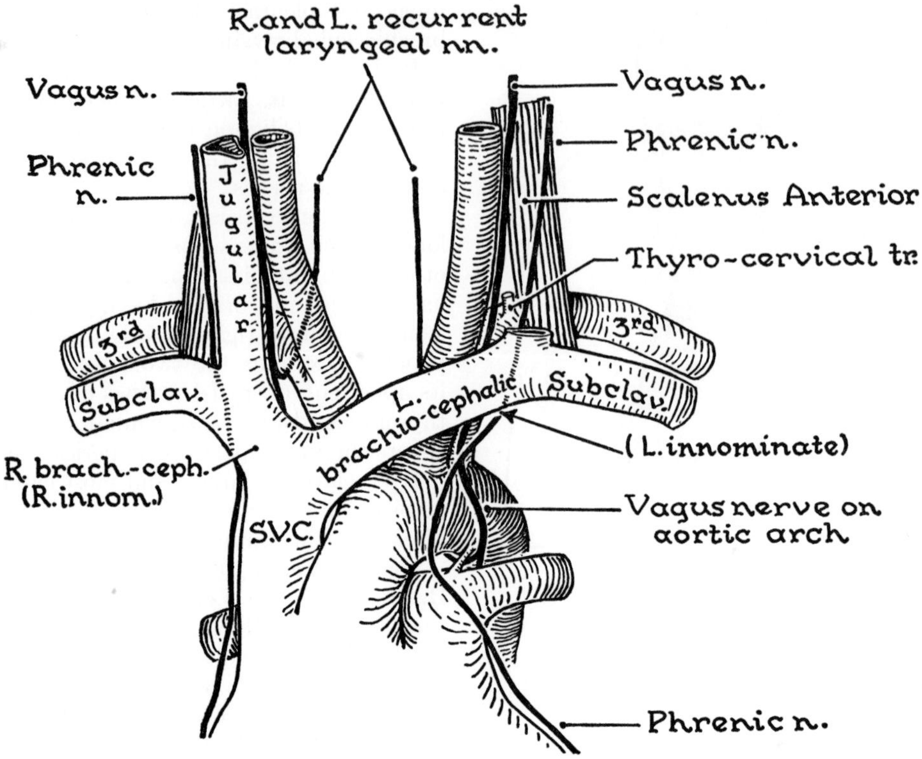

FIG. 630. The courses of the phrenic and vagus nerves

Along its right side runs the phrenic nerve (*fig. 630*). On its left side lie the ascending aorta, which is overlapping, and the brachiocephalic trunk (innominate artery). It is covered with pleura on three sides—in front, on the right, and behind. Before entering the pericardium and descending in front of the upper part of the root of the right lung, it is joined from behind by the arch of the azygos vein.

On each side, the phrenic and vagus nerves enter the thorax behind the brachiocephalic vein (*fig. 630*).

The Tributaries of the brachiocephalic veins fall into three groups:

1. Internal jugular and subclavian veins.
2. Thoracic or right lymph duct.
3. Veins returning blood delivered by the four branches of the subclavian artery, viz., vertebral, internal thoracic, inferior thyroid, and highest intercostal veins. The left brachiocephalic vein receives also the left superior intercostal vein (*fig. 726*). (These veins are discussed on p. 621.)

Prevertebral Structures

The esophagus, trachea, left recurrent nerve, and thoracic duct run through the superior mediastinum as a bundle or unit of four parallel structures (*fig. 631*).

The *esophagus* is directly applied to the bodies of the vertebrae of this region. The *trachea*, throughout its entire course, both cervical and thoracic, is in turn directly applied to the front of the esophagus. Below, it is indented and deflected to the right by the aortic arch. The *thoracic duct* ascends along the left border of the esophagus. The *left recurrent nerve* arises from the vagus nerve on the left side of the aortic arch, turns tightly round the arch beyond the attachment of the lig. arteriosum, and encounters tracheobronchial lymph nodes before ascending in the angle between the trachea and esophagus.

The **Trachea** (*fig. 708*) begins where the larynx ends—at the lower border of the cricoid cartilage, on a level with the 6th

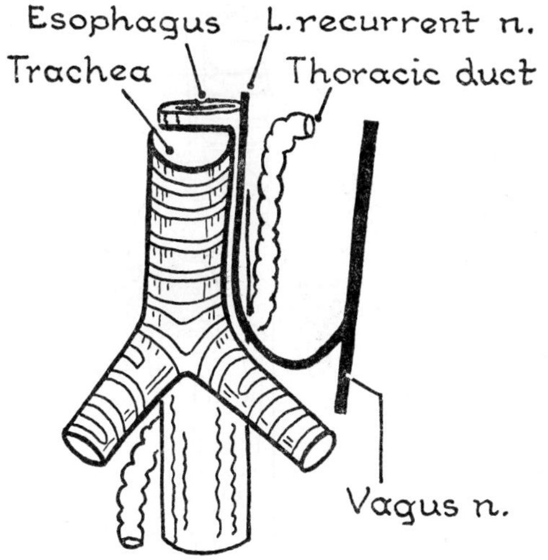

FIG. 631. A unit of four parallel structures runs through the superior mediastinum.

cervical vertebra. Since it ends by dividing into right and left bronchi, on the plane between the superior and posterior mediastina, it follows that it crosses 5 vertebral bodies (one cervical and four thoracic). By palpation you may easily determine on yourself that the cricoid is as far above the jugular notch (2″) as the sternal angle is below it (2″), making the total length of the trachea 4″ or more (up to 6″). Therefore, half the trachea lies within the superior mediastinum (*fig. 708*, p. 605). In life, the bifurcation lies at a lower level (p. 496), in virtue of the fact that the trachea and bronchi are fibro-elastic tubes capable of changing their diameters and lengths.

The trachea may be constricted by the thyroid gland at its upper end, by the aortic arch at its lower end, and by the brachiocephalic trunk (innominate artery) on its right side retrosternally. It occupies the median plane except at its lower end where the aortic arch deflects it to the right.

About 20 U-shaped rings of hyaline cartilage keep its lumen patent; the ring at the bifurcation has a *carina* or keel that supports the "crotch" of the trachea. Similarly shaped rings keep the extrapulmonary and 1st inch of the intrapulmonary bronchi patent.

Relationships of Trachea (*fig. 632*). Throughout its entire course the esophagus lies behind it, and the left recurrent nerve is in the angle between it and the projecting left border of the esophagus. The aortic arch, lying behind the lower half of the manubrium, is in contact with the anterior and left aspects of the lower end of the trachea and of the other constituents of the "unit". The brachiocephalic trunk (arising at the center of the manubrium), and the left c. carotid and left subclavian arteries (arising on the left of the center) wind round the trachea in semi-spiral fashion. In front of these three arteries runs the left brachiocephalic vein.

The right side is subpleural except where the brachiocephalic trunk, right vagus nerve, and azygos arch intervene.

The left side is excluded from contact with pleura by the left subclavian and left common carotid arteries and by the arch of the aorta.

Further, tracheobronchial lymph nodes occupy the three angles at the bifurcation of the trachea (*fig. 633*), and the cardiac plexus of nerves lies in front of the bifurcation.

Extrapulmonary Bronchi, right and left (*fig. 633*). Of these the right bronchus is 25 per cent the larger because it supplies the larger lung; it is the more vertical because the aortic arch deflects the trachea to the right. Hence, foreign bodies are more com-

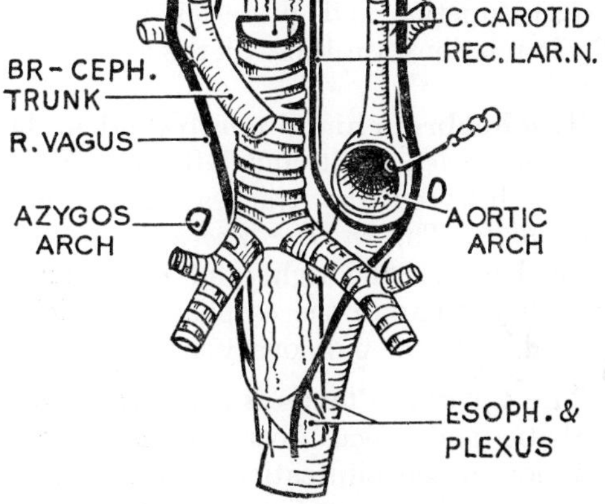

FIG. 632. Trachea and extrapulmonary bronchi, and their lateral relations.

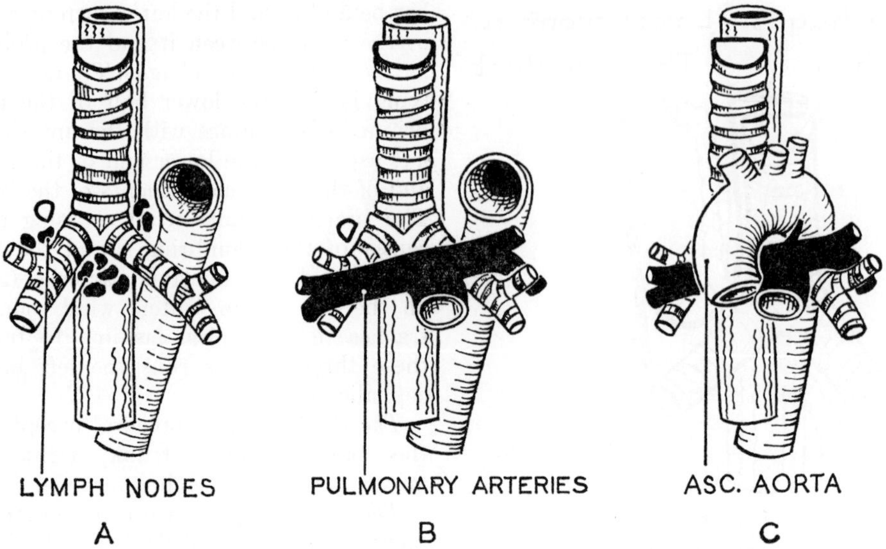

FIG. 633. Relations at the bifurcation of the trachea, shown serially

monly aspirated into the right lung than into the left.

The first branch of the right bronchus supplies the upper lobe of the right lung, passes above the right pulmonary artery (eparterial), and arises 1 inch or less from the trachea. Only the arch of the azygos vein passes above it.

The first branch of the left bronchus supplies the upper lobe of the left lung, but it passes below the left pulmonary artery and below the aortic arch; hence, it arises 2 inches from the trachea.

The bronchi arise to the right of the median plane, on the horizontal plane between superior and posterior mediastina. Their relations are those of the roots of the lungs.

Tracheobronchial Lymph Nodes. The *superior nodes,* right and left, occupy the angles between the trachea and bronchi (*fig. 633*). The *inferior nodes* occupy the angle between the right and left bronchi, and they separate the esophagus, which is behind, from the pulmonary artery in front.

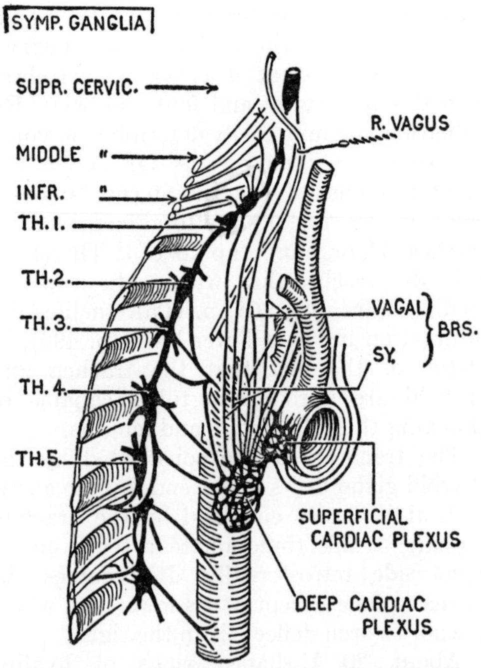

FIG. 634. The cardiac plexuses. (From White, after Kuntz and Morehouse.)

The Cardiac Plexus is a plexus of sympathetic and vagal fibers. It is situated anterior to the bifurcation of the trachea, superior to the bifurcation of the pulmonary trunk, and posteromedial to the arch of the aorta. A short extension of the plexus, which lies to the right of the lig. arteriosum and below the aortic arch, has been called the *superficial cardiac plexus* (*fig. 634*), in which case all the rest of the plexus is called the *deep cardiac plexus.* However, these terms describe an artificial condition (Mitchell;

Mizeres). The cardiac plexus lies on the adventitial wall of the pulmonary trunk at its bifurcation and consists of subsidiary plexuses named the *right and left pulmonary, right and left coronary, right and left atrial,* and the *plexus on the arch of the aorta.*

The plexus on the arch of the aorta is formed mainly by the left cervical and cervicothoracic cardiac branches. The right and left pulmonary plexuses are formed by the cervical, cervicothoracic, and thoracic cardiac branches of both sides. At the hilus of each lung the pulmonary plexuses receive both anteriorly and posteriorly branches of the vagus nerve and sympathetic trunk.

The coronary plexuses are formed mainly by extensions of the right pulmonary plexus with some contributions from the left pulmonary plexus and the plexus on the arch of the aorta. The coronary plexuses may also receive direct contributions from the cervical cardiac branches and usually send filaments into the anterior ventricular walls.

The right and left atrial plexuses are formed mainly by extensions of the pulmonary plexuses with direct contributions from the thoracic cardiac branches. The left atrial plexus also sends filaments into the posterior ventricular walls. All these plexuses are interconnected (*fig. 624.1*).

Cardiac Nerves. On each side, the plexus receives slender cardiac nerves from the sympathetic trunk and the vagus nerve, as described on page 518. Most of the vagal branches are interconnected with sympathetic branches before joining the plexus. Some branches are mere filaments or groups of filaments.

The origin and course of the cervical cardiac nerves, and occasionally lower branches, are extremely variable on both sides, arising from any part of the vagus nerve and cervical sympathetic trunk, and crossing either anterior or posterior to the arch of the aorta, in contrast to the usual teaching that the left cervical cardiac nerves tend to be the only ones that remain on the left (anterior) side of the aortic arch (Mizeres).

Functions and Cell Stations. All the cardiac nerves have both efferent and afferent fibers, except the superior cervical sympathetic cardiac nerve which is believed to have only efferent fibers.

The postganglionic efferent fibers of the sympathetic cardiac nerves produce acceleration of the heart's action and dilatation of the coronary arteries. Their cell stations are in the three cervical and upper four (or five) thoracic sympathetic ganglia. Afferent pain fibers from the heart and aorta run mainly, or entirely, in the sympathetic cardiac nerves to the sympathetic ganglia, and through these ganglia and their rami communicantes to the upper four (or five) spinal ganglia where, like somatic afferent nerves, they have their cell stations.

The preganglionic efferent fibers of the vagal cardiac nerves produce slowing of the heart's action and contraction of the coronary arteries. They synapse with postganglionic fibers in the ganglia of the cardiac plexus and in the intrinsic cardiac ganglia, which are practically confined to the atria and interatrial septum and areas near the roots of the great vessels. Afferent vagal fibers from the heart, ascending aorta, and great veins are concerned in reflexes that depress the heart. Their cell stations are in the inferior vagal ganglion (G. A. G. Mitchell).

Intermediate Structures

Aortic Arch and Its Three Branches. The following paragraphs are in large measure a review.

The thoracic aorta is divided into three parts—*ascending aorta, arch of the aorta,* and *descending aorta.* These occupy, respectively, the middle, superior, and posterior mediastina. To appreciate its course and relationships some knowledge of its development is essential (p. 520).

Topographically, the arch is the part of the aorta that rises above the plane dividing the superior from the posterior mediastinum. It is placed behind the lower half of the manubrium. Its direction is backward from the right border of the manubrium to the left border of the disc between the 4th and 5th thoracic vertebrae. A bullet entering the chest from the front might almost traverse the arch.

Surfaces and Relations. The arch has four aspects—left anterior, right posterior, convex upper, and concave lower.

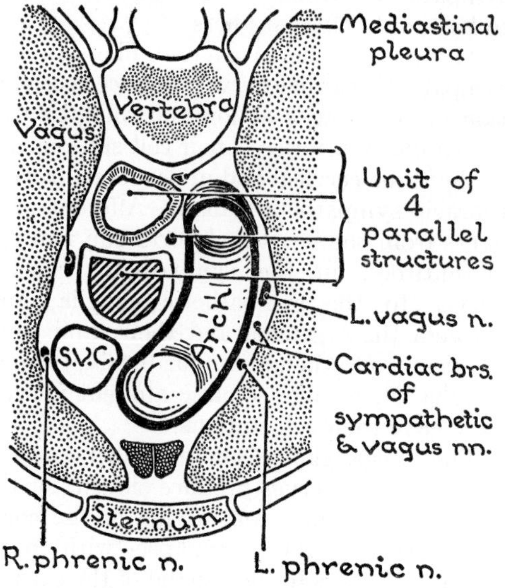

FIG. 635. Cross section of superior mediastinum showing the relations of the aortic arch.

The Left Anterior Aspect is touched by the right and covered by the left mediastinal pleura and lung. It is crossed by four nerves (*fig. 635*)—left phrenic, left vagus, and two cardiac nerves—and by the left superior intercostal vein. This vein bears the same relationship to these nerves as the azygos arch and the end of the s. v. cava bear to the corresponding right nerves, i.e., all nerves except the phrenic run medial to it.

The Right Posterior Aspect curves past the "unit" of four parallel structures (trachea, esophagus, recurrent nerve, and thoracic duct) and the nerves to the deep cardiac plexus that descend on the side of the trachea. The arch is, therefore, convex to the left as well as upward, i.e., it is convex in two planes.

Below, the pulmonary trunk bifurcates into right and left branches. The lig. arteriosum joins the left pulmonary artery to the concavity of the arch beyond the origin of the left subclavian artery. On the left of the ligament is the left recurrent nerve; on the right is the superficial cardiac plexus.

The left recurrent nerve, therefore, arises on the left, passes below, and ascends on the right of the aortic arch.

Above, its three branches arise, and in front of their stems lies the left brachiocephalic vein.

BRANCHES. The right and left coronary arteries being the first two branches of the aorta, the three great vessels arising from the arch are the 3rd, 4th, and 5th branches. As the three great vessels describe partial spirals around the "unit of four parallel structures," they necessarily have different relationships at different levels, as seen in figures 630, 632, and 628.

The brachiocephalic trunk (innominate a.) arises behind the center of the manubrium and ends behind the right sternoclavicular joint by dividing into right common carotid and right subclavian aa. The *left common carotid artery* arises close to the trunk, and the left subclavian artery arises behind the left carotid; both arteries ascend behind the sternoclavicular joint. On each side, however, two strap muscles (Sternohyoid and Sternothyroid) intervene between the arteries and the joint.

Anomalies of the Aortic Arch

1. Rarely both the right and the left arch persist, as in amphibia, forming an arterial ring through which the esophagus and trachea pass (*fig. 627*).

2. Rarely the right arch persists and the hinder part of the left arch disappears, as in birds, thus transposing the normal human scheme, with corresponding transposition of the courses of the recurrent nerves (*fig. 627*).

3. Sometimes (about 1 per cent) the anterior part of the right arch disappears and the posterior part persists to form the stem of the right subclavian artery. This stem becomes the 4th branch of the aortic arch and crosses behind the esophagus and trachea (*fig. 627*). The right recurrent laryngeal nerve, thus freed, behaves like the superior laryngeal nerve in taking a direct course to the larynx.

4. The isthmus of the aorta (i.e., the segment of the aortic arch between the left subclavian artery and the ductus arteriosus) is narrow at birth, but it enlarges soon afterward as the ductus closes (*fig. 636*). Occasionally, it fails to enlarge—a condition called coarctation of the aorta—and in con-

sequence a collateral circulation has to be established between the internal thoracic and costocervical branches of the subclavian arteries above and the aortic intercostals and inferior epigastric arteries below.

5. Commonly the left common carotid artery arises from the stem of the brachiocephalic trunk, as is usual in many primates.

6. Commonly the left vertebral artery arises from the aortic arch.

7. The ductus arteriosus may remain patent, generally in combination with cardiac anomalies.

Each **Vagus Nerve** descends through the neck, applied to the posterolateral side of the great carotid stem. Continuing into the thorax, it passes behind the sternoclavicular joint and the brachiocephalic vein (*figs. 630* and *632*). The *right vagus* must cross the origin of the right subclavian artery (in front) and the brachiocephalic trunk (laterally) in order to reach the trachea, which conducts it subpleurally to the back of the root of the right lung. Above the root, the azygos vein arches forward, lateral to the right vagus. The *left vagus* continues to descend along the posterolateral side of the left carotid stem, (and therefore in the angle between it and the left subclavian artery) to the aortic arch which it crosses far back in order to reach the back of the root of the left lung.

Branches of the Vagi in the Superior Mediastinum. Here each vagus is responsible for recurrent, cardiac, tracheal, and esophageal branches. The right recurrent nerve gives off a cardiac branch as it hooks round the right subclavian artery; the other right branches including one cardiac branch spring directly from the right vagus. All the left branches spring from the left recurrent nerve.

In the posterior mediastinum, each vagus breaks up to form a posterior pulmonary plexus, reunites, and breaks up again to form the *esophageal plexus*, which surrounds the esophagus and supplies it. It also sends filaments to the pericardium and pleura.

From the esophageal plexus two stems, each composed of fibers of both vagi and of sympathetic fibers, pass through the diaphragm, applied to the esophagus. There is usually one stem in front, the *anterior vagal trunk*, and one behind, the *posterior vagal trunk*.

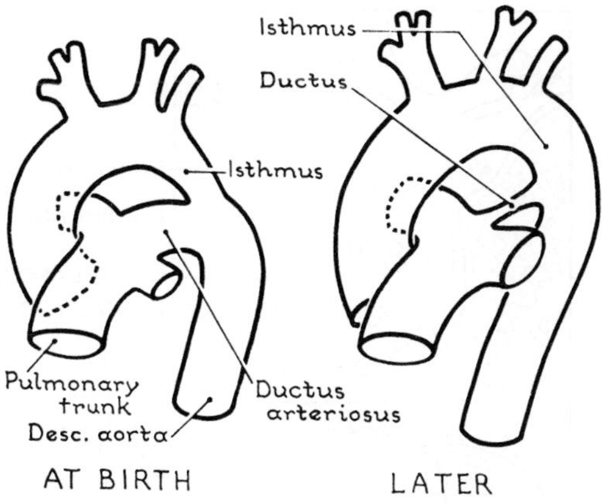

FIG. 636. Aortic isthmus and ductus arteriosus, at birth and a few months later. (After Patten.)

»» In about 8 per cent of 100 cases one or both stems was found to pass through as multiple branches. (Bradley, Small, Wilson, and Walters.)

Each **Phrenic Nerve** enters the thorax between the subclavian artery and the beginning of the brachiocephalic vein (*fig. 630*) where it lies lateral to the thyrocervical trunk, which separates it from the vagus—and each passes a finger's breadth in front of the root of the lung. The *right phrenic* follows subpleurally along the side of the great vertical venous channel (*fig. 569*). The *left phrenic nerve*, in its strictly subpleural course, is the most anterior of the four nerves that cross the aortic arch (*fig. 635*).

The nerves may profitably be sketched in figure 594.1.

POSTERIOR MEDIASTINUM

The Posterior Mediastinum is a passage or thoroughfare between the superior mediastinum above and the abdominal cavity below (*fig. 637*). For its vertical extent see figure 567.

Contents

A. Longitudinal tubular structures:
   1. Descending aorta.
   2. Thoracic duct.
   3. Azygos and hemiazygos veins.
   4. Esophagus (with vagus nerves).

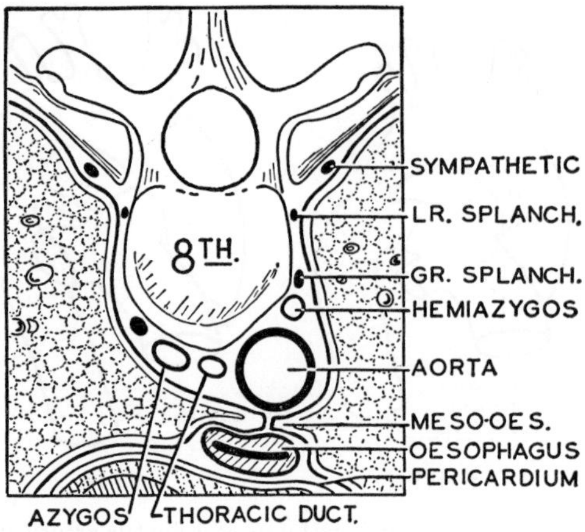

FIG. 637. The posterior mediastinum (in transverse section).

B. Transverse tubular structures:
1. Aortic intercostal arteries.
2. Thoracic duct (from right to left).
3. Certain posterior intercostal veins.
4. Hemiazygos veins (terminal parts).

The sympathetic trunks and the intercostal nerves are covered with costal pleura and therefore are wide of this region.

Postulate. The transversely running structures cling to the thoracic wall; they supply the wall and, like the ribs, are to be regarded as part of the wall (*fig. 638*).

In embryonic life, three pairs of symmetrically placed vessels ran side by side through the entire length of the posterior mediastinum (*fig. 639*). There were two arteries, two lymph trunks, and two veins. The two arteries were medianly placed and, so, fused—as medianly placed vessels commonly do—to form the descending aorta. Out of the laterally placed veins, the azygos and the hemiazygos veins took form. The right intermediately placed vessel became the posterior mediastinal portion of the thoracic duct; its left counterpart is rarely if ever present in man.

Descending Aorta. Being the continuation of the (*left*) aortic arch, the descending aorta runs the first part of its course on the left side of the bodies of the vertebrae (5, 6, and 7) and commonly it grooves or erodes them. Lower down, it gains the median plane and lies in front of the vertebrae (8–12) (*fig. 637*).

Relations. This great arterial trunk beats against the vertebral column throughout the whole length of the posterior mediastinum. Crossing it posteriorly are the terminal parts of the hemiazygos veins. Throughout its course, the thoracic duct and the azygos vein lie on its right posterolateral side, and accompany it through the aortic hiatus in the diaphragm where it becomes the abdominal aorta. The hemiazygos veins lie on its left posterolateral side.

On the left are the mediastinal pleura and lung. *On the right* are the esophagus in its upper part; the right mediastinal pleura and lung in its lower part.

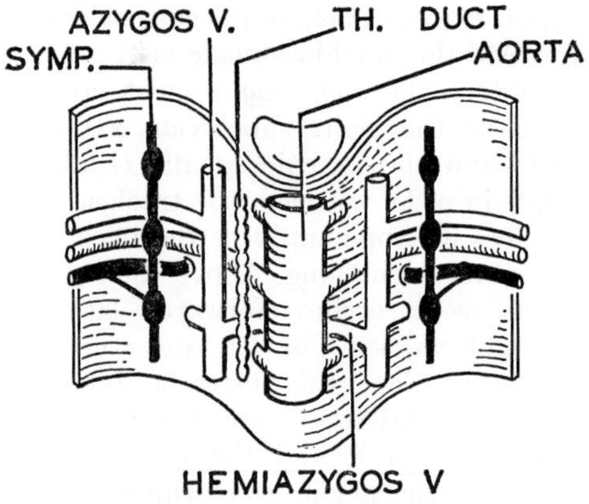

FIG. 638. Postulate: horizontal structures in the posterior mediastinum belong to the thoracic wall and pass external to longitudinal structures.

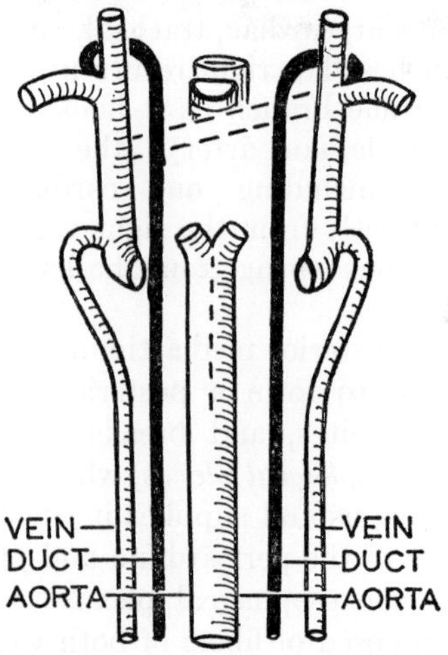

FIG. 639. Three symmetrically placed embryonic vessels.

In front are: (1) the root of the left lung; (2) the pericardium, which separates it from the oblique pericardial sinus and left atrium; (3) the esophagus, which was to its right opposite vertebrae 5, 6, and 7, is in front and passing to the left side opposite vertebrae 8, 9, and 10; (4) the diaphragm, at the level of the vertebrae 11 and 12, separates it from the upper recess of the omental bursa.

Branches (*fig. 642*)—(1) *visceral:* one to three bronchial aa. (p. 495), one to three esophageal aa. (p. 534), and twigs to the pericardium and diaphragm. (2) *parietal:* lower nine pairs of posterior intercostal and one pair of subcostal arteries.

Intercostal and Subcostal Arteries. The upper six **anterior intercostal arteries** are branches of the *internal thoracic artery;* the succeeding three are branches of the *musculophrenic artery*. The 10th and 11th intercostal spaces are short, open anteriorly and do not receive anterior intercostal arteries.

The 1st and 2nd **posterior intercostal arteries** arise indirectly from the subclavian artery (via the costocervical trunk and its supreme or highest intercostal branch) (*fig. 642*).

The remaining nine posterior intercostal arteries spring from the back of the descending aorta. Those to the 3rd and 4th spaces have necessarily to make a considerable ascent.

The **subcostal artery** with its vein and nerve leaves the thorax behind the lateral

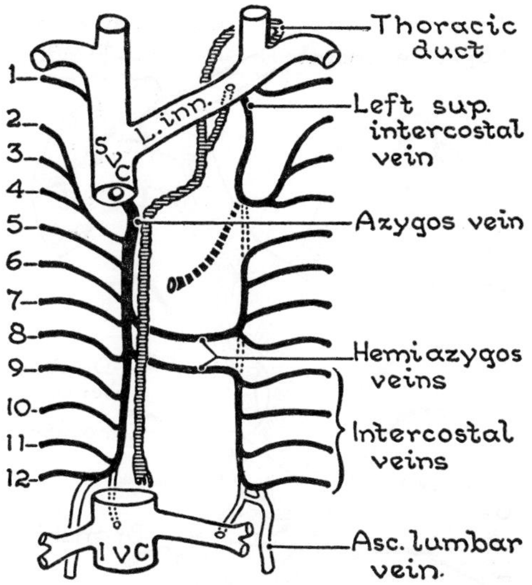

FIG. 641. The thoracic duct and the intercostal veins. (Continued from figure 677.)

arcuate lig. and runs in front of the Quadratus Lumborum.

Figure 638 schematically depicts the intercostal arteries leaving the aorta in the median plane; the intercostal veins returning to the azygos and hemiazygos veins near the median plane; and the intercostal nerves entering the thorax between the necks of the ribs and, therefore, far from the median plane.

These transversely running vessels and nerves cling to the thoracic wall which they supply and of which they are a part, no structure intervening. The terminal parts of the hemiazygos veins and the cross-channel of the thoracic duct cross the median plane transversely. They likewise cling to the wall.

Thoracic Duct (*figs. 639* to *641*).

»» The *primitive* lymph ducts were phylogenetically paired right and left vessels[8] that ascended through the posterior mediastinum on each side of the descending aorta, and through the superior mediastinum on each side of the esophagus till, reaching the root of the neck, each arched laterally immediately behind the carotid sheath to open into the angle between the subclavian and the internal jugular vein (*fig. 725*). Of the various prevertebral cross-communications between these right and left vessels, one lying on the plane between the posterior and superior mediastina, and therefore not subject to pressure by the aorta, enlarged.

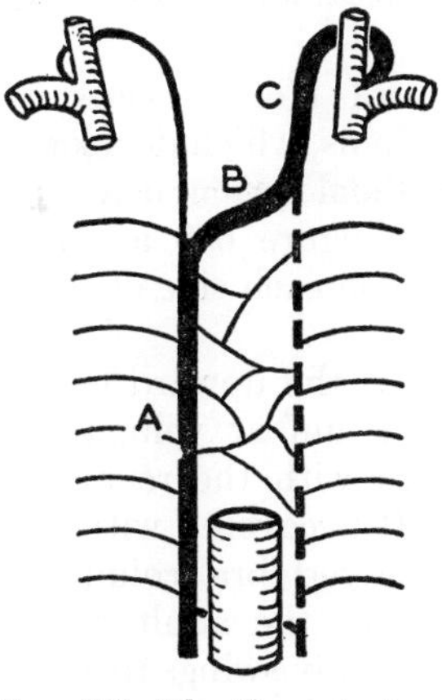

FIG. 640. The thoracic duct

[8] As in the frog and bird.

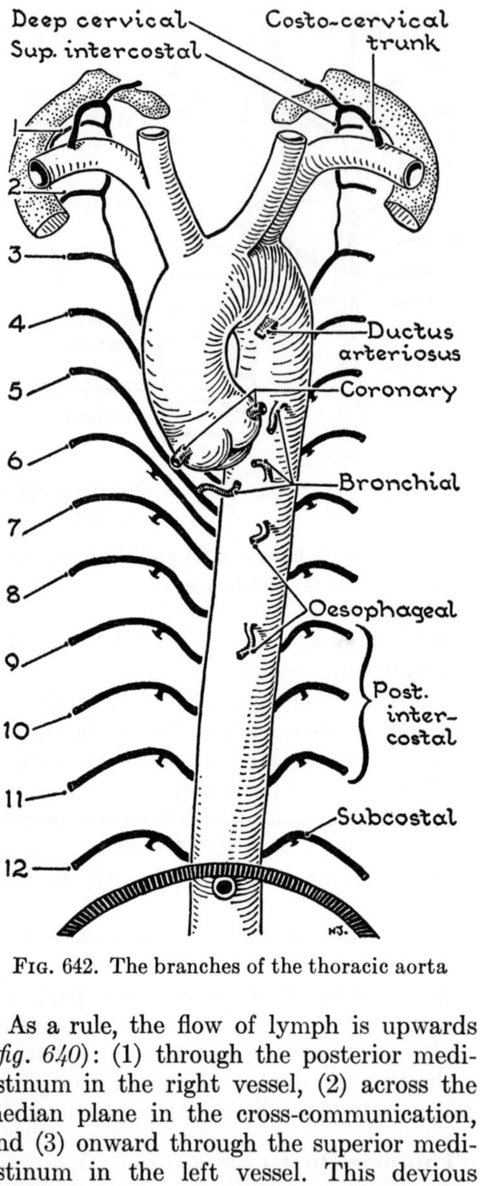

FIG. 642. The branches of the thoracic aorta

As a rule, the flow of lymph is upwards (*fig. 640*): (1) through the posterior mediastinum in the right vessel, (2) across the median plane in the cross-communication, and (3) onward through the superior mediastinum in the left vessel. This devious channel is known in adult anatomy as the thoracic duct. The diagonally opposite segments of the primitive lymph ducts severed connection with the thoracic duct. The lower left portion disappears (if indeed it ever existed in the human embryo) and the left intercostal lymph vessels mostly follow the example of the hemiazygos veins in crossing the median plane behind the aorta (according to postulate) and end in the thoracic duct (*fig. 640*).

The thoracic duct begins as the effluent from the cisterna chyli, enters the thorax through the aortic hiatus in the diaphragm, crosses the 12 thoracic vertebrae, and then at the level of vertebra C. 7, curves laterally in the neck (p. 622) to end in the left jugulo-subclavian angle (*fig. 725*).

The relationship of the thoracic duct to the vertebral column; to the aorta and azygos vein; to the right aortic intercostal arteries and hemiazygos veins; to the esophagus; and to the right and left mediastinal pleurae: needs no elaboration here.

Communications. If the thoracic duct be cut deliberately or by accident, chyle (the product of the digestion of fat) escapes from the cut end. Provided the duct is tied, evil results seldom follow, which indicates that accessory lymphaticovenous communications must exist (see p. 37).

Valves. The thoracic duct has few valves. There are usually two (or one) at the cephalic end; when only one, it is always inadequate (Rouviere).

Variations. Most of the variations possible from figure 640 have been observed. Commonly, the duct ends as a delta of two or three branches that open into the brachiocephalic (innominate) vein (or nearby veins) (*fig. 641*).

»» *Comparative Anatomy.* In the New World monkeys the lymph vessels of the digestive organs and of the posterior extremities end in the venous system near the renal veins and do not join the thoracic duct (Silvester). Note that in rats lymph trunks communicate with numerous veins including the renal, iliolumbar, portal, iliac, jugular, azygos, and vertebral; and that in cats there are communications with the azygos and intercostal veins. Man evidently possesses similar connections.

Azygos and Hemiazygos Veins (*fig. 641*). These veins, which developed from the posterior cardinal system of veins (*fig. 611*), are shown in figure 639 as paired venous channels, one on each side of the descending aorta.

Each vein is the upward continuation of the ascending lumbar vein, and it usually communicates with the renal vein (or inf. vena cava). It is covered with pleura and is applied to the vertebral column.

In its ascent, the adult right vein, the *azygos vein*, usually swings to, or beyond, the median plane and returns to arch over the root of the right lung to join the superior vena cava (Nathan).

The left vein, which early ended in the coronary sinus, definitively ends in the left brachiocephalic (innominate) vein. Usually it breaks into three segments (*hemiazygos, accessory hemiazygos,* and *left superior intercostal veins*) after two or more cross-branches have united it to the azygos vein. Alternatively, it may persist without breaks; it may even retain connection with the coronary sinus, when it is called the left superior vena cava.

TRIBUTARIES: posterior intercostal veins, vertebral venous plexus (*fig. 676*), and mediastinal, esophageal, and bronchial veins.

Intercostal Veins. The **anterior intercostal veins** on each side drain through the internal thoracic vein to the brachiocephalic vein.

From figure 641 observe: (1) that, of the 12 **posterior intercostal** and **subcostal veins** on each side, the 2nd, 3rd, and 4th unite to form the superior intercostal vein; (2) that the brachiocephalic veins drain the 1st, or supreme, right intercostal vein and the upper four (supreme and superior) left veins; and (3) that the azygos vein drains all others, that is, 11 of the 12 right veins and 8 of the 12 left veins via the hemiazygos veins.

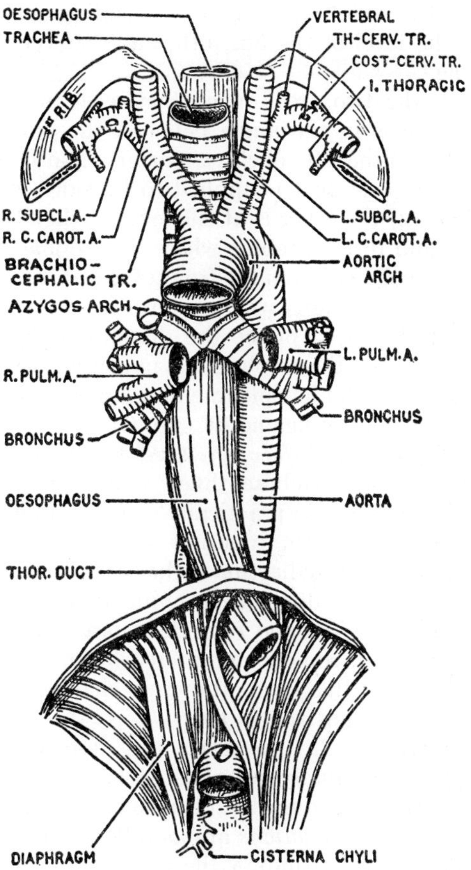

FIG. 643. The esophagus, the aorta, and the three branches of the aortic arch.

Esophagus

The esophagus extends from the pharynx to the stomach, and has, therefore, cervical, thoracic, and abdominal portions. Like the trachea, the esophagus begins at the lower border of the cricoid cartilage, at the level of the 6th cervical vertebra, and at a distance of 6 inches from the incisor teeth. It pierces the diaphragm behind the 7th left costal cartilage, an inch from the median plane, at the level of the 10th thoracic vertebra, and joins the stomach an inch beyond. It is 10 inches or more long (*fig. 643*).

It has *Four Constrictions*—at its origin, at the aortic arch, at the tracheal bifurcation, and where it passes through the diaphragm.

Its Curvatures are in two planes. Thus, in the midthoracic region it occupies the median plane; elsewhere it is slightly on the left, so, it is convex to the right. It is also convex dorsally in conformity with the curvature of the vertebral column.

THORACIC RELATIONSHIPS OF THE ESOPHAGUS. When considering these, have special regard to: (1) the mediastinal pleurae and lungs, (2) the heart and great arteries, (3) the respiratory tract, (4) the vertebral column, and (5) the thoracic duct. Ask yourself "Where could a sharp foreign body piercing its walls puncture these structures?"

Its right margin is in contact throughout with right mediastinal pleura and lung, except where the arch of the azygos vein interposes itself.

Its left margin is separated throughout from left mediastinal pleura and lung, (except at two areas) by the following four arteries: left common carotid, left subclavian, arch of the aorta (where it arches over the root of the left lung at the level of the 4th vertebra), and the descending aorta at the level of the 5th, 6th, and 7th vertebrae.

Of the two areas in contact with pleura (1) one is in the angle between the aortic arch and the left subclavian artery, and here the thoracic duct is applied to its side (*fig. 573*); (2) the other is at the level of the 8th, 9th, and 10th vertebrae where the esophagus is "suspended" from the front of the aorta by a meso-esophagus which allows it to curve forward and to pierce the diaphragm (*fig. 325.1*). Here the esophagus is in contact with both right and left pleurae and lungs behind the pulmonary ligaments (*fig. 637*).

Its posterior surface is related to the upper 10 thoracic vertebrae thus: with vertebral bodies 1–4 it is in practically direct contact. Intervening at the junction of the superior and posterior mediastina is the cross-channel of the thoracic duct. Intervening at the level of vertebrae 5, 6, and 7 are the thoracic duct, azygos vein, some right intercostal arteries, and (about this level) the cross-channels of the hemiazygos veins (*fig. 641*). At the level of vertebrae 8, 9, and 10, the descending aorta is gradually interposed. Finally, the esophagus lies to the left of the median plane.

Its anterior relations are as follows: in the superior mediastinum—the trachea and left recurrent nerve, with the left common carotid and subclavian arteries and the aortic arch crossing the projecting left margin; at the junction of superior and posterior mediastina—the bifurcation of the trachea, the bronchi (especially the left), and the inferior tracheobronchial nodes, all crossed ventrally by the right pulmonary artery; in the posterior mediastinum— the pericardium and oblique pericardial sinus, which alone separate it from the left atrium as far as vertebra 8; lastly, at the level of vertebra 9 and 10 is the diaphragm.

VESSELS. *The Arteries to the Esophagus* come from the inferior thyroid aa. in the neck; variably from the bronchial aa., right aortic intercostal aa., and descending aorta in the thorax; and the left gastric and inferior phrenic arteries in the abdomen.

Its veins drain to the inferior thyroid, azygos, and left gastric veins. Anastomoses between the last two veins unite the portal and caval systems (see esophageal varix, p. 247).

NERVES. The recurrent nerves and the sympathetic trunks in the neck; the right vagus and left recurrent nerve in the superior mediastinum. Below the bronchi the vagi, joined by branches from the sympathetic trunks and splanchnic nerves, form the esophageal plexus around the esophagus. From this plexus two nerves, the *anterior* and *posterior vagal trunks,* descend on the esophagus to the stomach.

SPHINCTERS. There is a sphincter at both ends of the esophagus. At the *gastric or cardiac end* the sphincter is a physiological one, supplied (1) by the vagus which conducts opening impulses (relaxes), and (2) by the sympathetic which conducts closing impulses (contracts). The sympathetic fibers partly ascend from the celiac plexus with the left gastric artery and partly descend in the thorax from the peri-aortic plexus (White and Smithwick).

At the *pharyngeal end* is the Cricopharyngeus (p. 665).

SECTION **VII**

Head and Neck

CHAPTER 34

FRONT OF SKULL, FACE, AND SCALP

SKULL, ON FRONT VIEW

(Norma Frontalis)

»» *Warning:* When handling a skull keep your fingers out of the orbital cavities or you will certainly break their medial walls which are papery in thinness.

Orientation: At a convention of anthropologists held in Frankfort (1882) it was agreed to examine skulls when so placed that the lower margins of the orbital apertures and the upper margins of the external acoustic (auditory) meatuses lie on a horizontal plane.

The Frankfort Plane. This most nearly approximates the Anatomical Position (*fig. 1*), in which the eyes look straight forward as, of course, they do in life. It is roughly achieved by placing a 2″ block under the foramen magnum, leaving the point of the chin resting on the table.

OUTLINE OF THE NORMA FRONTALIS (*fig. 645*). The *zygomatic arches* lie at the widest parts of the face. Above the arches, the outline of the skull is rounded because it is formed by the *cranium* or brain case, and it bulges a few millimeters beyond the zygomatic arches. Below the zygomatic

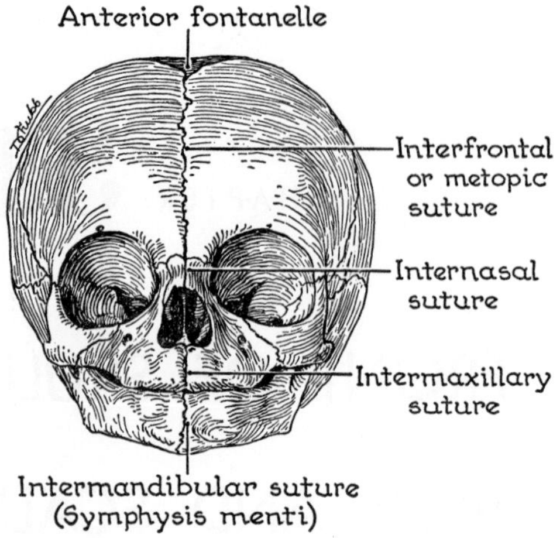

FIG. 644. The skull at birth, front view

arches the skull is angular and is outlined by the *posterior border of the ramus,* the *angle,* and the *base* or lower border of the mandible.

At Birth (*fig. 644*) a median suture line bisects the norma frontalis, separating the *parietal, frontal, nasal, maxillary,* and *mandibular* bones of opposite sides. The two halves of the human mandible fuse at the *symphysis menti* during the second year, but in most mammals they remain separate throughout life.

The two halves of the frontal bone likewise fuse about the 2nd year, but in some skulls they remain separate, i.e., the interfrontal or *metopic suture* persists. The interparietal or *sagittal suture* is usually obliterated by the age of 35 years (Todd and Lyon).

The *bregma* is the point at which the sagittal and coronal (frontoparietal) sutures intersect. It is situated 1″ in front of the *vertex* or highest point. The *nasion* is the point at the root of the nose where the frontonasal suture crosses the median plane.

Entrance to the Orbit [Aditus Orbitae]. The vertical diameter of the entrance is slightly less than the transverse. Each of three bones—frontal, maxillary, and zygomatic—forms approximately one-third of the orbital margin. The frontal bone forms the supra-orbital margin and descends lower medially, where it articulates with the *lacrimal bone* and *frontal process of the maxilla,* than laterally where its *zygomatic process* articulates with the *frontal process of the zygomatic bone* (*fig. 645*).

The fullness above the medial part of the supra-orbital margin of the frontal bone is the *superciliary arch.* The arches are well marked in the male and are a criterion of sex. The elevation between the superciliary arches, and therefore between the eyebrows, is called the *glabella* because the overlying skin is bald or glabrous.

The *piriform aperture* (anterior nasal aperture) lies below and between the orbital apertures. Its sharp, pear-shaped margin is formed by the nasal bones above; by the maxillae laterally and below. A median spine of bone, the *anterior nasal spine,* juts forward from the maxillae and helps to support the septal cartilage of the nose.

The upper border of the *zygomatic arch,* when traced forward, bends sharply upward, lateral to the orbit, and then, as the *temporal line,* it curves backward across the side of the cranium, separating the *temporal fossa* below from the *region of the scalp* above (*fig. 646*).

Now, if the temporal muscles are powerful and therefore large, and if the brain and therefore the brain case are small, then the temporal lines of the two sides approach each other more closely. In some dogs and apes they meet in the median plane and rise, like the crest on a Roman helmet (*fig. 647*).

The lower border of the zygomatic arch, when traced forward, curves downward and medially and becomes continuous with the lower border of the *zygomatic process* of the maxilla, which in turn becomes continuous with a ridge that descends to the second molar tooth. This ridge or buttress separates the *facial surface* of the maxilla from the *infratemporal surface.*

Teeth. There are 32 *teeth* in all, 16 in each jaw. Of the eight upper and lower teeth on each side, two are *incisors* or cutting teeth, one is a *canine,* two are *premolar* or bicuspid teeth for their crowns have two cusps, and three are *molar* or millstone teeth. The roots of the teeth are embedded in little troughs or alveoli con-

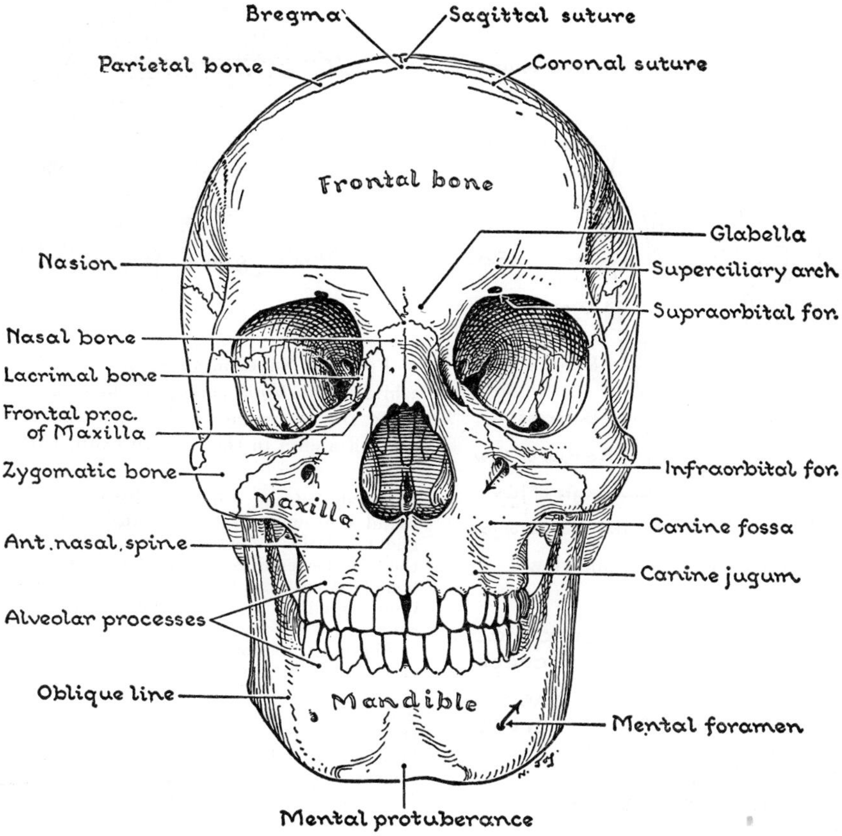

FIG. 645. The skull, on front view (Norma frontalis)

tained in the *alveolar processes* of the maxilla and mandible. (Also p. 683.)

Man alone has a *chin* and an *anterior nasal spine*. They are associated with recession of the teeth (*fig. 648*).

The skull has but one pair of movable joints, the *temporomandibular* or *jaw joints*. Here a bone of the face articulates with a bone of the cranium. When the teeth of the lower jaw close on the upper teeth, a force ranging from 150 to 300 pounds can be exerted. Therefore, to prevent the mandible from crushing the hollow maxilla beneath the cranium, a buttress or strengthening bar is provided in the form of a ridge that extends upward from the (1st or) 2nd molar tooth to the zygomatic bone. The force is then largely transmitted up the strong lateral orbital margin to be dispersed through the dome of the cranium. Stresses from the front teeth are mainly transmitted via the frontal process of the maxilla along the medial orbital margin.

The sockets for the canine teeth cause ridges on the upper and lower jaws. The area on each jaw medial to the canine ridge is the *incisive fossa*. The area on the upper jaw between the canine ridge and the zygomatic process of the maxilla is the *canine fossa*.

At the point of the jaw, there is a slightly raised triangular area, the *mental protuberance*. From its lateral angle an *oblique line* runs upward and backward to become continuous with the *anterior border of the ramus* of the jaw.

Foramina. Three intra-osseous foramina —*supra-orbital*, *infra-orbital*, and *mental*— open on to the face on a vertical line that passes between the premolar teeth. They penetrate the frontal, maxillary, and mandibular bones about 1¼″ from the median

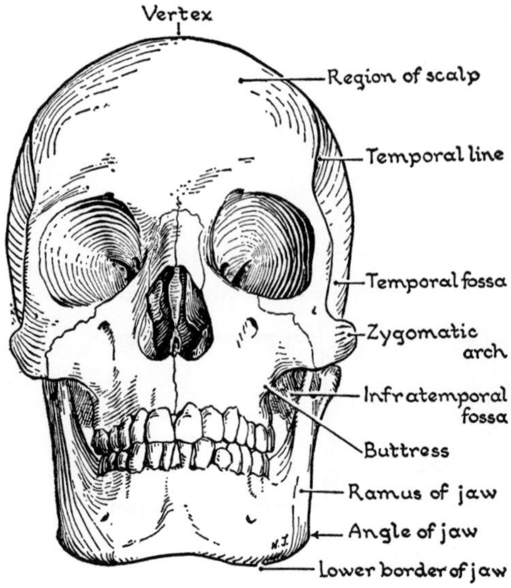

FIG. 646. The skull, on front view

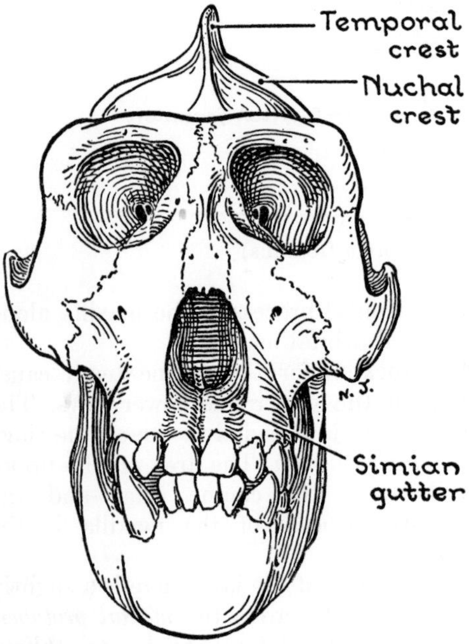

FIG. 647. The skull of a gorilla, front view. (After Gregory.)

plane and transmit sensory branches of the 1st, 2nd, and 3rd divisions, respectively, of the trigeminal nerve and their companion vessels (*fig. 658*).

»» During fetal life the supra-orbital and infra-orbital nerves and vessels run along the roof and floor, respectively, of the orbital cavity, the former turning round the supra-orbital margin on to the forehead, and the latter round the infra-orbital margin on to the face. Depending on the extent to which the frontal bone later envelops the supra-orbital nerve and vessels, there is either a supra-orbital notch—foramen—or canal.

Similarly, a process from the infra-orbital margin of the maxilla grows medially over the infra-orbital vessels and nerve forming a roof for them. The suture line may persist in the adult (*figs. 645* and *839*). In the hinder part of the floor of the orbital cavity they lie in a gutter, but in the anterior they run through a canal that opens inferomedially on to the canine fossa, 1 cm. below the infra-orbital margin.

In a similar fashion the mandible grows round the inferior alveolar (dental) nerve and vessels, thereby forming the mandibular canal. The mental foramen is the anterior orifice of this canal.

Two minute intra-osseous foramina pierce the zygomatic and nasal bones and open on to the face: the zygomatic bone is pierced near its center by the zygomaticofacial nerve and a twig of the lacrimal artery; the nasal bone by a vein from the nose.

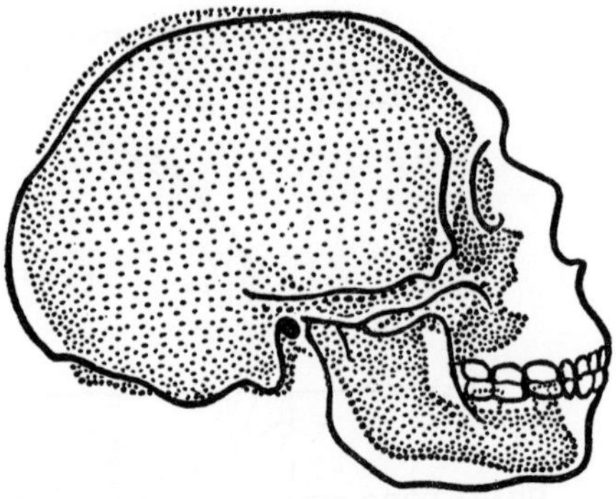

FIG. 648. Superimposed profiles of a modern white skull (*stippled*) and a prehistoric skull (*clear*). Note the recession of the face and the appearance of a chin in the modern skull. (After Boule.)

FACE

Muscles and Features of the Face

The facial muscles or muscles of expression are disposed around the orifices of the mouth, eye, nose, and ear, as sphincters and dilators (*fig. 649*). Developmentally, they took origin in the hyoid or 2nd pharyngeal arch and from it spread as a sheet over the face, dragging after them branches of the facial nerve, which is the nerve of this arch. The *Platysma*, which spread downwards over the neck, and the *Epicranius*, which spread upward over the cranium, are derived from the same source and are supplied by the same nerve.

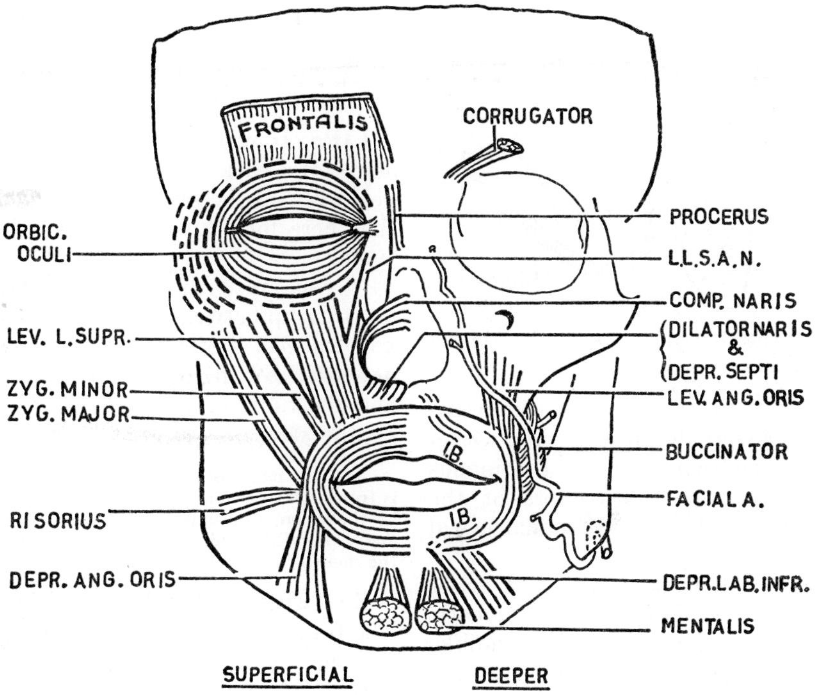

FIG. 649. The muscles of the face

One muscle on the face—the *Masseter*—is not supplied by the facial nerve. The Masseter covers the ramus of the jaw and is a muscle of mastication. Accordingly, it is supplied on its deep surface by the trigeminal nerve.

Muscles of Rima Oris (Aperture of Mouth). The *Orbicularis Oris,* or sphincter of the mouth, lies within the lips and encircles the oral aperture. It extends upward almost to the nose and downward to the horizontal skin crease midway between the chin and the mouth.

Converging on the angle of the mouth where they blend with the Orbicularis Oris are five muscles—the *Levator Anguli Oris* (Caninus), which arises below the infra-orbital foramen; the *Zygomaticus Major,* or smiling muscle, which arises from the bone of the same name; the *Risorius,* or grinning muscle, which arises from the parotid fascia and is joined by the posterior fibers of the *Platysma;* and the *Depressor Anguli Oris* (Triangularis), which arises from the oblique line on the mandible.

Muscles of the Lips (L. Labia). Attached to the upper lip are three bands, which arise from the medial and lower borders of the orbital margin. They are: *Levator Labii Superioris Alaeque Nasi,* **Levator Labii Superioris,** and *Zygomaticus Minor.*

The first gives a slip to the ala of the nose; the second is broad, quadrate, and arises above the infra-orbital foramen; the third is a mere slip.

Attached to the lower lip is the *Depressor Labii Inferioris* (Quadratus), which arises from the oblique line of the mandible between the mental foramen and the mental protuberance. It is rhomboidal. Its medial border decussates with that of its fellow above the horizontal skin crease, leaving a triangular space above the mental protuberance. This the Mentales occupy.

Muscles of the Chin (L. Mentum). Each *Mentalis* is conical and it passes from the lower incisive fossa, where it is submucous, downward to be attached widely to the skin of the chin. When it contracts, it puckers the skin of the chin.

Muscles of the Cheek (L. Bucca). The *Buccinator* is a flat muscle whose inner sur-

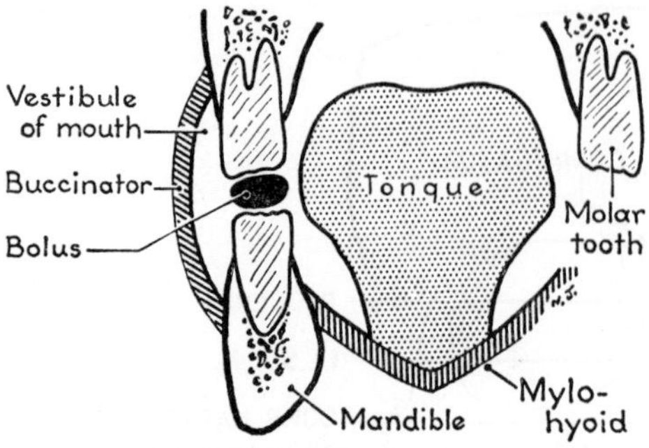

FIG. 649.1. The Buccinator and the tongue hold the food between the teeth.

face is lined with the mucous membrane of the cheek. Externally, it is covered with a thin areolar membrane which is continuous posteriorly over the Constrictors of the pharynx; hence, called the buccopharyngeal fascia.

Attachments. Above and below, it arises from the outer surfaces of the alveolar processes of the maxilla and mandible, lateral to the molar teeth. Posteriorly, it is continuous with the Superior Constrictor of the pharynx, the line of union being marked by an indefinite fibrous suture, the *pterygomandibular raphe* (*figs. 770* and *771*), that extends from the hamulus of the medial pterygoid plate to the mandible behind the 3rd molar tooth. Anteriorly, it extends into the upper and lower lips and there blends with the Orbicularis Oris; some fibers decussate behind the angle of the mouth, the upper fibers passing into the lower lip, the lower fibers into the upper lip.

Actions. The Buccinator aids in mastication by pressing the cheeks against the teeth, thereby preventing food from collecting in the vestibule of the mouth (*fig. 649.1*). Dogs have no cheeks and cannot chew. It also acts in blowing and in sucking.

»» In order to satisfy yourself of this, pass your left index finger well into the right side of the vestibule and perform chewing, sucking, and blowing movements.

Nerve supply: Facial nerve (nerve VII).

Structures piercing: Buccal branches of nerve V^3, which are sensory; parotid duct; and ducts of a cluster of small mucous glands, the *molar glands,* that lie on the buccopharyngeal fascia near the parotid duct.

The space between the Buccinator medially and the ramus of the jaw laterally is occupied by an encapsuled mass of lobulated fat, the *buccal pad* of fat.

LIPS. If you run the tip of your tongue across the back of your lower or upper lip, you will feel the small nodular *labial glands* that here form an incomplete subepithelial tunic.

If you grasp the margin of your upper or lower lip between your finger and thumb, you will feel the pulsations of a submucous *arterial ring* lying between the labial muscles and the tunic of labial glands. It is formed by the *superior* and *inferior labial arteries.*

»» The lip margins are red partly because the skin is translucent and partly because the vascular papillae or thelia are unusually long. Historically, the term "epithelium" was first applied to the cells covering the thelia of the lip (E. A. Schafer).

EXTERNAL NOSE (*figs. 650* and *651*). The framework of the external nose is made of bone, hyaline cartilage, and fibro-areolar tissue. The cartilages are: *septal, lateral,* and *alar.*

The *septal cartilage* lies in the parti-

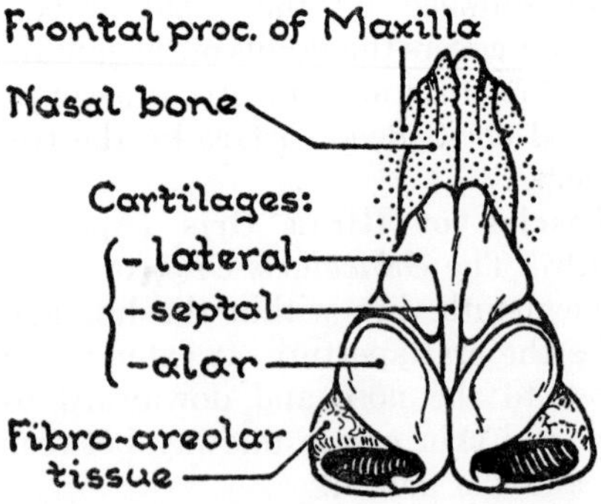

FIG. 650. The framework of the external nose (front view).

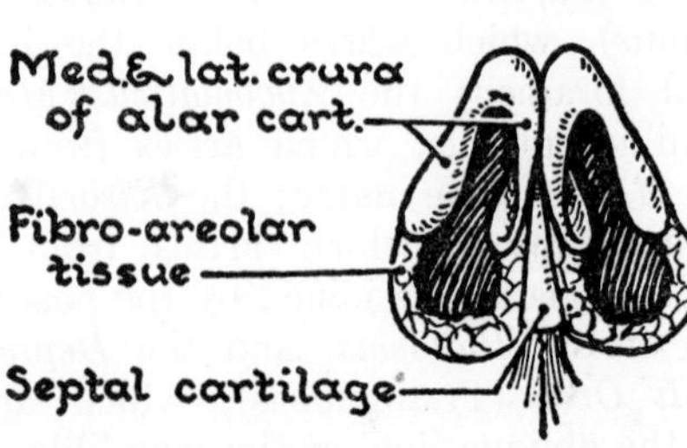

FIG. 651. The framework of the external nose (viewed from below).

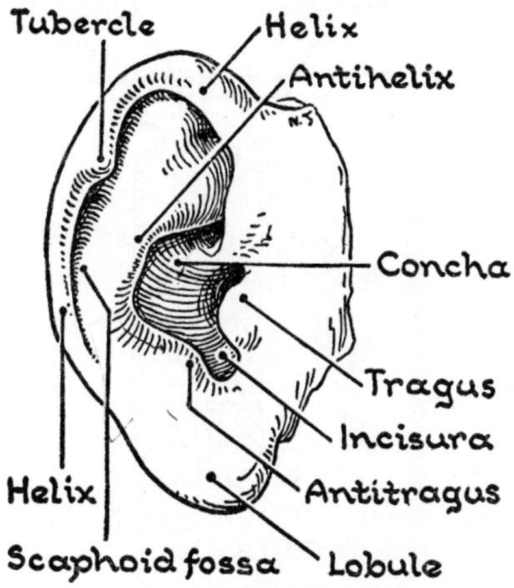

FIG. 652. The auricle

tion or septum between the right and left nasal cavities. Its lower free border, which projects far in front of the anterior nasal spine, is best felt between the tips of two fingers inserted within the nares or nostrils. The tip of the nose and the lower border of the nasal septum are supported by the medial limbs of the U-shaped alar cartilages. The lateral limb of the *alar cartilage* does not extend to the lower part of the *ala* of the nose, which is composed of fibro-areolar tissue. The right and left *lateral cartilages* are not entities but are winglike expansions of the septal cartilage. They are firmly united to the nasal bones above and maxillae behind, but are connected only loosely with the alar cartilages below.

» The apposed surfaces of the nasal bones are flat and triangular, the base being above (*figs. 799* and *844*). The posterior surface of each bone is covered with mucous membrane and is grooved by a branch of the anterior ethmoidal nerve. The nerve passes between the bone and lateral cartilage to the outer surface of the nose and, as the external nasal nerve, continues to the tip of the nose (*fig. 658*).

The alar cartilage is movable; and, when during deep inspiration, the *Levator Labii Superioris Alaeque Nasi* and other muscular slips pull on its lateral limb, the nostril dilates. The *Compressor Naris* joins its fellow to form a sling over the bridge of the nose.

AURICLE. The framework of the *auricle* is made of a single piece of elastic cartilage except at its most dependent part, the lobule, which is fibro-areolar. The cartilage is continuous with the cartilage of the external acoustic meatus (meatus. L = a canal) (see p. 706). Figures 652 and 653 provide the names of its elevations and depressions. Of these, note that *Darwin's tubercle* represents the primitive apex, and from the *tragus* grow hairs that guard the *external meatus*.

The skin is adherent on the lateral surface, but movable on the helix and on the cranial surface.

Muscles. The auricle has several rudimentary intrinsic muscles and three extrinsic muscles—Auriculares Posterior, Superior, and Anterior—all supplied by the facial nerve. The Posterior springs from the mastoid bone; the two others from the epicranial aponeurosis. The intrinsic muscles are easily displayed because of the absence of fat.

Sensory Nerves—auriculotemporal (V^3), great auricular (C. 2, 3), and lesser occipital (C. 2, 3), also two twigs, the *auricular branches of the vagus* and *facial nerves*. The twig from the facial nerve is postulated on clinical evidence.

Blood Supply—superficial temporal and posterior auricular arteries. Some branches of the latter turn round the helix to reach the lateral surface, while others pierce the cartilage.

EYELIDS, CONJUNCTIVAL SAC, AND TEAR APPARATUS. DEFINITIONS. The upper and lower eyelids, or *palpebrae*, are united at the medial and lateral angles by the corresponding *palpebral commissures*. The opening between the margins of the lids is the *palpebral rima* or *fissure*.

The posterior five-sixths of the outermost coat of the eyeball is white, tough, and

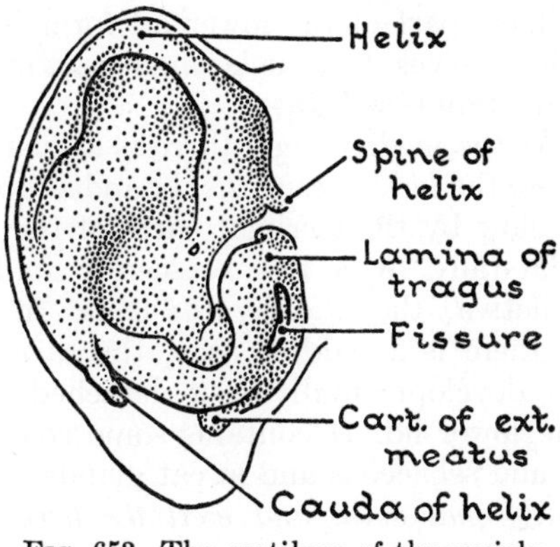

FIG. 653. The cartilage of the auricle

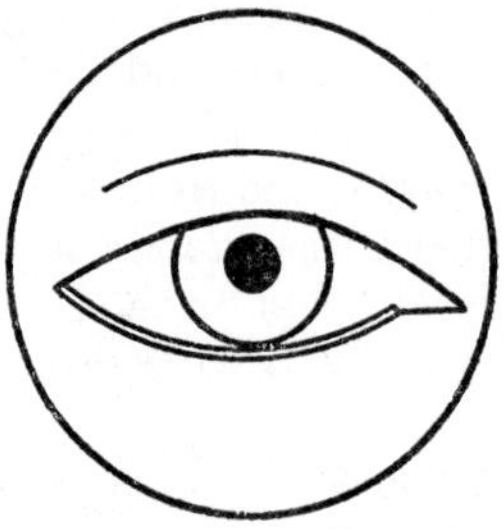

FIG. 654. The margins of the eyelids

called the *sclera;* its anterior one-sixth is transparent and called the *cornea.* Through the cornea the varicolored *iris* is seen, and in the center of the iris is the *pupil.*

The potential space between the eyeball and the eyelids is the *conjunctival sac.* The membrane lining the sac is the *conjunctiva.* At the upper and lower limits of the sac, called the *fornices,* the conjunctiva is reflected from eyeball to eyelid.

Inspection. When examining your eye in a looking glass, observe that:

1. The margin of the lower lid crosses the lower limit of the cornea; the margin of the upper lid crosses the cornea midway between the pupil and the corneal margin, so no sclera is seen either above or below the cornea, but only at its sides (*fig. 654*).

2. The lateral five-sixths of the margins of the lids are flat and carry eyelashes or *cilia.* They form the *ciliary parts* of the margins. The medial one-sixth are devoid of hairs and are rounded, and as the *canaliculi* that drain away the tears traverse them, they may be called the *lacrimal parts* of the lid margins.

3. The entire margin of the upper lid and the ciliary part of the lower lid form semi-elliptical curves; but the lacrimal part of the lower margin is straight.

4. At the medial angle there is a triangular area, the *lacus lacrimalis,* bounded above and below by the lacrimal parts of the lids and laterally by a free crescentic fold of conjunctiva, the *plica semilunaris.* In the lacus there is a reddish area, the *caruncle,* which developmentally is a detached part of the lower lid. It contains some colorless hairs and sebaceous and sweat glands.

Gently pull down and evert the lower lid and note that:

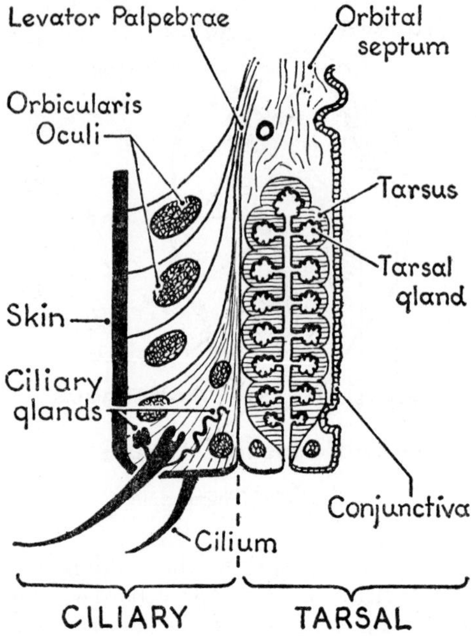

FIG. 655. Section through the upper eyelid. (After Whitnall.)

5. At the junction of the ciliary and lacrimal parts of its margin there is a *papilla* on which the *punctum,* or entrance to the inferior lacrimal canaliculus, can easily be seen. Because the punctum is directed backward so as to be applied to the eyeball, it is able to suck up tears. In the upper lid, the papilla and punctum are less well marked.

6. The conjunctiva is firmly adherent to the back of the lid and to the front of the cornea, but at the fornices and where it covers the sclera, it is loosely attached.

Evert the upper lid over a match stick and note that:

7. A sulcus lies near and parallel to the margin. Into it the foreign particles that chance to enter the sac are commonly caught.

8. The hairs or cilia projecting from the lid margins are in two or three irregular rows.

9. Hairs imply the presence of sebaceous glands, and such open into each hair follicle. Sweat glands likewise open into or beside the hair follicles (*fig. 655*). These *ciliary glands* are situated in front of the tarsus.

10. The *tarsal glands,* embedded in the

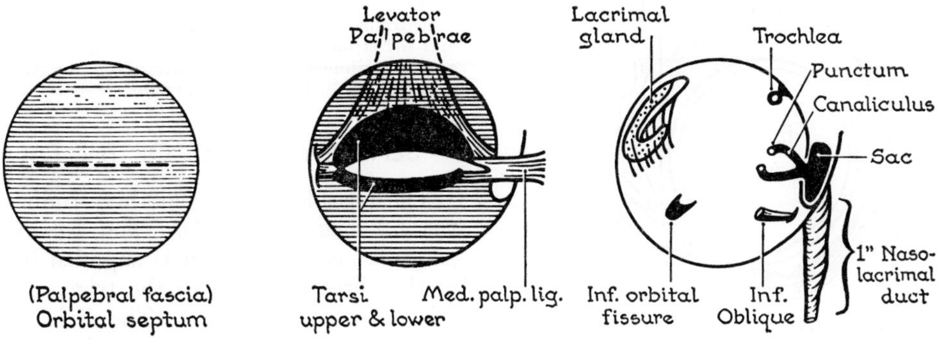

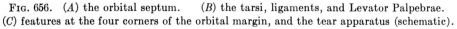

FIG. 656. (*A*) the orbital septum. (*B*) the tarsi, ligaments, and Levator Palpebrae. (*C*) features at the four corners of the orbital margin, and the tear apparatus (schematic).

tarsus, are modified sebaceous glands, visible as yellow streaks through the conjunctiva. On stroking them in the cadaver with the end of the handle of the scalpel, threads of white sebum are expressed on to the lid margin, like paste from a collapsible tube.

»» An obstructed and inflamed hair follicle or stye will project on the front of the lid; an obstructed tarsal gland on to the globe of the eye.

The chief duty of the lids is to keep a film of tears spread over the eyeball, and the upper lid wipes the eyeball free of dust and foreign particles.

Orbital Septum and Tarsi (*fig. 656*). The eyelids develop as folds of skin which come together and adhere along their edges during the middle 3 months of intra-uterine life. When they become free again, the palpebral rima is re-established. (In kittens, the lids remain adherent for some days after birth.)

While the lids are closed, the orbital septum, which is the framework of the eyelids, may be regarded as forming a complete diaphragm for the orbital cavity, for it is attached to the orbital margin all around, except medially where it passes behind the tear sac to gain attachment to the lacrimal bone, there creating a sharp ridge, the *posterior lacrimal crest* (*fig. 845*). Hence, operations on the sac are performed in front of the septum.

Condensation and thickening of the septum take place over an almond-shaped area in the upper lid and over a rod-shaped area in the lower lid, resulting in the formation of an upper and a lower *tarsus*. These plates are anchored to the orbital margin by the *medial* and *lateral palpebral ligaments*. The lateral lig. or raphe is merely a slight thickening of the orbital septum, whereas the medial lig. is a strong independent band that crosses in front of the tear sac to be attached to the frontal process of the maxilla.

Muscles of Eyelids. The *sphincter* of the palpebral fissure is the *Orbicularis Oculi*. The fibers within the lids, the *palpebral portion*, take an arched course from medial to lateral palpebral lig. in front of the orbital septum. Although striated and supplied by the facial nerve, they usually act involuntarily, closing the lids in sleep and in blinking.

The fibers of the peripheral or *orbital portion* pass in circles from the medial palpebral ligament and adjacent part of the frontal bone across the forehead, temple, and cheek back to the medial ligament and adjacent part of the maxilla. Having no lateral attachment, they draw the lids medially and thereby encourage tears and particles of dust to the medial angle of the eye. They are responsible for the "crow's foot" wrinkles seen at the lateral angles when the eyes are firmly closed.

»» Some muscle fibers, the *Pars Lacrimalis* (Tensor Tarsi), are carried medially behind the tear sac and there find attachment to the posterior lacrimal crest (*fig. 657*). They serve to keep the lids so closely applied to the eyeballs that foreign particles cannot readily accumulate behind them, and, perhaps by creating a vacuum in the sac, aspirate tears.

The *dilator* of the palpebral fissure is the Levator Palpebrae Superioris. Involuntary muscle fibers in both lids, the superior and inferior *tarsal muscles*, widen the fissure (*fig. 698*).

Muscles of Forehead, associated with the eyelids (*fig. 649*). The *Frontalis* causes

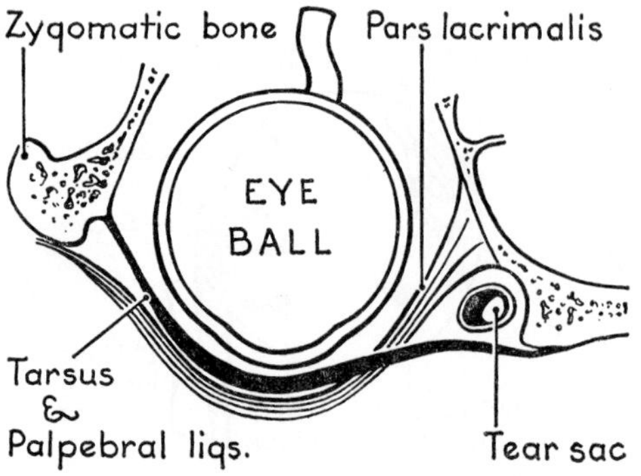

FIG. 657. Horizontal section of globe and upper lid. The upper lid, which moves like a visor and wipes the globe, is kept applied to it by the Pars Lacrimalis. (After Whitnall.)

the transverse wrinkles on the forehead, associated with a surprised and supercilious look. Raising the eyebrows brings it into play. It arises from the epicranial aponeurosis 2″ or 3″ above the brow. Its most medial fibers are prolonged on to the nose as the *Procerus*. The remaining fibers interlock with those of the Orbicularis. The fascia lining the deep surface of the Frontalis (*fig. 661*) is attached to the bone above the supra-orbital margin; it would prevent the downward spread of fluid into the eyelids.

The *Corrugator Supercilii* causes the short vertical wrinkles in front of the glabella on frowning, displaying annoyance, and exhibiting pain. It arises from the glabella deep to the Frontalis and, as a small band, runs laterally deep to the eyebrows and interlocks with the Frontalis and Orbicularis (*fig. 649*).

Lacrimal or Tear Apparatus (*fig. 656C*). The upper and lower *lacrimal canaliculi* are about 10 mm. long. They take a curved course near the free margin of the lid from *lacrimal punctum* to lacrimal sac, which they enter either separately or by a common orifice. The *lacrimal sac* is but the blind upper end of the *nasolacrimal duct* (*fig. 656C*). This membranous duct lies behind the medial palpebral lig. and in front of the Pars Lacrimalis of the Orbicularis Oculi and the orbital septum.

The *nasolacrimal duct* continues downward between lacrimal, maxillary, and inferior conchal bones to open into the inferior meatus of the nose (*fig. 799*).

»» It is surrounded with veins, and is separated from the atrium of the nose by the papery lacrimal bone and the strong frontal process of the maxilla, and an anterior ethmoidal air cell generally intervenes between its upper half and the atrium.

SENSORY NERVES OF THE FACE

The face develops from three rudiments, the *frontonasal, maxillary,* and *mandibular processes*, each of which is supplied by one of the three divisions of the trigeminal, or 5th cranial, nerve (N. V). The divisions are named the ophthalmic, maxillary, and mandibular nerves; they may be indicated by the signs V^1, V^2, and V^3.

The great auricular nerve (C. 2 and 3) encroaches on the face, sending branches across the parotid gland and the Masseter. The facial nerve mediates deep sensibilities. (see Nervus intermedius, page 714.)

The **Ophthalmic Nerve** (V^1). Of the 5 cutaneous branches of V^1, four are related to the upper lid; one to the nose (*fig. 658*). The *lacrimal branch* is a mere twig. It pierces the orbital septum in the lateral part of the lid.

The *supra-orbital branch* emerges through the supra-orbital notch or foramen, and divides into medial and lateral branches which ascend on the frontal bone, pierce the Frontalis, and extend almost to the lambdoid suture on the back of the skull.

The *supratrochlear branch* pierces the orbital septum above the trochlea for the Superior Oblique and, then pierces the Frontalis to supply the region above the glabella.

The *infratrochlear branch* pierces the same septum and muscle below the trochlea to supply the structures about the medial palpebral commissure, including the lacrimal sac. The four preceding nerves supply the whole thickness of the upper lid.

The *external nasal branch* emerges at the lower border of the nasal bone, which is easily palpated with the fingernail, and descends on the nasal cartilages to the tip of the nose.

Arteries. Branches of the ophthalmic art. accompany these five nerves, viz., lacrimal, supraorbital, supratrochlear, dorsal nasal (infratrochlear), and external nasal arteries (*fig. 703*).

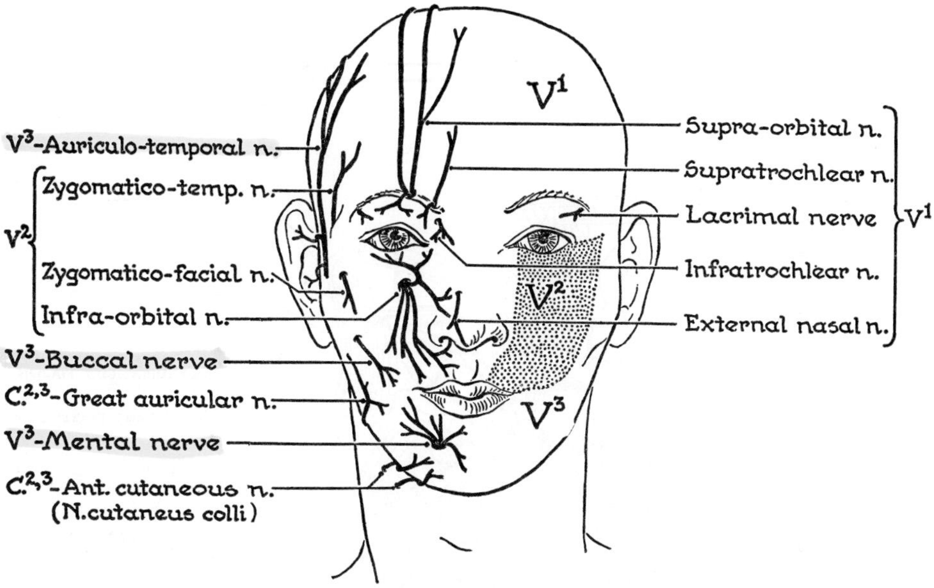

FIG. 658. The sensory nerves of the face and front of the scalp

The **Maxillary Nerve** (V^2). Of the 3 cutaneous branches of V^2, the **infra-orbital branch** emerges through the infra-orbital foramen, and finds itself between the Levator Labii Superioris and the Levator Anguli Oris. Its branches pass to the upper lip and to the mucous membrane of the cheek and upper gums. It also supplies the skin and conjunctiva of the lower eyelid, and the dorsum of the nose, and it sends branches below the ala of the nose to the skin of the vestibule.

»» The *zygomaticofacial branch* appears through the foramen of that name. It is but a twig. The *zygomatico-temporal* branch appears through the foramen of that name in the temporal fossa, pierces the temporal fascia behind the tubercle on the frontal process of the zygomatic bone, and supplies the anterior part of the temporal region.

Arteries of the same names accompany these nerves.

The **Mandibular Nerve** (V^3) (*fig. 658*). Of the 3 cutaneous branches of N. V^3, the *mental branch* emerges through the mental foramen and finds itself deep to the Depressor Anguli Oris. Its branches pass mainly upward to the skin and mucous membrane of the lower lip and to the gums and the chin (*fig. 793*).

The *buccal branch* appears deep to the anterior border of the Masseter, below the level of the parotid duct. It runs almost to the angle of the mouth to become cutaneous, and branches that pierce the Buccinator supply the mucous membrane of the cheek.

The *auriculotemporal branch* crosses the posterior root of the zygoma just in front of the ear and ascends behind the superficial temporal artery. Its name suggests its terminal distribution to auricle and temporal region, but it also supplies the outer surface of the tympanic membrane, the external meatus, and the mandibular joint.

Arteries. Branches of the maxillary artery (mental and buccal) accompany the mental and buccal nerves; and the superficial temporal art. accompanies the auriculotemporal nerve.

»» NOTE: The sensory pathway from (1) the *cornea* is via the ciliary nn. which travel between the scleral and choroidal coats of the eyeball; (2) the *tip of the nose* via the external nasal n.; (3) the *point of the chin* via the mental n.; and (4) the *tip of the auricle* via the lesser occipital nerve.

MOTOR NERVE OF THE FACE

The facial, or 7th cranial, nerve (N. VII) supplies the muscles of the face, auricle, and scalp, the Platysma, and, to be seen later, the Digastric (post. belly), Stylohyoid, and Stapedius.

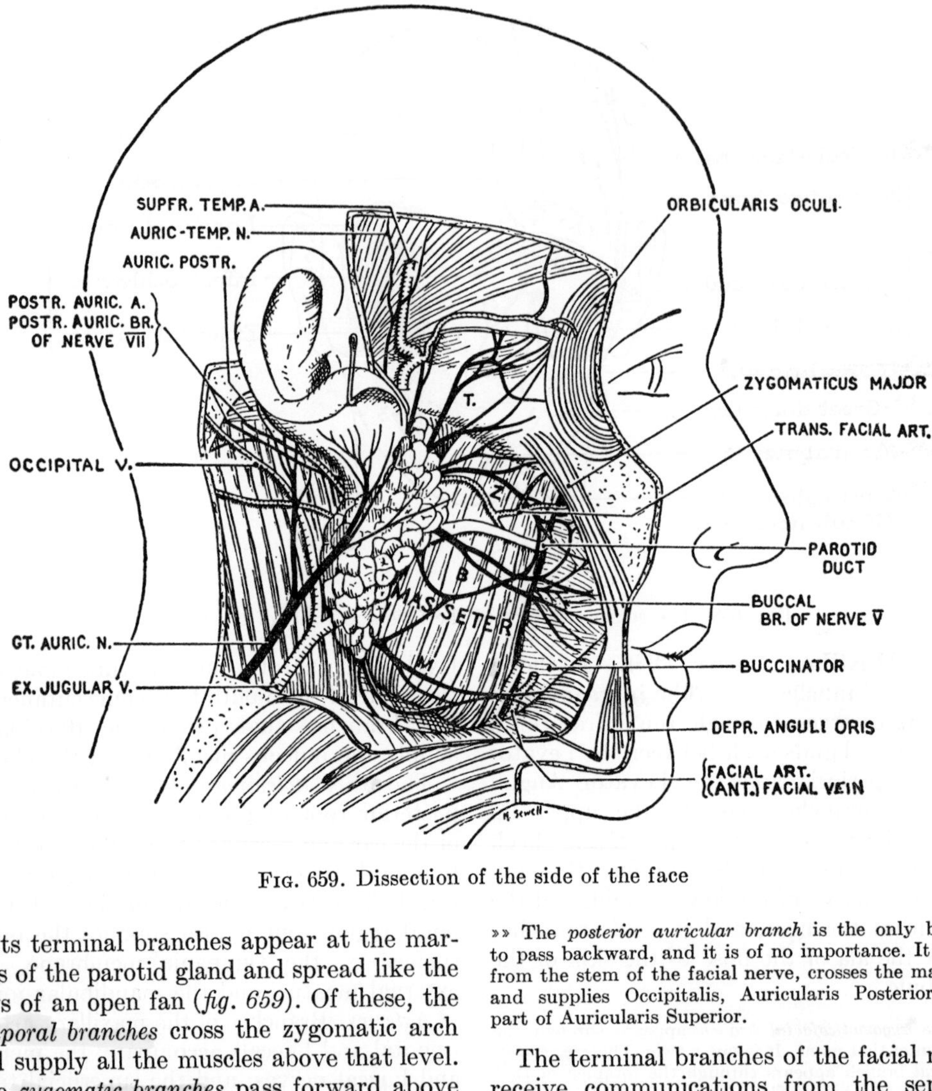

FIG. 659. Dissection of the side of the face

Its terminal branches appear at the margins of the parotid gland and spread like the rays of an open fan (*fig. 659*). Of these, the *temporal branches* cross the zygomatic arch and supply all the muscles above that level. The *zygomatic branches* pass forward above the parotid duct to supply the muscles of the infra-orbital region. The *buccal branch* takes the general direction of the buccal branch of the trigeminal nerve, but it is superficial to the Masseter. The *mandibular branch* supplies the muscles of the lower lip and chin.

The *cervical branches*, two in number, pass within a finger's breadth of the angle of the jaw: one descends, communicates with the anterior cutaneous nerve of the neck [n. transversus colli], and supplies the Platysma; the other curves forward, crosses the base of the jaw superficial to the *facial artery*, joins the mandibular branch, and assists it to innervate the muscles of the lower lip.

»» The *posterior auricular branch* is the only branch to pass backward, and it is of no importance. It arises from the stem of the facial nerve, crosses the mastoid, and supplies Occipitalis, Auricularis Posterior, and part of Auricularis Superior.

The terminal branches of the facial nerve receive communications from the sensory branches of the trigeminal nerve on the face and from C. 2 and 3 about the neck and ear.

BLOOD SUPPLY TO THE FACE

This is very free and anastomoses are numerous. In addition to the many branches of the *ophthalmic* and *maxillary arteries* that accompany the various branches of the 5th nerve on to the face, there are the *facial* and *transverse facial arteries* (*fig. 659*).

Facial Artery (Ext. maxillary art.). The facial artery appears on the face at the base of the jaw, immediately in front of the Masseter. There its vein lies behind it on the Masseter; part of the cervical branch of

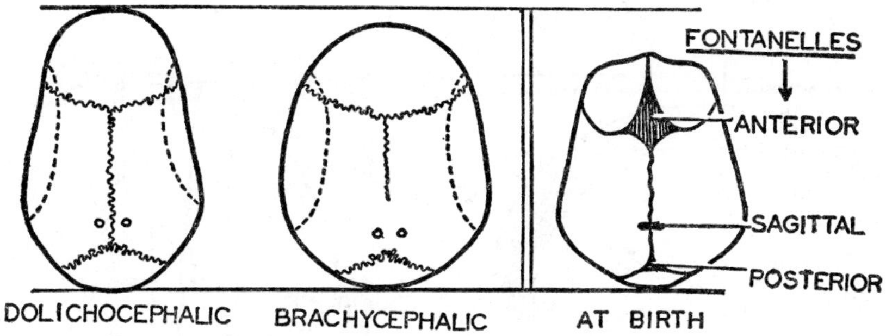

FIG. 660. Skulls viewed from above. Fonticuli or fontanelles

the facial nerve enters the face superficial to it; one or two lymph nodes lie beside it. In its sinuous course it passes about ½″ from the angle of the mouth and it ends at the side of the nose by dividing into the angular and the lateral nasal arteries.

»» The facial artery crosses, in turn, the lower jaw, Buccinator, upper jaw, and Levator Anguli Oris (*fig. 649*). And, it is crossed superficially by all the other muscles it meets (viz., Platysma, Risorius, Zygomaticus Major and Minor, and Levator Labii Superioris).

Branches: An **inferior** and a **superior labial** art. arise near the angle of the mouth, and with those of the opposite side, encircle the mouth between the Orbicularis Oris and the layer of labial glands. A *septal branch* springs from the superior labial art.

A large *unnamed branch* runs on the jaw toward the mental foramen.

Small branches pass posteriorly.

The *lateral nasal art.* follows the upper border of the alar cartilage.

The *angular art.* ascends to the medial palpebral commissure and anastomoses with the dorsal nasal branch of the ophthalmic artery.

The *submental art.* arises in the submandibular region and crosses the jaw near the chin to enter the face.

The **Superficial Temporal Artery** is one of the two terminal branches of the external carotid artery (*fig. 712*). It arises deep to the parotid gland, just behind the neck of the mandible. It crosses (the post. root of) the zygoma and ascends with the auriculotemporal nerve for 1 or 2″ before dividing into a **frontal** and a **parietal branch.** These are sinuous, and in older persons their pulsations can be seen through the skin. They run superficial to the temporal fascia to enter the subcutaneous layer of the scalp (*fig. 662*).

BRANCHES: The *transverse facial art.* crosses the Masseter between the zygoma and the parotid duct. It may be large.

Auricular branches anastomose on the ear.

The *middle temporal art.* pierces the temporal fascia just above the (post. root of the) zygoma and ascends in a groove on the temporal squama.

Terminal branches supply the temporal region and the scalp.

The **Facial Vein** (Ant. facial vein) is the distant companion of the facial artery. It runs behind the artery and takes a straighter and more superficial course. Its branches correspond to those of its artery. In addition, however, it receives the blood from the supra-orbital and supratrochlear veins. In fact, it is by union of these two veins that the facial vein arises.

Connections. It makes important connections (*fig. 664*): (1) with the *pterygoid plexus* through the *deep facial vein.* This vein curves backward below the zygomatic process of the maxilla to join the veins around the pterygoid muscles; these in turn communicate through the foramina at the base of the skull with the cavernous sinus; (2) with the *cavernous sinus* through the *superior ophthalmic vein.* This vein communicates in front with the supra-orbital and supratrochlear veins, and drains backward into the cavernous sinus, but the direction of flow may be reversed; (3) with the *frontal diploic vein.* This vein emerges from a pinpoint hole in the supra-orbital notch and joins the supra-orbital vein.

SKULL FROM ABOVE AND SCALP

»» **Normal Verticalis.** Viewed from above, a skull is roughly oval in outline, but it may have one of many shapes. In front, a glimpse may be had of the bridge of the nose, but the face is not projecting (prognathous) as in lower animals. At the sides, the zygomatic arches are hidden (cryptozygous) in white races, but visible in some others, e.g., certain Eskimos. Behind, the inion is not in view because it lies below the posterior pole of the skull.

The Cephalic Index. When the maximum width of a skull is less than 75 per cent of its maximum length it is said to be dolichocephalic or long headed; when

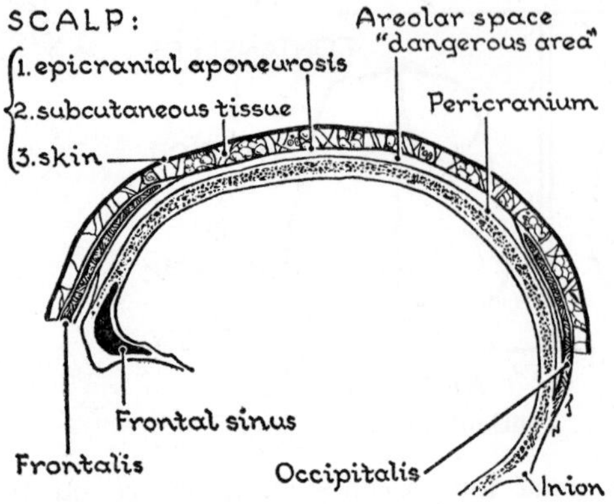

FIG. 661. Sagittal section of skull cap and overlying tissues. Note the fibrous bands, fat, vessels, and nerves in the scalp.

more than 80 per cent it is called brachycephalic or broad headed; when between 75 and 80 per cent it is mesaticephalic (*fig. 660*).

Three **sutures** related to three sides of the parietal bone are visible: the *coronal* (frontoparietal), the *sagittal* (or interparietal), and the *lambdoid* (parieto-occipital). The point of intersection of sagittal and coronal sutures is the *bregma*. The point of intersection of sagittal and lambdoid sutures is the *lambda*.

The bones of the roof of the skull develop in membrane, **ossification** of the frontal and parietal bones, beginning during the 2nd fetal month at their points of greatest fullness, called the *frontal* and *parietal tubers* (eminences).

At birth, ossification has not reached any of the four angles of the parietal bones; so, at these sites, called **fonticuli** (*fontanelles*), the brain is covered with membrane. Of these, the *anterior* fonticulus is 1″ by 2″ in diameter and is shaped like a flat kite (*fig. 660*) the long angle tapering into the interfrontal suture—a matter of obstetrical importance. It is obliterated before the end of the 2nd year—if not, there is something amiss. The bregma marks the site. The summits of the temporal lines and the pinpoint parietal emissary foramina are in view.

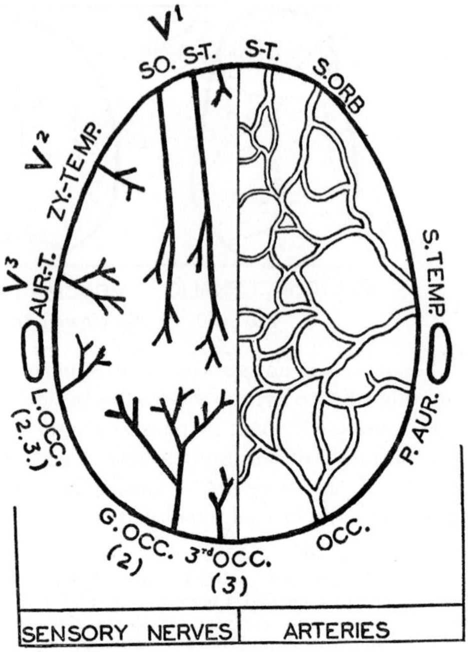

FIG. 662. The sensory nerves and the arteries of the scalp.

Scalp

The scalp is composed of skin, dense subcutaneous tissue, and Epicranius. All three are firmly bound together and are separated from the periosteum of the skull by a very loose areolar space, "the dangerous area"—dangerous to life, if infected (*fig. 661*).

Phylogentically, the Epicranius was a continuous sheet of muscle, now aponeurotic save at its anterior and posterior ends. Its posterior muscular end, the *Occipitalis*, is attached close above the superior nuchal line. Its anterior end, the *Frontalis*, extends right across the forehead blending with its fellow in the median plane and interdigitating in front with the Orbicularis Oculi.

The Occipitalis has a fixed bony attachment, whereas the Frontalis is free. Contraction of the Occipitalis draws the scalp backward, while contraction of the Frontalis causes horizontal wrinkles on the forehead. It may be called upon to assist feebly in raising the eyelids. Laterally, the *Epicranial Aponeurosis* gives origin to the superior and anterior auricular muscles, and elsewhere it fades away over the temporal fascia.

In the subcutaneous tissue, fibers run criss-cross in all directions, uniting skin to

Epicranius. Between the fibers fat is imprisoned, and there the vessels and nerves run.

Nerves (*fig. 662*). The sequence of the cutaneous (sensory) nerves in the scalp is orderly from front to back—V^1, V^2, V^3; ventral rami of cervical nerves 2 and 3; and dorsal rami of cervical nerves 2 and 3.

Arteries (*fig. 662*). The anastomosis between the arteries of the scalp is extremely free. These arteries are derived either indirectly from the *internal carotid* through its ophthalmic branch (viz., supratrochlear and supra-orbital) or directly from the *external carotid* (viz., superf. temporal, post. auricular and occipital).

CHAPTER 35

POSTERIOR TRIANGLE OF NECK

Boundaries; Sternomastoid; Trapezius.
Investing Fascia; Accessory Nerve; Cervical Nerves 3 and 4; Omohyoid; External Jugular Vein; Floor of Triangle; Fascial Carpet; Lymph Nodes.

BLOOD VESSELS IN TRIANGLE

Subclavian Vein and Artery and Branches; Other Arteries in Triangle.

NERVES IN POSTERIOR TRIANGLE

BRACHIAL PLEXUS.
NERVES TO FOUR MUSCLES—*Levator Scapulae; Rhomboids; Serratus Anterior; Diaphragm (Phrenic Nerve).*
CUTANEOUS NERVES.

»» If there were no obstructive clavicle to act as a barrier between the axilla and the posterior triangle of the neck, these two regions would be dissected together, for the reason that the nerves, arteries, veins, and lymph vessels are continued directly from the one to the other. The posterior triangle is, indeed, the root of the upper limb.

It is certainly profitable to review these two regions together, and optionally, if the clavicle is sawn through, at a point made obvious by figure 59, the two regions may be dissected together.

Boundaries. The middle third of the clavicle is the base of the triangle; the posterior border of the Sternomastoid is the anterior side; the anterior border of the Trapezius is the posterior side; the point where these two muscles meet on the superior nuchal line is the apex.

The posterior triangle is the result of a longitudinal cleavage of what in embryonic life was a single muscle mass, now the **Sternomastoideus** and the **Trapezius.** Above, these two muscles have a continuous attachment extending from the inion to the tip of the mastoid process. This attachment is aponeurotic, so it produces a ridge, the *superior nuchal line*. The mastoid process is the anterior extremity of this line drawn out by the Sternomastoid, so it takes the downward, forward, and medial direction of the Sternomastoid (*fig. 663*).

Below, the two muscles have a discontinuous attachment to the clavicle, the Trapezius being attached to the posterior border of its flattened lateral third; the Sternomastoid (clavicular head) to the superior border of its medial third. The sternal head crosses the sternoclavicular articulation and finds attachment to the sternum just below.

Action. If, while looking down to the ground, you flex your head and neck against

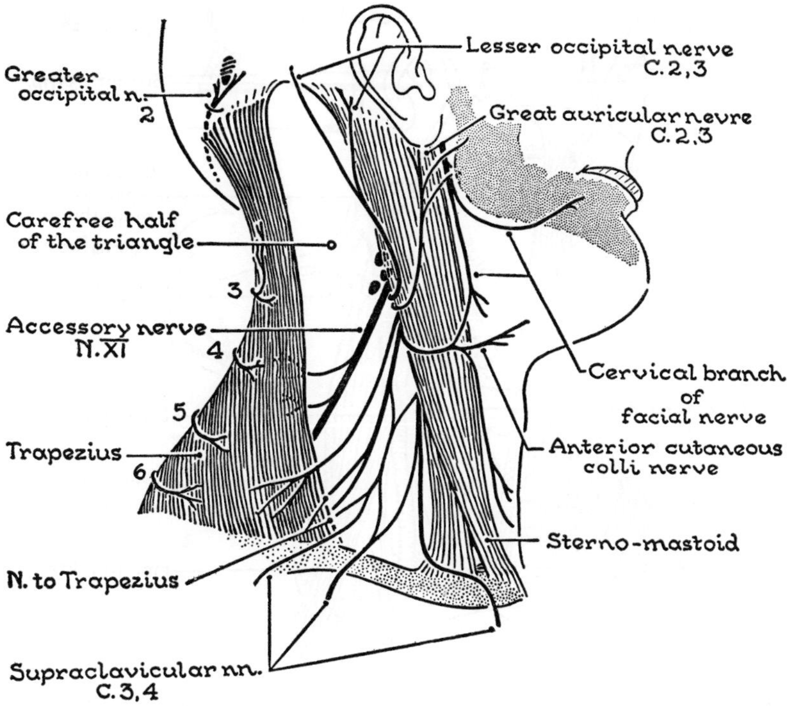

FIG. 663. The superficial nerves of the neck. Of these, the facial and accessory are motor. (*Nerves of neck: anterior cutaneous = transverse.*)

resistance, you will bring into action both Sternomastoids, as you can verify by palpation. If now you rotate your bent head and neck, so that you look sideways up, the Sternomastoid of the opposite side will become still more prominent.

Trapezius (see pp. 94–95 and *fig. 77*).

The Platysma is superficial to the lower part of the triangle (pp. 605–606).

The Investing Deep Fascia of the neck covers the posterior triangle and splits to envelop the Sternomastoid in front and the Trapezius behind, and it attaches itself to the clavicle below.

Crossing the triangle, embedded in the investing fascia, is the accessory nerve.

Accessory Nerve, external branch (N. XI). The accessory nerve is the nerve to the Sternomastoid and Trapezius, and it spans the gap between them. It is placed very superficially—embedded in the investing fascia. It divides the triangle into two nearly equal parts: in the part above the nerve you may dissect *carefree* for there is no important structure to damage; but below you must be *careful.*

The accessory nerve has a curious origin: arising from the upper five or six segments of the spinal cord, it enters the cranial cavity by the foramen magnum only to leave again by the foramen jugulare (*fig. 764*, p. 658).

In the neck it passes obliquely downward and backward from the transverse process of the atlas to the superior angle of the scapula (*fig. 77*). En route, it disappears under cover of the anterior border of the Sternomastoid less than 2½″ below the tip of the mastoid process. Here lymph nodes surround it.

It reappears at what you would estimate to be the middle of the posterior border of this muscle. Here more lymph nodes surround it, and the lesser occipital nerve takes a recurrent course below it. It then crosses the posterior triangle intrafascially, superficial to the Levator Scapulae, and disappears again, this time under cover of the

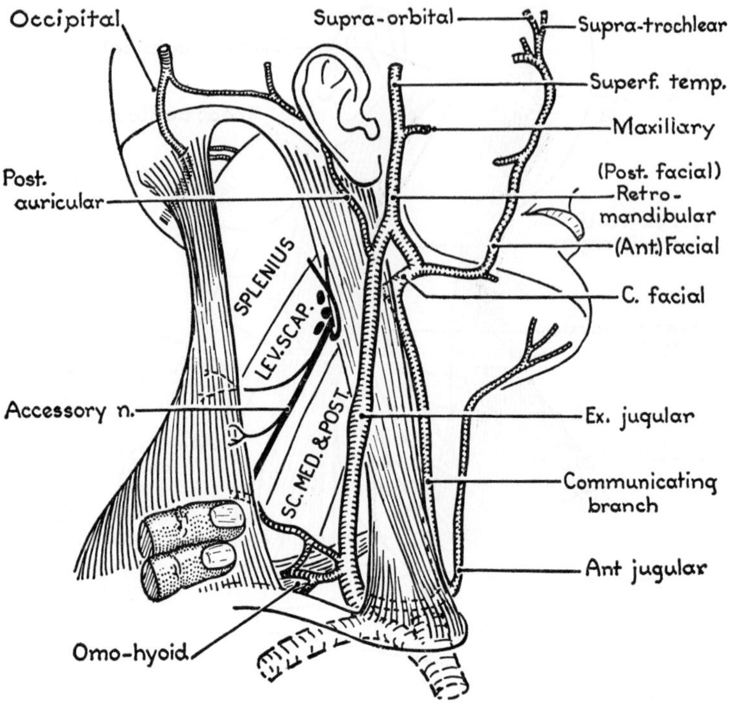

FIG. 664. The superficial veins of the face and neck

anterior border of the Trapezius, two to three fingers' breadth above the clavicle. Sensory (and possibly motor) twigs from C. 2, 3, and 4 join it in its course.

Branches of Cervical Nerves 3 and 4 cross the posterior triangle subfascially a finger's breadth or so below and parallel to the accessory nerve, and they are apt to be mistaken for it. Some of these parallel branches pass deep to the Trapezius and enter it (p. 95); others, *lateral brs. of the supraclavicular nerves*, pass superficial to it (*fig. 663*).

(See *Supraclavicular Nerves*, p. 558.)

Omohyoid (*fig. 664*). During development a backward extension (the inferior belly) of this straplike muscle passed from the anterior to the posterior triangle and gained attachment to the upper border of the scapula beside the suprascapular notch. It passed deep to the Sternomastoid, dragging its nerve after it.

The inferior belly of the Omohyoid rises one or two fingers' breadth above the clavicle. A layer of condensed areolar tissue binds it down to the fascia covering the Subclavius, forming an inverted sling for it. There is, therefore, a pouch between the "Omohyoid fascia" and the investing deep fascia.

External Jugular Vein (*fig. 664*). This large vein descends subcutaneously across the obliquely running Sternomastoid, pierces the investing deep fascia at the posterior border of the Sternomastoid an inch above the clavicle, pierces the fascia retaining the Omohyoid, and ends in the subclavian vein. The Platysma also covers its lower half.

Tributaries. The *transversa colli, suprascapular*, and *anterior jugular veins* communicate with each other in the pouch between the investing deep fascia and the fascia retaining the Omohyoid, and end in the external jugular vein. The terminal part of the anterior jugular vein lies along the upper border of the clavicle deep to the Sternomastoid.

Floor of the Triangle. The floor is formed by several muscles whose fibers run obliquely downward and backward (*figs. 664* and *666*). Of these, the *Levator Scapulae* occupies a middle position. It arises from the posterior tubercles of the transverse

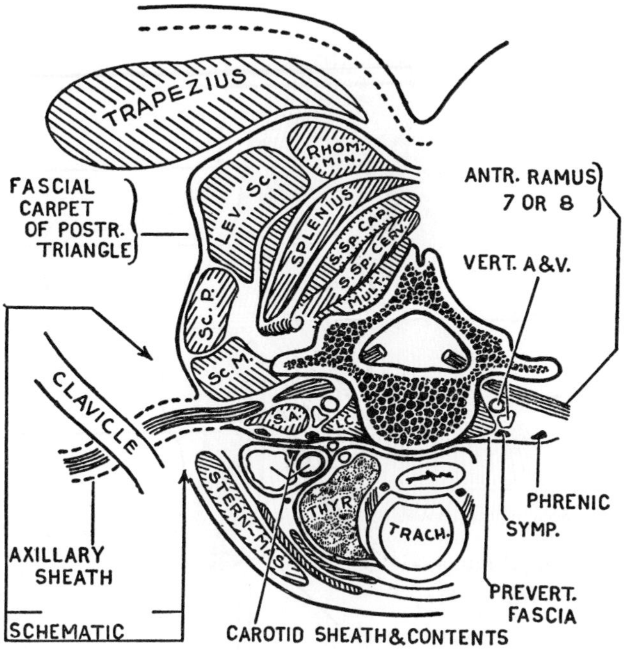

FIG. 665. Transverse section of the neck showing the pre- and postvertebral fasciae prolonged into the axilla as a tubular covering (axillary sheath) for the brachial plexus and subclavian vessels. The nerves shown in figure 666 remain deep to this fascia.

processes of the upper four cervical vertebrae, and it is inserted into the medial border of the scapula between the root of the spine and the superior angle. The accessory nerve is superficial to it, parallel to its fibers, and serves as a guide to it.

Above the Levator and parallel with it is soft-grained *Splenius.*

Below the Levator and parallel to it are the three Scaleni (*fig. 749*). Of these, the *Scalenus Medius* arises from the costotransverse bars of all the cervical transverse processes (or the homologue in the case of atlas and axis) (Cave); and it is inserted into the upper surface of the 1st rib between its neck and the groove for the subclavian artery. The *Scalenus Posterior* may be considered as the portion of the Medius that passes on to the 2nd rib.

The *Scalenus Anterior* is separated from the Scaleni Medius by the brachial plexus and the subclavian artery. It arises from the anterior tubercles of all the transverse processes that possess anterior tubercles (3, 4, 5, and 6). Its posterior border is nearly parallel with the posterior border of the Sternomastoid, and lies slightly behind it. Followed downward, its posterior border leads to its tendinous insertion into the scalene tubercle, situated on the 1st rib between the grooves for the subclavian artery and vein.

The lateral border of the 1st rib being the boundary between the floor of the posterior triangle and the medial wall of the axilla, it follows that the digitation of the *Serratus Anterior* that arises from the 1st rib forms part of the floor.

»» A small part of the *Semispinalis Capitis* may appear at the apex of the triangle, above the Splenius (*fig. 666*). It is told by its vertically running fibers. It is crossed by the occipital artery (*fig. 675*).

Fascial Carpet. The muscular floor of the triangle is carpeted with a layer of fascia. This fascia is part of the fascia that envelops like a sleeve the vertebral column and the pre- and postvertebral muscles of the neck. Of course, the cervical nerves leaving the intervertebral foramina, and the subclavian vessels leaving the thorax, are at first deep to this carpet.

The carpet, then, covers the subclavian

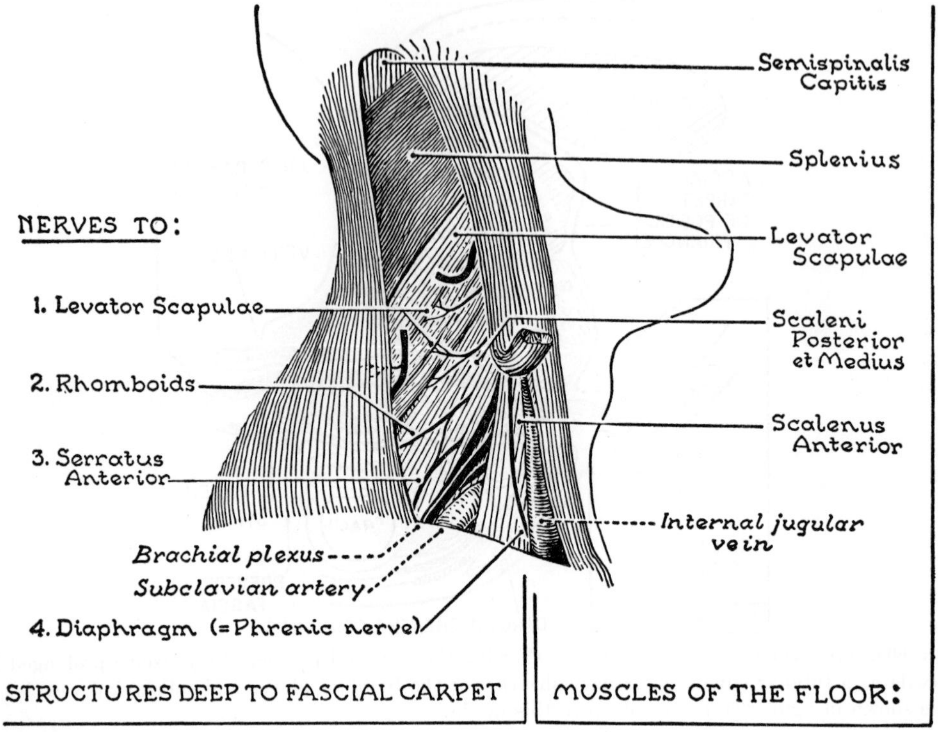

FIG. 666. The floor of the posterior triangle and the nerves that have no occasion to pierce its fascial carpet.

vessels and the roots of the brachial plexus and it provides them with a tubular sheath, the *axillary sheath,* as they enter the axilla (*fig. 665*). It also covers the motor nerves to four important muscles—Levator Scapulae, Rhomboids, Serratus Anterior, and Diaphragm. Now, these nerves are safe and cannot be damaged so long as the fascial carpet is left intact, for having no occasion to pierce the carpet they descend between it and the muscles of the floor.

To define and clean the carpet, use either the tips of your fingers or two pairs of blunt forceps.

Lymph Nodes. In the fat between the fascial roof of the triangle and the fascial carpet, superficial to the brachial plexus and the subclavian vessels, lie the *lateral group of inferior deep cervical* (supraclavicular) *lymph nodes.* They drain the back of the scalp and neck and they usually receive some efferent vessels from the upper deep cervical, axillary, and deltopectoral nodes. These nodes empty into the jugular lymph trunk. The axillary nodes empty into the subclavian lymph trunk, which follows the subclavian vein to the thoracic (or right lymph) duct.

BLOOD VESSELS IN POSTERIOR TRIANGLE

The **Subclavian Vein** is the continuation of the axillary vein. It begins at the lateral border of the 1st rib and ends at the medial border of the Scalenus Anterior by joining the internal jugular vein to form the brachiocephalic vein (innominate v.). The vein is separated from its artery by the Scalenus Anterior; both vessels groove the 1st rib. The rib is obliquely set, so the vein lies antero-inferior to the artery, and it does not rise above the clavicle.

Tributaries. Ext. jugular vein (*figs. 664, 726,* and *759*).

The **Subclavian Artery,** 3rd part, and the brachial plexus burst through the floor between the Scalenus Anterior and Scalenus Medius.

The 3rd part of the artery extends from the lateral border of the Scalenus Anterior to the lateral border of the 1st rib where it becomes the axillary artery.

Below—1st rib and the pleura.

Behind—Scalenus Medius and the lowest trunk of the brachial plexus.

In front—Platysma, cutaneous nerves, three layers of fascia, and a plexus of veins; the clavicle and the suprascapular artery.

Antero-inferiorly—subclavian vein.

Branch. Dorsal scapular art. usually.

Other Arteries in the Posterior Triangle. The *suprascapular* and *transversa colli arteries*, which spring from the 1st part of the subclavian art., via the thyrocervical trunk (*fig. 725*), pass laterally in front of the Scalenus Anterior and its fascia and the phrenic nerve, to appear at the posterior border of the Sternomastoid.

The **Suprascapular Art.** runs a retroclavicular course to the (supra)scapular notch.

The **Transversa Colli (Cervicis) Art.,** lying at a higher level, crosses the floor of the triangle and accompanies the accessory nerve to the Trapezius. It commonly (30 per cent) gives off the dorsal scapular art.

The **Dorsal Scapular Art.** Usually (67 per cent; Huelke) springs from the 2nd or 3rd part of the subclavian art. and follows the nerve to the Rhomboids [dorsal scapular n.] deep to the Levator Scapulae. Sometimes (20 per cent) it gives off the transversa colli art.

The **Occipital Art.** flits across the apex of the triangle.

NERVES IN POSTERIOR TRIANGLE

» *Terminology.* In the thoracic, lumbar, and sacral regions the spinal nerves are named numerically after the vertebrae above them. In the cervical region, however, they are named after the vertebrae below them. What of the nerve between vertebrae C. 7 and Th. 1? It is grouped with the cervical nerves, making the 8th.

The Transverse Processes of the cervical vertebrae have a downward tilt due to the pull of muscles, and each possesses a posterior tubercle. Anterior tubercles are absent from the 1st, 2nd, and 7th cervical transverse processes and present on the 3rd, 4th, 5th, and 6th; and the width of the groove between anterior and posterior tubercles depends on the size of the ventral ramus around which the process is molded, and it increases from 3rd to 6th (*fig. 668*).

The upper limb originally occupied the level of the segments from which it derives its nerves; but it descended, dragging them after it. This accounts for the obliquity of the plexus.

BRACHIAL PLEXUS: This plexus (*fig. 70*) is formed by the ventral rami of nerves C. 5, 6, 7, 8 and Th. 1. The ventral ramus just beyond each end of the series, namely, C. 4 and Th. 2, commonly contributes branches. Occasionally the plexus is moved more or less bodily a segment headward (prefixed) or tailward (postfixed).

Rami 5, 6, and 7 take descending courses, 8 runs horizontally, 1 ascends. The rami increase in size from each end of the series to C. 7, which is the middle and largest ramus of the plexus. The cervical pleura rises in front of ramus Th. 1 to the level of ramus C. 8 (*fig. 725*).

» The plexus is composed as follows (*fig. 70*): rami 5 and 6 unite to form an uppermost trunk; ramus C. 7 continues as a middle trunk; rami C. 8 and Th. 1 unite at the neck of the 1st rib to form a lowest trunk. The lowest trunk lies on the 1st rib behind the subclavian artery and is in part responsible for the groove on the rib often attributed to the artery.

Each of the three trunks divides into an anterior and posterior division. Behind the clavicle the three posterior divisions unite to form the posterior cord of the plexus, whereas the upper and middle anterior divisions unite to form the lateral cord, and the lowest anterior division continues as the medial cord.

The three cords of the plexus are disposed around the second part of the axillary artery, that is, behind the Pectoralis Minor, a finger's breadth from the tip of the coracoid process.

The roots of the plexus supply the Rhomboids, Serratus Anterior, and Diaphragm. They also supply the neighboring prevertebral muscles. They receive gray rami from the middle and inferior cervical and Th. 1 and 2 sympathetic ganglia (*fig. 44.4*).

If the handle of the knife is carried along the lateral border of the plexus, it will be lead away by the most lateral branch of the plexus, the *suprascapular nerve,* to the (supra)scapular notch at the root of the coracoid process.

Nerves to Four Muscles—Levator Scapulae, Rhomboidei, Serratus Anterior, and Diaphragm—course between the muscular floor of the triangle and its fascial carpet (*fig. 666*). The nerves to the first three are to be found between the accessory nerve above and the upper border of the brachial plexus below. They arise from the posterior aspects of the ventral rami, and they join in the general inferolateral slope. Thus:

1. A branch from C. 3 and one from C. 4 arise with the roots of the supraclavicular nerves, descend on the *Levator Scapulae*, and supply it within the triangle.

2. A branch from C. 5 supplies the *Rhomboids* and sends a twig to the Levator Scapulae. It crosses the Scalenus Medius, usually after piercing it, and disappears deep to the anterior border of the Levator Scapulae (*fig. 78*, p. 96).

3. Branches from C. 5, 6, and 7 supply the *Serratus Anterior*. Those from C. 5 and 6 join in front of the Scalenus Medius, usually after piercing it, with or just below the nerve to the Rhomboids. Branch C. 5 ends mainly in the highest digitation of the Serratus; branch C. 6 enters the axilla applied to the Serratus. Branch C. 7 is concealed by the brachial plexus which shelters it from danger.

»» To find it, pull the plexus forward and seek for a long, stout thread that leaves root C. 7 and descends behind it. This thread crosses in front of the Medius, passes on to the Serratus Anterior, and remains applied to it as far as its lowest digitation. It enters the axilla behind the brachial plexus and great vessels and is there joined by branch C. 6.

The **Phrenic Nerve** is not within the geometrical limits of the triangle, but it is in danger of injury when the Sternomastoid is retracted, so is the internal jugular vein, which descends anteromedial to the phrenic nerve. It would be an omission not to mention them.

The phrenic nerve arises from the ventral ramus of C. 4 and gets twigs from C. 3 and 5. It descends vertically on the Scalenus Anterior, crossing it from lateral to medial side, and is in naked contact with it.

»» *Nerve to Subclavius* (C. 5 and 6). This long thread descends in front of the plexus and the subclavian vessels. Commonly, it delivers to the phrenic nerve its twig from C. 5 which is surgically important when it joins that nerve beyond the vessels.

Cutaneous Nerves (*fig. 663*). Because nerve C. 1 has no cutaneous branch and because the ventral rami of C. 5—Th. 1 are carried bodily into the upper limb, as the brachial plexus, it falls to the rami of C. 2, 3, and 4 to supply the cutaneous territory between the trigeminal nerve above and the 2nd thoracic nerve below (*fig. 98*). This they do by means of four nerves that radiate from about the middle of the posterior border of the Sternomastoid. Thus:

1. *The Lesser Occipital N.* (C. 2, 3) hooks round the accessory nerve and ascends near the posterior border of the Sternomastoid. It gives off side branches and ends in the scalp.

2. *The Great Auricular N.* (C. 2, 3) runs vertically across the Sternomastoid towards the front of the lobe of the ear, being either in contact with the external jugular vein or at some distance behind it. *Mastoid* branches pass to the mastoid region, *auricular* branches to both surfaces of the auricle, and *facial* branches to the parotid and masseteric regions.

3. *The Anterior Cutaneous Colli N.* [N. transversus colli] (C. 2, 3) crosses the Sternomastoid transversely near its middle and supplies the skin between jaw and sternum.

»» It does so through two main branches: of these, one runs upward along the anterior border of the Sternomastoid and communicates with the cervical branch of the facial nerve; the other runs downward along this border. The stem of the nerve crosses either superficial or deep to the external jugular vein. The end twigs pierce the Platysma.

4. *The Supraclavicular Nerves* (C. 3, 4) arise from a stem that divides into three branches: the *anterior* branch descends along the posterior border of the Sternomastoid to the clavicle, turns forward and pierces the Platysma; the *middle* branch crosses the middle third of the clavicle; the *posterior* branch runs parallel to the accessory nerve and a little below it and passes superficial to the Trapezius.

The supraclavicular nn. are sensory to the lower part of the posterior triangle and to the pectoral, deltoid, and acromial regions above the level of the 2nd rib.

CHAPTER 36

BACK

SKELETAL PARTS

The bony parts covered by the deep or intrinsic muscles are: (1) the nuchal region of the skull; (2) the dorsal aspect of the vertebral column, and the ribs between the tubercles and angles; and (3) the posterior 3″ of the iliac crest.

SKULL FROM BEHIND (Norma Occipitalis). The **Outline** of the norma occipitalis is horseshoe-shaped and extends from the tip of one mastoid process over the vault to the tip of the other (*fig. 667*). On each side it crosses the mastoid and the parietal bone.

At the base of the skull the outline extends nearly horizontally from one mastoid process to the other. Medial to the mastoid process the outline crosses two grooves: the lateral one gives origin to the posterior belly of the Digastric; the medial one lodges the occipital artery. It then crosses the jugular process of the occipital bone, the occipital condyle, and the foramen magnum.

The **Surface** of the norma occipitalis is convex and includes parts of the parietal,

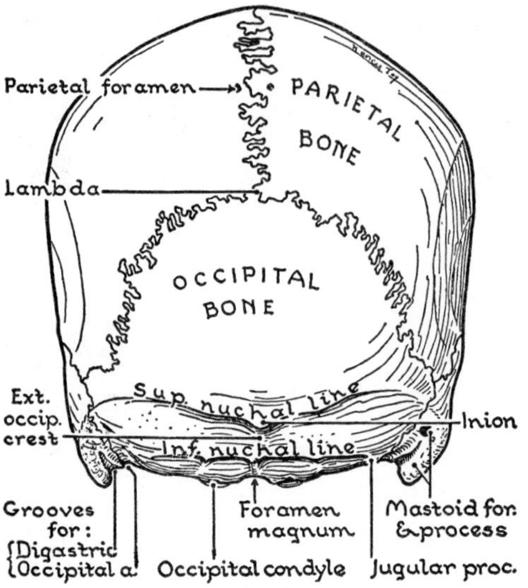

FIG. 667. The skull, from behind (Norma occipitalis.)

occipital, and temporal bones. At the center is the *lambda.* From it a *triradiate suture* runs: the sagittal (interparietal) suture to the vertex, the lambdoid (parieto-occipital) suture to the blunt postero-inferior angle of the parietal bone on each side. There the lambdoid suture divides into two limbs: one limb continues downward and forward as the occipitomastoid suture to the root of the styloid process; the other runs forward as the parietomastoid suture.

»» *Foramina.* On each side there are three *foramina* for emissary veins: (1) the *parietal foramen* situated close to the sagittal suture transmits a small vein from the superior sagittal sinus; (2) the *mastoid foramen* situated close to the occipitomastoid suture, and (3) the *condylar canal,* which opens on to the condylar fossa, transmit veins from the sigmoid sinus. Any of the three may be absent. (Meningeal twigs of the occipital artery traverse the mastoid and parietal *foramina.*)

The condylar fossa receives the rim of the articular process of the atlas when the head is extended. Midway between the lambda and the foramen magnum is the *inion* or *external occipital protuberance.* From it the *superior nuchal line* curves to the rough outer surface of the *mastoid process,* which indeed is the drawn out end of the superior line. The Trapezius creates the medial one-third of the line; the Sternomastoid creates its lateral two-thirds and draws out the process.

The surface above the superior nuchal line is divided unequally into the *area of the scalp, mastoid area,* and *temporal fossa.* The surface below the superior nuchal line is the **nuchal area** (nucha = neck).

When the muscles are massive, the inion and the superior nuchal lines mount high; but normally the positions of the external (inion) and internal occipital protuberances almost correspond.

The *external occipital crest* is a sharp median crest that gives attachment to the ligamentum nuchae and runs from the inion to the foramen magnum. The *inferior nuchal line* curves laterally from the mid-point of the external occipital crest.

VERTEBRAL COLUMN FROM BEHIND

The column is seen as two longitudinal gutters, one on each side of the median plane, between the tips of the spinous processes and the tips of the transverse processes.

Spinous Processes. Of the various spinous processes C. 1 (the atlas) is reduced to an upturned tubercle; C.2—C.6 are bifid in white races; C. 7 is less prominent than Th. 1; Th. 5–8 are almost perpendicular, and are markedly overlapping; Th. 10 is often disproportionately small; Th. 11 is directed horizontally backward, and the spines above it and below converge on it; the lumbar spinous processes are oblong plates; the upper three or four sacral spines form an irregular *median* crest; the lower sacral and the coccygeal spines are missing.

Supraspinous and interspinous ligaments unite the spines. In the neck the supraspinous ligament is the **ligamentum nuchae.** It is triangular. Its posterior border is free; its anterior border is attached to the cervical spines; its superior border is attached to the inion and external occipital crest. The pull of the lig. nuchae and Trapezius account for the direction of the inion.

The **Laminae** are band-like and tend to overlap the laminae below—testudo fashion. They are united to each other by ligamenta flava. Their inferolateral angles carry the inferior articular processes. These remarks do not hold for the laminae of C. 1, known

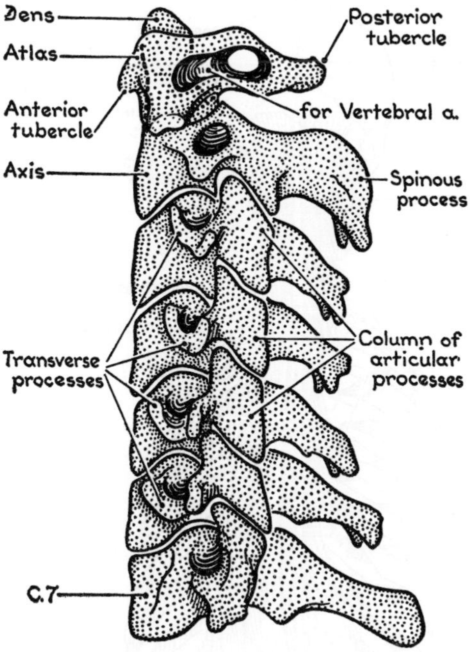

FIG. 668. Cervical vertebrae on side view

as the *posterior arch of the atlas*, which is slender, compressed from above downward, and grooved above by the vertebral arteries.

Above and below the posterior arch of the atlas there is a wide interlaminar space closed by membranes (posterior atlanto-occipital and atlanto-axial). The lumbar interlaminar spaces also are wide. Flexion of the spine, of course, enlarges all interlaminar spaces. The upper sacral laminae are fused. The lower sacral and the coccygeal laminae are absent.

The **Articular Processes** partaking in the atlanto-occipital and atlanto-axial joints lie on a plane anterior to the subsequent articular processes and are not serially homologous with them (*fig. 675.1*). The subsequent cervical articular processes are segments of a column cut obliquely.

The cervical articular processes afford attachment to the posterior roots of the transverse processes. The inferior articular processes are visible from behind in all regions. The posterior margins of the superior articular processes of the atlas and axis and of the lumbar and 1st sacral vertebrae are visible from behind.

The sacral articular processes amalgamate on each side to form an interrupted *crest of articular tubercles*. It lies medial to the dorsal sacral foramina, and it ends below as a *sacral cornu*, which by articulating with the corresponding *coccygeal cornu* completes a foramen for the 5th sacral nerve (*fig. 669*). On extension of the spine the lower borders of the inferior articular processes engage in pits on the laminae of the vertebrae next below, resisting hyperextension.

The **Transverse Processes** of C. 1 and C. 7 project far beyond those of C. 2–6 (*fig. 748*). Th. 1–12 diminish progressively in projection. L. 1–5 project farther than C. 1 and C. 7, L. 3 being the most projecting of all transverse processes. L. 5 lies below the level of the iliac crest and, due to its special function, is stout, directed upward and backward, and is conical (p. 320). The sacral transverse processes fuse to form an irregular crest of *transverse tubercles* which ends below as the *inferolateral angle of the sacrum*. A ligament, commonly ossified, joins this angle to the *transverse process of the coccyx*, thereby forming a foramen for the ventral ramus of the 5th sacral nerve.

The **Dorsal Sacral Foramina** are four in number on each side. They lie between the articular and transverse tubercles. They are sharp and round and admit a lead pencil, which may be passed straight forward through the pelvic sacral foramina to the front of the sacrum. Medially, they communicate with the sacral canal.

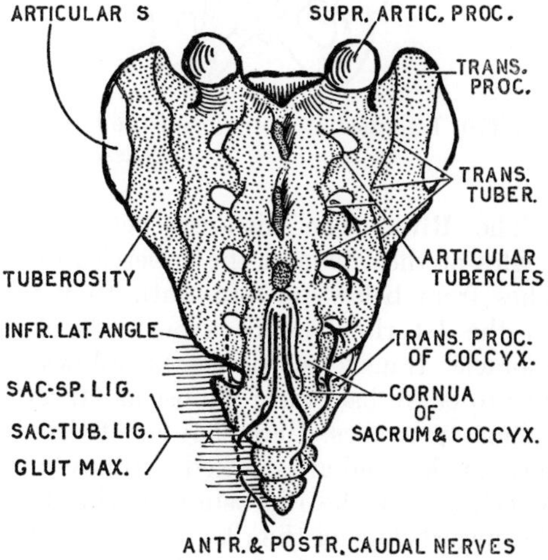

FIG. 669. Dorsal aspect of sacrum and coccyx

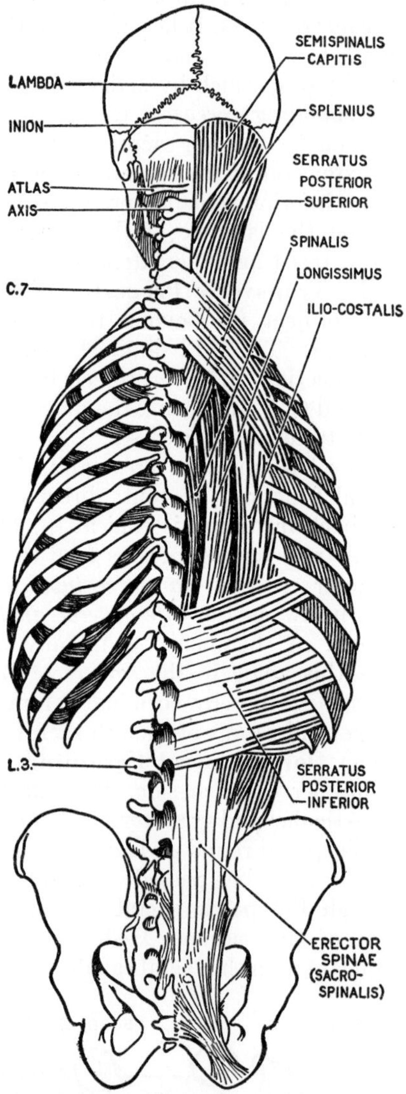

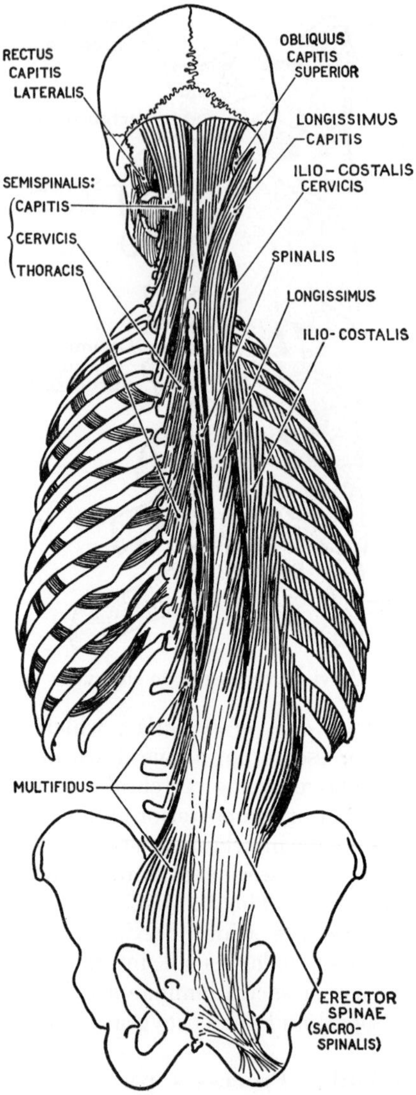

FIG. 670. Intermediate muscles of the back. FIG. 671. Deep muscles of the back.
(Dissections by Dr. V. P. Collins.)

The **Ribs.** The distance between the angles of the ribs and the tubercles diminishes from below upward until they meet on the 1st rib. The backward tilt of the thoracic transverse processes allows the ribs to curve backward almost as far as the spinous processes. Here they are twisted to form angles, and are marked by lines for the attachment of the Iliocostalis. Owing to the downward slope of the ribs, the angles lie on nearly the same horizontal plane as the tips of the spinous processes with which they correspond numerically.

»» *A lumbar transverse process* is morphologically a costal or rib element (*fig. 23.1*); a small tubercle, the *accessory process*, situated behind the root of a lumbar transverse process, is in series with the thoracic transverse processes and with the posterior roots and tubercles of the cervical transverse processes, i.e., it is the morphological transverse element. It gives insertion to slips of the Longissimus and is therefore pulled downward.

On the back of the rim of each lumbar superior articular process there is a larger tubercle, the *mamillary process.* It gives origin to the Multifidus and is therefore pulled upward.

The transverse processes of Th. 11 and 12 do not support ribs, so they are rudimentary, but they do have mamillary processes; and the 12th has also an accessory process.

Iliac Crest. The hinder 3″ of the iliac crest lies above the rough area, the *tuberosity,* for the interosseous sacro-iliac ligament and gives part origin to the Erector Spinae.

MUSCLES OF THE BACK

The muscles of the back are arranged in superficial, intermediate, and deep groups. The *superficial group* acts upon the upper limbs; the *intermediate group* is respiratory in action; and both have migrated or spread backward across the deep group of muscles. This is indicated by their nerve supply—accessory nerve and ventral nerve rami. The *deep group* is intrinsic to the back; it is composed of "native" muscles supplied by dorsal nerve rami (*figs. 670* and *671*).

Superficial

1. Trapezius and Latissimus Dorsi.
2. Levator Scapulae and Rhomboidei.

Intermediate

3. Serrati Posteriores (superior et inferior) (*fig. 670*).

Deep

4. Splenius (cervicis et capitis).
5. *Longitudinal muscles*
   Erector Spinae:
   Iliocostalis, Longissimus, Spinalis.
6. *Oblique muscles*
   Transversospinalis:
   Semispinalis, Multifidus, Rotatores.
7. *Remaining deep muscles:*
   Interspinales, Intertransversarii, Levatores Costarum, Suboccipital muscles.

»» It is profitless to memorize even for a short period the text book description of the attachments of the deep muscles of the back because you can make no use of the particular information. The back is, however, a region of such great importance that you should not neglect to obtain a grasp of the scheme of things.

If the part is moist and the knife sharp, you can rapidly trace the tendinous slips of the muscles to their attachments and make a pretty display, because there is no fat here.

Intermediate Muscles and Splenius

The deep muscles (longitudinal, oblique and others) are bridged by the *Serrati* in the thoracic region, by the *lumbar fascia* in the lumbosacral region, and by the *Splenius* in the cervical region.

The Serratus Posterior (*fig. 670*) has a superior and an inferior part. Each part has four slips with aponeurotic origins and fleshy insertions. The *Serratus Posterior Superior* arises from the lower cervical and upper thoracic spines and passes downward and laterally to the upper ribs (2–5) beyond their angles. The *Serratus Posterior Inferior* blends with the thoracolumbar fascia and through it gains attachment to the lower thoracic and upper lumbar spines. It passes transversely to the lower ribs (9–12) lateral to their angles.

Both parts of this muscle elongate the thoracic cavity and may act as muscles of inspiration. They have migrated medially, superficial to the deep muscles, and, so, are supplied by ventral nerve rami.

The Splenius (*figs. 666* and *670*) is a detached part of the deep group of muscles which it has come to bridge. In fact, it is wrapped around them as its name implies (splenius L. = a bandage). It arises from the lower half of the ligamentum nuchae and from the upper thoracic spines (Th. 1–6). Its fibers pass semispirally upward and laterally and separate into two parts—Splenius Cervicis and Splenius Capitis.

The Splenius Cervicis passes deep to the Levator Scapulae and shares the attachments of the Levator Scapulae to the cervical vertebrae (post. tubercles of C. 1–4). *The Splenius Capitis* passes deep to the Sternomastoid and shares the attachments of Sternomastoid to the superior nuchal line and mastoid process. It forms the floor of the posterior triangle of the neck above the Levator Scapulae.

The Thoracolumbar Fascia has two parts: thoracic and lumbar.

The **lumbar fascia** is the dorsal aponeurotic attachment of the Transversus Abdominis (*fig. 215*). Now, just as the Obliquus Abdominis Internus splits to form a sheath for the Rectus Abdominis, so the

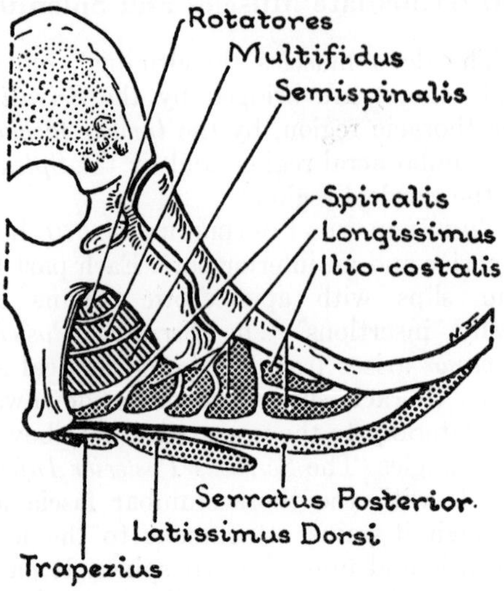

FIG. 672. The muscles of the back on cross-section (schematic). Note: the deeper the muscle the shorter its span and the nearer it is to the vertebral canal.

dorsal aponeurosis of the Transversus Abdominis splits to form a sheath for the deep dorsal muscles; and its fibers run transversely.

Its superficial layer (posterior lamina) is tough and thick. It passes behind the deep muscles to be attached to the lumbar spines. The Latissimus Dorsi and Serratus Posterior Inferior reinforce it.

Traced downward into the sacral region, it blends with the dense aponeurosis of origin of the Erector Spinae. Traced upward, as the **thoracic part** of *the thoracolumbar fascia*, it becomes a delicate sheet that stretches from the vertebral spines to the angles of the ribs, spanning the deep dorsal muscles.

Its deep layer (anterior lamella, *fig. 323*) passes between the deep muscles and the Quadratus Lumborum to be attached to the tips of the lumbar transverse processes, and also to the last rib above and to the iliac crest below.

Deep or Intrinsic Muscles

Erector Spinae (Sacrospinalis) (*fig. 672*). This muscle extends from the pelvis to the skull. It has: (1) a dense aponeurotic origin which, covering the fleshy origin of the

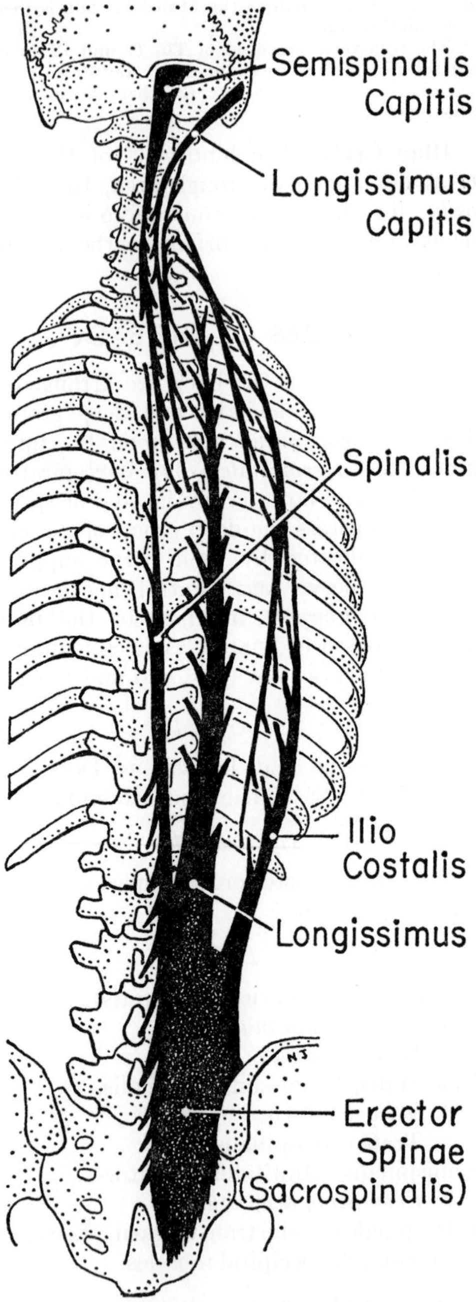

FIG. 672.1. Plan of the Erector Spinae and Semispinalis Capitis. (After Cunningham's Anatomy.)

Multifidus, arises from the lower two thoracic, the lumbar, and the sacral spines (= median sacral crest), the sacral transverse processes (= lat. sacral crest) and the various adjacent ligaments, and (2) a fleshy origin from the interosseous sacroiliac lig. and the part of the iliac crest above it (*fig. 672.1*).

A little below the last rib the Erector Spinae splits into 3 columns: Iliocostalis, Longissimus, and Spinalis.

»» *Observations.* More tendinous slips than can be accommodated endeavor to find attachment, one behind the other, on the posterior tubercles of the cervical transverse processes, so the hindmost are crowded on to the articular processes whose close proximity makes this simple (*figs. 673* and *674*).

The Iliocostalis is inserted into the angles of the ribs and into the cervical transverse processes (C. 4–6) by a series of relayed bundles that extend over about six segments—where one slip is inserted another slip arises on its medial side.

The Longissimus (thoracis, cervicis, and capitis) is inserted into lumbar accessory and transverse processes, and into thoracic transverse processes and nearby parts of the ribs (Th. 2–12). Bundles arising medial to these (Th. 1–4) are relayed to the cervical transverse processes (C. 2–6). Other bundles arising medial to these again (upper Th. transverse and lower C. articular processes) extend as a broad fleshy band to be attached to the mastoid process deep to the Splenius Capitis and Sternomastoid.

The Longissimus is the only column of the Erector Spinae to reach the skull. The

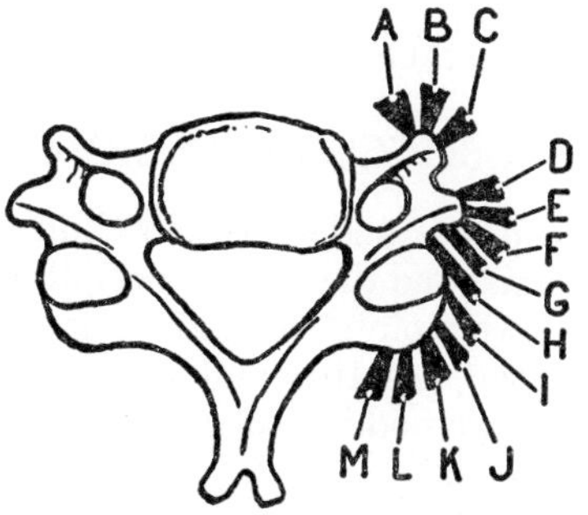

FIG. 673. The muscles attached to the transverse and articular processes of a cervical vertebra. *A*, Longus Colli. *B*, Longus Capitis. *C*, Scalenus Anterior. *D*, Scalenus Medius. *E*, Scalenus Posterior. *F*, Levator Scapulae. *G*, Splenius Cervicis. *H*, Iliocostalis Cervicis. *I*, Longissimus Cervicis. *J*, Longissimus Capitis. *K*, Semispinalis Capitis. *L*, Semispinalis Cervicis. *M*, Multifidus.

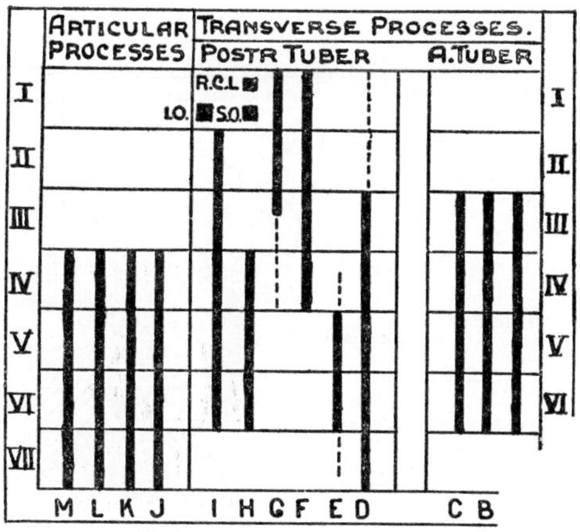

FIG. 674. Graphic representation of figure 673.

lateral branches of the lower dorsal nerve rami pass between it and the Iliocostalis.

»» *The Spinalis* is largely aponeurotic, flat, and ½″ wide. It extends from the upper lumbar to the lower cervical spines. Its lateral border is free.

Transversospinalis. This oblique group of muscles is concealed by the Erector Spinae. Its fibers pass obliquely upward and medially from transverse processes to spines. It is disposed in three layers: (1) *Semispinalis*, (2) *Multifidus*, and (3) *Rotatores*. The superficial layer (1) spans more segments than the intermediate layer, (2) and therefore takes a more vertical course, and (3) arises nearer the tips of the transverse processes and is inserted nearer the tips of the spinous processes. The same characteristics distinguish the intermediate layer from the deep layer.

The superficial layer spans about five segments; the intermediate about three; the deepest connects adjacent segments.

»» *The Semispinalis* (thoracis, cervicis, capitis) forms the superficial layer. Its thoracic and cervical parts arise from the thoracic transverse processes (Th. 1–10) and pass obliquely upward and medially across five segments to the cervical and upper thoracic spines (C. 2–Th. 4); that is to say, it extends to the axis—not to the atlas.

The Semispinalis Capitis passes from the upper thoracic transverse processes and lower cervical articular processes (C. 4–Th. 5) to the occipital bone between the superior and inferior nuchal lines. The fibers of this massive muscle run nearly vertically.

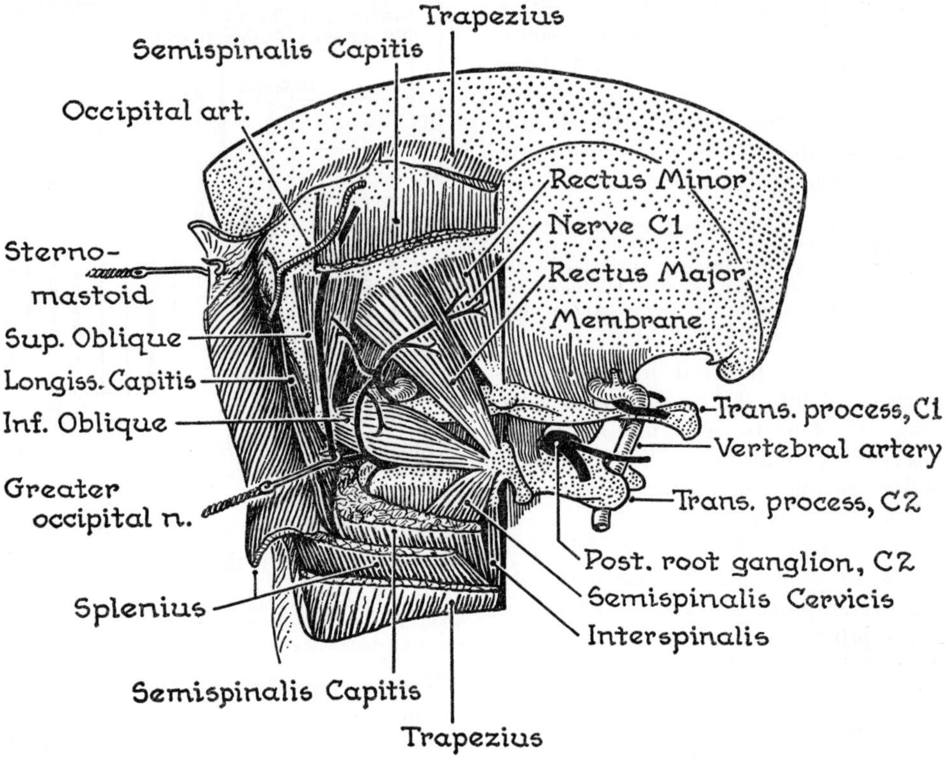

FIG. 675. The suboccipital region, containing the suboccipital triangle

The medial border is free and is separated from its fellow by the lig. nuchae.

The Multifidus arises as a thick, fleshy mass from the dorsal aspect of the sacrum between its spinous and transverse crests, from adjacent ligaments, from the dense aponeurosis of the overlying Erector Spinae, and from all transverse processes up to C. 4 (actually from mamillary processes in the lumbar region, transverse in the thoracic, and articular in the cervical). It spans about three segments to be inserted into the lower border of every spinous process (C. 2–L. 5). The atlas has no spine.

»» *The Rotatores* bridge one interspace. They are small slips that pass from the root of one transverse process to the root of the spinous process or lamina next above. They are best marked in the thoracic region.

OTHER DEEP MUSCLES. The *Interspinales* and *Intertransversarii* are well developed in the cervical and lumbar regions, and mostly absent from the thoracic region. The *Levatores Costarum*, though hidden by the Erector Spinae, are grouped with the thoracic muscles (p. 472). The *suboccipital muscles* are the deepest layer of muscles above the axis.

Interspinales are well developed median paired muscles. They unite the bifid tubercles of adjacent cervical spinous processes, and adjacent borders of the oblong lumbar spinous processes.

Intertransversarii (Anteriores and Posteriores) unite adjacent anterior tubercles and adjacent posterior tubercles of the cervical transverse processes; the highest Posterior Intertransverse muscle being the Rectus Capitis Lateralis (p. 644). In the lumbar region they are well marked.

Suboccipital Muscles, see below.

SUBOCCIPITAL REGION

Between axis and atlas and skull are the atlanto-axial and the atlanto-occipital joints. At the lower joints we shake our heads to indicate the negative and disapproval; at the higher we nod indicating the affirmative and approval.

Certain dorsal muscles ascend as far as the spine of the axis; others (Semispinalis Capitis, Splenius Capitis, and Longissimus Capitis) extending higher, span the atlas to reach the skull; but none stops at the spine of the atlas—it has no spine. Hence, the suboccipital region.

LOCATION. The suboccipital region lies deep to the apical part of the posterior triangle of the neck (*fig. 666*) and extends on both sides of it. The Semispinalis Capitis forms the immediate covering or lid; and lower is the Splenius.

BONY LIMITS OF THE REGION (*fig. 675*). *Above,* inferior nuchal line of occipital bone; *below,* axis; *laterally,* mastoid process, transverse process of atlas, and transverse process of axis; *medianly,* the massive spine of the axis and, above and on a deeper plane, posterior tubercle of atlas.

CONTENTS OF THE REGION.

Four muscles	Two oblique Two straight
Two nerves	Greater occipital Suboccipital
Two arteries	Vertebral Occipital

Muscles (*fig. 675*). The *Obliquus Capitis Inferior* is thick, fleshy, and rounded. It passes from the spine of the axis obliquely upward and forward to the tip of the transverse process of the atlas. It bounds the region inferiorly.

The three other muscles are flat and triangular. Of these, the *Obliquus Capitis Superior* passes from the tip of the transverse process of the atlas obliquely upward and backward to be inserted between the two nuchal lines of the occipital bone lateral to the Semispinalis Capitis. It bounds the region laterally.

The *Rectus Capitis Posterior Minor* arises from the posterior tubercle of the atlas; the *Rectus Capitis Posterior Major* from the spine of the axis. These two are attached side by side to the occipital bone between the inferior nuchal line and the foramen magnum.

» *Observation.* (1) Five muscles (paired) radiate from the end of the spine of the axis; namely, Rectus Capitis Posterior Major, Obliquus Capitis Inferior, Multifidus, Semispinalis Cervicis, and Interspinalis.

(2) Only one muscle, the Rectus Capitis Posterior Minor (paired), radiates from the posterior tubercle of the atlas. (3) The Obliquus Capitis Inferior is not attached to the caput or head, but it does cause the caput to rotate through pulling on the atlas.

Nerves and Arteries. Dissection is made difficult by the denseness of the areolar tissue. Begin by tracing a communicating branch from the greater occipital nerve (C. 2) across the Inferior Oblique to the suboccipital nerve (i.e., dorsal ramus of C. 1). This ramus supplies the four muscles of the region and sends a branch to the muscle covering the region.

Having found these, follow the stem of the nerve through the **suboccipital triangle**—bounded by the Rectus Capitis Posterior Major and the two oblique muscles—to the upper border of the posterior arch of the atlas.

The thin *posterior atlanto-occipital membrane,* in series with lig. flava, unites the posterior arch of the atlas to the margin of the foramen magnum. Find the *vertebral artery* winding medially, behind the superior articular process of the atlas; detach the membrane from the arch and follow the vertebral artery in its groove on the arch to where the dorsal ramus of C. 1 emerges between it and the arch. Muscular twigs of the artery pass through the triangle; and commonly a large vein from the vertebral plexus pierces the membrane and passes through the triangle to the *suboccipital plexus of veins.* The *occipital artery* crosses the Superior Oblique and there gives off its descending branch.

Actions of Deep Muscles of Back. The deep dorsal muscles acting together *extend* the vertebral joints, including the lumbosacral joint below and the atlanto-occipital joints above. They also prevent, or regulate, *flexion* of these parts, as is the case with the Triceps on the elbow joint. Much, however, of the apparent extensor and flexor movement of the vertebral column takes place actually at the hip joints. When the deep muscles of one side act, *lateral bending* and *rotation* occur, the oblique muscles being the chief rotators (see Functions etc.; p. 207).

Explanatory. It has been seen that the Semispinalis Cervicis and the Multifidus extend upward as far as the spine of the axis, and that the Semispinalis Capitis extends beyond this to the occipital bone—leaving the tubercle of the atlas free. Hence, while you are extending your neck and head, you can rotate your atlas from side to side, and the head rotates with it.

The above facts explain: (1) why the spine of the axis is downturned and massive—the laminae from which the spine springs are necessarily massive too; (2) why the "spine" of the atlas is upturned and reduced to a tubercle—the posterior arch (laminae) from which the tubercle springs is slender, its function being to prevent spreading of the lateral masses of the atlas; and (3) why the atlas has very long transverse processes, these being levers to facilitate rotation.

NERVES OF THE BACK

(Dorsal Rami of Spinal Nerves)

General Considerations. The dorsal rami of each of the 31 pairs of spinal nerves are similar in size, course, relations, and distribution, with the exception of the first two and last three.

The dorsal rami supply a serially segmented territory. They do not extend to the muscles of the limbs, nor are they involved in plexuses. They supply the skin and the "native" deep muscles of the back medial to the angles of the ribs. Hence, they are much smaller than the corresponding ventral rami (C. 1 and 2 excepted).

»» Certain cutaneous branches trespass beyond the angles of the ribs and a few wander afar, thus: C. 2 (greater occipital nerve) ascends to the top of the head; Th. 2 extends toward the acromion; L. 1, 2, and 3 descend to the buttock.

Like the ribs, the nerves slope downward and laterally and they supply a band of

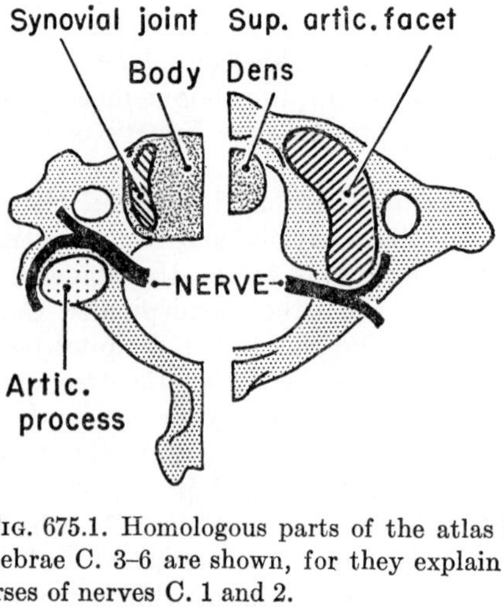

Fig. 675.1. Homologous parts of the atlas and vertebrae C. 3–6 are shown, for they explain the courses of nerves C. 1 and 2.

skin at a lower level than the intervertebral foramina from which they emerge. A given band is overlapped and supplied by the nerve above and the nerve below, so section of one nerve does not cause anesthesia.

»» Each dorsal ramus divides into a medial and a lateral branch (C. 1; S. 4, 5 and Co. 1 excepted), and one or other ends as a cutaneous nerve (C. 1; C. 6, 7, 8; and L. 4, 5 excepted). Above the midthoracic region the medial branches become cutaneous; below it, the lateral branches.

Spinal Ganglia (Post. Root Ganglia). Ganglion C. 1, when present, lies on the posterior arch of the atlas; C. 2 on the lamina of the axis; C. 3—L. 4 in the intervertebral foramina; L. 5—Co. 1 in the vertebral and sacral canals.

A *typical dorsal ramus* takes origin just beyond a spinal ganglion (*fig. 43*), and passes backward on the side of a superior articular process.

»» Here the lateral relation in the cervical region is a Posterior Intertransverse muscle; in the thoracic region, a costotransverse lig.; in the lumbar region, an Intertransverse muscle. The dorsal sacral rami emerge from the dorsal sacral foramina.

Courses of Nerve Trunks C. 1 and 2. *Explanatory:* These are peculiar because the articular processes of the atlanto-occipital and atlanto-axial joints are not the morphological equivalents of succeeding articular processes (*fig. 675.1*)—they occupy an anterior plane, their joint cavities being homologous with the joint cavities found on each side of a typical cervical intervertebral disc. Hence, they pass behind "articular processes." The dorsal ramus of C. 1 passes through the suboccipital triangle, supplies the four suboccipital muscles, and has no cutaneous branch; the dorsal ramus of C. 2 winds round the lower border of the Inferior Oblique and sends its large medial branch (greater occipital) through the Semispinalis Capitis and Trapezius to the top of the head. Its lateral branch is muscular.

Other Dorsal Rami. From C. 3–5 the medial branches run medially between the Semispinalis Capitis and Semispinalis Cervicis and pierce the overlying muscles. From C. 6–Th. 6 the medial branches behave similarly after running one layer deeper; that is, between the Semispinalis Cervicis and Multifidus. From Th. 7–12 the lateral branches run laterally and deep to the Longissimus, pass between it and the Iliocostalis, and pierce the overlying structures. L. 1, 2, and 3 pass through the Erector Spinae below its level of cleavage into Longissimus and Iliocostalis, pass to its lateral border, pierce the posterior lamina of the lumbar fascia, cross the iliac crest, and descend to the level of the greater trochanter of the femur. L. 4 and 5 do not become cutaneous.

Sacral and Coccygeal Nerves. The lower ends of the sacrum and the coccyx have, so to speak, been partly dissolved away, leaving the nerve trunks of S. 5 and Co. 1 exposed at the lower end of the sacral canal. The trunk of S. 5 passes through the foramen bounded posteriorly by the sacral and coccygeal cornua (the homologue of an intervertebral foramen) and divides into a ventral and a dorsal ramus (*fig. 669*). Trunk Co. 1 divides into a ventral and a dorsal ramus on the back of the coccyx.

The dorsal rami of S. 4, 5 and Co. 1 do not divide into medial and lateral branches, but unite to form a small descending cutaneous nerve that supplies the skin over the coccyx. This nerve is the homologue of the dorsal caudal nerve of the quadruped.

ARTERIES OF THE BACK

1. The **Vertebral Artery** is a branch of the subclavian (*fig. 725*). It can be exposed in the suboccipital triangle (*fig. 675*). On leaving the foramen transversarium of the atlas medial to the Rectus Capitis Lateralis (which is an enlarged posterior intertransverse muscle), it winds backward around the superior articular process of the atlas, passes in front of the lateral margin of the posterior atlanto-occipital membrane and in so doing enters the vertebral canal. It occupies the long groove on the posterior arch of the atlas. The suboccipital nerve (C. 1) passes between it and the arch. It sends twigs to accompany this nerve.

2. **Branches of the Vertebral, Intercostal, Lumbar, and Lateral Sacral Arteries** accompany the dorsal rami of the cervical, thoracic, lumbar, and sacral nerves.

3. The **Occipital Artery** is a branch of the external carotid (*fig. 712*). To expose it in its entirety the mastoid process and attached muscles (Sternomastoid, Splenius, Longissimus, and Digastric) require to be removed. It is then seen to follow the posterior belly of the Digastric across the carotid sheath (here containing: int. carotid a., nerves X, XI, and XII, and int. jugular vein), and then to cross the Rectus Capitis Lateralis, Obliquus Capitis Superior, and the apex of the posterior triangle, where, lying on the Semispinalis Capitis, it is joined by the greater occipital nerve (*fig. 675*), whereupon it pierces the Trapezius and ascends in the scalp (*fig. 662*). In its course it occupies a groove on the mastoid bone.

Branches of the Occipital Artery. Muscular branches, including the sternomastoid branch in the anterior triangle;

meningeal twigs which traverse the jugular, mastoid, and parietal foramina;

descending branch which splits near the lateral border of Semispinalis Capitis

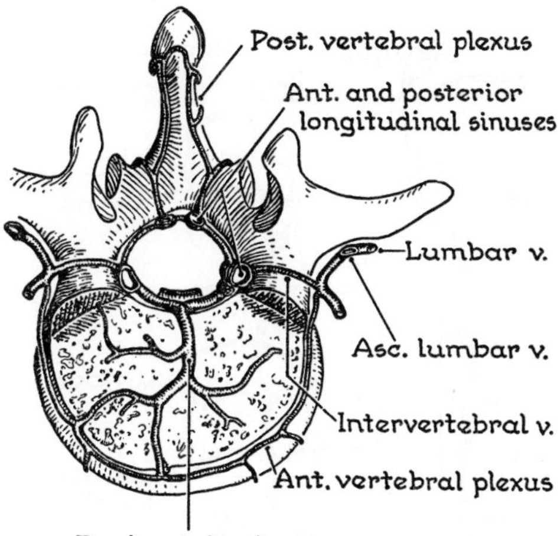

FIG. 676. The veins of the vertebral column

into two, a superficial and a deep branch, which pass to the two surfaces of that muscle. The superficial branch anastomoses with the transversa colli a.; the deep branch anastomoses with the profunda cervicis a.

4. The **Profunda Cervicis Artery** is one of the two terminal branches of the costocervical trunk. It enters the back by passing between the neck of the 1st rib and the transverse process of the 7th cervical vertebra. It ascends deep to the Semispinalis Capitis and anastomoses with the descending branch of the occipital a. and with branches of the vertebral a. This becomes a collateral circulation when the carotid a. is ligated.

VEINS OF THE BACK

»» These veins are large and they form plexuses which tend to follow the arteries. In the neck they mainly descend around the vertebral and profunda cervicis arteries. The profunda cervicis vein ends in the vertebral vein which in turn ends in the brachiocephalic vein.

The occipital vein ends in the suboccipital part of the plexus. It sends venae commitantes with its artery to the int. jugular vein, and it communicates with the post. auricular vein.

Veins of the Vertebral Column (Vertebral Venous System)

The vertebral canal contains a dense plexus of thin-walled, valveless veins which surrounds like a basket-work the spinal dura mater. Above, this plexus communicates

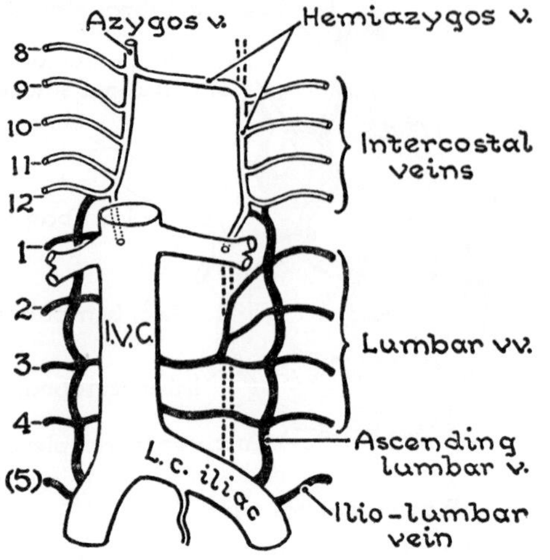

FIG. 677. The ascending lumbar vein. (Cont'd. on fig. 641.)

through the foramen magnum with the occipital and basilar sinuses of the cranium. Anterior and posterior longitudinal channels (venous sinuses) can be discerned in this internal *vertebral venous plexus* (*fig. 676*).

At several spinal segments (not every segment) the plexus receives a vein from the spinal cord and at each segment it receives a vein, the *basivertebral vein*, from the body of a vertebra; and in turn it is drained by intervertebral veins which pass through the intervertebral (and sacral) foramina to the vertebral, intercostal, lumbar, and lateral sacral veins.

Through the body of each vertebra come veins which form a meager *anterior vertebral plexus*, and through the lig. flava pass veins which form a well marked *posterior vertebral plexus*.

Other Longitudinal Channels. In the cervical region, these plexuses communicate freely with the occipital, vertebral, and profunda cervicis veins; and in the thoracic, lumbar, and pelvic regions, segment is linked to segment by the azygos (or hemiazygos), ascending lumbar, and lateral sacral veins.

The *ascending lumbar vein* (*fig. 677*) is an anastomotic vein that ascends in front of the lumbar transverse processes linking one lumbar vein to another, and connecting the common iliac vein with the azygos (or hemiazygos) vein.

Historical. Batson injected a thick radio-opaque solution into the central end of the *deep dorsal vein of the penis* of an adult cadaver. Under the fluoroscope he watched the fluid enter and pass through the prostatic plexus of veins and flow onward through the internal and common iliac veins of both sides to the inferior vena cava. Stereoscopic films showed that the lateral sacral veins were filled and that the fluid had entered the sacral and iliac bones. He noted the resemblance between this venous pattern and that of an early spreading carcinoma of the prostate.

Into another cadaver he injected a thinner solution in order to fill finer veins. Strangely, none of the solution entered the inferior vena cava, but it entered the sacrum and ilium and the veins of the lower lumbar spine.

Into subsequent cadavera he injected larger quantities (200 cc.) of thin solution and found that it progressed up the spine and entered the venous sinuses and veins of the cranial cavity—but it always by-passed the caval veins.

Into the deep dorsal vein of an anesthetized monkey he injected radio-opaque colloidal thorium. This was observed to pass into the i. v. cava; but, when a towel was tied around the monkey's abdomen in order to increase the intra-abdominal pressure and the injection repeated, some thorium passed for a short way into the i. v. cava but most passed into the vertebral system of veins and could be followed in radiograms past the zone of compression into the veins of the thoracic spine and out into the lower intercostal veins. A second experiment gave identical results, thereby demonstrating that the injections in the cadavera were not artifacts.

He injected a thin solution into a *venule of an adult female breast* and found that the fluid spread into the clavicles, head of the humerus, cervical vertebrae, intercostal and azygos veins, and into the transverse and sagittal venous sinuses of the skull. Here again the pattern was comparable to the metastatic spread in carcinoma of the breast.

These findings have led Batson to add to the recognized pulmonary, portal, and caval venous systems a fourth or **vertebral venous system.** This system may be considered a separate, although overlapping, system of veins. It comprises the veins of the brain, skull, neck, viscera, vertebral column (and their valveless connections in the limb girdles), and the veins of the body wall.

Clinical Significance. The foregoing experiments indicate (1) that compression of the thorax and abdomen with the larynx and other sphincters closed, as occurs in straining, coughing, and lifting with the upper limbs, not only prevents blood from entering the thoraco-abdominal veins but squeezes it out of them into the vertebral system; (2) that the increase in the intraspinal and intracranial pressure that occurs during coughing, sneezing, and straining is active—not passive; (3) that tumors and abscesses having connection with this venous system may spread anywhere along this system without involving the portal, pulmonary, or caval systems; and (4) that the cranial and spinal parts of the system, as well as being pathways, are blood depots or storage lakes of blood; further, (5) they reveal the channels through which blood from the lower limbs and pelvis may in favorable circumstances return to the heart after the i. v. cava has been obstructed below the renal veins.

CHAPTER 37

INTERIOR OF CRANIUM

Skull Cap or Calvaria

Structure. The bones of the roof of the skull consist of an *outer* and an *inner plate*, or *lamina*, of compact bone with a layer of spongy bone, called the *diploe*, sandwiched in between. Injuries to the roof of the skull, by compressing the inner plate, tend to cause it to splinter like glass; hence, it has been called the *vitreous layer*.

At birth, the bone consists of a single compact layer. Into this layer veins grow, branch, rebranch, and unite with neighboring veins; and marrow is laid down around

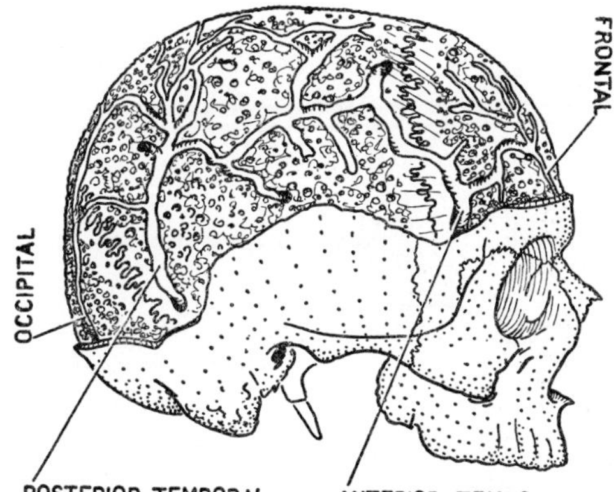

FIG. 678. The four diploic veins

them. Thus is the diploe formed and with it the outer and inner plates.

Diploe does not form in bone covered with thick, fleshy muscle: (1) the temporal squama and (2) the nuchal part of the occipital. In these parts the bone remains "infantile"—thin and translucent.

Hollow buds of mucous membrane sprout from the nasal cavity and mastoid antrum into the diploic layer of certain bones and, by replacing it, form *air sinuses.*

These three types of bone are revealed on the sawn surface of the skull: (1) undifferentiated nondiploic bone in the squama of the temporal bone, (2) air sinuses in the frontal bone, and (3) diploic bone elsewhere.

Blood Supply. There are *four diploic veins* on each side (*fig. 678*). The frontal diploic vein emerges from an obvious, though small, orifice in the supra-orbital notch and joins the supra-orbital vein. The anterior temporal diploic vein emerges from the greater wing of the sphenoid to join the sphenoparietal blood sinus; the posterior temporal diploic vein emerges from the postero-inferior angle of the parietal bone and joins the transverse sinus; and the occipital diploic vein emerges near the internal occipital protuberance and ends in the transverse sinus; but any of these may open into surface veins. There are no accompanying diploic arteries; the meningeal and pericranial arteries provide the arterial blood.

MENINGES

Three meninges or membranes envelop the brain—*dura mater, arachnoid mater,* and *pia mater* (*fig. 679*). Their names indicate their qualities: the dura is tough, the arachnoid is like a spider's web, and the pia clings faithfully to the brain surface like a skin, following all its irregularities. Between the dura mater and arachnoid mater there is a potential space, the *subdural space.*

Between the arachnoid mater and pia mater there is an actual space, the *subarachnoid space,* filled with *cerebrospinal fluid.* The arachnoid mater is attached to the pia mater by loose scattered threads. As the arachnoid does not dip into the sulci of the brain, but bridges them, innumerable small and several large *cisterns* filled with cerebrospinal fluid are seen in the carefully removed brain. It is the pressure of this fluid within the subarachnoid space that obliterates the subdural space. The arteries of the brain travel in the subarachnoid space.

The **Dura Mater** consists of two closely adherent fibrous layers—an outer and an inner.

The *outer layer* or *endocranium* is a periosteum. It is continuous through the foramina of the skull with the external periosteum or *pericranium.* Its outer surface is rough and shaggy (from vessels and fibers withdrawn from the bone).

In the parietal region particularly two

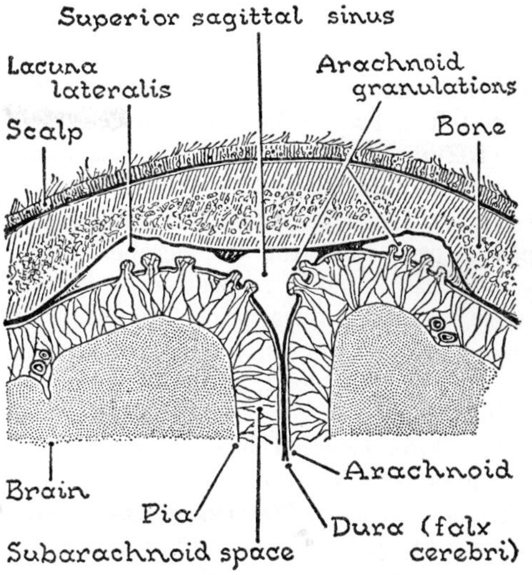

FIG. 679. The arachnoid granulations return the cerebrospinal fluid.

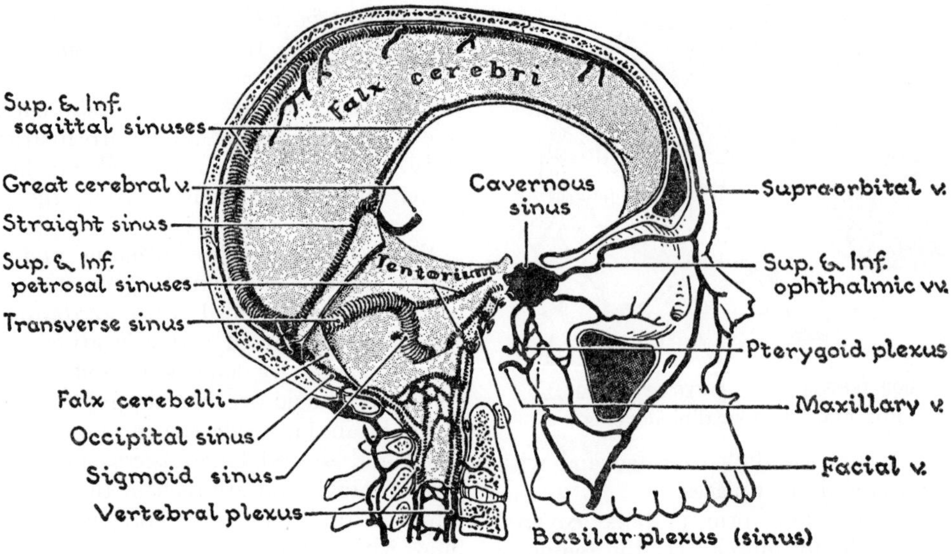

FIG. 680. The folds of the dura mater. Venous sinuses. Vertebral venous plexus

structures stand out from it in relief: (1) Cauliflower-like masses, *arachnoid granulations*, covered with a film of dura, grow widely (nearly 1″) from each side of the median plane (*fig. 679*). They are responsible for the marked pits on the parietal bone. (2) Branches of the *meningeal vessels* run in the outer layer of the dura and make grooves on the bones, notably the parietal bone.

The *inner layer of the dura* is smooth like a serous membrane. It is reduplicated to form **four inwardly projecting folds,** which partially subdivide the cranial cavity into compartments, and being taut they prevent shifting of the cranial cargo, which is the brain. Two of the folds, the *falx cerebri* and *falx cerebelli*, are sickle-shaped occupants of the median plane. The other two, the *tentorium cerebelli* and the *diaphragma sellae*, form roofs for the cerebellum and hypophysis cerebri, respectively. Between the layers of the dura lie certain canals and spaces, *venous sinuses*, lined with endothelium, filled with blood, and continuous with veins.

The **Falx Cerebri** is sickle-shaped, and it hangs between the two cerebral hemispheres (*fig. 680*). Its point is attached to the crista galli. Its convex upper border extends from the crista galli to the internal occipital protuberance. It finds attachment to the frontal crest and to the lips of the sagittal sulcus on the frontal, parietal, and occipital bones. The anterior part of its lower border is free; the posterior part suspends the tentorium cerebelli. Its anterior part may be cribriform. The superior sagittal venous sinus occupies its upper border; the inferior sagittal venous sinus occupies the free part of its lower border, and the straight venous sinus the attached part of its lower border (*fig. 680*).

The **Falx Cerebelli** is a slight fold attached to the internal occipital crest and to the tentorium. Its anterior border, which is free and is often bifid below, projects between the hinder parts of the cerebellar hemispheres. The occipital sinus lies in its attached posterior border.

The **Tentorium Cerebelli,** shaped like a bell tent with open flaps, forms a roof for the cerebellum and a floor for the hinder parts of the cerebrum.

Its *peripheral border* is attached on each side to the posterior clinoid process (which it drags laterally, downward, and backward) and to the lips of the groove on the superior border of the petrous bone, postero-inferior angle of the parietal bone, transverse groove on the occipital bone, and to the internal occipital protuberance.

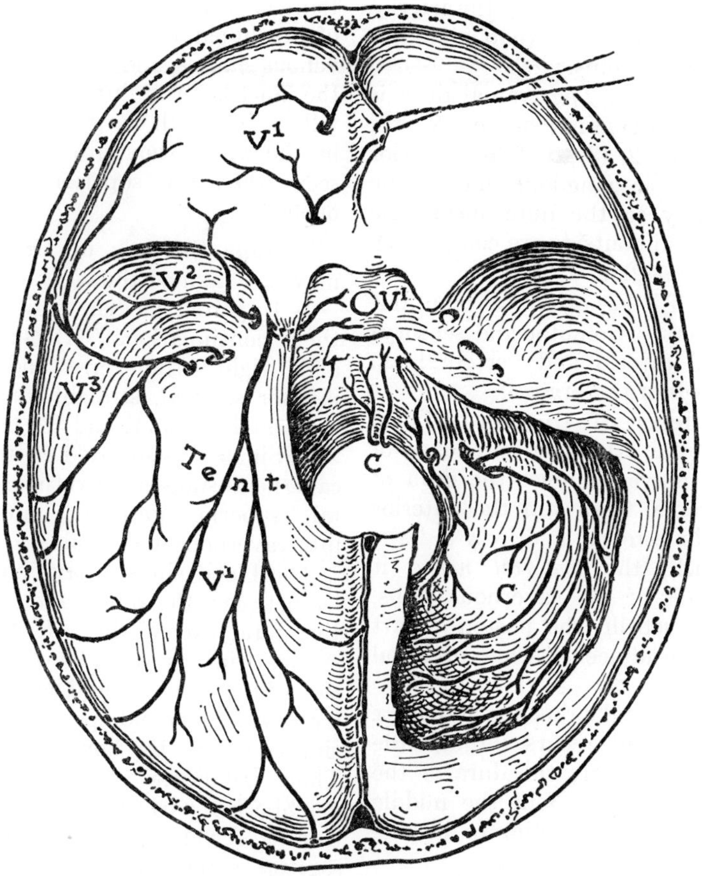

FIG. 680.1. Innervation of the cranial dura mater. (After Kimmel)

Its *medial border* is free; it bounds a large oval opening, the *incisura tentorii;* and it closely grips the sides of the midbrain. It is fixed in front to the anterior clinoid process, which it drags backward into a cone. To reach the anterior clinoid process, the free border crosses above the anterior end of the peripheral border and with it forms a *triangular field* at the side of the diaphragma sellae (*fig. 681*).

The tentorium is held taut by the falx cerebri (and falx cerebelli), the oblique line of union being occupied by the *straight sinus.* Its attached border is occupied on each side by the superior petrosal and transverse sinuses.

The **Diaphragma Sellae** forms a "tentorium" for the hypophysis cerebri and it has a large central aperture for the stalk of the hypophysis cerebri. Pia is reflected from the stalk to the margin of the aperture, thereby closing it. But with advancing age the pia and the subarachnoid space may descend to form a circular moat around the gland (cf., the circumvallate papillae of the tongue) (Sunderland).

Meningeal Arteries, being periosteal arteries, lie embedded in the outer layer of the dura mater. They supply—dura mater, inner table of the skull, and diploe. The **middle meningeal a.,** assisted by a branch of the *anterior ethmoidal a.* in the anterior cranial fossa, caters for the territory above the level of the tentorium cerebelli.

»» Other arteries make small contributions: the *posterior ethmoidal a.* in the anterior fossa; the *accessory meningeal* and *internal carotid aa.* in the middle fossa; the *occipital a.* (via jugular and mastoid foramina), the *ascending pharyngeal a.* (via jugular foramen and hypoglossal canal), and the *vertebral a.* in the posterior fossa.

MENINGEAL VEINS accompany the arteries and communicate with the venous sinuses and with the diploic veins.

Meningeal Nerves. The cranial dura is supplied by the trigeminal nerve (N. V), cervical nerves (1), 2, (3), and the superior cervical sympathetic ganglion. Indeed, the sources of supply to the dura inside the skull and to the skin outside are comparable (*fig. 680.1; cf. fig. 662*).

The brain itself is insensitive to pain, but sympathetic fibers (vasomotor and sensory) on the internal carotid and vertebral aa. supply the vessels of the brain.

Above the level of the tentorium: Nerve V^1, via the ethmoidal branches of the nasociliary nerve, supplies the dura of the anterior cranial fossa and the anterior part of the falx cerebri; and, via a large recurrent branch, the *tentorial nerve,* it supplies the walls of the cavernous sinus, the tentorium cerebelli, the posterior part of the falx, and the adjacent parieto-occipital dura.

Nerve V^2, via several branches and *nerve* V^3, via a branch that recurs through the foramen spinosum, supply the dura of the middle cranial fossa and, join the middle meningeal plexus (sympathetic) to be distributed throughout its territory.

Below the tentorium. The dura of the posterior cranial fossa is supplied by nerves C. (1), 2, (3) and the superior cervical ganglion. The branches accompany the vagus nerve (N. X) through the jugular foramen and N. XII through the hypoglossal canal, and branches ascending through the foramen magnum extend to the posterior clinoid process (Kimmel).

The **Cerebrospinal Fluid** (CSF) is secreted by the choroid plexuses of the lateral, 3rd, and 4th ventricles of the brain. It escapes through three orifices in the 4th ventricle into a subarachnoid cistern. The fluid diffuses over and around the brain and spinal cord and, though the spinal cord ends at the 2nd lumbar vertebra, the subarachnoid space with its contained fluid extends to the 2nd sacral vertebra (*fig. 42*, p. 40). The CSF returns to the blood stream via the arachnoid granulations and villi.

Arachnoid granulations are aggregations of large nonvascular villous processes of arachnoid tissue. They occur along the venous sinuses, and bulge into them through the inner layer of dura (*fig. 679*). Small and villous in youth, large and cauliflower-like in the aged, they are most conveniently seen when the superior sagittal sinus is opened.

Venous Sinuses of the Dura Mater may be classified thus (*fig. 680*):

1. Unpaired median sagittal sinuses and their continuations: (1) superior sagittal and (right) transverse and sigmoid; (2) inferior sagittal, straight, and (left) transverse and sigmoid; and (3) occipital.

2. Sinuses associated with the paired cavernous sinuses—cavernous, sphenoparietal, superior petrosal, inferior petrosal; intercavernous and basilar.

The blood sinuses have no valves. They lie between the outer and inner layers of the dura, except the inferior sagittal and straight sinuses which lie within a reduplication of the inner layer. The superior sagittal, transverse, sigmoid, petrosal, and occipital sinuses groove the bones on which they lie. Their tributaries mostly come from the neighboring parts of the brain; the middle meningeal veins partly end in the superior sagittal sinus; three of the four diploic veins of each side commonly end in the sinuses. All sinuses drain ultimately into the internal jugular veins. Accessory veins, called *emissary veins,* connect the sinuses with the extracranial veins (p. 577).

The superior sagittal sinus (unpaired) occupies the entire length of the attached margin of the falx cerebri, and at the internal occipital protuberance it usually becomes the right transverse sinus. Six or so cerebral veins enter it, against the bloodstream, and large meningeal veins join it. It increases in size from before backward; it is triangular on cross-section; fibrous strands cross its lumen. Arachnoid granulations bulge into it and into its lateral expansions, called *lacunae laterales.*

The inferior sagittal sinus (unpaired) is very small. It occupies the free edge of the falx cerebri. (It receives adjacent cerebral veins.) On being joined by the *great cerebral vein* (of Galen), which turns upward behind the corpus callosum, it becomes the straight sinus.

The straight sinus (unpaired) lies in the line of union between the tentorium cerebelli and the falx cerebri, and therefore, though straight, it is not horizontal. At the int. occipital protuberance it usually becomes the left transverse sinus.

"Lateral Sinus." This term is still in common use, although officially discarded in favor of the transverse and sigmoid sinuses—which are its two constituent parts.

The transverse sinus occupies the attached margin of the tentorium and grooves the occipital bone and postero-inferior angle of the parietal bone. It is triangular on cross-section. Leaving the tentorium it becomes the *sigmoid sinus* which takes a sigmoid course downward in the angle between the mastoid and petrous parts of the temporal bone and, returning to the occipital bone, passes forward over the jugular process and then downward through the jugular foramen to become the internal jugular vein. It is semilunar on cross-section.

The transverse sinus is joined by the superior petrosal sinus, and several veins.

The confluens sinuum is the dilatation commonly found at the beginning of the right transverse sinus. It may cause a depression (torcular Herophili) on the occipital bone beside the int. occipital protuberance. Here the right and left transverse sinuses communicate, usually widely; here the occipital sinus begins.

»» In 51 per cent of 100 cases, the right lateral sinus was larger than the left; in 29 per cent the left was larger than the right, and in 20 per cent the right and left were equal (Browning).

The occipital sinus (unpaired) is variable in size. It descends in the attached margin of the falx cerebelli, bifurcates, and after partly encircling the foramen magnum ends in the sigmoid sinuses. (It receives cerebellar veins and communicates with the vertebral venous plexus (*fig. 676*).)

The cavernous sinus (paired) is a trabeculated and expanded sinus lying at the side of the hypophyseal fossa and of the hollow body of the sphenoid. Laterally, it extends to the maxillary nerve and trigeminal ganglion; anteriorly, to the superior orbital fissure; and posteriorly, to the apex of the petrous bone (*fig. 680*). It receives the sup. and inf. ophthalmic veins (they have no valves), the superficial middle cerebral vein, and the sphenoparietal sinus. It is drained by the sup. and inf. petrosal sinuses and emissary veins. (Contd. on p. 587.)

»» *The sphenoparietal sinus* (paired), lying underneath the lesser wing of the sphenoid, connects the anterior branch of the middle meningeal vein to the cavernous sinus.

The intercavernous sinus connects the cavernous sinuses of opposite sides around and below the hypophysis cerebri.

The superior petrosal sinus (paired) occupies the groove on the superior border of the petrous bone in the attached margin of the tentorium. It drains the cavernous sinus into the transverse sinus. At its origin it bridges, like an aqueduct, the root of the trigeminal nerve.

The inferior petrosal sinus (paired) is larger than the superior. It occupies the groove dorsal to the suture between the basi-occipital and petrous bones, passes through the anterior compartment of the jugular foramen, and ends in the internal jugular vein ½" below the skull. It drains the cavernous sinus. It receives the labyrinthine vein (int. auditory vein) and local veins.

The basilar sinus is a wide trabeculated space behind the dorsum sellae and basi-occipital. It unites the cavernous and the inferior petrosal sinuses of opposite sides and communicates below with the vertebral venous plexus (*fig. 676*).

»» *Note:* All dural sinuses ultimately deliver their blood to the sigmoid sinuses and so to the int. jugular veins, except the inf. petrosal sinuses, which join the int. jugular veins directly.

Emissary Veins pass through the foramina of the skull and connect the sinuses inside with the veins outside, as follows:

Superior sagittal sinus: (1) via the foramen cecum, which lies between the ethmoid and frontal bones, to the veins of the nose. Present in the child, it seldom persists in the adult; (2) via the parietal foramina to the veins of the scalp.

Sigmoid sinuses: (3) via the mastoid foramen to the posterior auricular vein. This, the mastoid emissary vein, is large and fairly constant; (4) via the condylar canal (which opens behind the occipital condyle) to the suboccipital veins. This is often large, but it is inconstant.

Cavernous sinuses: (5) As there are no valves in the ophthalmic veins the blood by reverse flow can pass from the cavernous sinuses to the supra-orbital, facial, and other veins; (6) via the foramen ovale to the pterygoid plexus; (7) via the carotid canal (and for. lacerum) to the pharyngeal plexus.

Occipital and Basilar sinuses, via the foramen magnum (8) communicate with the vertebral venous plexus.

CRANIAL NERVES
(As seen during removal of the brain)

»» It is fortunate that the brain, floating in cerebro-spinal fluid and encased in its three membranes, has the monopoly of the cranial cavity. Not even fat is permitted within; the brain has no rival for space. This total absence of fat within the cranial cavity makes simple the work of the dissector.

Proceed to identify and examine the nerves and vessels as instructed below. For purposes of subsequent study, cut them long on one side and short on the other, using scissors—a knife would tear the nerves which are delicate because they have not yet acquired an epineural sheath from the dura mater.

Let the head fall back, and gently raise the frontal lobes of the brain.

On the floor of the anterior cranial fossa, about 0.5 cm. from the median plane, lies a long (3 cm.), fragile stalk with a slightly enlarged anterior end, the *olfactory tract* and *bulb* (*fig. 681*). The bulb is fixed to the floor by delicate *olfactory nerves* which descend from it and, in tubes of arachnoid mater, pierce the cribriform plate to supply a small area on the roof and walls of the nasal cavity.

»» Cut one *olfactory tract* far back and so leave the olfactory bulb resting on the cribriform plate; on the other side raise the olfactory tract and bulb with the frontal lobe.

The *optic chiasma* lies well behind the chiasmatic (optic) groove; from it the *optic nerve* passes on each side to the optic canal. The *internal carotid artery* ascends in the angle between the optic tract and optic nerve.

»» Cut one optic nerve long, the other short; then cut the internal carotid artery and the stalk of the *hypophysis cerebri* (pituitary gland) behind the optic chiasma and above the diaphragma sellae.

Ease the temporal pole from under cover of the lesser

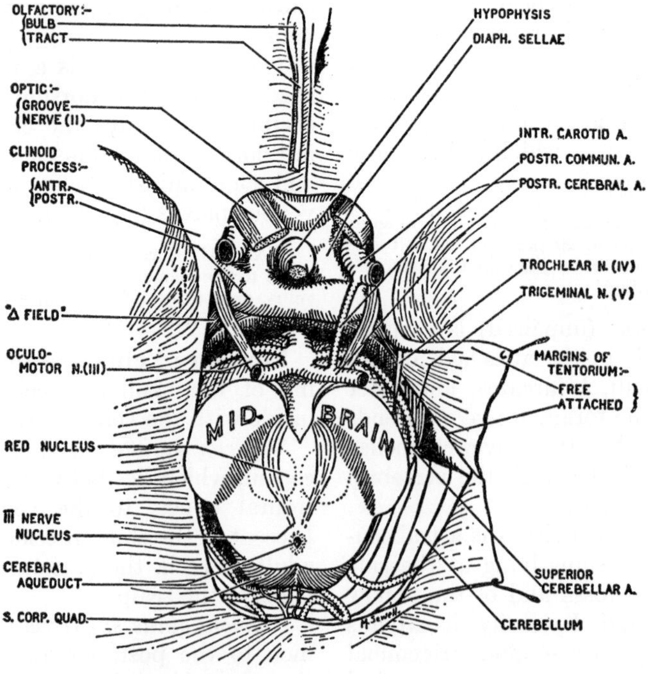

FIG. 681. A stage in the removal of the brain

wing of the sphenoid first on one side then on the other, turning the head from side to side, taking advantage of gravity, and all the time supporting the brain with the palm. With a knife cut through the upper part of the midbrain and let the forebrain fall away in your hand. For success in this last procedure the bell-tent shape of the tentorium cerebelli must be borne in mind, the blade kept above the clinoid processes and free margin of the tentorium, and the cut in the midbrain made to rise posteriorly (*fig. 680*).

On each side the *posterior cerebral artery* will be cut through where it winds around the midbrain, and the *great cerebral vein* will be cut in the median plane behind.

The *oculomotor nerve* (N. III) is large (*fig. 681*). It enters an arachnoid and dural cul-de-sac far forward in the triangular field between the attachments of the tentorium to the anterior and posterior clinoid processes. It may be traced backward and medially, past the posterior clinoid process and between the posterior cerebral and superior cerebellar arteries to the front of the midbrain just above the pons.

The *trochlear nerve* (N. IV), the most delicate of the cranial nerves, pierces the dura in the same triangle as nerve III, but far back, and it also passes between the same two arteries. Followed backward, around the midbrain, under shelter of the free edge of the tentorium—which requires to be raised to bring it into view—it leads to the back of the midbrain, where it arises.

»» Cut NN. III and IV and sever the attached margin of the tentorium cerebelli on both sides. On raising the flaps thus formed, the cerebellum is exposed.

The *trigeminal nerve* (N. V), the largest of the cranial nerves, arches over the most medial part of the upper border of the petrous bone below the attached margin of the tentorium. It curves backward and slightly downward to the side of the pons.

»» Cut N. V. With the handle of the knife hold the midbrain and pons back from the dorsum sellae and basi-occipital and, looking down, identify the *abducent nerve*.

The *abducent nerve* (N. VI). It arises at the lower border of the pons in line with N. III, ascends clamped to the pons by the ant. inf. cerebellar artery, and pierces the dura overlying the inferior petrosal sinus (*fig. 682*).

The *facial* (N. VII) and *vestibulocochlear* (N. VIII) *nerves* with the *nervus intermedius* (pars intermedia) between them arise at the lower border of the pons, abreast of

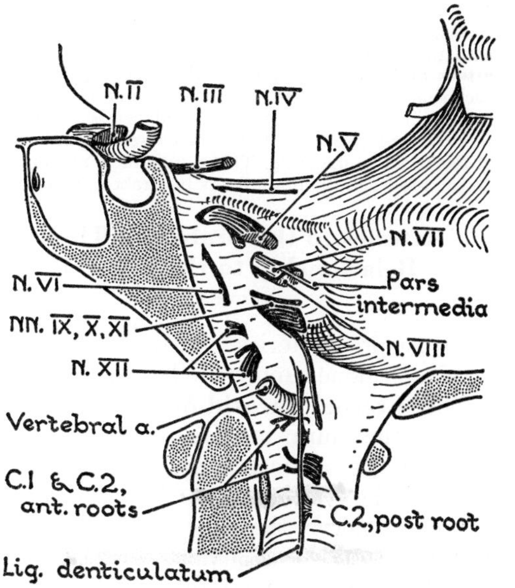

FIG. 682. The cranial nerves, piercing the dura mater.

N. VI and almost in line with N. V. They pass laterally and slightly upward into the internal acoustic meatus. The *labyrinthine artery* (int. auditory a.) accompanies them, and the *labyrinthine vein* ends in the inf. petrosal sinus.

The *glossopharyngeal* (N. IX), *vagus* (N. X), and *accessory* (N. XI) *nerves* arise by a row of fila from the medulla and spinal cord just below and in line with the NN. VII and VIII. They pass laterally (across the tuberculum jugulare), pierce the dura mater ½″ below the internal acoustic meatus, and enter the jugular foramen between the inferior petrosal and sigmoid sinuses. Nerve IX runs horizontally and pierces the dura independently in front of NN. X and XI. The root fila of NN. X and XI ascend with increasing degrees of obliquity and pierce together.

The *hypoglossal nerve* (N. XII) arises from the medulla between the pyramid and olive in line with the origin of nerves III and VI above and with the ventral root of the 1st cervical nerve below. Its root fila, like those of the ventral or motor root of a spinal nerve, converge laterally, and, piercing the dura through two apertures, enter the hypoglossal canal.

»» Cut nerves VI to XII. With a long scalpel inserted through the foramen magnum cut across the spinal cord (medulla) with one sweep. With it the vertebral artery and the spinal root of the accessory nerve on each side will be severed. Remove the midbrain and the hindbrain (i.e., pons, medulla, and cerebellum). Observe the groove on the cerebellum caused by the margin of the foramen magnum. This no doubt is not present during life when the brain floats in cerebrospinal fluid.

Arteries to the Brain and Their Relationship to the Cranial Nerves

Two paired arteries—*internal carotid* and *vertebral*—alone supply the brain.

The **Internal Carotid Artery** (*fig. 682.1*) pierces the dura medial to the anterior clinoid process, which it grooves. It at once gives off the *ophthalmic a.* which runs below the optic nerve through the optic canal, and the *posterior communicating a.* which runs backward, medial to N. III to unite with the posterior cerebral a. It then ascends in the angle between the optic nerve and tract, and ends as the *anterior* and *middle cerebral aa.* Of these, the ant. cerebral a., after running medially above the optic nerve, is joined to its fellow by the *ant. communicating a.*, whereas the middle cerebral a. runs laterally in the stem of the lateral cerebral sulcus.

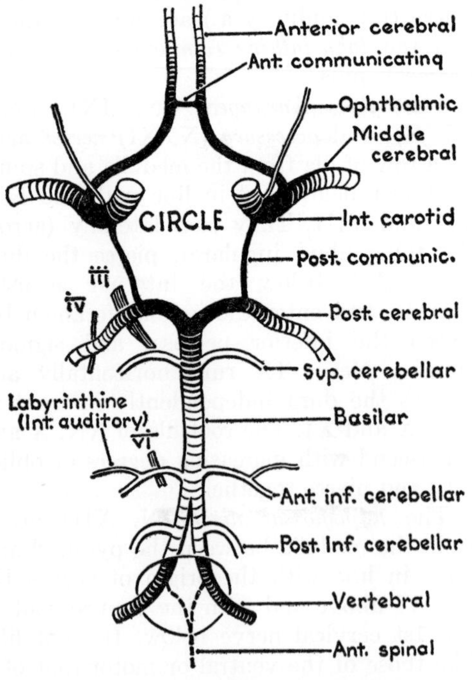

FIG. 682.1. The two vertebral and two internal carotid arteries supply the brain, and they join to form an arterial circle.

The **Vertebral Artery** (*fig. 682.1*) pierces the dura behind the occipital condyle and grooves the margin of the foramen magnum. Here it lies abreast of the interval between the last cranial (hypoglossal) and the 1st cervical nerve. It passes forward between these two nerves to the lower border of the pons where it unites with its fellow to form the basilar a.

The **posterior inferior cerebellar a.** is the largest branch of the vertebral a. On its course to the cerebellum it bears a variable relationship to IX, X, XI nerves—usually it descends in front of them and crosses below them, but it may pass between them, or throw a long loop over them.

The **basilar artery** ascends medianly from the lower border of the pons to the upper border where it ends in a T-shaped bifurcation, the *right* and *left posterior cerebral aa.* In front of it are the basi-occipital and dorsum sellae. Three large paired branches proceed horizontally from it: (1) the *anterior inferior cerebellar a.*, which arises near the lower border of the pons, clamps N. VI to the pons, runs tortuously above, below, or between nerves VII and VIII, and sends the labyrinthine a. to the inner ear; and (2) the *superior cerebellar a.* and (3) the *posterior cerebral a.*, between which run NN. III and IV.

FLOOR OR BASE OF THE SKULL

Three Cranial Fossae

Boundaries (*fig. 683*). The interior of the base of the skull has three terraces, or downward steps, called fossae—an *anterior*, a *middle*, and a *posterior*.

The anterior cranial fossa is sharply marked off from the middle fossa by three free concave crests, a median and two lateral, which are separated from each other by two prominent backwardly projecting tubercles, the *anterior clinoid processes*. The median concave crest connects the anterior clinoid processes of opposite sides above the

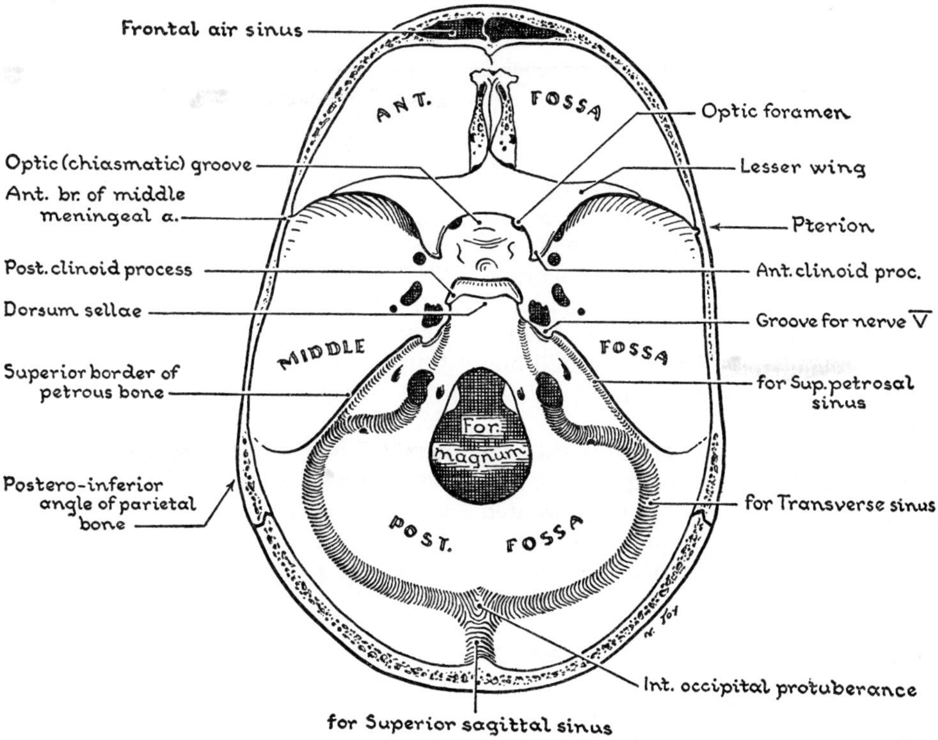

FIG. 683. The interior of the base of the skull—the three cranial fossae

optic canals and across the body of the sphenoid. Each lateral concave crest curves from the anterior clinoid process laterally toward the sharp antero-inferior angle of the parietal bone (**pterion**), but may fail to reach it. It is formed by the *lesser wing of the sphenoid*, and it overhangs the front of the middle fossa.

The middle cranial fossa is marked off from the posterior cranial fossa by a median, rectangular plate, the *dorsum sellae*, at whose free upper angles are tubercles, the *posterior clinoid processes*. On each side, it is marked off by the *superior border of the petrous bone*.

This border extends from the body of the sphenoid, slightly below the side of the dorsum sellae, horizontally laterally and backward toward a point about a finger's breadth behind the external acoustic meatus. The medial ½″ of the superior border of the petrous bone is crossed by the roots of nerve V, so it is rounded. Elsewhere it has a shallow groove for the superior petrosal sinus, bounded by two lines which give attachment to the tentorium cerebelli.

Lesser Wing of Sphenoid. Each lesser wing is triangular. Its attenuated *apex* reaches nearly to the pterion. Its base is attached to the body of the sphenoid by *two flat roots*, an anterior and a posterior, which embrace the optic nerve and ophthalmic artery, thereby forming the *optic canal.*

»» During the 1st year the anterior roots meet and fuse above the anterior part of the body, thereby forming a yoke, the *jugum sphenoidale* (*fig. 684*). The posterior edge of the jugum is the anterior edge of the *chiasmatic* (*optic*) *groove*.

The *posterior edge* of the lesser wing is concave, free, fits into the stem of the lateral cerebral sulcus (of the brain), and ends medially as the ant. clinoid process.

The **anterior clinoid process** is drawn, by the free edge of the tentorium, posteriorly between the int. carotid artery, which grooves it below and medially, and N. III (*fig. 681*).

Anterior Cranial Fossa (*fig. 685*). The upward extension of the nasal septum, called fancifully the *crista galli* or cock's comb, rises in the median plane from the anterior half of the anterior fossa. It is part of the ethmoid bone (ethmos, Gk. = a sieve). The crista extends backward to the sphenoid and forward to a blind canal, the **foramen cecum,** placed between the ethmoid and frontal bones, which in early life transmitted an emissary vein to the nose. Ascending in front of the foramen cecum is a median ridge, the *frontal crest.* The crista galli and the frontal crest give attachment to the falx cerebri.

For 3 mm. on each side of the crista galli the floor of the anterior fossa forms the roof of the nasal cavities, and it is perforated like a sieve by numerous olfactory nerves clothed in arachnoid sheaths that stream through it; hence, it is called the *cribriform plate* of the ethmoid (cribrum, L. = a sieve).

»» The medial ends of two short canals, the *anterior* and *posterior ethmoidal foramina,* which lead from the orbital cavity, open extradurally at the side of the cribriform plate. They are not readily located unless traced from the orbital cavity. They transmit from the orbital cavity to the nasal mucosa the ant. and post. ethmoidal arteries and the ant. ethmoidal nerve. These arteries give off meningeal branches. The anterior ethmoidal a. and n. descend into the nose through a slit, the *nasal slit,* at the side of the front of the crista galli.

Laterally, the fossa is formed by the **orbital plate of the frontal bone.** This thin plate is the roof of the orbital cavity, so it is rounded, and it rises high above the depressed roof of the nasal cavities. (It also forms a roof for the frontal and ethmoidal air sinuses.) Ridges corresponding to the cerebral sulci are conspicuous in the anterior fossa.

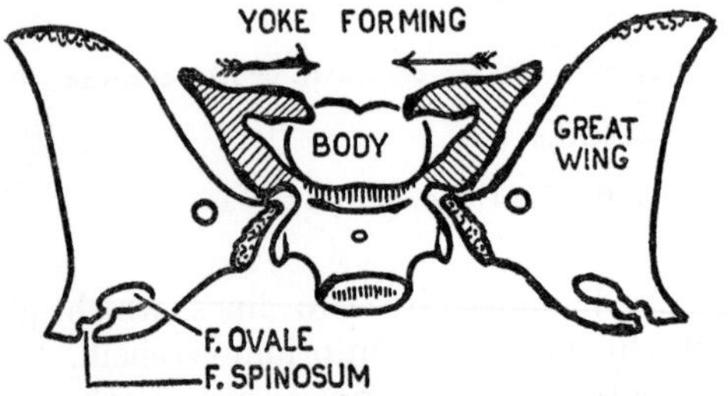

FIG. 684. The sphenoid bone at birth is in three parts. Note the lesser wings spreading above the body to form a yoke (jugum).

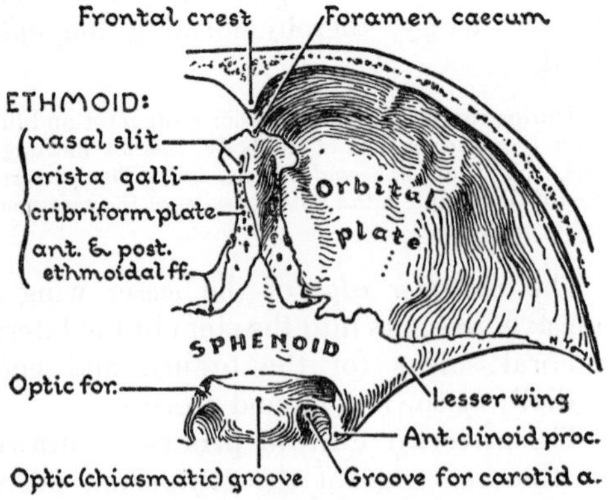

FIG. 685. The anterior cranial fossa (*Optic foramen and optic groove = optic canal and chiasmatic sulcus.*)

Middle Cranial Fossa (pages 583–586).

Posterior Cranial Fossa (*figs. 683* and *686*). This fossa lodges the hind brain, which comprises the cerebellum, medulla, and pons. In life it is roofed in by the tentorium cerebelli, so on each side it is limited above by: (1) the posterior clinoid process; (2) the superior border of the petrous bone; and (3) the lips of the broad shallow groove for the transverse sinus, which continue horizontally backward to the internal occipital protuberance.

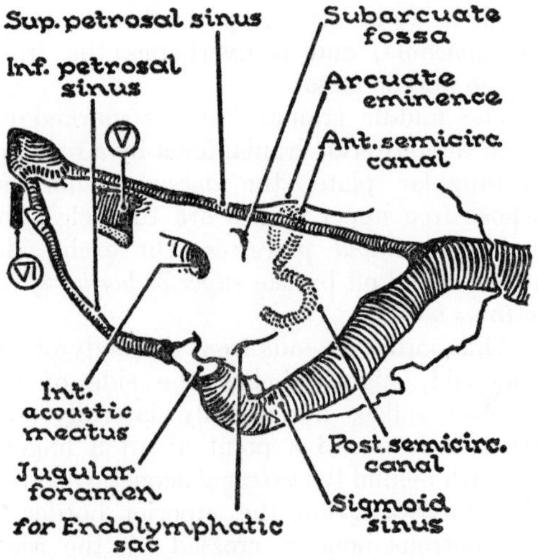

FIG. 686. The posterior surface of the petrous bone is bounded by venous sinuses.

» The *internal occipital protuberance* lies slightly above or below the level of the external occipital protuberance (or inion), depending upon the size of the cerebrum and the development of the nuchal muscles.

The *foramen magnum* is enormous, unpaired and oval. It lies at the lowest part of the posterior fossa. It is narrower in its anterior half, where the occipital condyles encroach on it, than behind. On the medial edge of each condyle there is a *tubercle* for the alar (check) ligament.

Stepping upward and laterally from this tubercle, in a coronal plane, are the essential features of the fossa: (1) the hypoglossal canal, which passes laterally and forward through the base of the condyle and transmits the hypoglossal (XII) nerve. (2) Superolaterally is a *strengthening bar of bone* (tuberculum jugulare) which the accessory (XI), vagus (X), and glossopharyngeal (IX) nerves cross on their way to (3) the *jugular foramen;* and (4) ½″ above this is the *internal acoustic meatus.* Into it the vestibulocochlear (VIII) and facial (VII) nerves disappear.

» *Surface Anatomy.* A straight rod connecting both *external acoustic meatuses* nearly passes through both internal acoustic meatuses. This fact will assist you readily to relate the last six cranial nerves to the surface of the skull.

The *jugular foramen* is an interosseous foramen between the occipital and the petrous temporal bones. Descending to its most anterior part is a narrow groove which lies behind the *petro-occipital fissure* and lodges the inferior petrosal sinus. Descending sinuously to its most posterior part is a wide groove for the *sigmoid sinus.* Nerves IX, X, and XI pass through its middle part.

The *groove for the transverse sinus* begins at the internal occipital protuberance and runs: (1) horizontally laterally on the squama of the occipital bone and postero-inferior angle of the parietal bone to a point ¾″ or less behind the external acoustic meatus; (2) there, as the groove for the sigmoid sinus, it curves downward and medially in the angle between the mastoid and petrous parts of the temporal bone and, leaving them, returns to the occipital bone—this time to the *jugular process;* (3) it then curves forward above the jugular process; and (4) descends in front of it to become the internal jugular vein.

Two foramina for emissary veins commonly pass backward from the groove: (1) the *mastoid foramen* leaves the mastoid part of the course and runs through or near the occipitomastoid suture; and (2) the *condylar canal* leaves the jugular part and opens behind the condyle.

The inclined surface rising from the foramen magnum to the dorsum sellae is the **clivus.** It comprises the upper surface of the basi-occipital [basilar part of occipital bone] and a small part (1 cm.) of the body of the sphenoid.

» In youth the two parts are united by a synchondrosis which is completely ossified by the 21st year (McKern and Stewart).

The basi-occipital is wide and thin below, where it cuts across the hypoglossal canal into the jugular foramen, and it becomes narrower and thicker as it ascends.

Between the foramen magnum and the internal occipital protuberance a thick bar, the *internal occipital crest,* gives attachment to the falx cerebelli. On each side of the crest, the bone is concave for a cerebellar hemisphere, thin, and translucent. Its external surface gives attachment to nuchal muscles.

The **posterior surface of the petrous bone** (*fig. 686*) is flat and triangular. It is defined by grooves for *three sinuses*—sup. petrosal, inf. petrosal, and sigmoid. Its apex is joined to the sphenoid bone by a synchondrosis. Posterosuperior to the internal acoustic meatus is a small laterally directed pit, the remains of a large pit (*fig. 834C*, p. 726) over which at birth the anterior (superior) semicircular canal arched, hence called the *subarcuate fossa.*

» Postero-inferior to the acoustic meatus is a medially directed *vertical slit,* the opening of the aqueduct of the vestibule, which lodges the *saccus endolymphaticus* (*fig. 816*). A *pyramidal notch* on the lower border of the petrous bone, just above the anterior end of the jugular foramen, lodges a ganglion of nerve IX. At the apex of the pyramid is the pinpoint opening of the cochlear canaliculus, which lodges the perilymphatic duct (aqueduct of cochlea).

MIDDLE CRANIAL FOSSA

The **middle cranial fossa** (*fig. 687*), shaped like a butterfly, has a median part and two lateral parts.

Median Part. The median part admits

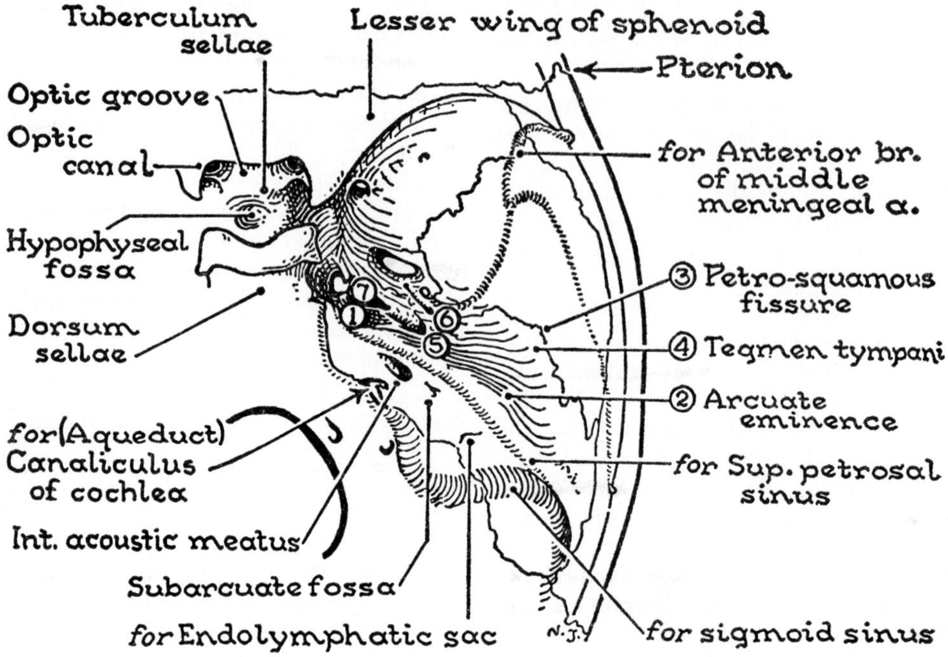

FIG. 687. The middle cranial fossa. Note the seven features on the cerebral surface of the petrous bone: (1) a depression for the trigeminal ganglion, (2) an elevation for the anterior semicircular canal, (3) the remains of the petrosquamous fissure, (4) the tegmen tympani, (5) hiatus for the greater petrosal nerve, (6) hiatus for the lesser petrosal nerve, (7) the roof of the carotid canal which is commonly membranous.

the end of a finger. It is likened to a bed with four clinoid processes, or bed posts (Kline, Gk. = a bed), each of which is pulled on by the tentorium. It lies above the body of the sphenoid, which is thin walled because it is inflated by the sphenoidal air sinuses. It is separated from the anterior cranial fossa by the curved line that unites the anterior clinoid processes and forms the anterior edge of the chiasmatic (optic) groove. It is bounded behind by the dorsum sellae whose superolateral angles are surmounted by the posterior clinoid processes.

Features: (1) the optic canals and the chiasmatic (optic) groove connecting them, and (2) the sella turcica.

The *optic canal* lies between the inflated body of the sphenoid and the two roots of the lesser wing of the sphenoid. The posterior root separates the canal from the groove for the internal carotid artery.

»» The *chiasmatic* (*optic*) *groove* connecting the optic canals behind the jugum, does not lodge the optic chiasma but part of the frontal lobe of the brain and related vessels.

The *sella turcica*, or Turkish saddle, lies behind the chiasmatic groove. It has three parts: (1) an olive-shaped swelling, the *tuberculum sellae* or pommel of the saddle; (2) behind this is the seat of the saddle, called the *hypophyseal fossa* because it lodges the hypophysis cerebri (pituitary gland); and (3) behind this rises the *dorsum sellae* or back of the saddle. At each side of the saddle, as though to accommodate the legs of the rider, is a foramen lacerum (*fig. 687.1*).

Foramen Lacerum. This ragged foramen is bounded by the body of the sphenoid, the attachment of the greater wing, the apex of the petrous temporal bone, and the basi-occipital. The carotid canal and the pterygoid canal open into it.

»» The ant. clinoid process is joined to the tuberculum sellae by a fibrous band (commonly ossified) that passes behind the internal carotid artery.

Lateral Part. Each lateral part is limited in front by the lesser wing of the sphenoid, and behind by the superior border of the petrous bone. Laterally, it extends from the sharp antero-inferior angle of the parietal almost to the blunt postero-inferior angle. It is narrowest and lowest medially at the side of the body of the sphenoid. It involves: (1) the *greater wing* of the sphenoid and (2) the squamous and (3) the petrous parts of the temporal bone.

Greater Wing of Sphenoid. The *feature of the cerebral surface of the greater wing is a* **crescent** *of foramina (fig. 688):* (1) The *superior orbital fissure* is comma-shaped and lies between the greater and lesser wings. It leads forwards into the orbital cavity. (2) Behind the medial end of the fissure is the *foramen rotundum.* This round orifice is directed forward toward the infra-orbital foramen but opens into the pterygopalatine fossa. (3) The *foramen ovale* lies ½″ posterolaterally and opens downward into the infratemporal fossa. And (4) the *foramen spinosum* lies immediately posterolaterally, and also opens into the infratemporal fossa.

Each of the first three foramina transmits a division of the trigeminal nerve, V^1, V^2, and V^3. The fourth, i.e., the foramen spinosum, is situated at the posterolateral angle of the greater wing. It takes its name from the spine that descends from the angle. It transmits the middle meningeal artery.

The superior orbital fissure is separated from the optic canal by one bar of bone and from the foramen rotundum by another bar. The foramina ovale et spinosum are parts of the sphenopetrosal fissure engulfed by the greater wing (*fig. 684*).

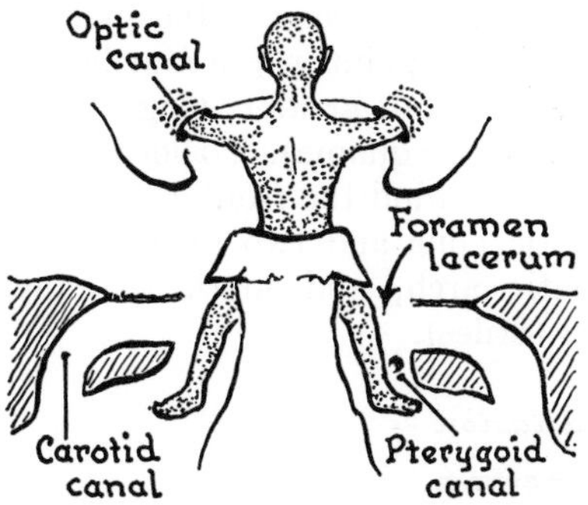

FIG. 687.1. The foramen lacerum
The rider, seated on the saddle, with his arms stretched forward through the optic canals, and his legs dangling through the lacerate foramina, should aid in locating the foramen.

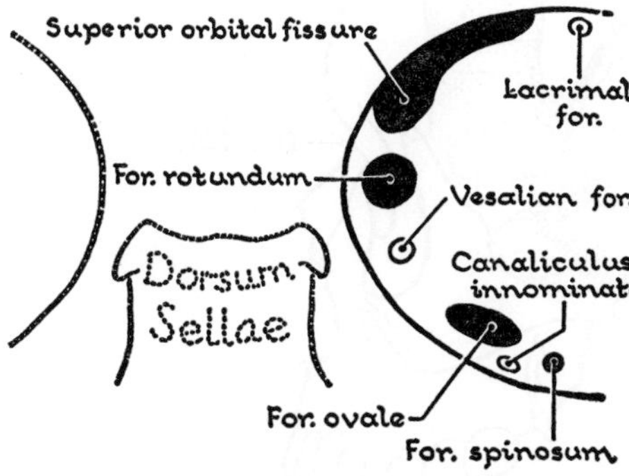

FIG. 688. The crescent of foramina about the greater wing. Of these foramina, 4 are constant and 3 (Lacrimal, Vesalian, and innominatus) are not.

»» *Three small and inconstant foramina* may appear on this crescent: (5) A foramen, situated lateral to the apex of the superior orbital fissure, allows the lacrimal a. to anastomose with the ant. branch of the middle meningeal a. (6) The foramen of Vesalius, situated between the foramen rotundum and foramen ovale, transmits an emissary vein. (7) The "canaliculus innominatus" transmits the lesser (superficial) petrosal nerve to the otic ganglion. Usually this nerve passes through either the petrosphenoidal fissure or the foramen ovale.

Squamous Part of Temporal Bone. The feature of the cerebral surface of this squama is the **groove for the middle meningeal artery** (*fig. 687*). This passes from the foramen spinosum on to the squama, curves forward and laterally to a point corresponding to the middle of the zygomatic arch, and there divides into two grooves for the anterior and posterior branches of the middle meningeal artery.

The important *anterior groove* regains the greater wing and proceeds to the sharp antero-inferior angle of the parietal bone (pterion) where it may remain an open groove, but more commonly it acquires overhanging edges or becomes a bony canal (*fig. 687*). Beyond the pterion it ascends to the vertex, again as an open groove that lies a finger's breadth (more or less) behind the anterior border of the parietal bone. Large grooves branch backwards from it, small ones forward.

»» The *posterior groove* curves backward a finger's breadth (more or less) above and parallel to the zygomatic arch and supramastoid crest. To confirm this, place your index finger above the arch and hold the squama to the light; its lower part is translucent.

The squama is also thin and translucent lateral to the foramen spinosum, where it overlies the mandibular fossa.

Petrous Part of Temporal Bone. The features of the *cerebral surface of the petrous bone* are a medley: a depression for the trigeminal ganglion; an elevation overlying the anterior semicircular canal; a suture line and thin bone (tegmen tympani) overlying the middle ear; and 2 small foramina and 2 grooves for 2 parasympathetic nerves (greater and lesser petrosal nn.) (*fig. 687*).

»» 1. On the apex is a *shallow depression* for the trigeminal (semilunar) ganglion. It is continuous behind with the rounded medial part of the superior border of the petrous bone over which the roots of the trigeminal nerve roll. In front, the bone is commonly deficiens, being replaced with fibrous tissue which here forms the roof of the carotid canal.

2. An elevation, the *arcuate eminence*, rises like the tip of a finger above the superior border, a finger's breadth from the side of the skull. It overlies the anterior semicircular canal.

3. The remains of the *petrosquamous fissure* run from behind the foramen spinosum first laterally, parallel to the superior border, and then backward in a curve to the transverse sinus. It can be identified with the fingernail. It is open until the 2nd year and veins pass through it to the tympanum.

4. Medial to the fissure is the ***tegmen tympani*** or roof of the bony auditory tube, tympanum (middle ear), and mastoid antrum (*fig. 817*). It is thin and can be broken with the point of the forceps.

5 and 6. *Two foramina* open 4 and 8 mm., respectively, behind the foramen spinosum, and from each a faint groove runs anteromedially, parallel to the superior border: (1) The lateral groove conducts the lesser (superficial) petrosal nerve to the canaliculus innominatus (p. 723). (2) The medial groove conducts the greater (superficial) petrosal nerve across the depression for the trigeminal ganglion to the foramen lacerum.

Surface Anatomy of Skull (*fig. 689*).

1. The stem of the *middle meningeal artery*, passing through the foramen spinosum, deep to the head of the mandible, which is readily located by palpation on opening and closing the mouth.

2. The *anterior branch* of the middle meningeal artery crossing the pterion. The **pterion** is the point where four bones meet (parietal, frontal, greater wing of sphenoid and temporal squama). To locate it, place the thumb behind the frontal process of the zygomatic bone and two fingers above the zygomatic arch, and mark the angle so formed (Stiles).

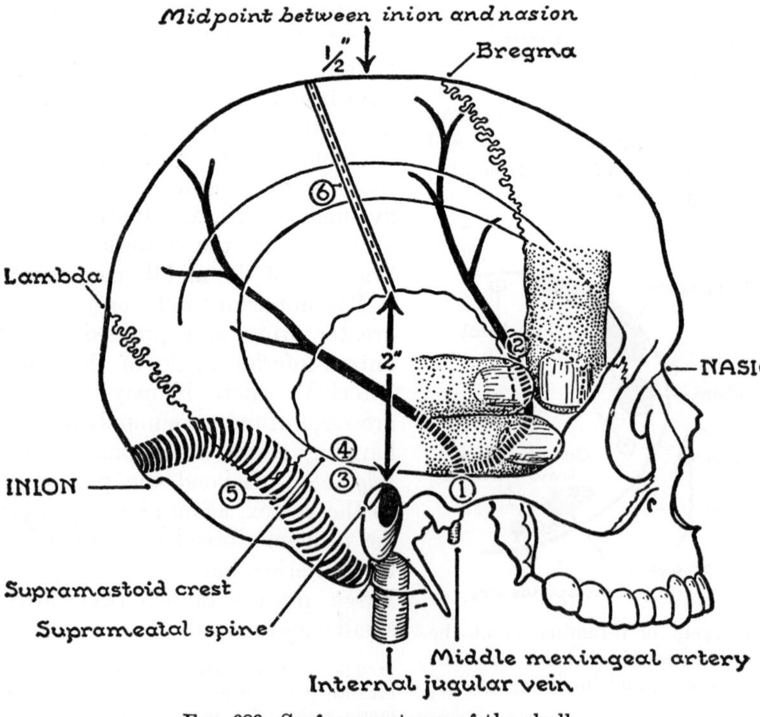

FIG. 689. Surface anatomy of the skull

This great landmark overlies (1) anterior branch of the middle meningeal art., and (2) stem of the lateral cerebral sulcus and, therefore, the insula, lentiform nucleus, internal capsule, etc.

3. The *Suprameatal Triangle* lies below the supramastoid crest and behind the suprameatal spine; a hole drilled here enters the *mastoid antrum.*

4. A hole drilled above the supramastoid crest enters the *middle cranial fossa.*

5. The "*lateral sinus,*" i.e., transverse and sigmoid sinuses, passing from the inion to a point ¾″ or less behind the external acoustic meatus to become the internal jugular vein deep to the anterior border of the mastoid process.

6. The *central sulcus* of the cerebrum running from a point ½″ behind the mid inion-nasion point to a point 2″ above the external acoustic meatus.

Application of Key Figure 688. Does it not follow that the valuable *crescent of foramina* in the greater wing extends, on surface projection, from the head of the mandible to the pterion?

CONTENTS OF MIDDLE CRANIAL FOSSA

1. *Inside both layers of dura mater:*
Optic chiasma and nerve.
Hypophysis cerebri (pituitary gland).
Temporal lobe of cerebrum.

2. *Between two layers of dura mater:*
Cavernous sinus.
Nerve V.
Nerves III, IV, VI.
Int. carotid art. and sympathetic plexus.

3. *Embedded in outer layer of dura:*
Middle meningeal vessels.
(Superficial) Petrosal nerves.

»» *Review.* The oculomotor (N. III), trochlear (N. IV), abducent (N. VI), and trigeminal (N. V) nerves run courses in the middle cranial fossa. Nerves III and IV were seen to pierce the dura mater in the triangle between the free and attached borders of the tentorium. Nerve V was seen ascending from the pons, curving over and therefore rounding off the medial part of the superior border of the petrous bone, and passing through the elliptical mouth of an evagination of arachnoid and dura maters, called the *trigeminal cave.* Nerve VI was seen piercing the dura in the posterior cranial fossa over the inferior petrosal sinus.

The **Trigeminal Nerve** (N. V) is described first because it can be dissected without disturbing the other nerves associated with the cavernous sinus.

On slitting up the mouth and roof of the trigeminal cave, the loose parallel fibers of nerve V are seen to become a plexiform swelling, called the **trigeminal ganglion** (semilunar ganglion). This ganglion is homologous with, and has the same structure as, a spinal ganglion. It lies in a "fingertip" depression above the apex of the petrous bone. The depression extends forward above the roof of the carotid canal, which here is usually fibrous, so the ganglion is subjected to the pulsations of the underlying internal carotid artery.

From the anterior border of the ganglion three divisions proceed: the *mandibular nerve* (V^3) drops almost straight down through the foramen ovale, as though through a trap door, into the infratemporal fossa; the *maxillary nerve* (V^2) passes straight forward through the foramen rotundum into the pterygopalatine fossa and ultimately appears on the face as the infra-orbital nerve; the *ophthalmic nerve* (V^1), which is the smallest of the three divisions, runs forward and upward and divides into three branches, *nasociliary, frontal,* and *lacrimal,* which pass through the superior orbital fissure into the orbital cavity.

The nasociliary nerve is the most important branch of V^1 for it is sensory to the eyeball, including the cornea. It arises from the medial side of N. V^1 and accompanies N. VI. It cannot be seen until N. V^1 is everted.

The trigeminal nerve also conveys motor fibers to the muscles of mastication, so it is a mixed nerve. Its motor root arises from the pons beside the sensory root, and joins that root beyond the ganglion—now in this it behaves like a spinal nerve. The motor root is distributed solely with V^3, so, it passes through the foramen ovale. This requires it to cross the ganglion from medial to lateral side; this it does inferiorly as a separate bundle of threads.

Cavernous Sinus (described on p. 577). Through it passes the internal carotid artery surrounded with sympathetic fibers; and applied to the lateral side of the carotid artery are the nerves of the ocular muscles—

III, IV, and VI (*fig. 690*). Nerve V[1] is a lateral relation of the anterior half of the sinus.

How do the nerves traversing the cavernous sinus gain entrance to the orbital cavity? All pass through the superior orbital fissure. In the ape this fissure is round—it has no lateral extension, as in man (*fig. 691*). In man it is the medial or primitive part of the fissure that the nerves utilize. *They crowd through it,* fairly tightly packed.

» The trochlear, frontal, and lacrimal nerves run side by side above the slender tendinous upper head of the Lateral Rectus, which separates them from the oculomotor, abducent, and nasociliary nerves, which pass between the two heads of the Lateral Rectus. But all are crowded together.

The **Internal Carotid Artery** lies in the carotid canal (*fig. 692*), separated from the trigeminal ganglion by a fibrous layer of

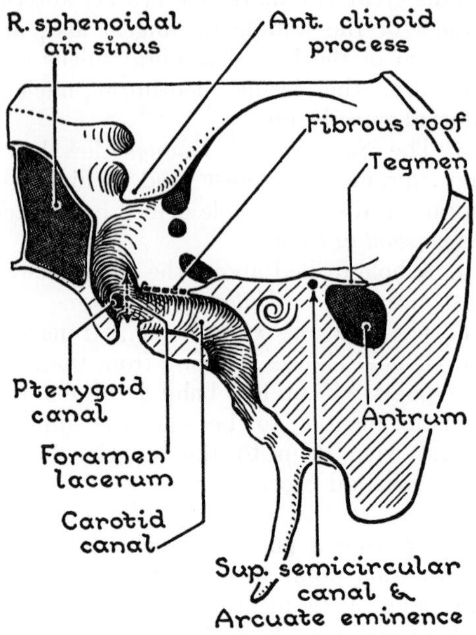

FIG. 692. The carotid canal, shaped like an inverted L, begins on the under surface of the petrous bone and ends at the apex by entering the foramen lacerum.

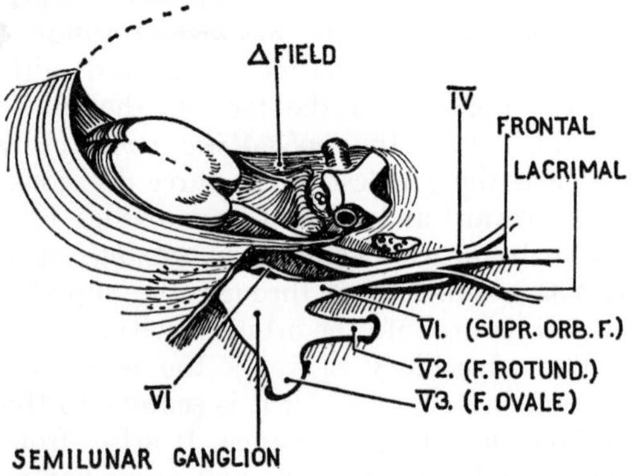

FIG. 690. The 3 divisions of the trigeminal nerve (N. V.). (*Ganglion: semilunar = trigeminal.*)

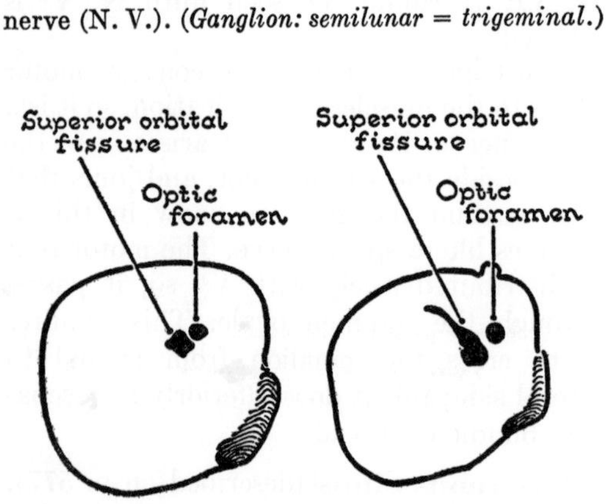

FIG. 691. The superior orbital fissure in the ape and in man. (*Optic: foramen = canal.*)

dura. It emerges from the apex of the petrous bone into the foramen lacerum—it does not pass through the f. lacerum—and bending upward enters the middle cranial fossa.

There, within the cavernous sinus, it ascends in a sulcus on the lateral wall of the body of the sphenoid (and therefore of the sphenoidal air sinus), makes a right angled turn, and passes horizontally forward to the anterior clinoid process. There, leaving the cavernous sinus, it makes an acute angled turn upward, medially, and backward below the anterior clinoid process and optic nerve to the angle between the optic nerve and tract where it divides into the *anterior* and the *middle cerebral artery*.

It sends twigs to the trigeminal ganglion and hypophysis and gives off the ophthalmic and posterior communicating arteries. Parkinson has demonstrated a rich anastomotic network across the midline, joining the two internal carotid arteries as they pass through the cavernous sinuses.

Its intimate relationship to the optic nerve

and the three motor nerves to the ocular muscles are shown in figure 693.

The **Abducent Nerve** (N. VI) supplies the chief abductor of the eyeball.

N. VI arises at the lower border of the pons, the width of the olive medial to the facial nerve. It has an ascending and a horizontal course: thus, it ascends clamped to the pons by the ant. inf. cerebellar artery, passes through the inf. petrosal sinus, bends sharply forward over the sphenopetrosal synchondrosis (or over the bone on one or other side of it), and enters on its horizontal course. In this it *curves tightly round* the lateral side of the int. carotid artery within the cavernous sinus, with nerves III, IV, and V^1. It crowds through the superior orbital fissure between the two heads of the Lateral Rectus, and enters this muscle on its ocular surface behind its middle.

Sympathetic fibers and twigs from nerve V^1 join it in the sinus.

If the Lateral Rectus is paralyzed, the oblique muscles can abduct the eye to, but not beyond, the normal resting position.

The **Trochlear Nerve** (N. IV) supplies the ocular muscle that plays in a trochlea. It is the only nerve to rise from the back of the brain. On this account it has the longest intracranial course. It is also the most slender—olfactory nerves excepted.

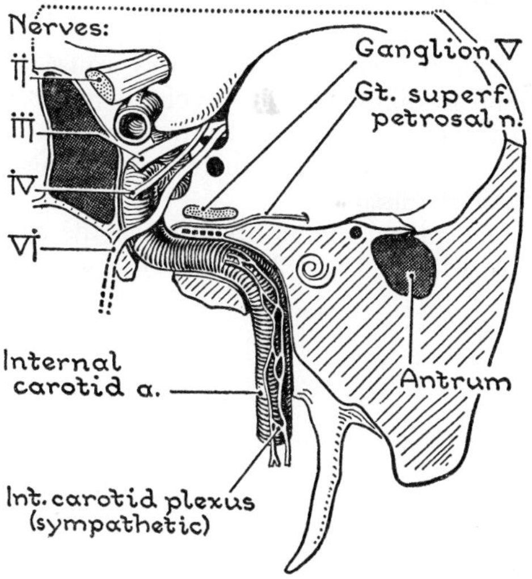

FIG. 693. The course and relations of the intrapetrous and intracranial parts of the internal carotid artery.

It arises from the midbrain, just below the inferior colliculus, winds forward round the midbrain under the free edge of the tentorium cerebelli (*fig. 681*), passes between the posterior cerebral and superior cerebellar arteries, pierces the triangle bounded by the free and attached margins of the tentorium, enters the cavernous sinus, runs forward lateral to the int. carotid art. with nerves III and VI (*fig. 693*).

Nerve III inclines downward medial to N. IV, and the frontal nerve adheres to the lateral side of N. IV as it passes through the superior orbital fissure, above the origin of the muscles.

In the orbit N. IV runs below the periorbita of the bony roof and enters the upper border of the Superior Oblique far back. In its course it crosses above the Levator Palpebrae and Superior Rectus.

If paralyzed, double vision (diplopia) results on trying to look downward.

The **Oculomotor Nerve** (N. III) is motor to all the ocular muscles, except the two supplied by nerves IV and VI. It is also motor to the Levator Palpebrae, and to the ciliary muscle and sphincter of the pupil.

It arises from the front of the midbrain, passes between the same two arteries as the trochlear nerve, and enters the same triangular field of the dura mater (*figs. 681* and *693*). In its course it runs lateral to the posterior communicating a., and posterior clinoid process. Then, within the cavernous sinus, where it is the highest structure, it crosses the int. carotid a. and grooves the anterior clinoid process. Then, it dips down

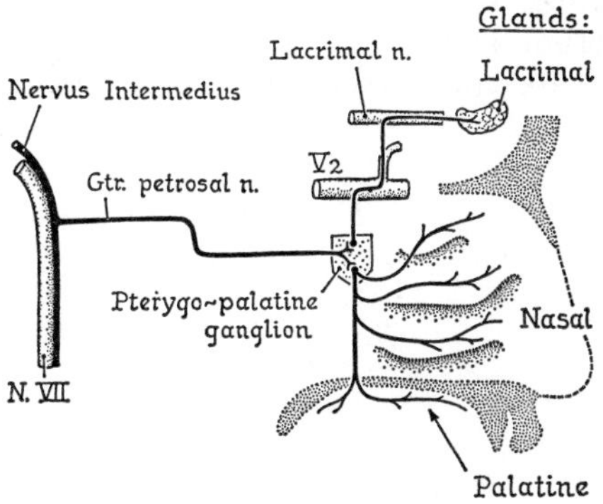

FIG. 693.1. Distribution of fibers in the greater petrosal nerve.

medial to the trochlear and frontal nerves, in order to enter the orbit with the abducent and nasociliary nerves, between the two heads of the Lateral Rectus. This it does in two branches.

Middle Meningeal Artery. This branch of the maxillary artery appears through the foramen spinosum, which is the hindmost foramen on the "crescent of foramina" (*fig. 688*), and occupies the grooves for the middle meningeal artery (and veins) (see p. 575).

Branches. Its *anterior and posterior terminal branches* are distributed above the level of the tentorium.

»» Just before entering the skull, the middle meningeal artery sends the *accessory meningeal artery* through the foramen ovale to the trigeminal ganglion and the dura. Just after entering the skull, it sends two large twigs, which accompany the two (superficial) *petrosal nerves*, into the petrous bone: one to supply the facial nerve and anastomose with the stylomastoid branch of the post. auricular art.; the other to the tympanum. The anterior branch of the artery commonly anastomoses through the superior orbital fissure with the lacrimal artery (*fig. 703*).

The **middle meningeal veins** pass through the foramen spinosum to the pterygoid plexus; they also join the superior sagittal sinus. And, since the grooves they occupy on the parietal bone widen above, it is possible that the venous blood mostly flows upward.

(Superficial) Petrosal Nerves. These two fine nerves, a greater and a lesser, appear in the middle cranial fossa through foramina in the petrous bone. (1) Both nerves run forward and medially, parallel to the superior border of the petrous bone, in faint furrows that conduct them to the for. lacerum and for. ovale, respectively; (2) both are embedded in the outer layer of dura mater; (3) both are secretory; and (4) both are relayed in parasympathetic ganglia, situated beneath the base of the skull (*fig. 797*).

»» *The greater petrosal nerve*, a branch of the nervus intermedius (i.e., of the facial nerve), passes below the trigeminal ganglion, and descends through the foramen lacerum where it is joined by a sympathetic twig from the carotid plexus (the deep petrosal nerve). Thereupon, it passes through the pterygoid canal (as the nerve of the pterygoid canal) to the pterygopalatine ganglion; whence it is relayed to the lacrimal, nasal, and palatine glands (*fig. 693.1*).

The lesser petrosal nerve is the continuation of the tympanic branch of the glossopharyngeal nerve (*fig. 761*). It appears in the middle cranial fossa lateral to the greater nerve, and leaves the skull through the foramen ovale to join the otic ganglion. Thence it is relayed to the auriculotemporal nerve, which conducts it to the facial nerve, and so it reaches the parotid gland (*fig. 797*).

Internal Carotid Nerve and Plexus (*fig. 693*). This branch (or branches) of the superior cervical ganglion, becoming plexiform, accompanies the int. carotid artery through the carotid canal and cavernous sinus to be distributed with the branches of the artery.

»» While in the carotid canal, it sends two twigs, **caroticotympanic nerves,** to the tympanic plexus, and one twig, **deep petrosal nerve,** to unite with the greater petrosal nerve to form the N. of the pterygoid canal and so to the pterygopalatine ganglion.

While in the cavernous sinus it sends twigs to nerves III, IV, V^1, and VI; other twigs pass through the superior orbital fissure to the ciliary ganglion.

Stimulation of these fibers causes the pupil to dilate and the involuntary muscles in the eyelids (sup. and inf. tarsal muscles, *fig. 698*) to contract, thereby widening the palpebral fissure.

The preganglionic fibers leave the spinal cord with T. 1 and 2 (*fig. 766*).

CHAPTER 38

ORBITAL CAVITY AND CONTENTS

BONY CAVITY—*Orbital Margin; Optic Canal; Fissures and Suture Lines; Walls and Beyond; Angles; Foramina.*

CONTENTS OF ORBITAL CAVITY

Bulbus Oculi; Definitions. *Optic Nerve.*

MUSCLES OF EYEBALL—*Four Recti; Two Obliqui; Cone of Muscles.*

MUSCLES OF EYELIDS—*Levator Palpebrae; Tarsal Muscles.*

Vagina Bulbi (Fascia Bulbi).

Actions of the Six Muscles.

NERVES OF THE ORBIT—*Special Sense; Motor; Sensory; Autonomic (Ciliary Ganglion); Nerves.*

Ophthalmic Artery and Branches; Ophthalmic Veins.

Lacrimal Gland. *Other Contents.*

DISSECTION OF EYEBALL

COMPOSITION OF EYEBALL OR BULB—*Three Outer Concentric Coats; Structures Revealed by Dissection of Ox Eye.*

DEVELOPMENT OF EYEBALL.

Bony Cavity [Orbita]. The orbital cavities are two pyramidal cavities each with four walls, an apex, and an *orbital margin*, or brim, which surrounds an *aditus*, or entrance.

The aditus faces forward and laterally. Because its diameters are less than those of the part of the cavity immediately behind it and moulded by the eyeball, a cast of the cavity has the appearance of a pear, the optic canal being the stalk.

Their medial walls are parallel, separated by the nasal cavities, and 1″ apart. Their lateral walls are at right angles to each other. The apex is at the optic canal (*fig. 694*).

Orbital Margin. Three bones—*frontal, maxillary*, and *zygomatic*—contribute nearly equal thirds to the orbital margin: the frontal forming the upper margin and parts of both sides, the others meeting at the middle of the lower margin where there is a tubercle, palpable through the skin. Each of these 3 bones transmits a cutaneous nerve—*supra-orbital, infra-orbital*, and *zygomaticofacial* (*fig. 658*, p. 547).

The lower margin of the orbit, traced medially, becomes the *anterior lacrimal crest* of the frontal process of the maxilla (*fig. 695*). The upper margin, traced medially, becomes the *posterior lacrimal crest* of the lacrimal bone. Thus, the two crests bound the fossa for the lacrimal sac in front and behind. The margin therefore is spiral, like the obturator foramen. The orbital septum (palpebral fascia) is attached to the posterior lacrimal crest and is responsible for its razor-like sharpness.

The margin is much stronger laterally, where it forms a pillar that transmits thrusts from the molar teeth, than medially (*fig. 696.*)

Optic Canal (optic foramen). This lies between the body of the sphenoid and the two roots of the lesser wing. It is 3 to 9 mm. long (about ¼″). Hence, the optic nerve is in contact with the papery wall of the sphenoidal (or post. ethmoidal) air sinus for 3 to 9 mm. (p. 696).

Fissures and Suture Lines (*fig. 695*). A narrow bar of bone (the lower root of the lesser wing) separates the optic canal from the upper limb of an extensive V-shaped fissure. The short upper limb of this V, the *superior orbital fissure*, separates the lesser and greater wings of the sphenoid. The long lower limb is the *inferior orbital fissure*. It completely separates the greater wing from the maxilla, and extends to the zygomatic bone.

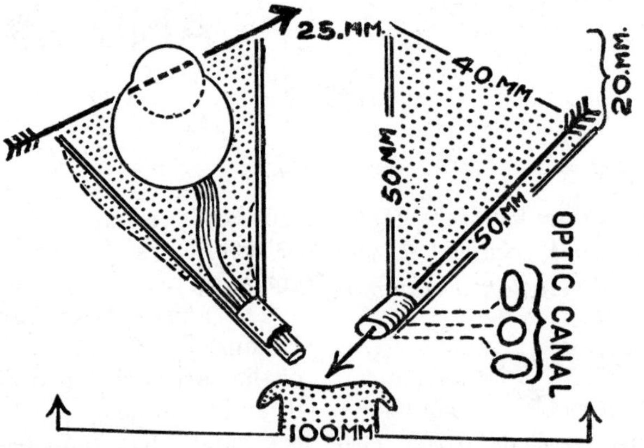

FIG. 694. The orbital cavities on horizontal section, and their dimensions

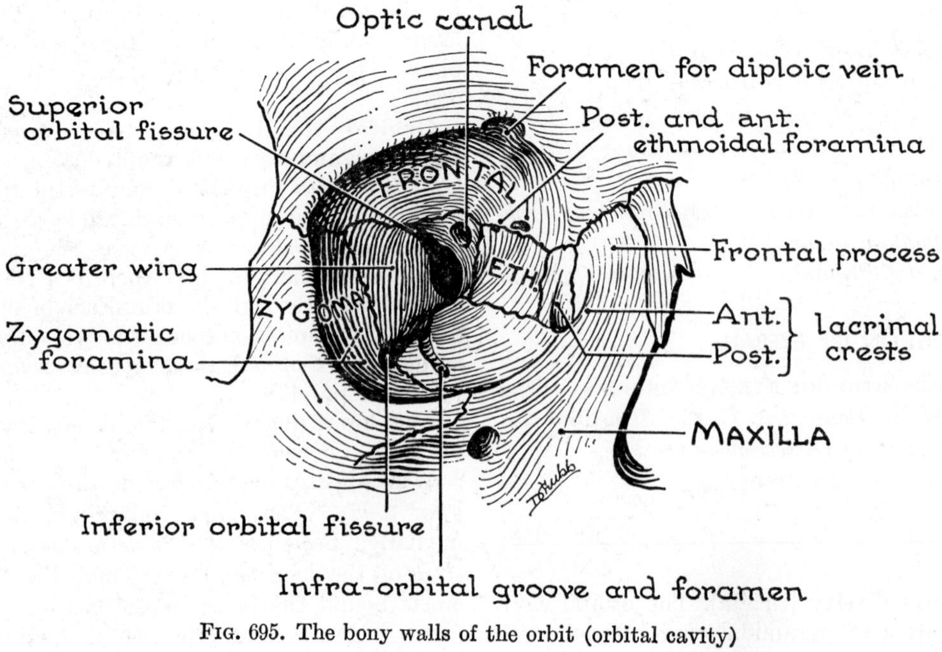

FIG. 695. The bony walls of the orbit (orbital cavity)

A curved probe, passed backward through the infra-orbital foramen, traverses the infra-orbital canal and appears in the infra-orbital groove on the orbital plate of the maxilla. This groove ends at the middle of the inferior orbital fissure.

»» Observe from figure 695 that the orbital part of the frontal bone forms the roof of the orbit and that it rests, like a lid, upon the lateral and medial walls, the suture line being horizontal. This suture line is prolonged as an arc across the face where the frontal bone rests on the frontal process of the maxilla and on the nasal bone. The anterior and posterior *ethmoidal foramina* lie in, or near, the fronto-ethmoidal suture.

Another suture line runs backward from the naso-lacrimal canal to the inferior orbital fissure, separating the lacrimal and ethmoidal bones medially from the maxillary (and palatine) bones below.

Walls and Beyond (*fig. 696*). The medial wall is thin and papery; the lateral wall is the strong wall.

»» *Comparative Anatomy.* This may seem strange because in mammals lower than primates the orbital cavity and temporal fossa are continuous; there is no bony lateral wall. And, in many mammals (cat, pig) even the lateral part of the orbital margin is missing.

A perforation made (1) in the *roof* leads to the anterior cranial fossa (if made anteriorly, it first traverses the frontal air sinus); (2) in the *floor*, to the maxillary air sinus; (3) in the *medial wall*, to the ethmoidal air cells; behind them, to the sphenoidal air sinus; and, *in front of them, to the atrium of the nasal cavity;* and (4) in the *lateral wall*, to the temporal fossa or, behind it, to the middle cranial fossa.

The *periorbita* (periosteum) is tough and easily detached, especially from the roof and medial wall—a matter of surgical importance.

Angles. Behind each of the 4 angles of the orbital margin there is a feature of note (*fig. 656*). Thus:

Superolaterally—fossa for the lacrimal gland.

Superiomedially—fovea (or spine) for the trochlea of the Superior Oblique.

Inferomedially—nasolacrimal canal and origin of the Inferior Oblique.

Inferolaterally—end of the inferior orbital fissure; ¾″ back.

Foramina. The *optic canal* is the royal entrance to the orbital cavity; through it pass the optic nerve (N. II) within its three meningeal tubes (*fig. 698*), and the

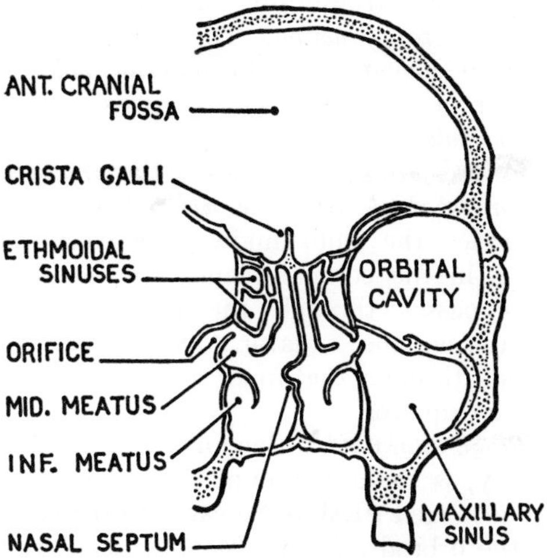

FIG. 696. The skull, on coronal section

ophthalmic artery which supplies this region (*fig. 703*).

The superior orbital fissure is the general entrance; through it pass motor nerves III, IV, and VI, sensory nerve V^1, sympathetic fibers, and ophthalmic veins.

The inferior orbital fissure is an accessory entrance; through it pass branches from V^2 (infra-orbital and zygomatic nerves), the infra-orbital artery, and a communicating vein from the inf. ophthalmic vein to the pterygoid plexus.

Other openings serve as exits—nasolacrimal canal, infra-orbital groove, ant. ethmoidal, post. ethmoidal, zygomatic, and supra-orbital foramina.

CONTENTS OF ORBITAL CAVITY

Bulbus Oculi. The eyeball is 1″ (24.5 mm.) long, or half as long as the orbital cavity. It occupies the anterior half of the cavity; muscles and fat largely fill the posterior half. It projects beyond the orbital margin to the extent that a needle passed from the lateral margin to the bridge of the nose would pass behind the lens (*fig. 694*). On the other hand, the projecting supra-orbital margin and the bridge of the nose prevent a flat surface, such as a book, from striking the eye.

DEFINITIONS. The white fibrous posterior five-sixths of the eyeball is the *sclera;* the transparent anterior one-sixth is the *cornea.*

These are structurally continuous at the *corneoscleral junction.* The center of the corneal curvature is the *anterior pole;* the center of the scleral curvature is the *posterior pole.*

A line joining the poles is the *anteroposterior, sagittal,* or *optic axis.* The *equator* encircles the bulb midway between two poles in the coronal plane. *The horizontal axis* passes through the right and left points on the equator. *The vertical axis* passes through the upper and lower points on the equator.

The orbital axis, or long axis of the orbital cavity, is the axis around which the Recti are arranged (from optic canal to the center of the orbital aditus). *The optic axes,* right and left, are parallel to each other and to the medial wall of the orbital cavity.

Vision is most acute where rays of light come to a focus on the retina at the posterior pole. This part of the retina is the yellow spot or *macula.* The optic nerve pierces the sclera 3 mm. to the medial or nasal side of the posterior pole at the *optic disc* (papilla), which is the blind spot. It is in line with the *orbital axis.*

Optic Nerve. The optic nerve is developmentally different from other nerves; it is a part of the brain and, like the brain, it is surrounded with meninges and is bathed in cerebrospinal fluid. The optic nerve takes a sinuous course from optic canal to optic disc and, so, does not restrain the movements of the eyeball. Its strong dural sheath begins at the optic canal and extends to the sclera and blends with it. A probe passed through the optic canal to the back of the globe lies within the subarachnoid space

If the nerve is cut across close behind the sclera, a central black spot—the *central artery and vein of the retina*—can be seen.

The nerve cannot be withdrawn from its sheath because it adheres to it at the upper part of the optic foramen.

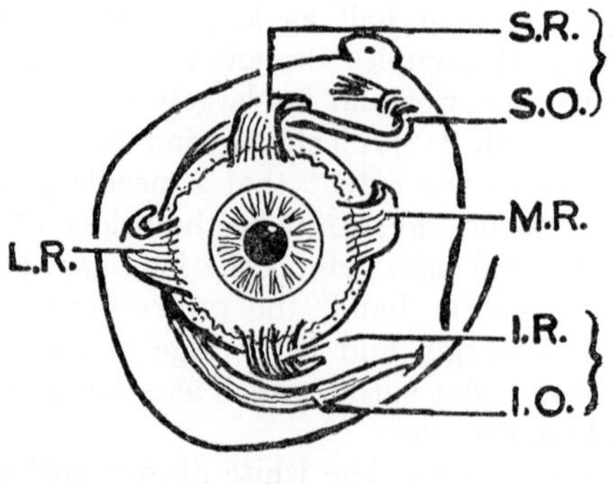

FIG. 697. The six muscles of the eyeball (from the front).

Muscles of the Eyeball. There are 4 straight and 2 oblique muscles of the bulb.

The Recti (superior, inferior, medialis, lateralis) arise from the margin of a fibrous cuff, which is fixed behind to the optic canal and to the dural sheath of the optic nerve, and which reaches laterally to embrace the medial end of the superior orbital fissure (*fig. 702*). They are inserted by band-like aponeuroses into the sclera, 6 to 8 mm. behind the corneoscleral junction (*fig. 697*) and are there loosely covered with conjunctiva.

The Recti spread like the staves of a barrel: behind they are applied to the four walls of the orbital cavity; in front they grasp the globe. Each Rectus has an areolar sheath, and adjacent sheaths are united by areolar tissue—just as the sheaths of Sternomastoid and Trapezius are united by the deep fascia of the posterior triangle: so, a cone is described, "*the muscle cone*" which encloses a space (*fig. 698*). A hammock of condensed areolar tissue, which is slung between the points of attachment of the palpebral ligaments to the orbital margin, supports the bulb, and extensions sent to the Medial and Lateral Recti act as check ligaments.

The origin of the Lateral Rectus is perforated by the nerves that enter the cone of muscles, so it has an upper and lower tendon of origin. Involuntary muscle fibers, the *Inferior Tarsal Muscle* (*fig. 698*), spread forward from the Inferior Rectus to the lower tarsus.

The Levator Palpebrae Superioris is delaminated from the upper part of the Superior Rectus, so they share the same nerve. When the Rectus raises the eye, the Levator raises the lid.

Attachments. The Levator arises with the Superior Rectus and is inserted in three layers. Of these: (1) The anterior layer passes

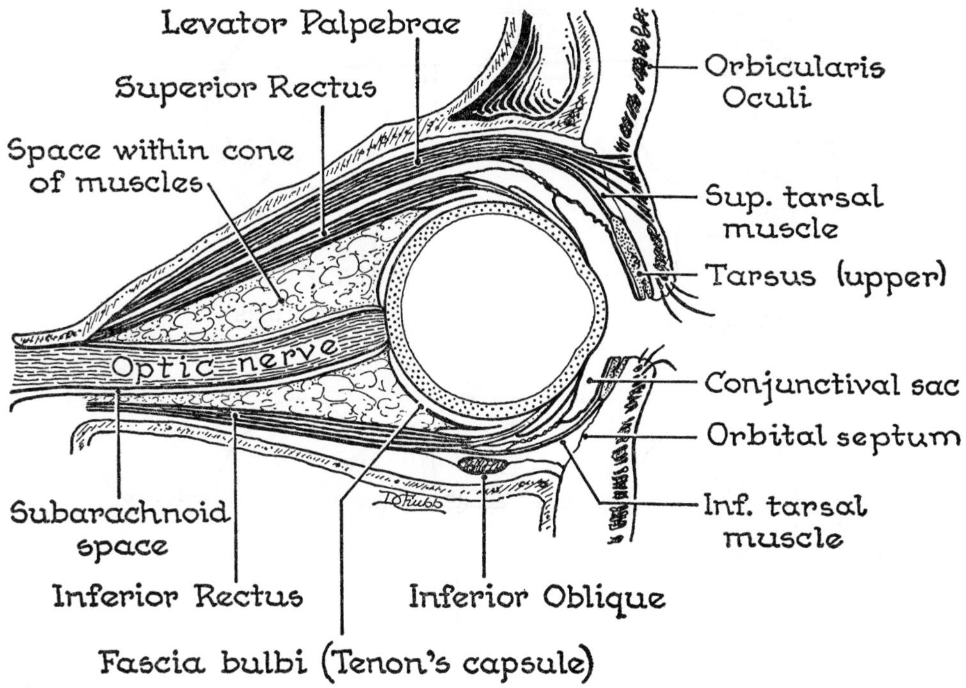

FIG. 698. Diagram of the orbital cavity, on sagittal section

through the Orbicularis and is attached to the skin of the lid. Its edges extend to the medial and lateral palpebral ligs. and are attached with them. (2) The intermediate layer is a sheet of involuntary muscle, the *Superior Tarsal Muscle*, which is attached to the upper tarsus. (3) The posterior layer is fascial and passes to the superior fornix of the conjunctiva (*fig. 655*, *656*, and *698*).

Vagina Bulbi (Fascia Bulbi) (*fig. 698*). The eyeball is invested in a bursal sheath, which extends from the optic nerve to the corneoscleral junction. This sheath of the bulb is necessarily pierced by the six tendons acting on the bulb, and it is reflected for a short distance along each of them; in the case of the Superior Oblique—backward beyond the trochlea.

The Obliqui (Superior et Inferior) are directed backward and laterally from just behind the superomedial and inferomedial angles, respectively, of the orbital margin, to be inserted by fan-shaped tendons into the superolateral quadrant of the posterior half of the bulb.

The Obliquus Inferior arises from the floor, lateral to the entrance to the naso lacrimal canal (*fig. 656*). The Obliquus Superior arose primitively from a corresponding point on the roof, but it migrated backward above the Medial Rectus to the fibrous cuff. It passes through a fibrocartilaginous loop, the *trochlea*, at the superomedial angle, so the direction of its pull remains the same as that of the Obliquus Inferior. The Superior Oblique is tendinous from pulley to insertion. It is not a digastric muscle.

The two Obliques cross below the corresponding Recti—S. Oblique below S. Rectus; I. Oblique below the I. Rectus.

The nerves enter the four Recti on their bulbar surfaces behind their midpoints, and the two Obliqui on their borders (upper and posterior; see *fig. 702*).

ACTIONS OF THE SIX MUSCLES (*fig. 699*). The actions should not be memorized. They can be worked out readily, provided it is appreciated: (1) that the eyeball has three axes on which to rotate (sagittal, horizontal, vertical); (2) that the four Recti are arranged around the orbital axis—

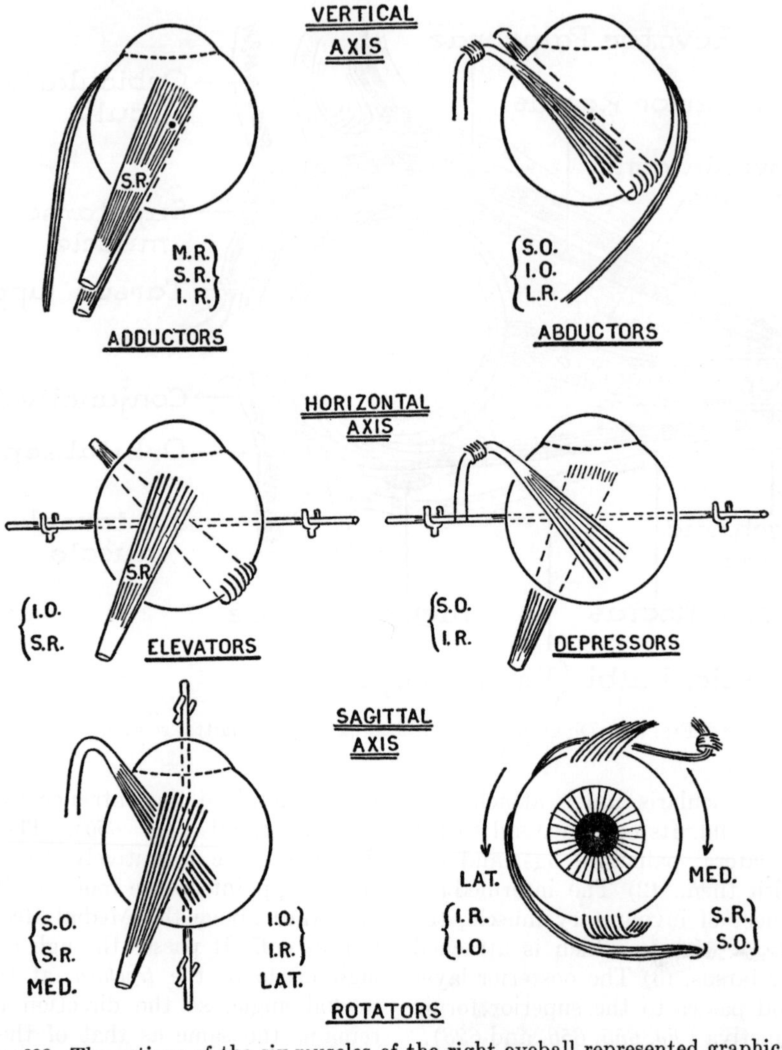

FIG. 699. The actions of the six muscles of the right eyeball represented graphically

not around the optic axis (p. 594)—hence, M., S., and I. Recti act as adductors; and (3) that the two Oblique muscles pass behind the vertical axis and are inserted behind the equator. Hence, they act as abductors.

The Medial and Lateral Recti act on one axis only; each of the other muscles act on multiple axes.

The Recti, acting together, retract the eyeball; and the Obliqui protract it.

Nerves of the Orbit

1. Special Sense—II.
2. Motor—III, IV, and VI.
3. Sensory—V[1] (frontal, lacrimal, and nasociliary branches).
4. Autonomic—(1) sympathetic fibers from the carotid plexus, and (2) parasympathetic fibers traveling with N. III.

Special Sense. *The Optic Nerve* (II) reaches the orbit through the optic canal and comes to lie within the cone of muscle (*fig. 698*).

All the other nerves crowd through the superior orbital fissure: three of these, the *trochlear*, *frontal*, and *lacrimal*, pass above the origin of the Lateral Rectus and lie between the roof of the orbit and the cone of muscles; the others pass as a bundle through the fibrous origin of the Lateral Rectus, and lie within the cone of muscles (*figs. 700–702*).

The Three Motor Nerves (*fig. 702*). *The Abducent Nerve* (VI) clings to the ocular surface of the Lateral Rectus and enters it behind its midpoint.

The Trochlear Nerve (IV) enters the upper border of the Superior Oblique far back.

The Oculomotor Nerve (III) supplies three Recti, Inferior Oblique, and Levator Palpebrae; and it conveys parasympathetic fibers to the ciliary ganglion, thence they are relayed to the ciliary muscle and Sphincter Pupillae.

Nerve III is employed when an object is examined close at hand, as in reading, because it causes convergence of the eyes (adductor muscles), accommodation of the lens or focusing (ciliary muscle), and contraction of the pupil (circular fibers of iris), thereby shutting out peripheral light.

»» Nerve III passes between the two heads of the Lateral Rectus as an upper and a lower division: of these, the upper supplies the Superior Rectus and Levator Palpebrae; the lower sends a branch below the optic nerve to the Medial Rectus, a branch to the Inferior Rectus, and a branch that runs along the lateral border of the Inferior Rectus to the Inferior Oblique. The nerve to the Inferior Oblique delivers the preganglionic fibers (motor root) to the ciliary ganglion.

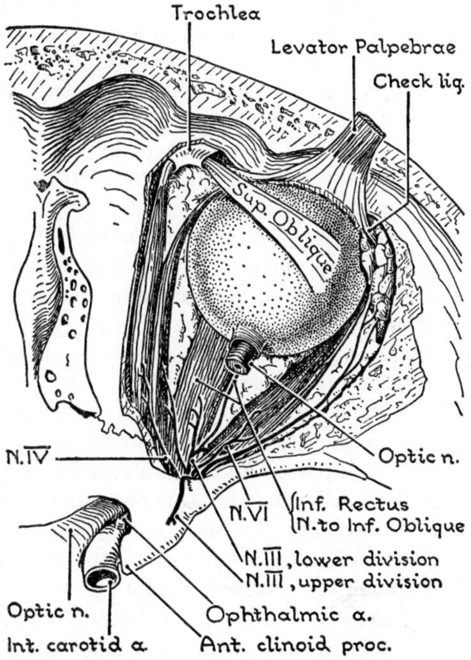

FIG. 700. Dissection of the orbital cavity, from above.

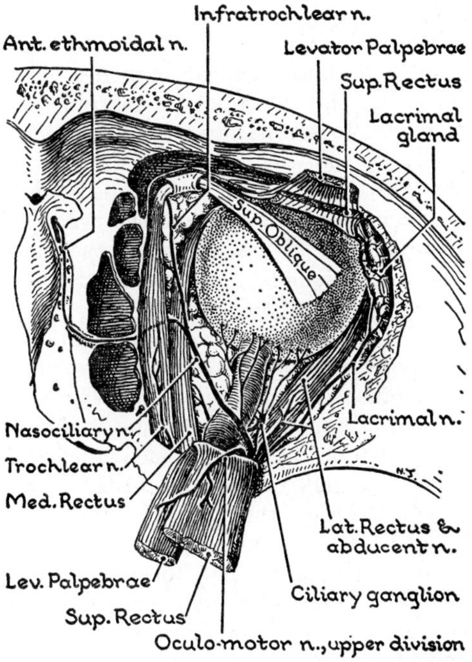

FIG. 701. Dissection of the orbital cavity, from above.

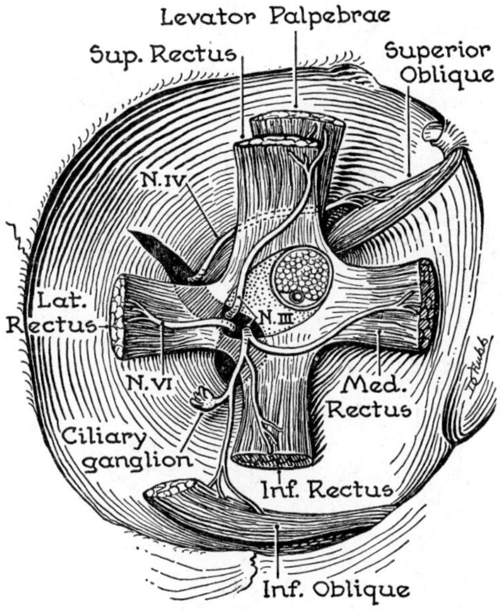

FIG. 702. Sketch of the distribution of cranial nerves III, IV, and VI.

Ophthalmic Nerve (V[1]). This sensory nerve passes through the superior orbital fissure as three branches: frontal, lacrimal, and nasociliary. The *frontal nerve* passes above the Lateral Rectus, runs between the orbital plate of the frontal bone and the Levator Palpebrae, and divides into supra-orbital and supratrochlear branches. These turn round the supra-orbital margin to be distributed to scalp and eyelid (*fig. 658*).

The *lacrimal nerve* follows the upper border of the Lateral Rectus and ends in the upper lid. It accepts from the zygomatic nerve secretory fibers, relayed in the pterygopalatine ganglion, and delivers them to the lacrimal gland (*fig. 693.1*).

The **nasociliary nerve** (*fig. 701*) is of supreme importance on account, not of the nasal branch, but of the ciliary. The nasociliary nerve passes between the two heads of the Lateral Rectus, crosses above the optic nerve, and runs on the medial wall of the orbit between the Superior Oblique and Medial Rectus. It sends (1) a twig through the posterior ethmoidal foramen to the sphenoidal and ethmoidal cells and (2) the *infratrochlear nerve* forward, below the trochlea, to the tear sac and the region all around it, and it continues as (3) the *anterior ethmoidal nerve.*

Two **long ciliary nerves** arise from the nasociliary nerve, as it crosses the optic nerve; they accompany the short ciliary nerves. They are mixed—sensory and sympathetic.

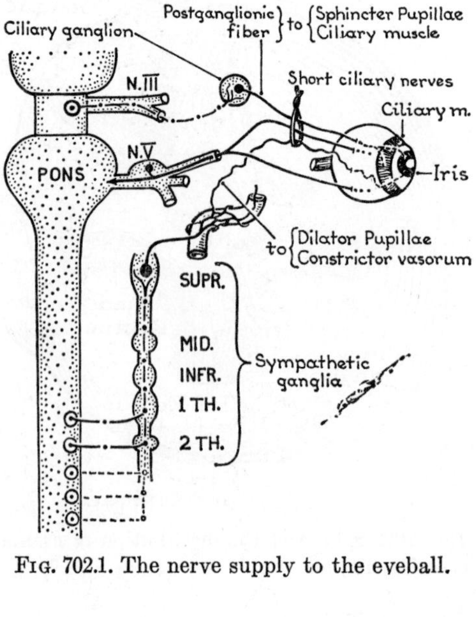

FIG. 702.1. The nerve supply to the eyeball.

Sensation from the tip of the nose and from the cornea is subserved by the respective divisions of the nasociliary nerve. A rough foreign body, such as a cinder, in the eye—if there were no ciliary nerves (afferent fibers of pain) to detect it—would cause inflammation and ulceration of the cornea (*fig. 702.1*).

»» The *anterior ethmoidal nerve* passes through the anterior ethmoidal foramen, and appears extradurally in the ant. cranial fossa. It then descends through the slit at the side of the crista galli into the nasal mucosa, and supplies ethmoidal cells and the front of the nasal cavity. Descending behind the nasal bone, it passes between nasal bone and cartilage to appear on the dorsum of the nose, where, as the *ext. nasal nerve*, it extends to the tip (*fig. 658*).

Autonomic and Ciliary Nerves (*fig. 701*). Far back between optic nerve and Lateral Rectus there is a small brown ganglion, the **ciliary ganglion.** It is the relay station for the parasympathetic fibers of nerve III. These fibers pass to the ganglion via the nerve to the Inferior Oblique and leave it via 12 or more *short ciliary nerves.* The short ciliary nerves pierce the scleral coat around the optic nerve and run forward between the scleral and choroidal coats. They are motor to the ciliary muscle and Sphincter Pupillae (circular fibers of the iris).

Short ciliary nerves, however, are not entirely parasympathetic. Thus, a branch from the sympathetic and another from the nasociliary nerve enter the ciliary ganglion and, without synapsing, pass out with the short ciliary nerves: the sympathetic fibers are vasoconstrictor; the nasociliary fibers are sensory.

The two *long ciliary nerves*, described with the nasociliary nerve (above), though particularly important for carrying sensory fibers to the cornea, also carry sympathetic fibers. These join the nasociliary nerve in the cavernous sinus and are motor to the Dilator Pupillae (radial fibers of the iris).

Ophthalmic Artery (*fig. 703*). This artery supplies the contents of the orbital cavity and sends branches beyond the cavity. It arises from the int. carotid artery, passes through the optic canal and, piercing the dural sheath of the nerve, finds itself free within the cone of muscles. It then crosses above the optic nerve between the ophthalmic vein in front and the naso-ciliary nerve behind.

Branches must be accounted for to the various structures within the orbit—three coats of the eyeball, optic nerve, muscles, fat, and lacrimal gland.

The **central artery of the retina,** with its companion vein, enters the sheath of the nerve ½″ behind the eyeball, runs in the center of the optic nerve through the sclera to the retina, and supplies its inner layer. It is an end artery. Obstruction leads to instant and total blindness.

Posterior ciliary arteries (six or more) pierce the sclera around the optic nerve to end in the choroid. Two of these arteries, *long posterior ciliary aa.*, run forward, one on each side, between sclera and choroid to anastomose with the anterior ciliary arteries.

Anterior ciliary arteries, derived from the muscular branches to the Recti, pierce the sclera behind the corneoscleral junction, anastomose with a long posterior ciliary artery on each side, and supply the ciliary body and iris. But before piercing the sclera, they supply twigs to the deep conjunctival plexus (episcleral) around the corneal margin. The cornea has no blood supply; the sclera has but little.

Six branches of the ophthalmic a. stream out of the orbit in company of correspondingly named nerves (*fig. 658*) and anastomose with branches of the ext. carotid artery. They are: *supra-orbital, supratrochlear, dorsal nasal* (with infratrochlear n.) and *lacrimal,* which end on the forehead or face, and *ant.* and *post. ethmoidal arteries,* which end in the nasal mucosa.

Ophthalmic Veins. *The superior ophthalmic vein* anastomoses with the facial vein and, since it has no valves, the blood can flow in either direction (*fig. 680*). It crosses above the optic nerve, passes through the sup. orbital fissure and ends in the cavernous sinus.

The inferior ophthalmic vein begins on the floor of the orbit, communicates through the inf. orbital fissure with the pterygoid plexus, crosses below the optic nerve, and ends either in the superior vein or in the cavernous sinus. Tributaries correspond to branches of the artery.

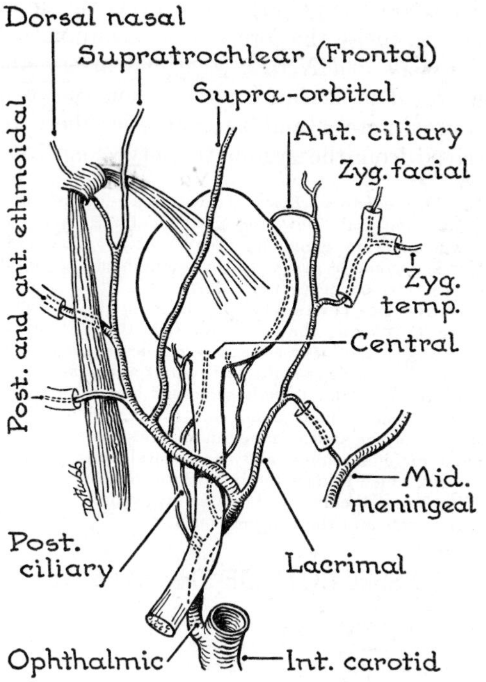

FIG. 703. Diagram of the ophthalmic artery and its branches.

LYMPH VESSELS have not been described definitely within the orbital cavity, excepting those from the lacrimal gland, and they pass to the parotid nodes.

Lacrimal Gland (*fig. 656C*). This serous gland is placed behind the *superolateral* angle of the orbital margin, between the orbital plate of the frontal bone and the conjunctiva. It is indented by the lateral border of the Levator Palpebrae and thereby made J shape. So, it has a deep (or orbital) lobe and a superficial (or palpebral) lobe. Less than a dozen ducts open near the superior fornix of the conjunctiva; those of the orbital lobe cross the palpebral lobe.

Exposure. (1) To expose the *orbital lobe* of the gland, cut through skin, Orbicularis Oculi, and orbital septum along the superolateral quadrant of the orbital margin. (2)

To expose the *palpebral lobe*, evert the upper lid and incise the fornix of the conjunctiva.

Vessels and Nerves: Lacrimal artery and nerve. The lacrimal nerve (sensory) conveys secretory and sympathetic fibers received from the zygomatic nerve (*fig. 795*).

»» The secretory fibers travel via intermediate, greater petrosal, and pterygoid canal nerves to the pterygopalatine ganglion; thence to be relayed by N. V^2, zygomatic nerve, and a communicating branch to the lacrimal nerve (*fig. 693.1*).

Other Contents Three branches of the maxillary nerve (V^2) enter the orbit through the inf. orbital fissure: (1) the *infra-orbital nerve*, lies embedded in the floor; (2) the *zygomatic nerve* clings to and perforates the lateral wall and sends secretory and sympathetic fibers to the lacrimal gland; and (3) the *orbital branch* of the pterygopalatine ganglion supplies the sphenoidal and ethmoidal sinuses and the Orbital muscle (involuntary) which bridges the inf. orbital fissure.

Twigs of the infra-orbital artery supply the floor of the orbit and the lacrimal sac.

DISSECTION OF THE EYEBALL

»» A convenient way to acquire a general knowledge of the anatomy of the human eyeball is through the dissection of the eyeball of the ox, because it is large and obtainable without difficulty. It is necessary to remove the adnexa preparatory to hardening the ball in formalin or alcohol overnight.

The *conjunctiva* is only loosely attached to the sclera and is easily separated from it up to the corneal margin. The epithelium of the *cornea* is firmly adherent and cannot wrinkle. In man it consists of five or six layers of cells.

The four Recti, two Obliqui, and the Retractor Bulbi (a muscle not present in man), are to be cleaned and removed with the fat around the ball. The thick *tube of dura mater* surrounding the optic nerve is to be cleaned and its attachment to the globe defined.

Composition of the Eyeball or Bulb

Three Outer Concentric Coats and their parts (*figs. 704* and *705*):

1. Outer or fibrous coat:
   Sclera and cornea.
2. Middle or vascular coat:
   Choroid, ciliary body, and iris.
3. Inner or retinal coat:
   Outer pigmented.
   Inner nervous.

Three Enclosed Refractive Media:
aqueous humor—lens—vitreous body.

»» DISSECTION. Holding the bulb firmly in the left hand, shave off from the neighborhood of the equator thin slices of the sclera, which is grayish in color, until the choroid, which is told by its jet blackness, is exposed. Then holding the bulb loosely so as to relieve tension carefully insert the point of a probe through the hole just made and detach the choroid all round it. With scissors snip away the part of the sclera so freed. And so, with the alternate aid of probe and scissors, and working meridionally, between anterior and posterior poles, remove a third or more of the outer coat. This will expose an underlying elliptical area of the choroid. The point of the probe must be directed continuously against the sclera in order that the delicate middle and inner coats shall not be punctured. With a sweeping movement detach the middle coat from the corneoscleral junction where it is firmly attached.

OBSERVATION. The space behind the cornea is the *anterior chamber*. It is continuous through the *pupil*, which is oval in the ox and circular in man, with the *posterior chamber*. Both chambers contained

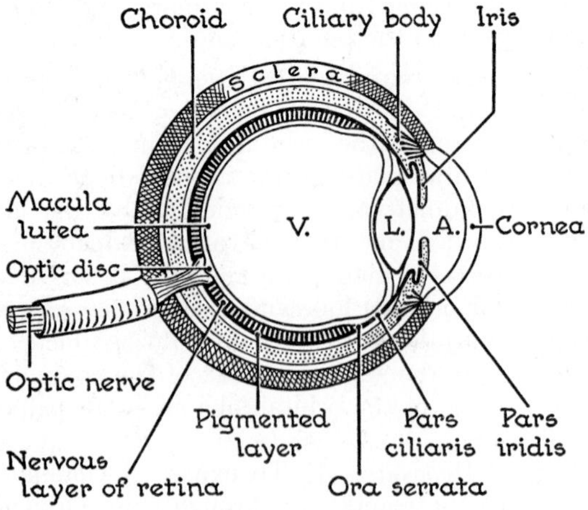

FIG. 704
Scheme of an eyeball, sagittal section

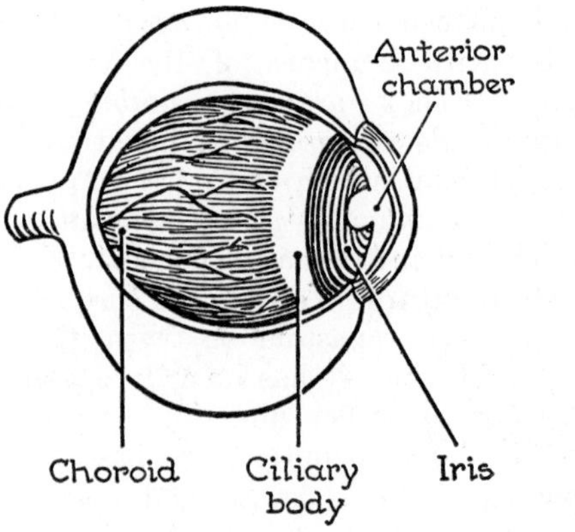

FIG. 705
Eyeball of an ox, middle coat exposed

aqueous humor in life. The lens touches the back of the *iris* at the pupillary margin. The probe should be passed through the pupil and behind the iris into the posterior chamber.

In man the *cornea* forms one-sixth of the outer coat of the bulb; the *sclera* five-sixths. The cornea is more convex than the sclera, i.e., it is a segment of a smaller sphere. The cornea is about 1 mm. thick; the sclera is thinner, especially at the equator. The two, however, are structurally continuous at the *corneoscleral junction*, where there are several features of note:

1. The edge of the cornea is overlapped by the sclera like a watch glass in its case.
2. Running circularly around the sclera there is a minute cleft, the *scleral sinus*, visible with a lens.
3. The middle coat has a white zone, 6 mm. broad, the *ciliary body*, which is continuous in front with the iris and behind with the choroid. The ~~ciliary muscle arises from the sclera at~~ the corneoscleral junction and is there firmly attached.
4. The acute angle between the cornea and the iris (actually between sclera and iris) is the *iridocorneal angle*. It is crossed by interlacing strands, the *pectinate ligament*, that pass backward from the edge of the posterior elastic membrane of the cornea to the region of the iris and sclera, and the spaces enclosed are lined with the mesothelium of the anterior chamber. The anterior chamber communicates through the spaces with the scleral sinus which in turn communicates with the scleral veins.

»» DISSECTION. Cut away the remaining part of the cornea and, after freeing structures with the probe, carefully enter the blade of the scissors through the pupil and cut a large square flap in the iris. Raise the flap and enlarge it backward through the ciliary body into the choroid, thereby exposing the jelly-like vitreous body.

OBSERVATION. On the surface of the raised flap (in front of the ciliary body) a number of short, black finger-like processes, the *ciliary processes*, are apparent. When in position, they occupy the peripheral part of the posterior chamber. They may reach to the periphery of the lens. Handle them with the probe. They are about 70 in number. They are black because the pigmented layer of the retina is adherent to them (see below).

The peripheral margin of the lens also is exposed; so is the transparent capsule of the vitreous body, called the *hyaloid membrane*. The hyaloid membrane passes forward in folds, which the ciliary processes occupy, to near the margin of the lens where it divides into an anterior and a posterior layer. The posterior layer continues to encapsule the vitreous. The anterior and stronger layer, the *suspensory ligament of the lens*, blends with the front of the lens capsule. A triangular canal, the *zonular spaces*, encircles the margin of the lens between the two layers, and it is possible with a hypodermic syringe to cause a colored fluid to flow round it.

The *ciliary muscle* (*fig. 706*) is triangular on cross-section. Its fibers radiate backward from the corneoscleral junction to the choroid which they pull forward when they contract, thereby causing relaxation of the suspensory ligament and allowing the lens to become more convex. The muscle also possesses an inner bundle of circular fibers.

»» DISSECTION. Using probe and scissors, cut circularly through each of the three coats at the equator: first through the remaining part of the sclera, next through the choroid, and then through the retina. The bulb can now be separated into anterior and posterior halves; the vitreous body remains with the anterior half.

OBSERVATION. In man the fibers of the optic nerve pierce the sclera in bundles, 3 mm. to the nasal side of the posterior pole of the bulb, and at this point the sclera is cribriform and weak. Next, they pierce the choroid and the outer layer of the retina, which adheres to the choroid, and then after forming a circle, the *optic disc* (papilla), which is a blind spot, 1.5 mm. in diameter, they spread out as the inner layer of the retina.

After death the retina is gray and lusterless like an exposed photographic film. No longer supported by the vitreous it detaches itself from the choroid everywhere except at the disc, and it becomes wrinkled and perhaps broken. The *central artery* and *vein* each pass through the disc as two vessels, which bifurcate and pass to the four quarters of the inner layer of the retina.

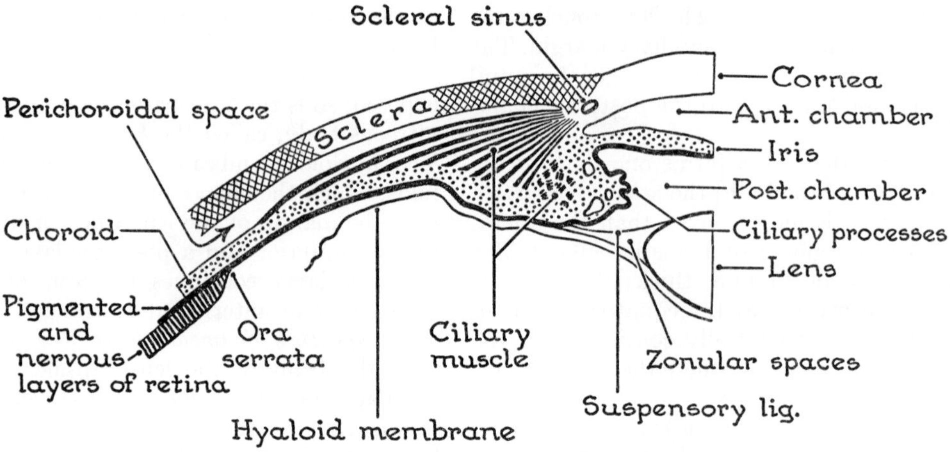

FIG. 706. The ciliary region, enlarged. (After Cunningham's Anatomy.)

The *choroid*, loosely adhering to the inner surface of the sclera, is easily detached and the *perichoroidal space* opened up. The inner surface of the sclera is stained with pigment, except along a number of meridional lines where the ciliary nerves adhere. If the choroid is sponged under water, the pigment is washed away and a network of vessels is seen.

Turn to the anterior half of the bulb. The *retina* becomes thin along a wavy line, the *ora serrata*, a short distance behind the ciliary muscle. Behind this the retina is true optic retina, but in front (where rays of light cannot reach) the retina is represented by two layers of cubical cells, the outer of which is pigmented. These two layers are carried forward over the ciliary body and iris to the margin of the pupil.

The Refractive Media. The *cornea* does the chief focusing; the lens is for fine adjustment. The *lens*, derived from the same layer as skin, hardens or cornifies with advancing age. The hardening begins at the center, and accommodation becomes increasingly difficult. The ox, being young, the lens is soft throughout. When hardened, a lens may be split into layers somewhat like an onion. The *vitreous body* is embryonic tissue comparable to that in the umbilical cord.

ARTERIES. Ciliary arteries, page 599.

The *central a.* supplies the inner layers of the retina; it is an end artery (pp. 598–599).

The function of the vascular choroid is to nourish by diffusion the outer layers of the retina; hence, where the retina is thin (i.e., in front of the ora serrata) the choroid is much less vascular.

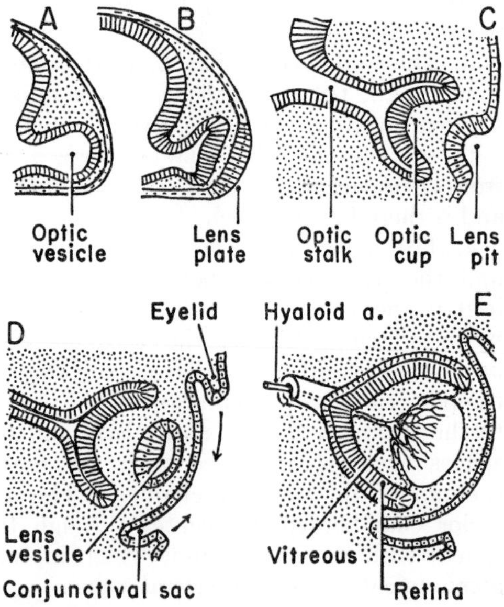

FIG. 706.1. Stages in the development of retina, lens, and conjunctival sac. (After Mann.)

The cornea is bloodless.

VEINS. Four choroidal veins, *vorticose veins*, pierce the sclera behind the equator to enter the ophthalmic vein.

NERVES (pp. 597–598).

DEVELOPMENT. The retina developed as an outgrowth from the brain and, so, is of ectodermal origin. In its early stage it resembled an inflated rubber balloon with a hollow stalk which was continuous with the cavity of the 3rd ventricle. On the appearance of the lens, which developed from the overlying skin surface and likewise is of ectodermal origin, the balloon was deflated and invaginated and made cup-shaped, hence the two layers of the retina (*fig. 706.1*).

The central artery originally passed through the hyaloid canal in the vitreous body and anastomosed in the capsule of the lens, which early was vascular. Before birth, this capsule atrophies and the artery, ceasing to supply it, confines itself to the retina and becomes an end artery.

CHAPTER 39

ANTERIOR TRIANGLE OF NECK

ANTERIOR TRIANGLE AND MEDIAN LINE OF NECK

Subdivisions; Landmarks.
Superficial Structures: Platysma; Deep Fascia; Superficial Veins and Nerves.

Median Line of the Neck

Boundaries; Median Structures.
Infrahyoid Muscles; Cervical Viscera.
Pharynx and Constrictors; Thyroid Gland.
Carotid Sheath.

Carotid Triangle

Posterior Belly of Digastric in Key Position.
Stylohyoid; Nerve Supply; Relations.
NERVES IN CAROTID TRIANGLE—*XI; XII; Ansa Cervicalis; X; Ext. and Int. Laryngeal Branches.*
ARTERIES IN CAROTID TRIANGLE—*Three Carotid Arteries; Six Collateral Branches of Ext. Carotid: Superior Thyroid; Lingual; Facial; Ascending Pharyngeal; Occipital and Posterior Auricular.*
Veins in Carotid Triangle.

Submandibular Triangle

Boundaries; Muscular Floor.
CONTENTS—*Submandibular Gland; Facial Artery and Its Branches; Facial Vein.*

ANTERIOR TRIANGLE AND MEDIAN LINE OF THE NECK

Subdivisions (*fig. 707*). The anterior triangle of the neck is bounded by the median line from chin to manubrium, by the anterior border of the Sternomastoid, and by the lower border of the jaw together with the hinder part of the posterior belly of the Digastric. It is subdivided into three subsidiary triangles—*submandibular* (digastric), *carotid*, and *muscular*—by the anterior and posterior bellies of the Digastric and the superior belly of the Omohyoid.

The region of the neck bounded below by the body of the hyoid bone and on each side by the anterior belly of the Digastric is the *submental triangle*. The region above the posterior belly of the Digastric and behind the ramus of the jaw is the *parotid region*. Though the parotid region is in the neck, it

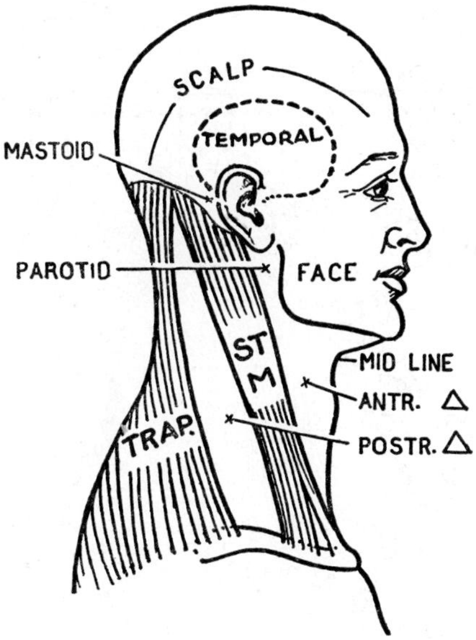

FIG. 707. The superficial regions of the head and neck.

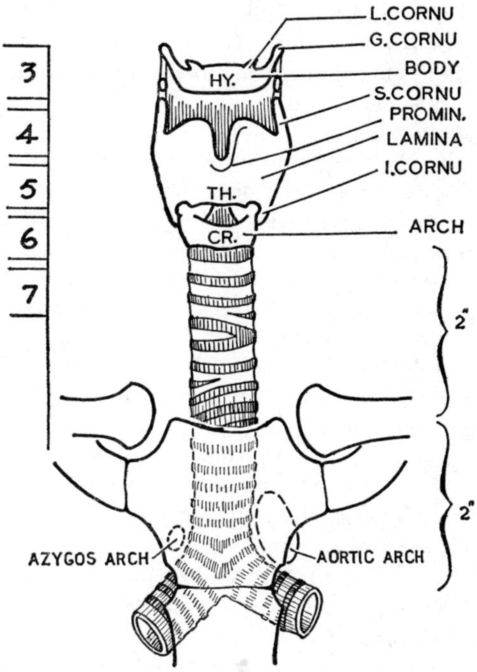

FIG. 708. Landmarks and vertebral levels

is beyond the confines of the anterior triangle.

Landmarks (*fig. 708*). The only vertebra that can be identified from the front is the *atlas* (*fig. 715*). The tip of its transverse process, much more prominent than all other cervical transverse processes, except the 7th, lies between the angle of the jaw and the tip of the mastoid process. It is best felt by pressing upward behind the angle of the jaw. The other transverse processes can be felt on deep pressure but not identified individually.

If you drop your chin slightly, in order to render the cervical fascia lax, and run your fingers downward in the median line of the neck from chin to jugular (suprasternal) notch, you will palpate in succession the *body of the hyoid bone*, the *laryngeal prominence* of the thyroid cartilage (Adam's apple), the *arch of the cricoid cartilage*, and 2″ of trachea.

With the head in the anatomical position (eyes looking forward) the hyoid bone lies above the level of the chin, at the angle between what are really the floor of the mouth and the top of the neck. While palpating your hyoid bone (your chin must be dropped —you must look at your toes—in order to relax the cervical fascia) perform the act of swallowing and note that the hyoid is pulled upward and forward. The thyroid and cricoid cartilages also are felt to rise.

Run the index fingers along the hyoid bone to the tips of its greater cornua, which lie near the anterior borders of the Sternomastoids, and note that the bone can be moved from side to side like a shuttle; so, to palpate one cornu it is necessary to steady the other. The right and left laminae of the thyroid cartilage and its superior cornua are also readily felt provided the opposite side is steadied. (Cornu, L. = horn; plural = cornua.)

»» The hyoid bone lies at the level of the body of the 3rd cervical vertebra, the thyroid cartilage at the level of the 4th and 5th, the **cricoid cartilage** at the very important level of the **6th**.

Superficial Structures

Platysma (Gk. = a plate). The Platysma is a rhomboidal, subcutaneous sheet of muscle. It extends from the face above to the level of the 2nd rib below. It is superficial to the first two bones in the body to ossify (i.e., clavicle and mandible) and it crosses the entire length of both. It is continuous above with the facial muscles, but the most anterior fibers are attached to the lower border of the mandible and others decussate with the opposite Platysma for an inch behind the chin. Its anterior border slopes from this point to the sternoclavicular joint. Hence, the Platysma leaves the median line of the neck and the lowest part of the anterior triangle uncovered; whereas it covers the lowest part of the posterior triangle. It is as though the sheet had been pulled off the anterior triangle in an attempt to cover the posterior one. (*figs. 708.1* and *708.2*).

Action. It clothes the side of the neck, which is concave, and when it contracts its fibers, by straightening, ease a tight collar and take pressure off the underlying veins of the neck. This action is antisphincteric. Its posterior fibers pull the angle of the mouth downward (see also p. 540).

Nerve supply: the facial nerve, cervical branch. Twigs of the trans. colli nerve (ant. cutaneous n.) pierce it.

Deep Fascia. The neck is enveloped in a sleeve of *investing deep fascia*, similar in texture to that enveloping the limbs. According to rule, it is attached to all the exposed bony parts and ligaments it encounters (*fig. 708.1*).

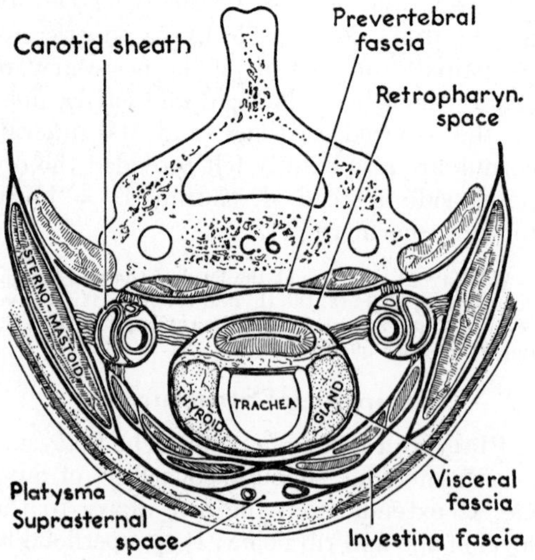

FIG. 708.1 Diagram of the front of the neck, on cross-section.

FIG. 708.2. The Platysma muscle

»» These are: *behind*, the lig. nuchae; in *front*, the whole length of the body and greater cornua of the hyoid bone; *above*, the lower border of the jaw, the zygomatic arch (to reach which it crosses the parotid gland), the cartilage of the ear, the mastoid process, and the superior nuchal line; *below*, it splits an inch or so above the manubrium into two layers, which are attached to the front and back of the jugular notch, thereby enclosing a space, the *suprasternal space*. Lateral to this it blends with the subcutaneous parts of the clavicle, acromion, and posterior border of the spine of the scapula between the attachments of the Sternomastoid and Trapezius above, and the Pectoralis Major and Deltoid below.

The deep fascia splits behind to enclose the Trapezius, covers the posterior triangle, splits in front to enclose Sternomastoid, and covers the anterior triangle. It encloses the submandibular and parotid salivary glands, and provides a sling to bind down the intermediate tendon of the Digastric.

The Omohyoid sling, carotid sheath, prevertebral fascia, and sheath of the thyroid gland, see pp. 554, 611, 623, and 644.

Superficial Veins (*fig. 664*). The *superficial temporal vein* and the *maxillary vein* unite in the parotid gland to form the *retromandibular vein* (post. facial v.). This divides into two branches: the posterior branch joins the *posterior auricular vein* to form the *external jugular vein;* while the anterior branch joins the *facial vein* at the angle of the jaw to form the *common facial vein.* The common facial vein pierces the deep fascia to join the *internal jugular vein* at the level of the hyoid bone.

The *external jugular vein* descends vertically, crosses the Sternomastoid, pierces the deep fascia at the posterior border of the Sternomastoid an inch above the clavicle, then receives the *transversa colli, suprascapular, anterior jugular* and other veins, and finally pierces a second layer of fascia, the Omohyoid fascia (p. 554), to end in the *subclavian vein.*

The right and left *anterior jugular veins,* unequal in size and asymmetrically placed, begin in the submental region, run near the median line, pierce the deep fascia an inch or so above the manubrium to enter the suprasternal space. Here a cross-channel unites them. Each then turns laterally and runs along the upper border of the clavicle between Sternomastoid and the infrahyoid ("strap") muscles (*fig. 709*) to end in the external jugular vein.

Not infrequently a *communicating vein,* lying along the anterior border of the Sternomastoid, connects the common facial and anterior jugular veins. It may equal in size the int. jugular vein and be mistaken for it.

Three Superficial Nerves appear in the anterior triangle (*fig. 663*): (1) the *great auricular nerve* which passes toward the ear where it divides, (2) the *transversus colli nerve* (ant. cutaneous nerve of neck) which supplies the entire front of the neck, and (3) the *cervical branch of the facial nerve.* The last named nerve, though subcutaneous (actually subplatysmal), is a motor nerve of importance (see p. 548).

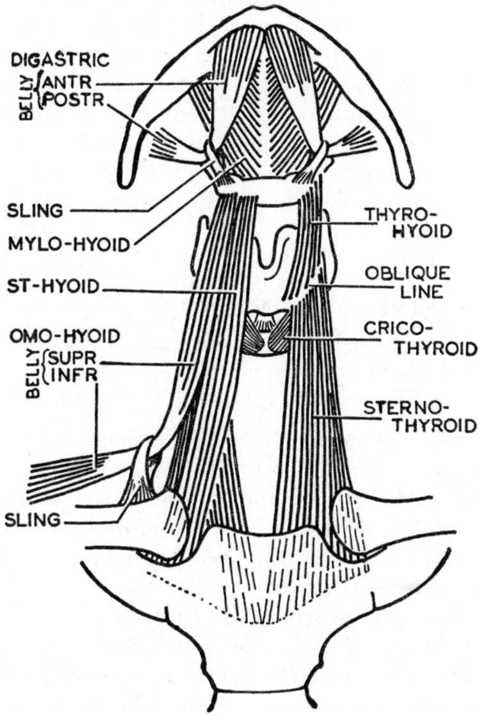

FIG. 709. The muscles bounding the median line of the neck.

Median Line of the Neck

BOUNDARIES AND SUBDIVISIONS (*fig. 709*). The median line is a broad strip bounded above by the slightly diverging *anterior bellies of the Digastrics,* below by the converging *Sternothyroids,* and between these by the nearly parallel *Sternohyoids.* It is divided into *suprahyoid* and *infrahyoid parts.* The suprahyoid part is limited below by the body of the hyoid and on the sides by the anterior bellies of the Digastrics, which converge to be attached to the digastric fossae at the sides of the symphysis menti. The triangle formed thereby is the *submental triangle.* The Mylohyoids form its floor. Here the anterior jugular veins begin; here lie the submental lymph nodes, which drain the median parts of the lower lip and floor of the mouth and the tip of the tongue.

»» If you examine the cadavera in the dissecting rooms, you will find the anterior bellies of the *Digastrics* and the *Mylohyoids* in process of change. Originally, they formed a single muscle sheet: in a percentage of subjects separation is complete; in others various types and degrees of incomplete separation are encountered. Having a common developmental origin, a common nerve supply may be inferred for these two muscles (*fig. 720*).

MEDIAN STRUCTURES AND VESSELS CROSSING THE MEDIAN LINE. The *hyoid bone* resembles the iliac crest in that no muscle crosses it from one end to the other. Being subcutaneous, the deep fascia is attached to it. The *thyrohyoid membrane* passes from the upper border of the thyroid cartilage to the body and greater cornua of the hyoid. The median *cricothyroid ligament* unites the adjacent borders of the cricoid and thyroid cartilages. It is very strong and is visible between the upwardly diverging borders of the Cricothyroid muscles. The *cricothyroid branch* of the superior thyroid artery anastomoses with its fellow in front of the ligament. (The Cricothyroids are the tensors of the vocal cords.) The *isthmus of the thyroid gland* generally covers the 2nd, 3rd, (and 4th) tracheal rings.

In front of the lower cervical rings of the trachea, and in surgical danger, are: (1) one or more cross communications between the anterior jugular veins within the suprasternal space, (2) the brachiocephalic trunk and (3) the left brachiocephalic, or innominate, vein may peep above the suprasternal notch. (4) The inferior thyroid veins descend to the brachiocephalic veins, and (5) an occasional thyroidea ima artery ascends from the brachiocephalic trunk to the thyroid gland.

The **Infrahyoid Muscles** (*fig. 709*). These four paired muscles are the depressors of the larynx and the hyoid bone. Often referred to as "strap muscles," they belong to the same superficial ventral sheet of muscles as the *Rectus Abdominis,* and it is helpful to think of them as the **"Rectus Cervicis."**

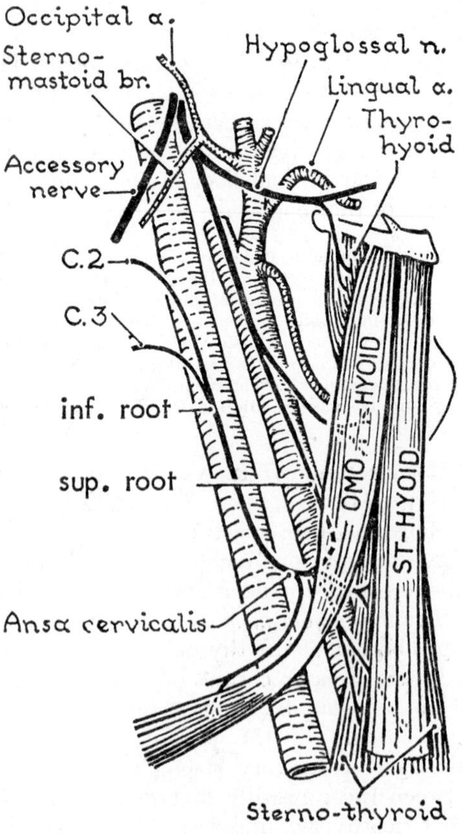

FIG. 710. Ansa cervicalis, its roots and its branches to Infrahyoid muscles.

The primitive infrahyoid muscle mass splits into a superficial and a deep layer; each of which splits again into two. The superficial layer splits longitudinally into medial and lateral parts, the *Sternohyoid* and *Omohyoid;* the deep layer becomes attached to the oblique line of the thyroid cartilage and is thus divided into upper and lower parts, the *Thyrohyoid* and *Sternohyoid*. The four infrahyoid muscles are supplied by the ventral rami of cervical nerves 1, 2, and 3 via the hypoglossal nerve and the ansa cervicalis (ansa hypoglossi) (*figs. 710* and *765*).

The **Sternohyoid** and **Omohyoid** arise side by side from the front of the body of the hyoid, and diverge very slightly from the median plane as they descend. The Sternohyoid is attached to the posterior aspect of the capsule of the sternoclavicular joint and to the bone on each side of the joint. The Omohyoid leaves the Sternohyoid abruptly below the level of the cricoid cartilage, passes deep to the Sternomastoid, crosses the posterior triangle, and reaches the upper border of the scapula beside the notch. These two muscles and their fellows of the opposite side lie within a common sheet of fascia which passes in front of the larynx and trachea, and which is attached to the carotid sheath laterally, and to the posterior surfaces of the manubrium and clavicle, inferiorly.

»» The Omohyoid, like the Digastric, has two bellies. They are united below the level of the cricoid cartilage by an intermediate tendon and are held down by a sling. Unlike the Digastric, the two bellies of the Omohyoid are supplied by the same nerve, for the inferior belly is but an extension backward of the superior belly.

The **Thyrohyoid** is superficial to the thyrohyoid membrane. It extends upward to the greater cornu and adjacent part of the body of the hyoid. It, therefore, projects posterior to the Omohyoid and appears in the carotid triangle.

The **Sternothyroid** converges on its fellow as it descends until their medial borders meet at the center of the posterior surface of the manubrium. The lower attachment extends from this center laterally to the 1st costal cartilage (*fig. 709*).

Cervical Viscera vs. Abdominal. *General Remarks.* There are similarities between the abdomen and the front of the neck which it is helpful to bear in mind.

»» Thus, posteriorly both regions are bounded by secondary flexures of the vertebral column, called the lumbar and cervical flexures, respectively.

Anteriorly, the one region extends from the lower end of the sternum to the symphysis pubis; the other, from the upper end of the sternum to the symphysis menti.

In the anterior wall of the abdomen the Rectus Abdominis extends from pubis to chest wall. It is a segmental muscle, supplied by somatic segmental (intercostal) nerves. Similarly, in what may be called the anterior wall of the neck, a muscle, which temporarily we shall call the "*Rectus Cervicis,*" because it is the upward continuation of the Rectus Abdominis, extends from chest wall to mandible. It likewise is a segmental muscle, supplied by somatic segmental (C. 1, 2, and 3) nerves.

The "Rectus Cervicis" has acquired attachments to the thyroid cartilage and to the hyoid bone. Its infrahyoid parts are the Sternohyoid and Omohyoid, the Sternothyroid and Thyrohyoid, described above; its suprahyoid part is the *Geniohyoid.* The Geniohyoid extends from the mental spine (genial tubercle) of the mandible (*fig. 735*) to the body of the hyoid bone (*fig. 721*).

Through the abdomen run the stomach and the intestines; through the neck run the pharynx and esophagus (with their off-shoot the larynx and trachea). These are but different levels of the digestive tube; and, in the vagus and sympathetic they have a common nerve supply. True, there is no peritoneal cavity in the neck.

To liken the thyroid gland to the pancreas does not strain the comparison, for both glands arise as hollow outgrowths from the wall of the digestive tract.

It is to these **four visceral tubes**—pharynx and esophagus larynx and trachea—and the *thyroid gland,* that we are applying the collective term, **"cervical viscera."**

It is desirable at this stage to master the following facts about "the cervical viscera" and to observe the attachments of the *constrictors of the pharynx* (*figs. 711* and *714*).

A constrictor is to the pharynx what circular muscle is to the intestine. On contracting it reduces the caliber. The nasal, oral, and laryngeal cavities open into the anterior wall of the pharynx, so the constrictors are present only in the posterior and side walls.

Pharynx. The pharynx, which is the upper end of the digestive and respiratory tubes, extends from the base of the skull to the level of the 6th cervical vertebra where, at the lower border of the cricoid cartilage, it is

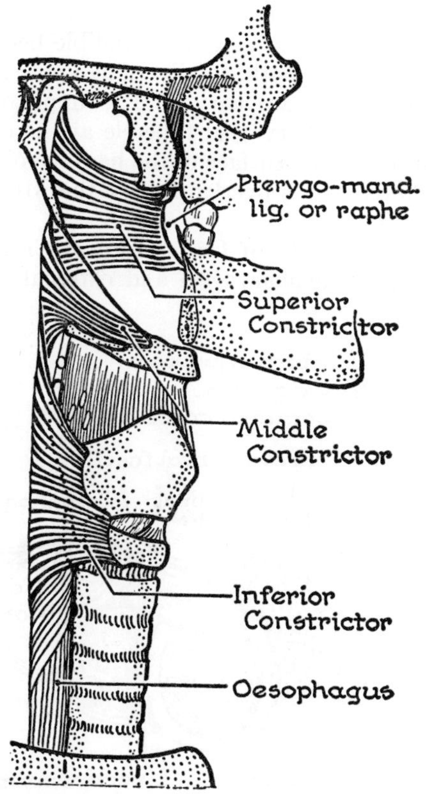

FIG. 711. The three Constrictors of the pharynx.

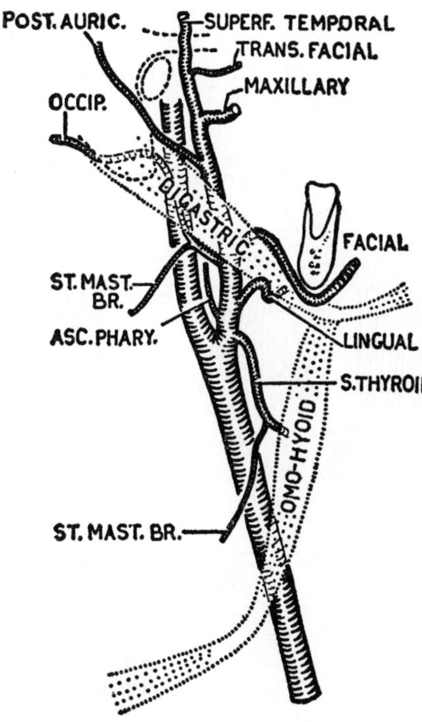

FIG. 712. The three carotid arteries and the branches of the external carotid.

continuous with the esophagus. At this same level the larynx is continuous with the trachea (*fig. 711*). The posterior wall of the trachea is applied throughout its entire length to the anterior wall of the esophagus.

There are three **Constrictors,** *Superior, Middle,* and *Inferior.* Each is fan-shaped, and each is fixed anteriorly by its narrower end or handle. The bases of the fans of opposite sides meet in the median plane behind. By "superimposing" figure 712 on figure 711, one gains an appreciation of important lateral relations of the Constrictors.

The Inferior Constrictor overlaps the Middle, and the Middle overlaps the Superior in telescope fashion; and on the side walls of the pharynx there are spaces above and below their narrow handles of origin. Through these spaces pass vessels, nerves, muscles, and the auditory tube.

Attachments of the Constrictors. It is simplest to begin by placing the Middle Constrictor (*fig. 711*). *The Middle Constrictor* arises in the angle between the greater and lesser horns of the hyoid bone and the lowest part of the stylohyoid ligament. From this its fibers fan out and meet those of the opposite side in the median plane.

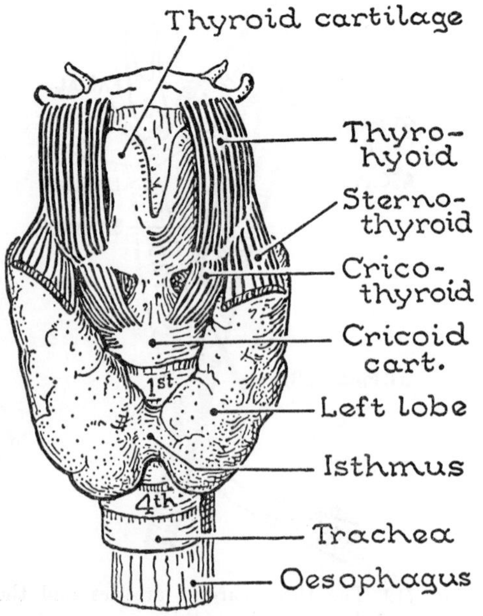

FIG. 713. The thyroid gland, front view

The origin of the *Inferior Constrictor* extends from the upper border of the thyroid cartilage to the lower border of the cricoid cartilage.

»» The thyroid part arises from the outer surface of the lamina of the thyroid cartilage and there assists the Sternothyroid and Thyrohyoid to create an oblique line, and also from a fibrous bridge over the Cricothyroid which extends from the tubercle on the lower border of the thyroid cartilage to the lower cornu. It is concerned with swallowing.

The cricoid part, the **cricopharyngeus,** arises from the triangular area on the cricoid between the Cricothyroid and the Post. Cricoarytenoid (R. Mackenzie). Closed to deny access of air to the esophagus, it relaxes during the act of swallowing.

The upper fibers of the Inferior Constrictor fan out and meet those of the opposite side outside those of the Middle Constrictor. Its lowest fibers are horizontal and blend with those of the esophagus.

The *Superior Constrictor* is continuous anteriorly with the Buccinator. It arises from the pterygomandibular raphe and from the bone at each end of the raphe, i.e., the lowest part of the posterior border of the medial pterygoid lamina, and the mandible behind the last molar tooth. Its diverging upper and lower borders are curved. The upper one reaches the pharyngeal tubercle at the center of the under surface of the basi-occipital; the lower one is overlapped by the Middle Constrictor.

Nerve supply of Constrictors: Cranial nerve XI via pharyngeal and external and

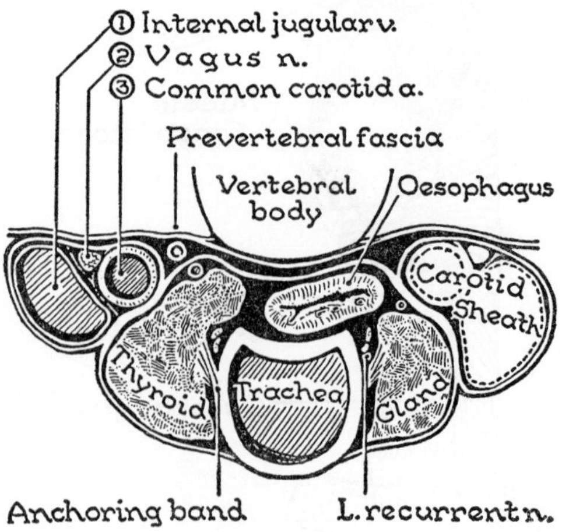

FIG. 714. The thyroid gland and the carotid sheath, on cross section.

recurrent laryngeal branches of the vagus (N. X).

Thyroid Gland (*fig. 713*). This gland is wrapped around the front and sides of the four cervical "visceral tubes." It consists of a right and a left lobe, connected near their lower poles by an isthmus, which crosses the (1st), 2nd, 3rd, (and 4th) rings of the trachea. Each lobe lies on the side of the trachea and esophagus, and extends upward on the side of the Inf. Constrictor until arrested by the attachment of the Sternothyroid to the oblique line on the thyroid cartilage. It intervenes between the "four visceral tubes" and the carotid sheath, and when enlarged it either overlaps the sheath or displaces it laterally (*fig. 714*). (See also pp. 622–623.)

Carotid Sheath. The common and internal carotid arteries, the internal jugular vein, and the vagus nerve extend from the cranial cavity to the thorax and in so doing traverse the neck in some condensed areolar tissue, called the *carotid sheath* (*fig. 714*). The arterial stem is medial, the vein lateral, and the vagus nerve posterior in the angle between the artery and the vein.

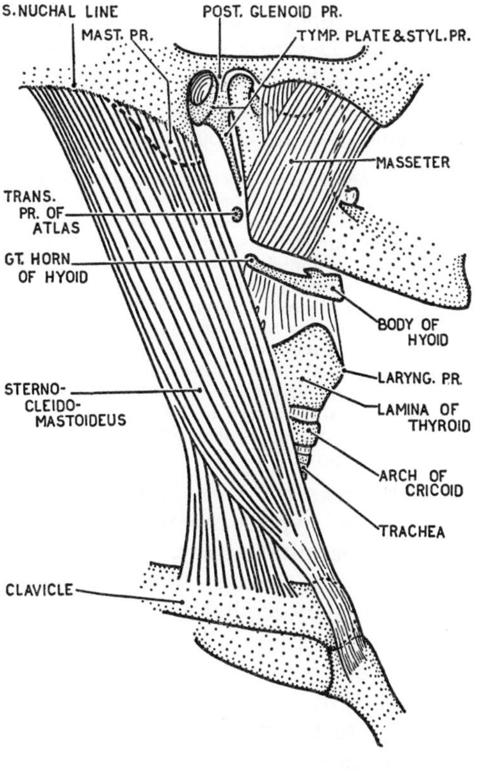

FIG. 715. The Sternomastoid and landmarks

Behind the arterial stem, but outside the sheath, is a smaller nerve, the *sympathetic trunk:* it likewise traverses the neck. In front of the arterial stem, but outside the sheath, is the superior root of the ansa cervicalis (descendens hypoglossi nerve) (*fig. 710*): it is confined to the carotid triangle. The sheath is applied to the side of the cervical viscera, and is partly under the cover of the Sternomastoid (*fig. 715*).

Carotid Triangle

The carotid triangle is bounded by the anterior border of the Sternomastoid, the superior belly of the Omohyoid, and the posterior belly of the Digastric.

Posterior Belly of the Digastric. This belly occupies a **key position** in the neck (*fig. 716*). It arises from the lateral of the two grooves on the under aspect of the mastoid bone. It is united to the anterior belly by an intermediate tendon which is held down to the junction of the body and greater cornu of the hyoid by a fascial sling.

Be sure to locate on yourself these two bony points, and to note that a straight line joining them crosses the tip of the transverse

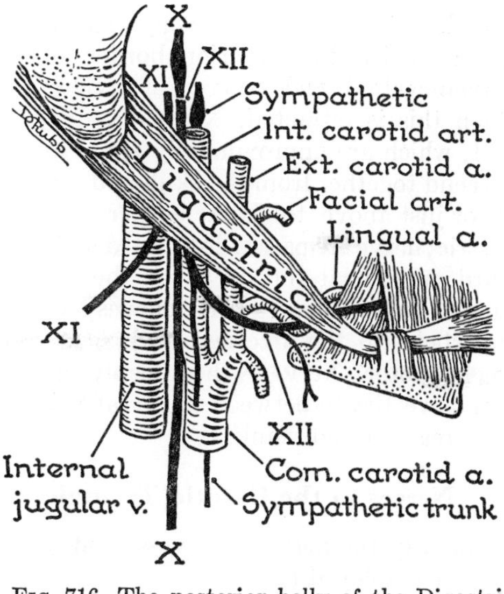

FIG. 716. The posterior belly of the Digastric in its key position.

process of the atlas and passes deep to the angle of the jaw.

»» *The Stylohyoid* is a slender portion of the posterior belly of the Digastric that has moved forward on to the root of the styloid process. It lies along the upper border of the posterior belly, splits to let the intermediate tendon pass through it, and it is inserted into the greater horn of the hyoid bone (*fig. 721*).

Nerve supply to Posterior Belly and Stylohyoid—the stem of the facial nerve.

Relations. The mastoid process and the muscles inserted into it conceal the origin of the posterior belly; and the parotid and submandibular glands overflow the posterior belly; but only three structures cross it superficially: (1) the two main tributaries of the *common facial vein*, (2) branches of the *great auricular nerve*, and (3) the *cervical branch of the facial nerve* (*figs. 663* and *664*). So, with care the posterior belly may be exposed freely.

Passing deep to the posterior belly of the Digastric and thereby placing it in a commanding or key position are the great vessels, the last three cranial nerves, and the sympathetic trunk. In fact, *all structures in the carotid triangle that reach to higher levels pass deep to the posterior belly of the Digastric* (*fig. 716*).

General Disposition of the Vessels and Nerves. The int. jugular vein, and the int. and ext. carotid arteries ascend side by side deep to the posterior belly. The vein is sheltered by the anterior border of the Sternomastoid and comes into view only when this is retracted. Nerves X, XI, and XII, which are approximately equal in size, descend together from the skull and separate at, or just above, the lower border of the Digastric; nerve XI passes downward and backward superficial (or deep) to the internal jugular vein; nerve XII curves forward superficial to the arteries. Both nerves are solely motor. Nerve X lies deeply and descends vertically between the great vein and the great arterial trunk.

Nerves in the Carotid Triangle

Identify the nerves and vessels in the sequence employed below.

Accessory Nerve (N. XI), *external branch* (*fig. 764*). The accessory nerve supplies the Sternomastoid and Trapezius and therefore courses backward. It appears from under cover of the Digastric, between the int. jugular vein and int. carotid artery. It crosses the int. jugular vein, which separates it from the transverse process of the atlas, and disappears into the deep surface of the Sternomastoid from 1½″ to 2½″ below the tip of the mastoid process. Here lymph nodes surround it. The sternomastoid branch of the occipital artery accompanies it. Commonly (58 of 197 specimens) the nerve crosses deep to the int. jugular vein and lies in contact with the transverse process of the atlas.

»» On everting the anterior border of the Sternomastoid, the accessory nerve can readily be found at this 1½″ to 2½″ point, and traced upward deep to the Digastric where it meets nerve XII.

Hypoglossal Nerve (N. XII) (*fig. 716*). The hypoglossal nerve appears from under cover of the Digastric in contact with the accessory nerve, or slightly medial to it. It is the motor nerve to the tongue, so it courses forward.

It passes under cover of the posterior belly of the Digastric a second time and so enters the submandibular (digastric) triangle, where it disappears between the Mylohyoid and the Hyoglossus.

»» In embryonic life, the nerve looped down to a lower level, but later it was dragged upward in front of the "*arterial plane*" until the occipital branch of the ext. carotid artery arrested its upward course. Therefore, in the adult it is found curving forward superficial to every artery it meets—int. carotid, ext. carotid, and lingual arteries always, and commonly either the superior thyroid or the facial artery, but never deep to these branches or they would arrest its ascent.

The hypoglossal nerve is most readily found just above the posterior end of the greater cornu of the hyoid bone, and from there traced backward. When cleaning it, keep to its upper border lest you damage two branches that spring from its lower or convex border.

Ansa Cervicalis (Ansa Hypoglossi) (*fig. 710*). As the hypoglossal nerve is curving round the occipital artery, it gives off the superior root of the ansa (descendens hypoglossi), and the occipital artery gives off its *sternomastoid branch.* The superior root, which is composed of fibers picked up from nerve C. 1, traverses the carotid triangle superficial to the internal and common carotid arteries and the carotid sheath. Near the intermediate tendon of the Omohyoid it joins the *inferior root of the ansa* (descendens cervicalis, C. 2 and 3) to form a loop, the *ansa cervicalis*. This inferior root necessarily crosses the internal jugular vein; it does so on either its medial or lateral side.

Distribution in the neck (*fig. 710*).

To Thyrohyoid (i.e., the short infrahyoid muscle) from C. 1, via nerve XII.

To the three long infrahyoid muscles from C. 1, 2, 3, via the ansa.

»» Each of the long muscles receives two twigs, one going to its upper part and one to its lower. These pass between the superficial and deep layers of muscles and enter them on their apposed surfaces.

Vagus Nerve (N. X) (*figs. 716* and *717*). The vagus runs vertically within the carotid sheath in the posterior angle between the int. jugular vein and the great arterial trunk.

To find the vagus nerve, ease N. XI and the int. jugular vein laterally, and N. XII and the int. carotid artery medially.

Branches appearing in carotid triangle: (1) cardiac br. which fuses with a *cardiac branch* of the sympathetic trunk (Mizeres), (2) the two terminal branches of the superior laryngeal nerve, the *internal laryngeal nerve* being sensory, and the *external laryngeal nerve* being motor.

The Internal Laryngeal Nerve is easily found where it pierces the thyrohyoid membrane a little in front of the superior cornu of the thyroid cartilage, deep, of course, to the posterior border of the Thyrohyoid. It runs along the upper border of the Inf. Constrictor and is accompanied by the sup. laryngeal branches of the sup. thyroid artery and vein, which pierce with it and lie below it—as, from a consideration of their origins, would be expected. It is sensory to the larynx above the level of the vocal cords.

The External Laryngeal Nerve, loosely bound to the sup. thyroid artery, descends obliquely between the fascia covering the Inf. Constrictor and the carotid sheath (which should be retracted), and passes deep to the Omohyoid to reach the Cricothyroid, which is the tensor muscle of the vocal cord.

»» EXPLANATORY. The *Cricothyroid is developmentally* a detached portion of the Inf. Constrictor, and the ext. laryngeal nerve sends twigs to the Inf. Constrictor before piercing it to end in the Cricothyroid. To get to the Cricothyroid the nerve must pass deep to the attachment of the Sternothyroid to the oblique line on the thyroid cartilage—so must the sup. thyroid artery. Indeed, the upper pole of the thyroid gland (depending upon its size) pushes the sup. thyroid a. either nearly to or against the ext. laryngeal nerve. Hence, the nerve is liable to be damaged in goitre operations with resulting weakness of the voice.

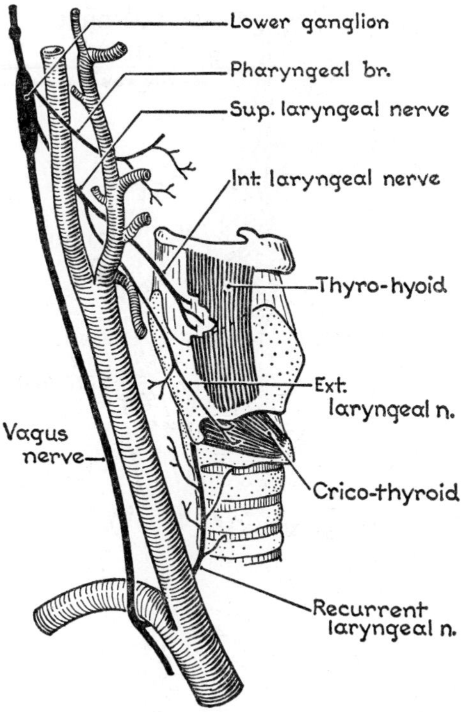

FIG. 717. The pharyngeal and laryngeal branches of the vagus.

ARTERIES IN THE CAROTID TRIANGLE

The arteries in this triangle are: (1) parts of the common, internal, and external carotid arteries, and (2) the stems of most of the six collateral branches of the external carotid artery (*fig. 718*).

Common Carotid Artery. This artery appears from under cover of the Omohyoid, ascends through the carotid triangle to the level of the upper border of the thyroid cartilage where it ends by dividing into two terminal branches of nearly equal size, the *internal* and *external carotid aa.*, the internal carotid to be distributed inside the skull, and the external outside.

These two arteries ascend side by side, the internal artery being posterolateral, the

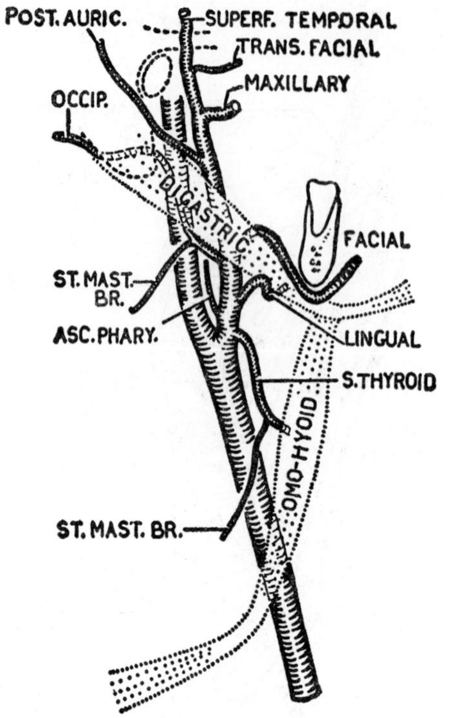

FIG. 718. External carotid artery and branches

external artery being anteromedial, and both pass deep to the posterior belly of the Digastric—the external carotid to enter the parotid gland; the internal carotid to pass deep to the parotid gland and styloid process.

Branches. The common and internal carotid aa. give off no collateral branches in the neck; so, it falls to the external carotid, assisted by the inferior thyroid artery, to supply the "cervical viscera."

External Carotid Artery. The external carotid extends from the upper border of the thyroid cartilage to the neck of the mandible where it divides into two terminal branches: *superficial temporal* and *maxillary aa.*

In its short course before entering a deep groove in the parotid gland, the ext. carotid artery is applied to the Inferior and Middle Constrictors.

Collateral Branches, six in all, radiate from the neighborhood of the posterior belly of the Digastric to reach the parts they supply.

Three of these—*superior thyroid, lingual,* and *facial*—arise from its anterior aspect close together below the Digastric (*fig. 718*). Now, this is their order of origin because the 1st has to descend to reach the thyroid gland, the 2nd has to pass forward to reach the tongue, and the 3rd has to ascend to reach the face. In this mobile part of the body all three take sinuous courses.

On apposing figure 712 to figure 711, it becomes apparent that the superior thyroid art. is applied to Inf. Constrictor; the lingual art. to Middle Constrictor; and the facial art. to Middle and Sup. Constrictors.

The **Superior Thyroid Artery** must pass deep to the three long infrahyoid muscles in order to reach the thyroid gland at its upper pole, where it divides into three glandular branches. Of these, one ramifies on the lateral surface of the thyroid gland; one on the medial surface; and one runs along the medial border to the isthmus where it anastomoses with its fellow.

»» *Other Branches* are: (1) *superior laryngeal branch,* which pierces the thyrohyoid membrane below the internal laryngeal nerve and supplies the larynx; (2) a *cricothyroid branch,* which passes either superficial or deep to the Sternothyroid, crosses the Cricothyroid muscle and ligament, anastomoses with its fellow, and sends twigs through the ligament into the larynx; (3) a sternomastoid branch, which follows the Omohyoid across the carotid sheath to the Sternomastoid.

The **Lingual Artery,** applied to the Middle Constrictor, loops upward and forward and, passing deep to the posterior belly of the Digastric, enters the submandibular triangle where it at once passes deep to the Hyoglossus. The hypoglossal nerve, looping downward and forward, crosses it superficially (*fig. 716*). (Continued on p. 682).

»» In 20 per cent of 211 specimens the lingual and facial arteries spring from a common linguo-facial stem (G. F. Lewis).

The **Facial Artery** (Ext. Maxillary a.) steers a course for a point on the lower border of the jaw just in front of the Masseter. It is, however, deflected from the straight path by the posterior belly of the Digastric, which passes deep to the ramus of the jaw and carries the artery upward before it. Hence, the " ∾ " shaped course of the artery.

The Middle and Superior Constrictors lie medial to the 1st, or cervical, loop of the artery, the Sup. Constrictor separating it from the tonsil (*fig. 719*). The Digastric and Stylohyoid, and the submandibular gland occupy the concavity of this loop and the Medial Pterygoid lies laterally. Then, to enter the face, it turns round the lower border of the jaw.

Branches are given on page 617.

The **Ascending Pharyngeal Artery** (best seen when the pharynx is being dissected) arises from the deep aspect of the ext. carotid artery near its origin, and ascends on the side wall of the pharynx as far as the base of the skull. The int. carotid artery is its lateral companion.

It supplies the pharynx, soft palate, tube, and meninges.

»» The meningeal twigs traverse the hypoglossal, jugular, and lacerate foramina, and a tympanic twig follows the tympanic branch of the glossopharyngeal nerve.

The **Occipital and Posterior Auricular Arteries** follow the lower and upper borders of the Digastric backward, and therefore cross superficial to the int. carotid artery, the last three cranial nerves, and the int. jugular vein. The mastoid then separates them. They end in the scalp and auricle.

The **Occipital Artery** occupies the groove on the mastoid bone medial to the groove for the Digastric. Therefore, it passes deep to the Digastric, the mastoid process, and the three muscles inserted into the mastoid process. It then flits across the apex of the posterior triangle and, joining the greater occipital n., pierces the Trapezius an inch inferolateral to the inion and ends in the scalp (*fig. 675*).

BRANCHES. Sternomastoid, meningeal, descending, and terminal, see page 569.

The **Posterior Auricular Artery** arises at or above the upper border of the Digastric, and follows that border to the mastoid bone. Then, behind the ear, it ascends on the bone, deep to Auricularis Posterior, to end in the scalp (*fig. 662*).

BRANCHES. Of its two important branches: (1) the *stylomastoid branch* follows the facial nerve through the facial canal to anastomose with a petrosal branch of the middle meningeal art., and (2) *auricular branches* supply the medial surface of the auricle and, then partly piercing the cartilage, but mainly by turning round the helix, anastomose with

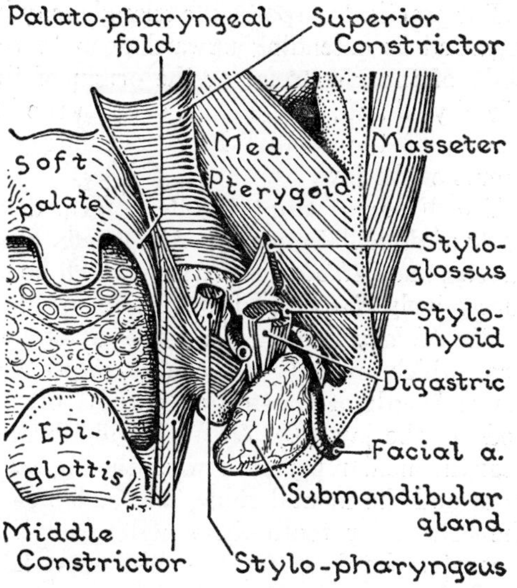

FIG. 719. To explain the S-shaped course of the facial artery, postero-inferior view.

branches of the superficial temporal art. and supply the lateral surface.

Veins of the Anterior Triangle (*figs. 664* and *759*). The *superior thyroid, lingual,* and *facial veins* as well as a *middle thyroid vein* cross superficial to the carotid arteries and join the int. jugular vein. The facial vein unites with the anterior branch of the retromandibular vein (post. facial vein) to form the *common facial vein* (*fig. 664*). The *pharyngeal plexus* is drained by several veins into the int. jugular vein (*fig. 759*).

»» The *occipital vein* partly ends in the internal jugular vein and partly in the posterior auricular vein but mostly in the vertebral plexus. The *posterior auricular vein* joins the posterior branch of the retromandibular vein to form the *external jugular vein* (*fig. 664*).

Submandibular Triangle

(Digastric Triangle)

The boundaries of the submandibular triangle are the two bellies of the Digastric and the lower border of the jaw. The anterior belly separates this triangle from the submental triangle; the posterior belly separates it from the carotid triangle; and a broad band of fascia, stretching from the styloid process to the posterior border of the ramus of the mandible, and hence called the *stylomandibular ligament*, separates it from the parotid region behind.

For practical purposes the triangle may be regarded as extending upward deep to the body of the jaw as far as the origin of the Mylohyoid and, behind this, deep to the insertion of the Medial Pterygoid into the ramus of the jaw.

The Floor of the triangle is formed by parts of three flat muscles—*Mylohyoid, Hyoglossus,* and *Middle Constrictor*—which lie on successively deeper planes (*fig. 720*).

The Mylohyoid arises from the mylohyoid line, which extends diagonally across the entire length of the medial surface of the body of the jaw (*fig. 735*). This line begins near the median plane, between the digastric fossa and the mental spine, and ends below the 3rd molar tooth. The mylohyoid line separates the fossa for the sublingual salivary gland anterosuperiorly from the fossa for the submandibular salivary gland postero-inferiorly.

The fibers of the Mylohyoid run inferomedially to be inserted into the body of the hyoid bone and a median raphe that extends from the hyoid bone to the mandible. It thus constitutes with its fellow a *Diaphragma Oris.* Its posterior border is oblique and free.

The Hyoglossus arises from the whole length of the greater cornu of the hyoid (and slightly from its body) (*fig. 721*). Its fibers run upward and forward to be inserted into the side of the tongue where they interdigitate with fibers of the Styloglossus. It is rhomboidal with free anterior and posterior borders. It is overlapped by the Mylohyoid, and in turn it overlaps the Middle Constrictor.

The Middle Constrictor has an angular origin from the whole length of the greater cornu, lesser cornu, and lowest part of the stylohyoid lig. deep to the Hyoglossus.

Contents of submandibular triangle:
(1) submandibular gland and lymph nodes,
(2) hypoglossal and (3) mylohyoid nerves,
(4) lingual and (5) facial arteries, and
(6) facial vein.

The **Submandibular Gland** (Submaxillary Gland) fills the submandibular triangle, overflowing the tendon of the Digastric below; extending upward into the angular space between the mandible laterally and the Mylohyoid medially; and extending backward to abut against the parotid gland, only the

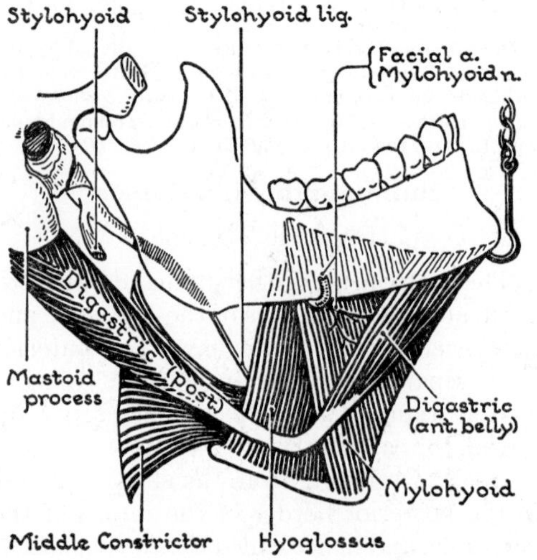

FIG. 720. The floor of the submandibular triangle.

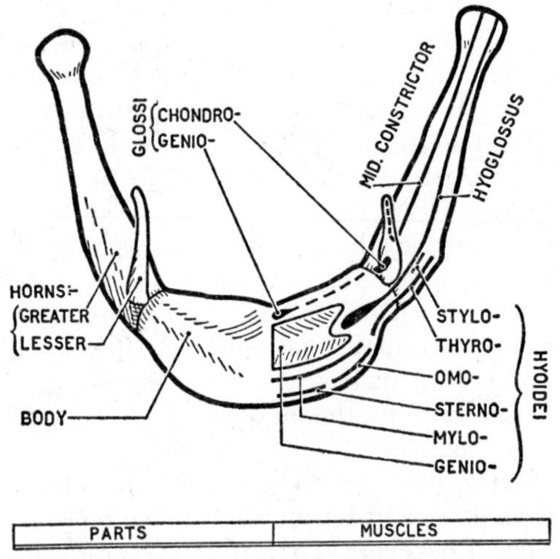

FIG. 721. The hyoid bone and its muscle attachments.

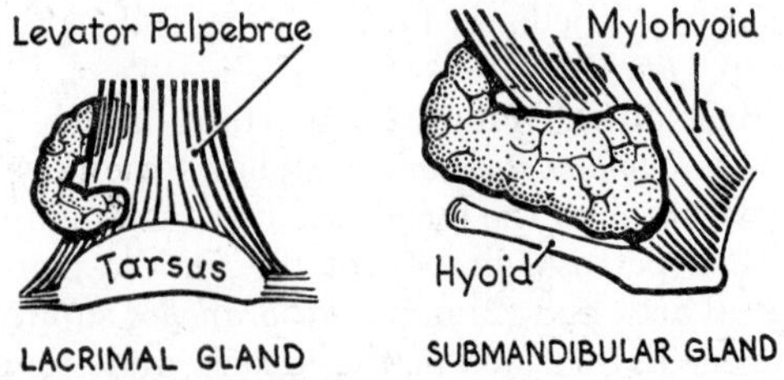

FIG. 721.1. Two U-shaped glands and the two responsible muscles.

stylomandibular lig. intervening. A process proceeds around the free posterior border of the Mylohyoid and along the floor of the mouth as far as the sublingual gland. The Mylohyoid may, indeed, be said to indent the gland and so to divide it into a superficial and a deep part, *cf.* Levator Palpebrae and lacrimal gland (*fig. 721.1*).

Its 2″ long duct, seen in figures 785 and 786, runs forward between the Mylohyoid and the Hyoglossus, and finally opens under the tongue (p. 678).

Superficial to the gland are: skin, Platysma, cervical branch of nerve VII (*fig. 659*), deep fascia and the facial vein. The facial artery, however, is deep.

»» The gland, with half a dozen lymph nodes applied to it, is loosely enveloped in deep cervical fascia, which splits below at the hyoid bone to enclose it. The superficial layer of this fascia ascends to the lower border of the jaw; the deep layer covers the floor of the region and ascends to the mylohyoid line of the jaw; and the stylomandibular lig. unites the two layers behind.

When the lower border of the gland is raised and the intermediate tendon of the Digastric pulled either up or down, the *hypoglossal nerve* can be traced forward superficial to the lingual artery and across the Hyoglossus to the posterior border of the Mylohyoid, deep to which it disappears. And, the *lingual artery* can be traced forward on the Middle Constrictor to the posterior border of the Hyoglossus deep to which it disappears.

When the anterior end of the gland is raised and pulled backward, the *mylohyoid nerve* (to Mylohyoid and ant. belly of Digastric), accompanied by the *submental branch* of facial artery, is seen. The nerve may be traced forward to the two muscles in which it ends, and backward to the interval between the anterior free border of the Medial Pterygoid and the ramus of the jaw.

Secretory Nerve Supply: the chorda tympani relayed in the submandibular ganglion (*fig. 786*, and p. 679).

The **Facial Artery** (cont'd from p. 615).

CERVICAL BRANCHES: ascending palatine, tonsillar, glandular, and submental.

The *ascending palatine and tonsillar branches* arise at the summit of the bend and ascend on the pharyngeal wall. The tonsillar branches pierce the S. Constrictor and descend with the Levator Palati to supply the soft palate and bed of the tonsil.

Glandular brs: to submandibular gland. The *submental artery* follows the end part of the mylohyoid nerve, sends twigs through the Mylohyoid to the floor of the mouth, and then turns round the lower border of the jaw to end in the chin.

(FACIAL BRANCHES: inf. labial, sup. labial, lat. nasal, and angular: see page 549).

The **Facial Vein** takes a straighter and more superficial course than the artery, being separated from it by the submandibular gland, Digastric, and Stylohyoid (*fig. 664*). It joins the retromandibular vein to form the common facial vein.

CHAPTER 40

ROOT OF NECK

Great Vessels. General Dispositions. The right common carotid and subclavian arteries arise from the brachiocephalic trunk (innominate a.) behind the right sternoclavicular joint. The left common carotid and subclavian arteries arise from the aortic arch, and after a course of an inch enter the neck by passing behind the left sternoclavicular joint.

On both sides, two infrahyoid muscles intervene between the arteries and the joint, and on the left side there is the left brachiocephalic vein as well. On both sides, the common carotid artery overlaps the subclavian artery at the entrance to the neck and it ends at the upper border of the thyroid cartilage by dividing into two terminal branches, the *internal* and *external carotid arteries*. It has no collateral branches.

The **Subclavian Artery** arches over the pleural cupola and 1st rib, and it becomes the axillary artery at the lower border of this rib.

Surface Anatomy. You will recall that the axillary artery passes a point lying a finger's breadth medial to the tip of the coracoid process (*fig. 67*). A curved line running from the sternoclavicular joint to this point, and rising an inch above the clavicle, marks the course of the subclavian artery and the 1st part of the axillary artery. This line crosses the clavicle near its midpoint (*fig. 722*).

The subclavian artery is divided into three parts—1st, 2nd, and 3rd—by the Scalenus Anterior which crosses in front of the 2nd part, separating it from its vein.

The **Subclavian Vein** (*fig. 725*) has only two parts. These correspond to the 3rd and 2nd parts of the artery; the beginning of the brachiocephalic vein substitutes for the 1st part.

»» The reason is that the subclavian vein lies within the concavity of its companion artery, whereas the int. jugular vein lies lateral to its companion, the common carotid artery, and so has to cross the 1st part of the subclavian artery in order to effect the union known as the brachiocephalic vein.

The termination of the internal jugular vein crosses and largely conceals the 1st part

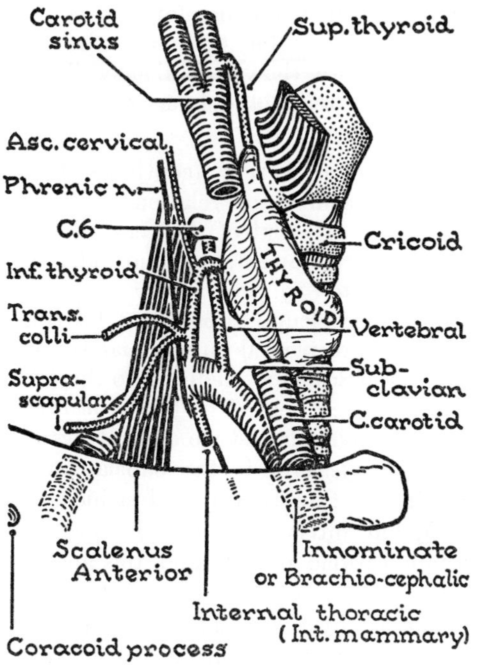

FIG. 722. The arteries at the root of the neck

of the subclavian artery and the stems of the branches arising from it.

»» It is, of course, legitimate to think in terms of the "1st part of the subclavian vein" and, when tributaries are under consideration, it is helpful to do so; but we must speak and write of the "beginning of the brachiocephalic vein".

"Triangle of the Vertebral Artery" (*figs. 723* and *725*). It saves much repetition if a digression is made in order to examine a triangle with the following boundaries:
Base—1st part of the subclavian artery.
Lateral side—Scalenus Anterior.
Medial side—Longus Colli (Cervicis).
Apex—anterior tubercle of the 6th cervical transverse process.

The Posterior Wall of the triangle includes the transverse process of C. 7, ventral ramus of nerve C.8 which runs laterally above the neck of the 1st rib, the neck of the 1st rib, and the pleural cupola, which rises to that neck.

Contents: *The vertebral artery*, which ascends from base to apex and there enters the foramen transversarium of vertebra C. 6.

The vertebral vein, which descends in front of the vertebral artery, crosses the subclavian artery, and ends in the brachiocephalic vein.

The sympathetic trunk with its ganglia and branches is shown in figure 724, and described on pages 660–661.

Ascending in front of the Triangle are:
1. The carotid sheath and contents.
2. The phrenic nerve.

Arching in front of the Triangle are:
3. The inferior thyroid artery.
4. The thoracic duct, on the left.

The *carotid sheath* and its three contents (common carotid a., int. jugular v., and vagus nerve) cover the triangle, their precise positions depending upon the size of the thyroid gland which thrusts them laterally,

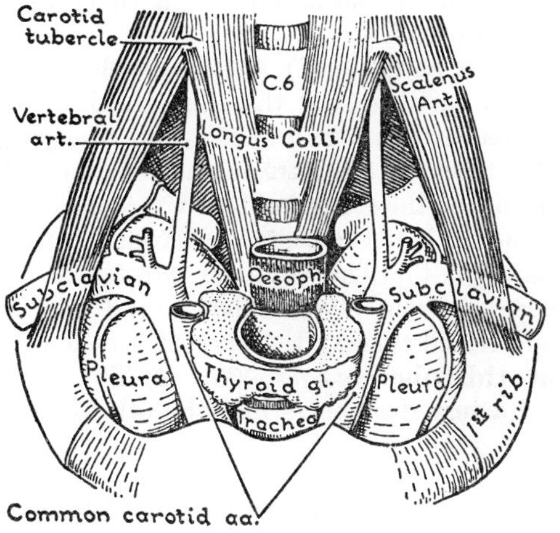

FIG. 723. "The triangle of the vertebral artery"

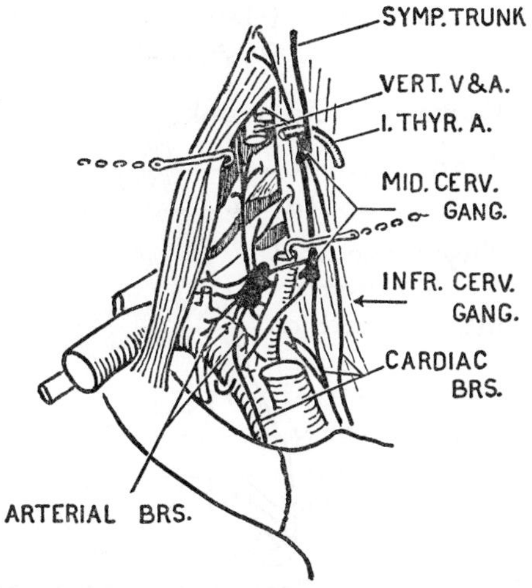

FIG. 724. The sympathetic trunk, ganglia, and branches, at the root of the neck.

away from the "cervical viscera". But the common carotid will overlap the subclavian artery, and the vein and the vagus will cross it (*fig. 725*).

The *phrenic nerve*, after descending in front of the Scalenus Anterior, slips off the anterior border of this muscle (on the left side) on to the subclavian artery (*fig. 725*).

The *inferior thyroid artery* and the *thoracic duct* arch between the vertebral vessels and the carotid sheath. The artery arches *medially;* the duct arches *laterally* (*fig. 725*).

LANDMARKS. The anterior tubercle of the transverse process of vertebra C. 6 is a landmark of importance. Its prominence is accentuated by the absence of a tubercle on vertebra C. 7.

Events at C. 6: (1) At this level lies the cricoid cartilage and therefore the junction of pharynx with esophagus, and of larynx with trachea. (2) Here is the intermediate tendon of the Omohyoid and therefore the boundary between the muscular and carotid triangles. (3) The common carotid artery passes in front of the tubercle and may be compressed against it. Hence, it is called the **carotid tubercle** (*fig. 723*). (4) The vertebral artery disappears into the 6th foramen transversarium and therefore passes behind the tubercle. (5) The tubercle is the apex of "the triangle of the vertebral artery" and the Scalenus Anterior and Longus Colli ascend to be attached to it.

Subclavian Artery (continued from p. 618). The course and relations of the right subclavian art. and of the cervical part of the left subclavian art. are almost identical—but not quite (*fig. 725*).

Below are pleural cupola and 1st rib.

Behind are pleural cupola and the insertion of the Scalenus Medius into the 1st rib, but the lowest root (Th. 1) of the brachial plexus grooves the 1st rib and intervenes.

Antero-inferiorly is the subclavian vein and its continuation (the brachiocephalic vein), but intervening are phrenic, vagus, certain cardiac nerves, and the ansa subclavia.

Anterior Relations. The 1st part of the subclavian artery lies medial to the Scalenus Anterior. It is covered anteriorly by Sternomastoid, sternal end of clavicle, transverse part of ant. jugular vein, which runs just above the clavicle, Sternohyoid and Sternothyroid, and deep to these by the internal

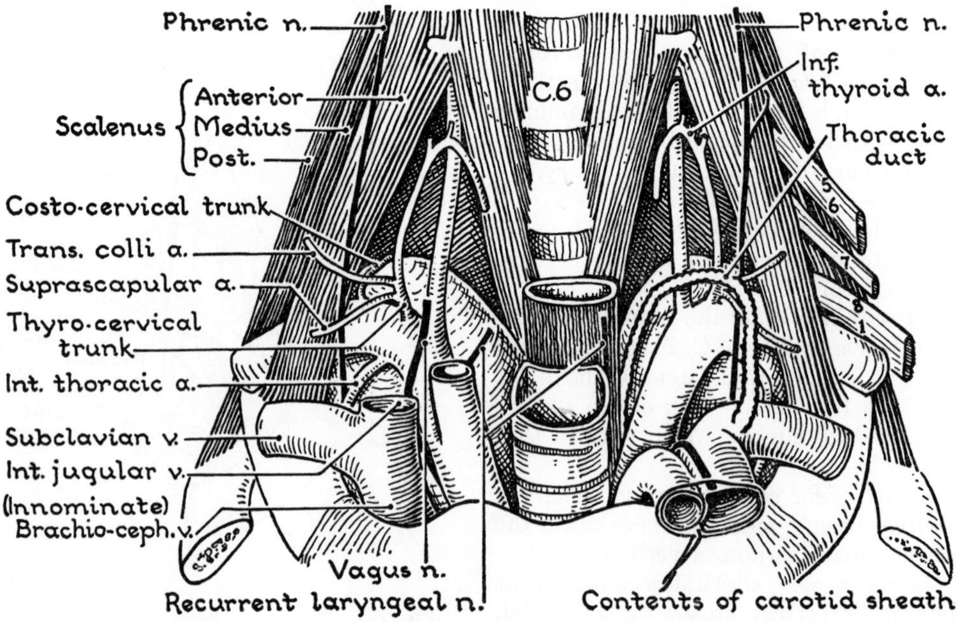

FIG. 725. The root of the neck

jugular vein, which is accompanied by the phrenic nerve (posterolaterally), vertebral vein (posteriorly), and vagus nerve (posteromedially).

The *right phrenic nerve* tends to cling to the anterior border of the Scalenus Anterior. For embryological reasons, the *right recurrent laryngeal nerve* arises from the vagus while it is crossing the subclavian artery, and it recurs below and behind the artery. The *left vagus nerve* descends into the thorax in the angle between the left subclavian and left common carotid arteries. On the left side the *thoracic duct*, on the right side the *right lymph duct*, are immediate anterior relations.

On *both sides* a thread, the *ansa subclavia*, which connects either the middle or the vertebral ganglion with the inferior cervical ganglion, loops in front, below, and behind the artery.

»» Cardiac branches of the vagus and sympathetic cross both in front of the artery and behind it.

The 2nd part is separated from its vein by the Scalenus Anterior.

Branches of subclavian artery (*fig. 725*). These mostly arise from the 1st part; so at their origin they are concealed by the internal jugular vein (*fig. 725*). They are:

1. Vertebral.
2. Thyrocervical trunk.
   - Inferior thyroid.
   - Transversa colli (cervicalis).
   - Suprascapular.
3. Internal thoracic (Int. mammary).
4. Costocervical trunk.
   - Deep cervical.
   - Highest intercostal.
     - 1st posterior intercostal.
     - 2nd posterior intercostal.
5. Dorsal scapular.

The Vertebral Artery ascends to the foramen transversarium of the 6th cervical vertebra. *In front* lies the carotid sheath, but arching between it and the sheath are the thoracic (or right lymph) duct and the inferior thyroid artery. *Behind* are the structures of the posterior wall of the vertebral triangle (p. 619).

(Continued on page 644.)

The Thyrocervical Trunk arises from the subclavian artery between the vagus and phrenic nerves. The trunk has no length but at once ends as three branches. Of these, (1) and (2), the *Suprascapular* and *Transversa Colli Arteries*, run laterally across the Scalenus Anterior to the posterior triangle and "clamp down" the phrenic nerve. (See page 557).

(3) *The Inferior Thyroid Artery* takes an S-shaped course. It ascends first near the medial border of the Scalenus Anterior, then arches medially between vertebral vessels and carotid sheath (therefore below the carotid tubercle) and either through, in front of, or behind the sympathetic trunk. It then descends toward the lower pole of the thyroid gland where it breaks up into an upper and a lower glandular branch.

Distribution. The artery supplies the thyroid and parathyroid glands and sends branches to the trachea and esophagus, pharynx and larynx.

»» The laryngeal branch, *inf. laryngeal art.* follows the recurrent nerve into the pharynx. A large muscular branch, the *ascending cervical artery*, which arises at or near the summit of the "∾" and ascends on the Scalenus Anterior medial to the phrenic nerve, is apt to be mistaken for the nerve.

The Internal Thoracic Artery (int. mammary a.) arises opposite the thyrocervical trunk, descends on the pleura behind the subclavian vein, and crosses the phrenic nerve (in front or behind).

(For thoracic part, see p. 472).

The Costocervical Trunk arises at or behind the border of the Scalenus Anterior, curves over the pleural cupola to the neck of the 1st rib, and there divides into two branches: The *deep cervical art.* (page 569) and the *supreme or highest intercostal art.* (*fig. 642*).

The *Dorsal Scapular Artery*, see p. 557.

Brachiocephalic Vein and Tributaries. The blood delivered by the four branches of the subclavian artery mostly returns to the brachiocephalic vein. The general venous pattern is shown in figure 726.

The internal jugular and subclavian veins each possess one double cusped **valve.** The former is situated a finger's breadth above the clavicle in a dilatation, the *inferior jugular bulb.* The latter is situated above the 1st rib (*fig. 759*).

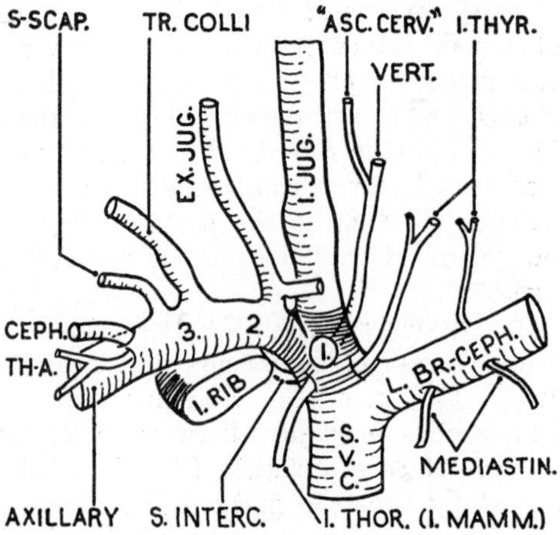

FIG. 726. The veins at the root of the neck. 1. = right brachiocephalic vein.

Phrenic Nerve. This branch of the cervical plexus (C. 4) receives contributions from C. 3 and C. 5 and gray rami communicantes. It starts deep to the prevertebral fascia (*fig. 665*) and, as its destination is the diaphragm, it has no occasion to pierce that fascia. It descends nearly vertically in naked contact with the obliquely placed Scalenus Anterior, crossing it from posterior to anterior border. It then crosses in front of the 1st part of the subclavian artery and enters the thorax by crossing the internal thoracic artery (in front or behind). (The right phrenic nerve commonly remains on the Scalenus Anterior until the subclavian artery is passed.)

In front of the phrenic nerve are (1) transversa colli and suprascapular arteries, which clamp it down and prevent it from being confused with the vagus; (2) end of the thoracic (or right lymph) duct; and (3) internal jugular vein and junction of the subclavian and brachiocephalic veins, which largely cover it.

Thoracic Course, see pp. 479, 480 and 483.

Distribution, see p. 292 and figure 326.

»» *Variations*. The slender branch from C. 5 commonly travels via the nerve to the Subclavius, and it may join the phrenic nerve low down, behind the 1st costal cartilage, crossing in front of the subclavian vein.

Thoracic Duct (continued from p. 532). The duct enters the neck on the left side of the esophagus and at once, at the level of the C. 7, arches laterally and forward on the pleural cupola. It opens into the angle between the left internal jugular and subclavian veins, and is there guarded by a bicuspid valve.

Its course is simple—it goes behind the 3 structures contained within the carotid sheath, and in front of "the plane of the subclavian artery and its branches", some or all of which it crosses anteriorly, depending on the extent of the arc it makes (*fig. 726.1*). Therefore, it crosses behind the vagus, which lies within the carotid sheath, and in front of the phrenic nerve, which is clamped down by the transversa colli and suprascapular arteries (*fig. 725*). The duct crosses either just in front of or just behind the vertebral vein.

On each side there are three lymph trunks, the *internal jugular*, *subclavian*, and *bronchomediastinal*, which open into the internal jugular, subclavian, and brachiocephalic veins, respectively, near the angle of union. On the left side, they may open into the thoracic duct; on the right side, they may unite to form a short stem (½"), the *right lymph duct*. The first two follow the veins of the same names; the bronchomediastinal duct is formed by the union of efferents from the tracheobronchial and parasternal nodes.

The tracheobronchial nodes receive the efferents from the lungs; the parasternal nodes drain territory supplied by the internal thoracic artery, including the anterior abdominal wall, thoracic wall, mamma, mediastinum, and diaphragm, and also the upper surface of the liver via the falciform ligament. These vessels contain lymph; the thoracic duct also contains digested fat (chyle).

Thyroid Gland (*fig. 713*). The thyroid

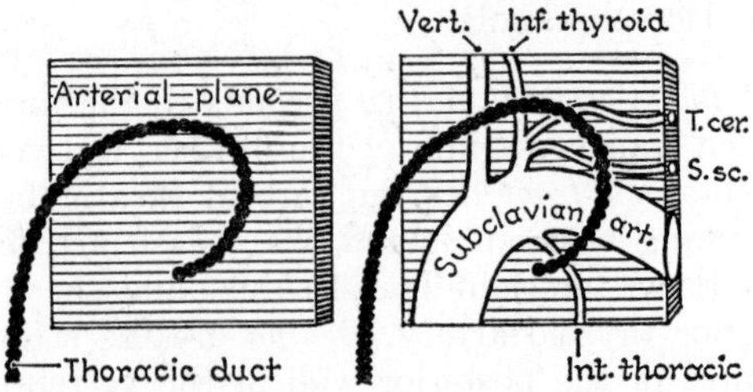

FIG. 726.1. The thoracic duct and the "arterial plane."

gland consists of a right and a left *lobe*, which are pointed above and rounded below and are connected with each other near their lower ends by a narrow *isthmus;* and, from the isthmus a finger-like process, the *pyramidal lobe*, commonly ascends near the median plane toward, or to, the hyoid bone.

The thyroid gland, like the prostate and the kidney, has a *capsule* and a loose *areolar sheath*.

Development. The mode of development (*fig. 727*) of the gland explains its relations. The thyroid gland arose as a median outgrowth of the pharynx between the anterior and posterior rudiments of the tongue. It grew downward under cover of the "Rectus Cervicis" (p. 608) ventral to the hyoid bone, thyroid and cricoid cartilages and upper rings of the trachea; and it spread out on the sides of the trachea into right and left lobes in much the same way as a large drop of candle grease might trickle down a candle, clinging to it. The foramen cecum of the tongue marks its site of origin; the pyramidal lobe when present indicates its course.

Relations. The isthmus crosses the upper two or three tracheal rings; and each lobe expands downward on the side of the trachea, backward on to the esophagus, and upward on to the pharynx and larynx. The upward expansion is, however, arrested by the attachment of the Sternothyroid to the oblique line of the thyroid cartilage. The gland clings closely to the "four visceral tubes" (p. 609) and forces the carotid sheath aside. When enlarged, it overflows laterally in front of the carotid sheath, and downward retrosternally in front of the great vessels and pleura.

When the isthmus is divided and pulled laterally, each lobe is seen to be bound to the cricotracheal ligament by a dense *fibrous band* (*fig. 728*) which compels the gland to follow the movement of the trachea. Also, the *recurrent laryngeal nerve*, commonly in two branches, is seen ascending on the side of the trachea (just in front of the tracheo-esophageal angle) to the back of the crico-thyroid joint where it disappears deep to the Inferior Constrictor. The nerve lies between layers of the sheath and passes either in front of, between, or behind the branches of the inferior thyroid artery. This mixed nerve is distributed not only to the larynx but also to the trachea, esophagus, and Inf. Constrictor.

Vascular and Nervous Supply. Its *Arteries* are the paired superior and inferior thyroid arteries, and the occasional median unpaired thyroidea ima. They anastomose freely.

Of its *Veins*, the superior thyroid vein follows the superior thyroid artery to end in

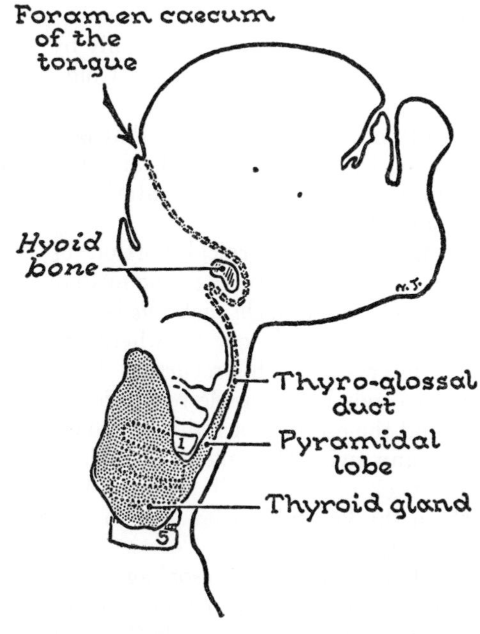

FIG. 727. The course of a developing thyroid gland. (From data by J. E. Frazer.)

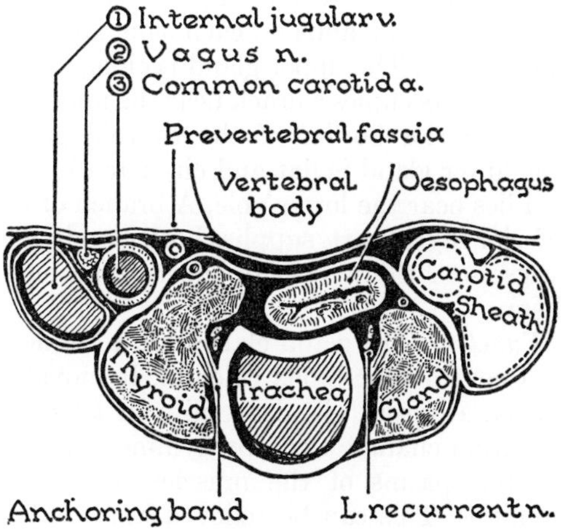

FIG. 728. The trachea and esophagus, on cross section.

the internal jugular vein; the inferior thyroid veins follow the thyroidea ima a. to the brachiocephalic vein; and the middle thyroid vein leaves the lateral border of the gland to end in the internal jugular vein.

Lymph Vessels pass from extensive lymph plexuses to the deep cervical, pretracheal, and paratracheal nodes. A vessel may pass directly to the right subclavian vein and another to the thoracic duct, without the intervention of a node.

Nerves: Sympathetic fibers from the superior and middle cervical ganglia travel along the superior and inferior thyroid arteries, middle thyroid vein, and the external and recurrent laryngeal nerves.

»» *Function.* The thyroid gland elaborates a hormone that controls the rate of oxidation in the body. Marked under-activity of the gland in childhood results in retarded skeletal growth, delayed epiphyseal union, and arrested sexual and mental development; this is called *cretinism.*

Marked under-activity of the gland in adult life results in an oedematous condition due to the subcutaneous accumulation of a mucinous substance, hence called *myxoedema.* Over-activity increases the metabolic rate and the heart rate and is usually associated with nervous instability and loss of weight. In the variety of hyperthyroidism called *exophthalmic goiter* the eyes are prominent.

Anomalies. A *pyramidal lobe* occurs very commonly. The *isthmus* rarely disappears; *ectopic lobules* may occur between the infrahyoid muscles; the *thyroglossal duct* may persist and open at the foramen cecum, or be broken up into one or more thyroglossal cysts. One or both *inferior thyroid arteries* may be absent.

Parathyroid Glands (*fig. 768*). These small glands, yellowish-brown like a bumble bee, lie along the posterior border of the thyroid gland between its capsule and sheath. There are two glands on each side, an upper and a lower. The upper gland is elongated (6 mm.) and occupies a crack near the middle of the posterior border of the thyroid gland. The lower gland is flat and circular (5 mm.) and lies near the lower pole. A branch of the inferior thyroid art. supplies both glands, and twigs from the nerves to the thyroid enter them.

Function. The gland elaborates a hormone that controls the blood calcium. Removal of the parathyroid glands results in *tetany*, a condition characterized by symmetrical and painful spasms of the muscles of the extremities. This can be relieved immediately by injections of calcium in readily ionizable form.

In *hyperthyroidism,* calcium is drained from the bones—particularly from the trabeculae in the metaphyses of growing bones. Since the resorbed bone is replaced by soft connective tissue, fractures are common.

Development. The inferior gland, like the thymus, is developed from the 3rd pharyngeal pouch and it follows the thymus to a lower level than the superior gland, which is developed from the 4th pouch. The lower gland may follow the thymus gland for some distance below the thyroid gland—its position is variable.

Trachea and Esophagus. These two tubes begin where the larynx and pharynx end, which is at the cricoid cartilage in front of the 6th cervical vertebra, 6″ from the incisor teeth. The trachea ends at the level of the sternal angle. If you measure from cricoid cartilage to sternal angle you will find the distance is 4½″; this is the length of the trachea. Its outside diameters in the cadaver are about ⅘″ by ⅗″.

The trachea occupies the median plane, except below where the aortic arch deflects it to the right. *Behind* it lies the esophagus, but between the two there is enough areolar tissue to allow each to dilate and contract independently, *cf.* the bladder and rectum. Behind the cervical part of the esophagus is the vertebral column, separated only by prevertebral fascia and the Longus Colli muscles.

The 18 or so U-shaped rings that keep the lumen of the trachea patent are deficient behind where applied to the anterior wall of the esophagus.

In front of the cervical portion of the trachea are the structures in the median line of the neck (p. 607). *On each side* is the common carotid artery, except where thyroid gland intervenes. The recurrent laryngeal nerve ascends in the angle between the trachea and the esophagus and it supplies them with many twigs. The pleural cupola as far as the neck of the 1st rib, and the thoracic duct on the left side as far as C. 7 are also lateral relations.

The left border of the esophagus projects beyond the trachea (*fig. 728*) and it is from this more accessible or left side that the surgeon prefers to approach the esophagus.

CHAPTER 41

SIDE OF SKULL, PAROTID, TEMPORAL, AND INFRATEMPORAL REGIONS

LATERAL ASPECT OF THE SKULL (NORMA LATERALIS)

A straight line carried from nasion to mastoid process divides the skull into cranial and facial parts with fair accuracy (*fig. 729*).

The **Cranium on lateral view** (*fig. 730*) presents three approximately "concentric" ovoid contour lines: (1) the outline of the cranium, (2) the outline of the temporal fossa, (3) the outline of the squama of the temporal bone.

THE OUTERMOST OVOID CONTOUR LINE is the outline of the cranium. Its features are: nasion, glabella, bregma, vertex, lambda, posterior pole of the skull, inion, and foramen magnum.

Above the level of the inion lies the cerebrum, and the outline of the cranium is here full; below lies the cerebellum, and the outline shelves to the foramen magnum, whose center is deep to the mastoid process. From nasion to foramen magnum the frontal, parietal, and occipital bones contribute nearly equally to the outline.

From the inion the *superior nuchal line* curves laterally to the rough outer surface of the *mastoid process*, which is the drawn out end of the line. To these the Trapezius and Sternomastoid are attached, and deep to the latter are the Splenius and Longissimus Capitis. The upper, smooth, triangular part of the mastoid bone lies behind the external acoustic meatus and closes the mastoid antrum laterally.

THE INNERMOST OVOID CONTOUR LINE is the border of the squama temporalis. Side by side below its middle are twin cavities, (1) *external acoustic meatus* and (2) *mandibular fossa* (*fig. 731*). From the squama projects the *zygoma* or zygomatic process of the temporal bone. This process articulates with the zygomatic bone, and both take part in the zygomatic arch.

The *lower border of the zygomatic arch* begins at the 2nd molar tooth and ascends as

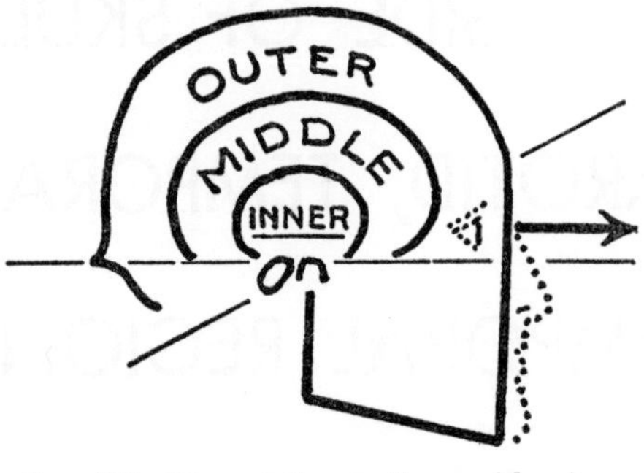

FIG. 729. Plan of the skull, on side view
The face is angular. The cranium is oval and is divided into three zones, placed above twin depressions (*fig. 731*).

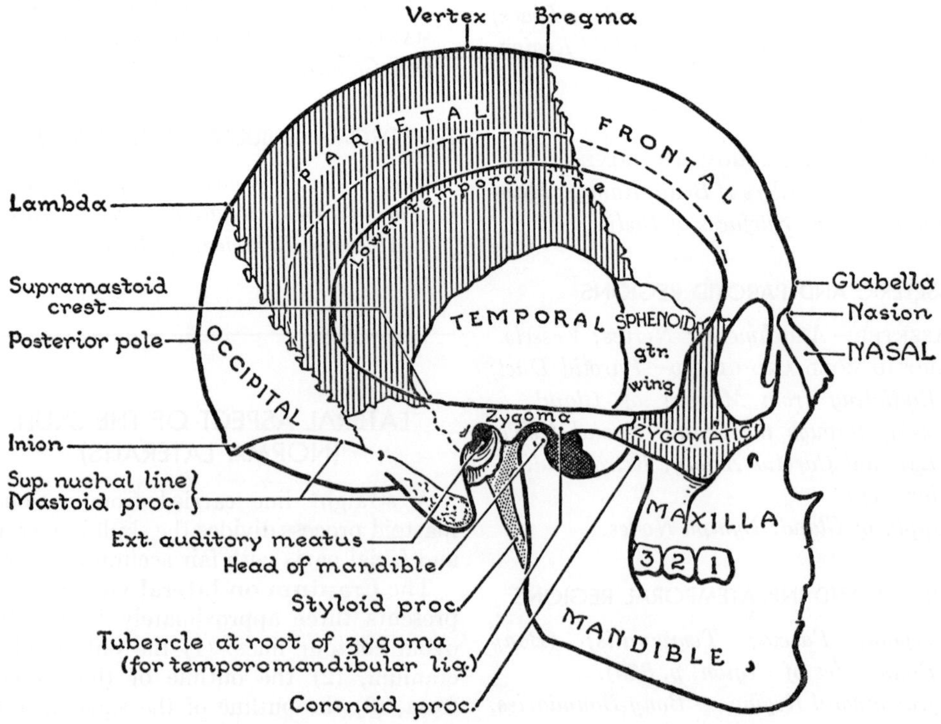

FIG. 730. The skull, on side view. (Norma lateralis)

a buttress to the zygomatic process of the maxilla, separating the facial aspect of the skull from the infratemporal fossa. It then curves backward along the lower border of the zygomatic bone and zygoma to the *tubercle* for the lateral (temporomandibular) lig. Then, as the *anterior root of the zygoma,* it makes a right angle turn medially and, ceasing to be free, ends as the *articular tubercle* (eminence), which bounds the mandibular fossa in front.

THE INTERMEDIATE OVOID CONTOUR LINE surrounds the **temporal fossa** and gives attachment to the temporal fascia. It comprises the following parts: the sharp *upper border of the zygoma,* which, when traced backward, first becomes the *posterior root of the zygoma,* next the *supramastoid crest* (which by coincidence lies between the mastoid antrum below and the middle cranial fossa above); then, as the *temporal line,* it curves across the parietal and frontal bones, and finally follows the angled *temporal border of the zygomatic bone,* and so completes the ovoid.

The *temporal fossa* is deepest where the Temporalis requires to be strongest, which is antero-inferiorly, above the coronoid process of the jaw. Parts of the zygomatic bone and greater wing of the sphenoid form its anterior wall and separate it from the orbital cavity. The temporal line separates it from the region of the scalp.

Four bones—temporal squama, greater wing of sphenoid, parietal, and frontal—take part in its medial wall and meet at a +-shaped or H-shaped suture called the **pterion.** The pterion is a landmark full of importance (pp. 586–587, *fig. 689*).

A ragged crest, the *infratemporal crest,* on the squama temporalis and greater wing of the sphenoid separates the temporal fossa from the infratemporal fossa.

Stylomastoid Region. The *mastoid process* is bounded medially by a (deep) groove that leads forward to the *stylomastoid foramen,* i.e., the orifice of the facial canal. Out of it comes the facial nerve; into it goes the stylomastoid artery.

In front of the foramen is the *styloid process,* 1″ or more long. This process and the lesser horn of the hyoid bone, having a common derivation (*fig. 744.1*), point at each other, as a stalactite points at a stalagmite.

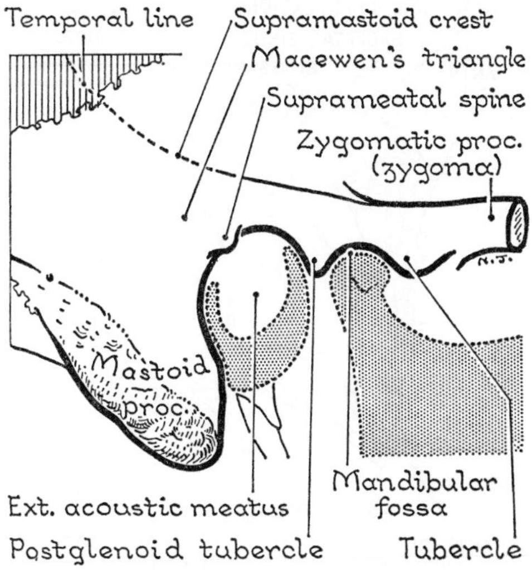

FIG. 731. Twin depressions (external acoustic meatus and mandibular fossa) with the postglenoid tubercle in between.

The U-shaped *tympanic bone* (*stippled* in *fig. 731*) forms two-thirds of the circumference of the *ext. acoustic meatus.* Its anterior part, the *tympanic plate,* is square, partly ensheaths the styloid process, and separates meatus from *mandibular fossa.*

The *postglenoid tubercle* descends from the posterior root of the zygoma behind the head of the jaw. The *suprameatal spine,* which is the surgeon's guide to the antrum, lies behind the external meatus (*fig. 731*).

THREE KEY BONES

Due to their central positions and simple features the **parietal bone** has been selected from among the cranial bones and the **zygomatic bone** from among the facial bones as "key bones" most worthy of individual treatment; and the **lower jaw,** which is the only movable bone in the skull. Although their details may be no more important than those of other bones, their appreciation will ensure a better understanding of the whole cranium.

Parietal Bone

The parietal bone is classified as a flat bone, with two surfaces, four borders, and

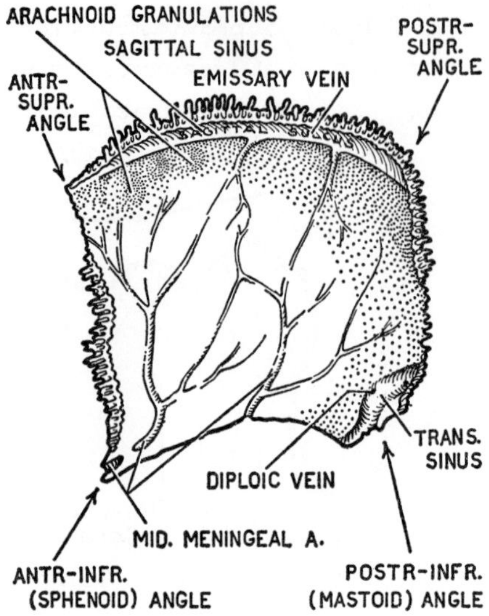

FIG. 732. The medial surface of the parietal bone.

four angles, and it is molded on the brain. Its features are its borders and its angles (*figs. 730* and *732*).

Borders. Three borders are straight and serrated and each articulates with one bone: the anterior with the frontal bone at the parietofrontal or *coronal suture*, the superior with the opposite parietal bone at the interparietal or *sagittal suture*, and the posterior with the occipital bone at the parieto-occipital or *lambdoid suture*. The inferior border is concave and has the appearance of having been scraped away externally to articulate with the squama of the temporal bone which overlaps it at the parietosquamous, or *squamosal, suture*.

Angles. Each of the four angles has a different shape and is in relation on its medial surface with an important vessel.

The antero-inferior angle is acute; it has on its medial surface either (1) a shallow groove, (2) a deep groove with overhanging edges, or (3) a canal for the anterior branch of the middle meningeal vessels; and it rests on the greater wing of the sphenoid at the *pterion*.

The anterosuperior angle is a right angle, is grooved medially by the superior sagittal sinus, and is situated at the junction of the coronal and sagittal sutures at the *bregma*.

The posterosuperior angle is rounded, is also grooved by the superior sagittal sinus, and is situated at the *lambda*.

The postero-inferior angle is blunt, is grooved medially by the transverse sinus, and it rests on the mastoid part of the petrous bone.

Surfaces. The external surface is convex. At the point of greatest fullness, the *parietal tuber*, ossification started and spread concentrically and therefore reached the four angles late. They are unossified at birth, and owing to the pulsations transmitted by the underlying brain, are called fonticuli (fontanelles, p. 550).

Two lines, the *upper* and *lower temporal lines*, placed ½″ apart, curve across the lateral surface from the postero-inferior angle to the anterior border, dividing it into an upper two-thirds covered with scalp and a lower one-third which forms part of the temporal fossa. The temporal fascia is attached to the upper line; the temporal muscle reaches to the lower line.

The internal surface is concave. Grooves for branches of the middle meningeal vessels ascend on it, one being commonly about a finger's breadth behind the anterior border. A groove, the *sagittal sulcus*, running along the superior border, lodges the superior sagittal sinus. By its side are depressions for arachnoid granulations, and a small foramen, the *parietal foramen*, transmits an emissary vein from the sinus to the surface veins.

Zygomatic Bone

The cheek bone is a flat bone, shaped somewhat like a conventional diamond (*figs. 730* and *733*). The slightly convex *lateral* (*facial*) *surface* is separated from the medial aspect by four angles and four borders. The medial aspect shares in the formation of the walls of the temporal and infratemporal fossae.

All four angles and the *maxillary border* (really a surface) are articular; three borders are free. Of these, the *orbital border* is concave and gives attachment to the orbital septum; the *masseteric border* is tubercular for the tendinous origin of the Masseter; and the *temporal border* is angled and sharp for the temporal fascia.

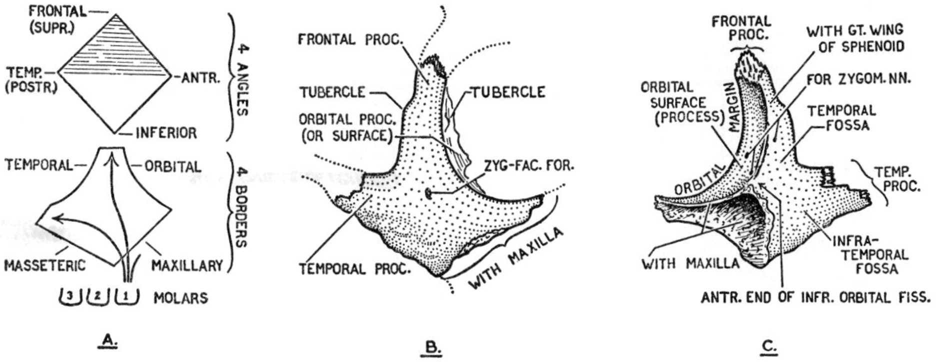

FIG. 733. The zygomatic bone. *A*, four angles, four borders, and lines of force transmission. *B*, the lateral surface. *C*, the medial aspect.

Functions of the Zygomatic Bone. Its frontal process, which is strong, transmits to the frontal bone for dispersion the force of impacts delivered during mastication. Its temporal process is one of the buttresses of the face (*fig. 739*). It also gives origin to the Masseter. Its worth is well appreciated on viewing the zygomatic process of the maxilla from below.

»» A process of the zygomatic bone, extending backward from the orbital margin, forms part of the lateral wall and floor of the orbital cavity. This "*orbital process*" reaches to the inferior orbital fissure.

The bone is traversed by a Y- or V-shaped canal. The stem of the canal opens onto the orbital surface in front of the inferior orbital fissure. One limb opens onto the facial surface; the other onto the temporal. These transmit the zygomatic nerve and artery and their zygomaticofacial and zygomaticotemporal branches (*fig. 703*).

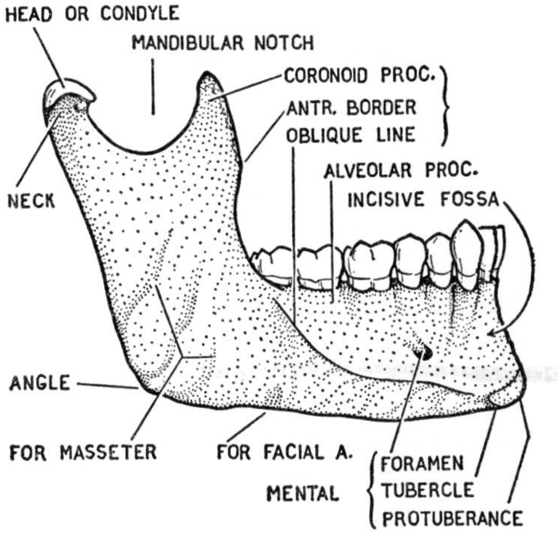

FIG. 734. The lateral aspect of the mandible

Mandible or Lower Jaw

The jaw is shaped like a horseshoe (*figs. 734* and *735*). Each half is L-shaped, consisting of two oblong parts. The horizontal parts of the two sides fuse at the *symphysis menti* in the median plane during the 2nd year to form the *body* of the jaw (although in most mammals they remain paired); the vertical parts are the *rami*.

BORDERS OF THE BODY. The *lower border* of the body is thick and rounded and is continuous behind with the lower border of the ramus, which is thin; together these form the *base of the jaw*. The *alveolar process*, or upper part of the body, carries eight teeth. The roots of the teeth (except the 2nd and 3rd molars) cause rounded ridges on the thin front wall of the alveolar process, that of the canine being the most prominent. Medial to the canine ridge is the *incisive fossa* from which the Mentalis takes origin.

THE RAMUS is an oblong, nearly vertical, flattened plate. It is surmounted by two processes, the *head* and the *coronoid process*, which are separated from each other by a U-shaped notch, the *mandibular notch*.

The head articulates with the mandibular fossa of the temporal bone, and is like a ¾″ segment of a lead pencil set horizontally but not in perfect alignment with its fellow, since the medial end is tilted backward. It is supported by a *neck*. In front of the medial part of the neck there is a *fossa* for the insertion of the tendon of the Lateral Pterygoid.

The coronoid process is a traction process, caused by the pull of the Temporalis (*cf.*

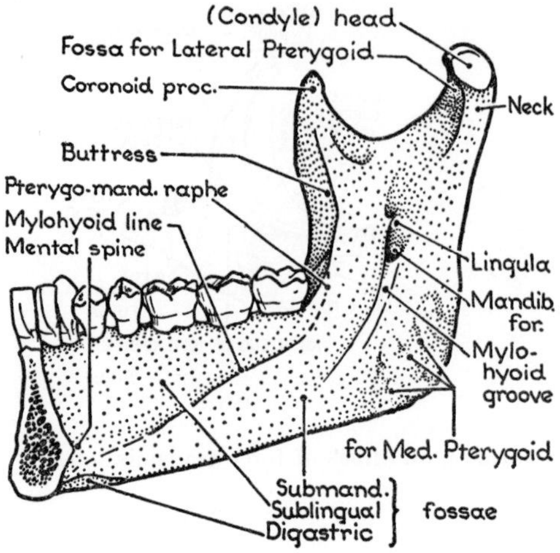

FIG. 735. The medial aspect of the mandible

the mastoid process and Sternomastoid). It rises under shelter of the zygomatic arch and is triangular (or, rather, like a crow's beak, being convex in front and concave behind).

The posterior and inferior borders of the ramus meet at the *angle* of the jaw. It is greater than a right angle, thin, rounded and either inverted or everted. Laterally it is ridged for tendinous septa of the Masseter, medially for tendinous septa of the Medial Pterygoid.

MANDIBULAR CANAL. Through the bone runs the *mandibular canal.* Its entrance, the *mandibular foramen,* lies at the center of the medial surface of the ramus, above the level of the crowns of the molar teeth. Guarding the foramen in front is a small, upwardly projecting tongue, the *lingula,* which gives attachment to the spheno-mandibular lig. A narrow groove, the *mylohyoid groove,* which lodges the mylohyoid nerve and artery, begins behind the lingula and runs for 1 inch obliquely downward and forward on the ramus.

The canal, conveying vessels and nerves to the teeth, continues to the symphysis menti, but it communicates with the outer surface of the body at the *mental foramen,* situated 1¼″ from the symphysis, in line between the premolar or bicuspid teeth, and midway between the upper and lower borders.

» The margin of the foramen is smooth above and laterally, because the emerging mental nerve and artery are mainly distributed in these directions.

THE SURFACES OF THE BODY. *External.* In front of the lower end of the symphysis menti there is a broad triangular elevation, the *mental protuberance.* From the infero-lateral angle of this protuberance (mental tubercle) an indefinite line, the *oblique line,* crosses the body diagonally upward and backward below the mental foramen to become continuous with the sharp anterior border of the ramus and coronoid process. To this line are attached the Depressor Labii Inferioris and Depressor Anguli Oris.

Internal. Projecting from behind the middle of the symphysis menti is the *mental spine* (genial tubercles), for the origin of the Geniohyoid and Genioglossus. From below the spine another oblique line, the *mylohyoid line,* crosses the body diagonally upward and backward to become (nearly) continuous with a strengthening *buttress* on the medial aspect of the ramus and coronoid process. To this line the Mylohyoid is attached. Between the mylohyoid line and the buttress the pterygomandibular raphe is attached (p. 542), and also the two muscles united by this raphe, viz., the Superior Constrictor behind and the Buccinator in front, the Buccinator extending forward on the aveolar process, lateral to the molar teeth.

Fossae are related to the mylohyoid line: (1) the *digastric fossa,* for the attachment of the anterior belly of the Digastric, resembles a fingertip impression made below the line, at the side of the symphysis; (2) the *sublingual fossa,* for the sublingual gland is above the line, and (3) the *submandibular fossa* for the submandibular gland is below it.

MASSETERIC AND PAROTID REGIONS

Masseter. The Masseter is rhomboidal. It arises by tendinous fibers from the anterior two-thirds of the lower border of the zygomatic arch, which accordingly is tubercular, and by fleshy fibers from the medial surface of the arch and posterior one-third of the lower border, which accordingly are smooth. It covers the lateral surface of the ramus and is inserted into it, but owing to its obliquity it leaves bare the area about the neck (*fig. 737*). It has a common developmental origin with the Temporalis and is partly united with it.

Nerves, p. 636. *Actions*, p. 639.

The *nerve* reaches the Masseter by crossing the mandibular notch above the Lateral Pterygoid; the *vessels* by crossing below it, which is in accordance with Nerve—Artery Relationship (p. 636).

The **Parotid Region** (Gk. para = near; ous (otos) = the ear) is a mold lined with fascia and filled with parotid gland. The gland fills the irregularities of the mold and overflows its brim in front and below, and through the gland pass certain vessels and nerves.

The parotid gland is invested in deep cervical fascia which splits to enclose it. The superficial layer reaches the zygoma; the deep layer lines the mold and reaches the lower border of the tympanic plate. The gland itself falls short of the zygoma.

»» If you make a careful study of the mold you need not spend time on the cast, which is but the counterpart.

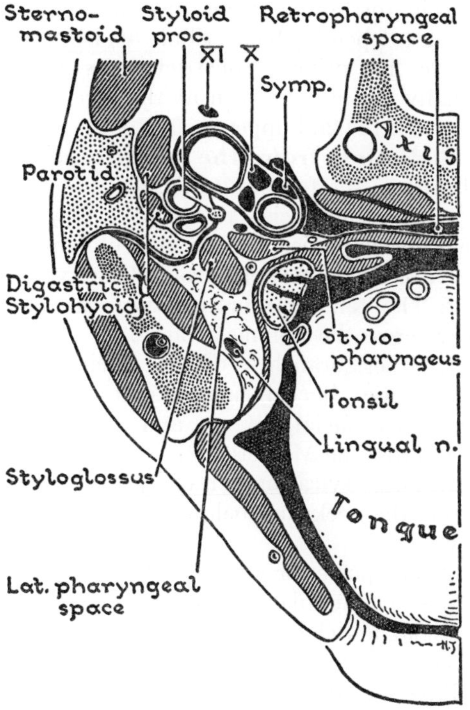

FIG. 736. Cross-section of the head, at the level of the parotid gland and the tonsil.

The Parotid Mold or Bed (*figs. 715* and *736*). This comprises—*Behind:* mastoid process and anterior border of the Sternomastoid. *In front:* posterior border of the ramus of the jaw and of the two muscles (Masseter and Medial Pterygoid) inserted into the ramus. Here the gland overflows on to the Masseter as the facial process. *Above:* anterior and posterior boundaries meet in the cleft between the capsule of the temporomandibular joint in front and the cartilaginous and bony external acoustic meatus behind. *Below:* Stylohyoid and the posterior belly of the Digastric. These the gland overflows, thereby encroaching on the carotid triangle.

The *bottom of the mold* is formed by: (1) the styloid process and the three muscles that arise from it. They intervene between the gland and the int. jugular vein, int. carotid artery, and the last four cranial nerves; (2) the fascial lining, which adheres to the styloid process and to the posterior border of the ramus of the mandible. Between these two bony parts the fascia is ballooned forward, like a sail before the wind, deep to the Medial Pterygoid. The lower part of this sheet, the *stylomandibular lig.*, is thickened and it separates the parotid from the submandibular gland.

Several tongue-like processes from the cast fill several crevices in the mold. Of these, (1) one passes forward between the upper part of the ramus and the Medial Pterygoid; (2) another passes upward between the external meatus and the capsule of the jaw joint; (3) another passes medially in front of the internal carotid artery to the Superior Constrictor; but (4) the largest projection is the facial process. It covers the hinder part of the Masseter (and the temporomandibular lig. and neck of the jaw) and is prolonged above the parotid duct as the *accessory parotid gland.*

The **parotid duct** crosses the Masseter horizontally a finger's breadth below the zygomatic arch, makes a right angled turn round the anterior border of the Masseter, and then pierces the buccal pad of fat, p 24 Pansky

Buccinator, and mucous membrane of the cheek to open in the vestibule of the mouth. There its orifice, constricted as orifices usually are, can be seen at the level of the crown of the 2nd upper molar tooth.

Radiating from the margin of the gland are the following (*fig. 659*):

1. The superficial temporal artery and vein, accompanied by the auriculotemporal nerve, cross the posterior root of the zygoma.
2. The temporal branches of the facial nerve cross the zygomatic arch.
3. Other branches of the facial nerve (zygomatic, buccal, mandibular) and the transverse facial artery, and the parotid duct, cross the Masseter.
4. The cervical branch of the facial nerve enters the neck just below the angle of the jaw.
5. The posterior auricular artery and the posterior auricular nerve, which supplies vestigial muscles (Occipitalis and auricular muscles), cross the mastoid.

Passing through the gland (*fig. 737*):

1. Facial nerve—foremost in importance.
2. Retromandibular (post. facial) vein.
3. External carotid artery.

FACIAL NERVE (**N. VII**) (*fig. 737*). The facial nerve enters the parotid region by the stylomastoid foramen, and it continues its downward course for ½ inch before plunging into the parotid gland, 1 inch below the head of the jaw. Within the gland it divides into an upper and a lower division from which branches of plexiform nature appear on the face (*fig. 659*).

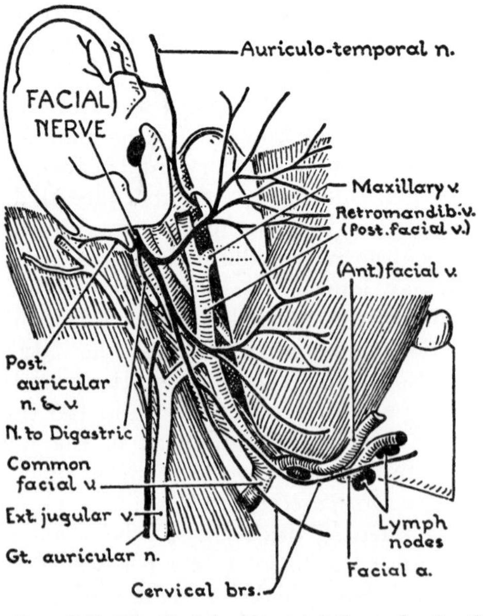

FIG. 737. The facial nerve and the veins in the parotid region.

Branches in this region: post. auricular n. and n. to Digastric (post. belly) and Stylohyoid.

Communicating nerves: (1) auriculotemporal n., behind the neck of the jaw, transfers to N. VII secretory fibers received from the otic ganglion; and (2) great auricular n., superficial to the Masseter, sends sensory fibers to N. VII.

The stem of the nerve is found by cutting down on the mastoid process (avoiding the post. auricular art. and nerve), and then with the handle of the scalpel easing the gland well forward from the process. The stem will lie exposed to the point where it disappears through the areolar capsule and into the gland.

At birth the child has no mastoid process, so the stylomastoid foramen is subcutaneous; consequently, the facial nerve may be severed accidentally by a deep skin incision made behind the ear. As the process develops the foramen and the stem of the nerve become submerged.

» The gland is divided into two almost equal parts, superficial and deep, by the plane of the facial nerve and its branches. The veins form a plexus on a plane immediately deep to that of the nerves. This combined fasciovenous plane is found by following the superficial temporal vein downward, or else the ext. jugular vein upward, and, in so doing, splitting the gland (Patey and Ranger).

The gland is likened to a creeping plant that weaves itself into the meshes of a supporting trellis of nerve and vein, as shown in figure 737.1 (McKenzie).

The **External Carotid Artery** appears from under cover of the Digastric and Stylohyoid. Deeply grooving the deep surface of the parotid gland, it ascends under shelter of the posterior border of the ramus of the jaw to the neck where it divides into its two terminal branches: (1) the *maxillary artery* which, hugging the neck of the jaw, passes forwards into the infratemporal region; and (2) the *superficial temporal artery* which, after giving off the transverse

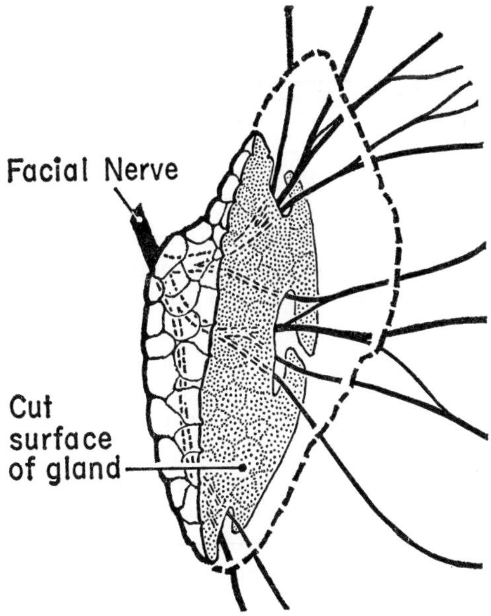

FIG. 737.1. To show the relation of the facial nerve to the parotid gland. (After McKenzie.)

facial artery, crosses the root of the zygoma, where its pulsations can be felt (*fig. 712*).

The **Retromandibular Vein** (post. facial vein), formed by the junction of the superficial temporal and maxillary veins, traverses the gland superficial to the external carotid artery, divides into two branches which pass superficial to the Digastric and help to form the common facial and the external jugular vein (*fig. 664*).

Supply of the Parotid gland. The *Arteries* traversing the gland supply it.

Nerves: The glossopharyngeal nerve (via its tympanic br., lesser petrosal nerve, otic ganglion, auriculotemporal nerve, and facial nerve) provides the secretory fibers (*figs. 737.2* and *797*). Sympathetic fibers reach the gland via the external carotid plexus.

Lymph Nodes, superficial and deep to the parotid fascia, drain cutaneous areas mostly above the zygomatic arch (scalp, eyelids, and auricle). Their efferents follow the ext. jugular vein; others enter the upper deep cervical nodes. Nodes *within the parotid* drain deeper parts (external meatus, tympanum, soft palate, deep parts of the cheek) and drain into deep cervical nodes.

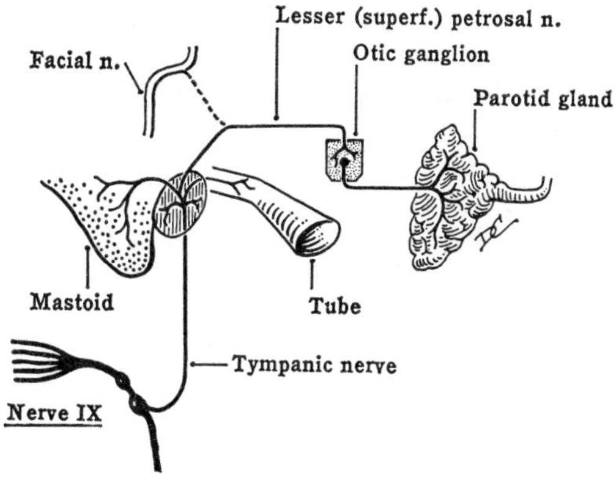

FIG. 737.2. Secretometer nerve to parotid gland

TEMPORAL AND INFRATEMPORAL REGIONS

Temporal Fascia. This strong fascia is attached to the limits of the temporal fossa (described on page 627 as an intermediate ovoid contour line). It splits below into two layers which enclose some fat; the superficial layer is attached to the upper border of the zygomatic arch rendering it sharp; the deep layer descends deep to the Masseter.

»» The middle temporal artery, a branch of superf. temporal art., pierces the fascia and ascends in a groove on the squamous temporal; the zygomaticotemporal nerve also pierces this fascia.

Temporalis. The Temporal muscle arises by fleshy fibers from the whole temporal fossa between the lower temporal line and the infratemporal crest—except in front where a pad of fat separates it from the lateral wall of the bony orbit. It also arises from the temporal fascia (*cf.* origin of Gluteus Medius, *fig. 424.1*).

»» *Comparative Anatomy.* It is only in the primates that the temporal and orbital cavities are separated by bone; e.g., in the dog they are separated by a membrane.

The handle of this fan-shaped muscle is necessarily largely tendinous; it is attached to the circumference of the coronoid process, which is an "epiphysis" without a separate center of ossification. The tendon necessarily begins on the superficial surface because the fleshy fibers are all of approximately the same length and the lowest pass directly to the medial surface of the coronoid process.

INFRATEMPORAL REGION. This region lies below the temporal fossa and deep to the ramus of the mandible. Without some preliminary knowledge of the bony boundaries of the region the contents cannot usefully be discussed.

Bony Boundaries (*figs. 738* and *740*):

The **Lateral Wall** is the ramus of the mandible. Near the center of its medial surface, just above the plane of the crowns of the molar teeth is the *mandibular foramen* (*fig. 735*). The anterior margin of the foramen projects upward as a small tongue, the *lingula*, and from the foramen the *mylohyoid groove* runs downward and forward for 1″. The area between the groove and the angle is ridged for the fibrous attachment of the Medial Pterygoid.

The *head* and *neck* of the jaw extend medial to the plane of the ramus. In front of the neck there is a pit for the insertion of the Lateral Pterygoid.

The *Coronoid Process*, which limits the mandibular notch anteriorly, is recurved and strengthened medially by a bar of bone. This process is to the temporal muscle what the mastoid process is to the sternomastoid muscle.

The **Anterior Wall** of this bony fossa is formed by the inflated body of the maxilla and is of eggshell thinness. It is separated from the facial surface of the maxilla by the *buttress* that descends from the zygomatic arch to the 2nd molar tooth. It is limited below by the 2nd and 3rd molar teeth and the part of the alveolar process behind them, called the *tuberosity of the maxilla;* above, by the *inferior orbital fissure;* and medially by the *pterygopalatine fossa.*

The **Medial Wall** is the *lateral plate* of the pterygoid process. This muscular lamina (for the origin of the two pterygoid muscles) is ½″ wide.

The *pterygoid process* of the sphenoid bone is a flying buttress for the anterior wall; accordingly, it slopes downward and forward so as to abut against the maxilla above the tuber. It assists the zygomatic arch in preventing the face from being driven backward under the cranium (*fig. 739*). The triangular cleft above the site of abutment is the *pterygopalatine fossa.* It is the hiding place of the pterygopalatine ganglion and of the 3rd part of the maxillary artery. The opening into the pterygopalatine fossa is the *pterygomaxillary fissure,* which joins the inferior orbital fissure at a right angle (*fig. 740*).

The Roof of the infratemporal fossa is flat and is formed by the under surface of the *greater wing of the sphenoid* (and slightly by the squamous temporal). A ragged edge, the *infratemporal crest,* separates the roof from the medial wall of the temporal fossa.

The *foramen ovale* perforates the roof at the posterior border of the lateral pterygoid plate—and the plate is the guide to the

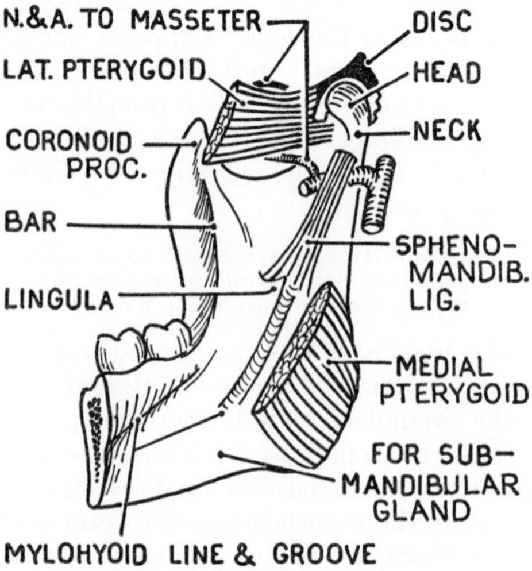

FIG. 738. The lateral wall of the infratemporal fossa: i.e., the ramus of the jaw.

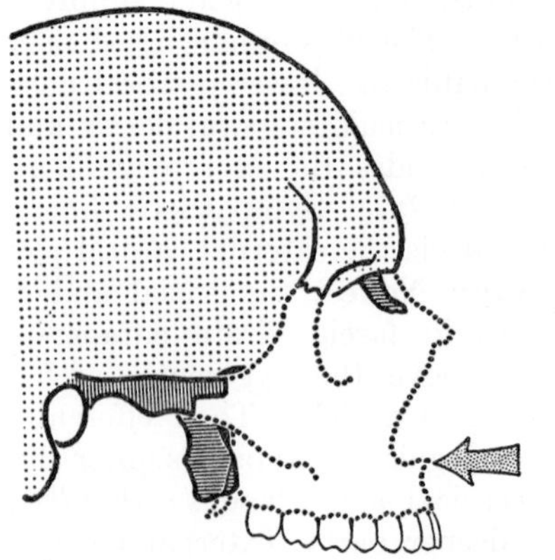

FIG. 739. The chief buttresses of the face—the pterygoid and zygomatic processes.

foramen. The *foramen spinosum,* which is the detached posterior end of the oval foramen, perforates at the *spine of the sphenoid,* which forms the medial limit of the mandibular fossa.

A Key Feature. A pencil passed through both mandibular notches and across the base of the skull encounters no obstruction (*fig. 741*). It lies immediately behind the roots of the pterygoid plates and below the oval foramina.

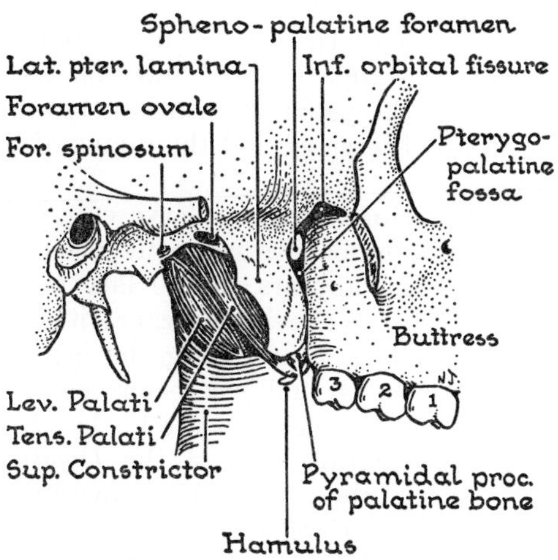

FIG. 740. Anterior wall, medial wall, and roof of the infratemporal fossa.

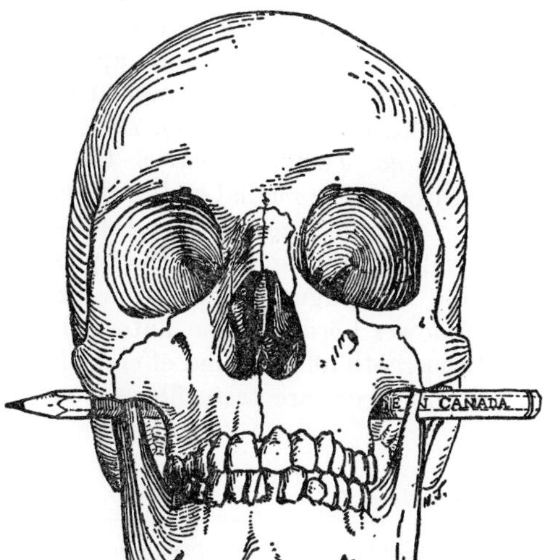

FIG. 741. A pencil can be passed through both mandibular notches. A key feature.

CONTENTS OF INFRATEMPORAL REGION:

1. Pterygoideus Medialis.
2. Pterygoideus Lateralis.
3. Mandibular nerve. √3
4. Maxillary artery.
5. Maxillary vein.
6. Otic ganglion.

The **Medial Pterygoid** is the most medial structure in the infratemporal region (*fig. 742*). It arises from the medial surface of the lateral pterygoid lamina.

»» A few fibers, it is true, creep round below the lamina on to the pyramidal process (*fig. 740*).

It crosses from the medial to the lateral wall of the fossa in a downward and backward direction to be attached to the medial surface of the ramus postero-inferior to the mandibular foramen (*fig. 738*).

Both the Medial Pterygoid and the Masseter are rhomboidal; both take downward and backward courses; and both are inserted into roughly corresponding areas on the two surfaces of the ramus. The difference to note is the added lateral direction of the Medial Pterygoid.

The **Lateral Pterygoid** has a continuous origin from almost the entire roof and medial wall of the infratemporal fossa. The

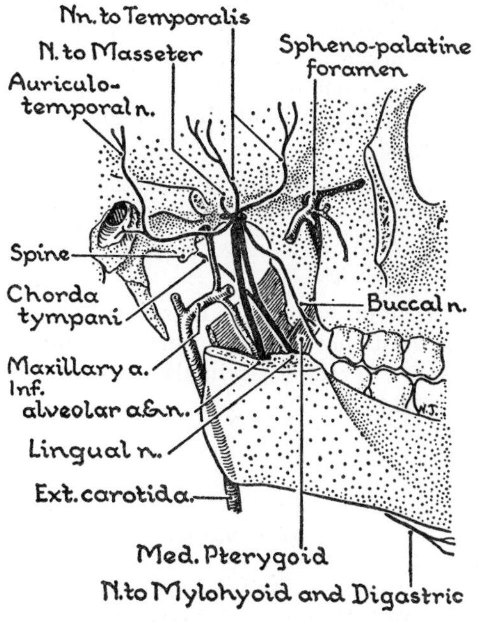

FIG. 742. The mandibular nerve

fibers converge as they pass backward and laterally to be inserted by tendon into the pit in front of the neck of the jaw and into the articular disc.

Nerve–Artery Relationship (*fig. 742*). The *maxillary artery* enters the region in contact with the neck of the jaw—i.e., in contact with the hindmost part of the lateral wall of the infratemporal fossa. Its name indicates its ultimate distribution, but it also supplies the area through which it passes. The *mandibular nerve* (V^3) enters through the foramen ovale—i.e., through the most medial part of the roof of the fossa. Now, the foramen ovale lies above a pencil passed through both mandibular notches. Obviously, therefore, it lies above and in front of a line joining the necks of the jaw. Hence:

1. The nerve has its entrance above, in front of, and medial to the artery.
2. The artery has its entrance below, behind, and lateral to the nerve.
3. These relative positions are maintained by the stems and branches of the nerve and artery.

Mandibular Nerve (V^3) (*fig. 742*). Developmentally, the mandibular nerve is the nerve of the mandibular arch. It is a mixed nerve, for added to its sensory fibers is the entire motor root of the trigeminal nerve. Descending through the foramen ovale, nerve V^3 breaks up at once into branches, each of which begins its career deep to the horizontally running Lateral Pterygoid.

»» Because of the obliquity of the Medial Pterygoid, only the descending branches of the nerve actually cross it; but the nerve and all its branches are at first superficial to the Tensor Palati, which lies medial to the foramen ovale (*fig. 740*).

Branches supply the muscles of mastication (but not the Buccinator) and are sensory to the mandibular process (see table 22.)

»» 1. Certain branches remain deep to the Lateral Pterygoid, viz., (1) motor branches that pass directly to the *two Pterygoids* and indirectly, via the otic ganglion, to the *two Tensors* (Palati and Tympani) and (2) a *sensory twig* to the dura, via the foramen spinosum.

2. Other branches appear at the borders of the Lateral Pterygoid or perforate it. Thus: running between its upper border and the roof of the fossa are two branches to the *Temporalis* and one to the *Masseter*. The latter crosses the mandibular notch behind the tendon of the Temporalis and sends a twig to the joint.

The Buccal Branch is the sensory nerve of the cheek. It sends many fibers through the Buccinator to the mucous membrane of the cheek and lower gums (*fig. 793*), and some to the skin at the angle of the mouth (*fig. 658*).

The Inferior Alveolar (Dental) and *the Lingual nerve* appear at the lower border of the Lateral Pterygoid and continue between the Medial Pterygoid and the ramus of the jaw.

The **Inferior Alveolar Nerve** enters the mandibular foramen, traverses the mandibular canal, and appears on the face as the mental nerve. While in the canal it sends twigs to the teeth (including the incisors) and to the gums; and just before entering the canal it gives off the nerve to the *Mylohyoid* and anterior belly of the *Digastric*, which runs in the mylohyoid groove to the submandibular triangle.

The **Lingual Nerve** supplies the anterior two-thirds of the tongue, the floor of the mouth, and the gums (p. 679), so naturally it lies in front of the inferior alveolar nerve. It enters the mouth between the Medial Pterygoid and the ramus, and, applied to the jaw, it runs forward submucously just below the 3rd molar tooth (*fig. 794*).

The Chorda Tympani leaves the tympanum through the medial end of the petrotympanic fissure (*fig. 756*), grooves the medial side of the spine of the sphenoid, and joins the lingual nerve from behind, near the lower border of the Lateral Pterygoid. It has both afferent and efferent fibers: the afferent fibers are taste fibers from the

TABLE 22

The Branches of the Mandibular Nerve

Muscular Branches	Sensory Branches	Other Branches
Temporalis and Masseter	Auriculotemporal	Taste
Medial and Lateral Pterygoids	Inferior alveolar	Secretory
Tensores Palati and Tympani	Lingual	Articular
Mylohyoid and Digastric (anterior)	Buccal	

anterior two-thirds of the tongue; the efferent fibers are secretory to the submandibular and sublingual salivary glands. (Continued on p. 679).

The **Auriculotemporal Nerve,** as it courses backward, applied to the roof of the fossa (*fig. 742*), splits to encircle the middle meningeal artery and passes lateral to the spine of the sphenoid. It then winds laterally behind the capsule of the joint, crosses the posterior root of the zygoma, and accompanies the superficial temporal artery.

Distribution:

1. Cutaneous fibers to the auricle and the temporal region (*fig. 737*), and (via twigs that pass between the bony and cartilaginous meatuses) to the external meatus and the outer surface of the ear drum.
2. *Articular twigs* to the jaw joint.
3. *Secretory fibers* to the parotid gland, which are received from the otic ganglion and are conveyed to the facial nerve (*fig. 797*).

»» *An Aid to Location and Function.* One could imagine a fracture of the spine of the sphenoid interfering with the secretion of the three great salivary glands (parotid, submandibular, sublingual) and with taste in the anterior two-thirds of the tongue, for the spine is in contact with the auriculotemporal nerve laterally and the chorda tympani medially (*fig. 742*).

Maxillary Artery (Int. maxillary art.) (*fig. 743*). This is the larger of the two terminal branches of the external carotid. It begins at the neck of the jaw, runs forward in contact with the neck, crosses the lateral (sometimes medial) surface of the Lateral Pterygoid, and disappears into the pterygopalatine fossa, where it breaks up into its end branches.

It is divided by the Lateral Pterygoid into three parts—1st, before crossing; 2nd, crossing; 3rd, after crossing.

DISTRIBUTION. The branches of the 1st and 2nd parts of the artery are distributed with the branches of the mandibular (V^3) nerve to the territory of the lower jaw (mandibular process); whereas the branches of the 3rd part are distributed with the branches of the maxillary (V^2) nerve to the territory of the upper jaw (maxillary process). Hence, the term "mandibulo-maxillary artery" might have been more apt.

BRANCHES. All branches of the 1st and

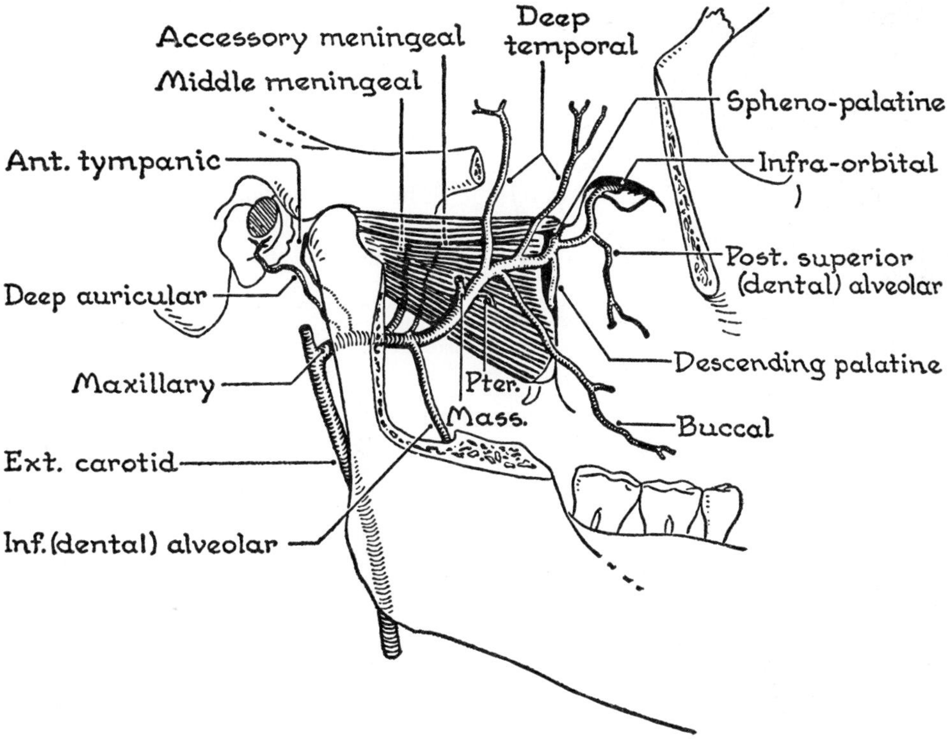

FIG. 743. The maxillary artery

3rd parts pass through foramina; the branches of the 2nd part are muscular.

From the 1st Part: (1) *The deep auricular a.* follows the branch of the auriculotemporal nerve between the cartilage and bone of the acoustic meatus to supply the skin of the meatus and (outer surface of) the ear drum. (2) *The anterior tympanic a.* ascends behind the capsule of the joint and through the petrotympanic fissure into the tympanum. (3) The **middle meningeal a.** ascends medial to the Lateral Pterygoid and passes through the foramen spinosum. (4) The *accessory meningeal a.* ascends through the foramen ovale to supply the trigeminal ganglion and adjacent dura mater. (5) The **inferior alveolar a.** accompanies the nerve of the same name and has corresponding branches.

From the 2nd Part: Muscular branches to Lateral and Medial Pterygoids, branches that join the nerves to Temporalis and Masseter, and a branch follows the buccal nerve.

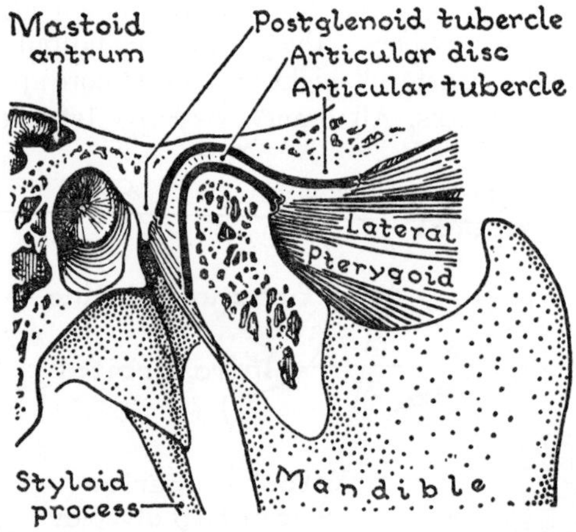

FIG. 744. The mandibular joint, on sagittal section.

From the 3rd Part: (see page 690).

Maxillary Vein (Internal). Veins corresponding to branches of the maxillary artery form a plexus, the **pterygoid plexus,** around the pterygoid muscles (*fig. 680*).

It has important connections (1) with the cavernous sinus via the foramen ovale, (2) with the facial vein via the deep facial vein, and (3) with the pharyngeal plexus.

The plexus ends as the *maxillary vein,* which follows its artery deep to the neck of the jaw and joins the superficial temporal vein to form the retromandibular vein (post. facial vein).

Otic Ganglion (*fig. 737.2*). This, a parasympathetic ganglion, is a relay station on the course of the *secretory fibers* of nerve IX (and nerve VII) to the parotid gland.

The lesser (superficial) petrosal nerve descends through the foramen ovale bringing preganglionic fibers to the ganglion; the postganglionic fibers travel with the auriculotemporal nerve as far as the neck of the jaw where they join the facial nerve to be distributed with it (*figs. 761* and *797*).

»» *Motor fibers* from the mandibular nerve (via the n. to the Medial Pterygoid) pass through the ganglion en route to the Tensor Palati and Tensor Tympani. *Sympathetic fibers,* brought by the middle meningeal artery, pass through the ganglion.

The otic ganglion, about 3 by 3 mm. in diameter, is situated below the foramen ovale, deep to the mandibular nerve.

»» It is best seen (i.e., with least disturbance to its branches) from the interior of the pharynx after removal of the Tensor Palati.

TABLE 23

Movements of the Mandible

Depress (Open Mouth)	Elevate (Close Mouth)	Protract (Protrude Chin)	Retract (Withdraw Chin)	Side to Side (Grinding, Chewing)
L. Pterygoid Digastric (anterior) Mylohyoid Geniohyoid Infrahyoid muscles Gravity	Temporal Masseter M. Pterygoid	L. Pterygoid M. Pterygoid	Temporal (mid. and post.) Masseter (deep part)	Temporal (mid. and post.) of same side Pterygoids of opposite side Masseter

Temporomandibular Joint
(Jaw Joint)

Bony Parts. The bony parts of this joint are: (1) the head of the jaw; (2) the articular surface of the mandibular fossa of the temporal bone (*fig. 744*).

The posterior border of the ramus of the jaw expands above into a triangular process, the *neck*, the upper border of which, the *head*, is rounded like a roller.

The head projects farther medially than laterally. The long axes of the heads of opposite sides are not in line, but are inclined posteromedially, and would, if produced, meet at the anterior border of the foramen magnum. In front of the neck is a *pit* for the tendon of the Lateral Pterygoid.

The Mandibular Fossa lodges: (1) the head of the jaw and (2) a process of the parotid gland. It has an anterior articular part formed by the temporal squama and a posterior nonarticular part formed by the tympanic plate. The two parts converge medially on the spine of the sphenoid, and they meet above at the tympanosquamous (squamotympanic) fissure. (Continued on p. 650).

Ligaments. The *strength* of this joint depends obviously on the bony conformation and on muscles. The *capsule* is necessarily lax, and posteriorly it is necessarily attached in front of the tympanosquamous fissure, since through this fissure passes an artery (ant. tympanic a.). It is thickened laterally to form a triangular bundle, the *lateral* or *temporomandibular ligament*, the fibers of which pass downward and backward from the tubercle of the zygoma to the posterior border of the neck of the jaw.

An *articular disc* caps the head of the jaw and projects forward under the articular tubercle, dividing the joint cavity into an upper and a lower compartment. This disc is firmly fixed to the medial and lateral ends of the condyle; the capsule blends with its circumference and the tendon of the Lateral Pterygoid is partly inserted into its anterior margin.

***AXIOM:** In man, an articular disc implies two types of movement, one on each side of the disc. In the lower cavity simple hinge movements between the head and disc occur; in the upper cavity the disc and head together glide on the articular tubercle.*

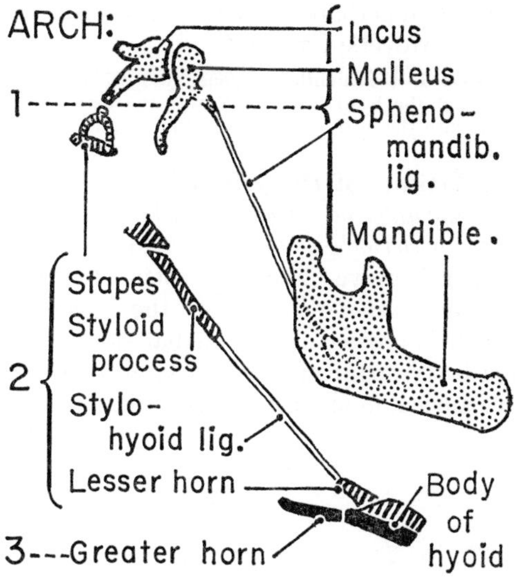

Fig. 744.1. Two vestigial ligaments (sphenomandibular and stylohyoid) derived from the cartilages of the 1st and 2nd pharyngeal arches.

Palpation—Surface Anatomy. The heads can be palpated first by placing a finger in front of each tragus and then in each cartilaginous external meatus, and their movements analyzed on opening and closing the mouth, on protruding and retracting the chin, and on performing grinding movements. You should do this.

Actions of Muscles (table 23).

The various movements of the jaw are produced by cooperative activity of several muscles bilaterally or unilaterally. Mandibular elevation is performed by the Temporalis, Masseter, and Medial Pterygoids and depression by the Lateral Pterygoids and Digastrics. The Digastrics show their greatest activity in forceful openings of the mouth at the limit of depression of the mandible.

Lateral movements are performed by the ipsilateral Temporalis and Masseter and the contralateral Medial Pterygoid (and, to a lesser extent, the Lateral Pterygoid).

Protraction is performed by the Medial and Lateral Pterygoids while retraction is by the Temporalis, chiefly its posterior fibers, and perhaps the deep part of Masseter (Latif; Moyers; Carlsoo).

»» *Note:* If the mouth is opened too widely (as in yawning) the head may move over the articular tubercle into the infratemporal fossa, undergoing dislocation.

Relations of the joint. *Lateral*—subcutaneous; *anterior*—insertion of Lateral Pterygoid; *posteriorly*—parotid gland, auriculotemporal nerve, and superficial temporal vessels; *medial*—spine of the sphenoid (which is crossed on its medial side by the chorda tympani and on its lateral side by the auriculotemporal nerve) and just in front of the spine is the foramen spinosum for the middle meningeal vessels.

Nerve Supply. V^3 via (1) auriculotemporal n. and (2) nerve to Masseter.

Accessory Bands. (1) The *sphenomandibular ligament* is a vestige of the cartilage of the 1st pharyngeal arch. It extends from the spine of the sphenoid to the lingula of the mandible (*fig. 744.1*). (2) The *stylomandibular ligament* is a sheet of fascia condensed between the parotid and submandibular glands, and connecting the styloid process to the angle of the mandible

CHAPTER 42

CERVICAL VERTEBRAE, PREVERTEBRAL REGION, AND EXTERIOR OF BASE OF SKULL

CERVICAL VERTEBRAE

Typical; Atypical: Atlas and Axis, and 7th; Anomalies.

Articulated Cervical Vertebrae.

DEEP CERVICAL STRUCTURES

MUSCLES.

Prevertebral Fascia.

VERTEBRAL VESSELS.

VENTRAL RAMI OF CERVICAL NERVES.

Cervical Plexus.

CRANIOVERTEBRAL JOINTS

Transverse Ligament of Atlas; Alar Ligament.

General Ligaments and Homologues; Membrana Tectoria; Ligamentum Nuchae.

EXTERIOR OF THE BASE OF THE SKULL

Transverse Lines, Anterior and Posterior.

ANTERIOR AREA

Bony Palate (Alveolar Process and Tuber Maxillae); Foramina (Greater and Lesser Palatine and Incisive).

Pyramidal Process; Incisive Bone (Premaxillae).

Choanae.

Pterygoid—Laminae; (Fossa); Hamulus and Canal.

Zygomatic Arch.

INTERMEDIATE AREA

Basi-occipital, (Pharyngeal Tubercle).

Oblique Line; Spine of Sphenoid.

Mandibular Fossa; Tympanic Plate; Articular Tubercle; Tympanosquamous Fissure; Postglenoid Tubercle.

Carotid Canal and Jugular Foramen.

POSTERIOR AREA

Features; Occipital Bone; Condyle and Jugular Process.

CERVICAL VERTEBRAE

Man, the giraffe, and the mouse and, indeed, all other mammals (the manatee and certain sloths excepted) have seven cervical vertebrae. The 1st and 2nd are peculiar; the 3rd, 4th, 5th, and 6th are typical; the 7th is transitional. All have one distinguishing feature—their transverse processes are perforated.

Typical Cervical Vertebra (*fig. 745*). The *body* is slightly elongated from side to side and is equal in height ventrally and dorsally. The upper surface resembles a shallow seat in having a raised lip at the sides and in being rounded in front. The inferior surface is the counterpart.

The *pedicles* arise from the middle two-fourths of the side of the body, so the upper and lower *vertebral notches* are of equal depth. Moreover, the pedicles project laterally as well as backward, so the *vertebral foramen* is triangular.

The *laminae* are not especially noteworthy.

The *articular processes* are placed at the junction of the pedicles and laminae. They form a bony column cut obliquely into segments that permit flexion and extension of the neck, i.e., the lower rounded facet faces downward and forward and therefore can glide forward on the upper facet of the process of the vertebra below.

The *spinous process* is short, downturned, bifid, and V-shaped on cross-section.

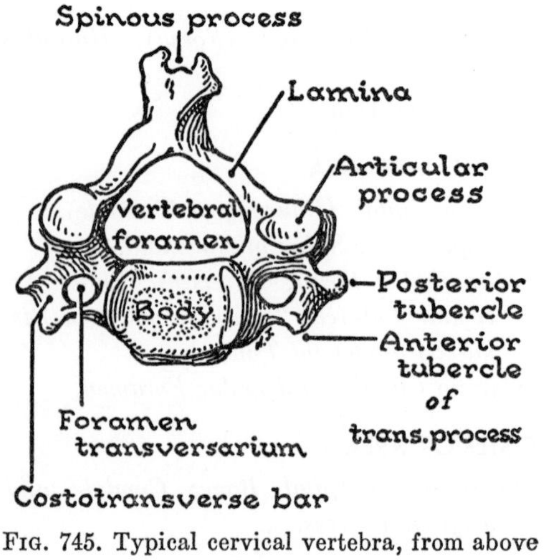

FIG. 745. Typical cervical vertebra, from above

The *transverse processes* have two roots, a perforation, and two tubercles. The *anterior root* is a costal or rib element and, like a rib, it is attached to the side of the body and therefore is in front of the vertebral notch (*fig. 23.1*). The *posterior root* is developmentally a true transverse process and, as such, it is attached to the junction of pedicle and lamina and therefore is behind the vertebral notch. The foramen transversarium transmits the vertebral artery, so it is circular. It is closed laterally by a plate, the *costotransverse bar*, which forms a gutter on which lies the ventral ramus of a spinal nerve, and its size varies with the size of the ramus it supports. The transverse processes are directed laterally and slightly downward and forward in conformity with the pull of the tendons attached to them and with the directions of the nerves resting on them.

Muscles are attached to the posterior tubercles of all cervical transverse processes, but only the 3rd, 4th, 5th, and 6th have anterior tubercles (*figs. 673* and *674*).

The 1st Cervical Vertebra supports the skull, so it is called the **atlas.** It loses its body and acquires an anterior arch. The lost body becomes the *dens* of the axis, so the atlas rotates around its own lost body. It also loses its spine; at least the spine is represented by a tubercle.

The atlas (*fig. 746*) is a ring divided into 5 equal areas—the anterior arch, right and left lateral masses, and a posterior arch composed of right and left halves. A transverse process projects from each lateral mass.

The *anterior arch* is anterior to the dens and to the plane of the bodies of the other

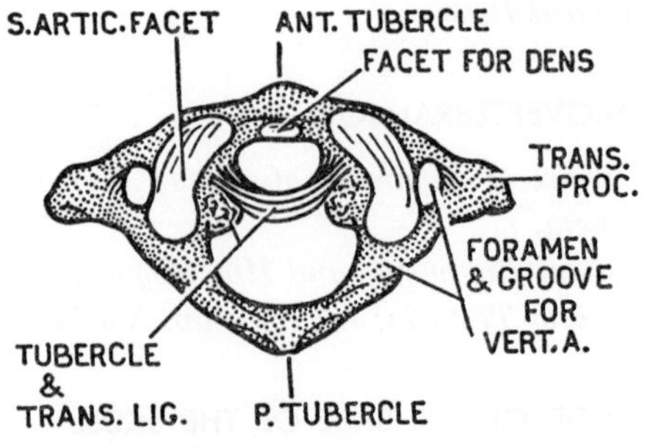

FIG. 746. The atlas and the transverse ligament. (Posterosuperior view.)

vertebrae. It has a facet behind for the dens, and a prominent tubercle in front to which the anterior longitudinal lig. and the Longus Colli muscles ascend; so, it is downturned.

The *tubercle* on the posterior arch gives attachment to two small muscles only, the right and left Recti Capitis Posteriores Minores (*fig. 675*), so it is upturned and the *posterior arch* has no occasion to be strong. Further, it is flattened from above downward and grooved for the vertebral artery, just behind the lateral mass.

Each lateral mass has an upper and a lower weight-bearing facet. The upper facet articulates with the occipital condyle and, being its counterpart, is oval and concave and it converges anteriorly on its fellow. The lower facet articulates with the corresponding facet on the axis, is circular, and faces downward and medially. A *tubercle* for the transverse lig. of the atlas, which retains the dens in position, projects medially from each mass.

The *transverse process* projects laterally and, being a lever that helps to rotate the atlas, it is long—only lumbar transverse processes are longer (*fig. 748*).

The *vertebral foramen* at this most movable part of the column is capacious; so, the spinal cord is not liable to compression.

The 2nd Cervical Vertebra or **Axis** is typical in its lower part and atypical in its upper. The *dens,* which projects from the upper surface of the body, is constricted at its root where the transverse ligament grips it, and it has a facet in front for the atlas.

The *superior articular facet,* being weight-bearing, is large—it extends beyond the body on to the transverse process, overhanging the foramen transversarium. It lies entirely in front of the plane of the inferior articular process. The *transverse process* is short and downturned. The bifid *spine* is massive because large deep muscles (e.g., Multifidus, Semispinalis Cervicis) extend upward to it—but no farther—thereby leaving the atlas free to rotate around the dens while they are extending the vertebral column. The *vertebral arch,* from which the massive spine springs, is necessarily massive too.

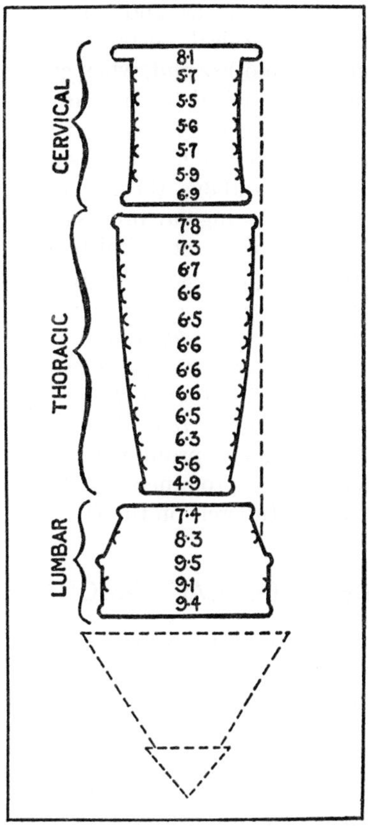

FIG. 748. Diagram showing the mean spread of the transverse processes (to scale).

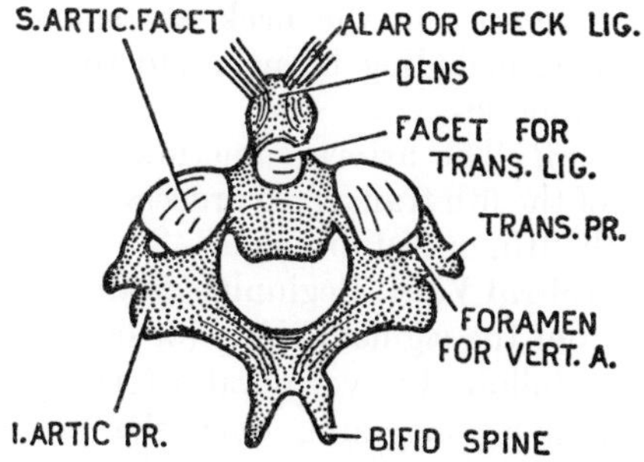

FIG. 747. The axis (epistropheus). (Postero-superior view.)

The 7th Cervical Vertebra has a long nonbifid spine—nearly as prominent as that of Th. 1. The foramen transversarium transmits small veins.

Anomalies. (1) The occipital bone and atlas are occasionally fused. (2) The axis and vertebra C. 3 are commonly fused. (3) Vertebra C. 7 may carry cervical ribs (*fig. 556*).

Articulated Cervical Vertebrae, on

front view. The bodies and transverse processes of the cervical vertebrae are nearly abreast of each other and, when clothed with the muscles attached to the anterior tubercles of the transverse processes, they present a relatively flat prevertebral surface. The basi-occipital is above the anterior arch of the atlas and the jugular process (i.e., transverse process) of the occipital bone is above the transverse process of the atlas. The 1st and 7th transverse processes project far beyond the 2nd–6th (*fig. 748*).

All cervical transverse processes have posterior tubercles, but *only the 3rd, 4th, 5th, and 6th have anterior tubercles*, and the 6th, which is the most prominent of these, is rendered doubly prominent by the absence of an anterior tubercle on the 7th.

DEEP CERVICAL STRUCTURES

Deep Anterior Cervical Muscles grouped according to their relations to the roots of the cervical and brachial plexuses (*fig. 749*):

Muscles Medial to the Plexuses:

1. Rectus Capitis Anterior.
2. Longus Colli (Cervicis).
3. Longus Capitis.
4. Scalenus Anterior.

Muscles Lateral to the Plexuses:

1. Rectus Capitis Lateralis.
2. Scalenus Medius and Posterior.
3. Levator Scapulae.

The following section recapitulates facts scattered elsewhere and previously learned; it also presents matter that requires appreciation but not memorization.

»» The *Longus Colli* extends from the body of the 3rd thoracic vertebra to the anterior tubercle of the atlas, and it is attached to the bodies of the vertebrae in between. It sends slips to the 3rd, 4th, 5th and 6th anterior tubercles and it receives slips from them.

The *Longus Capitis* arises from the 3rd, 4th, 5th, and 6th anterior tubercles and ascends to the basi-occipital to be attached behind the plane of the pharyngeal tubercle. It fills the hollows between the bodies and transverse processes.

The *Scalenus Anterior* arises from the 3rd, 4th, 5th, and 6th anterior tubercles and descends to the scalene tubercle of the 1st rib.

The *Rectus Capitis Anterior* covers the atlanto-occipital joint. It extends from the front of the lateral mass of the atlas to the basi-occipital.

The *Rectus Capitis Lateralis* extends from the transverse process of the atlas to the jugular process of the occipital bone.

The *Scalenus Medius* arises from all, or most of, the posterior tubercles and costotransverse bars of the transverse processes. It descends to the upper surface of the 1st rib between the groove for the subclavian artery and the tubercle on the neck. The *Scalenus Posterior* is its most posterior part continued to the 2nd rib behind the impression for the Serratus Anterior.

There is an angular gap between the transverse process of the atlas and the Scalenus Medius. This gap is occupied by the *Levator Scapulae* (*fig. 749*), which arises from the 1st, 2nd, 3rd, and 4th (posterior) tubercles.

Note that: (1) the jugular process is the "transverse process" of the occipital bone. (2) Well developed Ant. and Post. Intertransverse muscles unite the respective ant. and post. tubercles of the transverse processes. (3) The Rectus Capitis Anterior and Rectus Capitis Lateralis represent modified Anterior and Posterior Intertransverse muscles, and the ventral ramus of C. 1 appears between them. (4) Structures descending from the jugular foramen cross in front of the jugular process, Rectus Capitis Lateralis and the transverse process of the atlas—and lower down, Levator Scapulae, Scalenus Medius and Scalenus Anterior. (5) The Scaleni are modified Intercostal muscles; and (6) the brachial plexus represents enlarged and modified lateral branches of intercostal nerves piercing them (*fig. 95*).

The **Prevertebral Fascia** covers the prevertebral muscles and is continuous with the deep fascia that forms the carpet for the posterior triangle of the neck (p. 555). It is part of a strong sleeve that envelops the deep muscles of the neck. Above, it is attached to the base of the skull behind the jugular foramina. Below, it is lost in front of the thoracic vertebrae.

The roots of the cervical and brachial plexuses emerge from the vertebral column deep to the fascia, and of course the branches to the four muscles described above (p. 557 and *fig. 666*) remain deep to it. And, it must be pierced by all cutaneous branches (lesser occipital, great auricular, transversus colli, and supraclavicular), by branches of C. 1 and 2 to nerve XII, of C. 2 and 3 to ansa cervicalis, and of C. 2, 3, and 4 to nerve XI.

Vertebral Artery. *Its Origin and Course* are given in figure 725 and page 619. (See also *fig. 750.*)

Its Function is to supply the cervical segment of the cord and part of the brain.

Its Branches in the neck are spinal and muscular, including branches to the suboccipital muscles.

Variant. The artery sometimes passes in front of the 6th transverse process and enters the 5th, 4th, or 3rd foramen.

Vertebral Vein. Beginning as an emissary vein from the sigmoid sinus (or occipital sinus), it follows the vertebral artery through the foramen magnum, over the posterior arch of the atlas, and through the upper six transverse processes where it forms a net-

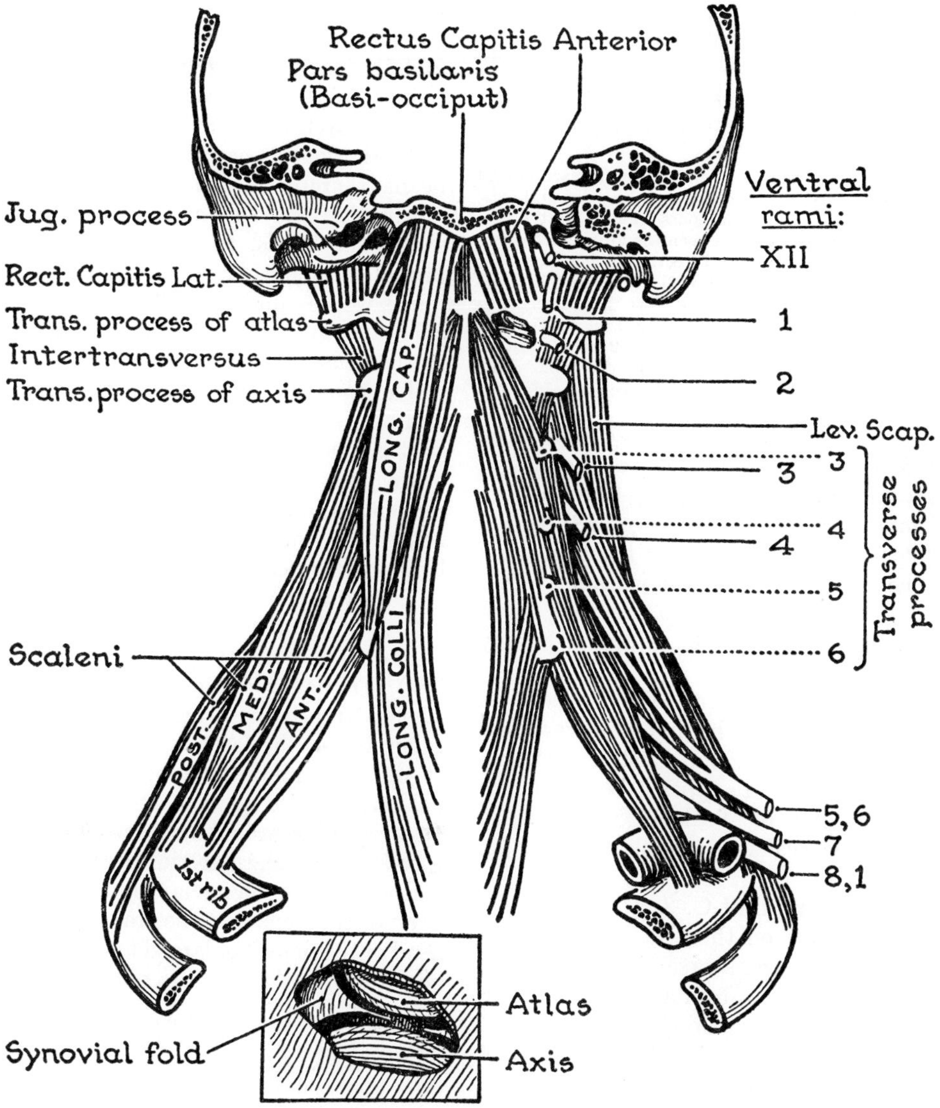

FIG. 749. The prevertebral muscles: Deep anterior cervical muscles

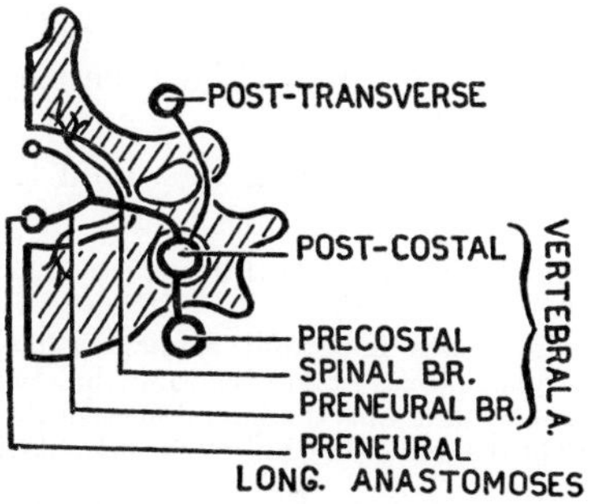

FIG. 750. Diagram to explain on developmental grounds the zig-zag course of the vertebral artery.

work around the artery. Leaving the 6th foramen, it descends in front of its artery to join the brachiocephalic vein. It communicates freely with the other veins of the vertebral venous system (*fig. 676*, and p. 569).

Ventral Rami of Cervical Nerves. The cervical plexus is formed by the ventral rami of C. 1, 2, 3, 4; the brachial plexus by the rami of C. 5, 6, 7, 8, and Th. 1. Ramus C. 4 sends a communication to ramus C. 5 and therefore is divided between two plexuses, just as L. 4 is divided between the lumbar and sacral plexuses, and S. 4 between the sacral and coccygeal plexuses (table 13, p. 334).

The courses of nerves C. 1 and 2 are peculiar, as explained by figure 675, and on p. 568.

»» The ventral rami of C. 1 and 2 curve forward lateral to the superior articular processes of the atlas and axis, respectively; that of C. 1 then passes medial to the vertebral artery and appears between the adjacent borders of Rectus Capitis Anterior and Rectus Capitis Lateralis; whereas that of C. 2 passes lateral to the vertebral artery, appears between (Ant. and) Post. Intertransverse muscles, and divides into ascending and descending branches. This ascending branch of C. 2 joins most of C. 1 in front of the trans. process of the atlas. This united stem joins the hypoglossal nerve (*fig. 765*).

Distribution of the Cervical Plexus. The *phrenic nerve* is the chief nerve of the plexus. It is a mixed nerve from C. 3, 4 and 5.

Cutaneous Branches (see page 558).

Motor Branches supply the local muscles; branches of C. 2, 3, and 4 join nerve XI, branches of C. 2 and 3 join the ansa cervicalis; and branches of C. 3 and 4 supply Levator Scapulae.

The ventral rami of the lower six cervical nerves run laterally behind the vertebral artery, between Ant. and Post. Intertransverse muscles, and appear between the Longus Capitis or Scalenus Anterior in front and the Scalenus Medius behind (*fig. 749*).

The ventral rami of C. 3, 4, 5, and 6 occupy the gutters on the 3rd, 4th, 5th, and 6th gargoyle-like transverse processes. These rami increase in size from above downward; so do the gutters in which they lie. The rami of C.8 and Th. 1 are related to the neck of the 1st rib: the former runs nearly horizontally above it, the latter ascends obliquely in front of it and they meet and unite at the medial border of the rib to form the lowest trunk of the brachial plexus. This trunk is in part responsible for the groove on the 1st rib commonly attributed to the subclavian artery.

CRANIOVERTEBRAL JOINTS

Joints between Skull, Atlas, and Axis

Five synovial joints are here involved, two paired and one median.

The paired joints are between the articular processes of the atlas and axis, and between the superior articular processes of the atlas and the occipital condyles; the median unpaired joint is between the dens and the anterior arch of the atlas.

At the *atlanto-occipital joints* we nod our heads thereby indicating approval or the affirmative; at the *atlanto-axial joints* we shake our heads, thereby indicating disapproval or the negative. At the other cervical joints we flex and extend the neck and look sideways up. This last movement occurs also at the atlanto-occipital joints.

The movements between skull and atlas and between atlas and axis have wide range, so, the ligaments of the vertebral arches and of the processes, being far from the centers of movement, are loose and weak. Near the centers of movement strong and peculiar ligaments appear:

1. Transverse ligament of the atlas.
2. Alar ligaments.

Peculiar Ligaments (*figs. 746, 747*, and *751*). **Transverse Lig. of the Atlas.** This strong arched band extends between the tubercles on the lateral masses of the atlas. It passes behind the root of the dens and holds it forward against the atlas. There is a synovial joint (a bursa) between the front of the dens and the anterior arch of the atlas and a bursa (or synovial joint) between the back of the dens and the transverse lig. The head of the dens is enlarged and cannot easily be withdrawn from its osseofibrous ring.

»» Weak upper and lower bands pass from the transverse lig. to the basi-occipital above and to the body of the axis below, giving the whole the appearance of a cross; hence, called the *cruciform lig.*

Alar Ligament (*fig. 747*). This short, very stout cord (one on each side) passes from the side of the apex of the dens laterally and slightly upward to the tubercle on the occipital condyle.

Together the two alar ligs. hold the skull tightly applied to the atlas, and they check rotation of the skull and atlas on the axis.

»» A pair of less important special ligaments—the *accessory atlanto-axial*—takes the same direction as the alar ligaments and joins the lateral mass of the atlas to the body of the axis. They likewise check rotation.

General Ligaments and Homologues (*fig. 751*). The *Anterior Longitudinal Liga-*

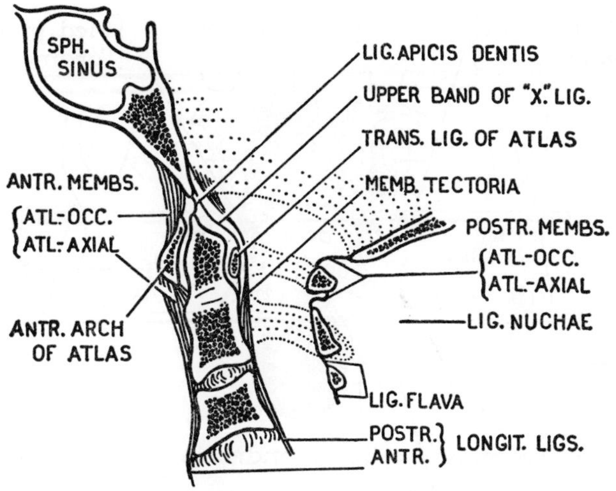

FIG. 751. Ligaments connecting the skull to the vertebral column (paramedian section)

ment of the bodies of the vertebrae becomes a cord at the axis, and as a cord it ascends to the anterior tubercle of atlas and on to the basi-occipital. Above the atlas its side parts are membranous, the *anterior atlanto-occipital membrane.*

The Posterior Longitudinal Ligament of the bodies passes from the posterior surface of the body of the axis to the inner surface of the basi-occipital, spanning the atlas and the transverse lig. It is broad and strong and called the **membrana tectoria.**

»» The intervertebral disc between the dens and the basi-occipital persists as a vestigial thread, the *lig. apicis dentis,* which transmitted the notochord.

The supraspinous and interspinous ligs. form the *ligamentum nuchae* (p. 520).

The ligamenta flava become weak closing *fibrous membranes* between occipital bone, atlas, and axis (see suboccipital region, *fig. 675* on p. 566).

The *ligaments* uniting the skull to the vertebral column are shown by figure 751 to be, from before backward—ant. atlanto-occipital membrane, (lig. apicis dentis, upper band of cruciform lig.), an alar lig. on each side, membrana tectoria, post. atlanto-occipital membrane, and lig. nuchae.

The *short muscles* joining the upper cervical vertebrae to each other and to the occipital bone give security to the joints of the neck (*cf.* the short muscles round the shoulder and the hip).

EXTERIOR OF THE BASE OF THE SKULL

The under surface of the base of the skull will be considered in three areas:
—anterior, intermediate, and posterior—separated by an *anterior* and a *posterior transverse line* (*fig. 752*).

These two imaginary lines cross most of the foramina at the base of the skull. Accordingly, they serve as reliable keys to the relationships of the nerves and vessels transmitted by these foramina. They can be used in conjunction with figures 755 and 688.

The anterior transverse line is found by passing a pencil through both mandibular notches and across the base of the skull. The fact that this can be done without the pterygoid laminae obstructing is proof that they lie anteriorly (*fig. 752*).

On removing the mandible, the line is seen to cross: (1) foramen ovale at (2) the root of the lateral pterygoid lamina, (3) foramen lacerum and (4) entrance to the pterygoid canal at (5) the root of the medial pterygoid lamina, and (6) the synchondrosis between the basi-occipital and the sphenoid.

The posterior transverse line unites the anterior margins of the right and left mastoid processes. It crosses: (a) stylomastoid foramen between (b) the styloid and mastoid processes, (c) posterior margin of jugular foramen, (d) hypoglossal canal, and (e)

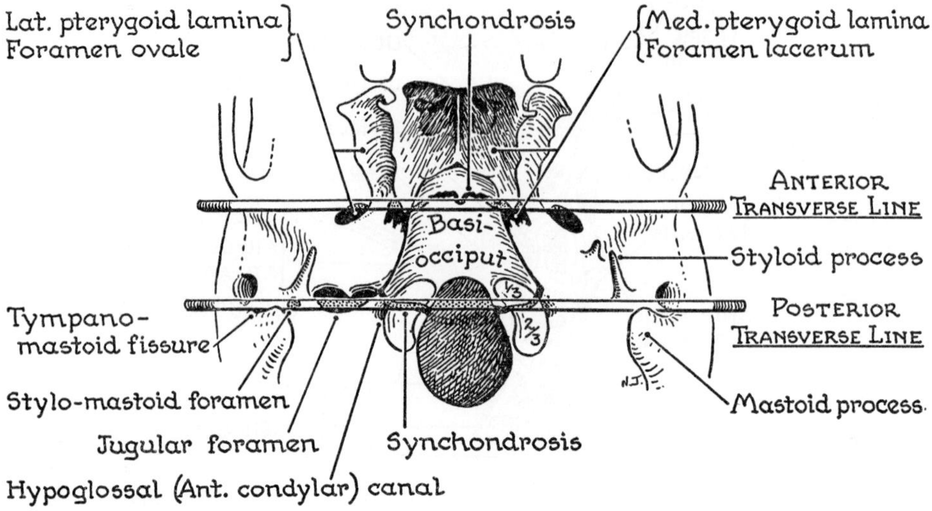

FIG. 752. The "anterior transverse line" and "posterior transverse line" on the exterior of the base of the skull.

junction between anterior ⅓ and posterior ⅔ of occipital condyle. Features d and e lie on the synchondrosis between the basilar and lateral (condylar) parts of the occipital bone.

Anterior Area (*fig. 753*). The bony palate is bounded by the alveolar process except behind where it has a free, sharp, crescentic border on each side separated by the *posterior nasal spine.* The *superior alveolar process* is U-shaped, carries 16 teeth, and has on each side a free posterior end, the *tuber maxillae,* palpable within your own mouth.

The bony palate is divided by a cruciform suture into an anterior ⅔, the *palatine processes of the maxillae,* and a posterior ⅓, the *horizontal plates of the palatine bones.* (See *figs. 841–843* on page 731.)

The foramen of the *greater palatine canal* lies medial to the 3rd molar tooth and from it a groove runs forward. This interosseous foramen is situated between the horizontal plate of the palatine bone and the alveolar process of the maxilla. On the sagittal limb of the suture, just behind the incisor teeth, the *incisive foramen* is situated.

» The remains of an irregular suture line, which runs from the incisive foramen to between the canine and the lateral incisor teeth, bounds the *incisive bone* (premaxilla) posteriorly.

The medial and lateral pterygoid laminae end freely between the levels of the bony palate and the tuber maxillae; but, a portion of the palatine bone, the *pyramidal process* (tubercle), interposes itself like a buffer between the plates and the maxilla. Two branches of the greater palatine canal, the *lesser palatine canals,* descend through the pyramidal process.

CHOANAE (Post. Nasal Apertures). These two oblong apertures are twice as deep as they are wide (1″ x ½″). Each choana is bounded on three sides by a sharp, free edge belonging to the *medial pterygoid lamina,* the *horizontal plate of the palatine bone,* and the *vomer;* and on the fourth side by the meeting of the *ala of the vomer* with the *vaginal process* of the medial pterygoid lamina below the body of the sphenoid.

PTERYGOID LAMINAE. These two plates bound a space, the *pterygoid fossa.*

The lateral lamina gives origin to the Lateral Pterygoid laterally and to the Medial Pterygoid medially; hence, it is a muscular lamina and it is everted by the pull of these two muscles.

The medial lamina is the hind part of the lateral wall of the nasal cavity. Its free border ends below in a hook, the *hamulus,* which is in echelon with the *tuber maxillae,* and the crown of the *3rd molar tooth* (*fig. 754*).

» It ends above conically as the *pterygoid tubercle* at the anterior border of the lower end of the foramen lacerum. Lateral to this tubercle is the entrance to the *pterygoid canal,* which leads forward to where the pterygopalatine ganglion is situated in the pterygopalatine

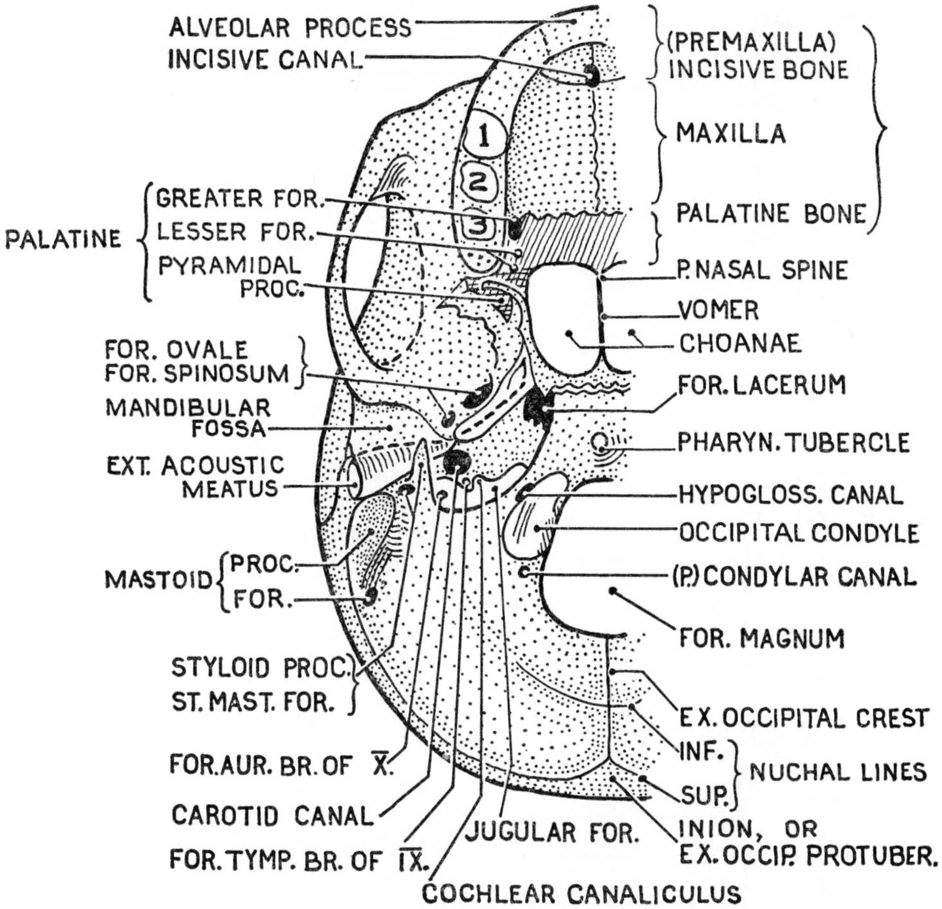

FIG. 753. The exterior of the base of the skull

fossa. The superomedial part of the pterygoid fossa is continued toward the spine of the sphenoid as a *canoe-shaped fossa* (the scaphoid fossa) which gives origin to the Tensor Palati.

LOWER BORDER OF THE ZYGOMATIC ARCH. This arch is described on pp. 626–627.

The Intermediate Area. Medianly is the basi-occipital, which widens as it passes backward. Near its center, which lies above the anterior tubercle of the atlas, is the *pharyngeal tubercle* for the raphe of the constrictors of the pharynx.

"OBLIQUE LINE AT BASE OF SKULL" (*fig. 755*). This imaginary line extends from the (tubercle at the) root of the medial pterygoid plate, which lies on the anterior transverse line, to the front of the ext. acoustic meatus. At the midpoint of this oblique line the **spine of the sphenoid** stands out like a sentinel guarding many strategic points. Thus, (1) anteriorly lies the foramen spinosum which transmits the middle meningeal vessels; (2) posteriorly is the opening of the carotid canal; (3) medially is the orifice of the bony auditory tube, and a bristle entering here emerges through the ext. acoustic meatus; and, (4) laterally is the mandibular fossa—indeed, the spine would serve as a buttress to resist medial displacement of the head of the mandible, which occupies the fossa.

The half of the line anteromedial to the spine lodges the cartilaginous part of the auditory tube; the half posterolateral is the tympanosquamous fissure.

Mandibular Fossa (*fig. 755*). This fossa of the temporal bone lies between the infratemporal fossa in front, the external meatus

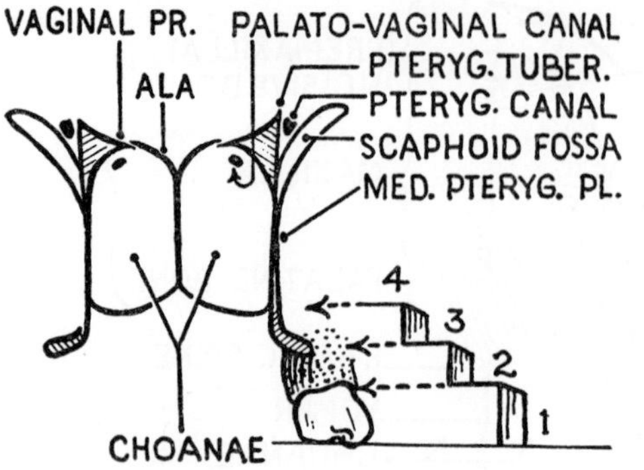

FIG. 754. Showing (*1*) 3rd molar tooth, (*2*) tuber maxillae, (*3*) hamulus, and (*4*) bony palate in echelon.

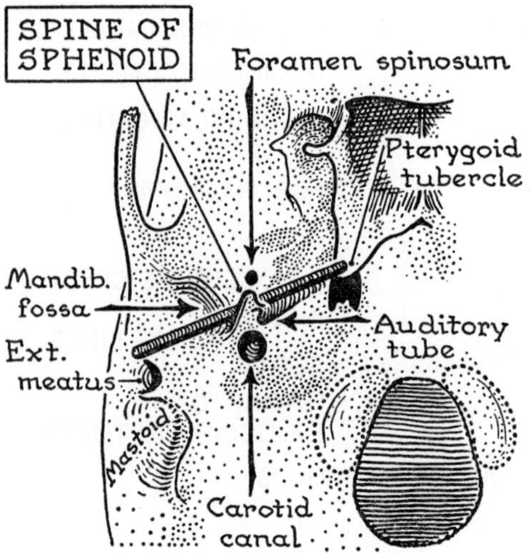

FIG. 755. The oblique line on the exterior of the base of the skull.

behind, and the spine of the sphenoid medially.

The *tympanic plate* forms the square, posterior wall of the fossa. At the upper limit of this plate, and lying on the "oblique line," is the tympanosquamous fissure. It is the temporal squama (i.e., the part of the fossa in front of the fissure) that is hollowed out to articulate with the mandible; it forms the dome and the anterior wall. The antero-inferior border of the fossa, the *articular tubercle* (eminence), is rounded, for it too is articular when the mouth is open. The dome is thin and translucent and it may be fractured by a blow on the chin.

At the lateral end of the fissure, the tem-

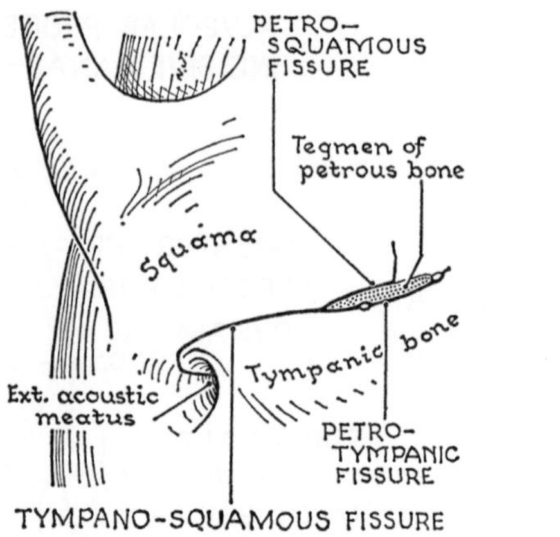

FIG. 756. Explanation of terms. The tympanosquamous fissure bifurcates.

poral squama is prolonged downward behind the head of the mandible as the *postglenoid tubercle*.

»» *Explanation of Terms* (*fig. 756*). The thin anterior edge of the tegmen tympani, which forms part of the floor of the middle cranial fossa, projects into the medial part of the *tympanosquamous fissure*, thereby dividing it into a *petrosquamous fissure* and a *petrotympanic fissure*.

Carotid Canal and Jugular Foramen. The entrance to the carotid canal lies immediately behind the entrance to the bony auditory tube and it is separated from the jugular foramen (compartment for int. jugular vein) by a *bony wedge* on the apex of which there is a pinpoint opening for the *tympanic branch of nerve IX* (*fig. 821*).

The carotid canal curves upward, forward, and medially in the long axis of the petrous bone and opens into the foramen lacerum (*fig. 692*).

The jugular foramen lies between the petrous temporal bone and the jugular process of the occipital bone. Immediately lateral to the foramen is the styloid process, and separated from it medially by a wedge of bone is the hypoglossal canal.

AXIOM: Canals separated by wedges of bone transmit structures (vessels or nerves) that are either converging or diverging.

The Posterior Area is limited behind and at the sides by the inion, superior nuchal lines, and mastoid processes. It includes most of the foramen magnum, two-thirds of the occipital condyles, the jugular processes, and the nuchal portion of the occipital and mastoid bones.

Its *features,* considered with the norma occipitalis on page 560, are: the grooves on the mastoid for the occipital artery and Digastric, the mastoid foramen, condylar canal, inferior nuchal line, and external occipital crest.

Occipital Bone. At birth, this bone consists of four pieces, disposed around the foramen magnum (*fig. 827*): basilar part (basi-occipital) in front; squamous part or squama behind; and a lateral part on each side.

These names are retained for the parts of the adult bone (see p. 720).

The external surface of the lateral part consists of an oval articular eminence, the *occipital condyle,* which skirts the anterior half of the foramen magnum, and the *jugular process,* which projects lateral to the condyle, and is homologous with the transverse process of a vertebra.

CHAPTER 43

GREAT VESSELS AND NERVES OF NECK: REVIEW AND SUMMARY

General Dispositions.

COMMON AND INTERNAL CAROTID ARTERIES—*Relations; Branches; Carotid Sinus; Posterior and Lateral Relations.*

INTERNAL JUGULAR VEIN—*Relations; Bulbs; Tributaries.*

LAST FOUR CRANIAL NERVES—*Glossopharyngeal; Sinus Nerve; Vagus; Accessory; Hypoglossal.*

SYMPATHETIC TRUNK—*Ganglia; Branches; Horner's Syndrome.*

The structures deep to the parotid region are:

1. Internal jugular vein.
2. Internal carotid artery.
3. Last four cranial nerves.
4. Sympathetic trunk.

»» *Preliminary.* The complete cervical courses of these structures cannot be seen until the parotid and infratemporal regions have been dissected, and the posterior belly of the Digastric with its two associated arteries (occipital and post. auricular), and the styloid process with its three attached muscles (Stylohyoid, -glossus, and -pharyngeus) have been severed and thrown aside.

General Dispositions. These deep and inaccessible structures enter or leave the skull through one of *three openings:*

1. Jugular foramen—internal jugular vein and nerves IX, X, and XI.
2. Hypoglossal canal—nerve XII.
3. Carotid canal—internal carotid artery and sympathetic prolongations.

The *jugular foramen* has three compartments: (1) a lateral for the internal jugular vein, (2) an intermediate for nerves IX, X, and XI, and (3) a medial for the inf. petrosal sinus.

Now, the *hypoglossal canal,* which transmits the hypoglossal nerve, converges on the jugular foramen, being separated from it by a wedge-shaped bar of bone. But for this wedge, all four nerves would traverse a single foramen.

The *carotid canal,* being an intra-osseous canal in the petrous bone, is obviously in front of the jugular foramen, which is an interosseous foramen between the petrous and occipital bones. Hence, at the base of the skull the int. carotid artery lies in front

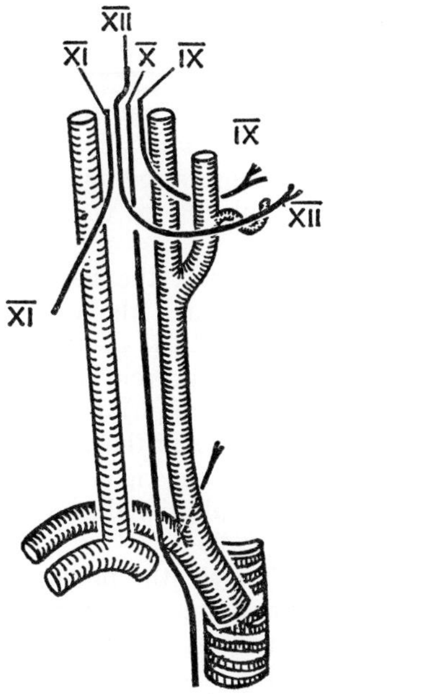

FIG. 757. The relations of the last four cranial nerves to the great vessels.

in the angle between them. The sympathetic trunk runs through the neck behind the artery, but it is outside the carotid sheath.

Medial Relations. As this arterial stem travels through the neck from sternoclavicular joint to carotid canal, it is applied to the side of the digestive and respiratory tubes. The width of the esophagus (1″) separates the right and left common carotids at the root of the neck; the width of the pharynx, which is twice that of the esophagus, separates the right and left internal carotids where they enter the carotid canals at the base of the skull (2″ apart); so, they diverge as they ascend.

The rounded posterior border of the *thyroid gland* usually insinuates itself between the common carotid artery and the esophagus, trachea, and recurrent nerve and forces the artery laterally (*fig. 728*).

The *superior laryngeal nerve* and its two end branches, the *internal* and *external*, descend applied to the pharyngeal wall.

of (and slightly medial to) the int. jugular vein, being separated from it by a thin wedge of bone (*fig. 818*). The four nerves lie medially in the angle between the artery and vein. *These two vessels and four nerves and the sympathetic trunk are compactly placed together* (*fig. 768*).

All *four nerves* descend together for a short distance between the int. jugular vein and the int. carotid artery (*fig. 757*). The X or *vagus nerve* continues vertically through the neck between the great artery and vein. The IX or *glossopharyngeal nerve*, in order to reach the pharynx and posterior third of the tongue, passes forward superficial to the int. carotid artery; the XI or *accessory nerve*, in order to reach the Sternomastoid, passes backward either superficial or deep to the int. jugular vein. The XII or *hypoglossal nerve*, in order to reach the tongue, passes forward superficial to the int. and ext. carotid arteries.

Common and Internal Carotid Arteries (*fig. 758*). This great arterial stem, the internal jugular vein, and the vagus nerve travel through the neck enveloped in the carotid sheath. The artery is medial, the vein lateral, and the nerve is posterior

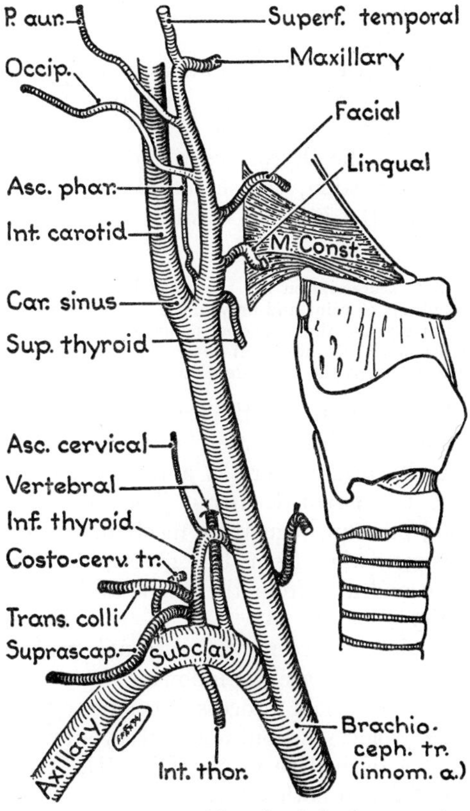

FIG. 758. The carotid and subclavian arteries

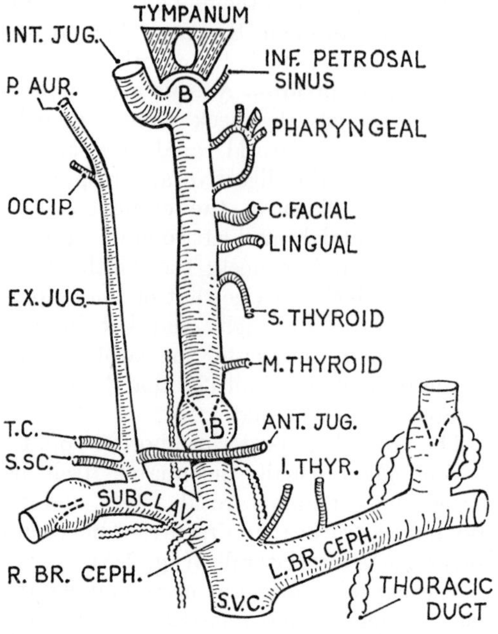

FIG. 759. The internal jugular vein

They pass medial to the int. and ext. carotids (*fig. 763*).

Branches. The common carotid artery bifurcates into internal and external carotid arteries about the level of the upper border of the thyroid cartilage. Just above the bifurcation, the external carotid lies between the internal carotid and the pharyngeal wall.

»» In this description the pharyngeal fascia, pharyngeal plexus of veins and nerves, the ascending pharyngeal artery and the ascending palatine and the tonsillar branches of the facial artery are considered as constituents of the pharyngeal wall—which they are.

The internal carotid artery gives off no branches in the neck.

At its origin there is a fusiform dilatation, the **carotid sinus.** The sinus is a blood pressure regulating mechanism which receives twigs from the glossopharyngeal nerve and also from the vagus and sympathetic.

Passing between the external and internal carotids are the following:

1. The styloid process, Stylopharyngeus and Styloglossus—but not Stylohyoid which, being a derivative of the Digastric, passes superficial to both arteries.
2. The glossopharyngeal nerve and pharyngeal branches of the vagus—but not the superior laryngeal nerve—for reasons given in figure 763.
3. A portion of the parotid gland.

Posterior Relations. The great arterial stem may be compressed against the prominent carotid tubercle of vertebra C. 6 (*fig. 723*).

Below the tubercle, the beginning of the subclavian artery and the vertebral artery and vein lie behind the great arterial stem; and the inferior thyroid artery and the thoracic (or right lymph) duct arch between the carotid sheath and the vertebral vessels; on the right side, the right recurrent laryngeal nerve is an additional posterior relation (*figs. 725* and *763*).

Above the tubercle, the prevertebral fascia and prevertebral muscles separate the artery from the transverse processes. At the base of the skull, the last four cranial nerves are behind the artery. The sympathetic trunk is posterior throughout, except below, where it passes behind the subclavian artery.

Lateral Relations. Laterally are the int. jugular vein and the vagus nerve. The vein is on a posterior plane at the jugular foramen and on an anterior plane where it crosses the subclavian artery (*fig. 725*); elsewhere it is overlapping. Cardiac branches of the vagus and sympathetic accompany the artery.

VARIATION. The int. carotid a. may describe a loop that brings it close to the tonsil.

Internal Jugular Vein. This vein is the continuation of the sigmoid sinus. It begins at the jugular foramen and ends, after crossing the subclavian artery, by joining the subclavian vein to form the brachiocephalic vein behind the sternoclavicular joint, two infrahyoid muscles intervening (*fig. 709*).

At the base of the skull the vein lies on the *posterior transverse line* (*fig. 752*), medial to the styloid process and stylomastoid foramen and therefore medial to the facial nerve; it is behind the carotid canal and therefore behind the int. carotid artery and the cranial prolongations of the sympathetic trunk; and it is posterolateral to the last four cranial nerves.

In the carotid sheath, it is separated by

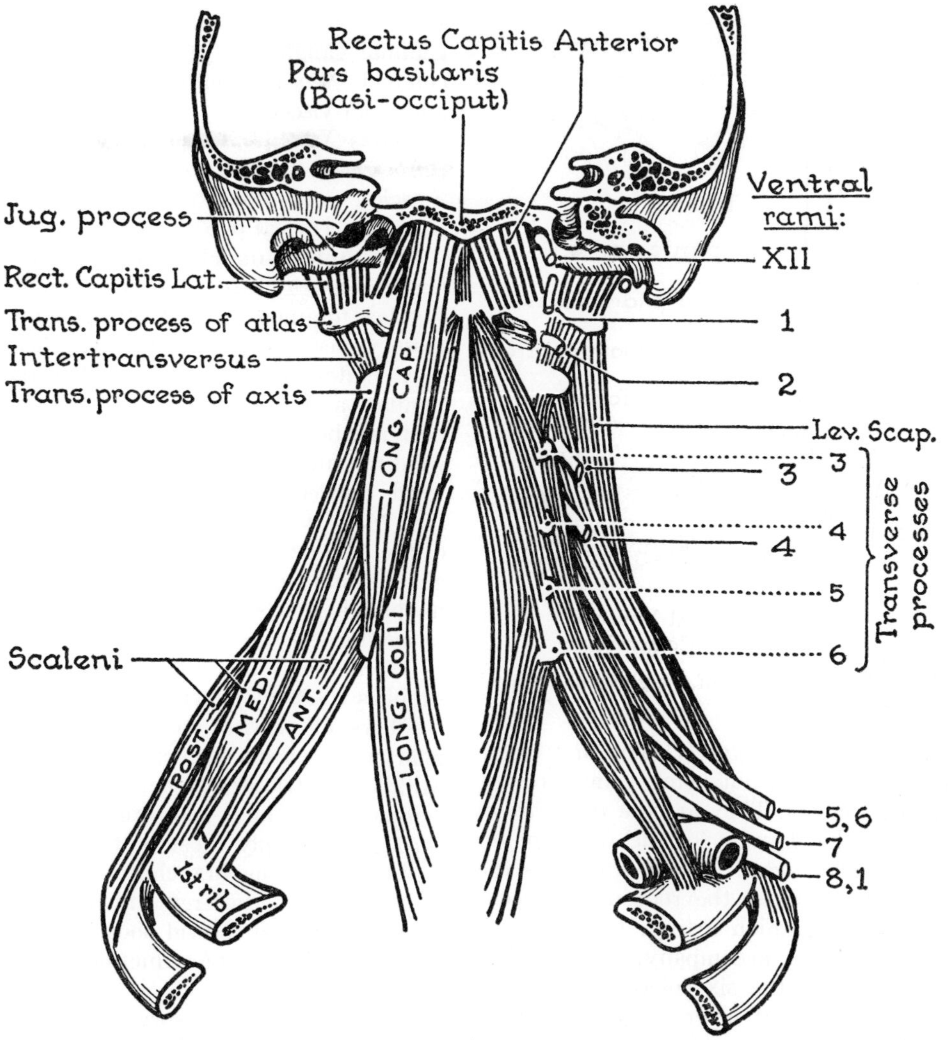

FIG. 760. Cranial nerve XII and the roots of the cervical and brachial plexuses emerging

prevertebral fascia from the deep cervical muscles and the cervical plexus (*fig. 760*).

»» From figure *760*, it can be seen that it crosses the jugular process, Rectus Capitis Lateralis, transverse process of atlas, Intertransversarius, Levator Scapulae, Scalenus Medius and cervical plexus, and Scalenus Anterior.

Bulbs. The vein has a bulb at both ends. The *upper bulb* is an outpouching of the wall of the vein (*fig. 818*). The *lower bulb* is a dilatation of the vein below the bicuspid valve situated about ½ inch above the clavicle.

At the root of the neck (*fig. 725*), it crosses in front of: (1) the subclavian artery and its branches; (2) the phrenic and vagus nerves separated from each other by the thyro-cervical trunk; (3) the thoracic (or right lymph) duct, which arches between the carotid sheath and the vertebral vessels, and (4) it makes contact with the pleural cupola.

The accessory nerve and the inf. root of the ansa cervicalis (descendens cervicalis) (C. 2, 3) cross either superficial or deep to the vein.

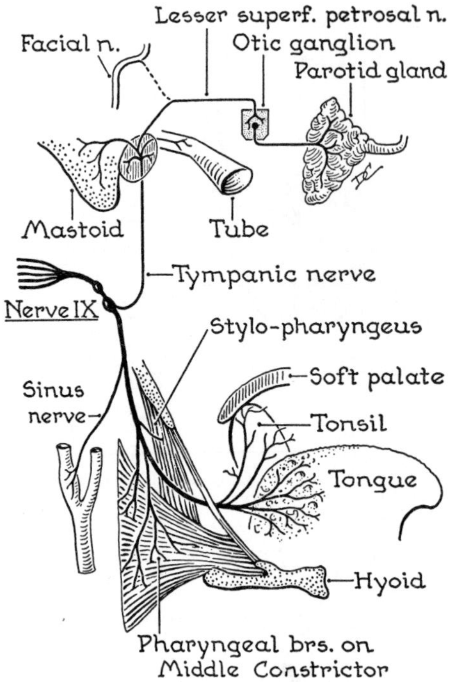

FIG. 761. Distribution of the glossopharyngeal (IX) nerve.

Tributaries (*fig. 759*). (1) The first tributary and the last, not being veins, are apt to be overlooked. They are the *inf. petrosal sinus* and the *thoracic* (or the *right lymph*) *duct.* (2) The *middle thyroid vein* joins the int. jugular vein at the root of the neck; it has no companion artery. (3) The four other tributaries accompany, more or less closely, four of the six collateral branches of the ext. carotid artery (*fig. 758*), and, accordingly, they are named: *superior thyroid, lingual,* and *common facial veins* (which join at and below the level of the hyoid bone), and the *pharyngeal veins* (which join at and above the level of the Digastric).

The terminations of the *occipital vein* (p. 569) and of the *posterior auricular, maxillary,* and the *superficial temporal veins* are shown in figure 664, page 554).

The Last Four Cranial Nerves (EXTRACRANIAL COURSES). The general dispositions of these four nerves on leaving the skull are given on page 652.

Nerves IX and X, at the base of the skull, each possess two ganglia, an upper and a lower. These ganglia are the equivalent of spinal ganglia to spinal nerves and of the trigeminal ganglion to nerve V. Both nerves conduct efferent and afferent impulses to and from viscera.

Nerves XI and XII conduct efferent impulses only, their fibers supplying striated muscles, and both receive contributions from the cervical plexus.

Glossopharyngeal Nerve (N. IX). This nerve (*fig. 761*) leaves the skull through the jugular foramen with the vagus and accessory nerves, but in its own sheath of dura mater. It descends between the int. jugular and int. carotid vessels to the posterior border of the Stylopharyngeus and, winding superficially round it, passes forward between the int. and ext. carotids (*fig. 763*). It then follows the upper border of the Middle Constrictor deep to the Hyoglossus and so enters the pharynx where it spreads out submucously over the posterior third of the tongue.

Distribution: Its one *muscular* branch supplies the Stylopharyngeus.

Fibers of *general sensation* pass to the pharyngeal plexus—which is formed on the Middle Constrictor by branches of the vagus, sympathetic, and glossopharyngeal—and through it supply most of the pharyngeal wall (*fig. 784*). One branch, the **sinus nerve,** consists of the afferent fibers from the carotid sinus and carotid body; when stimulated it brings about a reduction of the blood pressure.

The terminal fibers spread over the posterior third of the tongue, extending forward beyond the vallate papillae as fibers of general sensation and of *taste* (*fig. 778*); other branches are sensory to the tonsil, palatine arches, and soft palate. These fibers initiate the swallowing reflex.

Tympanic Nerve. This branch of nerve IX ascends into the tympanum through the minute canal on the apex of the wedge between the carotid canal and jugular foramen (*fig. 818*); it is sensory to the auditory tube, tympanum, medial surface of the ear drum, mastoid antrum, and mastoid air cells.

It is joined in the tympanum by sympathetic twigs from around the carotid artery. It leaves the tympanum and in the petrous bone is joined by a twig from the geniculate ganglion to form the *lesser* (*superficial*) *petrosal nerve*, which passes to the otic ganglion, there to be relayed via the auriculotemporal nerve to the parotid gland as its *secretory nerve*.

Vagus Nerve (N. X). This vagrant or wandering nerve (*fig. 762*) leaves the skull through the middle compartment of the jugular foramen in the same sheath of dura mater as nerve XI. It descends through the *neck* within the carotid sheath, occupying the posterior angle between the internal jugular vein and the great carotid stem as far as the sternoclavicular joint. There it crosses behind the brachiocephalic vein to enter the superior mediastinum.

In the Superior Mediastinum the courses are subpleural, but they differ on the two sides (*fig. 630*). *On the right side,* the vagus, having crossed the subclavian artery (IV primitive aortic arch), descends to the back of the root of the lung, lying first on the side of the brachiocephalic trunk (innominate art.), and then on the trachea. *On the left side,* the vagus continues its descent along the side of the carotid artery to the aortic arch (IV primitive aortic arch), and crosses the left side of the arch to reach the back of the root of the lung.

In the Posterior Mediastinum the courses are similar on the two sides. Each nerve forms a posterior pulmonary plexus, from which one or two stems emerge and pass to the esophagus, around which they form the esophageal plexus. From the plexus an anterior and a posterior vagal trunk emerge and descend on the respective surfaces of the esophagus, through the esophageal hiatus in the diaphragm, to the stomach.

In the Abdomen the two nerves lie close to each other at the lesser curvature of the stomach. The *anterior* (left) *gastric nerve* supplies the anterior surface of the stomach, and sends branches to the liver, pylorus, and first part of the duodenum. The *posterior gastric nerve* supplies the posterior surface of the stomach and sends one or two large branches alongside the stem of the left gastric artery to the celiac plexus, whence it travels with blood vessels to be distributed to the intestine as far as the left colic flexure

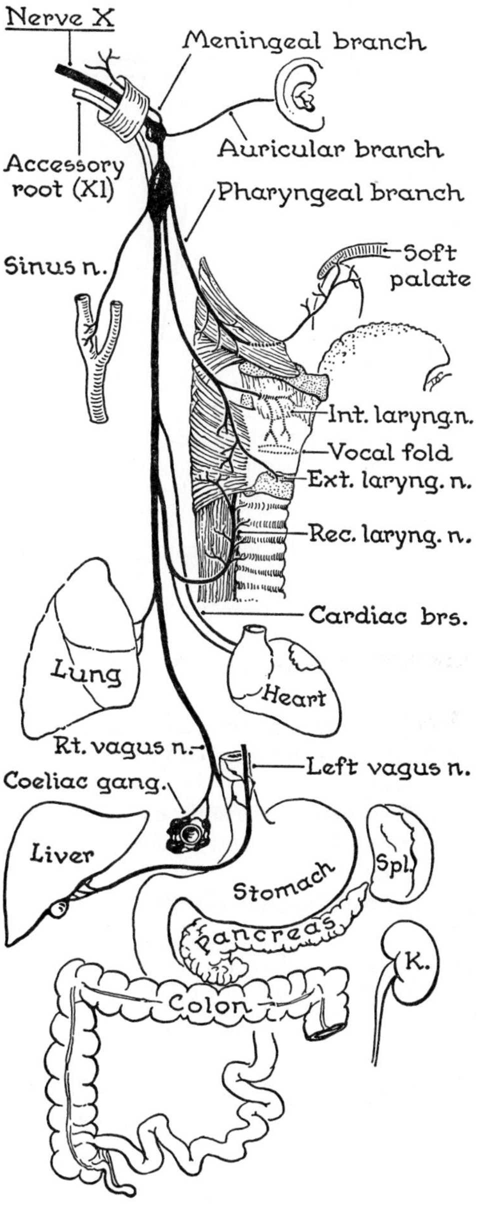

FIG. 762. Distribution of the vagus (X) nerve

and to the pancreas and other abdominal viscera.

Of the *two ganglia* of the vagus, the superior is small, the inferior is an inch long and lies just below the base of the skull. The cranial or *accessory root* of the accessory nerve joins the vagus at and beyond the ganglia and brings to it the

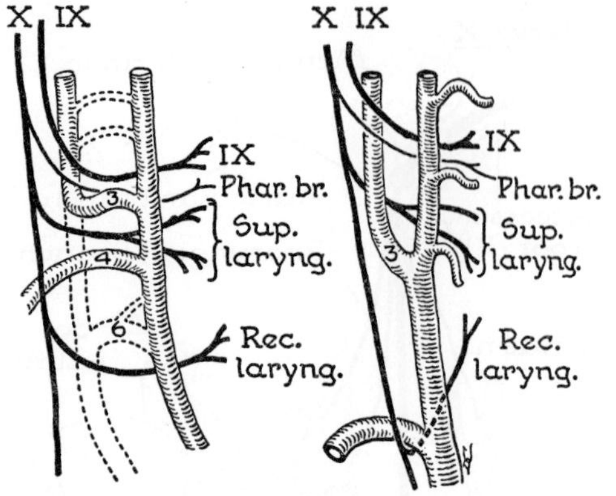

FIG. 763. Developmental explanation of the relationship of the glossopharyngeal, superior laryngeal, and recurrent laryngeal nerves to the carotid arteries.

motor fibers for the muscles of the pharynx, soft palate, and larynx.

BRANCHES arise from the vagus thus:

In the jugular fossa:

Meningeal and auricular.

In the neck:

Pharyngeal, superior laryngeal, sinus, cardiac, and right recurrent laryngeal.

In the thorax:

Cardiac, left recurrent laryngeal, pulmonary, esophageal, and tracheal.

In the abdomen:

To most abdominal viscera.

»» The *meningeal twigs* are derived from C. 1 and 2 and sup. cervical ganglion, and they are distributed to the dura of the posterior cranial fossa. The *auricular branch* crosses behind the int. jugular vein and enters a canal in the lateral wall of the jugular fossa, which conducts it past the facial nerve to the tympanomastoid fissure, through which it emerges. It assists the auriculotemporal n. to supply the outer surface of the tympanic membrane, and the external acoustic meatus. It also sends twigs to the cranial surface of the auricle.

Explanatory of figure 763. In the neck, the chief duty of the vagus is to supply the alimentary and respiratory tubes. This it does via three branches: pharyngeal, superior laryngeal, and recurrent laryngeal. In the embryo, these three pass between the primitive ventral and dorsal cephalic aortic arches. Postnatally, the pharyngeal branch continues this course.

With the breaking down of the segment of the primitive dorsal aorta between the 3rd and 4th arches, he *superior laryngeal nerve* is enabled to rise to a higher tevel and to slip behind the int. and ext. carotids.

On the disappearance of the right 5th and 6th primitive aortic arches, the *right recurrent laryngeal,* l*nerve* rises to the 4th primitive arch (subclavian artery) recurs below it, and passes behind the common carotid artery. The *left recurrent laryngeal nerve* continues its original course round the primitive 6th arch (ductus arteriosus).

The *Pharyngeal Branch* pierces the Superior Constrictor and supplies all the muscles of the pharynx and soft palate, except Stylopharyngeus, Tensor Palati, and Inferior Constrictor.

The *Superior Laryngeal Nerve* passes medial to the int. and ext. carotids and, lying on the Middle Constrictor, divides into an internal and an external branch; the *internal branch* pierces the thyrohyoid membrane and is sensory to the larynx above the level of the vocal cords and to the region of the pharynx around the entrance to the larynx (p. 704); the *external branch,* after partly supplying the Inferior Constrictor, ends in the Cricothyroid.

The *Recurrent Laryngeal Nerves* are mixed nerves. The *right nerve* arises from the vagus where it crosses in front of the subclavian artery. It recurs below the subclavian and is there in contact with the pleural cupola; it then crosses behind the common carotid artery and ascends in the angle between the trachea and esophagus (*fig. 717*).

The *left nerve* arises from the vagus where it crosses the aortic arch. It recurs around the lig. arteriosum, passes below and medial to the aortic arch and may there be surrounded by tracheobronchial lymph nodes. It then ascends in the angle between the trachea and esophagus, as on the right side.

Both recurrent laryngeal nerves give off cardiac, esophageal, and tracheal branches and branches to the Inferior Constrictor. They supply all the muscles of the larynx (Cricothyroid excepted), and they are sensory to the larynx below the vocal cords.

A branch of the vagus passes to the *carotid sinus* and carotid body.

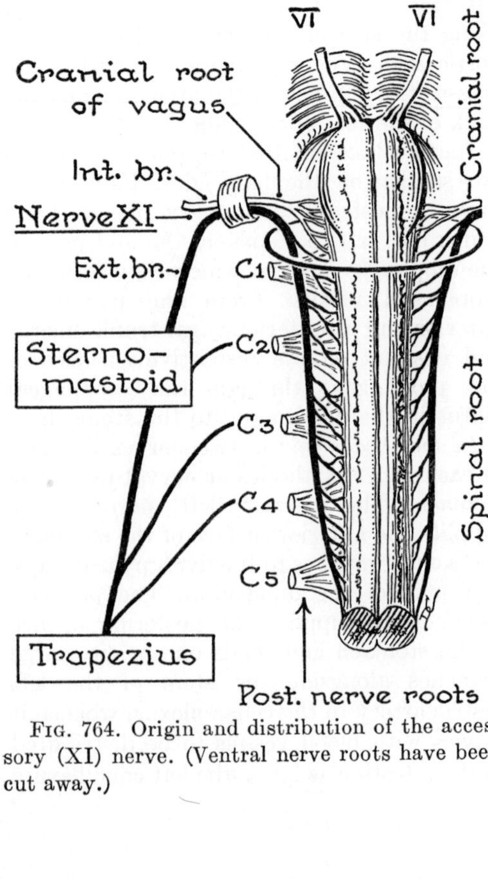

FIG. 764. Origin and distribution of the accessory (XI) nerve. (Ventral nerve roots have been cut away.)

Cardiac branches are described on page 518; *pulmonary* branches on page 527.

DISTRIBUTION. The vagus supplies: (1) the *striated muscles* of the pharynx (except Stylopharyngeus), soft palate (except Tensor Palati), and larynx; (2) the *heart* muscle, and the *smooth muscle* of the esophagus, stomach, and intestines down to the left colic flexure, and the gall bladder; and it contains (3) the *secretory* fibers for these organs. It contains (4) *afferent* fibers from these organs and from the larynx and lower respiratory passages, and (5) a few *taste* fibers from the region of the epiglottis.

Accessory Nerve (N. XI) (Spinal accessory nerve). The accessory nerve (*figs. 764* and *768*) has a double origin—*spinal* and *cranial.*

The *spinal root* arises from the anterior gray column of the upper five or six segments of the spinal cord, ascends behind the lig. denticulatum, and enters the posterior cranial fossa through the foramen magnum. The *cranial root* arises from the medulla as several fila in line with those of the vagus. The two roots unite as they enter the middle compartment of the jugular foramen (within the same dural sheath as the vagus), and as they leave the foramen, they separate.

The *cranial part* at once joins the vagus, bringing to it fibers for the muscles of the pharynx, soft palate, and larynx—it is accessory to the vagus.

The *spinal part* courses downward and backward superficial to the int. jugular vein (or deep to it) and the transverse process of the atlas. It makes a brief appearance in the carotid triangle between Digastric and Sternomastoid. Surrounded by lymph nodes and accompanied by the sternomastoid branch of the occipital artery, it enters the deep surface of the Sternomastoid 1½ to 2½" below the tip of the mastoid process.

It next appears at the posterior border of the Sternomastoid near its midpoint and here again it is surrounded by lymph nodes. Lying on the Levator Scapulae, it crosses the posterior triangle within the deep fascia, above and parallel to branches of C. 3 and 4 (*fig. 663*). It passes under cover of the anterior border of the Trapezius two or three fingers' breadth above the clavicle. Continuing deep to the Trapezius it crosses the superior angle of the scapula (*fig. 77*).

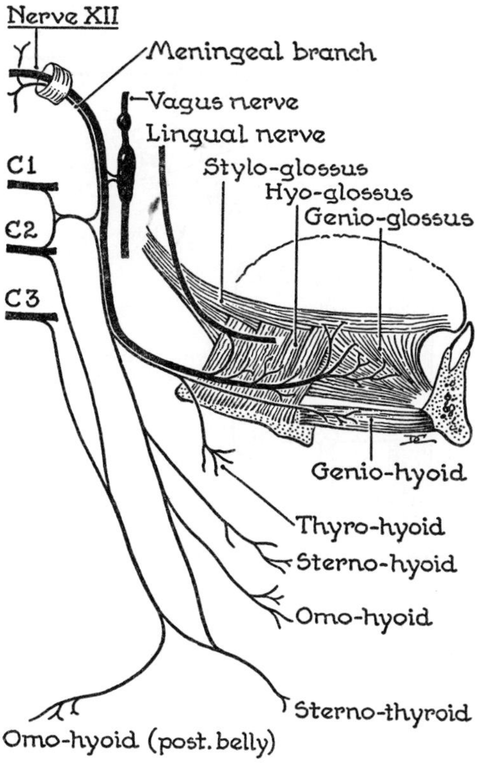

FIG. 765. Distribution of the hypoglossal (XII) nerve.

Distribution. The spinal part of the accessory nerve supplies the Sternomastoid and Trapezius. Within the Sternomastoid it is joined by a branch of C. 2, and deep to the Trapezius by branches of C. 3 and 4.

Functions. See pages 553 and 95.

Hypoglossal Nerve (N. XII) (*fig. 765*). This, the motor nerve of the tongue, emerges from its canal between the atlanto-occipital joint and the jugular foramen. It descends, making a half spiral turn behind the vagus and picking up a motor branch from C. 1 and a sensory branch from C. 2 (Pearson). It continued between the internal jugular vein and internal carotid artery to the lower border of the Digastric and Stylohyoid and so enters the carotid triangle. There it hooks around the occipital artery and, while doing so, gives off its *descendens branch, the superior root of the ansa cervicalis.*

It makes a gentle loop downward and forward superficial to the "arterial plane"

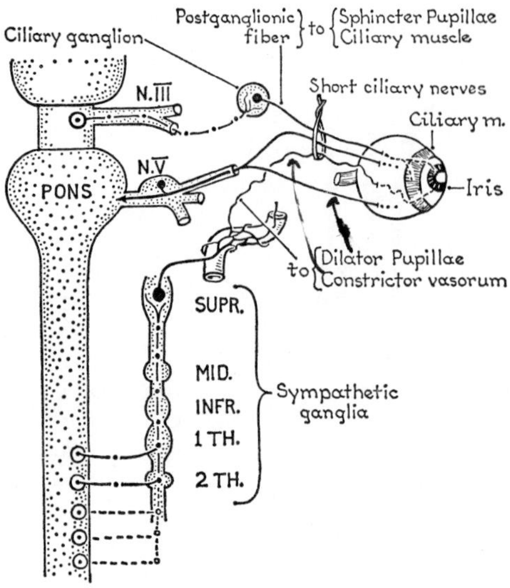

FIG. 766. The nerve supply to the eyeball

(i.e., the plane of the three carotid arteries and the three forward running branches called sup. thyroid, lingual, and facial) and, passing deep once again to the Digastric and Stylohyoid, it enters the submandibular triangle. There, concealed by the submandibular gland, it continues forwards superficial to the Hyoglossus, which now separates it from the lingual artery, and passes deep to the free posterior border of the Mylohyoid. Arriving at the anterior border of the Hyoglossus it swings medially and its branches ascend in the substance of the tongue.

Distribution. The hypoglossal nerve supplies all three extrinsic muscles of the tongue (Stylo-, Hyo-, and Genioglossus) and all the intrinsic muscles. The contribution from C. 1 is distributed to Geniohyoid, Thyrohyoid and long infrahyoid muscles.

Its meningeal branches come from C. 1 and 2 and sup. cervical ganglion, and pass to the post. cranial fossa.

Sympathetic Trunk, cervical part. This part of the trunk is an upward extension of the thoracic part (*fig. 766*). It ascends through the neck behind the common and internal carotid arteries, but outside the carotid sheath. It is medial to the vagus, which lies inside the carotid sheath. It is also thinner than the vagus, except at the sites of its ganglia (*fig. 768*). Entering the carotid sheath at the base of skull, it becomes the *internal carotid nerve or plexus* which accompanies the int. carotid artery through the carotid canal (*fig. 693*).

Followed downwards into the root of the neck, the trunk usually splits to encircle, or throw loops (ansae) around, three arteries: (1) inferior thyroid, (2) vertebral, and (3) subclavian, the last loop being the *ansa subclavia.*

The **Ganglia.** On the trunk there are three (or four) ganglia: superior, middle, (vertebral), and inferior. *The superior ganglion* is fusiform and over an inch long. It descends to the level of the greater horn of the hyoid bone.

»» *The middle ganglion* (inconstant), the size of a large pin's head, lies above the arch of the inf. thyroid artery. *The vertebral ganglion,* also inconstant and the size of a pin's head, lies in front of the vertebral artery, below the arch of the inf. thyroid artery. (The middle and vertebral ganglia are both present in about 50 per cent of specimens, but singly the vertebral ganglion is present much more often than the middle. (Becher and Grunt.)

The inferior ganglion lies behind the vertebral artery and in front of the 7th cervical transverse process. It commonly fuses in front of the neck of the 1st rib with the 1st thoracic sympathetic ganglion to form the *cervicothoracic* or *stellate ganglion,* which is large, nodular, and bristling with branches.

Branches (*fig. 766*). *Rami Communicantes.* The cervical part of the sympathetic trunk receives no white rami communicantes (preganglionic fibers) from the cervical segments of the spinal cord, but it delivers gray rami communicantes (postganglionic fibers) to each of the 8 cervical nerves.

»» It does so roughly thus: 1–4 spring from the superior ganglion; 5 and 6 from the middle ganglion; 6 or 7 from the vertebral ganglion; and 7 and 8 from the inferior ganglion.

Cardiac Branches, up to three in number, descend from the cervical ganglia or intervening parts of the trunk to the cardiac plexus (*fig. 634*).

Vascular Branches, carrying both efferent and afferent fibers, pass from each ganglion to blood vessels.

From the **superior cervical ganglion** postganglionic fibers pass to everything in its neighborhood—gray rami to the first *four cervical nerves*, mainly to be distributed with branches of the cervical plexus (p. 646); to the last *four cranial nerves* or their branches; to the *pharyngeal plexus*, to the *larynx* via laryngeal branches of the vagus; to the *cardiac plexus;* to the *orbital cavity* (see below); and to the *carotid sinus*, and the meninges.

Vascular branches of the superior ganglion follow the int. and ext. carotids and their branches thus:

»» With the *superior thyroid artery* to the thyroid gland; with the *facial artery* to the submandibular ganglion and on to the submandibular and sublingual glands, and to the cutaneous structures on the face (blood vessels, sweat glands, and arrectores); and with the *asc. pharyngeal and mid. meningeal arteries* to the dura (p. 576), and, via the otic ganglion, to the parotid gland.

The **internal carotid nerve** (plexus) (*figs. 692* and *693*), accompanying the int. carotid art., sends the deep petrosal n. to join the greater (superficial) petrosal n. and travel with it through the pterygoid canal to the pterygopalatine ganglion to be distributed with branches of the maxillary nerve; it sends (caroticotympanic) twigs to the *tympanic plexus* in the middle ear; to the *dura;* to the *four nerves* in the cavernous sinus (III, IV, V, and VI); to the *trigeminal ganglion;* to the *hypophysis cerebri;* to the *terminal branches* of the int. carotid artery (mid. cerebral, ant. cerebral, and ophthalmic) and their branches; to the tarsal muscles; and by a branch that either joins the nasociliary nerve or runs independently through the superior orbital fissure to the ciliary ganglion and through it, via ciliary nerves, to the Dilator Pupillae, and to the vessels of the eyeball. (The plexus around the ophthalmic artery may carry some of these fibers.)

From the **middle, vertebral,** and **inferior ganglia,** gray rami pass to the *brachial plexus* (*figs. 724* and *444*); cardiac branches to the *heart;* and vascular branches to be distributed thus: from the middle ganglion with the *inferior thyroid artery;* from the inferior ganglion to the *subclavian artery* (*fig. 724*); and from the vertebral and inferior ganglia to the *vertebral* (sympathetic) *plexus.* As this plexus ascends through the foramina transversaria, it receives twigs from the middle and superior ganglia, and it delivers "accessory gray rami communicantes" to the cervical nerves.

Cutting the Cervical Sympathetic Trunk results in **Horner's syndrome**—drooping of the upper eyelid (ptosis) due to paralysis of the superior tarsal muscle (*fig. 698*), contraction of the pupil due to the unopposed action of the oculomotor nerve, and vasodilatation and absence of sweating on the affected side of the face.

CHAPTER 44

PHARYNX AND PALATE

EXTERIOR OF PHARYNX

»» The skull, pharynx, great vessels, last four cranial nerves, and sympathetic trunk (in short, all structures in front of the prevertebral fascia) have been detached from the vertebral column.

Structures on the Posterior Transverse Line (*fig. 767*) are to be identified. They are (*fig. 768*): the styloid process with the *facial nerve* descending on its lateral side from the stylomastoid foramen, and the *internal jugular vein* descending on its medial side from the jugular foramen; also, the hypoglossal canal, separated from the jugular foramen by a wedge-shaped bar of bone. Were it not for this bar the jugular and hypoglossal openings would be one. Because the *glossopharyngeal*, *vagus*, and *accessory nerves* emerge from the jugular foramen, and the *hypoglossal nerve* from the hypoglossal canal, it is evident that these four nerves are very close together below the base of the skull and that the hypoglossal is the most medial. Anterior to these four nerves is the *sympathetic trunk;* and anterior to the trunk is the *internal carotid artery.*

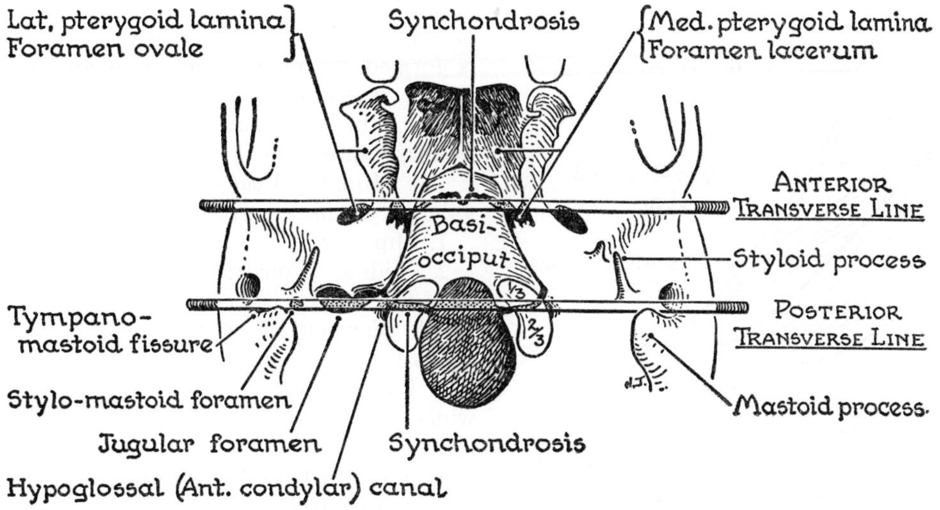

FIG. 767. The anterior and posterior transverse lines on the exterior of the base of the skull

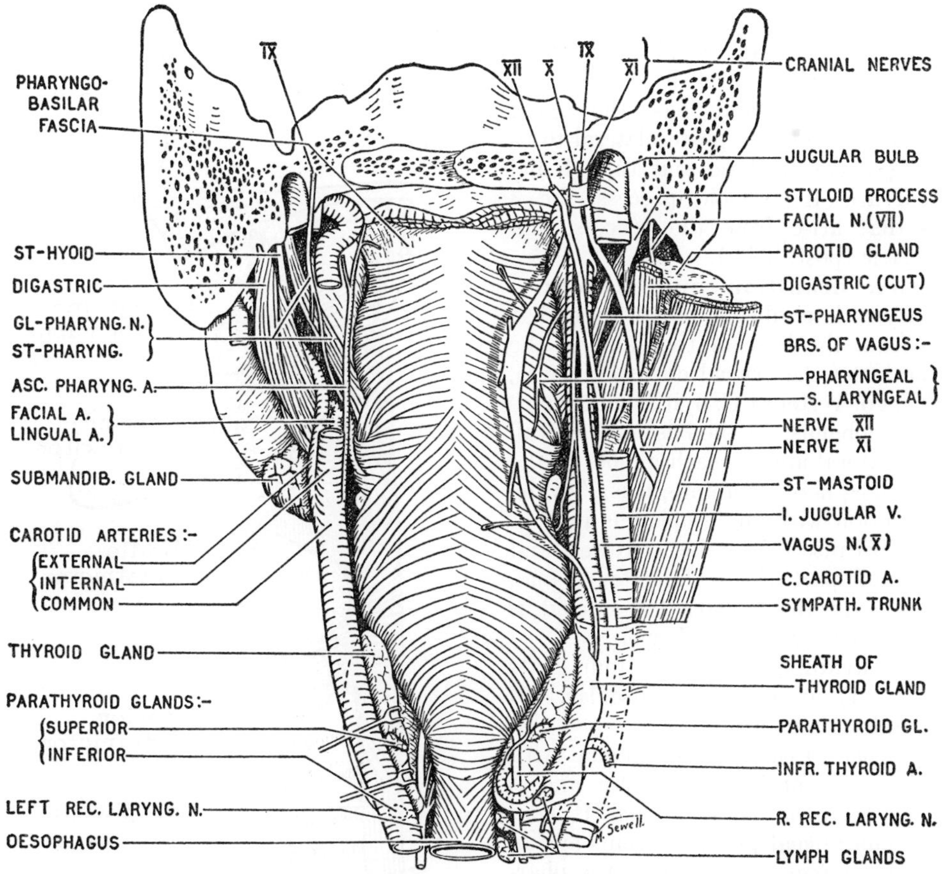

FIG. 768. The pharynx, last four cranial nerves, sympathetic trunk and great vessels—from behind. (The skull has been sectioned in "the posterior transverse line.")

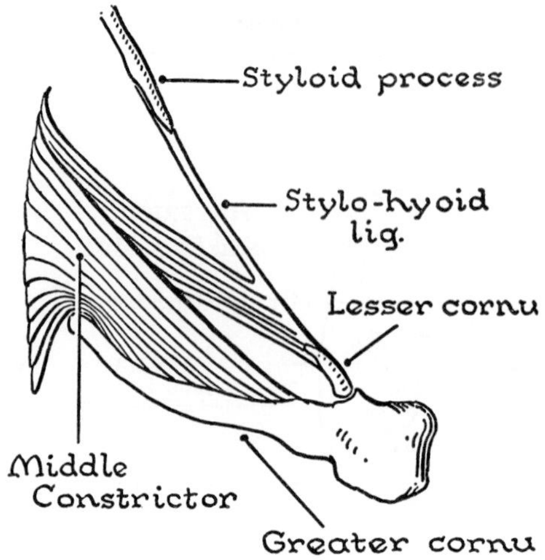

FIG. 769. The angular origin of the Middle Constrictor.

Indeed, the nerves and the trunk almost succeed in concealing the carotid from behind.

The posterior wall of the pharynx hangs from the basi-occipital well in front of the foramen magnum, and has the great vessels and nerves lying posterolateral to it. And lying between these and the Medial Pterygoid are: the styloid process, the 3 muscles that arise from the process, and the Digastric (post. belly).

Pharynx, definition and structure. The pharynx is a fibromuscular tube that extends from the base of the skull to the lower border of the cricoid cartilage where, at the level of vertebra C. 6, it is continuous with the esophagus. At the base of the skull its posterolateral angles reach almost to the carotid canals; here, therefore, it is 2″ wide. At its junction with the esophagus it is 1″ wide and, because this is the narrowest and least dilatable part of the alimentary canal, a foreign body that passes the cricoid is not likely to be arrested farther on.

THE PHARYNGEAL WALL has four coats or tunics: (1) areolar, (2) muscular, (3) fibrous, and (4) mucous.

The Areolar Coat is continuous with the areolar coat of the Buccinator and is called the *buccopharyngeal fascia.* It contains the pharyngeal plexus of veins and of nerves. The *venous plexus* drains the pharynx including the soft palate and tonsil; it communicates with the pterygoid plexus, and it ends in the internal jugular vein near the angle of the jaw. The *nervous plexus* is formed by pharyngeal branches of the vagus, glossopharyngeal, and sympathetic nerves, which are motor, sensory, and vasomotor, respectively.

The Muscular Coat comprises five paired voluntary muscles, namely—

1. Superior }
2. Middle } Constrictors
3. Inferior }

which represent an outer "circular" coat,

4. Stylo- }
5. Palato- } pharyngeus

which represent an inner "longitudinal" coat.

The **Three Constrictors** (*fig. 770*). Continued from page 610.

It is easiest to begin by placing the Middle Constrictor, thus:

The **Middle Constrictor** (*fig. 769*) arises from the angle between the greater and lesser cornua of the hyoid and from the lower end of the stylohyoid ligament.

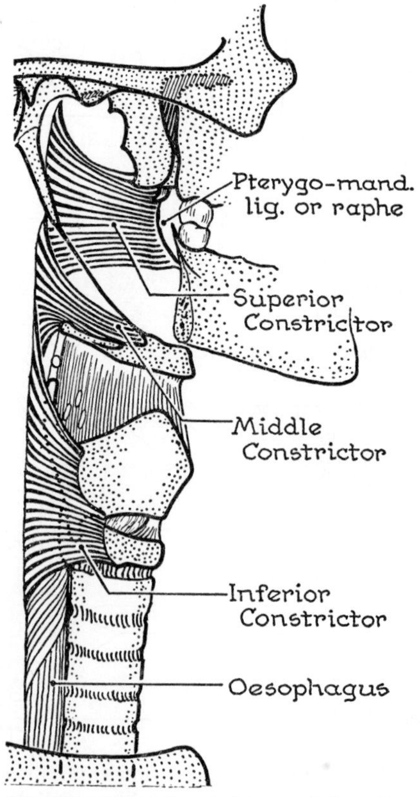

FIG. 770. The three Constrictors of the pharynx

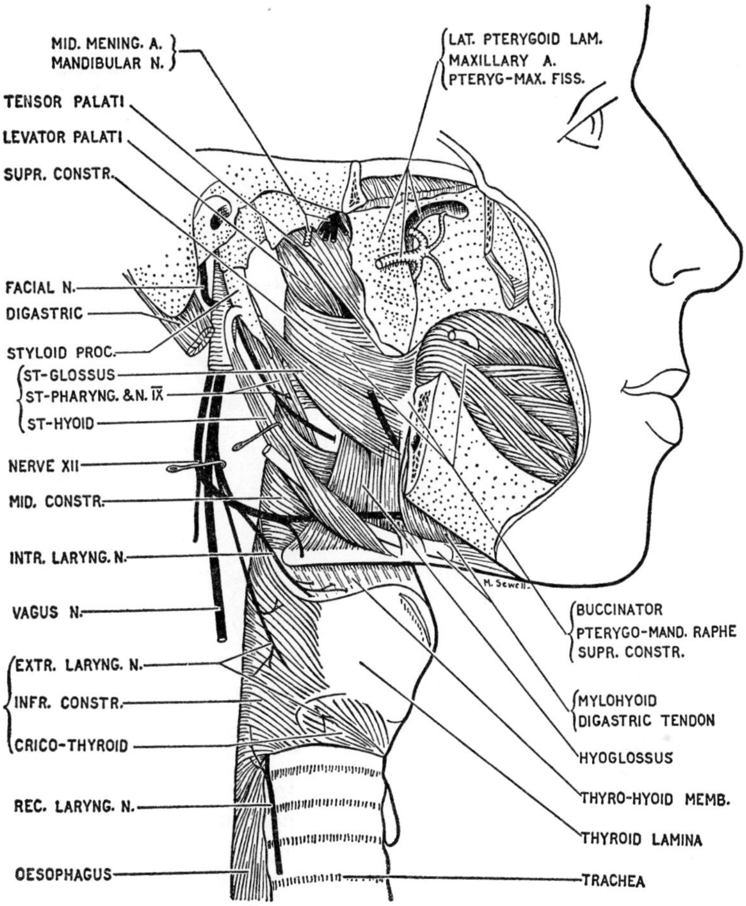

FIG. 771. The lateral aspect of the pharynx

Relations. To expose the origin of this constrictor, the Hyoglossus must be detached from the greater cornu and raised, together with the hypoglossal nerve which runs across its superficial surface, and the lingual artery, which runs across its deep surface.

The **Inferior Constrictor** has a continuous origin extending from the upper border of the thyroid cartilage to the lower border of the cricoid.

»» The *thyropharyngeal part* arises from the oblique line of the thyroid cartilage and from a fibrous bridge over the Cricothyroid. This bridge stretches between the tubercle on the lower border of the thyroid cartilage and the inferior horn.

The *cricopharyngeal part* arises from the triangular area on the cricoid below the inferior horn (between the origins of the Cricothyroid and the Posterior Crico-arytenoid).

The cricopharyngeal part, the **Crico-pharyngeus,** being normally in a state of contraction, guards the esophagus like a sphincter and prevent air from being sucked into it during inspiration (Negus; Raven).

The **Superior Constrictor** arises from the pterygomandibular raphe and from the bony point at each end of the raphe, i.e., the lower end of the medial pterygoid plate and the mandible behind the 3rd molar tooth. Some fibers spring from the tongue.

The longitudinal muscular coat comprising Palatopharyngeus and Stylopharyngeus, see pages 669–670.

The Fibrous Coat, called the **pharyngo-basilar fascia,** corresponds to a tunica submucosa. It is especially strong above, where it serves to anchor the pharynx to the posterior border of the medial pterygoid plate, to the basi-occipital, and the petrous bone. At the upper concave border of the Superior Constrictor a semilunar portion of the fascia is visible from without (*fig. 768*).

The Mucous Coat is described with the interior of the pharynx.

Structures Crossing the Borders of the Constrictors (*fig. 771*). Certain nerves, vessels, muscles, and the auditory tube pass through the four angular gaps that occur above and below the handle-like origins of the Constrictors:

1. *The recurrent laryngeal nerve* and its companion artery, the *inferior laryngeal a.*, pass through the gap between the esophagus and the Inf. Constrictor. The nerve is closely applied to the back of the cricothyroid joint and it may readily be involved in inflammation of the joint.

2. *The internal laryngeal nerve* and *superior laryngeal vessels* pierce the thyrohyoid membrane in the gap between the Inf. and Mid. Constrictors.

3. *The Stylopharyngeus* passes through the gap between the Mid. and Sup. Constrictors, amalgamates with the Palatopharyngeus, and gains attachment to the greater horn of the hyoid and posterior border of the thyroid cartilage. *The glossopharyngeal nerve*, after making a partial spiral around the Stylopharyngeus, passes through the same gap.

4. The *auditory tube*, the *Levator Palati*, and the *ascending palatine artery* pass through the gap between the Sup. Constrictor and the base of the skull.

INTERIOR OF PHARYNX AND THE PALATE

Inspection (*fig. 772*).

Opening into the pharynx anteriorly are orifices leading from the cavities of the nose, mouth, and larynx. Accordingly, the pharynx is divided into three parts: the *nasal pharynx*, *oral pharynx*, and *laryngeal pharynx*. The soft palate, ending in the uvula, hangs down and separates the nasal pharynx above from the oral pharynx below.

The **Nasal Pharynx** (Nasopharynx) lies above the soft palate and behind the nasal cavities. It is, in fact, the backward extension of the nasal cavities and it cannot be shut off from them.

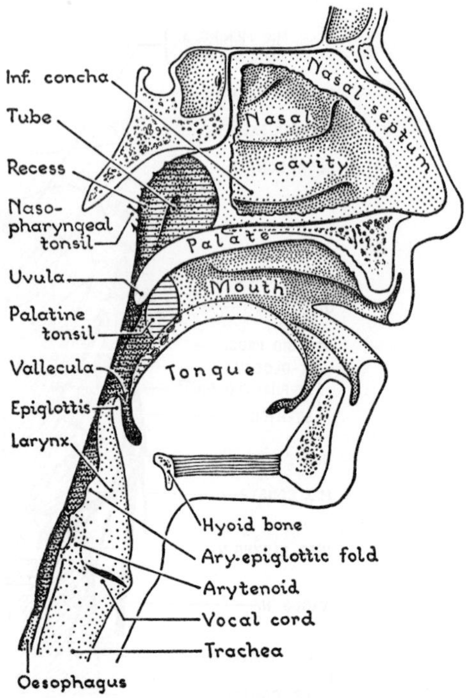

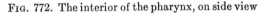

FIG. 772. The interior of the pharynx, on side view

In front, are two oblong rigid orifices, the *choanae* (post. nasal apertures), described on page 648. On looking through these apertures the posterior ends of the middle and inferior conchae are seen.

On the side wall of the pharynx, ½ inch behind the inferior concha, is the orifice of the *auditory tube*. Its upper and posterior lips are prominent and cartilaginous. A fold of mucous membrane, the *salpingopharyngeal fold*, overlying a muscle of the same name, descends from the postero-inferior part of the orifice giving it the appearance of a hook. Behind the orifice of the tube there is a vertical cleft, the *pharyngeal recess*.

The *roof*, formed by basi-occipital and petrous bones, is rounded off into the posterior wall which lies in front of the atlas and axis but with prevertebral fascia and prevertebral muscles intervening. On the roof there is some lymphoid tissue, the *(naso-)pharyngeal tonsil*, which when overgrown is known as "adenoids" (*fig. 798*). This tissue extends into the pharyngeal recess (behind the auditory tube) and,

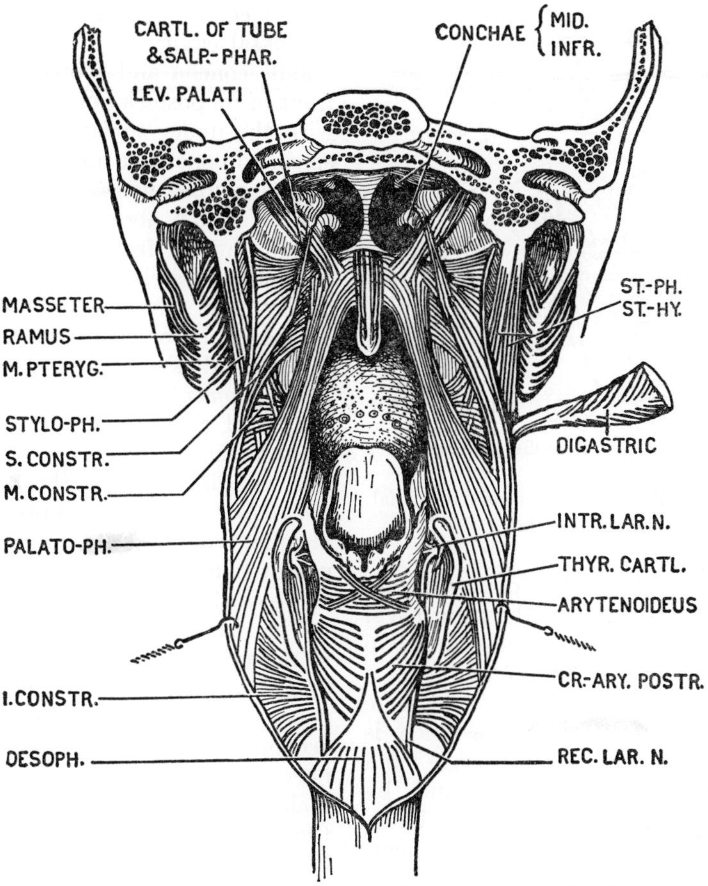

FIG. 773. The muscles of the pharynx, from behind

when hypertrophied, it may interfere with access of air to the middle ear with resulting deafness.

The **Oral Pharynx** is placed below the soft palate and behind the mouth and the posterior one-third of the tongue.

From the soft palate two folds of mucous membrane arch downward on each side. The anterior fold, the *palatoglossal arch*, overlies a muscle of the same name and descends to the junction of the anterior two-thirds and posterior one-third of the tongue. It lies at the dividing line between mouth and pharynx (oropharyngeal isthmus). The posterior fold, the *palatopharyngeal arch*, also overlying a muscle of the same name, arches downward to be lost on the side wall of the pharynx.

»» On each side, the two palatine arches and the triangular area between them, occupied by the tonsil, is called the *fauces*. The space between the right and left fauces is called the *isthmus of the fauces*, and the soft palate is its roof.

The **Laryngeal Pharynx** lies behind and around the freely projecting upper end of the larynx.

The *inlet of the larynx* is oval and obliquely placed. In front it is formed by the free, curved upper end of the *epiglottis;* behind, by the mucous membrane clothing the apices of the *arytenoid cartilages* and the *Arytenoideus* which unites these cartilages; on each side, by the *aryepiglottic fold* which extends from epiglottis to arytenoid. Slightly in front of the apex of the arytenoid cartilage, which is surmounted by the *corniculate cartilage*, is the rounded end of the *cuneiform cartilage*.

Three folds of mucous membrane leave the epiglottis: one, the *median glosso-epiglottic fold*, connects it in the median plane with the back of the tongue; one on each side, the

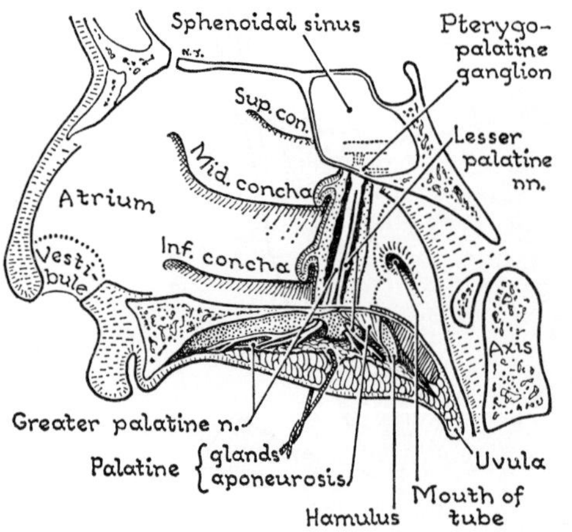

FIG. 774. Exploration of greater palatine canal. Dissection of under surface of palate.

lateral glosso-epiglottic fold (pharyngo-epiglottic fold), connects it with the pharyngeal wall. Between these three folds are two fingertip depressions, the *valleculae*.

On each side, behind the lateral fold there is a space, the *piriform recess*, which is bounded by the thyroid cartilage and thyrohyoid membrane laterally and by the free upper end of the larynx medially. On the posterior wall of the pharynx numerous *lymphoid follicles* are scattered. They may become enlarged.

EXPOSURE OF THE LARYNGEAL NERVES. Two nerves, being submucous, are readily exposed (*fig. 773*). The *internal laryngeal nerve*, having pierced the thyrohyoid membrane, runs transversely in a fold across the front of the piriform recess; it is a sensory nerve. The *recurrent laryngeal nerve* runs vertically, applied to the back of the cricothyroid joint. It is a mixed nerve which supplies all the muscles of the larynx except the Cricothyroid.

Palate

»» When the skull is correctly oriented, e.g., during assumption of erect posture, the hard palate is seen to be almost horizontal and its plane, if produced backward, strikes the vertebral column just below the foramen magnum; and the anteromedian point of that foramen is slightly (1 to 5 mm.) higher than the posteromedian point.

Exploration of the sphenopalatine foramen. Push the end of a seeker through the mucous membrane and lateral wall of the nasal cavity at a point just above the middle concha and a quarter of an inch in front of its posterior end. This point is flush with the under surface of the body of the sphenoid bone. The hole entered is called the *sphenopalatine foramen* because the sphenoid bounds it above and the palatine bone bounds it in front, below, and behind. The chief vessels and nerves of the nasal cavity pass through this foramen; so, in a sense it is for them the "porta" or door of the nasal cavity (*figs. 774* and *799*).

Development. Before the palate appeared the nasal and oral cavities were one, the *stomodaeum*, and the greater part of its side wall developed in the *maxillary process* (*fig. 775*), the nerve supply of which is the maxillary nerve (V^2). Subsequently, as the palate takes form, this nerve becomes the nerve of the palate also.

The maxillary artery (3rd part) was seen to disappear into the pterygopalatine fossa (*fig. 743*). There it meets the maxillary nerve and breaks up into branches that accompany the branches of the maxillary nerve through various bony apertures, including the sphenopalatine foramen and the greater and lesser palatine canals (*fig. 796*).

Structure of the Palate. The anterior two-thirds of the palate is called the *hard palate* because its framework is the bony palate; the posterior third is called the *soft palate* because it is composed of muscles and soft tissues. At its anterior part are several

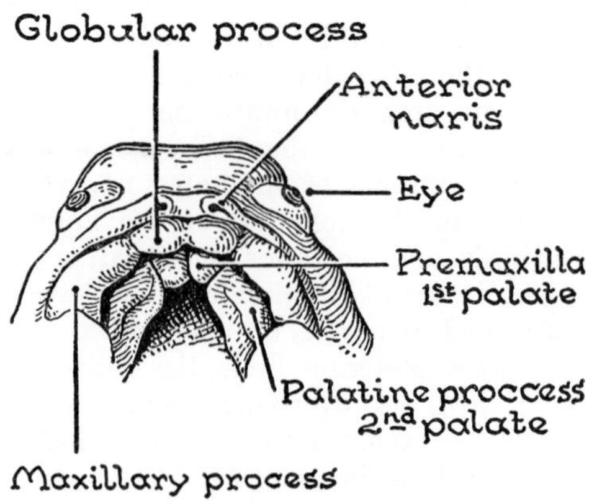

FIG. 775. The palate develops from 3 shelves—anterior, right, and left.

rudimentary ridges. In most mammals these are numerous and prominent and against them the tongue triturates food. Pinpoint orifices of the *ducts of mucous glands* are dotted over the hard palate, giving it an orange-skin appearance, and they are abundant over the soft palate.

Piercing the bony palate medial to the 3rd molar tooth is the *greater palatine foramen*. It lies almost vertically below the sphenopalatine foramen. The greater (anterior) palatine vessels and nerve emerge from this foramen and run forwards in two grooves, separated by a sharp crest, on the under aspect of the bony palate near the alveolar process.

»» There is, of course, no muscle under the hard palate—it could there have no function. The brown tissue seen there is a carpet of racemose *mucous glands*, which becomes much thicker under the soft palate. The periosteum adheres more intimately to the mucous membrane than to the bone; hence, the two are referred to as *mucoperiosteum*.

The *palatine aponeurosis* in which the bony palate ends is the pliable basis of the soft palate; it may be regarded as its unossified skeleton.

Piercing the bony palate behind the incisor teeth is the *incisive canal*.

»» The incisive canal runs between two developmental areas (1) the *primary palate* which developed from the globular (frontonasal) process and which is part of the premaxilla or bone bearing the incisor teeth (*fig. 775*); and (2) *the secondary palate* which developed from the right and left maxillary processes. A process of the vomer (*fig. 847*) descends into the incisive canal dividing it into right and left sides. Through each side a branch of the *greater palatine artery* ascends to anastomose on the nasal septum with a posterior septal artery, and the *nasopalatine nerve* (*fig. 794*) descends to the under surface of the premaxilla.

The thickness of the *soft palate* is due to glands and to a smaller extent to muscles; its strength depends upon the aponeurosis which occupies its anterior half. A stitch will tear through muscle and gland; so, the palatine aponeurosis should be included in the grip of a stitch that is intended to hold (*fig. 783*).

Exploration of greater palatine canal. Incise the mucoperiosteum of the nose along the line joining the sphenopalatine and greater palatine foramina (*fig. 774*). The fleshy tips of the middle and inferior conchae will be severed because they extend backward onto the vertical plate of the palatine bone, and the knife will be arrested below by the horizontal plate of the palatine bone. Then, with the handle of the knife strip back the mucoperiosteum for the requisite half inch, in order that the entire medial aspect of the medial pterygoid lamina may be exposed and its posterior border, which gives attachment to the pharyngobasilar fascia, defined.

Pass a long needle into the greater palatine foramen and upward through the greater palatine canal and pterygopalatine fossa to the level of the sphenopalatine foramen and leave it in situ. Then, with a strong probe proceed to break down the delicate intervening portion of the lateral wall of the nose formed by the *vertical plate of the palatine bone*. This exposes the greater palatine nerve and artery.

The greater palatine nerve may be followed to the *pterygopalatine ganglion* (sphenopalatine g.) which hangs from the maxillary nerve (p. 796); the artery, being a branch of the maxillary artery, naturally lies lateral to the nerve.

»» Between the greater palatine foramen and the hamulus is the pyramidal process of the palatine bone. It is pierced by two small foramina, the *lesser palatine foramina*, which transmit the lesser palatine vessels and nerves to the neighborhood of the soft palate and tonsil.

Soft Palate, continued on page 674.

Palatoglossus, Palatopharyngeus, and **Stylopharyngeus.** On freeing the mucous membrane from the palatoglossal arch, the *Palatoglossus* is displayed as a small bundle of fibers that extends from the soft palate above, where its fibers mingle with those of the opposite side, to the tongue below, where the fibers enter as transverse fibers. A more or less circular sphincter is thus formed which guards the entrance to the pharynx or isthmus of the fauces.

The *Palatopharyngeus* is to be regarded as a delaminated portion, or detached inner sheet, of the Sup. Constrictor which has been called into being with the appearance of the palate.

Explanatory. A palate is peculiar to mammals including man. Mammals require lips with which to grasp the nipple of the mammary gland—otherwise they could not suck. Equally, they require an extensive hard and soft palate with which to shut off the nasal cavities and nasopharynx from the mouth when sucking—otherwise air would be inspired with greater ease than milk could be imbibed, as happens in children born with cleft palates.

With the appearance of the palate new muscles are not called into being but pre-existing ones are modified. These may be derived either from the immediate neighborhood or from a distance. The muscles may, so to speak, be *native* or *immigrant*.

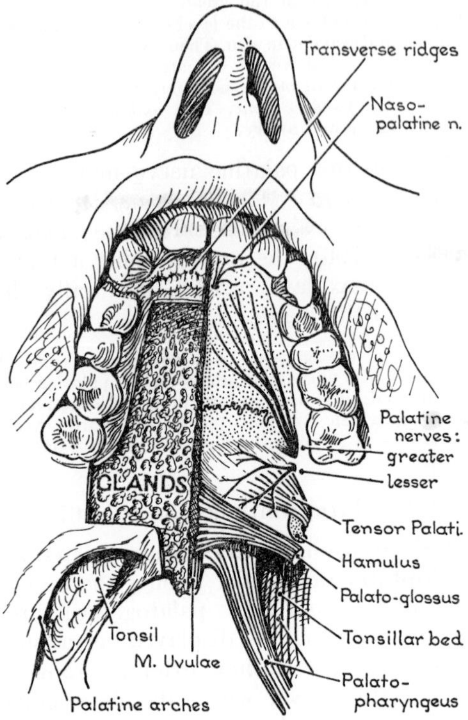

FIG. 776. Dissection of the palate and palatine arches.

All the muscles of the soft palate, save one, are native. They belong to the same group as the Superior Constrictor and have the same nerve supply—the accessory nerve via the pharyngeal plexus. The *Tensor Palati* is the immigrant; its nerve comes from the mandibular nerve (V^3) via the otic ganglion.

»» Traced upward, the *Palatopharyngeus* is found to separate into three distinct parts—tubal, palatine, and tonsillar. Its *tubal fibers*, the Salpingopharyngeus, form a slender bundle that ascends in the salpingopharyngeal fold to the lower edge of the cartilage of the auditory tube. Its *palatine fibers* spread out in the posterior or muscular part of the soft palate. Its *tonsillar fibers* spread out within the tonsillar bed.

Traced downward, the Palatopharyngeus spreads out so as to form an almost complete inner longitudinal sheet of muscle in the lower parts of the pharynx; some fibers pass to the posterior border of the thyroid cartilage and some to the hyoid.

»» *Dissection.* The posterior edge of this muscle is easily identified because its fibers run nearly vertically whereas those of the Constrictor lie outside it and take a more horizontal course.

The Stylopharyngeus arises from the pharyngeal side of the styloid process, as might be expected, passes through the gap between the Sup. and Mid. Constrictors, and blending with Palatopharyngeus, is inserted with it (see above) (*fig. 771* and *778*). It is the only muscle supplied by the glossopharyngeal nerve.

Palatine Tonsil

The tonsil resembles an ovary in shape and size (*figs. 776* and *777*). It is embedded in the side wall of the pharynx in the triangular interval between the palatoglossal and palatopharyngeal arches and the posterior third of the tongue.

»» An upper and a lower fold of mucous membrane may extend from the palatoglossal arch backward over its anterior part forming an upper and a lower pocket.

Removal of the tonsil (*figs. 779* and *780*). This is easily done because the rounded lateral aspect of the gland has a *fibrous capsule* which is separated from the pharyngobasilar fascia and the muscular wall of the pharynx by a layer of *loose areolar tissue* in which free dissection is readily made.

»» As at the bare area of the liver, so here loose areolar tissue allows the covering muscle (Diaphragm or Palatopharyngeus) to contract without hindrance from the covered organ (liver or tonsil).

As a result of tonsillitis, the areolar space may be obliterated and dissection difficult. The *upper pole* extends far upward into the soft palate beyond the arches and is there buried.

The upper pole of the tonsil is buried in the soft palate. The lower pole is continuous

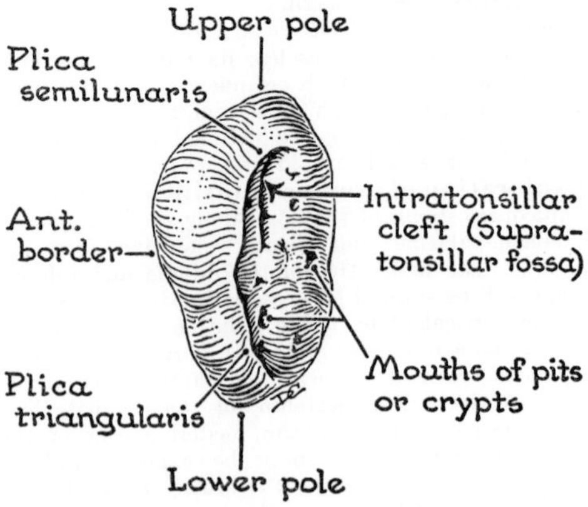

FIG. 777. The tonsil, medial aspect

with the lymphoid follicles on the dorsum of the tongue, collectively called the **lingual tonsil;** this pole is not visible in life unless the tongue is depressed. A prominent anterior pillar may largely conceal even an enlarged tonsil.

The lower part of the tonsil is moored to the tongue by a fibrous band and by some muscle fibers which help to prevent it from being swallowed. These and the vessels and nerves, which enter near the lower pole, must be severed during the removal of the tonsil.

White test-tube-like *crypts* extend from its free surface almost to the very capsule.

Tonsillar Bed. Lateral to the loose areolar tissue surrounding the fibrous capsule of the tonsil there are four thin sheets—two areolar and two fleshy—which constitute the tonsillar bed. From within outward they are (1) the *pharyngobasilar fascia* which forms a complete filmy sheet, (2) the *Palatopharyngeus* and (3) the *Superior Constrictor*, both of which are deficient below (*fig. 778*), and (4) the *buccopharyngeal fascia* (p. 664).

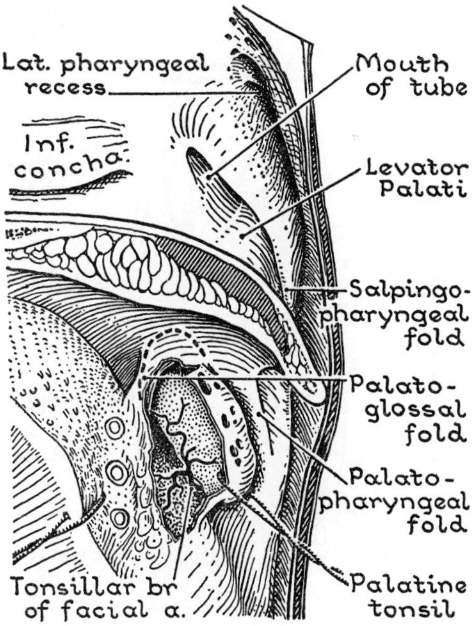

FIG. 779. First stage in the removal of the tonsil. The side wall of the pharynx.

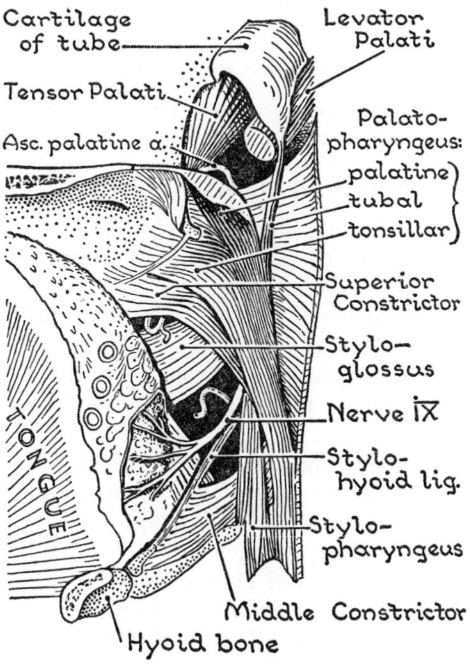

FIG. 778. A stage in the dissection of the side wall of the pharynx from within, showing particularly the relations of the tonsil. (By Dr. B. L. Guyatt.)

A large vein, the *paratonsillar vein*, descending from the soft palate and receiving tributaries from the tonsil, pierces the lower part of the bed to join the pharyngeal plexus; it is inconspicuous, unless engorged.

Two structures passing to the tongue, (1) *Styloglossus* and (2) *glossopharyngeal nerve*, form immediate lateral relations of the lower third of the tonsillar bed (*fig. 778*).

»» They can be exposed and cleaned by removing the thin fascial sheath which alone covers them here, the muscle sheets having faded off into delicate arched borders

The Styloglossus is a broad thick fleshy band that commonly stands out in relief as it passes downward, medially, and forward to the horizontal part of the tongue (i.e., anterior two-thirds) where its fibers interdigitate with those of the Hyoglossus (*fig. 788*).

It arises from the tip of the styloid process and the adjacent part of the stylohyoid ligament.

The Glossopharyngeal Nerve, larger than the int. laryngeal nerve, is placed far back.

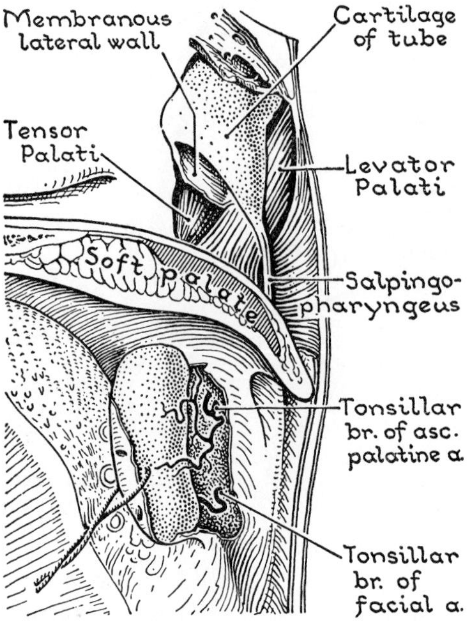

FIG. 780. Second stage in the removal of the tonsil. Dissection of nasopharynx. (Dissections by Dr. P. G. Ashmore.)

On appearing from under cover of the lower arched borders of the muscular sheets, it passes downward, medially, and forward to spread out submucously over the vertical part of the tongue (i.e., posterior one-third). Look for it immediately lateral to the palatopharyngeal arch, two-thirds of the way down the tonsillar bed.

»» *Other Relations.* The posterior belly of the Digastric and the submandibular gland, with the facial artery arching over them, are lateral relations of the lowest part of the bed. Farther laterally are the Medial Pterygoid and the angle of the jaw.

VESSELS AND NERVES OF THE TONSIL: the *tonsillar branch of the facial artery* (*figs. 779* and *780*); veins which pass through the tonsillar bed to the *pharyngeal plexus* of veins and to the common facial vein; *lymph vessels,* which pass through the bed to a *deep cervical gland* below the angle of the jaw (*fig. 824.1*); and nerve twigs from *nerve IX* and the *lesser palatine nerves.*

The *Tonsillar Bed* receives arterial twigs from the *tonsillar* and *ascending palatine branches* of the facial a., the *dorsales linguae aa., ascending pharyngeal a.,* and *lesser palatine aa.* In the event of hemorrhage, they are controlled by tying the external carotid a. at its origin.

Hyoid bone as a landmark. No muscle crosses the hyoid bone; so, it is subcutaneous in the neck and submucous in the pharynx (*fig. 778*).

»» **Dissection.** Pull backward the epiglottis and incise the mucous membrane along the body and greater horn of the hyoid down to the bone. The incision will pass between the epiglottis and the tongue, across the valleculae and the median and lateral glosso-epiglottic folds. To get free exposure carry the incision along the greater horn to its tip and beyond this to the median plane; then strip the mucous membrane from the pharyngeal wall (*fig. 778*). Find the lesser horn, which till after middle life is cartilaginous, and carry the point of the knife upward and backward along the anterior free edge of the stylohyoid lig. toward the styloid process of the temporal bone, but stop at the curved lower border of the Palatopharyngeus.

Since the *Middle Constrictor* takes origin in the angle between the two horns of the hyoid and the lower end of the stylohyoid lig., it also is submucous at its origin. Being fan-shaped, its borders curve up and down; and along its upper border runs the IX nerve.

»» A few deep fibers of the Hyoglossus pass from the cartilaginous lesser horn to the tongue—hence called the *Chondroglossus*—and when removed, the lingual artery and the Hyoglossus are in view.

The Hyoglossus arises from the whole length of the greater horn.

Side Wall of Nasal Pharynx

The following have been observed:

1. Orifice of the auditory tube, ½″ behind the inferior concha.
2. Pharyngeal recess, behind the orifice of the tube, and
3. (Naso-)pharyngeal tonsil, on the posterior wall of the pharynx and extending into the recess.

The following are now to be observed:

1. Upper border of Sup. Constrictor,
2. Pharyngobasilar fascia,
3. Auditory tube,
4. Levator and Tensor Palati,
5. Ascending palatine artery.

Upper Concave Border of the Superior Constrictor (*fig. 781*). The choana is bounded by bone, so it cannot be closed. Certainly, the Sup. Constrictor makes no attempt to close it; in fact, it is deficient behind the

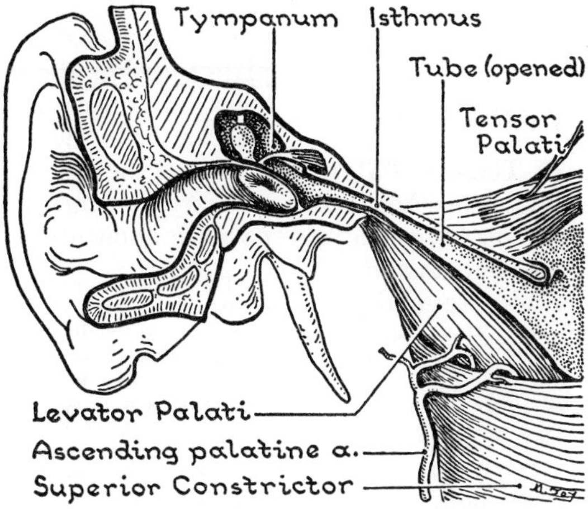

FIG. 781. The auditory tube (pharyngotympanic tube), after removal of the membranous and bony lateral wall.

choana. Its upper border curves from the hamulus and the lowest limit of the medial pterygoid plate to the pharyngeal tubercle on the basi-occipital (*fig. 753*).

Pharyngobasilar Fascia. This fascia which represents a submucous coat, largely closes the gap between the Sup. Constrictor, the medial pterygoid plate, and the base of the skull. It suspends the pharynx from the base of the skull and, accordingly, it is stronger there than lower down. The *tube*, the *Levator Palati*, and the *ascending palatine artery* pass through the gap (*fig. 781*).

The Auditory Tube (Pharyngotympanic Tube). This air duct is developmentally continuous with the tympanum and the mastoid antrum; so, its direction is backward, laterally, and slightly upward toward the mastoid process (*fig. 817*). A bristle passed along it in this direction for 1½″ appears through the anterior wall of the tympanum.

»» Fluid syringed through the nose is in danger of entering the forwardly directed mouth of the tube and of travelling to the tympanum. This, indeed, is the route by which infections spread from the throat to the middle ear.

The medial inch of the tube is *cartilaginous;* the lateral half inch is *bony*. The narrowest part, called the *isthmus*, is where bone and cartilage meet medial to the spine of the sphenoid. Here the lumen is only 2 to 3 mm. high and 1.0 to 1.5 mm. wide (*fig. 781*).

The cartilaginous part lies below the fissure between the petrous bone and the greater wing of the sphenoid. The cartilage of the tube, curved like an inverted J, forms only the upper and medial walls of the tube; the lower and lateral walls are membranous.

Except at the funnel-shaped *mouth* or *pharyngeal orifice*, the membranous lateral wall is applied to the cartilaginous medial wall, so that the lumen is closed to form a vertical slit. The mouth is firmly bound to the posterior border of the medial pterygoid plate and there rests on a projecting spine. The Levator Palati runs submucously below the mouth of the tube, raising its floor (*figs. 780* and *781*).

Function. When relaxed, the slit-like lumen of this air duct is closed, but during the act of swallowing and also of yawning and of sneezing, though apparently by no other natural means, it is opened reflexly through the action of the Tensor Palati (Rich). As a result, the atmospheric pressure on each side of the eardrum is maintained in equilibrium. While awake, one swallows once every minute; while asleep, once every 5 minutes (Graves and Edwards). Hence, while ascending and descending in an aeroplane it is wise to be awake.

Nerve Supply. Via its tympanic branch the glossopharyngeal nerve (IX) is sensory to the tube, and via its pharyngeal branch it is sensory to the mouth of the tube. Perhaps the pharyngeal branch of the maxillary nerve (V^2) helps to supply the mouth of the tube.

SOFT PALATE: REVIEW AND SUMMARY

Levator Palati and Tensor Palati. These two muscles arise close together from the base of the skull, one on each side of the tube. Both muscles descend to the soft palate, the Levator to elevate and pull backward the posterior part, the Tensor to depress and render tense the anterior part, and also to open the tube (*fig. 780*).

The Levator Palati is as stout as a lead pencil. It arises from the under surface of the apex of the petrous bone in front of the carotid canal. It runs beneath the whole length of the membranous floor of the tube, accompanying it downward, forward, and medially and across the upper border of the Sup. Constrictor. Below the mouth of the tube it enters the upper surface of the soft palate and there spreads out to join its fellow and the palatine aponeurosis.

The asc. palatine branch of the facial art. accompanies it into the soft palate.

The Tensor Palati is thin and fan-shaped. Its origin extends from the spine of the sphenoid to the scaphoid fossa at the root of the medial pterygoid plate. It also arises from the whole length of the membranous lateral wall of the tube. It descends lateral to the Sup. Constrictor and medial pterygoid plate to below the level of the hard palate. Then, after piercing the attachment of the Buccinator to the pterygomandibular raphe, it utilizes the hamulus as a pulley and takes a recurrent course to its insertion into the palatine aponeurosis.

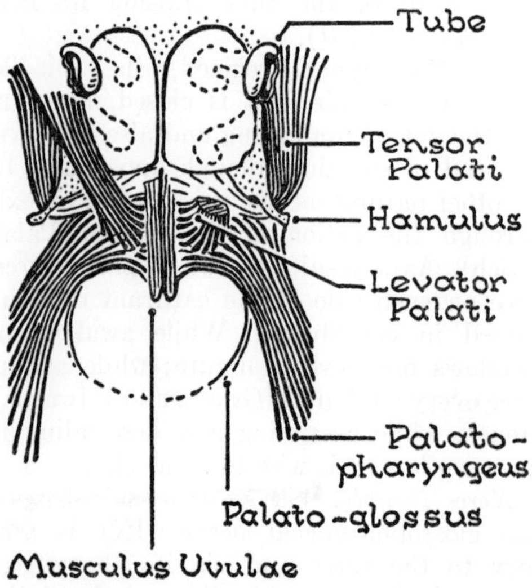

FIG. 782. The muscles of the soft palate—five on each side.

»» The Tensor must on principle be tendinous where it turns around the pulley; and on principle there must be a bursa to facilitate the play of the tendon on the pulley. These conditions are similar to those encountered by the Obliquus Oculi Superior at its pulley.

Palpation. The hamulus, or hook-like lower end of the medial pterygoid plate, is situated about half an inch behind the greater palatine foramen. It can be palpated in life from the mouth by pressing upward immediately posteromedial to the maxillary tuberosity. This point is a little in front of the palatoglossal arch.

Structure of Soft Palate. It is a general principle that free surfaces that are subjected to friction, pressure, or other rough treatment are lined with *stratified squamous epithelium.* The under aspect of the soft palate comes into contact with food, and the posterior part of its upper surface strikes the posterior pharyngeal wall during the act of swallowing; so, these parts are lined with stratified squamous epithelium. The remainder of its upper aspect is lined with *ciliated epithelium,* as is most of the nasal cavity and nasopharynx.

A thick carpet of racemose mucous *glands* covers the under surface of the soft palate (*fig. 783*).

It is important to note that the anterior one-third of the soft palate is *aponeurotic* and the posterior two-thirds *fleshy;* but it is not important to know the detailed arrangement of the fleshy fibers by layers. There is, then, a *bony palate,* an *aponeurotic palate,* and a *fleshy palate.* The aponeurosis is continuous in front with the sharp, posterior border of the hard palate, and laterally

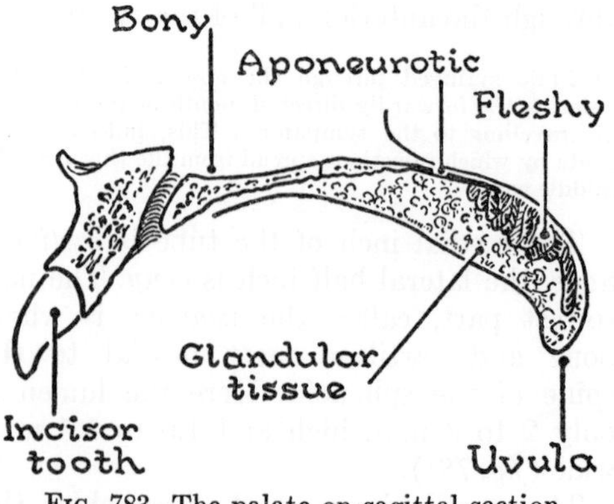

FIG. 783. The palate on sagittal section

with the pharyngobasilar fascia. In essence, it is the aponeuroses of the two tensor muscles, though the other palatine muscles gain partial attachment to it.

The Muscles, 5 in number, are paired:

Tensor Palati and Levator Palati
Musculus Uvulae
Palatoglossus and Palatopharyngeus (p. 669)

The two **Musculi Uvulae** (*fig. 782*) arise beside the posterior nasal spine and, like two closely applied fingers, they descend near the dorsum of the soft palate into the uvula, which they stiffen when they contract.

Vessels and Nerves of Pharynx and Soft Palate. Arteries. The pharynx is supplied mainly by the *ascending pharyngeal*, sup. and inf. thyroid, and pharyngeal aa.; the soft palate by the *ascending palatine branch of the facial a.;* and the tonsil by the *tonsillar branch of the facial a.* These anastomose with each other and with the *lesser palatine* and *dorsales linguae aa.*

Veins go to the pharyngeal plexus, and thence to the internal jugular vein.

Lymph vessels pass to the upper deep cervical nodes; those from the nasopharynx pass to nodes between the pharynx and the prevertebral fascia; those from the tonsil to a node below the angle of the jaw (*fig. 824.1*).

Motor Nerves. Nerve XI (through the vagus) via the pharyngeal plexus supplies all the pharyngeal and palatine muscles, except:

{Stylopharyngeus (nerve IX)
{Tensor Palati (nerve V^3).

The external and recurrent laryngeal branches of the vagus also supply the Inferior Constrictor.

The Sensory Nerve of the pharynx, including the soft palate and tonsil, is the glossopharyngeal (IX). But the maxillary nerve (V^2), via its pharyngeal br., supplies the roof of the pharynx; and, via the lesser palatine nerves, helps to supply the soft palate and the adjacent part of the tonsil. The vagus (X) via the int. laryngeal nerve, supplies the region round the entrance to the larynx (*fig. 784*).

Sucking. Place a finger in your mouth and, while sucking it, note that your lips grasp it, that a groove forms along the middle of the tongue, and that the tongue recedes from the palate, thereby creating a vacuum. Note also that, while sucking fluid through a straw, you can breathe in and out through the nose. This is possible, since the Palatoglossi shut the mouth off from the pharynx. A child with a cleft palate cannot suck effectively, because air, drawn in through the cleft, prevents the formation of a vacuum within the mouth.

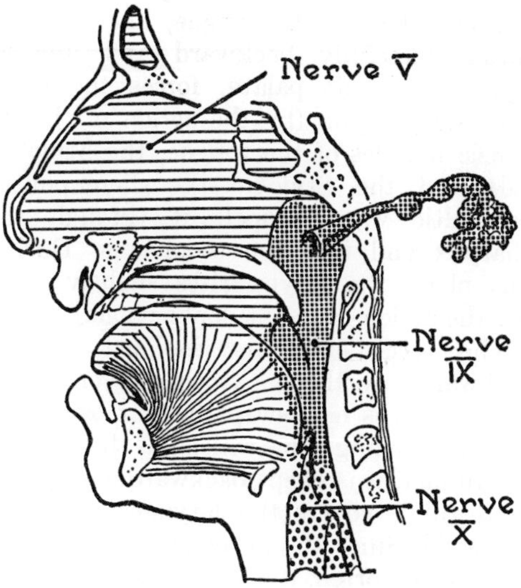

FIG. 784. The sensory distribution of the glossopharyngeal nerve. (After Edwards.)

Mechanism of Swallowing (Deglutition). Swallowing begins as a voluntary movement and continues as an involuntary one. Thus, the lips are closed and the Buccinators are pressed against the teeth. The lingual muscles pass the bolus of food backward on the dorsum of the tongue to the palatoglossal arch, and there, at the entrance to the pharynx, it may rest, the voluntary stage of deglutition being completed.

If, however, some saliva, fluid or portion of food enters the pharynx, the involuntary stage is started reflexly by stimulation of the glossopharyngeal nerve. The jaws are held closed by the Masseters and Temporals, while the hyoid bone and the larynx rise, as by palpation you can determine on yourself (probably by the action of the Digastrics). The tongue, like a piston thrust forcefully backward and upward against the soft palate, forces the bolus into the pharynx (by the action of the intrinsic muscles of the tongue, the Mylohyoids and the Styloglossi), whereupon a peristaltic wave propels it through the pharynx and into the esophagus. During this phase the larynx rises slightly more (by the action of the Stylopharyngei).

The erect epiglottis, inclined slightly backwards by the backward movement of the tongue, is now swept farther backward by the oncoming bolus which fills the valleculae. In fact, it is swept backward and downward till it covers the laryngeal aperture like a lid. Since the aryepiglottic folds can be seen to shorten, it is not unlikely that the Aryepiglottic muscles pull the epiglottis while the bolus pushes it.

The entrance to the larynx and the vestibule are tightly closed by the sphincteric muscles (*fig. 811*), which also tilt the apices of the arytenoid cartilages against the tubercle of the epiglottis and approximate the vocal cords. Although the epiglottis closes like a lid, the sphincteric mechanism is alone sufficient to prevent the entrance of food into the larynx.

»» The movements that take place during the act of swallowing are too rapid for the eye to perceive. For example, the epiglottis bends from the erect position to 60° below the horizontal and recovers in about 1/15 of a second. Hence, high speed cineradiography using 30 and 60 frames per second was employed by Saunders, Davis, and Miller, who in more senses than one have thrown new light on the mechanism of deglutition. It is on their paper, excellently illustrated, that the foregoing account is based.

Further, note that during the act of swallowing two apertures are closed and two are opened:

1. The entrance to the nasopharynx, called the *pharyngeal isthmus*, rendered narrower by the contracting Palatopharyngeus, is closed by the Levatores Palati which draw the soft palate upward and also backward so that its upper surface is pressed against the wall of the narrowing pharynx.

Lubricating mucus is necessary to seal the isthmus and render it air tight. (Contrast the effectiveness of a hand pump when the plunger is wet and when dry.)

2. The Tensores Palati open the auditory tubes, and render taut the anterior half of the soft palate.

3. The entrance to the larynx, as stated above, is closed by the sphincteric muscles (p. 701).

4. The Cricopharyngeus relaxes its guard over the esophagus to let the bolus pass.

5. The three pharyngeal constrictors contract vigorously only for 1/3 of a second each. Their contractions occur in series but overlap, resulting in a peristaltic wave that continues on to the esophageal muscles (Basmajian and Dutta).

Two Deep Cervical Spaces of Surgical Importance

Retropharyngeal Space (*fig. 736*). During the act of swallowing, the pharynx and esophagus must have freedom of movement. Accordingly, between the prevertebral fascia, which covers the prevertebral muscles, and the buccopharyngeal fascia, there is an areolar space called the *retropharyngeal space.* This potential space is closed above by the base of the skull, and on each side by the carotid sheath; caudally it opens into the superior mediastinum.

Lateral Pharyngeal Space (*fig. 736*). This is a space lined with areolar fascia, filled with fat and containing branches of the maxillary nerve and maxillary vessels.

It extends from the base of the skull and the auditory tube above, where it is widest, to the level of the hyoid bone below, where its apex lies. The pharynx is situated medially; the parotid gland posterolaterally; the Medial Pterygoid and the ramus of the jaw anterolaterally; and the styloid process and its muscles largely separate the space from the carotid sheath, which is posterior.

Its practical importance is surgical: (1) infection may spread to the space from the tonsil; (2) the dentist when injecting the lingual and inferior alveolar nerves may carry infection to it, and (3) when infected, infection may spread by the veins to the internal jugular vein.

The space communicates with the parotid space and with the submandibular space, but not with the retropharyngeal space.

CHAPTER 45

MOUTH, TONGUE, AND TEETH

MOUTH

INSPECTION AND PALPATION. The cavity of the mouth has two parts—a *vestibule* and a *cavity proper*. These are separated from each other by the teeth, alveolar processes, and gums; and they communicate with each other on each side through a space between the last molar teeth and the ramus of the mandible.

The **Vestibule** is bounded externally by the lips and cheeks. It opens on to the skin surface at the *aperture of the mouth*. The upper and lower lips are attached to the gums in the median plane by folds of mucous membrane, the *frenula*. The constricted orifice of the parotid duct opens opposite the 2nd upper molar tooth.

The Lips have four layers: *cutaneous*, *muscular*, *glandular*, and *mucous*. Between the muscular and glandular layers lies an *arterial circle*, formed by the upper and lower labial branches of the facial artery. Its pulsations can be felt on grasping the lip between the finger and thumb. The *glands* can be felt with the tip of the tongue.

The Cheek has the same four layers as the lips together with the buccal pad of fat, molar glands, and buccopharyngeal fascia. Where the *facial artery* crosses from lower to upper jaw, it is applied to the Buccinator an inch or less from the angle of the mouth.

Palpation. With the index finger in the vestibule *palpate* (1) the *Masseter,* which is rendered prominent when the teeth are alternately clenched and relaxed; (2) the lower border of the *zygomatic arch,* and the facial and infratemporal surfaces of the maxilla; and (3) the anterior border of the *ramus of the jaw,* and trace it to the *coronoid process* and to the tendon of the *Temporalis.*

Nerve Supply of Lips and Cheek. The *motor* nerve is the facial. When it is paralyzed the lips cannot be moulded to whistle, and food collects in the vestibule.

Sensory: The skin and mucous surfaces of the upper lip, lower lip, and cheek near the angle of the mouth are supplied by the infraorbital (V^2), mental (V^3), and buccal (V^3) nerves, respectively. *Lymph vessels* (p. 717).

Cavity Proper of the Mouth [Oral Cavity]. *Inspection.* The cavity is roofed in by the hard and soft palates. The *soft palate* ends medianly in the *uvula.* Two folds on each side arch downward from the soft palate: the anterior fold, the *palatoglossal arch,* ends at the side of the tongue and marks the entrance to the pharynx. On looking beyond it into the pharynx the posterior fold, the *palatopharyngeal arch,* is seen to pass from the margin of the uvula to the side wall of the pharynx.

Between these two palatine arches and the posterior one-third of the tongue a portion of the *palatine tonsil* is seen with the aid of a tongue depressor. The anterior two-thirds of the *tongue* rises from the floor and covers the structures on the sides and front of the floor, known as the sublingual region.

When the tip of the tongue is raised, a short median fold of mucous membrane, the *frenulum linguae,* is seen running from the tongue to the floor of the mouth. On each side, just in front of the frenulum there is a papilla on which opens the duct of the submandibular gland. Running posterolaterally from this orifice is a rounded ridge, the *plica sublingualis,* which overlies the upper border of the sublingual salivary gland.

Palpation. With the index finger palpate (1) the tuber of the maxilla behind the 3rd upper molar tooth (*fig. 754*); (2) the hamulus posteromedial to the tuber and below the level of the palate; (3) the anterior border of the Medial Pterygoid lateral to the palatoglossal arch; and (4) try to roll the lingual nerve against the jaw medial to the root of the lower 3rd molar tooth (*fig. 785*).

Sublingual Region

(Structures in the floor of the mouth.)

»» To display the structures, pull the right half of the tongue medially. Incise the mucous membrane along the bottom of the furrow between the mandible and the plica sublingualis and, keeping close to the bone, prolong the incision backward to the 2nd molar tooth, and forward to the frenulum (*fig. 785*). With the handle of the knife displace the sublingual gland (and with it the tongue) medially, but avoid injuring the lingual nerve which lies behind the incision.

The fossa on the jaw for the sublingual gland is exposed, and below it the origin of the Mylohyoid is seen. Next, incise the mucous membrane along the bottom of the furrow between the plica sublingualis and the tongue, and with the handle of the knife displace the gland laterally. The extensive fan-shaped muscle displayed, passing from mental spine to the tongue, is the Genioglossus.

There being no concealing fat, the structures within the mouth are readily displayed with the aid of two pairs of forceps and occasional touches with the knife.

The **Sublingual Gland** is enveloped in a sheath of areolar tissue which like a mesentery fixes it to the floor of the mouth. The artery to the gland, the sublingual branch of the lingual artery, reaches it through this "mesentery." Running diagonally across the medial aspect of the sublingual gland and adhering to it is the *submandibular duct.* On teasing between the upper border of the sublingual gland and the plica, a row of a dozen *short ducts* is seen leaving the gland to open on the plica.

In front, the sublingual gland is in contact with its fellow of the opposite side.

Behind, it abuts against the *submandibular* (submaxillary) *gland.*

Laterally, it occupies the sublingual fossa of the jaw.

Medially, the submandibular duct and the lingual nerve run forward between the gland and the Genioglossus (and Hyoglossus).

Below, is the Mylohyoid.

The **Lingual Nerve** (*fig. 785*) is a branch of nerve V^3. It appears in the mouth from under cover of the Sup. Constrictor, behind the last molar tooth, and has the chorda tympani incorporated in it. When the Sup. Constrictor is detached from the pterygomandibular raphe, the nerve is seen to be

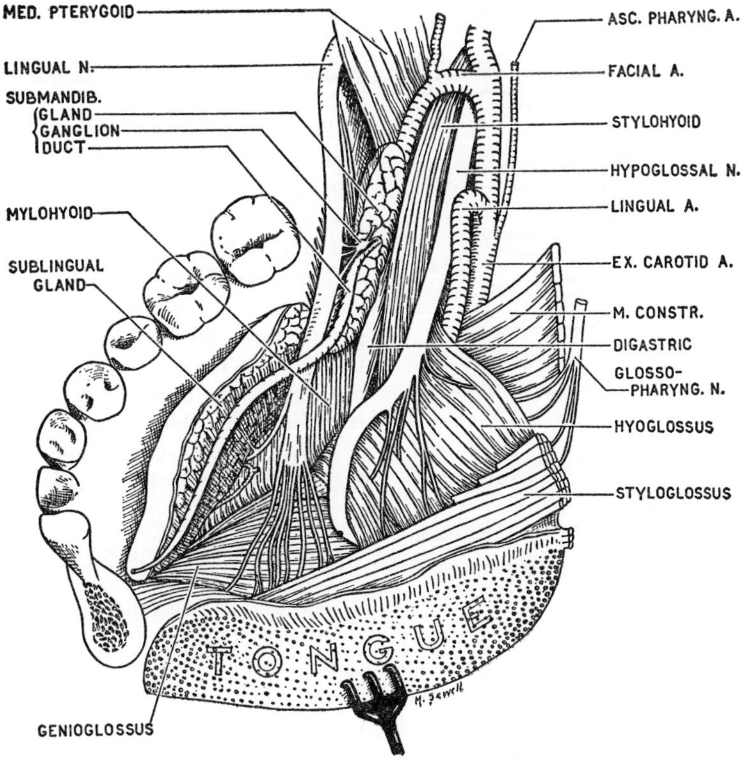

FIG. 785. Dissection of right side of floor of mouth

clamped to the ramus of the jaw by the Medial Pterygoid.

The lingual nerve passes forward from the lateral wall of the mouth, across the floor, to the side of the tongue. In its course it *describes a spiral* around the submandibular duct, lying successively above, laterally, below, medially, and above. Finally, it spreads out within the anterior two-thirds of the tongue as the nerve of general sensation, its fibers ending mainly in the filiform and fungiform papillae. It also supplies the sublingual region, including the floor of the mouth and the gums. As it crosses the Hyoglossus, two stout branches pass between it and the submandibular ganglion (see below) (*fig. 786*).

The **Chorda Tympani**, which joined the lingual nerve in the infratemporal fossa, contains both efferent and afferent fibers: (1) secretory fibers for the submandibular and sublingual glands and (2) taste fibers from the anterior two-thirds of the tongue.

The *secretory fibers* are preganglionic parasympathetic fibers whose relay station is the submandibular ganglion (*fig. 786.1*).

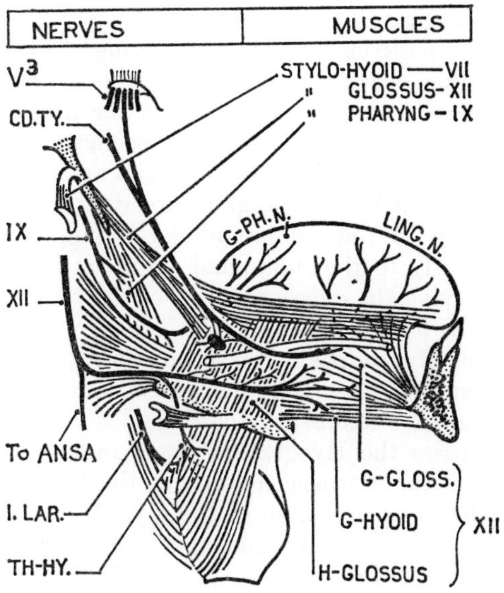

FIG. 786. The nerves and muscles of the tongue on lateral view.

The *taste fibers* accompany the lingual nerve to the anterior two-thirds of the tongue where they end in the taste buds; their cell station is the geniculate ganglion.

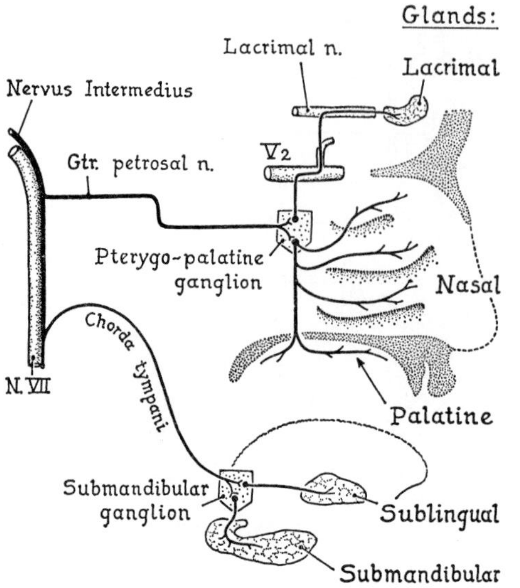

FIG. 786.1. Distribution of parasympathetic fibers of the nervus intermedius.

The **Submandibular (Submaxillary) Ganglion** is a parasympathetic ganglion—a relay station on the course of the efferent fibers of the chorda tympani. It is suspended from the lingual nerve by two roots, and it lies on the Hyoglossus medial to the submandibular gland.

The *posterior root* (or *roots*) brings to the ganglion *secretory fibers* from the chorda tympani and *sensory fibers* from the lingual nerve; *sympathetic fibers* (vasoconstrictor) join it from the plexus on the facial artery.

Branches of the ganglion are distributed directly to the submandibular gland, and indirectly to the sublingual gland by fibers traversing the *anterior root* to be distributed via the lingual nerve (*fig. 785*).

The **Hypoglossal Nerve** runs forward between the submandibular gland and the Hyoglossus well below the lingual nerve. As it crosses the Hyoglossus, fibers radiate to supply the extrinsic muscles of the tongue; at the anterior border of the Hyoglossus, it plunges into the tongue to supply the intrinsic muscles.

Muscles. The **Mylohyoids** (paired) arise from the mylohyoid lines on the mandible and they are inserted into the body of the hyoid bone. Their anterior borders are united in a median raphe that extends from the symphysis menti to the hyoid. The two Mylohyoids constitute the *Diaphragma Oris*. (See also p. 616 and *figs. 720 to 721.1.*)

Nerve supply: Mylohyoid n. from V^3 (*fig. 742*).

The **Genioglossi** (paired) arise from the mental spine (genial tubercle) and, like two vertically placed fans, pass backward into the tongue—their medial surfaces being in contact with each other.

The **Geniohyoids** (paired) also arise from the mental spine and, like two horizontally placed fans, pass backward to the body of the hyoid bone (*fig. 721*)—their medial borders being in contact with each other; they lie below the tongue.

Nerve supply. Genioglossus by N. XII. Geniohyoid by C. 1 via N. XII (*fig. 765*).

TONGUE

The tongue is a muscular organ concerned with mastication, deglutition, speech, and taste. It has two parts—an anterior two-thirds and a posterior one-third. These differ topographically, developmentally, structurally, functionally, in nerve supply, and in appearance.

The anterior ⅔ rises from the floor of the mouth and hence is called the *oral part* (body); the posterior ⅓ forms part of the anterior wall of the pharynx and hence is called the *pharyngeal part* (root). The boundary between the oral and pharyngeal parts is marked on the dorsum of the tongue by a V-shaped line, the *sulcus terminalis*, which runs medially and backward on each side from where the palatoglossal arch joins the side of the tongue to a median pit, the *foramen cecum linguae*.

Mucous Membrane. A mucous membrane of stratified squamous epithelium resting on a fibrous stroma, the *tunica propria*, covers the *dorsum*, or upper surface, of both parts of the tongue, as well as the tip, lateral margins, and under surface of the oral part. It is firmly adherent except on the posterior third of the dorsum where a submucous coat is present.

Two median, crescentic folds of mucous membrane, one fore and the other aft, are attached to the tongue. The anterior fold, the *frenulum linguae*, passes from its under

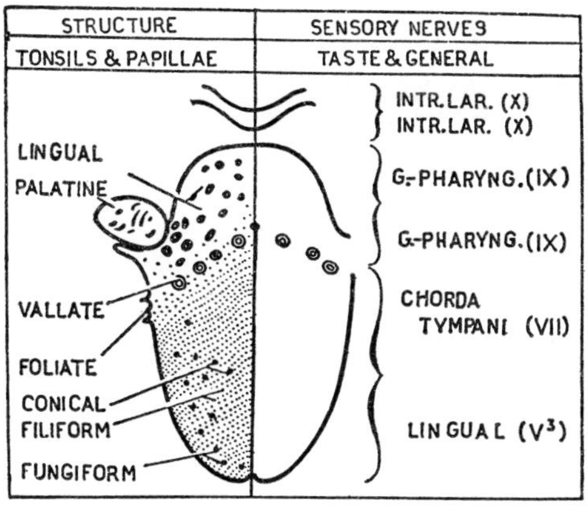

FIG. 787. The dorsum of the tongue showing structure (*left*) and sensory nerve supply (*right*).

surface to the floor of the mouth and separates the orifices of the submandibular ducts; the posterior fold, the median *glosso-epiglottic fold*, passes from its dorsum to the epiglottis and separates the valleculae.

The mucous membrane differs conspicuously on the two parts of the dorsum (*fig. 787*): on the *oral part* it is covered with papillae and is velvety; on the *pharyngeal part* it is studded with tubercles between which it is smooth and glistening.

The **Papillae** are of four varieties: filiform, fungiform, vallate, and foliate. They consist of a fibrous core derived from the tunica propria, covered with stratified squamous epithelium.

Filiform papillae are tapering and thread-like and are arranged in V-shaped rows that cover the dorsum of the oral part of the tongue. They contain touch corpuscles. Their epithelium is scaly and in some animals (e.g., cat, cow) it is cornified and is used as a rasp to grasp food.

Fungiform papillae have globular heads and are red because the core is more vascular and the epithelium not scaly. Like daisies on a lawn, they lie scattered singly among the filiform papillae at the tip and margin of the tongue, but they do not rise above them.

Vallate papillae are circular, about 2 mm. in diameter, and are surrounded by a moat which is 2 to 3 mm. deep. Twelve or less in number, they also are arranged in a V-shaped row just in front of the sulcus terminalis. Their flat tops hardly rise above the general surface.

Foliate papillae, rudimentary in man, are three to four short, vertical folds at the hinder part of the sides of the tongue.

Taste buds occur on most fungiform papillae, on the opposed sides of the foliate, and on both walls of the vallate. They also occur sparsely on the soft palate, epiglottis, and posterior wall of the pharynx.

On the *pharyngeal third* of the tongue there are no papillae. The numerous tubercles seen there are encapsuled *lymphoid nodules*. Each nodule surrounds a crypt, which receives the ducts of underlying mucous glands and opens conspicuously on the surface at the center of the nodule. The nodules are known collectively as the *lingual tonsil*. They are indefinitely separated from the lower pole of the palatine tonsil.

The mucous membrane on the under surface of the tongue is smooth, and on each side the lingual vein shines purple through it. Lateral to the vein is the fimbriated fold.

» *The Anterior Lingual Gland* (paired) is a cluster of mucous and serous racemose glands, ½ inch long, situated under the apical part of the tongue. Below it, there is a thin covering of longitudinal muscle fibers; above it, the terminal parts of the lingual artery and nerve run.

Muscles of the Tongue. There are 3 extrinsic and 3 intrinsic muscles on each

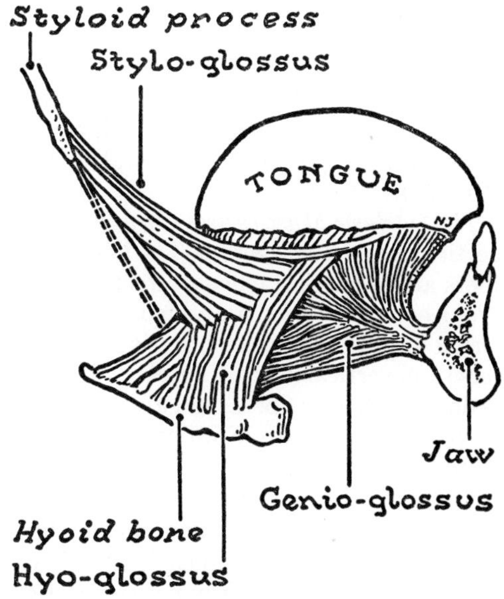

FIG. 788. The 3 extrinsic muscles of the tongue and their 3 bony origins.

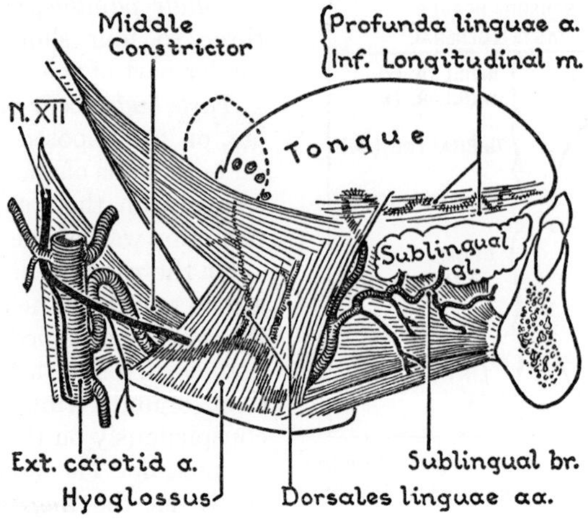

FIG. 789. The lingual artery

side—all supplied by the hypoglossal nerve. The former move the tongue bodily and alter its shape; the latter only alter its shape.

The Extrinsic Muscles (*fig. 788*) are—Genio-, Hyo-, and Stylo-glossus. Their actions are obvious. The middle and posterior fibers of the Genioglossi protrude the tongue; the anterior fibers withdraw the tip. The Styloglossi withdraw and raise the tongue. The Hyoglossi draw the sides downwards and backwards.

The Genioglossi as protruders of the tongue are "*safety muscles*", and if put out of action—the result of paralysis, fracture of the jaw, or during anesthesia—the tongue falls back and suffocation results. If only one Genioglossus is paralyzed, the protruded tongue points to the paralyzed side (*fig. 814*).

The Intrinsic Muscles are—Longitudinalis, Verticalis, and Transversus. The longitudinal fibers are in part attached posteriorly to the hyoid bone. They form an incomplete outer cortex deep to the tunica propria. The transverse and vertical fibers decussate with them; so do the extrinsic fibers, and give the tongue its distinctive feature of interwoven skeletal muscle fibers.

Strangely there are *areas of fat* among the posterior muscle fibers. The tongue has a median *fibrous septum* which is attached to the hyoid bone. It does not reach the dorsum.

»» ACCESSORY MUSCLES. (1) The *Palatoglossus*, supplied by nerve XI via the vagus, though primarily a palatine muscle, helps to narrow the isthmus of the fauces during the act of swallowing. (2) The *Geniohyoid*, by pulling the hyoid or tongue bone forward, comes into play on swallowing, as you can determine on yourself by palpation. (3) The *Chondroglossus* is a slip of the Hyoglossus that arises from the cartilaginous lesser horn of the hyoid bone.

Vessels and Nerves of Tongue

The Lingual Artery alone supplies the tongue. It arises from the external carotid at the level of the greater horn of the hyoid (*fig. 789*). It runs forward applied to the Mid. Constrictor, which separates it from the mucous membrane of the pharynx, and it continues its course to the tip of the tongue applied to the Genioglossus.

»» Its other relations are superficial ones. Its course is necessarily sinuous. In the carotid triangle it arches upward and is crossed by nerve XII which arches downward. It passes deep to the posterior belly of the Digastric and Stylohyoid and enters the submandibular triangle, where nerve XII crosses it again. It runs deep to the Hyoglossus, which now separates it from nerve XII, and under cover of the anterior border of the Hyoglossus, it ascends on the Genioglossus. Finally, it runs tortuously deep in the furrow between the Genioglossus and Longitudinalis Inferior.

In the last part of its course it is called the *profunda artery*. Its only anastomosis with its fellow is at the tip of the tongue; so, the tongue can be bisected almost bloodlessly.

BRANCHES: *Two dorsales linguae aa.*, which ascend deep to the Hyoglossus to supply the posterior third of the tongue and anastomose in the tonsil bed (p. 672); numerous *muscular twigs;* and a *sublingual a.*, which supplies the sublingual gland and the floor of the mouth. It anastomoses with the submental branch of the facial artery.

Small *venae comitantes* accompany the lingual artery, but the chief vein of the tongue (the profunda vein) is the conspicuous submucous vein. It follows nerve XII across the Hyoglossus, and is then joined by the venae comitantes to form the lingual vein which ends in the internal jugular vein.

Lymphatics of the Tongue (p. 717).

Development and Nerve Supply. Like the palate, the anterior two-thirds of the tongue has a bilateral origin. It develops from two ingrowing shelves, one on each side of the 1st or mandibular arch. This explains the nerve supply from the lingual branch of the mandibular nerve (V^3), and also why the tip is sometimes bifid, as is the serpent's tongue. With this part is incorporated posteriorly a median eminence (*tuberculum impar*) which makes its appearance between the 2nd arches. This briefly explains the nerve supply from the chorda tympani branch of the facial nerve.

The posterior one-third of the tongue is unpaired. It develops from a median bar, placed between the ends of the 3rd and 4th arches. This explains the nerve supply from the glossopharyngeal and superior laryngeal nerves.

The vallate papillae are supplied by the glossopharyngeal nerve.

The foramen cecum is the persisting end of the thyroglossal duct.

The muscles of the tongue are supplied by the hypoglossal nerve. They are somatic muscles that have migrated into both parts of the tongue.

Afferent Nerves. The *lingual nerve* is for general sensation; the *chorda tympani* is for taste; the *glossopharyngeal* and *superior laryngeal nerves* are both for general sensation and for taste (*fig. 787*).

TEETH

Parts (*fig. 790*). Each tooth has a root buried in the jaw, a *crown* projecting beyond the gum, and a *neck* encircled by the gum. At the apex of each root a pinpoint foramen, the *apical foramen*, leads through a widening *root canal* to the *tooth cavity*.

Each tooth is composed of *dentine* which is the exquisitely sensitive, yellowish basis of the tooth; *enamel*, which is the white insensitive covering of the crown, *cement* which

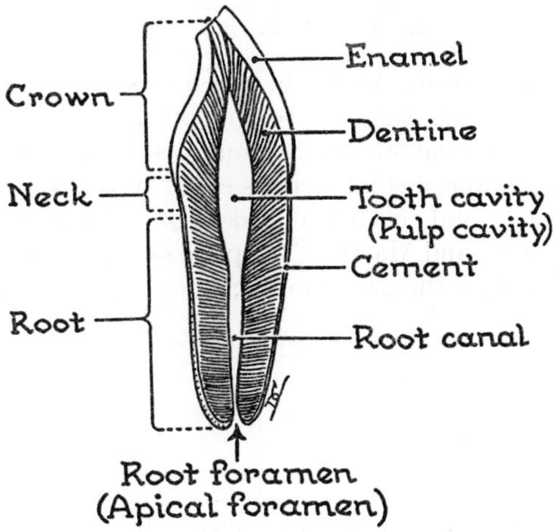

FIG. 790. A tooth, on longitudinal section

is a bony covering for the root and neck of the tooth; and *pulp* which is a fibrous material containing the nerves and vessels that pass through the pinpoint, root canal. The pulp occupies the tooth cavity within the dentine.

Each tooth lies in a bony socket or *alveolus* which narrows toward its bottom; thus a large pressure surface is afforded the tooth and extraction of a tooth made possible. Between the tooth and the socket there is a vascular membrane, the *periodontal membrane.* This modified periosteum is continuous with the lamina propria of the gum and is attached both to the cement and to the alveolar wall.

There are *32 permanent teeth*, 16 in the upper dental arch and 16 in the lower. Of the eight on each side of each arch—two are incisors, one canine (cuspid), two premolars (bicuspids), and three molars. The formula therefore reads:

$$\frac{3.\ 2.\ 1.\ 2.}{3.\ 2.\ 1.\ 2.}\left|\frac{2.\ 1.\ 2.\ 3.}{2.\ 1.\ 2.\ 3.}\right.$$

All except the molars are preceded by deciduous or primary teeth.

There are *20 deciduous teeth* (primary, temporary, or milk teeth), two incisors, one canine, and two molars on each side of each arch. The formula therefore reads:

$$\frac{2.\ \ 1.\ \ 2.}{2.\ \ 1.\ \ 2.}\ \Bigg|\ \frac{2.\ \ 1.\ \ 2.}{2.\ \ 1.\ \ 2.}$$

Eruption. At birth, the jaws are rigid bony bars, suitable to grasping a nipple. Between the 6th and 8th months the deciduous, lower, medial incisors erupt through the gums, and eruption proceeds as follows (Schour and Massler), the process being completed by the 24th month:

Order and Time of Eruption of Deciduous Teeth

Teeth	Med. Incisor	Lat. Incisor		1st Molar	Canine	2nd Molar
Order	a	b		d	c	e
Months	6–8	8–10	10–12	12–16	16–20	20–24

Then comes an *interval of 4 years.* At the 6th year the permanent teeth begin to erupt, and, because the 1st molars are the first permanent teeth to erupt, they are commonly called the *6th year molars.* The deciduous teeth are next replaced by permanent teeth in the following order: medial incisors, lateral incisors, 1st premolars, canines, and 2nd premolars. The 2nd molars erupt about the 12th year and the 3rd molars about the 18th year (15th–21st), but not uncommonly they fail to erupt.

Order and Time of Eruption of Permanent Teeth

Teeth	1st Molar	Med. Incisor	Lat. Incisor		1st Pre-molar	2nd Pre-molar Canine	2nd Molar
Order	f	a	b		d	c, e	f
Years	6	7	8	9	10	11	12

Descriptive Terms. It is convenient to refer to the anterior surfaces of the front teeth and lateral surfaces of the side teeth as *labial* (or buccal) surfaces; and to refer to the opposite surfaces as *lingual* surfaces: to refer to the medial surfaces of the front teeth and anterior surfaces of the side teeth as *proximal* surfaces, and to the opposite surfaces as *distal* surfaces. The biting surfaces may be referred to as the *masticatory* or occlusal surfaces. With the exception of the distal surfaces of the last molars, proximal and distal surfaces are *contact* surfaces.

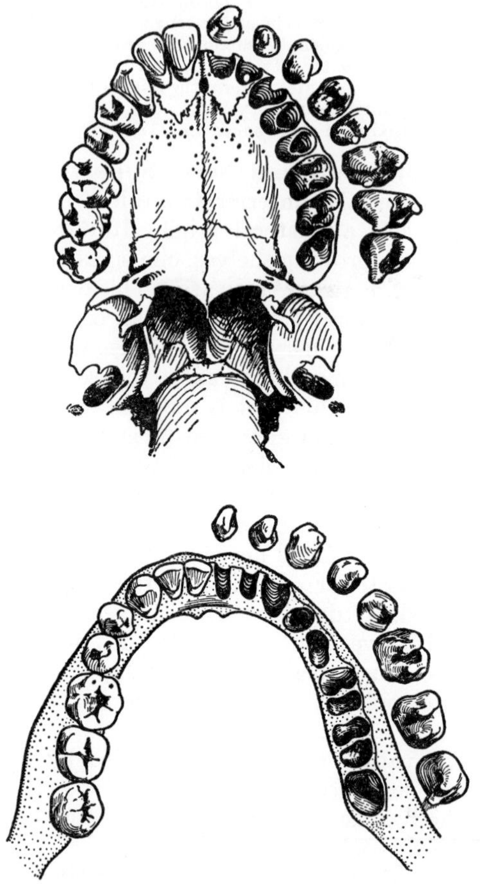

FIG. 791. The upper and lower teeth and their sockets. (The 2nd upper premolar or bicuspid, as well as the 1st, happens to have two roots.)

Crowns. There is evidence that the crowns of the human teeth have evolved from a tritubercular or tricuspid tooth. And two labial tubercles and one lingual tubercle are detectable on each tooth.

In the *incisors,* the labial tubercles fuse to form a cutting edge which is joined to an indistinct lingual tubercle by two faint lines (the cingulum) that enclose a triangular space. Among the North American Indians these are pronounced and give the incisors a shovel-like appearance.

In the *canines,* the labial tubercles fuse to form a single large cone and a lingual tubercle is often well defined.

In the *premolars* or bicuspids, the labial tubercles fuse to form a medium sized cone

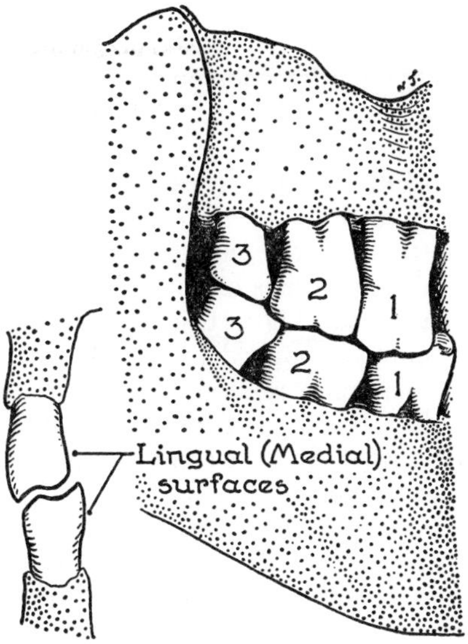

FIG. 792. The right molar teeth in occlusion. Teeth, when in occlusion, bite on two teeth, except the distal maxillary tooth and the proximal mandibular tooth.

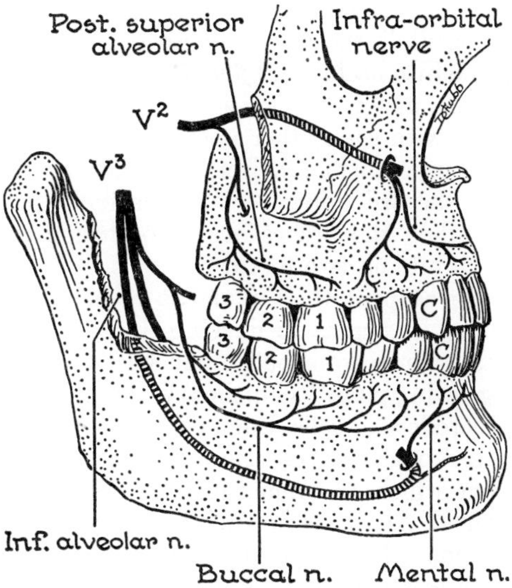

FIG. 793. Nerve supply to the outer aspect of the gums. Teeth in occlusion.

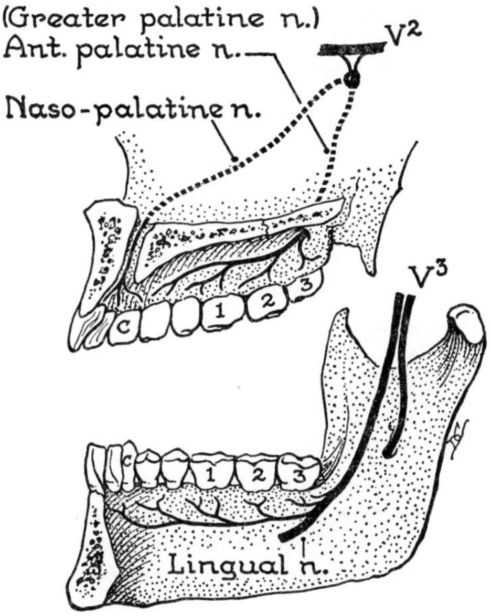

FIG. 794. Nerve supply to the inner aspect of the gums. Branches also reach the gums between the tooth sockets (*fig. 795*).

and the lingual tubercle or cusp is pronounced.

All *molars* have as a basis two labial tubercles and a proximal lingual tubercle. The *upper molars* characteristically have an additional lingual tubercle placed distally, making four in all—the 1st molar always has four, the 2nd commonly, and the 3rd variably. The *lower molars* characteristically have five tubercles, two being labial, two lingual, and a fifth distal—these tend to be reduced on the 3rd lower molar.

Roots (*fig. 791*). The roots of the incisors, canines, and premolars are single. (The first upper premolar has commonly a bifid or even a double root.) The lower molars have two flattened roots, a proximal and a distal; the upper molars have three conical roots, two smaller labial and one larger lingual.

The roots of all teeth tend to be flattened proximodistally, and in all lower teeth the flattening is pronounced. In the upper teeth there is a compromise between being rounded and conical on the one hand and being flattened on the other. The upper medial incisor has the roundest root; the canines have the longest roots; and the roots of the molars are commonly recurved.

Occlusion. The teeth of the upper arch project labially beyond the teeth of the lower arch. As a result, the labial borders of the masticatory or occlusal surfaces of the lower premolars and molars tend to be worn off and rounded and the lingual borders are sharp. The reverse is true of the upper premolars and molars. The upper incisors in most races "overbite" the lower incisors and do not come into occlusion (*figs. 792* and *793*).

The upper and lower dental arches end flush with each other posteriorly (*fig. 792*). The upper medial incisors are relatively large and the 3rd upper molars relatively small; so, when the arches are in occlusion most teeth bite on two teeth.

Development. Enamel is of ectodermal origin. It begins to develop during the 3rd fetal month from buds that sprout from an ingrowing plate (the primary dental lamina) of ectodermal cells. Each bud takes the form of a cap that covers the mesodermal papilla from which the remainder of the tooth is formed. At the same time buds, from which the enamel of the corresponding permannte teeth arises, sprout from the lingual surface of the dental plate, but they remain quiescent temporarily. The three permanent molars develop similarly from a backward extension of the plate.

Growth and Calcification of the Permanent Teeth begin in the 1st molars (6th year molars) about the time of birth; in the incisors and canines (the upper lateral incisors excepted) from 4th to 6th month; in upper lateral incisors from 10th to 11th month; and in premolars and 2nd molars early in the 2nd year.

»» Therefore, metabolic disturbances occurring in early infancy (from gastrointestinal and other causes), while affecting the anterior teeth, will omit the upper lateral incisors. And, no amount of dietary regulation or calcium therapy can ever correct enamel defects once they have occurred (Schour and Massler).

Nerve Supply to the Teeth and Gums. The maxillary nerve (V^2) supplies the teeth and gums of the upper jaw; the mandibular nerve (V^3) supplies those of the lower (*figs. 793, 794, and 795*).

The teeth of the *upper jaw* and also their periodontal membranes are supplied by the post. and ant. superior alveolar nerves. The lingual part of the upper gums related to molars and premolars is supplied by the greater (anterior) palatine nerve; the part related to the canine and incisors by the nasopalatine nerve. The labial part of the upper gums related to the molars is supplied by branches of the post. superior alveolar nerve (which descends on the infratemporal surface of the maxilla); the part related to the premolars, canine, and incisors by the infra-orbital nerve. (See the infra-orbital nerve, p. 689.)

The teeth of the *lower jaw* and their periodontal membranes are supplied by the inf. alveolar nerve. The entire lingual part of the lower gum is supplied by the lingual nerve. The labial part related to the molars and premolars is supplied by the buccal nerve; the part related to the canine and incisors by the mental nerve (*fig. 793*).

Variations in Distributions:

1. The pulp of the lower teeth may retain residual sensation after injection of the inf. alveolar nerve. There is evidence to show that this is mediated by fibers of the lingual and buccal nerves that pierce the alveolar walls to reach the pulp;

2. branches of the inferior alveolar nerve to the incisor teeth may decussate in the mandibular canal with those of the opposite side and supply the opposite incisors;

3. similarly, branches of the mental nerves of opposite sides decussate in front of the symphysis menti and supply the gum of the opposite side;

4. the anterior limits of the distribution to the gums of the lingual and buccal nerves varies, as is evidenced by the variable loss of sensation on injecting these nerves. Thus, the lingual nerve, though usually extending to the median plane, sometimes stops abreast of the canine tooth, and the lingual nerve of the opposite side crosses to supplement it. Similarly, the buccal nerve distribution may cease at the 2nd molar or extend to the canine; the posterior limits of the mental nerve vary inversely with this (Stewart and Wilson).

5. Apparently, the buccal nerve may help to supply the upper gum, and the post. sup. alveolar nerve the lower.

The **lymph vessels** of the pulp of the upper and lower teeth pass to the submandibular and upper deep cervical nodes.

CHAPTER 46

NOSE AND RELATED AREAS

PTERYGOPALATINE FOSSA

The pterygopalatine fossa (*fig. 740*) is the elongated triangular space between the rounded posterior border of the maxilla and its buttress, the *pterygoid process.* The fragile vertical plate of the palatine bone forms its medial wall; the greater wing of the sphenoid forms its roof. If each of its walls were included in its name, it would be designated pterygo-(maxillospheno-)palatine fossa.

The *sphenopalatine foramen,* as might be inferred from its name, is situated at the junction of the roof and medial wall (*figs. 796* and *799*). It is large and round, and is the main door for the vessels and nerves to the nasal cavity. A wire or a bristle passed through the foramen follows the roof of the nasal cavity on to the nasal septum. Thin wires passed up the *greater* and the *lesser palatine canals* enter the fossa from below. Wires passed through the *foramen rotundum* and *pterygoid canal* enter it from behind. The pterygoid canal is demonstrated by passing a wire forward from a point immediately superolateral to the pterygoid tubercle (*figs. 692* and *755*).

The fossa communicates with the orbit through the hinder part of the *inferior orbital fissure,* and with the infratemporal fossa through the *pterygomaxillary fissure.* Its contents are:

1. Maxillary nerve (in part).
2. Pterygopalatine ganglion.
3. Maxillary artery (3rd part) and veins.

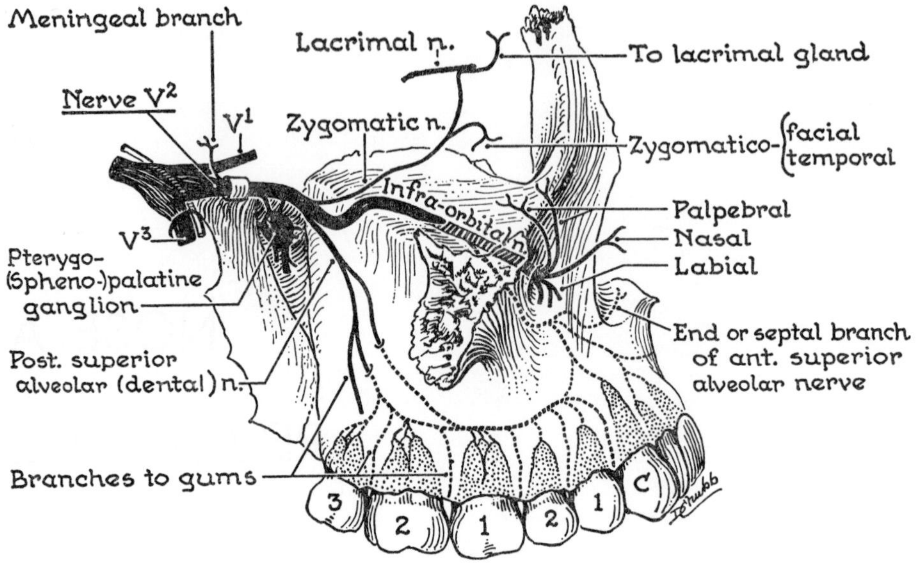

FIG. 795. Distribution of the maxillary (V^2) nerve

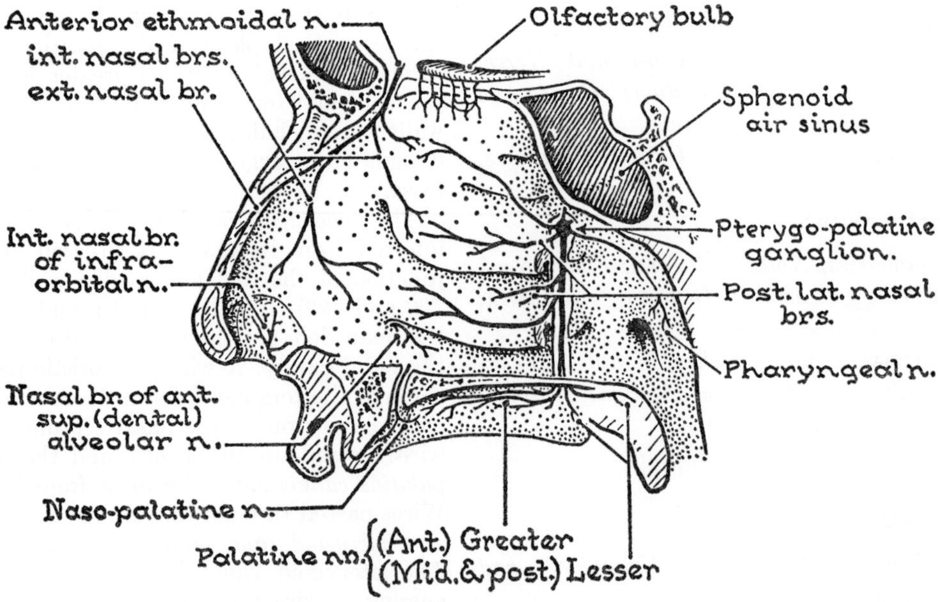

FIG. 796. The nerves of the nose and palate

The **Maxillary Nerve** (*figs. 795* and *796*), (V^2), or 2nd division of the trigeminal nerve, arises from the trigeminal ganglion, and is purely sensory. It is distributed to what developmentally is the maxillary process.

The wavy route taken by the nerve may be indicated by threading a wire from the middle cranial fossa through the foramen rotundum, across the pterygopalatine fossa to the inferior orbital fissure, and thence through the infra-orbital sulcus, canal, and foramen to the face. (On entering the infra-orbital sulcus it is called the infra-orbital nerve.)

In the cranium the nerve runs along the

inferolateral border of the cavernous sinus; in the foramen rotundum it commonly creates a ridge on the lateral wall of the sphenoidal sinus (*fig. 801*); in the pterygopalatine fossa it is surrounded by branches of the maxillary artery and veins, and the pterygopalatine ganglion is suspended from it; in the infra-orbital sulcus and foramen it creates a ridge on the roof and anterior wall of the maxillary air sinus.

Branches: (1) *A meningeal twig* goes to the dura mater. (2) An *orbital twig* supplies the periorbita and conveys sympathetic fibers to the *Orbitalis muscle,* which bridges and extends beyond the margins of the inferior orbital fissure. (3) *Two roots* go to the pterygopalatine ganglion, to be distributed to the nasal cavity, nasopharynx, and palate, as described on this page. (4) *The zygomatic nerve* passes through the inferior orbital fissure to the orbit, enters a V- or Y-shaped canal in the zygomatic bone, from which it emerges as two cutaneous branches, the *zygomaticofacial* and *zygomaticotemporal;* one on the cheek, the other in the temporal fossa (*fig. 658*). The secretory fibers to the lacrimal gland travel with the zygomatic nerve into the orbit, and there, leaving it, ascend on the lateral wall of the orbit to join the lacrimal nerve, which conveys them to the gland.

The **Infra-orbital Nerve** (*fig. 795*) is the continuation of nerve V^2. It begins at the inferior orbital fissure and ends on the face, between the Levator Labii Superioris and the Levator Anguli Oris, by dividing into many branches (*fig. 658*). These radiate to the cutaneous and conjunctival surfaces of the lower eyelid, to the skin of the side of the nose, to the vestibule of the nose, to the mobile part of the nasal septum, to the cutaneous and mucous surfaces of the upper lip and cheek, and to the gum.

In its course, it gives off two branches, the post. and ant. *superior alveolar* (dental) *nerves.* These descend in the infratemporal and facial walls of the maxilla—which are almost eggshell in thinness—and there form loops from which twigs proceed to the teeth, periodontal membranes, and mucous membrane of the maxillary sinus. The molar and premolar teeth are supplied by the posterior nerve, and the canine and incisor teeth by the anterior nerve.

The posterior superior alveolar nerves (usually two) arise in the infratemporal fossa and, descending, supply twigs to the labial portion of the gum over the molar teeth before entering their canals about the center of the infratemporal surface of the maxilla.

The anterior superior alveolar nerve, arising far forward, curves medially below the infra-orbital foramen and is apt to be damaged in opening into the maxillary sinus from the front; it sends a twig to the inferior meatus, floor, and septum of the nose (*figs. 795* and *796*).

Pterygopalatine Ganglion (Sphenopalatine ganglion). This parasympathetic ganglion is situated in the upper part of the pterygopalatine fossa. It is best displayed by breaking down the papery medial wall of the fossa. It has three roots: *secretory, sympathetic,* and *sensory;* but it is essentially a relay station on the secretory pathway of the greater (superficial) petrosal branch of the facial nerve, which reaches the ganglion as the nerve of the pterygoid canal. The fibers of the other roots pass through the ganglion without interruption (*fig. 797*).

The **sensory root** descends from nerve V^2 to the ganglion in order to be joined by the secretory and sympathetic fibers. The composite nerves leaving the ganglion are distributed to the mucosa of the nasal cavity, nasopharynx, and palate as follows:

Through the Sphenopalatine Foramen pass three nerves: (1) *Posterior lateral nasal nerves* run forward to the upper parts of the side wall of the nasal cavity and to ethmoidal cells. (2) The *nasopalatine nerve* (long sphenopalatine n.) crosses the under surface of the body of the sphenoid and, reaching the nasal septum, descends in the mucoperiosteum in a groove on the vomer to the incisive foramen, through which it passes. It supplies the septum, under surface of the front of the hard palate, and the gums (*fig. 776*). (3) *The pharyngeal nerve* runs backward to supply the roof of the nasopharynx and the sphenoidal sinus. It occupies the groove or canal on the under

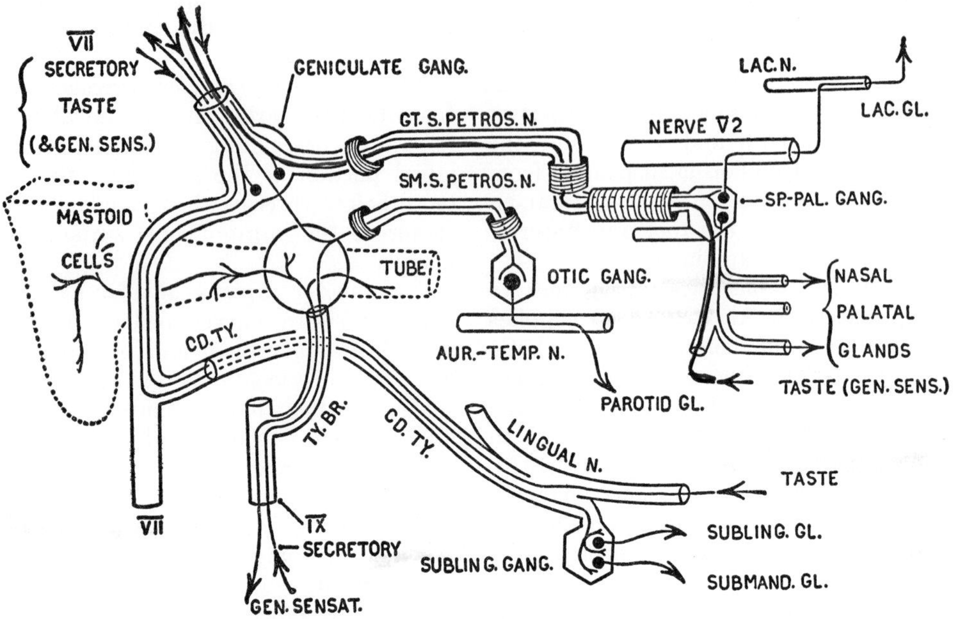

FIG. 797. Parasympathetic ganglia on the branches of nerves VII and IX: pterygo-(spheno-)palatine, otic, and submandibular (sublingual).

surface of the vaginal process of the medial pterygoid plate.

Through the greater palatine canal, the Greater (Anterior) Palatine Nerve descends to the under surface of the hard palate medial to the 3rd molar tooth. Thereafter, as two branches, it runs forwards in the mucoperiosteum near the alveolar process and supplies the remainder of the hard palate and the adjacent portion of the gums. It gives off (1) *posterior lateral nasal nerves,* which pierce the vertical plate of the palatine bone and pass forward to the inferior concha and inferior meatus; and (2) *two lesser palatine nerves,* which traverse the lesser palatine canals, appear close behind the parent nerve and supply the mucous membrane of the soft palate and adjacent parts of the tonsillar region.

The **sympathetic fibers** (mainly vasoconstrictor) pass from their relay station in the superior cervical ganglion through the carotid canal to the foramen lacerum, where (as the deep petrosal nerve) they leave the carotid artery and join the **secretory fibers** (greater petrosal nerve) to form the nerve of the pterygoid canal.

The Nerve of the Pterygoid Canal passes forward, through its canal, to the pterygopalatine ganglion and, after being relayed, is conveyed with the various branches of V^2 to the glands of the nose, nasopharynx, and palate; and some fibers travel with the zygomatic nerve, thence to the lacrimal nerve, and so to the lacrimal gland (*fig. 797*).

The secretory root also contains a few *taste fibers* which are distributed to the soft palate. It has therefore the same composition as the chorda tympani and they both share the geniculate ganglion as a cell station for taste fibers.

Maxillary Artery, 3rd part (continued from page 637 and *fig. 743*). This artery passes through the pterygomaxillary fissure into the pterygopalatine fossa and there gives off its branches.

Branches. The branches all escape through foramina (*fig. 743*) in company of the branches of the maxillary nerve and pterygopalatine ganglion, shown in figures 795 and 796, namely:

Posterior superior alveolar
Infra-orbital
    anterior superior alveolar
Artery of pterygoid canal

Descending palatine
  greater palatine
  lesser palatine
Sphenopalatine
  pharyngeal
  posterior lateral nasal
  posterior septal

The corresponding *veins* form the pterygoid plexus, and out of this the maxillary vein emerges.

NASAL CAVITIES

The right and left nasal cavities are situated above the hard palate and are separated from each other by the nasal septum. Each cavity has an anterior and a posterior aperture, a floor, roof, median wall or septum, and a lateral wall.

THE NARIS, nostril, or anterior nasal aperture, is directed downward on to the face. It is oval, mobile, and kept patent by the U-shaped alar cartilage and is controlled by muscles (*figs. 650* and *651*).

THE CHOANA or posterior nasal aperture is directed backward into the nasopharynx. It is oblong, rigid, bounded by bone, 1″ high and ½″ wide (*fig. 754*).

THE FLOOR, formed by the superior surface of the hard palate, is smooth, concave from side to side, ½ inch or more wide, about 3 inches long from the tip of the nose to the posterior border of the septum, and nearly horizontal (*fig. 798*).

THE ROOF has: (1) an *anterior part* whose slope corresponds to the slope of the bridge of the nose (formed by the lateral nasal cartilage, nasal bone, and spine of the frontal bone); (2) an *intermediate part*, formed by the cribriform plate, which is horizontal, 2 to 3 mm. wide, thin, delicate, and perforated by the olfactory nerves and ethmoidal vessels. It is situated beneath the anterior cranial fossa and is easily fractured, with consequent risk of meningitis. (3) *A posterior part* is formed by the anterior and the inferior surface of the body of the sphenoid, and has therefore a vertical and a sloping portion, which meet at an obtuse or a right angle. This part is about ⅓ of an inch wide, and is confluent with the roof of the nasopharynx.

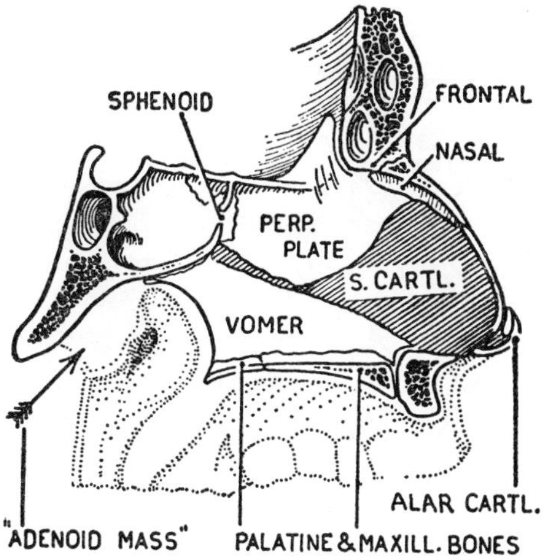

FIG. 798. Bones and cartilages of nasal septum

The **Nasal Septum** or Medial Wall has three main skeletal parts (*fig. 798*):

1. The thin *perpendicular plate of the ethmoid* lies above.
2. The *vomer* lies below and behind.
3. The *septal cartilage* lies in front and extends backward into the angle between the ethmoid and the vomer.

Slight *crests* on the palatine, maxillary, nasal, frontal, and sphenoidal bones form peripheral parts of the bony septum.

The posterior border of the vomer is free and extends from the posterior nasal spine to just in front of the junction of the sphenoid and basi-occipital.

The anterior part of the inferior border of the septal cartilage extends from the anterior nasal spine toward the apex of the nose. And, below this is the mobile part of the septum, which is strengthened by the medial crura of the alar cartilages (*fig. 650*).

»» *Deflected Septum.* If the septum is not quite straight, the deflection usually takes place at the junction of the cartilage with the vomer, and the bony and soft parts of the middle concha on the concave side are enlarged, as though to reduce the excess space.

At Birth, except for a miniature vomer, the framework of the septum and of the crista galli is cartilaginous. The definitive septal cartilage remains cartilaginous; the perpendicular plate of the ethmoid (and crista galli) is converted into bone; but the cartilage that precedes the vomer disappears, the vomer developing in right and left halves from the perichondrium on each side of the primitive septal cartilage. The alae of the vomer and the groove along the upper border of the vomer into which the definitive septal cartilage fits bear evidence of this bilateral origin.

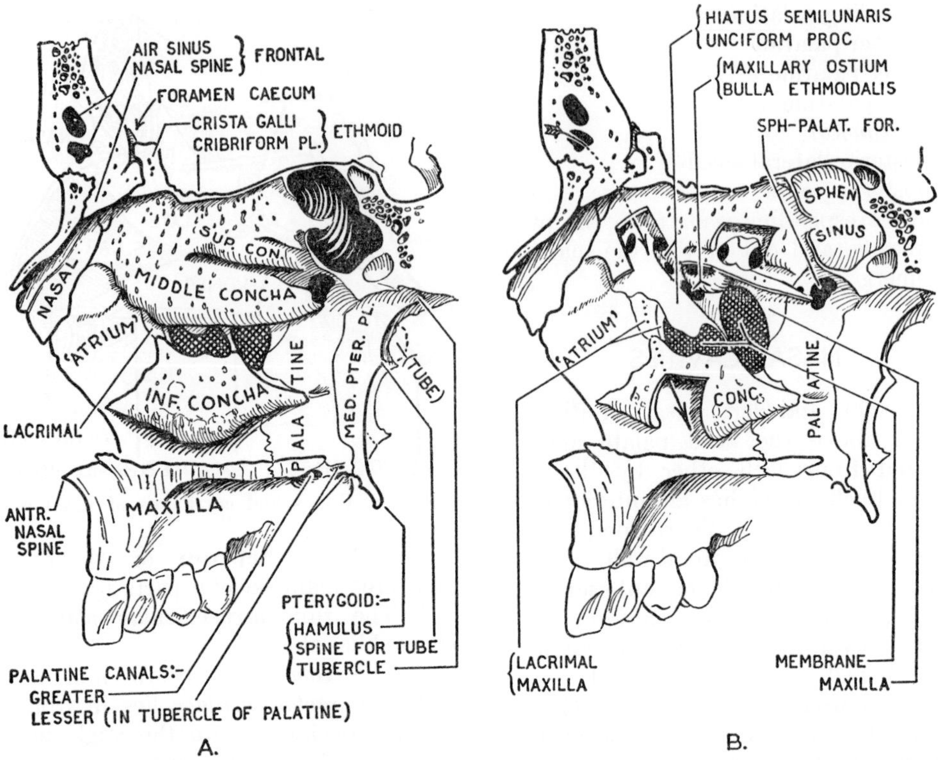

FIG. 799. *A*, bones of lateral wall of nasal cavity. *B*, orifices of air sinuses and nasolacrimal canal, revealed by cutting away parts of the conchae. (*Arrows* lead from frontal sinus and nasolacrimal canal.)

On removing the bony and cartilaginous parts of the septum but leaving the mobile septum and the mucoperiosteum on the far side intact, the injected arteries can be seen and the nerves perhaps dissected.

VESSELS AND NERVES of the Septum. The *arteries* form an open network or *rete*. Descending from above are the branches of the ant. and post. ethmoidal arteries and of the olfactory and ant. ethmoidal nerves. Running obliquely forward, in a groove on the vomer, to the incisive canal is the nasopalatine nerve, and near it are companion arteries (post. nasal septal aa.). The nerve descends through the incisive canal to the palate; a branch of the greater palatine artery ascends through the canal to anastomose with the septal rete, and a branch of the superior labial art. also joins the rete. The infra-orbital nerve supplies the vestibular part of the septum.

Lateral Wall (*figs. 799* and *800*). Two downwardly curved shelves, the *inferior* and *middle conchae*, project from the lateral wall of the cavity and conceal the *inferior and middle meatuses.* A third shelf, the *superior concha*, quite short and oblique, projects from the posterosuperior part of the lateral wall and conceals the *superior meatus*. The area above and behind the superior concha is the *spheno-ethmoidal recess.*

The inferior and middle conchae extend backward almost to the nasopharynx. The lower border of the inferior concha is free, horizontal, and ends ½″ in front of the auditory tube. The lower border of the middle concha is largely horizontal but with the addition of a short vertical or oblique anterior limb and, consequently, of an antero-inferior angle. It is on a level with the lower surface of the body of the sphenoid.

The part of the nasal cavity between the conchae and the septum is the *meatus communis*. The part anterior to the conchae is divided into two areas—a *vestibule* and an *atrium* (*fig. 800*).

The *vestibule,* or entrance chamber, lies in front of the inferior meatus, its lateral wall being the medial surface of the mobile ala of the nose. It is lined with stratified squamous epithelium, guarded by hairs, and lubricated by sebaceous and sweat glands—in short, by skin. Further, as the *apical recess,* it extends forward toward the tip of the nose. The U-shaped alar cartilage keeps the vestibule patent.

The *atrium* lies in front of the middle meatus and above the vestibule. A ridge or limen, caused by the upper edge of the alar cartilage, separates the atrium from the vestibule. It is lined with the mucoperiosteum covering the frontal process of the maxilla. Anterior to the atrium the lateral wall is formed by the nasal bone and the lateral nasal cartilage.

» Cut away the inferior concha and note its curved attachment to the side wall of the nose.

Inferior Meatus. A blunt probe passed from the orbital cavity down the *nasolacrimal duct* into the inferior meatus, travels downward and slightly backward and laterally, and traverses the mucous membrane obliquely like a ureter entering the bladder. The flap *valve* thus formed opens anywhere on the line between the summit of the curved attachment of the inferior concha and the floor of the nose.

The *(bony) nasolacrimal canal* opens at the summit of attachment of the inferior concha, which is at the junction of its anterior one-third with its posterior two-thirds. The thinnest part of the lateral wall of the inferior meatus is situated behind the nasolacrimal canal.

» This thin area, triangular in shape, is formed by the maxillary process of the inferior concha (*fig. 846*). Its apex falls far short of the floor of the nose. Its center lies about 2½" from the tip of the nose, or 1¼" from the anterior bony aperture. Through this triangular area the surgeon may pass a hollow needle into the maxillary sinus. Behind, it articulates with the vertical plate of the palatine bone; in front, with the medial wall of the maxilla, which is strong and will not give way before the probe. A sensory twig, the *nasal branch of the anterior superior alveolar nerve* with its companion artery, pierces the lateral wall abreast of the incisive foramen (*figs. 795* and *796*).

Middle Meatus. A probe passed from *the lowest part of the frontal sinus* into the nose enters the middle meatus at the anterior

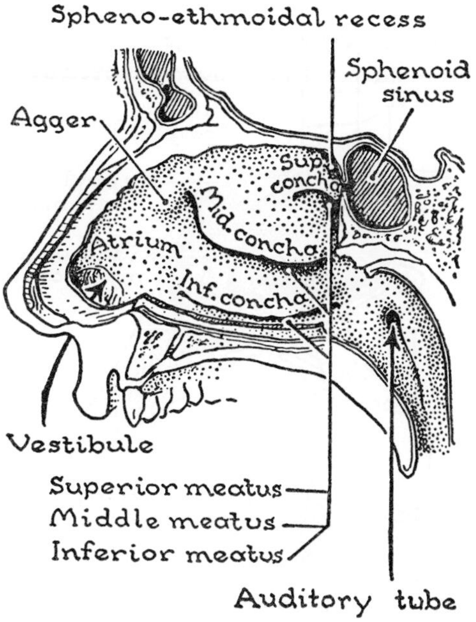

FIG. 800. The lateral wall of the nasal cavity

end of a curved groove, the *hiatus semilunaris.* The hiatus has a sharp lower edge; above it there is an ovoid swelling, the *bulla ethmoidalis.* Behind its midpoint the hiatus opens through an *ostium* of variable size into the *maxillary sinus at its highest part* (*fig. 803*). An *accessory* (an acquired) *ostium* is often to be seen about half an inch behind the (primary) ostium. The papery lacrimal bone lies immediately behind the strong force-transmitting frontal process of the maxilla.

» With a sharp probe, one may break through the lacrimal bone and then open into the lacrimal sac, as the surgeon may do to afford drainage when the nasolacrimal duct is obstructed.

The orifices of several anterior ethmoidal cells are seen under cover of the middle concha. The cell (or cells) in the bulla is the *bullar cell* (or cells).

Superior Meatus. The large orifices of one or more posterior ethmoidal cells open here.

Spheno-ethmoidal Recess. The circular orifice of the sphenoidal air sinus opens here, high up (*fig. 800*).

» On picking away, one by one, the partitions between the ethmoidal cells, the delicate orbital plate of the ethmoid, which closes the cells laterally and at the same time forms the medial wall of the orbital cavity, is displayed.

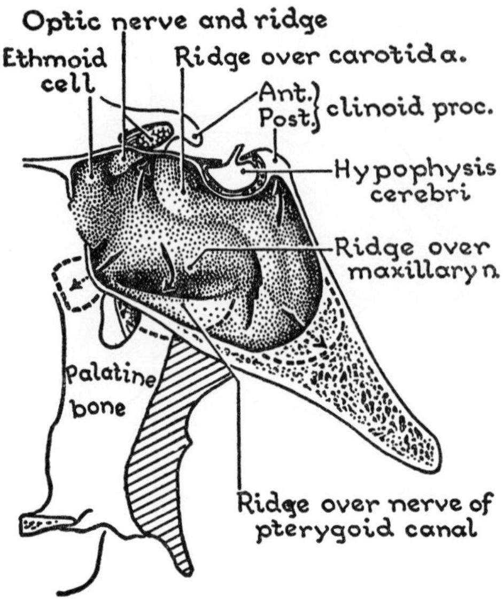

FIG. 801. A large sphenoidal sinus with many diverticula. Its important relationships are indicated by the contours of the bone.

Blood Supply to the Nasal Cavities. The arterial network is very free and is derived from:

1. The *ophthalmic artery*, via its ant. and post. ethmoidal branches, supplies the upper and front parts of the lateral wall and septum.

2. The *maxillary artery*, via its sphenopalatine branch, which traverses the sphenopalatine foramen, supplies the posterior parts of the lateral wall and septum. To reach the septum the artery (post. septal a.) must cross the roof of the cavity. This it does at the junction of the anterior and inferior aspects of the body of the sphenoid.

3. The *facial artery*, via the superior labial art., supplies the antero-inferior part of the septum.

The *venous network* forms a distensible cavernous tissue, especially over the inferior and middle conchae, its function being to warm and humidify the inspired air. Following the arteries, the veins drain: (1) upward via the ethmoidal veins into the superior ophthalmic vein; one vein, however, piercing the cribriform plate, joins the veins beneath the frontal lobe of the brain; (2) mainly backward through the sphenopalatine foramen to the pterygoid plexus; and (3) forward to the (anterior) facial vein.

The *lymphatics* (p. 717).

Perineural spaces. Around the filaments of the olfactory nerve distributed in the nasal mucosa are perineural spaces. These have been shown by experiment to be prolongations of the cranial subarachnoid space and to have no connection with lymph vessels (Faber).

Nerve Supply of the Nasal Cavities. The upper parts of the septal and lateral walls (over a total area of 2 sq. cm.) are supplied by the *olfactory nerves*, which, ensheathed in their membranes, pierce the cribriform plate in twenty or so filaments. These end in the olfactory bulb.

Ordinary sensation is carried mostly by V^2 with some help anteriorly from V^1. Figure 796 provides a summary.

»» *To cut off the sensory nerve supply:* (1) inject with a curved hollow needle an anesthetic through the sphenopalatine foramen; (2) put a plug of gauze (soaked in anesthetic) in the angle between the nasal bone and the septum (3) and another plug of guaze under the anterior end of the inferior concha (*fig. 796*).

The 1st anesthetizes the branches of the pterygopalatine ganglion, viz., post. lateral nasal and post. septal (nasopalatine) nerves (p. 689).

The 2nd catches the internal nasal branches of the anterior ethmoidal nerve. It is the medial of these branches that grooves the nasal bone and appears on the dorsum nasi as the ext. nasal nerve.

The 3rd catches the nasal branch of the anterior superior alveolar nerve which pierces the medial wall of the maxilla deep to the inferior concha. The branches of the *infra-orbital nerve* to the vestibule and mobile part of the septum would remain intact (*fig. 658*).

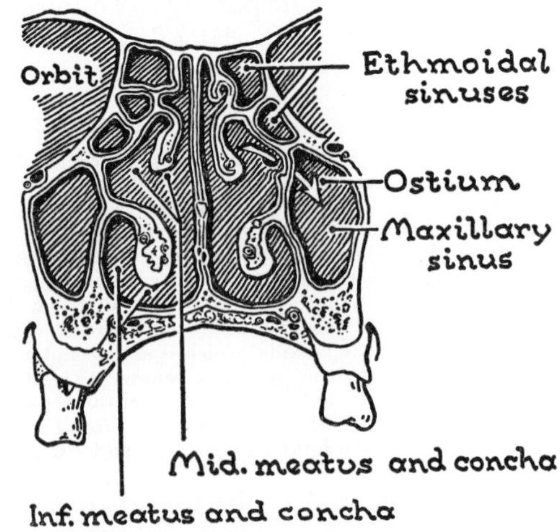

FIG. 802. The nasal cavities and adjacent air sinuses, on coronal section.

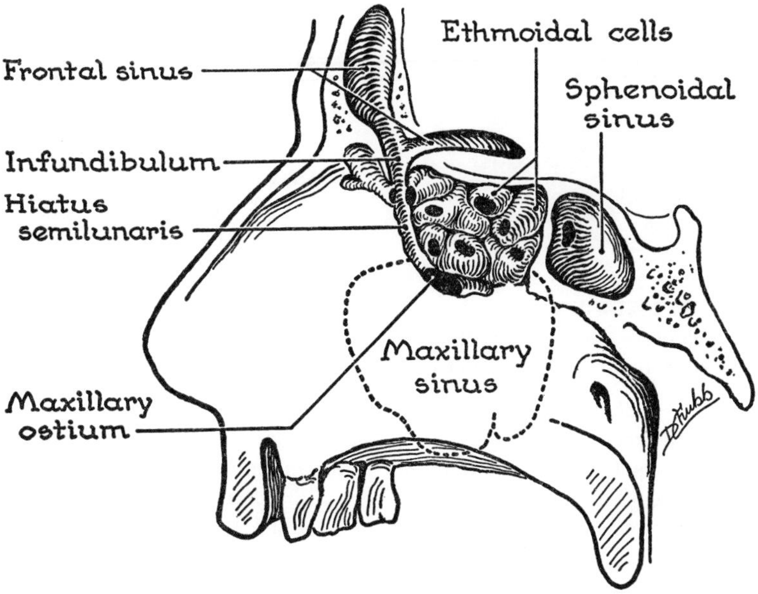

FIG. 803. Diagram of the paranasal sinuses

Note that if there were fluid in the frontal sinus, it would drain down the infundibulum, along the hiatus, and into the maxillary sinus, for the orifice of the frontal sinus is at its floor and that of the maxillary sinus at its roof. The sphenoidal ostium is in the upper half of its anterior wall. The ethmoidal ostia are variable.

Paranasal Air Sinuses

The paranasal sinuses (sphenoidal, ethmoidal, frontal, and maxillary) are paired, but they are commonly asymmetrical (*figs. 801* to *805*).

The *Sphenoidal Sinuses* are two in number—a right and a left (*fig. 803*). They are variable in extent, rarely symmetrical, and the partition between them is usually deflected. They occupy the body of the sphenoid, but may extend backward even into the basi-occipital and into the anterior and posterior clinoid processes, and the root of the pterygoid process (*fig. 801*).

The optic nerve, maxillary nerve, and nerve of the pterygoid canal are in contact with, and may raise ridges on the roof, lateral wall, and floor of the sinus. Observe the relationship of the sinus to the hypophysis cerebri above, and to the cavernous sinus and carotid artery laterally.

The circular ostium of the sinus is near either the middle or upper part of the anterior wall.

Maxillary Sinus (ANTRUM). Between the inferior concha and the ethmoidal bulla the lateral wall of the nose is largely membranous (*fig. 799B*), and a pin pushed through it will enter the sinus, but unless directed downward there is danger that it may enter the orbit.

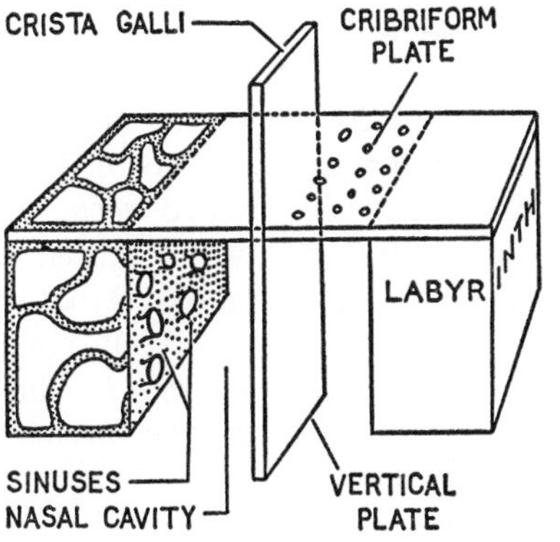

FIG. 804. Scheme of the ethmoid bone

The maxillary *ostium* (*fig. 803*) opens into the hiatus semilunaris, near the roof of the sinus. It is usually an oval or slit-like canal, 4.5 mm. long. Hence, when the mucous membrane lining it is congested,

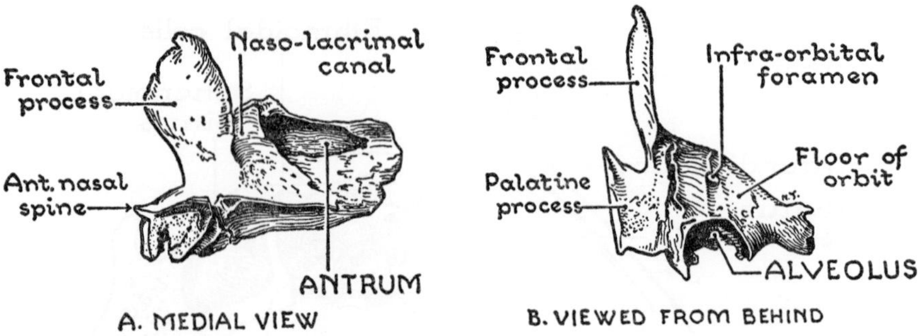

FIG. 805. The maxillary bone at birth, showing (*A*) the developing sinus (antrum), which (*B*) has not yet separated the alveolus from the floor of the orbit.

the canal may be obstructed temporarily. It may, however, be very large.

The maxillary sinus (*fig. 802*) is a *three-sided, hollow* pyramid. The base contributes to the lateral wall of the nasal cavity and is partly membranous (*fig. 799*). The apex stretches toward, or even into, the zygomatic bone. The three sides are translucent: one facing the infratemporal fossa, one the face, and one the orbital cavity. Because the floor of the orbital cavity is concave, the roof or orbital surface of the maxillary sinus is convex. The *infra-orbital canal* creates a ridge on the orbital and facial walls.

The floor or lower border of the sinus lies below the level of the floor of the nose. From the floor one or two *septa* project upward according as two or three molar teeth have erupted. The roots or root of any *tooth* might project into the bony maxillary sinus, save those of the incisors for they are embedded in the incisive bone (premaxilla). Those of the molars commonly do; hence, infection may readily spread from a decaying tooth to the sinus. Again, during the extraction of such a tooth the mucous membrane over the projecting root may be torn with the result that the empty socket connects the sinus to the mouth.

On removing the mucoperiosteal lining from the sinus, the *ant. and post. superior alveolar vessels* and *nerves,* derived from the infra-orbital vessels and nerve, are exposed (*fig. 795*). Where there is diploe they run in bony canals, but for the most part—on the infratemporal and facial walls—the bone is of eggshell thinness, and there the vessels and nerves occupy bony grooves, as they loop downward, and are covered with mucous membrane.

The **Ethmoidal Sinus or Cells** (*figs. 803* and *804*) may be likened to 8 or 10 rubber balloons placed in an oblong box and inflated through their stalks, which project through holes in the side of the box. The result must be an oblong mass of inflated balloons, but the shape of a particular balloon (or cell) depends upon the degree to which it and its neighbors are inflated. All air cells vary much in shape and in extent. A small air cell calls for a large adjacent cell or for several small cells. The ethmoidal cells are limited laterally by the orbital plate (lamina papyracea) of the ethmoid, but the surrounding bones (lacrimal, frontal, sphenoid, palatine, and maxillary) help to close the cells.

(Ethmoid bone, see page 724.)

The **Frontal Sinus** is merely an anterior ethmoidal cell that has extended beyond the ethmoid into the squama (vertical part) and orbital plate of the frontal bone. Topographically, it is frontal; developmentally, it is ethmoidal. It drains downward. Any fluid (mucus) that might be formed in the sinus would gravitate down the infundibulum and along the hiatus semilunaris into the maxillary sinus whose orifice is near its roof. Indeed, the arrangement is such as to tempt you to think that the maxillary sinus is a cesspool into which the frontal sinus drains (*fig. 803*).

One or more of the ethmoidal cells commonly extend into the orbital plate of the frontal bone and even into the lesser wing of the sphenoid.

Development of the Sinuses. The upper and lower jaws and the other bones of the face require to enlarge progressively as the teeth erupt. Enlargement is most economically achieved by the development of hollow bone; hence, the marrow cavities in long bones and the air sinuses in skull bones.

The sinuses appear between the 3rd and 4th intra-uterine months as evaginations of the nasal mucosa. At birth they are shallow depressions. The *frontal sinus* begins to invade the vertical plate of the frontal bone about the 8th month, but it does not rise above the nasion until the 3rd year. Occasionally, it extends but slightly into the vertical plate and extensively into the orbital plate. The *sphenoidal sinus* at the 6th year measures about $\frac{1}{4}''$ in all dimensions. The *maxillary sinus* is the size of a small pea at birth; at the 6th year it is about $\frac{3}{4}''$ in all dimensions (*fig. 805*).

Average Dimensions (width, height, and anteroposterior depths) in the adult are: frontal sinus, $1''$ x $1\frac{1}{4}''$ x $\frac{1}{2}''$; sphenoidal sinus, $\frac{2}{3}''$ x $1''$ x $1''$; maxillary sinus, $1''$ x $1\frac{1}{3}''$ x $1\frac{1}{3}''$.

The *Mucoperiosteum* of the sinuses has a ciliated epithelium like that of the nasal cavities. Being less glandular, it is less vascular and thinner; and it is more readily detached from the bone.

Nerve Supply. The sinuses are supplied by the ophthalmic (V^1) and the maxillary (V^2) nerves—the *frontal sinus* via the supra-orbital nerve; the anterior *ethmoidal sinus* via the anterior ethmoidal nerve; the posterior ethmoidal and *sphenoidal sinus* via the posterior ethmoidal nerve and the pharyngeal and other branches of the maxillary nerve traveling through the pterygopalatine ganglion; and the *maxillary sinus* via the superior alveolar nerves.

CHAPTER 47

LARYNX

The larynx is the upper end of the lower respiratory passages, the pharynx and the nasal cavities being the upper respiratory passages. The *superior laryngeal aperture*, or *aditus laryngis*, rises freely into the pharynx and is separated on each side from the hinder part of the thyroid cartilage by a space, the *piriform recess*, and from the back of the tongue by a depression, the *vallecula*. The valleculae of the two sides are separated by a median fold of mucous membrane, the *median glosso-epiglottic fold*.

EXTERNAL STRUCTURES (*fig. 807*). The **Cricoid Cartilage** (Gk. = like a ring) has two parts: a *lamina* or signet plate more or less quadrilateral and placed behind, and an *arch* with horizontal lower border and oblique upper border. It is the only complete cartilaginous ring in the respiratory passage. Its lumen is circular and it can with difficulty be slipped over a finger (*fig. 806*).

It lies in front of the 6th cervical vertebra.

The **Thyroid Cartilage** (Gk. = like a shield) consists of two quadrilateral plates, the *right and left laminae*, which converge to meet in the median plane in front at an angle. After puberty the angle varies with the sex, being like the subpubic angle—greater in the female than in the male (*fig. 809*). The upper border of each lamina is sinuous, and in the male it projects forward beyond the anterior attached border, thereby creating a projection, the *laryngeal prominence* or Adam's apple. The *posterior border* is free, rounded, and prolonged into an *upper* and a *lower horn*, the upper being the longer (*fig. 807*). The lateral surface is crossed by an *oblique line*, which extends from a tubercle near the upper border to a tubercle on the lower border, and gives attachment to 3 muscles—Sternothyroid, Thyrohyoid, and Inferior Constrictor.

The upper border of the thyroid is attached to the upper border of the body and greater horn of the hyoid by the *thyrohyoid membrane*, the posterior edge of which is thickened to form the (*lateral*) *thyrohyoid ligament*. This ligament joins the tips of the adjacent horns of the thyroid cartilage and hyoid bone, and it contains a nodule (cartilago triticea).

The **Cricothyroid Joint.** There is a *circular facet* on the medial aspect of the tip of the inferior horn of the thyroid cartilage for articulation with a corresponding facet on the side of the lamina of the cricoid. *Radiating fibers*, arranged in three bands, moor the lower horn of the thyroid to the cricoid and allow it to rotate up and down like the visor of a helmet, and perhaps to glide forward slightly. This is a synovial joint.

The *median cricothyroid ligament* is a strong, elastic, triangular band with truncated apex which unites adjacent borders of the cricoid and thyroid in the median plane.

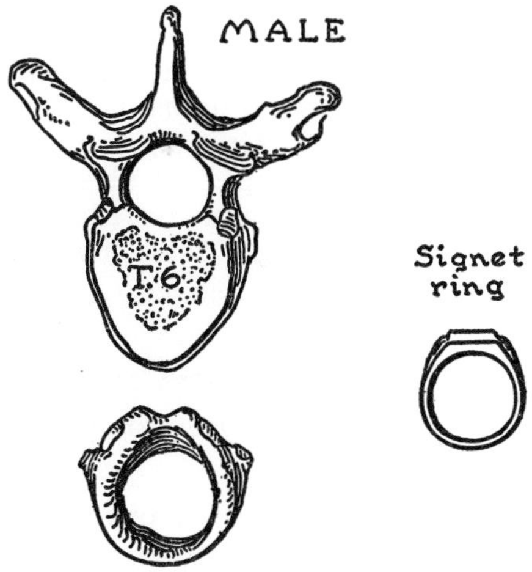

FIG. 806. Compare the lumina of a cricoid cartilage, a vertebral foramen, and a signet ring.

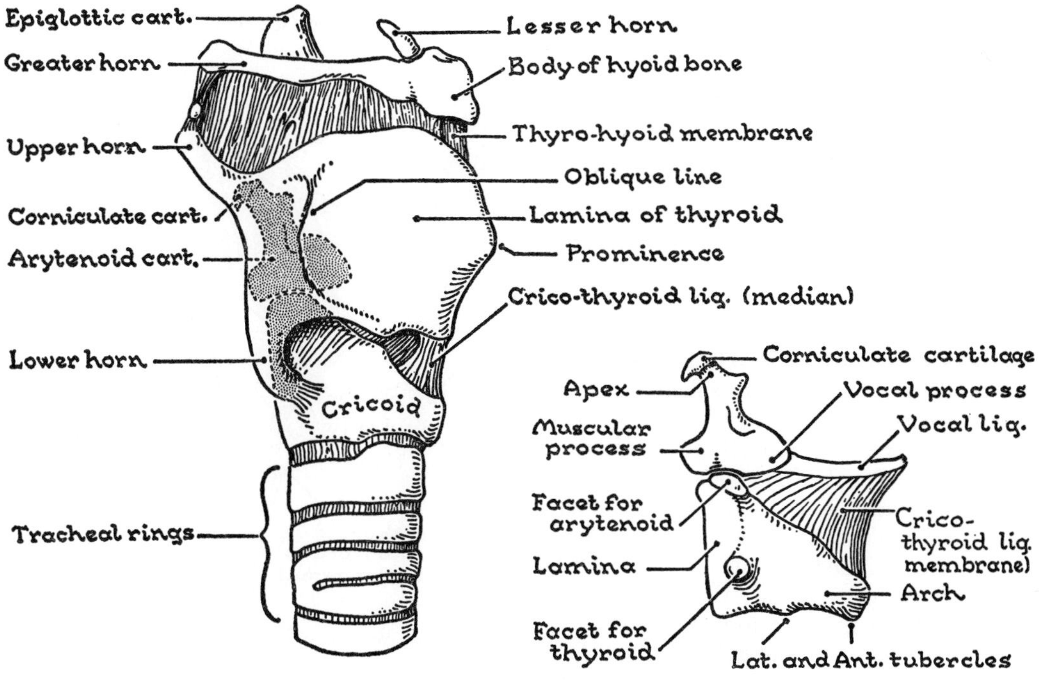

FIG. 807. The cartilages of the larynx, side view
Three ligaments—median cricothyroid, cricothyroid and vocal—constitute the conus elasticus.

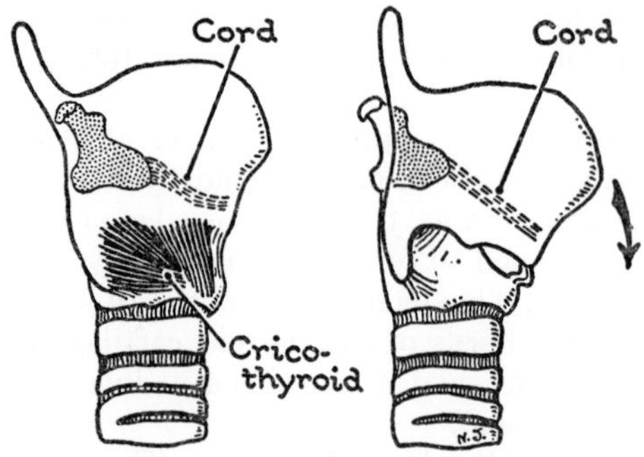

FIG. 808. The Cricothyroids render tense the vocal cords. (*Cricothyroid lig. also called cricothyroid membrane, cricovocal lig., and conus elasticus.*)

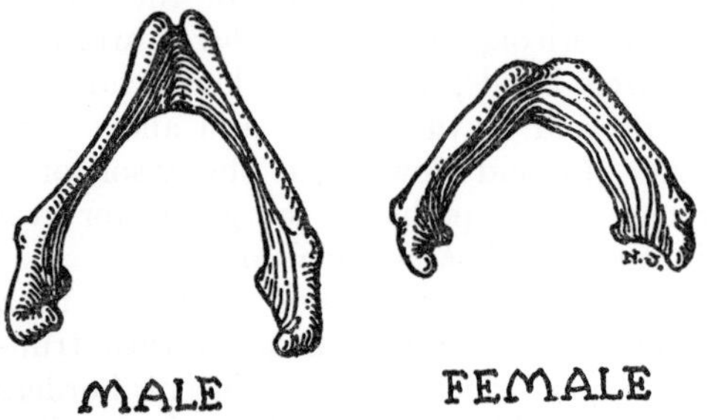

FIG. 809. The angle at which the laminae of the thyroid cartilage meet compares with the subpubic angle of that sex.

The Cricothyroid is the rotator muscle (*fig. 808*). It arises from the outer surface of the arch of the cricoid, which it monopolizes, and it is inserted into the lower border of the lamina of the thyroid cartilage and into the anterior border of the inferior cornu.

Nerve Supply: Ext. laryngeal nerve.

The lower border of the cricoid is attached to the first tracheal ring by the *cricotracheal ligament.*

INTERNAL FRAMEWORK. The inner parts of the larynx are shielded by the thyroid cartilage.

The **Arytenoid Cartilage** (paired) is like the quadrant of a cone. [Actually, the medial surface is flat; the posterior and inferior are concave; and the anterolateral is irregularly rounded.] It has 3 pronounced angles—a sharp anterior, the *vocal process;* a blunt lateral, the *muscular process;* and a recurved superior, the *apex* (*fig. 809.1*).

VOCAL AND CRICOTHRYOID LIGAMENTS. From the end of the vocal process a band, the *vocal ligament,* passes horizontally forward to the angle between the thyroid laminae at its midpoint. It is the framework of the vocal fold (vocal cord). The triangular membrane of which it forms the upper border is the *cricothyroid ligament* or *conus elasticus.* This membrane is attached below to the whole length of the upper border of the arch of the cricoid; in front it blends with the median cricothyroid ligament; and, after curving medial to the lower border of the thyroid cartilage, it ends above in a free upper border, the *vocal ligament.*

The **Epiglottic Cartilage** (unpaired) is a curved leaf-shaped cartilage, pitted to accommodate glands. Its stalk is attached by a ligament, the *thyro-epiglottic*

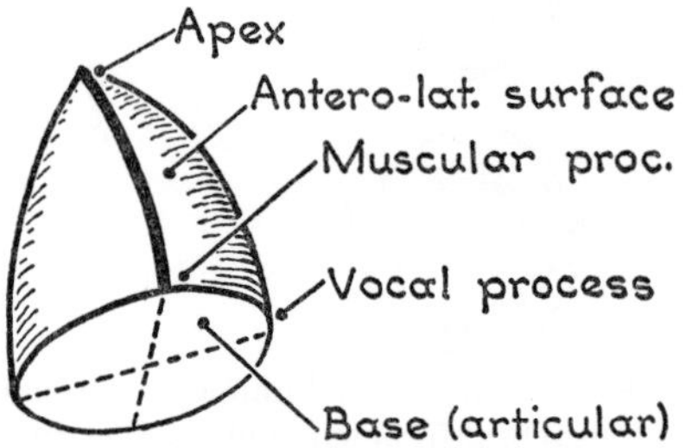

FIG. 809.1. Scheme for naming the parts of the arytenoid cartilage (see text).

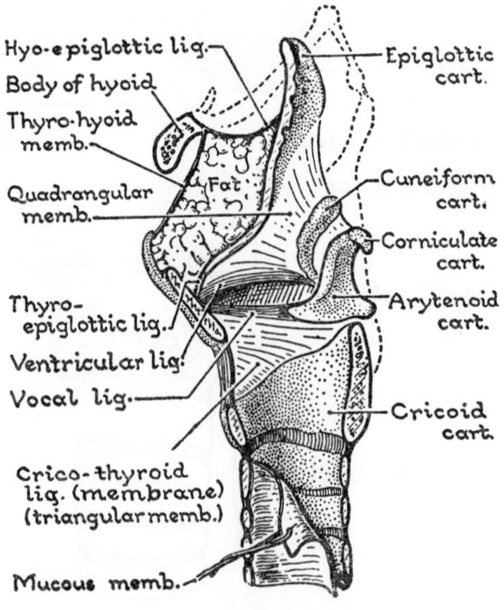

FIG. 810. The cartilaginous and membranous skeleton of the larynx, on median section.

lig., to the angle of the thyroid laminae above the vocal ligaments. Its rounded tip rises above the level of the hyoid bone. Its anterior surface is attached to the hyoid bone by a fibrous band, the *hyo-epiglottic lig.* (*fig. 810*). From its lateral border a fibro-elastic sheet, the *quadrangular membrane*, more delicate than the cricothyroid lig., curves backward to the lateral border of the arytenoid cartilage. The free upper edge of the quadrangular membrane is slightly thickened (the *aryepiglottic lig.*); the free lower border is markedly thickened to form the vestibular ligament, which is the basis of the vestibular fold (false vocal cord).

The recurved cornu or apex of the arytenoid, the *corniculate cartilage*, is separated from the main cartilage by a film of perichondrium. In the hinder part of the quadrangular membrane a detached portion of the side of the epiglottic cartilage was stranded during development; like the epiglottic cartilage it is pitted by glands. It is called the *cuneiform cartilage*, but it resembles a club more than a wedge. Its lower end is fixed to the arytenoid cartilage.

This internal framework of cartilage, fibro-elastic membrane, and ligament is covered with a sheet of muscle on the outside and is lined with mucous membrane on the inside. This being so, the framework is most readily revealed by splitting the larynx and trachea from behind by a median incision and peeling off the mucous membrane.

Between the vestibular and vocal ligaments the membrane is thin and is ballooned laterally to form a canoe-shaped depression.

Definitions. The term *"glottis"* is sometimes applied to the vocal folds. The term *"rima glottidis"* is applied to the narrow or cleft-like portion of the air passages bounded on each side by a vocal fold and the base of an arytenoid cartilage (*fig. 813*).

Extrinsic muscles move the larynx as a whole (e.g., Sternothyroid, Omohyoid, Digastric); whereas *intrinsic muscles* move the parts of the larynx on each other.

Mechanics of the Crico-arytenoid Joint. On the hinder part of the rounded upper border of the cricoid an elliptical facet (6 mm. long) slopes laterally, downward, and forward. Articulating with it is the (deeply) grooved base of the arytenoid, whose long diameter is set at a right angle to that of the cricoid.

The movements permitted the arytenoid are: (1) gliding down the sloping surface on abduction, and up on adduction; (2) rocking (rotating forward and backward) around the long axis of the elliptical facet. This rocking is such that, on abduction, the vocal process of the arytenoid (which dips downward and forward on adduction) moves upward, laterally, and backward, and the apices curve laterally. (3) A very slight pivotal movement, on a vertical axis, around the strong, steadying posterior crico-arytenoid lig. (von Leden and Moore).

INTRINSIC MUSCLES (*figs. 811* and *812*). The intrinsic muscles of the larynx (Cricothyroid excepted) are applied to the sides and back of the internal framework like a sphincter, imperfectly subdivided into several parts.

LATERALLY, it forms a sheet in five parts:

1. *The Lateral Crico-arytenoid* is applied to the cricothyroid ligament. It arises from the upper border of the arch of the cricoid,

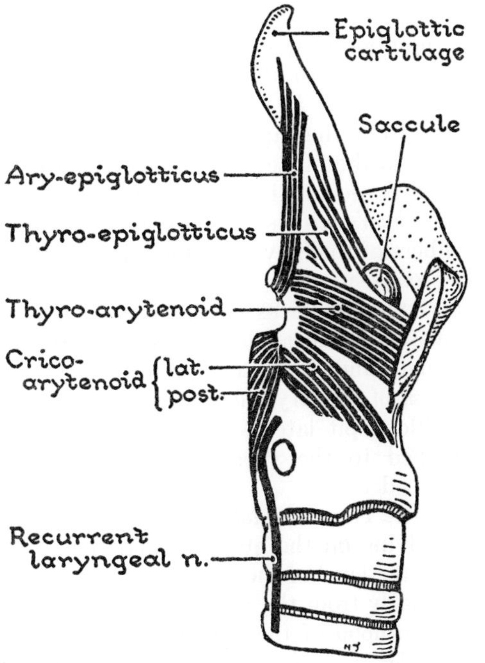

FIG. 811. The intrinsic muscles of the larynx, on side view.

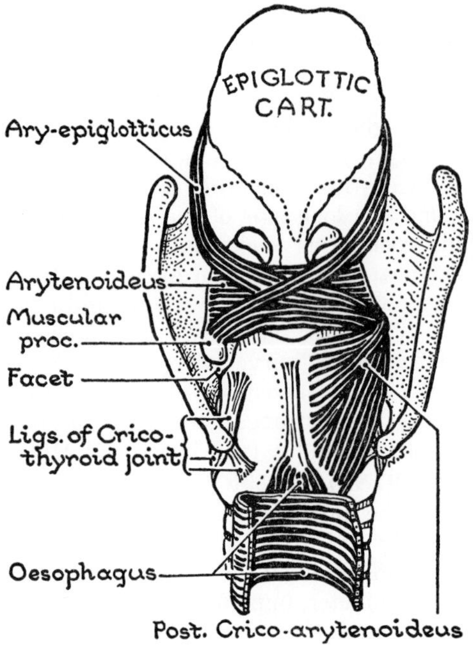

FIG. 812. The intrinsic muscles of the larynx, on posterior view.

passes backwards deep to the lower border of the thyroid and is inserted into the muscular process of the arytenoid.

2. *The Thyro-arytenoid* is the upward continuation of the Lateral Crico-arytenoid. It is applied to the vocal and vestibular ligaments and it extends above them. It arises from the lamina of the thyroid adjacent to the angle and is inserted into the lateral border of the arytenoid.

3. *The Vocalis* is the most medial bundle of fibers of the Thyro-arytenoid. Triangular on cross-section, it is applied to the under and lateral surfaces of the vocal ligament. It arises in the angle between the thyroid laminae, and it is inserted into the vocal process of the arytenoid cartilage and into an oblong pit lateral to it. That fibers are attached to the vocal ligament is denied (von Leden).

4. *The Thyro-epiglotticus.* Wisps of muscle fiber, lying on the quadrangular membrane above the level of the Thyro-arytenoid, pass irregularly from the thyroid cartilage to the neighborhood of the epiglottic cartilage.

5. *The Aryepiglotticus* is applied to the upper free margin of the quadrangular membrane. It is a continuation of the Arytenoideus Obliquus, described below.

POSTERIORLY, there are two parts: (1) *The Arytenoideus* is a thick transverse muscle that covers the arytenoid cartilages (save their apices) posteriorly. It extends from the lateral border and adjacent part of the posterior surface of one arytenoid to the same parts of the opposite arytenoid. The *oblique fibers* arise from the muscular process, decussate with fibers arising from the muscular process of the opposite side, and are partly inserted into the apex of the opposite arytenoid and partly continued as the *Aryepiglotticus* to or towards the epiglottic cartilage. (2) *The Posterior Crico-arytenoid,* though the last muscle to be described, is perhaps the most important of all. Its action is to separate the vocal cords, thereby widening the rima glottidis. All other intrinsic muscles have a sphincteric action on the larynx. The Posterior Crico-arytenoids are, therefore, *"safety muscles."* Bilateral paralysis results in closure of the rima glottidis with the attendant risk of suffocation. For a similar reason, the Genioglossi are *"safety muscles"* (see p. 682).

The Posterior Crico-arytenoid arises from its own half of the posterior surface of the lamina of the cricoid and is there separated from its fellow by a ridge from which the esophagus takes origin. The upper fibers pass horizontally, the lower vertically to the muscular process of the arytenoid.

Muscle Actions and Uses (*figs. 812* and *813*). The muscles of the larynx have three functions, (1) to open the rima glottidis, allowing entry of air so that we can breathe; (2) to close the rima glottidis and vestibule, denying entry to food when we swallow; (3) to regulate the tension of the vocal cords when we speak.

The first two actions are automatic and are controlled by the medulla; the third is voluntary and is controlled by the cerebral cortex.

MUSCLES ABDUCTING AND ADDUCTING THE CORDS, i.e., opening and closing the rima glottidis (*fig. 813*). The paired *Posterior Crico-arytenoids* are the only abductors. Their horizontal fibers rotate the arytenoids laterally; their vertical fibers

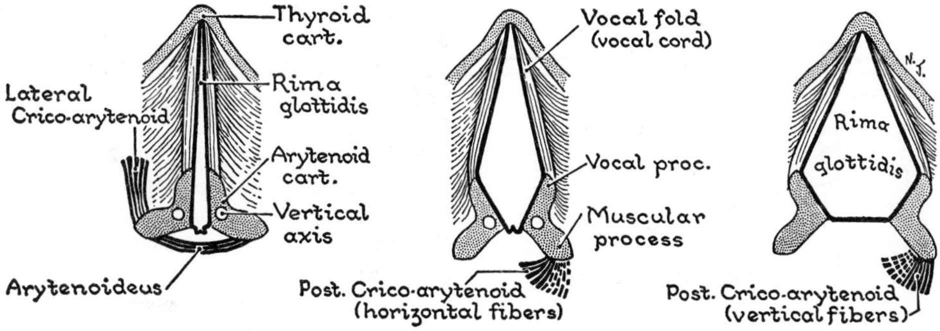

FIG. 813. Scheme of glottis, from above, to explain the actions of the Lateral and Posterior Crico-arytenoids. (The vertical axis is not a stationary one—see text.)

draw the arytenoids down the sloping facets on the cricoid. The Posterior muscles, therefore, abduct the cords, i.e., widen the rima glottidis.

The *Lateral Crico-arytenoids* and the *Thyro-arytenoids* rotate the arytenoids medially and, so, adduct the cords. The *Arytenoideus* approximates the arytenoid cartilages.

MUSCLES CLOSING THE VESTIBULE, as in the act of swallowing. The rima glottidis being closed, the *Thyro-arytenoids* with the help of the *Aryepiglottic* and *Thyro-epiglottic* muscles close the vestibule of the larynx, and tilt the arytenoid cartilages forward and downward.

MUSCLES AFFECTING THE TENSION OF THE CORDS. The cords being adducted, the *Cricothyroids* rotate the thyroid cartilage downward and forward, away from the arytenoid cartilages (*fig. 801*). At the same time the *Posterior Crico-arytenoids* steady (or perhaps tilt backwards) the arytenoid cartilages on the cricoid cartilage. The "slackness" of the cords being thus removed, the Vocales muscles are in a condition to contract effectively. The Vocales may, indeed, be regarded as controlling the fine adjustment of tension.

If one Cricothyroid is inactive (e.g., paralyzed), the opposite Cricothyroid pulls the thyroid cartilage to the inactive side and the cord of the inactive side is rendered slack (*fig. 814*). Similarly, if one side of the tongue is paralyzed, the muscles of the opposite side protrude the tongue to the paralyzed side.

DURING THE ACT OF SWALLOWING the

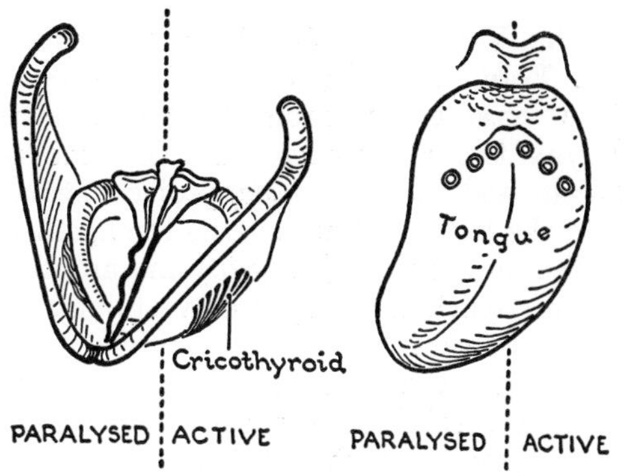

FIG. 814. Unilateral action of the Cricothyroid and of the Genioglossus projects the thyroid cartilage and the tongue to the contralateral side, i.e., inactive or paralyzed side.

Aryepiglottics constrict the entrance to the larynx; the *Thyro-arytenoids* constrict the vestibule and tilt the arytenoid cartilages forward so that their apices touch the tubercle of the epiglottis; the *Arytenoideus* brings the arytenoid cartilages together and the Lateral *Crico-arytenoids* swing the vocal processes medially, thereby closing the rima glottidis.

INTERIOR OF THE LARYNX. The larynx extends from the tip of the epiglottis, which projects above the level of the hyoid bone, to the lower border of the cricoid cartilage.

The Aditus or Entrance to the larynx is oblique. It is bounded by the upper border of the epiglottis, the aryepiglottic fold with the contained upper ends of the cuneiform and corniculate cartilages, and the mucous membrane covering the upper border of the Arytenoideus.

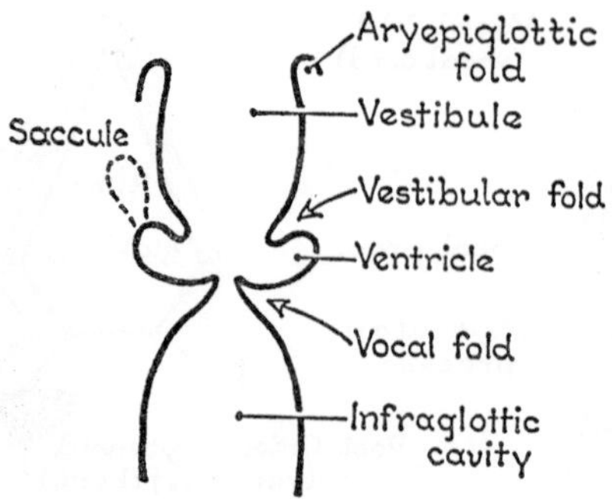

FIG. 814.1 The three parts of the laryngeal cavity, coronal section.

The **Vestibular** (Ventricular) and **Vocal Folds** are also called the false and true vocal cords. From each side of the larynx two anteroposterior folds, the *vestibular* and the *vocal folds*, project medially into the larynx. These overlie the ligaments of the same names (*fig. 810*) and are about 5 mm. apart. The upper or vestibular fold extends forward from the middle of the anterolateral surface of the arytenoid; the lower or vocal fold extends forward from the vocal process of the arytenoid; and both folds reach the angle between the laminae of the thyroid cartilage near its midpoint.

The vocal folds are visible from above because their attachments are medial to those of the vestibular folds. They form the anterior two-thirds or *intermembranous part* of the rima glottidis; the medial borders of the bases of the arytenoids form its posterior one-third or *intercartilaginous part.*

The Three Parts of the Laryngeal Cavity (*fig. 814.1*). The vestibular (ventricular) and vocal folds divide the cavity of the larynx into three parts:

1. In the upper part or *vestibule* of the larynx, a median swelling, the *tubercle of the epiglottis,* lies just above the thyro-epiglottic ligament, and a much smaller swelling on each side overlies the cuneiform cartilage.

2. On each side of the *middle part* the canoe-shaped depression between the vestibular and vocal folds is called the laryngeal *ventricle* (sinus). From the anterior end of the ventricle a cul-de-sac of mucous membrane, the *laryngeal saccule* (appendix), extends upward for about ½ inch. It lies between the quadrangular membrane and the Thyro-arytenoid. Occasionally, it extends above the thyroid cartilage and through the thyrohyoid membrane. In the gorilla, the saccule is of enormous size, extending to the axilla.

3. The inferior part, the *infraglottic cavity,* when viewed from below, is seen to be roofed over, except medianly, by the cricothyroid ligs. [conus elasticus]; it is circular on cross-section.

Nerve Supply. The vagus nerve, via its superior and recurrent laryngeal nerves and aided by the sympathetic (vasomotor), supplies the larynx, providing motor, secretomotor, and sensory fibers. The superior nerve supplies the Cricothyroid muscle and sensation to the larynx above the vocal folds; the recurrent supplies all the internal muscles and sensation below the vocal folds.

The *recurrent laryngeal nerve* enters the pharynx by passing deep to the lower border of the Inferior Constrictor and in contact with the back of the cricothyroid joint. There (or lower down) it divides into: an *anterior branch* which ascends on the lateral sheet of muscles and supplies them; and a *posterior branch* which supplies the two posteriorly placed muscles and communicates with the internal laryngeal nerve.

The *superior laryngeal nerve* divides into the internal and the external laryngeal nerve (*fig. 762*). The *internal laryngeal nerve* perforates the thyrohyoid membrane as several branches, crosses the anterior wall of the piriform recess, reaches the lateral sheet of muscles, and is sensory to the larynx above the glottis, and to the region immediately around the entrance of the larynx. The *external laryngeal nerve* supplies the Cricothyroid.

Blood Supply. The *superior laryngeal branch* of the sup. thyroid a. and the *inferior laryngeal branch* of the inf. thyroid a. supply the larynx. Twigs of the cricothyroid a. assist (p. 607).

Lymph vessels (p. 717).

Structure. *The Mucous Membrane* has a *stratified ciliated epithelium.* Goblet cells, mucous glands, lymph follicles, and diffuse lymphoid tissue are present, as elsewhere in the respiratory passage. *Ciliated* epithelium gives place to *nonciliated* where vibration and impact occur, i.e., over the *vocal folds;* and to *stratified squamous epithelium* over the upper part of the back of the epiglottis due to the friction of passing food. The mucous membrane is *adherent* over the epiglottis and vocal folds; elsewhere and especially behind, where movements are most free, it is loose. *Mucous glands* are abundant in the pits of the epiglottic, cuneiform, and arytenoid cartilages, about the ventricles, and in the saccules.

The Vocal Folds comprise the vocal ligament, the Vocalis muscle, and a covering of thick nonciliated epithelium. They are nonvascular and therefore pale. They contain little submucous tissue and no glands and therefore they do not easily become swollen with risk of suffocation.

» Types of Cartilage. The thyroid, cricoid, and arytenoid cartilages and the tracheal rings are *hyaline* in type. They tend to calcify before middle life and later to turn into bone, as does the hyoid bone at an earlier age. The thyroid cartilage in youth can be cut with a knife; in later life it requires to be sawn. The epiglottic and cuneiform cartilages are formed of *elastic cartilage* and, like the cartilages of the external ear and auditory tube, the corniculate cartilages and the vocal processes of the arytenoid cartilages, they neither calcify nor ossify.

CHAPTER 48

EAR

EXTERNAL EAR

The ear has three distinct parts—external, middle, and internal (*fig. 815*).

The external ear consists of an auricle and an external acoustic meatus.

AURICLE. This is described on p. 543.

MEATUS. This canal is 1″ (24 mm.) long from the bottom of the concha (or $1\frac{1}{2}$″ from the surface of the auricle) (*fig. 816*). It is closed at its fundus by the *tympanic membrane* or ear drum. It is oval on cross-section; so, an oval speculum should be selected when examining the membrane.

The Lateral Third of the meatus (8 mm.) is *cartilaginous*, except behind, where it is completed by fibrous tissue, and it is attached to the thick outer edge of the *bony* meatus. The cartilage of the auricle and the cartilage of the meatus are one piece of elastic cartilage.

With the tip of a finger in the meatus, you can feel the head of your jaw move, when you open your mouth.

The meatus is sinuous, being convex upward and convex backward. So, pulling the auricle upward, backward, and laterally straightens the cartilaginous part, thereby making inspection of the drum, through a speculum, possible.

The Medial Two-Thirds of the canal (16 mm.) is *bony* and is formed by the tympanic bone, except above, where it is completed by the temporal squama. The canal is narrowest some millimeters from the tympanic membrane. Owing to this and to the upward convexity of the canal, the lowest part of the membrane cannot be seen.

»» **Structure.** The cartilaginous part of the meatus is lined with skin in which there are hairs, sebaceous

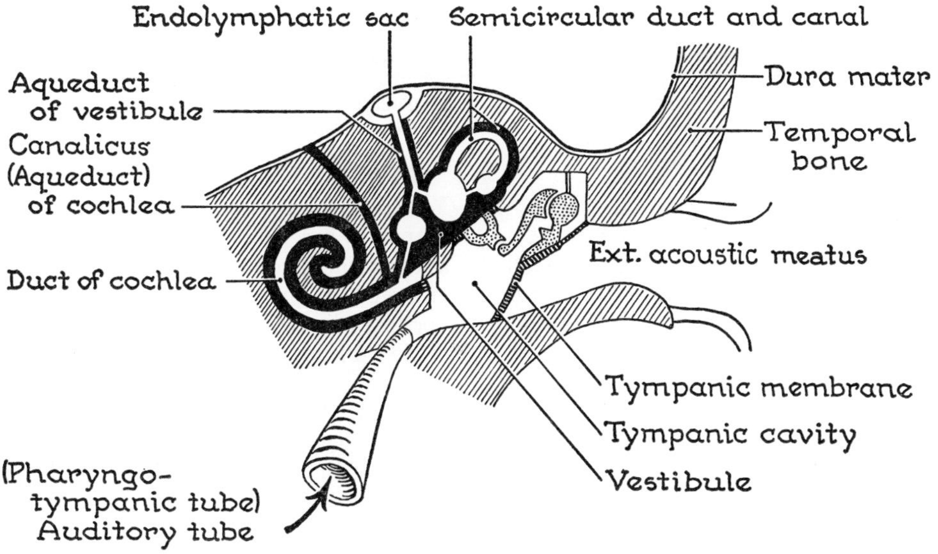

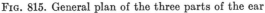

FIG. 815. General plan of the three parts of the ear

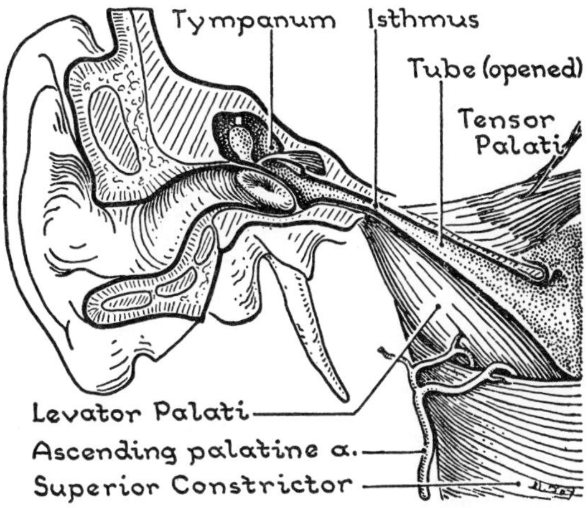

FIG. 816. The auditory tube, opened throughout by removal of its membranous wall and lateral part of its bony wall.

glands, and modified sweat glands which secrete cerumen or wax; hence, boils may occur here. The glands may extend for a short distance along the posterosuperior part of the bony meatus. Otherwise the bony meatus is lined with thin stratified squamous epithelium which is adherent to the periosteum and to the ear drum.

Vessels and Nerves of the Meatus. Arteries: posterior auricular, superficial temporal, and deep auricular branch of the maxillary. *Lymph vessels:* to mastoid, parotid, and superficial cervical nodes. *Sensory nerves:* auriculotemporal and auricular branch of the vagus (which emerges through the tympanomastoid fissure).

MIDDLE EAR or TYMPANUM

The auditory tube (pharyngotympanic tube) and middle ear are derived from the 1st and 2nd pharyngeal pouches, and the aditus to the mastoid antrum and the antrum itself are backward extensions of the middle ear (*fig. 817*).

During the act of swallowing, the tube is opened (page 673).

A chain of three ossicles (malleus, incus, and stapes; *fig. 815*) passes from the tympanic membrane across the cavity to a membrane which closes an oval window, the

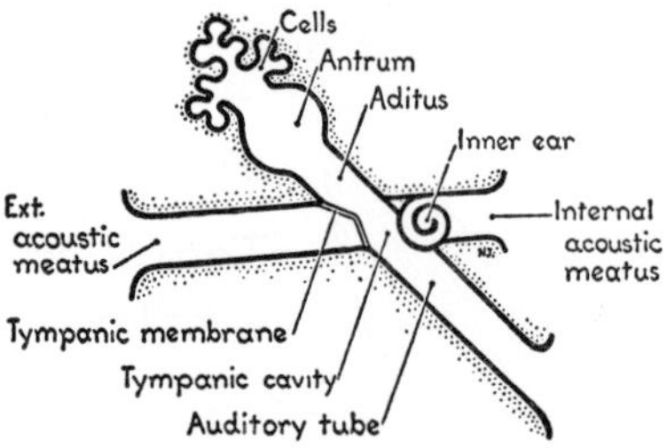

FIG. 816.1. The two meatuses, which have blind ends, and the line of the airway (tube, cavity, aditus, and antrum), which passes between them, viewed from above.

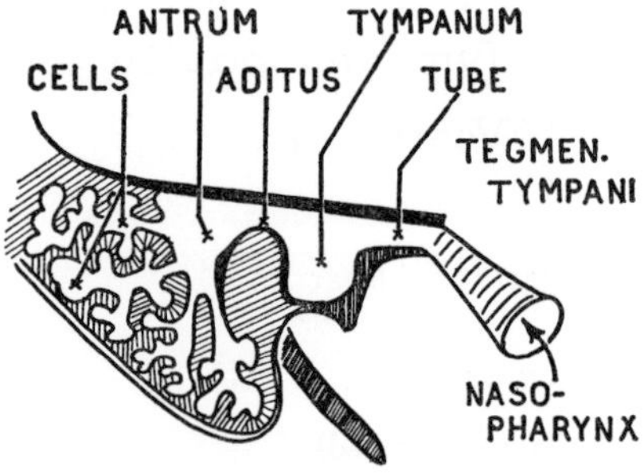

FIG. 817. The tegmen tympani and the passages it covers.

fenestra vestibuli, leading to the internal ear. By this means vibrations in the air are amplified and conducted to the internal ear.

»» **Bony Surroundings in Review.** The features presented by the sloping anterior surface of the petrous bone, described on page 586, and of the vertical posterior surface (p. 583) should be read again.

The floor of the *middle cranial fossa* (*fig. 687*) is commonly papery in thinness along a narrow band that runs from a few millimeters behind the foramen spinosum toward the suprameatal spine, which lies posterosuperior to the orifice of the external acoustic meatus. This narrow band can be broken through with a seeker and picked away with strong forceps. It forms a continuous roof for the tube, tympanum, aditus, and antrum and it is called the **tegmen tympani** (*fig. 817*).

On the *under surface of the skull* (*fig. 755*) a fissure runs from the pterygoid process to the anterior border of the external meatus. The projecting spine of the sphenoid divides the fissure into two halves: the anteromedial half lodges the cartilaginous part of the tube; the posterolateral half encloses the bony part of the tube and extends to the tympanum.

On the *lateral aspect of the skull* (*fig. 731*) the upper border of the zygoma is continued backwards above the external meatus as the *posterior root of the zygoma*, and above the mastoid as the *supramastoid crest*. The crest and the floor of the middle cranial fossa usually lie at exactly the same level; hence, a hole drilled above the supramastoid crest will enter the middle cranial fossa.

The lower part of the mastoid process is rough for the aponeuroses of the Sternomastoid and Splenius. The upper part, called the *postauditory process* (*fig. 834A*), is smooth and triangular; developmentally, it is a downgrowth from the squama of the temporal bone and it closes the mastoid antrum laterally, just behind the suprameatal spine. The *suprameatal spine* lies just behind the posterosuperior part of the orifice of the external meatus.

TYMPANIC CAVITY AND ITS WALLS. The cavity bears remote resemblance to a red blood cell—in being narrow and rounded, compressed at the center, and enlarged peripherally. It is 15 mm. in vertical diameter; 2 mm. across at the center, 4 mm. at the floor, and 6 mm. at the roof.

Again, the tympanic cavity may be likened to a sump pit, or trap, on the sloping course of the aditus ad antrum, epitympanic recess, and auditory tube (*fig. 818*). The floor of the pit overlies the jugular bulb; the anterior wall is the "carotid wall," and the posterior wall is the "facial nerve wall." The tympanic membrane occupies the lateral wall, and the inner ear the medial wall.

As the internal jugular vein and the internal carotid artery, both lying within

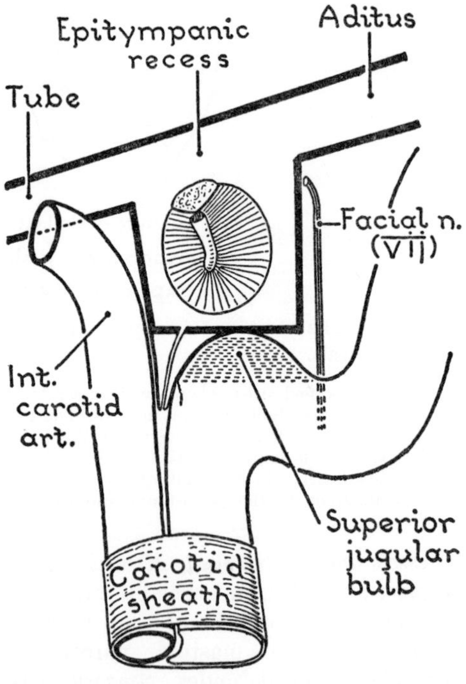

FIG. 818. The tympanic cavity likened to a sump pit on the course of the auditory tube, epitympanic recess, and aditus.

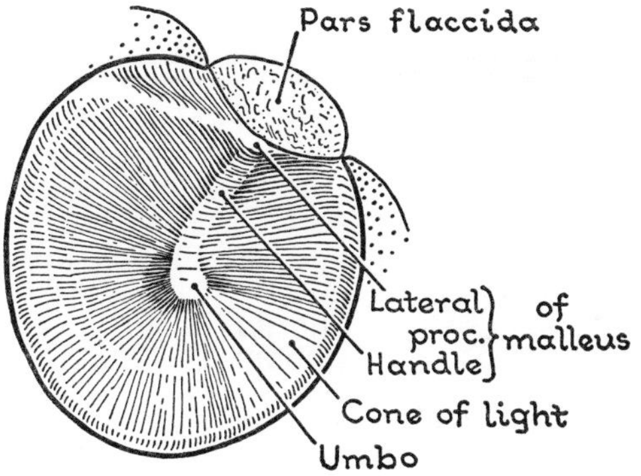

FIG. 819. The tympanic membrane, on lateral view.

the carotid sheath, are followed upward to the base of the skull, they diverge—the vein, as the sigmoid sinus, curving posterolaterally and the artery curving anteromedially. Running through the wedge of bone between the diverging vein and artery is the minute canal for the tympanic branch of the glossopharyngeal nerve.

The Lateral Wall of the tympanic cavity is closed by the tympanic membrane, but the cavity rises a few millimeters above the membrane, this part being the *epitympanic recess* (*fig. 820*).

The Floor is thin and it rests upon the jugular bulb.

The Roof or tegmen tympani is thin and sloping, and the dura mater is adherent to it; and when broken through from above, the malleus and incus are seen rising into the epitympanic recess.

Anteriorly, the roof and floor converge to become the auditory tube. A thin bony shelf divides the tube and provides an upper compartment occupied by the *Tensor Tympani* (*fig. 820*). The free lateral edge of the shelf projects into the middle ear and curls upward to form a pulley (the processus cochleariformis) around which the tendon of the muscle turns to run laterally to its insertion. The ascending part of the *carotid canal* forms the anterior wall below the orifice of the tube (and it ascends medial to it), a delicate plate of bone intervening.

The Posterior Wall in its uppermost part has a tunnel, the *aditus*, through which the epitympanic recess communicates with the mastoid antrum. The aditus has the tegmen for its roof, is a few millimeters long, and scarcely admits a quill. Below this, the *facial nerve* descends in the posterior wall; and jutting forward from this wall is a minute elevation, the *pyramid*. At the apex of the pyramid there is a pinpoint orifice through which the tendon of the Stapedius passes forwards to the neck of the stapes.

The Medial Wall (*fig. 821*) has at its center a swelling, the *promontory*, which overlies the first coil of the cochlea.

On an oblique line between the promontory and the roof of the aditus are (1) the fenestra vestibuli, (2) the canal for the facial nerve, and (3) the lateral semicircular canal. The *fenestra vestibuli* is an oval window opening into the vestibule. It is three mm. in the horizontal axis and it is closed by the footplate of the stapes. The *canal for the facial nerve* curves backward on the medial wall (between the oval window and pyramid below and the lateral semicircular canal above) and descends within the posterior wall. The wall of the canal may be dehiscent in its curved part. The *lateral semicircular canal* lies horizontally, bulges into the aditus and extends forward above the fenestra vestibuli. The bone over it is raised and smooth.

The *fenestra cochleae* is a round window opening into the scala tympani of the cochlea, and closed by the *secondary tympanic membrane*. It lies postero-inferior to the promontory, but it is not evident, since it lies sheltered at the bottom of a depression that faces backward.

TYMPANIC MEMBRANE. This membrane or eardrum (*fig. 819*) is nearly circular, being 9 mm. high and 8 mm. wide. Set in the sulcus of the tympanic bone, it faces laterally, forward, and downward as though to catch sounds reflected from the ground as one advances. It is composed of circular and radial fibers and is lined with epidermis laterally and mucous membrane medially, and the handle of the malleus is incorporated in it. In fact, the radial fibers of the membrane radiate everywhere from the handle except over a triangular area, the *pars flaccida*, between the upper end of the handle (lateral process) and the roof of the meatus.

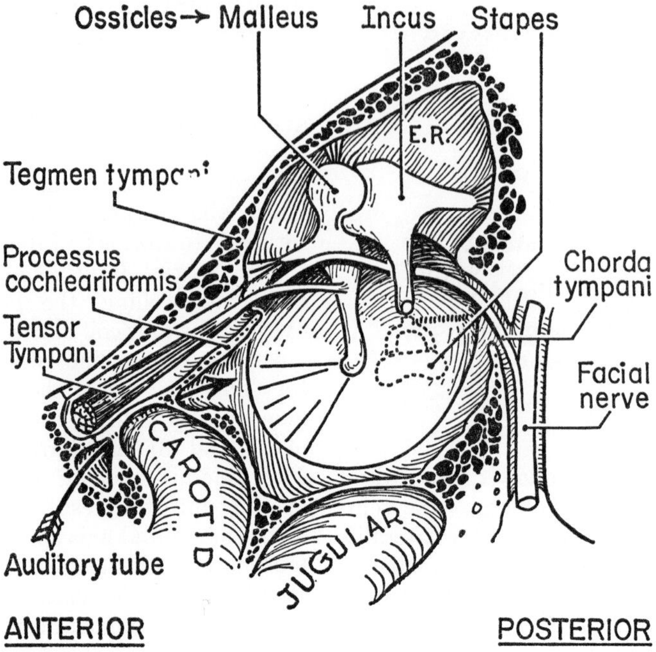

FIG. 820. Lateral wall of the tympanic cavity and the ossicles

At the lower end of the handle the membrane is indrawn: this point, called the *umbo*, lies antero-inferior to the center of the membrane.

The chorda tympani crosses medial to the upper end of the handle of the malleus and is slung from the membrane by an anterior and posterior fold of mucous membrane (anterior and posterior mallear folds).

AUDITORY OSSICLES, JOINTS, AND MUSCLES. Ossicles. There are three ossicles—malleus (hammer), incus (anvil), and stapes (stirrup) (*fig. 820*). The **Malleus** is 8 mm. long. It has a round head with a facet posteriorly, which ends below in a cog; a neck; a long handle embedded in the membrane and ending above in a lateral process, which is short and conical; and an anterior process which is very slender.

The **Incus** is shaped like a molar tooth. It has a body (i.e., the crown), two diverging processes (i.e., roots), a short horizontal one and a long vertical one. The body articulates with the head of the malleus; the long process is parallel to the handle of the malleus and from its end a (lentiform) nodule projects medially to articulate with the stapes.

The **Stapes** has a head with a concave socket for the incus; a short neck; anterior and posterior limbs, which are attached to an oval foot plate. The footplate is attached by an anular ligament to the margin of the fenestra vestibuli.

Joints of the Ossicles. The joints between the malleus and incus, and the incus and stapes have synovial cavities. The head of the malleus and the body and short process of the incus lie within the epitympanic recess. A ligament suspends the head of the malleus from the roof of the cavity, another suspends the body of the incus. Ligaments attach the anterior process of the malleus and the short process of the incus to the front and back of the cavity; and around this axis the ossicles move.

When the vibrating tympanic membrane moves medially, the handle of the malleus moves too and with it the incus, forced by the cog. The stapes is driven into the perilymph, which, being incompressible, causes the secondary tympanic membrane closing the fenestra cochleae to bulge.

» **Sound Conduction.** The effective vibratory area of the tympanic membrane is 55 sq. mm. and the average size of the footplate of the stapes is 3.2 mm. Hence,

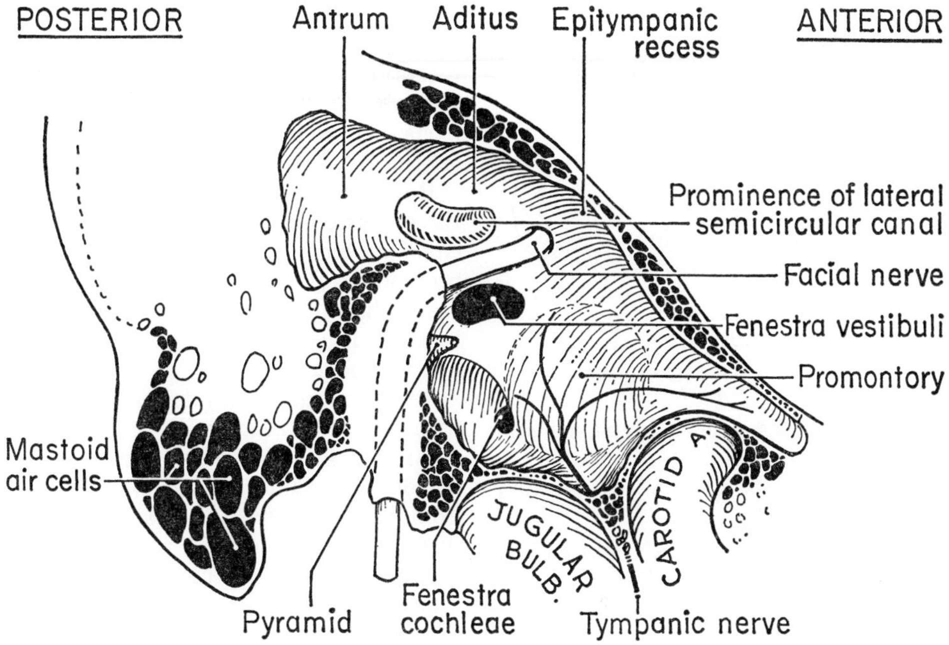

FIG. 821. Medial wall of the tympanic cavity

the hydraulic ratio (membrane to footplate) is as 17 to 1.

The lever ratio of malleus to incus being as 1.3 to 1.0, the total transformer ratio is as 22 to 1 (von Békésy).

The average size of the round window is 3.0 mm.

When the tympanic membrane is forced laterally (e.g., when holding the nostrils and inflating the middle ear), the malleus moves also; the cog disengages, and the incus is released. This ensures against the stapes being torn from the window.

Muscles of the Ossicles. The *Tensor Tympani* is about 2 cm. long. As its tendon leaves its canal (p. 709) it turns laterally round the processus cochleariformis to the upper end of the handle of the malleus; this it pulls medially thereby rendering the membrane tense. It is supplied by the mandibular nerve (V^3) (see otic ganglion, p. 638).

The Stapedius occupies the hollow pyramid and is but a few millimeters long. Its tendon, on leaving the foramen at the apex of the pyramid, passes forward to the neck of the stapes, and on contracting it pulls the anterior end of the foot plate laterally. It is supplied by the facial nerve.

Mucous Membrane lines the walls, closes the hole in the stapes, and covers the ossicles, ligaments, and tendons, forming many folds and pockets. It has no mucous glands, but there are goblet cells where the tube enters.

»» In the tube, however, the lining is in part ciliated and it contains goblet cells and mucous glands—particularly toward the pharyngeal end.

Vessels and Nerves. The *Tympanic Membrane* has two surfaces, each supplied by different nerves and different arteries. Lateral surface—auricular br. of vagus and auriculotemporal nerve; deep auricular br. of maxillary art. Medial surface—tympanic nerve (a branch of nerve IX; see *fig. 761*); and tympanic branches of the maxillary and stylomastoid arteries.

The Tympanum, Mastoid Antrum, and *Mastoid Air Cells* are supplied by the tympanic nerve (*fig. 821*).

»» This ascends through the minute canal between the ugular foramen and the carotid canal and ramifies on jthe promontory, which it grooves and where it is joined by two caroticotympanic twigs of the internal carotid plexus. It supplies the *tube* also.

The arterial supply is (1) the tympanic br. of the maxillary art. which enters through the tympanosquamous fissure (*fig. 756*), (2) the tympanic br. of the ascending pharyngeal art. which follows the tympanic nerve, (3) caroticotympanic twigs of the internal carotid art., which pierce the wall of the carotid canal, (4) the stylomastoid br. of the posterior auricular art., and (5) petrosal brs. of the middle meningeal art.

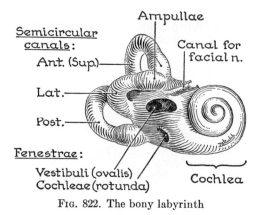

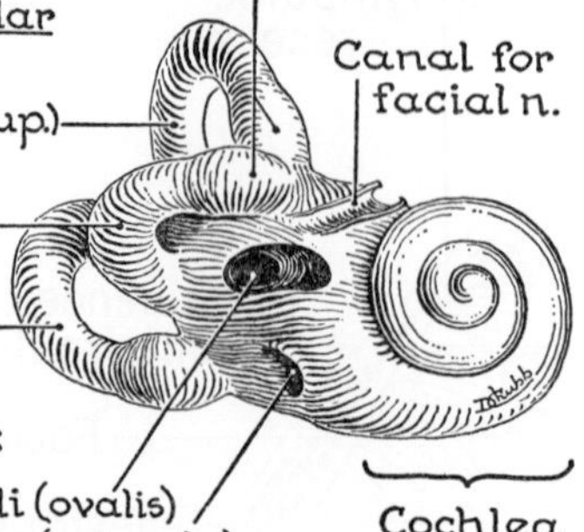

FIG. 822. The bony labyrinth

Veins pass to the pterygoid plexus and inferior petrosal sinus.

Lymph vessels pass to the parotid and retropharyngeal nodes.

MASTOID ANTRUM AND CELLS. The antrum is slightly smaller than the tympanic cavity of which it is a backward extension through the aditus into the petromastoid bone. It occupies the diploic layer at the expense of bone marrow. Its roof, the *tegmen tympani,* which is thin, separates it from the middle cranial fossa. The *sigmoid sinus* is very close behind it, separated by some diploe and a semicylindrical plate of bone, which is part of the inner table of the skull.

»» The *lateral wall,* though described as part of the mastoid, is in reality a downward extension of the temporal squama. It is about 1 mm. thick at birth and it increases by about 1 mm. a year until it is about 15 mm. thick. The antrum is large *at birth,* but there are no mastoid air cells and there is no mastoid process.

The **Mastoid Cells** sprout from the antrum soon after birth and grow like racemose glands, but they are not fully developed till puberty. The cells may be few and small and the mastoid relatively solid, or many and inflated and the mastoid "pneumatic". They may rupture into the groove for the Digastric. They may invade the squama and the roof of the tympanum.

Another collection of air cells, the *tubal* or *tympanic cells,* sprout from the medial wall of the tympanum near the orifice of the auditory tube and, like the branches of a vine, twine themselves around the carotid canal reaching toward, or even to, the apex of the petrous bone.

INTERNAL EAR

The internal ear is concerned with the reception of sound and with balancing. It lies within the petrous bone and has two parts, (1) the *bony labyrinth,* which contains (2) the *membranous labyrinth.*

Bony Labyrinth (*fig. 822*). This has three parts—*cochlea, vestibule,* and *semicircular canals.* The cochlea lies deep to the promontory, the vestibule to the fenestra vestibuli, and the lateral semicircular canal to the aditus. The whole apparatus is but 17 mm. long.

The Cochlea resembles a snail's shell with two and a half coils. It has a central pillar, the *modiolus,* whose base lies at the bottom of the internal acoustic meatus; and from it an *osseous spiral lamina,* like the thread of a screw nail, projects half way across the canal of the cochlea and, with the *basilar membrane,* which stretches across the other half, it divides the canal into two: (1) the *scala vestibuli,* which opens into the vestibule, and (2) the *scala tympani,* which is separated from the tympanic cavity, at the fenestra cochleae, by the *secondary tympanic membrane.*

The two scalae are continuous at the apex of the cochlea, called the *helicotrema.*

A minute duct, the *canaliculus* (aqueduct) *of the cochlea,* runs from the scala tympani through the petrous bone to the notch at the anterior margin of the jugular foramen straight below the internal acoustic meatus. The aqueduct brings the perilymph within the bony labyrinth and the cerebrospinal fluid within the subarachnoid space into communication—such is the general teaching.

»» Recent investigations indicate that the aqueduct of the cochlea is closed by a membrane and not open at depicted in figure 815 (Wharton Young).

The Vestibule communicates *in front* with the cochlea; *behind* with the three semicircular canals; and *medially* with the posterior cranial fossa through the aqueduct of the vestibule (*fig. 815*). When the stapes is removed, the vestibule communicates through the fenestra vestibuli (oval window) with the tympanic cavity.

The Three Semicircular Canals—anterior

(superior), posterior, and lateral—are set at right angles to each other and occupy three planes in space. The lateral canals of opposite sides are horizontal and lie in the same plane. The anterior canal of one side is parallel with the posterior canal of the other side, but they vary somewhat from specimen to specimen.

They are from 12 to 22 mm. long, the lateral being the shortest. Each is less than 1 mm. in diameter, except at one end where there is a swelling, the *ampulla*. They communicate at both ends with the vestibule. There are, however, but five openings, the anterior and posterior canals having a *crus commune*.

The *anterior* (superior) *canal* lies at a right angle to the posterior surface of the petrous bone and produces the arcuate eminence on the anterior (cerebral) surface (*fig. 687*). The *posterior canal* is immediately deep to the posterior (cerebellar) surface of the petrous bone and is parallel to it. It comes to within a third of an inch of the sigmoid sinus (*fig. 686*). The *lateral canal* is deep to the medial wall of the aditus and it runs above the canal for the facial nerve.

Membranous Labyrinth. This comprises (1) the cochlear duct, (2) the saccule, and utricle, and (3) the three semicircular ducts. It is a closed system containing endolymph. A stalk, the *ductus endolymphaticus*, passes from the saccule and utricle through a canal (aqueduct of the vestibule) in the petrous bone to the fissure half an inch lateral to the internal acoustic meatus. There the duct, which acts as a "safety" expansion sac, is placed extradurally. The *cochlear duct* lies on the vestibular side of basilar membrane. It is triangular on section and has a blind end. The *saccule* and *utricle* occupy the vestibule. The *semicircular ducts* only partially fill their canals.

Vessels and Nerves pass through the internal acoustic meatus. The *labyrinthine artery* (int. auditory a.) is a branch of the ant. inf. cerebellar a. The *labyrinthine vein* passes to the inferior petrosal sinus. The cochlear branch of the *acoustic nerve* is auditory; the vestibular branch (distributed to the utricle, saccule, and semicircular canals) is for equilibrium.

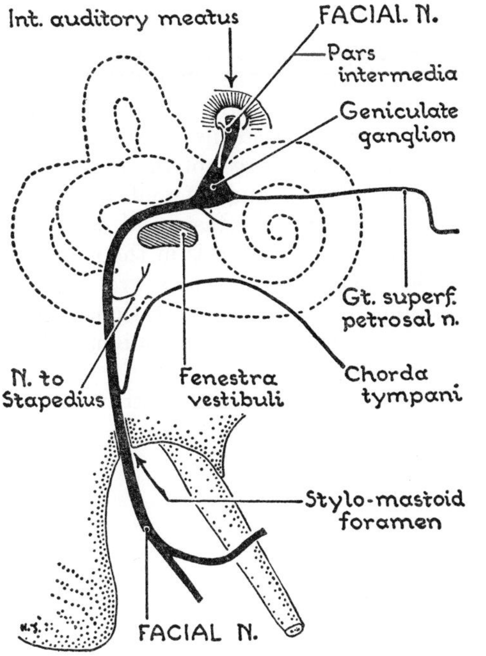

Fig. 823. The intrapetrous course of the facial nerve.

FACIAL NERVE, *Intrapetrous Part.* In the internal acoustic meatus, the facial nerve lies in a groove on the acoustic nerve and is there joined by its sensory root, the *nervus intermedius*, which enters the meatus with it. At the lateral end of the meatus, the nerve enters the facial canal and travels through it to the stylomastoid foramen, whence it issues into the parotid region (p. 632; *fig. 737*).

Its Course takes it laterally, above the vestibule of the bony labyrinth (*fig. 823*), to the medial wall of the tympanic cavity. There it makes an abrupt bend, the *genu*. It then arches backward and downward above the fenestra vestibuli on the medial wall and finally descends in the bony posterior wall of the cavity.

At the genu lies the *geniculate ganglion* (ganglion of the facial nerve) and there the *greater* (*superficial*) *petrosal* and a *root of the lesser* (*superficial*) *petrosal* leave it and *sympathetic twigs* (external petrosal nerve) join it. In its descending part it supplies the *Stapedius* and gives off the *chorda tympani*.

The Geniculate Ganglion (Ganglion of the

facial nerve) is the cell station of the taste fibers in the greater petrosal nerve and chorda tympani. The secretory fibers of the nervus intermedius pass "nonstop" through the ganglion (*fig. 797*).

The Nervus Intermedius (Pars Intermedia) or so-called *sensory root* of the facial nerve, has both afferent and efferent fibers. The *afferent fibers* subserve taste and deep sensibility—their cell station is in the geniculate ganglion. The *efferent fibers* are secretory (autonomic)—their relay stations are in the pterygopalatine, and submandibular ganglia (*fig. 797*).

The Chorda Tympani is distributed with the lingual nerve, so it leaves the facial nerve a few millimeters above the stylomastoid foramen, passes forward between the mucous and fibrous layers of the tympanic membrane, crosses medial to the handle of the malleus, and emerges through the medial end of the petrotympanic fissure. It then crosses medial to the spine of the sphenoid and joins the lingual nerve some distance below on the surface of the Medial Pterygoid (*figs. 786*, *742*, and *820*).

Indeed, the chorda tympani is to lower jaw (mandibular nerve) territory what the greater petrosal nerve is to upper jaw (maxillary nerve) territory.

CHAPTER 49

LYMPHATICS OF HEAD AND NECK

Main Chain of Nodes; Horizontal Series.
LYMPH VESSELS OF VARIOUS PARTS—*Tongue; Tonsil; Upper and Lower Teeth; Gums; Larynx; Ear; Nasal Cavity.*

The Main Chain of Lymph Nodes of the head and neck, called the *deep cervical nodes*, extends along the internal jugular vein from the base of the skull above to the clavicle below (*fig. 824*). Here it forms a *jugular lymph trunk*, which either opens independently into the angle between the internal jugular and subclavian veins or else joins the thoracic duct on the left side (right lymph duct on the right). Though the deep cervical nodes are largely covered by the obliquely set Sternomastoid, a few of them spread forward into the upper part of the anterior triangle and many spread backward beyond the posterior border of the Sternomastoid into the posterior triangle.

All these nodes lie superficial to the prevertebral fascia, which serves to separate them from the prevertebral muscles, and the roots of the cervical and brachial plexuses. The inferior belly of the Omohyoid subdivides them into an upper and a lower group. A few nodes of the *upper group*, which extend medially behind the nasopharynx, are called the *retropharyngeal nodes.* Their afferents come from the nasopharynx and soft palate, middle ear and auditory tube.

Two nodes are specially to be noted (*fig. 824.1*): (1) the *jugulo-digastric node*, which lies below the posterior belly of the Digastric where the common facial vein enters the internal jugular; and (2) the *jugulo-omohyoid*, which lies above the inferior belly of the Omohyoid where it crosses the internal jugular. The accessory nerve is surrounded by nodes both where it enters the Sternomastoid and where it leaves it. The upper group of nodes drains into the lower group. The *lower group* (supraclavicular nodes) communicates with the nodes of the axilla and with the lymph vessels of the mamma.

All parts of the head and neck drain through the deep cervical chain. The chain has a few forward outposts in the neck, e.g., *infrahyoid* (on the thyrohyoid membrane) whose afferents follow the superior laryngeal artery and come from the larynx above the vocal cords; *prelaryngeal* (on the cricothyroid lig.) and *paratracheal* (in the groove between the trachea and esophagus) follow the inferior thyroid artery. These receive afferents from the larynx below the vocal

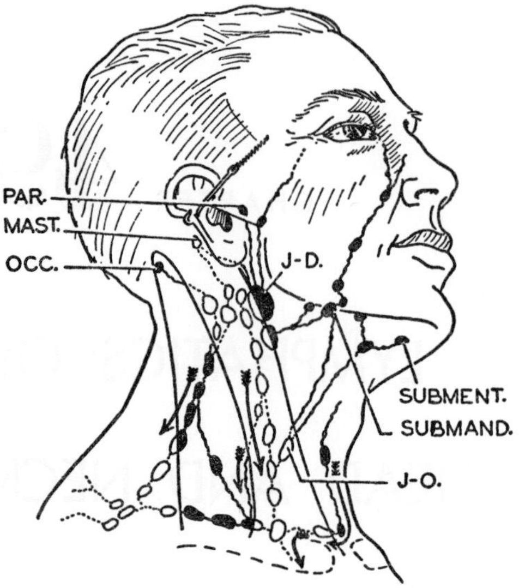

FIG. 824. The lymphatics of the head and neck. (After Rouvière.)

cords and from the thyroid gland and adjacent parts.

A Horizontal Series of superficial nodes surrounds the junction of head and neck. These nodes are placed on the stem of named blood vessels and they receive afferents from corresponding territories. Thus:

One or two *occipital nodes* lie on the Trapezius where it is pierced by the occipital artery, an inch inferolateral to the inion. Their afferents are from the scalp; their efferents pass deep to the posterior border of the Sternomastoid. They are palpable in German Measles.

One or two *retro-auricular nodes* (mastoid nodes) lie on the mastoid with the posterior auricular artery. Their afferents come from the scalp and auricle; efferents pass to the deep cervical nodes.

Several *superficial parotid nodes* (preauricular nodes) lie superficial to the parotid fascia near the superficial temporal and transverse facial arteries. Their afferents come from the scalp, auricle, eyelids, and cheek. Their efferents pass to the deep parotid and superficial cervical nodes.

[The *deep parotid nodes* may conveniently be described now. Embedded in the parotid salivary gland, they receive afferents from the superficial parotid nodes and from the external acoustic meatus, tympanum, deep

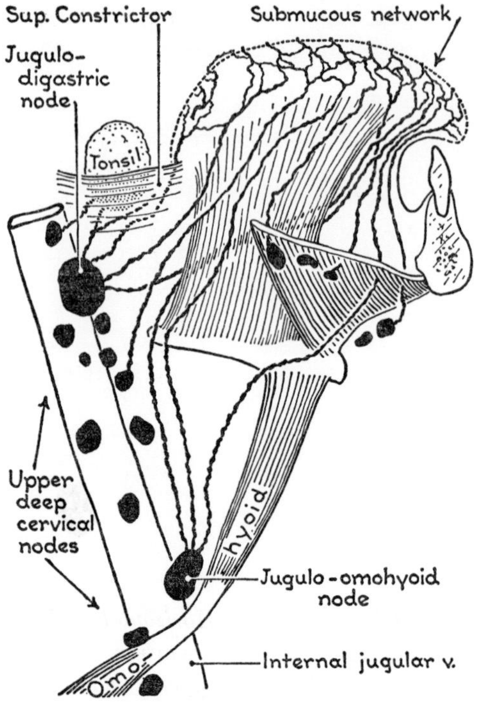

FIG. 824.1. The lymphatics of the tongue and tonsil. (After Jamieson and Dobson.)

parts of the cheek, soft palate, and posterior part of the nasal cavity. Their efferents pass to the deep cervical nodes.]

The superficial cervical nodes are small and are placed beside the external jugular vein on the upper part of the Sternomastoid. They are an offshoot of the superficial parotid nodes.

Half a dozen *submandibular nodes* lie on the surface of the submandibular salivary gland and also between it and the lower jaw, beside the facial artery. They have two extensions: (1) upward in the face along the course of the facial artery; the *facial nodes* are small and inconstant, except one or two at the lower border of the jaw: (2) forward along the submental artery; the *submental nodes* lie on the Mylohyoid below the symphysis menti. They receive afferents from the lower lip and chin and also from the tip of the tongue by vessels that pierce the Mylohyoid in company with anastomotic branches of the sublingual artery. The efferents pass to the submandibular nodes and also to the jugulo-omohyoid node.

The *submandibular nodes* receive afferents

from their 2 extensions, and from the face, cheek, nose, upper lip, gums, and tongue. The efferents pass to the upper deep cervical nodes. To examine these nodes the subject should be told to drop his chin in order to slacken the cervical fascia. One index finger should then be placed below the tongue, and the fingers of the other hand should be placed below the jaw and the structures between them palpated.

The **Lymph Vessels of the Tongue** (*fig. 824.1*) spring from an extensive submucous plexus and all vessels drain ultimately into the deep cervical nodes alongside the internal jugular vein, between the levels of the Digastric and the Omohyoid, the uppermost node being the *jugulo-digastric node;* and the lowest the *jugulo-omohyoid node* (*fig. 824*).

The nearer the tip of the tongue the vessels arise, the lower is the recipient node; and the farther back, the higher the node.

Course. The vessels from the apex of the tongue pierce the Mylohyoid and are mostly intercepted by the submental nodes. The marginal or lateral vessels of the anterior two-thirds partly pierce the Mylohyoid to end in the submandibular nodes, and partly follow the blood vessels across both surfaces of the Hyoglossus to the deep cervical nodes. The medial vessels, however, descend in (or near) the septum, between the Genioglossi, and, after either piercing or passing below that muscle, follow the lingual artery to the deep cervical nodes. The vessels from the posterior one-third pass through the pharyngeal wall below the tonsil.

Crossing in part to Nodes of the Opposite Side are vessels near the median plane, and also vessels leaving the submental nodes (*fig. 824.2*).

The **Lymph Vessels of the Tonsil** pierce or run below the Sup. Constrictor mainly to the jugulo-digastric node.

The **Lymph Vessels of the Upper Teeth** pass through the infra-orbital foramen and run with the facial artery to the submandibular nodes. Those from the **Lower Teeth** run through the mandibular canal to the deep cervical nodes.

The vessels from the buccal surfaces of the **Upper and Lower Gums** run to the submandibular nodes; those from the lingual part of the lower gums end in the submandibular and deep cervical nodes; those from the lingual part of the upper gums run dorsally with the palatine vessels to the deep cervical or retropharyngeal nodes.

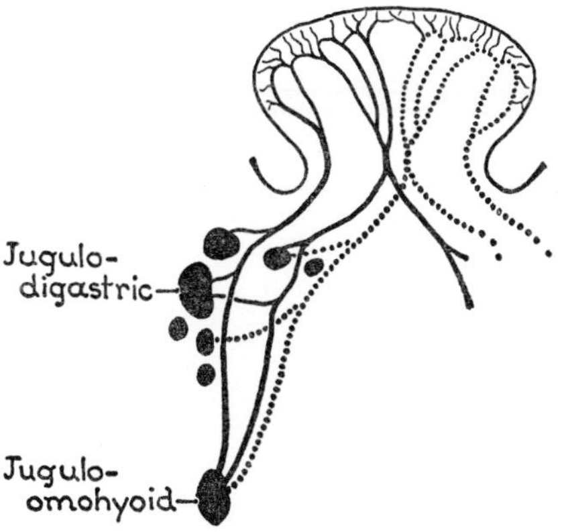

FIG. 824.2. Lymphatics of the tongue decussating. (After Jamieson and Dobson.)

The **Lymph Vessels of the Larynx** *above the vocal cords* follow the superior laryngeal artery through the thyrohyoid membrane to the upper deep cervical nodes after partial interception by the infrahyoid nodes; those *below the vocal cords* pierce the cricothyroid and cricotracheal ligaments and pass to the deep cervical nodes after partial interception by the prelaryngeal and paratracheal nodes. Vessels of the upper and lower parts of the larynx anastomose submucously in the posterior wall of the larynx but not in the region of the cords, which act as a barrier, comparable to the one erected at the pyloric sphincter.

The **Lymph Vessels of the Ear.** Those of the auricle and external meatus pass to the retro-auricular, upper cervical, and parotid nodes; those of the tympanic membrane and lateral wall of the tympanum pass to the parotid nodes; those of the auditory tube and medial wall of the tympanum pass to the retropharyngeal and deep cervical nodes.

The **Lymph Vessels of the Nasal Cavity** from the anterior part run with those of the external nose to the submandibular nodes; those from the posterior pass to the retropharyngeal, deep parotid, and deep cervical nodes.

CHAPTER 50

BONES OF SKULL

FRONTAL BONE—*Supra-orbital Margin and Outer Aspect of Squama; Under Surface; Inner or Cerebral Surface; Articulations; Ossification.*

PARIETAL BONE—*Ossification.*

OCCIPITAL BONE—*Squama; Condylar Parts; Basilar Part or Basi-Occipital; Articulations; Variations.*

SPHENOIDAL BONE—*Parts; Body and Lesser Wings; Greater Wing and Its Foramina; Pterygoid Process and Laminae; Ossification; Variations.*

ETHMOID BONE—*Shape; At Birth; Labyrinth and Cells; Conchae.*

TEMPORAL BONE—*Squamous Part; Tympanic Part (and Ring); Petromastoid Part.*

MAXILLA—*Facial Surface; Frontal Process; Infratemporal (Posterior) Surface; Orbital (Superior) Surface; Nasal (Medial) Surface; Ossification.*

ZYGOMATIC BONE—*Ossification.*

PALATINE BONE—*Plates; Processes; Greater Palatine Canal; Ossification.*

NASAL BONE—*Surfaces and Markings.*

LACRIMAL BONE.

INFERIOR CONCHA.

VOMER.

MANDIBLE—*Ossification.*

HYOID BONE—*Development and Ossification; Variations; Muscle Attachments; Fibrous Attachments.*

SKULL AT BIRTH.

»» It is, generally speaking, much more important to be familiar with the skull as a whole than with the individual bones that comprise it, because (except in the cases of the mandible and the ossicles of the ear) the bones are united to each other either by suture or synchondrosis and there is no movement between them. Muscle attachments, bony fossae, bony lines and ridges, blood sinuses, fasciae, and so on extend from bone to bone without respect to such joints, so the locations of the immovable joints that outline the individual bones are of little account. How different this is from the limbs, where the joints are of the first importance.

The bones of the skull may be classified as:

1. *Bones of the cranial cavity:* frontal, parietal, occipital, sphenoid, ethmoid, and temporal. (Of these only the parietal and temporal are paired.)

2. *Bones of the face and nasal cavities:* maxilla, zygomatic, palatine, nasal, lacrimal, inferior concha, vomer, and mandible. (Of these only the vomer and mandible are unpaired.)

FRONTAL BONE

The frontal bone (os frontale) (*figs. 825* and *826*) is shaped like a cockle shell and has two parts: a vertical part, the *squama*, in the forehead; and a horizontal part, the two *orbital parts* or *plates*, which forms the greater part of the roof of each orbit. Between the two orbital plates there is an oblong space, the *ethmoidal notch.*

Supra-orbital Margin and Outer Aspect of Squama. Between the squama and each orbital plate is the *supra-orbital margin;* this is concave, forms a third of the margin of the orbit, and has either a notch, foramen, or canal, the *supra-orbital* *notch* (f. or c.) 1¼″ from the median plane. The supra-orbital margin ends laterally in a stout projection, the *zygomatic process;* medially it ends at a point (*medial angular process*).

Between the right and left medial angular processes there is a broad semilunar surface, the *nasal margin* or *notch,* for articulation with the nasal bones and frontal processes of the maxillae. The point in the median sagittal plane between nasal and frontal bones, i.e., on the nasal notch, is the *nasion.*

The prominence half an inch above the nasion is the *glabella,* so called because it is situated between the eyebrows and is bald or glabrous. Lateral to it on each side a fullness, the *superciliary arch,* extends to, or beyond, the supra-orbital notch.

A sharp line, the *temporal line,* curves upward and backward from the zygomatic process and separates the temporal fossa below from the region of the scalp above. A fullness at the center of each half of the squama, the *tuber frontalis* (or *frontal eminence*), marks the site where ossification began. Vertical grooves for branches of the supra-orbital nerves are sometimes seen on the squama.

The Under Surface. Each orbital plate is very thin, and has laterally just behind the supra-orbital margin a *fossa* for the lacrimal gland, and medially a *spine* (or depression) for the trochlea of the Obliquus Oculi Superior.

The *ethmoidal notch* lodges the cribriform plate of the ethmoid. Skirting the notch on each side are broken cells which overlie the ethmoidal labyrinth and form the roofs of the *ethmoidal air cells* or *sinuses.* Two half canals, *anterior* and *posterior ethmoidal canals* (foramina), run in the walls of the cells from orbit to ethmoidal notch. The most anterior cell (sometimes the second most anterior) opens into the *frontal air sinus.*

Descending from the nasal notch is a broad triangular process, the *nasal spine.* In front it buttresses the nasal bones; behind these bones it articulates on each side with the frontal process of the maxilla; posteriorly it has a median crest for the vertical plate of the ethmoid, and on each side of this a longitudinal groove (4 mm. wide) forms part of the roof of the nasal cavity. The latter facts are best appreciated on inverting a skull and looking at the narrow roofs of the nasal cavities just above the nasal bones.

The Inner or Cerebral Surface takes

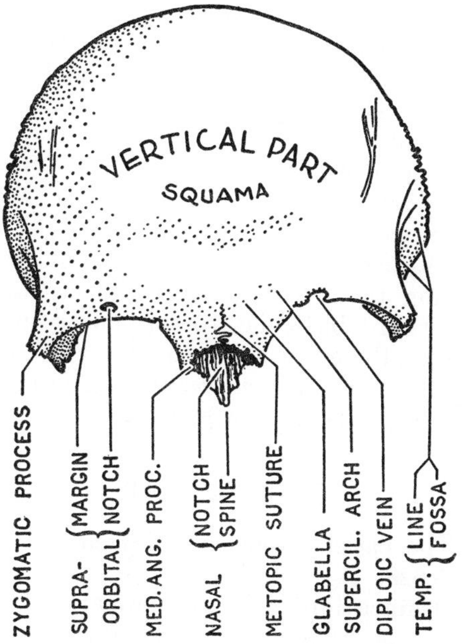

FIG. 825. Frontal bone—from in front

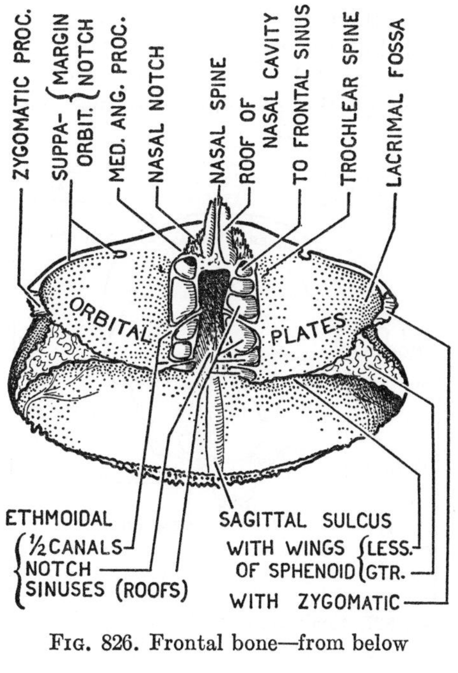

FIG. 826. Frontal bone—from below

part in the anterior cranial fossa. A median ridge, the *frontal crest* extends upward from the ethmoidal notch to a broad shallow groove, the *sagittal sulcus*. The upper surface of each orbital plate is convex and is marked by ridges which occupy sulci of the brain.

Articulations. Just as you raise your hat from your head, so you may raise a frontal bone from off the other bones of the skull (nasal, maxillary, lacrimal, ethmoid, sphenoid, and zygomatic), because it rests on them; it is true that at the upper part of the coronal (frontoparietal) suture the frontal bone overlaps the parietal; however, at the lower part it is overlapped by the parietal.

Ossification is in membrane; it begins during the 7th fetal week at the frontal tubers. At birth the frontal bone is in two halves; these fuse about the 2nd year at the *frontal* or *metopic suture*. Remnants of this suture persist at the glabella.

PARIETAL BONE

The parietal bone is described on pages 627–628.

Ossification is in membrane; it begins about the 7th fetal week at the *tuber parietale* or parietal eminence, that is at the point of fullness at the center of the bone. The parietal bone therefore corresponds closely to the frontal, but the two parietal bones do not fuse till the 3rd decade. Areas around the margins of the parietal bone may ossify

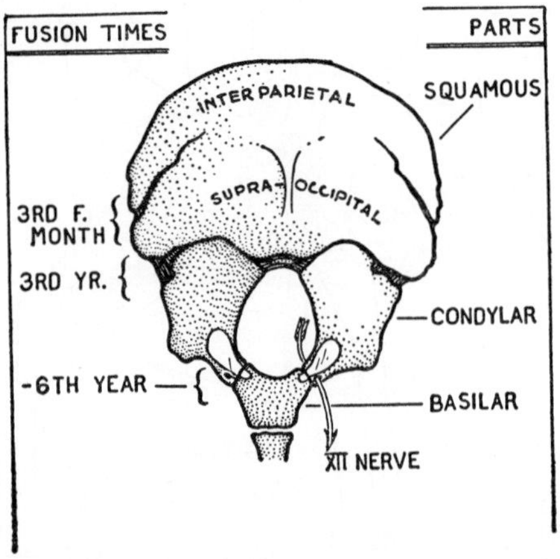

FIG. 827. Occipital bone at birth, exterior view. (*Condylar part = lateral part.*)

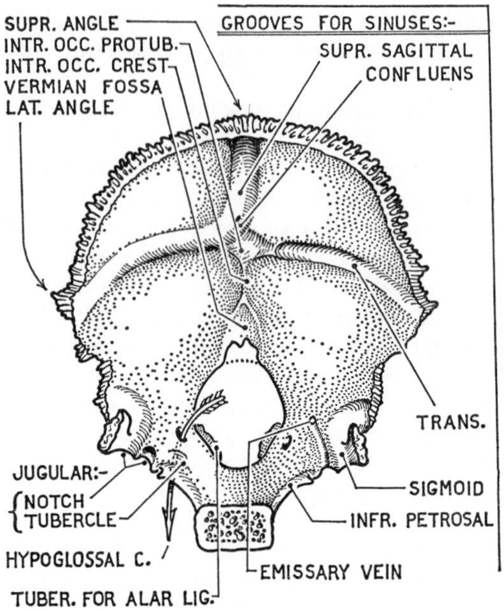

FIG. 828. Adult occipital bone (inner surface)

separately giving rise in the sutures to small independent bones, commonly the size of a finger nail, called *sutural* (*Wormian*) *bones.*

OCCIPITAL BONE

The occipital bone (unpaired) lies at the back and base of the spheroidal brain case. *At birth* (*fig. 827*) and until the 3rd or 4th year, it consists of four pieces, disposed around the *foramen magnum* thus: the squamous part or *squama* behind, a *lateral* (*condylar*) *part* on each side, and the *basilar part* or basi-occipital in front. These names are retained for parts of the adult bone.

Squama. Near the center of the outer surface of the squama is a boss, the *external occipital protuberance* or more briefly the *inion*. From the inion a line, the *superior nuchal line*, curves on each side to the lateral border, separating the area for the scalp above from the area for the muscles of the neck, the *nuchal area*, below. A median crest, the *external occipital crest*, runs from inion to foramen magnum; and from near the midpoint on this crest an *inferior nuchal line* curves laterally on each side.

Below the center of the inner surface is an elevation, the *internal occipital protuberance.*

From it a cruciate arrangement of lines radiates (*fig. 828*). The upper lines bound the *sagittal sulcus;* two transverse lines on each side bound the *transverse sulcus;* and, a prominent median line, the *internal occipital crest* descends to the foramen magnum, occasionally splitting below to enclose a triangular depression, the *vermian fossa.*

The cruciate lines divide the inner surface of the squama into four fossae—two upper ones for the occipital lobes of the cerebrum, and two lower ones for the hemispheres of the cerebellum. The upper fossae are covered externally merely with scalp, and the bone is thick; the lower fossae are protected externally by nuchal muscles, and the bone is thin and translucent.

Lateral (Condylar) Parts. On the under surface of each lateral part (and extending on to the basilar part) an oval articular eminence, the *occipital condyle,* skirts the anterior half of the foramen magnum. Behind each condyle there is a *condylar fossa* into which usually opens a *condylar canal* for an emissary vein. Lateral to the posterior two-thirds of each condyle projects a bar of bone, the *jugular process,* which is homologous with the transverse process of a vertebra.

The anterior one-third of each condyle extends forward onto the basilar part of the bone. The site of union between the basilar and condylar parts is marked by the *hypoglossal* (*anterior condylar*) *canal,* for the transmission of the hypoglossal nerve. The external orifice of this canal lies anterolateral to the condyle; the internal orifice lies within the margin of the foramen magnum above the middle of the condyle and is overhung by the *jugular tubercle.* The jugular process is grooved both above and in front by the *sigmoid sinus,* which here becomes the internal jugular vein. Posteriorly it is continuous with the squama.

Basilar Part or Basi-Occipital is a bar of bone that extends upward and forward from the foramen magnum to the sphenoid. It is thin and wide at the foramen magnum, but narrow and nearly square on cross-section where it joins the sphenoid. Its cerebral surface, concave from side to side, supports the pons and medulla, and along each side has a half of the groove for the *inferior petrosal sinus,* the petrous temporal having the other half. Each lateral margin is united by synchondrosis to the petrous temporal bone.

The under surface carries one-third of a condyle on each side, and in front of these are rough markings for the attachments of the Longus Capitis and Rectus Capitis Anterior. At the center is the *pharyngeal tubercle* for the attachment of the fibrous median raphe of the pharynx.

The basi-occipital and the sphenoid are united by cartilage which is usually completely ossified by the 19th year and never later than the 21st year (McKern and Stewart).

Articulations: With both parietals, both petrous temporals, the sphenoid and the atlas.

Variations. The occipital bone develops in cartilage, except the portion above the superior nuchal line, which develops in membrane; this superior part may fail to fuse with the rest of the bone thereby constituting an *interparietal bone.* The interparietal bone itself develops from several centers any of which may remain discrete, thereby simulating a large sutural bone. The *paramastoid process* is an occasional bar of bone that descends from the jugular process toward the transverse process of the atlas. The *3rd occipital condyle* is an occasional tubercle that projects from the anterior border of the foramen magnum to articulate with the dens of the axis. A *median cleft* may extend from the foramen magnum backward into the squama. It is due apparently to the nonappearance of an ossific center (*fig. 828*). *Fusion of the atlas* and *occipital bone* may occur.

SPHENOID BONE

Viewed from the front the sphenoid resembles a bat or an owl with wings outstretched and legs dependent. It extends across the base of the skull, articulates with numerous bones, takes part in many fossae and possesses many foramina. It comprises a body, two lesser wings, two greater wings and two pterygoid processes.

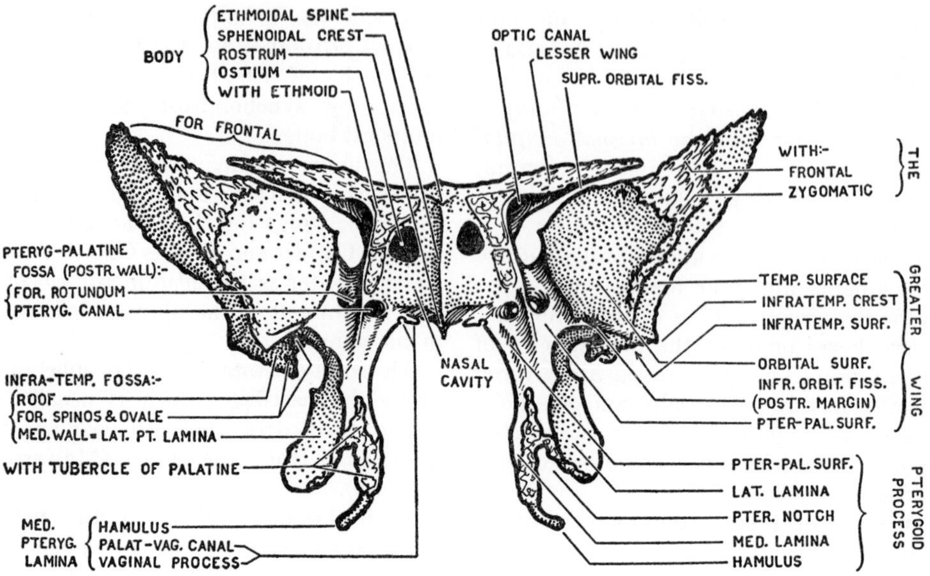

FIG. 829. Sphenoid bone—front view
(*Of palatine: tubercle = pyramidal proc.; Surface: pterygopalatine = maxillary.*)

At birth it is in three pieces, the body and lesser wings forming one piece, the greater wing and pterygoid process on each side forming two others (*fig. 684*). It becomes one bone during the 1st year. The cubical body contains two air sinuses, the right and left sphenoidal air sinuses (*fig. 829*).

Body and Lesser Wings—viewed from above. The attenuated lesser wing of each side has a free concave posterior border which ends medially in a blunt triangular spine, the *anterior clinoid process*. Medial to this it is attached to the anterior half of the body by two roots which bound the *optic canal* (foramen) above and below. After birth the upper root of each side extends like a sliding door across the upper surface of the anterior half of the body and, joining, they form a yoke, the *jugum*, which conceals this part of the body. The upper surface of the lesser wings and jugum forms the hinder part of the anterior cranial fossa. This surface is narrow and flat, and is pointed at each lateral end; in front it articulates with the orbital plates of the frontal bone and between these with the ethmoid, which it also overlaps (*fig. 829*).

The posterior edge of the jugum is also the anterior edge of a groove, the *chiasmatic sulcus* (*optic groove*), that connects the optic canals of opposite sides. The part of the body behind the groove is the *sella turcica* (Turkish saddle); it is subdivided into a pommel, a seat, and a back. The pommel of the saddle is a transversely set olive-like eminence, the *tuberculum sellae*, each end of which may form a spine, the *middle clinoid process*. Behind the tuberculum sellae is the excavated seat, the *hypophyseal* or *pituitary fossa*. Behind this rises a square plate of bone, the *dorsum sellae*, whose upper angles are tubercular, the *posterior clinoid processes*.

The side of the hollow body gives attachment antero-inferiorly to the greater wing; postero-inferiorly it articulates with the apex of the petrous temporal; and between these lies the foramen lacerum where the internal carotid artery enters the skull. Between the foramen and the anterior clinoid process the bone is faintly grooved by the artery. The side of the body extends forward beyond the optic canal, superior orbital fissure, and foramen rotundum.

The hinder part of the body is a square "epiphyseal" surface which fuses with the basi-occipital, usually by the 19th year.

The anterior surface of the body has a median crest, the *sphenoidal crest*, which forms part of the nasal septum. This crest begins above in a spine, the *ethmoidal spine*, and ends below in a beak, the *rostrum*, which is received between the alae of the vomer. A vertical triangular area at the side of the sphenoidal crest forms part of the roof of the nasal cavity. Near the midpoint of this area is the orifice of the *sphenoidal air sinus*. Lateral to this the body articulates with the ethmoidal labyrinth.

The mouths of five *bony passages* lie grouped at the side and under aspect of the front of the body. They are: (1) optic canal (foramen) between the roots of the lesser wing, (2) foramen rotundum at the root of the greater wing, (3) pterygoid canal at the root of the pterygoid process, (4) superior orbital fissure between the lesser and greater wings, and (5) palatinovaginal canal below the vaginal process. The anterior (antero-inferior) surface of the lesser wing forms the hinder part of the roof of the orbit.

Greater Wing. This projects from the side of the body and its inner or cerebral surface forms the anterior part of the lateral subdivision of the middle cranial fossa. It is separated from the lesser wing by a comma-shaped fissure, the *superior orbital fissure*, which opens from the middle cranial fossa to the orbit.

The *foramen rotundum* is situated below the medial end of the superior orbital fissure, and passes forwards through the root of the greater wing to the pterygopalatine fossa. This fossa lies below the level of the orbit and is seen from the side of the skull.

Behind its site of attachment to the body, the wing has a posterior border which ends posterolaterally in an angle. On the under surface of the angle there is a spine, the *spine of the sphenoid*. The posterior border grew around and engulfed the mandibular nerve thereby forming the *foramen ovale* and more laterally, at the root of the angular spine, it engulfed the middle meningeal artery thereby forming the *foramen spinosum*. These two foramina open downward into the infratemporal fossa.

The lesser (superficial) petrosal nerve may be similarly engulfed resulting in the formation of a third foramen, the *canaliculus innominatus*—a minute foramen between the foramen ovale and foramen spinosum. The superior orbital fissure and three foramina—rotundum, ovale, spinosum—lie on a crescent (*fig. 688*). The wing is grooved near its tip by the anterior branch of the middle meningeal artery.

The greater wing forms part not only of the middle cranial fossa, but also of the orbit, and of the temporal, infratemporal and pterygopalatine fossae. Between the temporal and infratemporal surfaces, which are set at a right angle to each other, is the sharp and often spinous *infratemporal crest*.

Pterygoid Process. A stout process, it descends obliquely from the junction of the body and greater wing (*fig. 830*). It consists of two plates, the *medial* and *lateral pterygoid laminae*. They are fused in front, but free behind and below. Between them is the *pterygoid fossa*. At the lower end of the posterior border of the medial pterygoid lamina is a delicate hook, the *hamulus*, at the upper end is a conical tubercle, *pterygoid tubercle*. This tubercle is the guide to the *pterygoid canal*, which lies just above and passes forward to the pterygopalatine fossa, where lies the pterygopalatine ganglion.

From the root of the medial lamina a plate, the *vaginal process*, runs medially toward the ala of the vomer. On the under surface of this process a groove or canal, the *palatinovaginal canal*, runs backward. The superomedial part of the pterygoid fossa is carried backward toward the spine of the sphenoid as a sharply defined fusiform fossa, the *scaphoid fossa*.

The medial lamina forms part of the lateral wall of the nasal cavity. Its posterior border is free and sharp for the pharyngeal aponeurosis and has a spine for the support of the mouth of the auditory (pharyngotympanic) tube.

The lateral lamina forms the medial wall of the infratemporal fossa. Its posterior border is free and serrated; followed upward it leads to the foramen ovale. Its medial surface gives origin to the Medial Pterygoid, its lateral surface to the Lateral Pterygoid—so it is a muscular process.

Ossification (*fig. 684*). The body and lesser wings develop in cartilage; so does the root of the greater wing and its down-

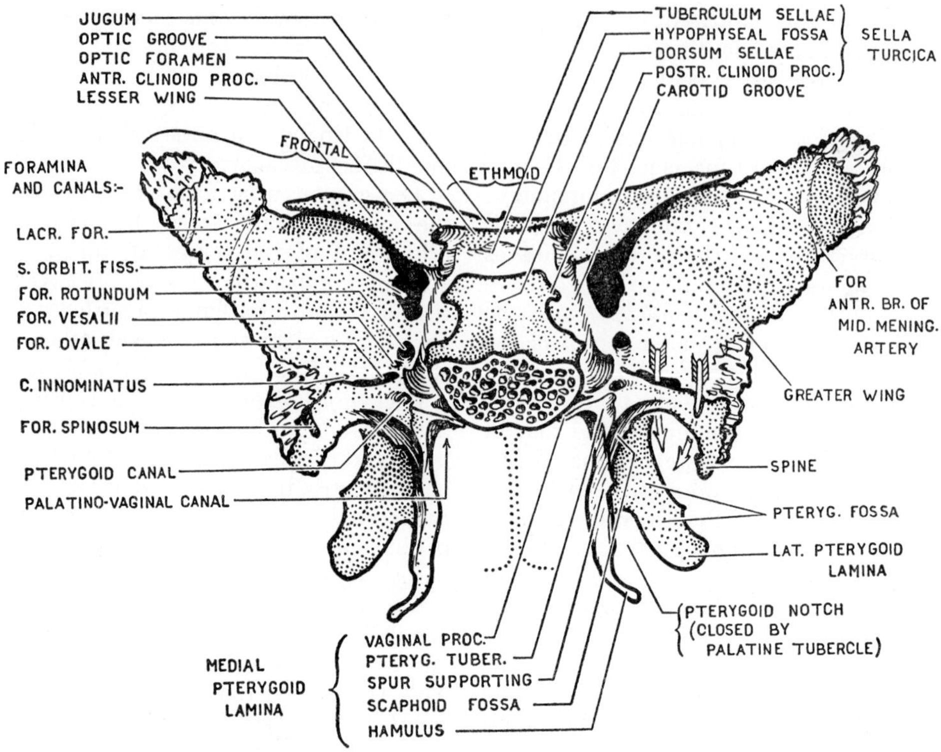

FIG. 830. Sphenoid bone—from behind
(Optic: foramen = canal; Groove: optic = chiasmatic; Palatine: tubercle = pyramidal proc.)

growth, the lateral pterygoid lamina. The remainder of the greater wing develops in membrane. The medial pterygoid lamina also develops in membrane, and its line of fusion with the body and greater wing is usually obvious; it runs above the vaginal process and pterygoid tubercle and crosses through the pterygoid canal. Further, two paired fragments ossify independently in cartilage: one is a curved plate of bone, the *lingula,* which lies above the posterior orifice of the pterygoid canal and sweeps laterally in front of the carotid artery; the other is a triangular plate, the *sphenoidal concha,* which is applied to the anterior and inferior surfaces of the body of the sphenoid. About the 3rd year the mucous membrane of the nasal cavity bursts through the right and left sphenoidal conchae into the body of the sphenoid, thereby forming the right and left *sphenoidal air sinuses.*

Variations. The septum between the right and left sinuses is usually greatly deflected. The sinus is commonly over-inflated, so to speak, with the result that it partly surrounds the optic canal, the pterygoid canal, and the foramen rotundum so that they project as ridges within it. The walls of the ridges may be resorbed; the optic nerve, nerve of the pterygoid canal, the maxillary nerve and also the cavernous sinus and carotid artery are then brought close to the mucoperiosteum of the sinus.

ETHMOID BONE

The ethmoid bone may be likened to a St. George's cross made of planks and having an oblong box suspended from each end of the cross-piece (*fig. 831*). The boxes are the *ethmoidal labyrinths;* the cross-piece is the *cribriform plate* (lamina cribrosa); the part of the upright above the cribriform plate is the *crista galli;* and the part below is the *vertical* or *perpendicular plate* (*fig. 832*).

The ethmoid is developed from the cartilaginous nasal capsule. *At birth* it is in three pieces—a median plate, and a right and a left labyrinth. The median plate, which forms part of the nasal septum, and the crista galli (cock's comb), which is its upward extension into the anterior cranial fossa, are cartilaginous; these begin to ossify during the 1st year. The labyrinths, however, are bony at birth and are joined to the median plate by a fibrous lamina cribrosa. Fusion is complete by the 5th or 6th year.

The *crista galli* is thick and triangular. The falx cerebri is attached to its posterior border and apex; the anterior border splits into two *alae* which, with the frontal bone, enclose the *foramen cecum* (*fig. 833*).

The *cribriform plate* is a fragile, sieve-like plate lying at each side of the crista galli and occupying the ethmoidal notch of the frontal bone. It forms part of the floor of the anterior cranial fossa and of the roof of the nasal cavities. Through the perforations pass the olfactory nerves in their arachnoid coverings, also the anterior ethmoidal nerve and nasal branches of the anterior and posterior ethmoidal arteries—the anterior ethmoidal nerve and artery passing through a special opening, the *nasal slit.*

The *vertical plate* forms the postero-superior third of the nasal septum (*fig. 798*).

Labyrinth. Each box-like labyrinth is composed of a dozen or less air cells, the *ethmoidal cellules* or *sinuses*, which open medially into the nasal cavity; laterally, it has a smooth, oblong, fragile wall, the *orbital plate* (lamina papyracea); above, it is covered by the medial part of the orbital plate of the frontal bone and slightly by the sphenoid.

The cells in places break through the (bony) walls of the labyrinth; those that break through the roof proper adopt the orbital plate of the frontal as their new roof, and one cell (or more) constantly extends even into the frontal bone itself and becomes the *frontal air sinus*, its stalk being the *infundibulum;* others are limited by the surrounding lacrimal, maxillary, palatine and splenoid bones.

From the hinder part of the medial surface of the labyrinth a scroll, the *superior concha*, hangs downward; and the medial surface itself continues downward as the *middle concha.* A hook of bone, the *uncinate process*, curves backward from the anterior end of this surface to meet the corresponding process of the inferior concha, thereby forming the lower limit of the hiatus semilunaris. The oblong posterior surface of the labyrinth abuts against the anterior surface of the body of the sphenoid.

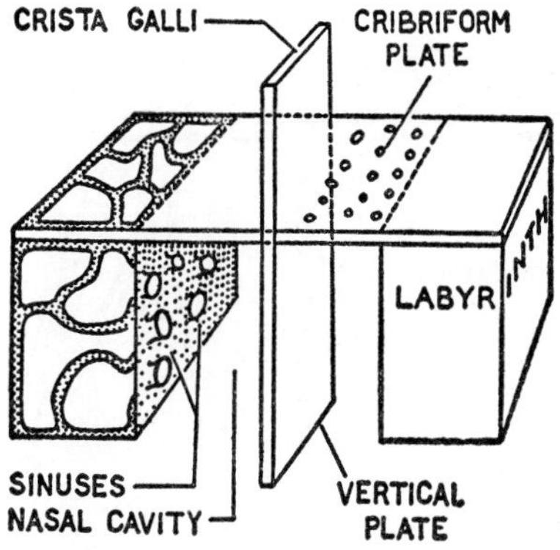

FIG. 831. Scheme of ethmoid bone

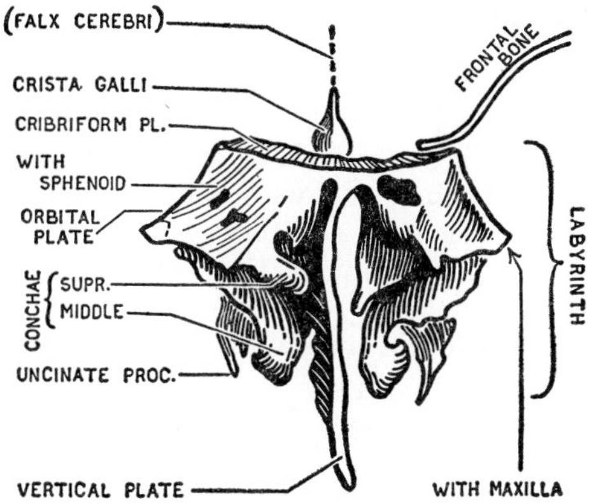

FIG. 832. Ethmoid bone—from behind

TEMPORAL BONE

The temporal bone is a composite bone, situated at the base and side of the skull between the sphenoid in front and the occipital behind. **At birth** it is in 3 parts—the squamous, tympanic, and petrous (petromastoid)—which fuse during the 1st year (*fig. 834*). The inner ear lies within the petrous part. The tympanic cavity, which developed from the first and second pharyngeal clefts, is enclosed by the three parts of

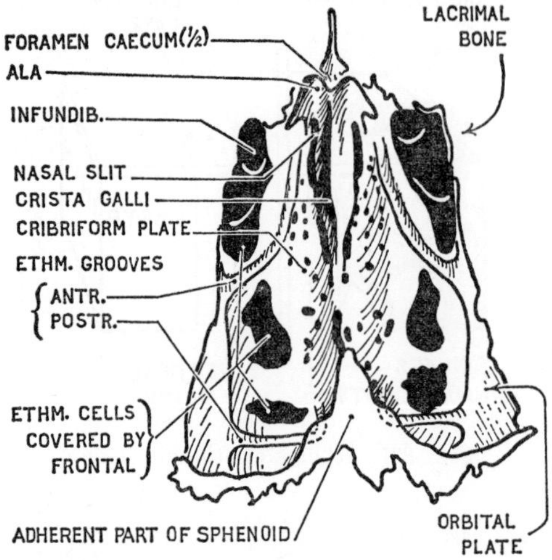

FIG. 833. Ethmoid bone—from above

the bone; it communicates with the mastoid antrum behind, and with the nasopharynx in front via the auditory (pharyngotympanic) tube. Through the bone runs the facial nerve. The squamous and tympanic parts develop in membrane; the petrous in cartilage.

Squamous Part. The squama, resembling a pilgrim's shell, forms part of the lateral wall of the cranium (*fig. 835*). Its medial surface, described fully on page 585, is grooved by the middle meningeal artery. From the lower part of its lateral surface the finger-like *zygoma* (zygomatic process) curves forward (p. 626). On the under surface is a translucent, oval socket, the *mandibular* (articular) *fossa* for the head of the lower jaw (p. 639). An angular part, the *postauditory process*, described in the adult bone as part of the mastoid, projects downward for half an inch below the level of the middle cranial fossa, closing the mastoid antrum laterally.

Tympanic Part. At birth it is a *ring* open above. It is grooved for the tympanic membrane, and attached to it laterally is the cartilage of the external acoustic (auditory) meatus. During the early years of life the ring becomes oval and elongated to form the anterior wall, floor, and lower part of the posterior wall of the bony external acoustic meatus. It also extends downward into a plate, the *tympanic plate*, which forms

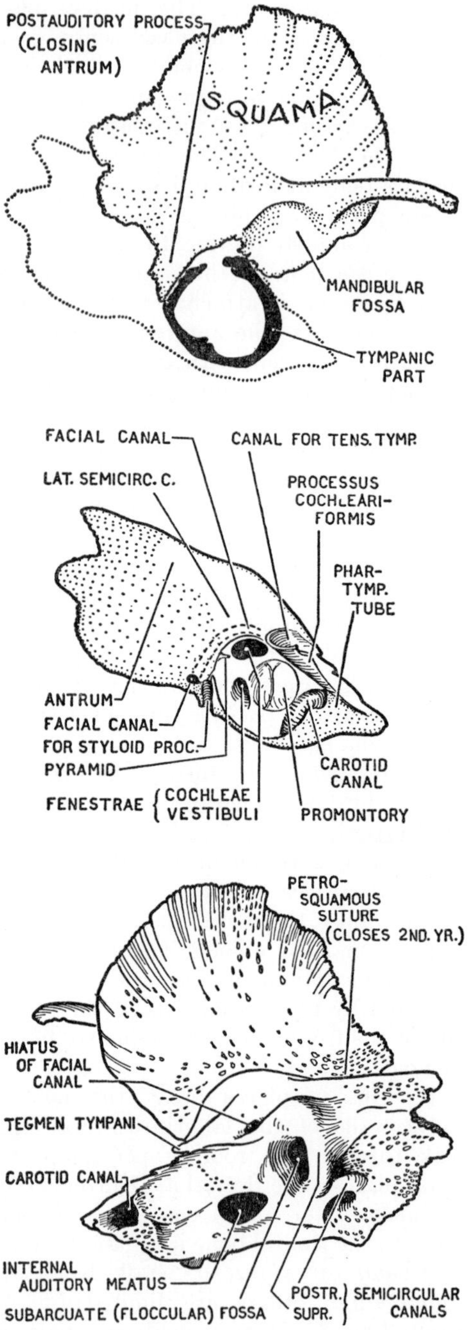

FIG. 834. The three parts of the temporal bone at birth. *Upper*, lateral aspect of squamous and tympanic parts. *Middle*, lateral aspect of petromastoid part. (The squamous and tympanic parts have been removed to show the medial wall of the tympanum and the mastoid antrum.) *Lower*, inner aspect.

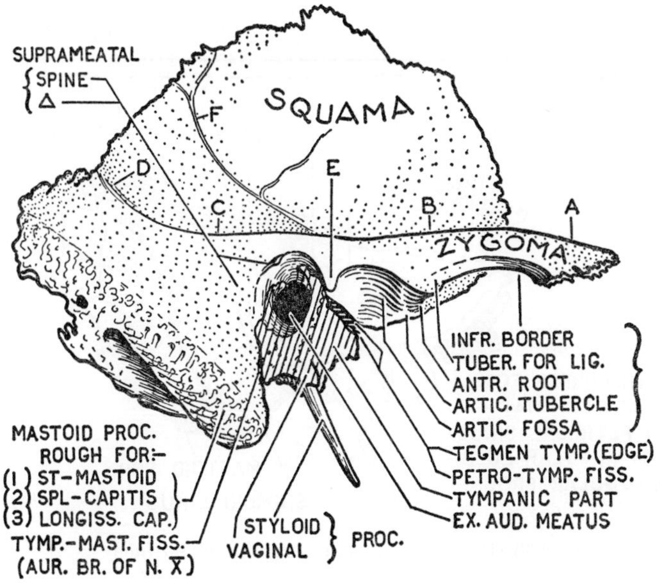

FIG. 835. Temporal Bone—lateral aspect

the posterior wall of the mandibular fossa and, splitting below to form the *vaginal process*, partly ensheaths the styloid process.

The Petrous Part (*fig. 836*) is the most important and also the most difficult part of the bone to understand. Its surfaces have been dealt with (pp. 583, 586, 626–627). In brief: it is pyramidal; its base is lateral; its apex is medial lying at the foramen lacerum. It has three surfaces, an anterior and a posterior which form parts of the middle and posterior cranial fossae, respectively, and an inferior which forms part of the under surface of the base of the skull.

The *carotid canal* begins on the under surface of the bone (*fig. 837*) and takes an inverted L-shaped course through it, opening into the foramen lacerum at the apex. The hinder part, the *mastoid bone*, is grooved internally, at its junction with the petrous, for the *sigmoid sinus;* externally it is prolonged downward into a nipple, the *mastoid process*, but this is not present during the 1st year of life, so the *stylomastoid foramen*, situated where its name suggests, opens subcutaneously and there discharges the facial nerve.

For features of the anterior or cerebral surface see figure 838 and also figure 687, for features of the posterior or cerebellar surface see figure 686, and for features of the inferior surface see figure 753.

MAXILLA

The maxilla or upper jaw (paired) has a body and four processes. The body is a hollow pyramid with three surfaces, an apex, and a base.

The most conspicuous feature of the bone is the *alveolar process*. It carries eight teeth, and ends behind the 3rd molar tooth in a free rounded part, the *maxillary tuberosity* (*fig. 839*). As in the lower jaw so in the upper, the roots of the teeth (2nd and 3rd molars excepted) cause ridges on the thin outer wall of the alveolar process, but not on the thick inner wall, that for the canine tooth being the largest.

From the 1st or 2nd molar tooth a rounded buttress ascends to the lower end of a large triangular prominence, the *zygomatic process*, which forms the truncated apex of the bone and is placed where the three surfaces (orbital, facial, and infratemporal) meet. It ends in a rough triangular area for articulation with the zygomatic bone. The buttress and the process separate the facial (anterior) surface from the infratemporal (posterior) surface.

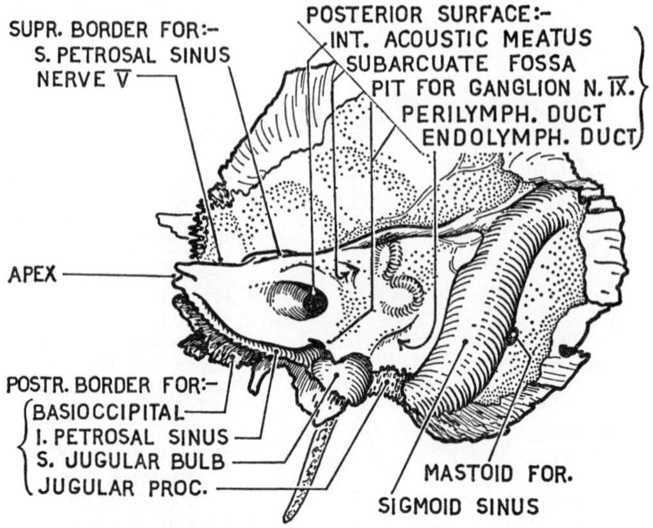

FIG. 836. Petromastoid part—cerebellar surface

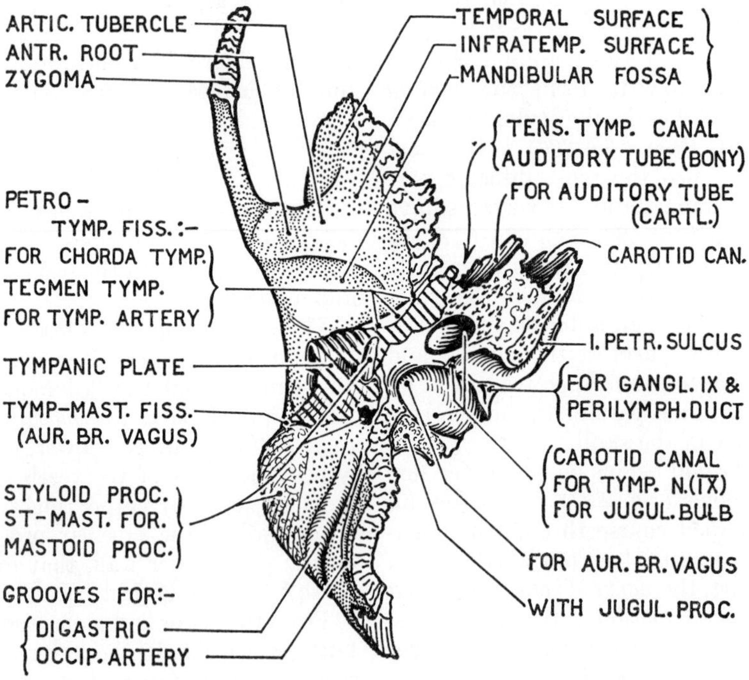

FIG. 837. Temporal bone—inferior aspect

Facial (Anterior) Surface. The facial surface is flat on a powerful skull, like that of the Eskimo, but concave in skulls of white races. The area medial to the ridge for the canine tooth, i.e., between the incisor teeth and the anterior nasal orifice, is the *incisive fossa;* the area lateral to this ridge is the *canine fossa.*

Opening on to the canine fossa is the *infra-orbital foramen,* i.e., the anterior orifice of the infra-orbital canal. It is placed 1 cm. below the infra-orbital margin and its direc-

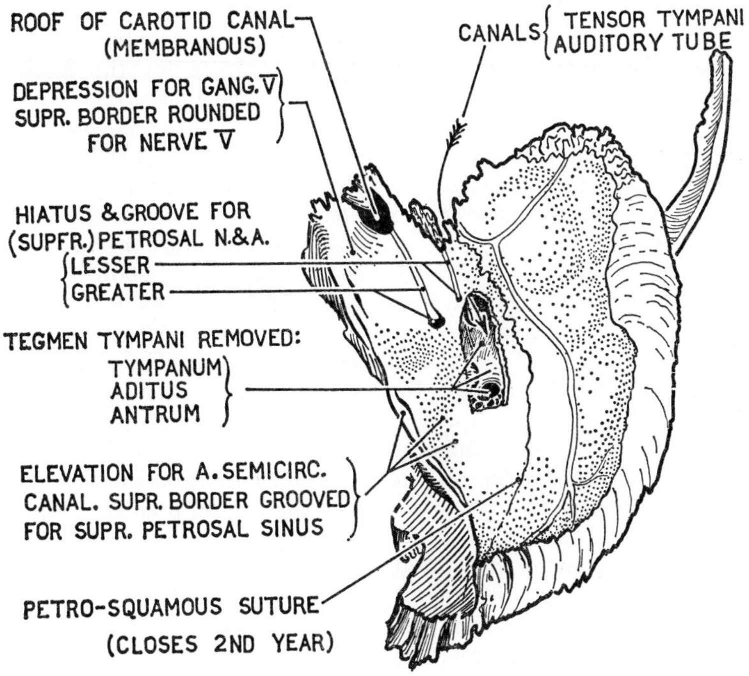

Fig. 838. Petrous part—cerebral surface

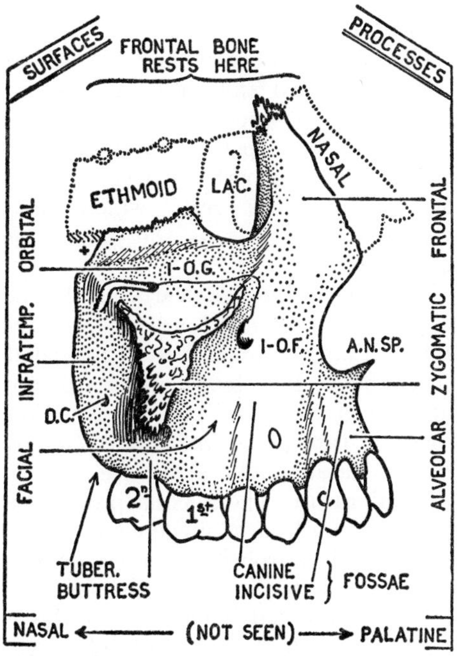

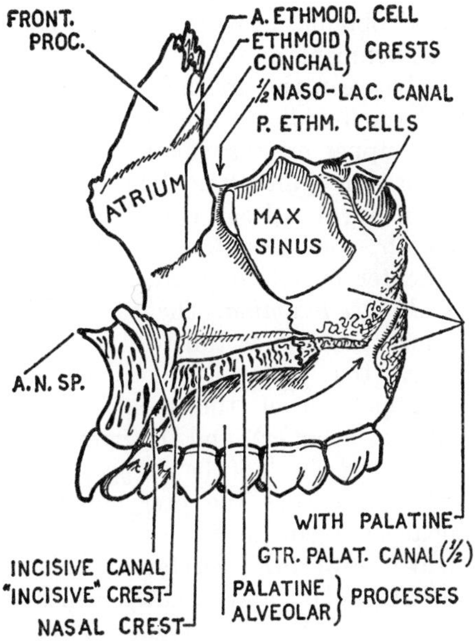

Fig. 839. Maxilla—lateral aspect Fig. 840. Maxilla—medial aspect

D.C. = dental canals; I-O.G. and I-O.F. = infra-orbital groove and canal; A.N.Sp. = Anterior nasal spine; + = space for orbital process of palatine bone.

tion contrasts with that of the mental foramen in the mandible, since it opens inferomedially. The *infra-orbital canal* can be followed backward below the infra-orbital margin to the middle of the orbital surface where, ceasing to have a roof, it becomes the *infra-orbital groove;* this in turn may be followed backward to the upper border of the infratemporal surface.

The facial surface is limited superiorly by the infra-orbital margin and is continuous superomedially with the lateral surface of the frontal process.

Frontal Process. This is triangular. Its apex articulates with the nasal notch of the frontal bone; its anterior border supports the nasal bone; its posterior border articulates with the lacrimal bone.

The infra-orbital margin is continued, as the *anterior lacrimal crest,* on to the lateral surface of the frontal process, dividing it into a convex area, which is part of the bridge of the nose, and a concave area, the *lacrimal groove.*

The medial or nasal surface of the frontal process is partly crossed by an oblique crest, the *ethmoidal crest,* for the attachment of the middle concha. Two-thirds of an inch below this, on the body of the maxilla, there is a second oblique crest, the *conchal crest,* for the attachment of the inferior concha. The area between the crests is part of the *atrium* of the middle meatus of the nose. Above the upper crest a small area forms the anterior wall of an ethmoidal cell.

Infratemporal (Posterior) Surface. This smooth, convex surface is perforated near its center by one or more *alveolar* (or *posterior dental*) *foramina.* The part of this surface just above the tuberosity is buttressed by the pterygoid laminae (the pyramidal process of the palatine bone intervening as a buffer), and the part above this is the anterior wall of the *pterygopalatine fossa,* wherein resides the pterygopalatine (sphenopalatine) ganglion.

Orbital (Superior) Surface. This is smooth, triangular, and slightly concave. Its apex extends on to the zygomatic process; its anterior border is the infra-orbital margin; its posterior border is the anterior margin of the inferior orbital fissure; its medial border is formed by the margin of the nasolacrimal notch and behind this by articular areas for the lacrimal, ethmoid, and palatine bones. The surface is crossed posteriorly by the *infra-orbital groove.* Just lateral to the nasolacrimal notch there is a *depression* for the origin of the Obliquus Oculi Inferior.

Nasal (Medial) Surface (*fig. 841*). This is the base of the hollow pyramidal body. Its anterior two-thirds is separated from the alveolar process by a horizontal plate, the *palatine process.* The nasal surface presents, in the disarticulated bone, an opening large enough to admit the thumb. This, the *maxillary hiatus,* is the bony *orifice of the maxillary air sinus* or antrum. Between this and the frontal process is a groove (lacrimal groove) which forms one-half of the circumference of the *nasolacrimal canal.*

The part of the nasal surface behind the maxillary orifice is overlaid by the palatine bone; and when this is in position a perpendicular canal, the *greater palatine canal,* is formed. The maxillary half of this canal is continued forward as two grooves on the under surface of the palatine process of the maxilla.

The medial border of the palatine process is slightly raised and with its fellow forms the *nasal crest,* which articulates with the vomer and forms part of the nasal septum. Its most anterior part is markedly raised to form the "*incisive crest,*" which ends anteriorly on the face as the *anterior nasal spine.*

The part of the bone carrying the incisor teeth is the *incisive bone* (or *premaxilla*), which in most mammals is an independent, paired bone. It extends backwards to the junction of the nasal and "incisive" crests where a canal, the *incisive canal,* passes from its nasal to its oral surface.

Ossification. The maxilla proper ossifies in membrane from a single center; the premaxilla ossifies from two centers or perhaps more. At birth the maxillary sinus is the size of a pea, and it enlarges as the teeth erupt. At birth the infra-orbital nerve lies free on the floor of the orbit just as the supra-orbital nerve lies free on the roof. As the maxilla enlarges the nerve sinks into a groove whose lateral edge then folds over the nerve, thus forming the infra-orbital canal and foramen.

ZYGOMATIC BONE

The zygomatic bone is described on page 628.

OSSIFICATION is in membrane.

PALATINE BONE

The palatine bone (paired) gives many students undue concern. It is a fragile L-shaped bone comprising an oblong vertical plate, a square horizontal plate, and three processes—the pyramidal, orbital, and sphenoidal (*figs. 841* and *842*).

Plates. *The vertical or perpendicular plate* forms the portion of the lateral wall of the nasal cavity just in front of the medial pterygoid lamina. It is applied to the hinder part of the nasal surface of the maxilla, but projects backward behind this so as to form the medial wall of the pterygopalatine fossa (seen from the side of the skull) and projects forward closing the hinder part of the opening into the maxillary sinus.

The horizontal plate articulates with its fellow to form the posterior third of the bony palate, the site of union being raised to form a *nasal crest,* for articulation with the vomer and ending behind in the *posterior nasal spine.* The anterior border of this plate articulates with the palatine process of the maxilla; the posterior border is sharp and concave.

Processes (*fig. 843*). An inverted pyramid, the *pyramidal process* (*tubercle*) projects from behind the lower part of the vertical plate and interposes itself like a buffer between the posterior border of the maxilla (just above the tuberosity) and the medial and lateral pterygoid laminae of the sphenoid. The process has a gutter for each lamina, and between the gutters a triangular area forms the lowest part of the pterygoid fossa.

Surmounting the upper border of the vertical plate are the orbital and sphenoidal processes, separated from each other by the U-shaped sphenopalatine notch—much as

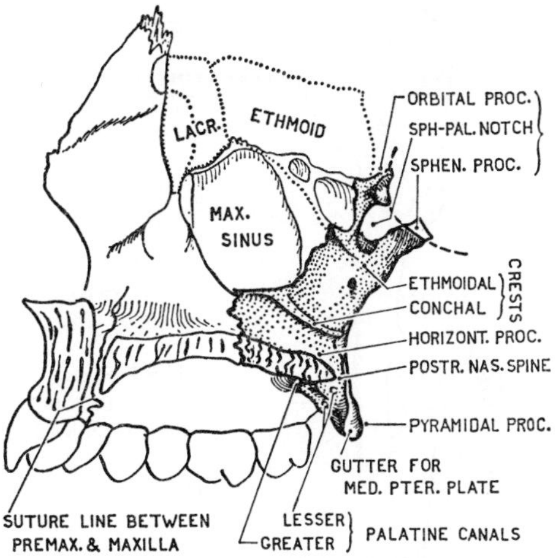

FIG. 841. Palatine bone (*stippled*) in articulation with maxilla—medial aspect.

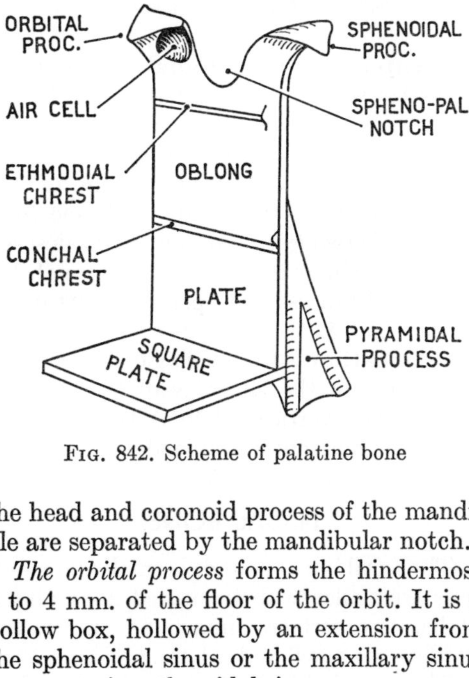

FIG. 842. Scheme of palatine bone

the head and coronoid process of the mandible are separated by the mandibular notch.

The orbital process forms the hindermost 3 to 4 mm. of the floor of the orbit. It is a hollow box, hollowed by an extension from the sphenoidal sinus or the maxillary sinus or a posterior ethmoidal sinus.

The sphenoidal process is a small plate applied to the under surface of the body of the sphenoid and reaching to the ala of the vomer. It converts the groove below the vaginal process of the sphenoid into the *palatinovaginal canal* (pharyngeal canal). *The sphenopalatine notch* is converted by the sphenoid into the sphenopalatine foramen; it is the gateway to the nasal cavity.

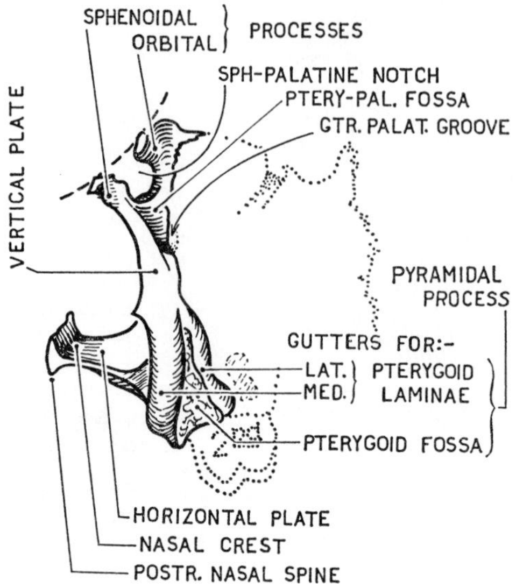

FIG. 843. Palatine bone—posterior aspect

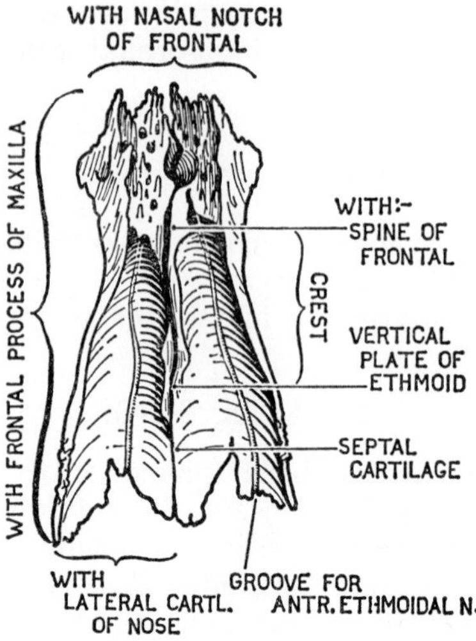

FIG. 844. Nasal bones articulated—posterior aspect.

Greater Palatine Canal. This canal drops between the body of the maxilla and the vertical plate of the palatine bone and opens between the alveolar process of the maxilla and the horizontal plate of the palatine bone as the greater palatine foramen, while two *lesser palatine canals* descend from the greater palatine canal through the pyramidal process and open on to its under surface (*fig. 841*).

Ossification is from a single center in the membrane in the lateral wall of the nasal cavity. The vertical plate is the primitive plate, the horizontal is secondary.

NASAL BONE

The nasal bone (paired) is small and stout; it is triangular with truncated apex above. It has two surfaces (inner and outer), two borders, an apex, and a base.

The *apex* is blunt, thick, and serrated; it articulates with the nasal notch of the frontal bone (*fig. 844*). The *base* is broad, thin, and notched; attached to it is the lateral nasal cartilage. The *lateral* (posterolateral) *border* is thin; it articulates with the frontal process of the maxilla. The *medial border* is a flat, triangular area which articulates with its fellow.

The outer or *facial surface* of the paired bones is saddle-shaped, being convex from side to side and concave from above downward. Near the center is a foramen for an emissary vein from the nasal mucosa.

The inner or *nasal surface* of the paired bones presents a median *crest* which articulates with the nasal spine of the frontal bone above, with the vertical plate of the ethmoid below, and perhaps with the septal cartilage still lower—depending upon how far the vertical (perpendicular) plate of the ethmoid has replaced the septal cartilage (*see fig. 798*). Lateral to the crest, the nasal surface of each bone is concave from side to side, grooved longitudinally for the anterior ethmoidal nerve, and covered with mucous membrane.

The paired bones form the upper part of the bridge of the nose. The brunt of a blow on the nose is transmitted from the nasal bones to the frontal processes of the maxillae, the nasal notch and spine of the frontal, the vertical plate of the ethmoid, and septal cartilage. The nasal bone develops in the membrane covering the cartilage of the nasal capsule.

LACRIMAL BONE

The lacrimal bone (paired) resembles a fingernail but is much thinner. It has two surfaces (lateral and medial) and four borders which articulate thus—in front with the frontal process of the maxilla, behind with the orbital plate of the ethmoid, above with the orbital plate of the frontal, and below with the orbital plate of the maxilla.

The lateral surface (*fig. 845*) is divided into an anterior and a posterior part by a razor-like crest, the *posterior lacrimal crest,* which gives attachment to the orbital septum and to the Pars Lacrimalis of the Orbicularis Oculi. The crest ends below in a hook, the *lacrimal hamulus,* which may or may not reach the margin of the orbit. The posterior part of this surface is flat and forms part of the medial wall of the orbit. The anterior part, the *lacrimal groove,* together with the grooved surface on the frontal process of the maxilla, forms a half-tube in which lodges the lacrimal sac. This part is prolonged downward into a *descending process* which articulates with the lacrimal process of the inferior concha and with it forms the medial wall of the nasolacrimal canal.

The medial or nasal surface of the lacrimal bone is covered with mucous membrane. A needle perforating it from the lateral surface will enter the atrium of the middle meatus of the nose, unless the perforation is made posteriorly when it will enter an ethmoidal cell, or made above when it will enter either the infundibulum of the frontal sinus or an intervening ethmoidal cell.

The lacrimal bone ossifies in membrane.

INFERIOR CONCHA

The inferior concha (turbinate bone) hangs downward like a scroll from the side wall of the nasal cavity. In the articulated skull it can be seen from the anterior and posterior apertures of the nose because it extends from a crest on the frontal process of the maxilla to a crest on the vertical (perpendicular) plate of the palatine bone. The lower border is thickened and gently curved, and the ends are pointed.

There are three fragile processes—one is large and downturned; two are small and upright (*fig. 846*). The *maxillary process* curves downward and laterally and forms part of the medial wall of the maxillary sinus; it is large, thin and triangular.

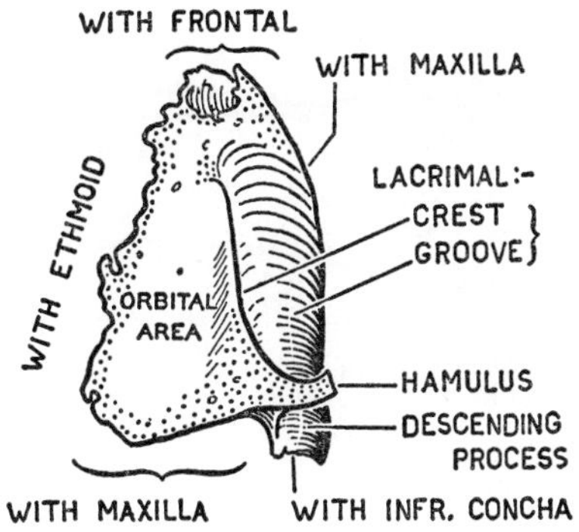

FIG. 845. Lacrimal bone—lateral aspect

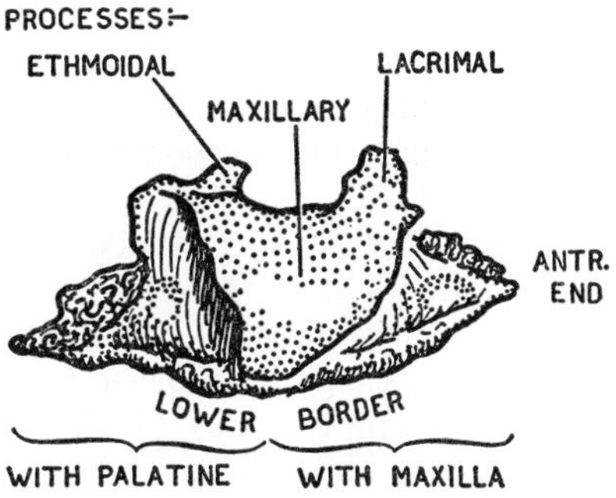

FIG. 846. Inferior concha—lateral aspect

The *lacrimal process* ascends from near the anterior end of the maxillary process and, by joining the descending process of the lacrimal bone, completes the nasolacrimal canal medially.

The *ethmoidal process* ascends from near the posterior end of the maxillary process and, by joining the uncinate process of the ethmoid, completes the lower border of the hiatus semilunaris of the middle meatus of the nose.

The inferior concha ossifies in the cartilage of the nasal capsule.

VOMER

The vomer or plowshare (unpaired) forms the entire postero-inferior third of the nasal septum. When the skull is viewed from behind, the free posterior border is seen dividing above into right and left alae. Viewed from the front the oblique anterior border is seen to be grooved in its lower part to receive the septal cartilage, and to be thin

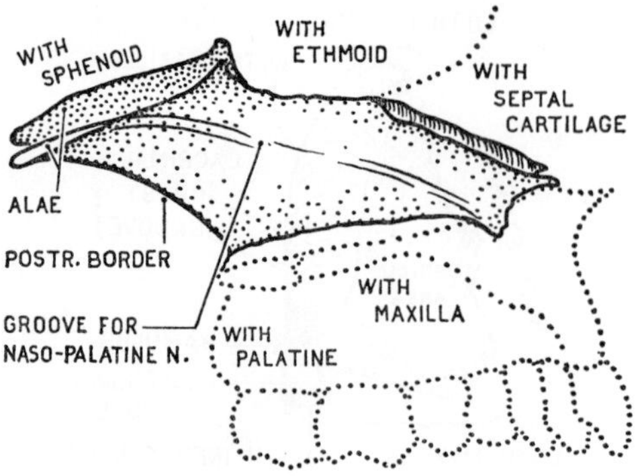

FIG. 847. Vomer—right side

in its upper part for articulation with the vertical plate of the ethmoid. Each surface is grooved longitudinally by the nasopalatine (long sphenopalatine) nerve and companion vessels (*fig. 847*).

The vomer develops in the postero-inferior part of the membrane that lies on each side of the "primitive" septal cartilage. The intervening cartilage is absorbed thus allowing the membrane bones of the opposite sides to fuse; evidence of the bilateral origin of the vomer is still seen, however, in the groove for the septal cartilage and in the alae.

MANDIBLE

The mandible is described on page 629.

Ossification. The lower jaw is the second bone in the body to start ossifying (6th fetal week), the clavicle being the 1st. Each half of the jaw ossifies from a single center which appears in the membrane overlying the anterior half of Meckel's cartilage, i.e., the cartilage of the first or mandibular arch. In front of the mental foramen, however, ossification involves a small part of Meckel's cartilage, and posteriorly the condyle and part of the coronoid process passed through a cartilaginous stage.

At birth each half of the jaw is a fragile trough in which the five milk teeth and 6th year molar (i.e., first permanent molar) lie buried (*fig. 848*). The mandibular canal—in part open above—runs along the bottom of the trough. The ramus meets the body at a very obtuse angle, the two being almost in

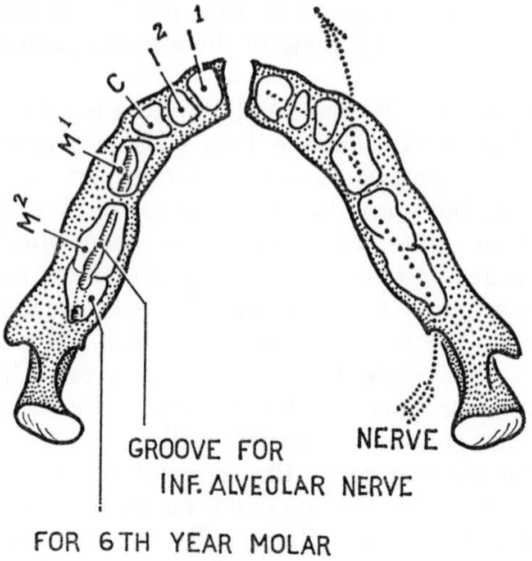

FIG. 848. Mandible at birth

line. The eruption of the teeth separates the upper and lower jaws; hence the angle decreases; conversely, it increases again if the jaws become edentulous. Growth takes place mainly through additions to the outer surface of the bone and to the posterior and inferior borders.

HYOID BONE

The hyoid bone is shaped like the letter U, hence its name (Gk. (H)U-eidos = U-like). It comprises a quadrate middle part, the *body*, and two processes on each side, the *greater* and *lesser horns* (cornua) (*fig. 849*). Muscles ascend to the hyoid and muscles descend to the hyoid, but no muscle crosses it, so the entire length of the bone (from the tip of one greater horn to the tip of the other) is subcutaneous externally and submucous internally (*fig. 810*).

It is readily palpated at the angle where the upper part of the neck meets the floor of the mouth (pp. 605, 607). Theoretically, the simplest way to open the pharynx is (1st) to cut transversely through the skin, (2nd) to saw through the hyoid, and (3rd) to cut transversely through the mucous membrane.

Attached to the entire length of the body and greater horns is the thyrohyoid membrane. Oddly, the attachment is along the upper border of the body—not the lower—

and the posterior aspect is free, smooth and in contact with a bursa.

Development and Ossification. The hyoid bone is one of the structures developed from the six paired cartilages of the branchial (pharyngeal) arches (*fig. 744.1*).

Each 1st cartilage (Meckel's) is converted into the incus, malleus, sphenomandibular ligament, and one-half of the body of the mandible.

Each 2nd cartilage (Reichert's) is converted into the stapes, styloid process of the temporal bone, stylohyoid ligament, lesser horn of the hyoid, and upper part of the body of the hyoid.

The dorsal halves of the 3rd, 4th, and 6th cartilages are resorbed. The ventral halves of the 3rd become the greater horns and lower part of the body of the hyoid; the ventral halves of the 4th become the thyroid cartilage; the ventral halves of the 6th become the arytenoid cartilages and (?) the cricoid cartilage.

The body and the greater horns begin to ossify independently about the time of birth, and remain united by synchondroses until middle life, when synostosis occurs. The lesser horns articulate by synovial joints with the junction of the body and greater horns, and are partly cartilaginous at middle life; synostosis may occur.

Variations. The upper part of the stylohyoid ligament may ossify, that is, the styloid process may be unduly long and be a lateral relation of the tonsil bed. The lower part may ossify, that is, the lesser horn may be unduly long (as normally in many mammals).

Muscle Attachments (*fig. 849*).

Fibrous Attachments are: the thyrohyoid membrane, lateral thyrohyoid ligaments, hyo-epiglottic ligament, the deep fascia of the neck and the septum of the tongue.

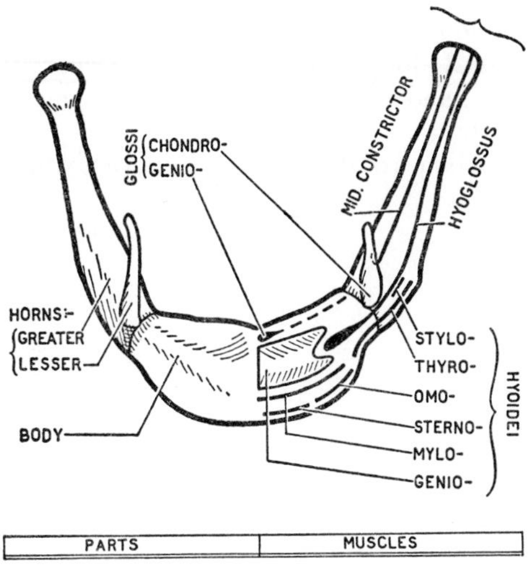

Fig. 849. Hyoid bone—anterosuperior aspect

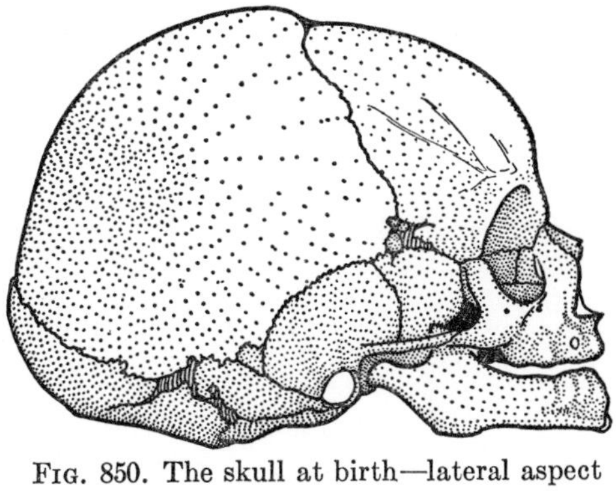

Fig. 850. The skull at birth—lateral aspect

THE SKULL AT BIRTH

The teeth of the newborn child are rudimentary and unerupted; the child can suck but cannot chew. Accordingly, the facial or masticatory portion of the skull is very small, being about one-seventh the size of the cranium or brain case (in the adult it is one-half the size); the ramus of the mandible is almost in line with the body (*fig. 850*); the mandibular (articular) fossa is very shallow (*fig. 834*); the air sinuses, which enlarge as the teeth erupt, are rudimentary; and the nasal cavities are small. The orbits are nearly circular.

There being no mastoid process, the stylomastoid foramen, through which the facial nerve emerges, is exposed. The tympanic bone being but a ring, the eardrum is exposed. At the sites where ossification began in the frontal and parietal bones, there are eminences, the *tubers*, which are almost conical.

Ossification not having reached the four angles of the parietal bone, the skull is still membranous at these areas; that is, there is a fontanelle or *fonticulus* at each angle (*fig. 660*). There is also a median fontanelle (sagittal fontanelle) in the interparietal suture, and another (metopic fontanelle) in the frontal (or metopic) suture.

The bones of the skull are thin, easily bent, and, having no diploe, consist of a single plate. The occipital bone is in four pieces; (*fig. 827*); the sphenoid is in three (*fig. 684*); the temporal is in three (*fig. 834A*); the ethmoid is in three; and the frontal bone and the mandible are each in two halves.

REFERENCES

GENERAL CONSIDERATIONS

Barclay, A. E., Barcroft, J., Barron, D. H., Franklin, K. J., and Prichard, M. M. L.: Studies of the foetal circulation and of certain changes that take place after birth. Am. J. Anat., *69:* 383, 1941.

Barnett, C. H., Davies, D. V., and MacConaill, M. A.: *Synovial Joints*. Longmans, Green and Company, London, 1960.

Basmajian, J. V.: *Muscles Alive: Their Functions Revealed by Electromyography*. The Williams & Wilkins Company, Baltimore, 1962.

Book, M. H.: The secreting area of the glomerulus. J. Anat., *71:* 91, 1936.

Brash, J. C.: Some problems in the growth and developmental mechanics of bone. Edinburgh M. J., *41:* 305, 363, 1934.

Brash, J. C.: *Neuro-Vascular Hila of Limb Muscles*. E. & S. Livingstone Ltd., Edinburgh, 1955.

Bridgman, C.: Changes in intramuscular pressure during contraction (abstract). Anat. Rec., *148:* 263, 1964.

Brookes, M., Elkin, A. C., Harrison, R. G., and Heald, C. B.: A new concept of capillary circulation in bone cortex: some clinical applications. Lancet, *1:* 1078, 1961.

Charnley, J.: Articular cartilage. Brit. M. J., *2:* 679, 1954.

Charnley, J.: How our joints are lubricated. Triangle, Sandoz J. M. Sc., *4:* no. 5, 1960.

Charnley, J.: Arthroplasty of the hip: a new operation. Lancet, *1:* 1129, 1961.

Clark, E. R., and Clark, E. L.: Further observations on living lymphatic vessels in the transparent chamber in the rabbit's ear. Am. J. Anat., *52:* 273, 1933.

Clark, W. E. Le Gros: *The Tissues of the Body*, Ed. 2. Clarendon Press, Oxford, 1945.

Coventry, M. B. *et al.:* The intervertebral disc etc. J. Bone & Joint Surg., *27:* 105, 1945.

Cronkite, A. E.: The tensile strength of human tendons. Anat. Rec., *64:* 173, 1936.

Cox, H. T.: The cleavage lines of the skin. Brit. J. Surg., *29:* 234, 1941.

Davies, D. V.: Observations on the volume, viscosity and nitrogen content of synovial fluid, etc. J. Anat., *78:* 68, 1944.

Dawson, B. H., and Hoyte, D. A. N.: Observations on premature fusion of the sutures of the cranial vault (abstracts). J. Anat., *91:* 590, 583, and 613, 1957.

Digby, K. H.: The measurement of diaphysial growth, etc. J. Anat., *50:* 187, 1916.

Duchenne, G. B. A.: *Physiologie des mouvements, etc.*, (translated by Kaplan, see below.) Paris, 1867.

Edwards, E. A.: The orientation of venous valves in relation to body surfaces. Anat. Rec., *64:* 369, 1936.

Ekholm, R.: Nutrition of articular cartilage. Acta anat., *24:* 329, 1955.

Gardner, E.: Physiology of movable joints. Physiol. Rev., *30:* 127, 1950.

Gardner, E.: The anatomy of the joints. Am. Acad. Orthop. Surgeons, Instruction course. *9:* 149, 1952. (Edwards, Ann Arbor, Mich.)

Girgis, F. G., and Pritchard, J. J.: Effects of skull damage on the development of sutural patterns in the rat. J. Anat., *92:* 39, 1958.

Haines, R. W.: On muscles of full and of short action. J. Anat., *69:* 20, 1934.

Haines, R. W.: The laws of muscle and tendon growth. J. Anat., *66:* 578, 1932.

Ham, A. W., and Leeson, T. S.: *Histology*, Ed. 4. J. B. Lippincott Company, Philadelphia, 1961.

Harris, H. A.: *Bone Growth in Health and Disease*. Oxford University Press, London, 1933.

Hughes, H.: The factors determining the direction of the canal for the nutrient artery in the long bones of mammals and birds. Acta anat., *15:* 261, 1952.

Inman, V. T., Saunders, J. B. deC. M., and Abbott, L. C.: Observations on the function of the shoulder joint. J. Bone & Joint Surg., *26:* 1, 1944.

Inman, V. T., and Saunders, J. B. deC. M.: Anatomicophysiological aspects of injuries to the intervertebral disc. J. Bone & Joint Surg., *29:* 461, 1947.

Kaplan, E. B.: *Physiology of Motion*. J. B. Lippincott Company, Philadelphia, 1949. (This is a translation of *Physiologie des mouvements* by Duchenne, see above.)

Keegan, J. J., and Garrett, F. D.: The segmental

distribution of the cutaneous nerves in the limbs of man. Anat. Rec., *102:* 409, 1948.

Keith, A.: *Menders of the Maimed.* Froude, London, 1919.

Kimmel, D. L.: Innervation of spinal dura mater and dura mater of the posterior cranial fossa. Neurology, *11:* 800, 1961.

Kimmel, D. L.: The nerves of the cranial dura mater and their significance in dural headache and referred pain. Chicago M. Sch. Quart., *22:* 16, 1961.

Langworthy, O. R. *et al.: Physiology of Micturition.* The Williams & Wilkins Company, Baltimore, 1940.

Learmonth, J. E.: A contribution to the neurophysiology of the urinary bladder in man. Brain, *54:* 147, 1931.

Le Double, A. F.: *Traité des variations du système musculaire de l'homme.* Paris, 1897.

MacConaill, M. A.: The movements of bones and joints. The synovial fluid and its assistants. J. Bone & Joint Surg., *32B:* 244, 1950.

MacDonald, I. B. *et al.:* Anterior rhizotomy. The accurate identification of motor roots at the lower end of the spinal cord. J. Neurosurg., *3:* 421, 1946.

McKern, T. W., and Stewart, T. D.: Skeletal age changes in young American males, analysed from the standpoint of age identification. Smithsonian Institution, 1957.

Mednick, L. W., and Washburn, S. L.: The role of the sutures in the growth of the braincase of the infant pig. Am. J. Phys. Anthropol., *14:* 175, 1956.

Mitchell, G. A. G.: *Anatomy of the Autonomic Nervous System.* E. & S. Livingstone, Ltd., Edinburgh, 1953.

Mortensen, O. A., and Guest, R. L.: The absorption of thorium dioxide by the reticuloendothelial system in the dog. Anat. Rec., *70:* 58, 1938.

Patten, B. M.: *Human Embryology,* Ed. 2. McGraw-Hill Book Company, Inc., New York, Toronto, London, 1953.

Petter, C. K.: Methods of measuring the pressure of the intervertebral disc. J. Bone & Joint Surg., *15:* 365, 1933.

Phemister, D. B.: Bone growth and repair. Ann. Surg., *102:* 261, 1935.

Pressman, J. J., and Simon, M. B.: Experimental evidence of direct communications between lymph nodes and veins. Surg. Gynec. & Obst., *113:* 537, 1961.

Pressman, J. J., Simon, M. B., Hand, K. and Miller, J.: Passage of fluids, cells, and bacteria via direct communications between lymph nodes and veins. Surg. Gynec. & Obst., *115:* 207, 1962.

Rappaport, A. M. *et al.:* Subdivision of hexagonal liver lobules into a structural and functional unit. Anat. Rec., *119:* 11, 1954.

Rappaport, A. M.: *The Liver,* Vol. 1. Academic Press, Inc., New York, 1963.

Rau, R. K.: Skull showing absence of coronal suture. J. Anat., *69:* 109, 1934.

Roofe, P. G.: Innervation of annulus fibrosus etc. J. Neurol. Neurosurg. & Psychiat., *44:* 100, 1940.

Rusznyák, I., Földi, M., and Szabo, G.: *Lymphatics and Lymph Circulation.* Pergamon Press, London, 1960.

Smith, C. G.: Changes in length and position of the segments of the spinal cord, etc. Radiology, *66:* 259, 1956.

Sunderland, S.: Blood supply of the nerves of the upper limb in man. Arch. Neurol. & Psychiat., *53:* 91, 1945.

Todd, T. W., and Pyle, S. I.: A quantitative study of the vertebral column, etc. Am. J. Phys. Anthropol., *12:* 321, 1928.

Trueta, J., and Cavadias, A. X.: A study of the blood supply of the long bones. Surg. Gynec. & Obst., *118:* 485, 1964.

Walls, E. W.: The fibre constitution of the human gastrocnemius and soleus muscles. J. Anat., *87:* 437, 1953.

Walmsley, T.: The articular mechanism of the diarthroses. J. Bone & Joint Surg., *10:* 40, 1928.

Weinmann, J. P., and Sicher, H.: *Bone and Bones,* Ed. 2. C. V. Mosby Company. St. Louis, 1955.

White, J. C., and Smithwick, R. H.: *The Autonomic Nervous System.* The Macmillan Company, New York, 1946.

Woodburne, R. T.: The sphincter mechanism of the urinary bladder and the urethra. Anat. Rec., *141:* 11, 1961.

UPPER LIMB

Basmajian, J. V., and Latif, A.: Integrated actions and functions of the chief flexors of the elbow. J. Bone & Joint Surg., *39A:* 1106, 1957.

Beevor, C. E.: Croonian lecture on muscular movements, etc. Brit. M. J., *1:* 1357, 1417, 1480, *2:* 12, 1903.

Bing, R.: *Compendium of Regional Diagnosis in Lesions of the Brain and Spinal Cord,* Ed. 11, translated and edited by W. Haymaker. C. V. Mosby Company, St. Louis, 1940.

Braithwaite, F. *et al.:* The applied anatomy of the lumbrical and interosseous muscles of the hand. Guy's Hosp. Rep., *97:* 185, 1948.

Bunnell, S.: *Surgery of the Hand.* J. B. Lippincott Company, Philadelphia, 1944.

Corbin, K. B., and Harrison, F.: The sensory innervation of the spinal accessory and tongue musculature in rhesus monkey. Brain, 62: 191, 1939.

Cummins, H., and Midlo, C.: *Finger Prints, Palms, and Soles*. Blakiston Company, division of Doubleday & Company, New York, 1943.

Flecker, H.: Time of appearance and fusion of ossification centers as observed by roentgenographic methods. Am. J. Roentgenol., *47:* 97, 1942. Also with similar title in J. Anat., *67:* 118, 1932.

Gardner, E.: The innervation of the elbow joint. Anat. Rec., *102:* 161, 1948.

Garn, S. M. *et al.*: A rational approach to the assessment of skeletal maturation. Ann. radiol., *V–VI*, 1964.

Greulich, W. W., and Pyle, S. I.: Radiographic atlas of skeletal development of the hand and wrist, Ed. 2. Stanford University Press, Stanford, Calif., 1959.

Haines, R. W.: The mechanism of rotation at the first carpo-metacarpal joint. J. Anat., *78:* 44, 1944.

Haines, R. W.: The extensor apparatus of the finger. J. Anat., *85:* 251, 1951.

Halls, A. A., and Travill, A.: Transmission of pressures across the elbow joint. Anat. Rec., *150:* 243, 1964.

Haymaker, W., and Woodhall, B.: *Peripheral Nerve Injuries: Principles of Diagnosis*, Ed. 2. W. B. Saunders Company, Philadelphia and London, 1953.

Inman, V. T., Saunders, J. B. deC. M., and Abbott, L. C.: Observations on the function of the shoulder joint. J. Bone & Joint Surg., *26:* 1, 1944.

Jones, F. W.: *The Principles of Anatomy as Seen in the Hand*, Ed. 2. Baillière, Tindall & Cox, London, 1941.

Kanavel, A. B.: *Infections of the Hand*, Ed. 7. Lea and Febiger, Philadelphia, 1939.

Landsmeer, J. M. F.: The anatomy of the dorsal aponeurosis of the human finger, etc. Anat. Rec., *104:* 31, 1949.

Rowntree, T.: Anomalous innervation of the hand muscles. J. Bone & Joint Surg., *31B:* 505, 1949.

Salsbury, C. R.: The interosseous muscles of the hand. J. Anat., *71:* 395, 1937.

Stopford, J. S. B.: *Sensation and the Sensory Pathway*. Longmans, Green & Co., Inc., London, 1930.

Sunderland, S.: The innervation of the first dorsal interosseous muscle of the hand. Anat. Rec., *95:* 7, 1946.

Sunderland, S.: Voluntary movements and the deceptive action of muscles in peripheral nerve lesions. Australian & New Zealand J. Surg., *13:* 160, 1944.

Wilder, H. H.: *The History of the Human Body*, Ed. 2. Henry Holt & Co., New York, 1923.

ABDOMEN

Alvarez, W. C.: *An Introduction to Gastro-enterology*. Heinemann, London, 1940.

Anson, B. J., and McVay, C. B.: Inguinal hernia. The anatomy of the region. Surg. Gynec. & Obstet., *66:* 186, 1938.

Basmajian, J. V.: The marginal anastomoses of the arteries to the large intestine. Surg. Gynec. & Obst., *99:* 614, 1954.

Basmajian, J. V.: The main arteries of the large intestine. Surg. Gynec. & Obst., *101:* 585, 1955.

Benjamin, H. B., and Becker, A. B.: A vascular study of the small intestine. Surg. Gynec. & Obst., *108:* 134, 1959.

Boyden, E. A.: The accessory gall-bladder. Am. J. Anat., *38:* 202, 1926.

Boyden, E. A.: The anatomy of the choledochoduodenal junction in man. Surg. Gynec. & Obst., *104:* 641, 1957.

Boyden, E. A.: *Gallbladder. McGraw-Hill Encyclopedia of Science and Technology*. New York, 1960.

Cullen, T. S.: *Embryology, Anatomy and Diseases of the Umbilicus*. W. B. Saunders Company, Philadelphia, 1916.

Curtis, G. M., and Movitz, D.: The surgical significance of the accessory spleen. Ann. Surg., *123:* 276, 1946.

Daseler, E. H., Anson, B. J., Hambley, W. C., and Reimann, A. F.: The cystic artery and constituents of the hepatic pedicle. A study of 500 specimens. Surg. Gynec. & Obst., *85:* 45, 1947.

Dawson, W., and Langman, J.: An anatomical-radiological study on the pancreatic duct pattern in man. Anat. Rec., *139:* 59, 1961.

Drummond, H.: The arterial supply of the rectum and pelvic colon. Brit. J. Surg., *1:* 677, 1914.

Edwards, E. A.: Functional anatomy of the porta-systemic communications. A. M. A. Arch. Int. Med., *88:* 137, 1951.

Falconer, C. W. A., and Griffiths, E.: The anatomy of the blood-vessels in the region of the pancreas. Brit. J. Surg., *37:* 334, 1950.

Finlayson, J.: Herophilus and Erasistratus. Glasgow M. J., May, 1893.

Franklin, K. J.: *A Monograph on Veins*. Charles C Thomas, Springfield, Ill., 1937.

Graves, F. T.: The anatomy of the intrarenal arteries and its application to segmental resection of the kidney. Brit. J. Surg., *42:* 132, 1954.

Halbert, B., and Eaton, W. L.: Accessory spleens: a pilot study of 600 necropsies (abstract). Anat. Rec., *109:* 371, 1951.

Harrison, R. G.: The distribution of the vasal and cremasteric arteries to the testis, etc. J. Anat., *83:* 267, 1949.

Healey, J. E., and Schroy, P. C.: Anatomy of the biliary ducts within the human liver. Arch. Surg., *66:* 599, 1953.

Healey, J. E., Schroy, P. C., and Sorensen, R. J.: The intrahepatic distribution of the hepatic artery. J. Internat. Coll. Surgeons, *20:* 133, 1953.

Hjortsjo, C.-H.: The topography of the intrahepatic duct systems (and of the portal vein). Acta Anat., *11:* 599, 1951.

Hjortsjo, C.-H.: The intrahepatic ramifications of the portal vein. Lunds Universitets Arsskrift., *52:* 20, 1956.

Hyde, J. S., Swarts, C. L., Nicholas, E. E., Snead, C. R., and Strasser, N. F.: Superior mesenteric artery syndrome. Am. J. Dis. Child., *106:* 25, 1963.

Jamieson, J. K., and Dobson, J. F.: The lymphatic system of the stomach, and of the caecum and appendix. Lancet, April 20 and 27, 1907.

Jamieson, J. K., and Dobson, J. F.: The lymphatics of the testicle. Lancet, Feb. 19, 1910.

Jamieson, J. K., and Dobson, J. F.: The lymphatics of the colon. Proc. Roy. Soc. Med., March, 1909.

Jay, G. D. III *et al.*: Meckel's diverticulum: survey of 103 cases. Arch. Surg., *61:* 158, 1950.

Lofgren, F.: *Some Features in the Renal Morphogenesis and Anatomy with Practical Considerations.* Institute of Anatomy, University of Lund, Sweden, 1956.

Lofgren, F.: An attempt at homologizing different types of pyelus (renal pelvis). Urologia Internat., *5:* No. 1, 1956.

Lytle, W. J.: The internal inguinal ring. Brit. J. Surg., *32:* 441, 1945.

Maisel, H.: The position of the human vermiform appendix. Anat. Rec., *136:* 385, 1960.

Mann, C. V., Greenwood, R. K., and Ellis, F. H., Jr.: The esophagogastric junction. Surg. Gynec. & Obst., *118:* 853, 1964.

Michels, N. A.: *Blood Supply and Anatomy of the Upper Abdominal Organs.* J. B. Lippincott Company, Philadelphia, 1955.

Michels, N. A., Siddharth, P., Kornblith, P., and Parke, W. W.: The variant blood supply to the small and large intestine: its import in regional resections. J. Internat. Coll. Surgeons, *39:* 127, 1963.

Millbourn, E.: On the excretory ducts of the pancreas, etc. Acta anat., *9:* 1, 1950.

Mitchell, G. A. G.: *Anatomy of the Autonomic Nervous System.* E. & S. Livingstone, Ltd., Edinburgh, 1953.

Moody, R. O., and Van Nuys, R. G.: Some results of a study of roentgenograms of the abdominal viscera. Am. J. Roentgenol., *20:* 348, 1928.

Moody, R. O., Van Nuys, R. G., and Kidder, C. H.: The form and position of the empty stomach in healthy young adults. Anat. Rec., *43:* 359, 1929.

Moody, R. O., and Van Nuys, R. G.: The position and mobility of the kidneys in healthy young men and women. Anat. Rec., *76:* 111, 1940.

Patey, D. H.: Some observations on the functional anatomy of inguinal hernia, etc. Brit. J. Surg., *36:* 264, 1949.

Pierson, J. M.: The arterial blood supply of the pancreas. Surg. Gynec. & Obst., *77:* 426, 1943.

Reeves, T. A.: A study of the arteries supplying the stomach and duodenum and their relation to ulcer. Surg. Gynec. & Obst., *30:* 374, 1920.

Rienhoff, W. F., and Pickrell, K. L.: Pancreatitis. An anatomic study of the pancreatic and extrahepatic biliary systems. Arch. Surg., *51:* 205, 1945.

Roche, M. B., and Rowe, G. G.: The incidence of separate neural arch, etc. J. Bone & Joint Surg., *34A:* 491, 1952.

Ross, J. A.: Vascular patterns of small and large intestine compared. Brit. J. Surg., *39:* 330, 1952.

Rowe, G. G., and Roche, M. B.: The etiology of separate neural arch. J. Bone & Joint Surg., *35A:* 102, 1953.

Shah, M. A., and Shah, M.: The arterial supply of the vermiform appendix. Anat. Rec., *95:* 457, 1946.

Sheehan, D.: The afferent nerve supply of the mesentery, etc. J. Anat., *67:* 233, 1933.

Steward, J. A., and Rankin, F. W.: Blood supply of the large intestine: its surgical considerations. Arch. Surg., *26:* 843, 1933.

Stewart, T. D.: The age incidence of neural arch defects in Alaskan natives. J. Bone & Joint Surg., *35A:* 937, 1953.

Tobin, C. E., and Benjamin, J. A.: Anatomic and clinical re-evaluation of Camper's, Scarpa's, and Colles' fasciae. Surg. Gynec. & Obst., *88:* 545, 1949.

Underhill, B. M. L.: Intestinal length in man. Brit. M. J., *2:* 1243, 1955.

Wakeley, C. P. G.: The position of the vermiform appendix, etc. J. Anat., *67:* 277, 1933.

Wells, L. J.: Descent of the testis: anatomical and hormonal considerations. Surgery, *14:* 436, 1943.

Wells, L. J.: Observations on the development of the diaphragm in the human embryo. Anat. Rec., *100:* 778, 1948.

Wells, L. J.: Contributions to embryology, Carnegie Institute, *35:* 107, 1954.

Wharton, G. K.: The blood supply of the pancreas, etc. Anat. Rec., *53:* 55, 1932.

Wilkie, D. P. D.: The blood supply of the duodenum, etc. Surg. Gynec. & Obst., *13:* 399, 1911.

Woodburne, R. T., and Olsen, L. L.: The arteries of the pancreas. Anat. Rec., *111:* 255, 1951.

PERINEUM AND PELVIS

Blair, J. B., Holyoke, E., and Best, R. R.: A note on the lymphatics of the middle and lower rectum and anus. Anat. Rec., *108:* 635, 1950.

Braithwaite, J. L.: Vesiculo-deferential artery. Brit. J. Urol., *24:* 64, 1952.

Braus, H.: *Anatomie des menchen*, Ed. 2. Springer-Verlag, Berlin, 1929.

Caldwell, W. E., and Moloy, H. C.: Anatomical variations in the female pelvis, etc. Am. J. Obst. & Gynec., *26:* 479, 1933.

Derry, D. E.: The innominate bone and the determination of sex. J. Anat., *43:* 266, 1908.

Greulich, W. W., and Thoms, H.: A study of pelvic type and its relationship to body build in white women. J. A. M. A., *112:* 485, 1939.

Greulich, W. W., and Thoms, H.: The dimensions of the pelvic inlet of 789 white females. Anat. Rec., *72:* 45, 1938.

Keith, A.: *Human Embryology and Morphology*, Ed. 6. Edward Arnold & Company, London, 1948.

Langworthy, O. R. *et al.*: *Physiology of Micturition.* The Williams & Wilkins Company, Baltimore, 1940.

Leaf, C. H.: *The Lymphatics by Poirier and Cuneo.* (translation) Constable, London, 1903.

Learmonth, J. E.: A contribution to the neurophysiology of the urinary bladder in man. Brain, *54:* 147, 1931.

Mitchell, G. A. G.: *Anatomy of the Autonomic Nervous System.* E. & S. Livingstone, Ltd., Edinburgh, 1953.

Moloy, H. C.: *Evaluation of the Pelvis in Obstetrics.* W. B. Saunders Company, Philadelphia, 1951.

Ricci, J. V. *et al.*: The female urethra: a histological study, etc. Am. J. Surg., N. S. *79:* 499, 1950.

Rouvière, H.: Anatomie des lymphatiques de l'homme. Masson & Cie, Paris, 1932 (translated into English by Tobias, see below).

Sheehan, D.: *Annual Review of Physiology*, Vol. 3, 1941.

Stopford, J. S. B.: The autonomic nerve supply of the distal colon. Brit. M. J., *1:* 572, 1934.

Thoms, H.: *Pelvimetry.* Paul B. Hoeber, Inc., 1956.

Tobias, M. J.: *Anatomy of the Human Lymphatic System.* Edwards, Ann Arbor, Mich., 1938 (translation of the work of Rouvière, see above).

Washburn, S. L.: Sex differences in the pubic bone. Am. J. Phys. Anthropol., N. S. *6:* 199, 1948.

Hanna, R. E., and Washburn, S. L.: The determination of the sex of skeletons as illustrated by a study of the Eskimo pelvis. Human Biol., *25:* 21, 1953.

Wilde, R. F.: The anal intermuscular septum. Brit. J. Surg., *36:* 279, 1949.

LOWER LIMB

Basmajian, J. V.: The distribution of valves in the femoral, external iliac and common iliac veins, etc. Surg. Gynec. & Obst., *95:* 357, 1952.

Basmajian, J. V., and Bentzon, J. W.: An electromyographic study of certain muscles of the leg and foot, etc. Surg. Gynec. & Obst., *98:* 662, 1954.

Bing, R.: *Compendium of Regional Diagnosis in Lesions of the Brain and Spinal Cord*, Ed. 11, translated and edited by W. Haymaker. C. V. Mosby Company, St. Louis, 1940.

Gardner, E.: The innervation of the hip joint. Anat. Rec., *101:* 353, 1948.

Gardner, E.: The innervation of the knee joint. Anat. Rec., *101:* 109, 1948.

Haxton, H.: The functions of the patella and the effects of its excision. Surg. Gynec. & Obst., *80:* 389, 1945.

Haymaker, W., and Woodhall, B.: *Peripheral Nerve Injuries: Principles of Diagnosis*, Ed. 2. W. B. Saunders Company, Philadelphia and London, 1953.

Hicks, J. H.: The mechanics of the foot: The joints. J. Anat., *87:* 345, 1953. The plantar aponeurosis and the arch. J. Anat., *88:* 25, 1954. The foot as a support. Acta anat., *25:* 34, 1955.

Jack, E. A.: Naviculo-cuneiform fusion in the treatment of flat foot. J. Bone & Joint Surg., *35B:* 75, 1953.

Jones, F. W.: *The Foot, Structure and Function.* Ballière, Tindall & Cox, London, 1949.

Jones, R. L.: The human foot . . . the role of its muscles and ligaments in the support of the arch. Am. J. Anat., *68:* 1, 1941.

Keegan, J. J., and Garrett, F. D.: The segmental distribution of the cutaneous nerves in the limbs of man. Anat. Rec., *102:* 409, 1948.

Last, R. J.: The popliteus muscle and the lateral

meniscus. J. Bone & Joint Surg., N. S. *32B:* 93, 1950.

Mitchell, G. A. G.: *Anatomy of the Autonomic Nervous System.* E. & S. Livingstone, Ltd., Edinburgh, 1953.

Morton, D. J.: *The Human Foot.* Columbia University Press, New York, 1937.

O'Rahilly, R.: A survey of carpal and tarsal anomalies. J. Bone & Joint Surg., *35A:* 626, 1953.

Singer, C.: *The Evolution of Anatomy.* Kegan Paul, etc., 1925.

Trueta, J.: The normal vascular anatomy of the femoral head during growth. J. Bone & Joint Surg., *B39:* 358, 1957.

Trueta, J., and Harrison, M. H. M.: The normal vascular anatomy of the femoral head in adult man. J. Bone & Joint Surg., *35B:* 442, 1953.

Tucker, F. R.: Arterial supply to the femoral head and its clinical importance. J. Bone & Joint Surg., *31B:* 82, 1949.

Walmsley, T.: The articular mechanism of the diarthroses. J. Bone & Joint Surg., *10:* 40, 1928.

Wolcott, W. E.: The evolution of the circulation in the developing femoral head and neck. Surg. Gynec. & Obst., *77:* 61, 1943.

THORAX

Boyden, E. A.: *Segmental Anatomy of the Lungs.* McGraw-Hill Book Company, Inc., New York, 1955.

Bradley, W. F. *et al.:* Anatomic considerations of gastric neurectomy. J. A. M. A., *133:* 459, 1947.

Brock, R. C.: *The Anatomy of the Bronchial Tree.* Oxford University Press, London, 1946.

Foster-Carter, A. F.: Broncho-pulmonary abnormalities. Brit. J. Tuberc., Oct., 1946.

Gradwohl, R. B. H.: *Clinical Laboratory Methods and Diagnosis,* Vol. II, Ed. 4. Mosby, St. Louis, 1948.

Grant, R. T.: Development of the cardiac coronary vessels in the rabbit. Heart, *13:* 261, 1926.

Gross, L.: *The Blood Supply to the Heart.* Paul B. Hoeber, Inc., New York, 1921.

Harper, W. F.: The blood supply of human heart valves. Brit. M. J., *2:* 305, 1941.

Hayek, H. von: *The Human Lung.* Translated by Krahl, V. E. Illustration based on figure 216, by courtesy of Hafner Publishing Company, Inc., New York, 1960.

Jackson, C. L., and Huber, J. F.: Correlated applied anatomy of the bronchial tree and lungs with a system of nomenclature. Dis. Chest, *9:* 319, 1943.

James, T. N.: The arteries of the free ventricular walls in man. Anat. Rec., *136:* 371, 1960.

James, T. N.: Anatomy of the human sinus node. Anat. Rec., *141:* 109, 1961.

James, T. N., and Burch, G. E.: The atrial coronary arteries in man. Circulation 2, *17:* 90, 1958.

Jones, D. S., Beargie, R. J., and Pauly, J. E.: An electromyographic study of some muscles of costal respiration in man. Anat. Rec., *117:* 17, 1953.

Krahl, V. E.: Translation of Hayek's *The Human Lung,* Hafner Publishing Company, Inc., New York, 1960.

Lachman, E.: The dynamic concept of thoracic topography, etc. Am. J. Roentgenol., *56:* 419, 1946.

Lachman, E.: A comparison of the posterior boundaries of lungs and pleura, etc. Anat. Rec., *83:* 521, 1942.

Macklin, C. C.: Bronchial length changes and other movements. Tubercle, Oct.–Nov., 1932.

Macklin, C. C.: The dynamic bronchial tree. Am. Rev. Tuberc., *25:* 393, 1932.

Mainland, D., and Gordon, E. J.: The position of organs determined from thoracic radiographs, etc. Am. J. Anat., *68:* 457, 1941.

Miller, W. S.: *The Lung,* Ed. 2. Charles C Thomas, Springfield, Ill., 1921.

Mitchell, G. A. G.: *Anatomy of the Autonomic Nervous System.* E. & S. Livingstone, Ltd. Edinburgh, 1953.

Mizeres, N. J.: The cardiac plexus in man. Am. J. Anat., *112:* 1963.

Morris, E. W. T.: Some features of the mitral valve. Thorax, *15:* 70, 1960.

Nathan, H.: Anatomical observations on the course of the azygos vein. Thorax. *15:* 229, 1960.

Nelson, H. P.: Postural drainage of the lungs. Brit. M. J., *2:* 251, 1934.

Reed, A. F.: The origins of the splanchnic nerves. Anat. Rec., *109:* 81, 1951.

Ross, J. K.: Review of the surgery of the thoracic duct. Thorax, *16:* 207, 1961.

Rouvière, H.: *Anatomie des lymphatiques de l'homme.* Masson & Cie, Paris, 1932.

Silvester, C. F.: On the presence of permanent communications between the lymphatic and the venous system at the level of the renal veins in South American monkeys. Am. J. Anat., *12:* 447, 1912.

Singer, R.: The coronary arteries of the Bantu heart. South African M. J., *33:* 310, 1959.

Tobin, C. E.: The bronchial arteries and their connections with other vessels in the human lung. Surg. Gynec. & Obst., *95:* 741, 1952.

Tobin, C. E.: Human pulmonic lymphatics. Anat. Rec., *127:* 611, 1957.

Tobin, C. E., and Zariquiey, M. O.: Arteriovenous shunts in the human lung. Proc. Soc. Exper. Biol. & Med., *75:* 827, 1950.

Thoracic Society: The nomenclature of bronchopulmonary anatomy. Thorax, *5:* 222, 1950.

Trotter, M.: Synostosis between manubrium and body of the sternum in whites and negroes. Am. J. Phys. Anthropol., *18:* 439, 1934.

Truex, R. C., and Warshaw, L. J.: The incidence and size of the moderator band, etc. Anat. Rec., *82:* 361, 1942.

Walls, E. W.: Dissection of the atrio-ventricular node and bundle in the human heart. J. Anat., *79:* 45, 1945.

Walmsley, T.: The Heart, in *Quain's Anatomy,* 1929).

White, J. C., and Smithwick, R. H.: *The Autonomic Nervous System,* Ed. 2. The Macmillan Company, New York, 1946.

Woodburne, R. T.: The costomediastinal border of the left pleura in the precordial area. Anat. Rec., *97:* 197, 1947.

Zoll, P. M., Wessler, S., and Schlesinger, M. J.: Interarterial coronary anastomoses, etc. Circulation, *4:* 797, 1951.

HEAD AND NECK

Basmajian, J. V., and Dutta, C. R.: Electromyography of the pharyngeal constrictors and levator palati in man. Anat. Rec., *139:* 561, 1961.

Batson, O. V.: The function of the vertebral veins and their role in the spread of metastases. Ann. Surg., *112:* 138, 1940.

Békésy, G.: See von Békésy, G., *below.*

Browning, H.: The confluence of dural venous sinuses. Am. J. Anat., *93:* 307, 1953.

Carlsöö, S.: Nervous co-ordination and mechanical function of mandibular elevators. Acta odont. Scandinav., *10:* suppl. 11, 1952.

Cave, A. J. E.: A note on the origin of the m. scalenus medius. J. Anat., *67:* 480, 1933.

Graves, G. O., and Edwards, L. F.: The eustachian tube. Arch. Otolaryng., *39:* 359, 1944.

Jamieson, J. K., and Dobson, J. F.: The lymphatics of the tongue, etc. Brit. J. Surg., *8:* 80, 1920.

Kimmel, D. L.: Innervation of spinal dura mater and dura mater of the posterior cranial fossa. Neurology, *11:* 800, 1961.

Kimmel, D. L.: The nerves of the cranial dura mater and their significance in dural headache and referred pain. Chicago M. Sch. Quart., *22:* 16, 1961.

Latif, A.: An electromyographic study of the temporalis muscle, etc. Am. J. Orthodontics, *43:* 577, 1957.

Leden, H. and Moore, P.: See von Leden, H. and Moore, P., *below.*

Lewinsky, W., and Stewart, D.: An account of our present knowledge of the innervation of the teeth and their related tissues. Brit. Dent. J., Dec. 1, 1938.

Mann, Ida: *The Development of the Human Eye.* Cambridge University Press, 1928.

McKenzie, J.: The parotid gland in relation to the facial nerve. J. Anat., *82:* 183, 1948.

Mitchell, G. A. G.: *Anatomy of the Autonomic Nervous System.* E. & S. Livingstone, Ltd., Edinburgh, 1953.

Moyers, R. E.: An electromyographic analysis of certain muscles involved in temporomandibular movement. Am. J. Orthodontics, *36:* 481, 1950.

Negus, V. E.: *The Comparative Anatomy and Physiology of the Larynx.* William Heinemann, Ltd., London, 1949.

Parkinson, D.: Collateral circulation of cavernous carotid artery: anatomy. Can. J. Surg., *7:* 251, 1964.

Pearson, A. A.: The hypoglossal nerve in human embryos. J. Comp. Neurol., *71:* 21, 1939.

Pearson, A. A. *et al.*: Cutaneous branches of the dorsal (primary) rami of the cervical nerves. Am. J. Anat., *112:* 169, 1963.

Powell, T. V., and Brodie, A. G.: Closure of spheno-occipital synchondrosis. Anat. Rec., *147:* 15, 1963.

Pressman, J. J., and Simon, M. B.: Experimental evidence of direct communications between lymph nodes and veins. Surg. Gynec. & Obst., *113:* 537, 1961.

Saunders, J. B. deC. M., Davis, C., and Miller, E. R.: The mechanism of deglutition as revealed by cine-radiography. Ann. Otol. Rhin. & Laryng., *60:* 897, 1951.

Schour, I., and Massler, M.: The development of the human dentition. J. Am. Dent. A., *28:* 1153, 1941.

Stiles, H. J.: In *Cunningham's Text-Book of Anatomy.* Oxford University Press, London, 1913.

Stewart, D., and Wilson, S. L.: Regional anaesthesia and innervation of the teeth. Lancet, *Oct. 20:* 809, 1928.

Sunderland, S.: The meningeal relations of the human hypophysis cerebri. J. Anat., *79:* 33, 1945.

von Békésy, G.: The ear. Scientific American, August, 1957.

von Békésy, G.: *Experiments in Hearing,* translated and edited by E. G. Wever. McGraw-Hill Book Company, Inc., New York, 1960.

von Leden, H. and Moore, P.: The mechanics of the cricoarytenoid joint. Arch. Otolaryngol., *73:* 541, 1961.

von Leden, H.: The mechanism of phonation. Arch. Otolaryngol., *74:* 660, 1961.

Watt, J. C., and McKillop, A. N.: Relation of arteries to roots of nerves in posterior cranial fossa. Arch. Surg., *30:* 336, 1935.

Young, M. W.: The termination of the perilymphatic duct. Anat. Rec., *112:* 404, 1952.

INDEX

O

U

W

Z